CO$_2$ EMISSIONS FROM FUEL COMBUSTION

ÉMISSIONS DE CO$_2$ DUES À LA COMBUSTION D'ÉNERGIE

2008
EDITION

INTERNATIONAL ENERGY AGENCY

The International Energy Agency (IEA) is an autonomous body which was established in November 1974 within the framework of the Organisation for Economic Co-operation and Development (OECD) to implement an international energy programme.

It carries out a comprehensive programme of energy co-operation among twenty-eight of the OECD thirty member countries. The basic aims of the IEA are:

▌ To maintain and improve systems for coping with oil supply disruptions.

▌ To promote rational energy policies in a global context through co-operative relations with non-member countries, industry and international organisations.

▌ To operate a permanent information system on the international oil market.

▌ To improve the world's energy supply and demand structure by developing alternative energy sources and increasing the efficiency of energy use.

▌ To promote international collaboration on energy technology.

▌ To assist in the integration of environmental and energy policies.

The IEA member countries are: Australia, Austria, Belgium, Canada, Czech Republic, Denmark, Finland, France, Germany, Greece, Hungary, Ireland, Italy, Japan, Republic of Korea, Luxembourg, Netherlands, New Zealand, Norway, Poland, Portugal, Slovak Republic, Spain, Sweden, Switzerland, Turkey, United Kingdom and United States. The European Commission also participates in the work of the IEA.

ORGANISATION FOR ECONOMIC CO-OPERATION AND DEVELOPMENT

The OECD is a unique forum where the governments of thirty democracies work together to address the economic, social and environmental challenges of globalisation. The OECD is also at the forefront of efforts to understand and to help governments respond to new developments and concerns, such as corporate governance, the information economy and the challenges of an ageing population. The Organisation provides a setting where governments can compare policy experiences, seek answers to common problems, identify good practice and work to co-ordinate domestic and international policies.

The OECD member countries are: Australia, Austria, Belgium, Canada, Czech Republic, Denmark, Finland, France, Germany, Greece, Hungary, Iceland, Ireland, Italy, Japan, Republic of Korea, Luxembourg, Mexico, Netherlands, New Zealand, Norway, Poland, Portugal, Slovak Republic, Spain, Sweden, Switzerland, Turkey, United Kingdom and United States. The European Commission takes part in the work of the OECD.

AGENCE INTERNATIONALE DE L'ÉNERGIE

L'Agence Internationale de l'Énergie (AIE) est un organe autonome institué en novembre 1974 dans le cadre de l'Organisation de coopération et de développement économiques (OCDE) afin de mettre en œuvre un programme international de l'énergie.

Elle applique un programme général de coopération dans le domaine de l'énergie entre vingt-huit des trente pays membres de l'OCDE. Les objectifs fondamentaux de l'AIE sont les suivants :

▪ Tenir à jour et améliorer des systèmes permettant de faire face à des perturbations des approvisionnements pétroliers.

▪ Œuvrer en faveur de politiques énergétiques rationnelles dans un contexte mondial grâce à des relations de coopération avec les pays non membres, l'industrie et les organisations internationales.

▪ Gérer un système d'information continue sur le marché international du pétrole.

▪ Améliorer la structure de l'offre et de la demande mondiales d'énergie en favorisant la mise en valeur de sources d'énergie de substitution et une utilisation plus rationnelle de l'énergie.

▪ Promouvoir la collaboration internationale dans le domaine de la technologie énergétique.

▪ Contribuer à l'intégration des politiques d'énergie et d'environnement.

Les pays membres de l'AIE sont : Allemagne, Australie, Autriche, Belgique, Canada, Danemark, Espagne, États-Unis, Finlande, France, Grèce, Hongrie, Irlande, Italie, Japon, Luxembourg, Norvège, Nouvelle-Zélande, Pays-Bas, Pologne, Portugal, République de Corée, République Slovaque, République Tchèque, Royaume-Uni, Suède, Suisse et Turquie. La Commission Européenne participe également aux travaux de l'AIE.

ORGANISATION DE COOPÉRATION ET DE DÉVELOPPEMENT ÉCONOMIQUES

L'OCDE est un forum unique en son genre où les gouvernements de trente démocraties œuvrent ensemble pour relever les défis économiques, sociaux et environnementaux que pose la mondialisation. L'OCDE est aussi à l'avant-garde des efforts entrepris pour comprendre les évolutions du monde actuel et les préoccupations qu'elles font naître. Elle aide les gouvernements à faire face à des situations nouvelles en examinant des thèmes tels que le gouvernement d'entreprise, l'économie de l'information et les défis posés par le vieillissement de la population. L'Organisation offre aux gouvernements un cadre leur permettant de comparer leurs expériences en matière de politiques, de chercher des réponses à des problèmes communs, d'identifier les bonnes pratiques et de travailler à la coordination des politiques nationales et internationales.

Les pays membres de l'OCDE sont : Allemagne, Australie, Autriche, Belgique, Canada, Danemark, Espagne, États-Unis, Finlande, France, Grèce, Hongrie, Irlande, Islande, Italie, Japon, Luxembourg, Mexique, Norvège, Nouvelle Zélande, Pays-Bas, Pologne, Portugal, République de Corée, République slovaque, République tchèque, Royaume-Uni, Suède, Suisse et Turquie. La Commission européenne participe aux travaux de l'OCDE.

FOREWORD

Recent years have witnessed a fundamental change in the way governments approach energy-related environmental issues. Promoting sustainable development and combating climate change have become integral aspects of energy planning, analysis and policy making in many countries, including all IEA member states.

In recognition of the importance attached to the environmental aspects of energy, the IEA has prepared this edition of its published statistics on CO$_2$ emissions from fossil-fuel combustion. These data are also available on CD-ROM and on the Internet.

The purpose of this volume is to put our best and most current information in the hands of those who need it, including in particular the participants in the UNFCCC process. The IEA is a contributor to the official Intergovernmental Panel on Climate Change (IPCC) methodologies for estimating greenhouse gas emissions. The IEA's basic energy balance data are the figures most often cited in the field. For these reasons, we felt it appropriate to publish this information in a comprehensive form.

It is our hope that this book will assist the reader in better understanding the evolution of CO$_2$ emissions from fuel combustion from 1971 to 2006 for more than 140 countries and regions, by sector and by fuel. This publication incorporates comments and suggestions received since the first edition in November 1997.

Most of the data presented in this publication are only for energy-related CO$_2$. Thus they may differ from countries' official submissions of emissions inventories to the UNFCCC Secretariat.

In addition, summary data for CO$_2$ from non-energy-related sources and gas flaring, and emissions of CH$_4$, N$_2$O, HFC, PFC and SF$_6$ are shown in Part III in cooperation with the Netherlands Environmental Assessment Agency (PBL).

The publication also includes information on "Key Sources" from fuel combustion, as developed in the *IPCC Good Practice Guidance and Uncertainty Management in National Greenhouse Gas Inventories*.

This report is published under my responsibility as Executive Director of the IEA and does not necessarily reflect the views of IEA member countries.

Nobuo Tanaka
Executive Director

AVANT-PROPOS

Ces dernières années, l'attitude des gouvernements à l'égard des problèmes d'environnement liés à l'énergie a radicalement changé. L'action en faveur du développement durable et la lutte contre le changement climatique sont désormais des aspects intégrés à la planification, l'analyse et la prise de décisions dans le domaine de l'énergie dans nombre de pays, et notamment dans tous les pays Membres de l'AIE.

Reconnaissant l'importance attachée aux aspects environnementaux de l'énergie, l'AIE a préparé cette édition de ses statistiques sur les émissions de CO_2 imputables à la combustion de combustibles fossiles. Ces données sont également disponibles sous forme de CD-ROM et sur Internet.

Le présent ouvrage a pour objet de mettre nos informations les meilleures et les plus récentes à la disposition de ceux qui en ont besoin, et tout particulièrement des participants aux travaux relatifs à la CCNUCC. L'AIE contribue à l'élaboration des méthodologies officielles du Groupe d'experts intergouvernemental sur l'évolution du climat (GIEC) pour l'estimation des émissions de gaz à effet de serre. Les données de base des bilans énergétiques de l'AIE sont les chiffres les plus fréquemment cités dans ce domaine. Il nous a donc semblé opportun, pour ces motifs, de publier ces informations de manière très complète.

Nous avons bon espoir que le présent ouvrage aidera le lecteur à mieux appréhender l'évolution des émissions de CO_2 dues à la combustion d'énergie entre 1971 et 2006 dans plus de 140 pays et régions, par secteur et par combustible. Cette publication tient compte des observations et suggestions qui nous ont été communiquées depuis la première édition de novembre 1997.

La majorité des données concernent seulement les émissions de CO_2 liées à l'énergie. Elles peuvent donc différer des données figurant dans les communications nationales officielles des inventaires des émissions transmises au Secrétariat de la CCNUCC.

De plus, des données synthétiques relatives aux émissions de CO_2 liées à des sources non-énergétiques et au gaz brûlé à la torche, et aux émissions de CH_4, N_2O, HFC, PFC et SF_6 figurent dans la Partie III en coopération avec la Netherlands Environmental Assessment Agency (PBL).

La publication comprend aussi des informations sur les « sources principales » dues à la combustion d'énergie, comme l'indique le IPCC *Good Practice Guidance and Uncertainty Management in National Greenhouse Gas Inventories* (Guide de bonne pratique et gestion des incertitudes dans les inventaires nationaux de gaz à effet de serre) du GIEC.

Le présent rapport est publié sous ma responsabilité, en qualité de Directeur exécutif de l'AIE, et ne traduit pas nécessairement les points de vue des pays Membres de l'AIE.

Nobuo Tanaka
Directeur exécutif

TABLE OF CONTENTS

INTRODUCTION

PART I: METHODOLOGY

PART II: CO₂ EMISSIONS FROM FUEL COMBUSTION

SUMMARY TABLES

GLOBAL AND REGIONAL TOTALS

COUNTRY TABLES

PART III: GREENHOUSE GAS EMISSIONS

Kyoto Protocol base years

The year 1990 should be the base year for the estimation and reporting of inventories. According to the provisions of Article 4.6 of the Convention and Decisions 9/CP.2 and 11/CP.4, the following Annex I Parties that are undergoing the process of transition to a market economy, are allowed to use a base year or a period of years other than 1990, as follows:

Bulgaria:	to use 1988
Hungary:	to use the average of the years 1985 to 1987
Poland:	to use 1988
Romania:	to use 1989
Slovenia:	to use 1986

TABLE DES MATIERES

INTRODUCTION

PARTIE I: METHODOLOGIE

PARTIE II : EMISSIONS DE CO₂ DUES A LA COMBUSTION D'ENERGIE

TABLEAUX RECAPITULATIFS

TOTAUX MONDIAUX ET REGIONAUX

TABLEAUX PAR PAYS

PARTIE III : EMISSIONS DE GAZ A EFFET DE SERRE

Années de référence du Protocole de Kyoto

L'année de référence pour l'estimation et la notification des inventaires devrait être 1990. En application des dispositions de l'article 4.6 de la Convention et des Décisions 9/CP.2 et 11/CP.4, les Parties de l'Annexe I citées ci-après qui sont en transition vers une économie de marché sont autorisées à utiliser une année ou période d'années de référence autre que 1990, à savoir :

Bulgarie : 1988
Hongrie : moyenne des années 1985 à 1987
Pologne : 1988
Roumanie : 1989
Slovénie : 1986

Important cautionary notes

- The estimates of CO_2 emissions from fuel combustion presented in this publication are calculated using the IEA energy balances and the default methods and emission factors from the *Revised 1996 IPCC Guidelines for National Greenhouse Gas Inventories*. There are many reasons why **the IEA estimates may not be the same as the numbers that a country submits to the UNFCCC**, even if a country has accounted for all of its energy use and correctly applied the *IPCC Guidelines*.

- In this publication, the IEA presents CO_2 emissions calculated using both the IPCC Reference Approach and the IPCC Tier 1 Sectoral Approach. In some of the Non-OECD countries, there can be **large differences between the two sets of calculations** due to various problems in some energy data. As a consequence, this can lead to different emission trends between 1990 and 2006 for certain countries. Please see Chapter 1, "IEA emissions estimates" for further details.

- Information on "key sources" from fuel combustion, as developed in the *IPCC Good Practice Guidance and Uncertainty Management in National Greenhouse Gas Inventories*, are only given for combustion sources and will not include key sources from fugitive emissions, industrial processes, solvents, agriculture and waste. Please see Chapter 1, "IEA emissions estimates" and Chapter 5, "IPCC methodologies" for further information.

Energy data on OECD and Non-OECD countries are collected by the Energy Statistics Division (ESD) of the IEA Secretariat, headed by Mr. Jean-Yves Garnier. Ms. Karen Tréanton, with the assistance of Ms. Ana Padilla and Mr. Stève Gervais, is responsible for the estimates of CO_2 emissions from fuel combustion. Secretarial support was supplied by Ms. Sharon Burghgraeve.

CO_2 emission estimates from 1960 to 2006 for the Annex II countries and from 1971 to 2006 for all other countries are available on CD-ROM suitable for use on IBM-compatible personal computers. To order, please see the information provided at the end of this publication.

In addition, a data service is available on the Internet. It includes unlimited access through an annual subscription as well as the possibility to obtain data on a pay-per-view basis. Details are available at http:\\www.iea.org.

Enquiries about data or methodology should be addressed to:

Ms. Karen Tréanton:
Telephone: (+33-1) 40-57-66-33,
Fax: (+33-1) 40-57-66-49,
E-mail: emissions@iea.org.

Note	See multilingual glossary at the end of the publication.
Attention	Voir le glossaire en plusieurs langues à la fin du présent recueil.
Achtung	Deutsches GLOSSAR auf der letzten Umschlagseite.
Attenzione	Riferirsi al glossario multilingue alla fine del libro.
注意事項	巻末の日本語用語集を参照
Nota	Véase el glosario plurilingüe al final del libro.
Примеч.	Смотрите многоязычный словарь в конце книги.

Avertissement important

- Les estimations des émissions de CO$_2$ dues à la combustion d'énergie présentées dans cette publication sont calculées à partir des bilans énergétiques de l'AIE ainsi qu'à l'aide des méthodes et des coefficients d'émission par défaut des *Lignes directrices du GIEC pour les inventaires nationaux de gaz à effet de serre - Version révisée 1996*. Pour de nombreuses raisons, **les estimations de l'AIE peuvent différer des chiffres communiqués par un pays à la CCNUCC**, même si ce pays a rendu compte de la totalité de sa consommation d'énergie et correctement appliqué les *Lignes directrices du GIEC*.

- Dans cette publication, l'AIE présente les émissions de CO$_2$ calculées selon deux méthodes : la méthode de référence du GIEC et la méthode sectorielle du niveau 1 du GIEC. Dans certains pays non-membres de l'OCDE, **d'importantes différences entre les deux méthodes** peuvent apparaître suite à des problèmes dans les données énergétiques. En conséquence, la tendance pour certains pays entre 1990 et 2006 peut différer selon la méthode de calcul choisie. Le lecteur est invité à se reporter au chapitre 1, "Estimations des émissions de l'AIE", pour plus de détails.

- Des informations sur les sources principales dues à la combustion d'énergie, selon la méthodologie développée dans le *Good Practice Guidance and Uncertainty Management in National Greenhouse Gas Inventories* (Guide de bonne pratique et gestion des incertitudes dans les inventaires nationaux de gaz à effet de serre), concernent uniquement les sources de combustion et ne comprennent pas les émissions fugitives, ainsi que les émissions liées aux procédés industriels, aux solvants, à l'agriculture et aux déchets. Pour plus d'informations, consultez le chapitre 1, « Estimations des émissions de l'AIE » et le chapitre 5, « Méthodologies GIEC ».

Les données énergétiques concernant les pays Membres et non membres de l'OCDE sont recueillies par la Division des statistiques de l'énergie (ESD) du Secrétariat de l'AIE, dirigée par M. Jean-Yves Garnier. Mme Karen Tréanton, avec l'assistance de Mme Ana Padilla et M. Stève Gervais, est responsable des estimations des émissions de CO$_2$ dues à la combustion d'énergie. Les travaux de secrétariat ont été assurés par Mme Sharon Burghgraeve.

Les estimations des émissions de CO$_2$ entre 1960 et 2006 pour les pays de l'Annexe II et entre 1971 et 2006 pour tous les autres pays sont disponibles sur CD-ROM utilisables sur ordinateur personnel compatible IBM. Pour les commander, on trouvera des informations à la fin de la présente publication.

En outre, un service de données est disponible sur Internet. Ce service comprend un abonnement annuel pour un accès illimité ou bien la possibilité de payer uniquement pour des données sélectionnées. Pour plus de détails, veuillez consulter http://www.iea.org.

Les demandes d'information sur les données ou la méthodologie doivent être adressées à :

Mme Karen Tréanton:
Téléphone: (+33-1) 40-57-66-33,
Fax: (+33-1) 40-57-66-49,
E-mail: emissions@iea.org.

Attention	See multilingual glossary at the end of the publication.
Attention	Voir le glossaire en plusieurs langues à la fin du présent recueil.
Achtung	Deutsches GLOSSAR auf der letzten Umschlagseite.
Attenzione	Riferirsi al glossario multilingue alla fine del libro.
注意事項	巻 末 の 日 本 語 用 語 集 を 参 照
Nota	Véase el glosario plurilingüe al final del libro.
Примеч.	Смотрите многоязычный словарь в конце книги.

ABBREVIATIONS

Btu:	British thermal unit
GJ:	gigajoule
Gt C:	gigatonnes of carbon
GWh:	gigawatt hour
J:	joule
kcal:	kilocalorie
kg:	kilogramme
kt:	thousand tonnes
ktoe:	thousand tonnes of oil equivalent
kWh:	kilowatt hour
MJ:	megajoule
Mt:	million tonnes
Mtoe:	million tonnes of oil equivalent
m^3:	cubic metre
PJ:	petajoule
t:	metric ton = tonne = 1 000 kg
t C:	tonne of carbon
Tcal:	teracalorie
TJ:	terajoule
toe:	tonne of oil equivalent = 10^7 kcal
CEF:	carbon emission factor
CHP:	combined heat and power
GCV:	gross calorific value
GDP:	gross domestic product
HHV:	higher heating value = GCV
LHV:	lower heating value = NCV
NCV:	net calorific value
PPP:	purchasing power parity
TPES:	total primary energy supply
AGBM:	Ad Hoc Group on the Berlin Mandate under the United Nations Framework Convention on Climate Change
AIJ:	Activities Implemented Jointly under the United Nations Framework Convention on Climate Change
Annex I:	See Chapter 4, Geographical coverage
Annex II:	See Chapter 4, Geographical coverage
CDM:	Clean Development Mechanism
Convention:	United Nations Framework Convention on Climate Change
COP:	Conference of the Parties to the Convention
EITs:	Economies in Transition (see Chapter 4, Geographical coverage)
IEA:	International Energy Agency
IPCC:	Intergovernmental Panel on Climate Change
OECD:	Organisation for Economic Co-Operation and Development
OLADE:	Organización Latino Americana De Energía
SBI:	Subsidiary Body for Implementation
SBSTA:	Subsidiary Body for Scientific and Technological Advice
TCA:	Technology Co-operation Agreement
UN:	United Nations
UNECE:	United Nations Economic Commission for Europe
UNFCCC:	United Nations Framework Convention on Climate Change
..	not available
-	nil
x	not applicable
+	growth greater than 1 000%

ABREVIATIONS

Btu:	unité thermique britannique
GJ:	gigajoule
Gt C:	gigatonne de carbone
GWh:	gigawattheure
J:	joule
kcal:	kilocalorie
kg:	kilogramme
kt:	millier de tonnes
ktep:	millier de tonnes d'équivalent pétrole
kWh:	kilowattheure
m^3:	mètre cube
MJ:	mégajoule
Mt:	million de tonnes
Mtep:	million de tonnes d'équivalent pétrole
PJ:	pétajoule
t:	tonne = 1 000 kg
t C:	tonne de carbone
Tcal:	téracalorie
tep:	tonne d'équivalent pétrole = 10^7 kcal
TJ:	térajoule
ATEP:	approvisionnements totaux en énergie primaire
CEC:	coefficient d'émission de carbone
PCI:	pouvoir calorifique inférieur
PCS:	pouvoir calorifique supérieur
PIB:	produit intérieur brut
PPA:	parité de pouvoir d'achat
AGBM:	Groupe spécial du Mandat de Berlin sous couvert de la Convention-cadre des Nations Unies sur les changements climatiques
AIE:	Agence internationale de l'énergie
AIJ:	Activités exécutées conjointement en application de la Convention-cadre des Nations Unies sur les changements climatiques
Annexe I:	Voir chapitre 4, couverture géographique
Annexe II:	Voir chapitre 4, couverture géographique
CCNUCC:	Convention-cadre des Nations Unies sur les changements climatiques
CEE(ONU):	Commission économique pour l'Europe des Nations Unies
Convention:	Convention-cadre des Nations Unies sur les changements climatiques
COP:	Conférence des Parties à la Convention
EET:	Economies en transition (voir chapitre 4, couverture géographique)
GIEC:	Groupe d'experts intergouvernemental sur l'évolution du climat
OCDE:	Organisation de coopération et de développement économiques
OLADE:	Organización Latino Americana D'Energía
ONU:	Organisation des Nations Unies
SBI:	Organe subsidiaire de mise en œuvre
SBSTA:	Organe subsidiaire de conseil scientifique et technologique
..	non disponible
-	néant
x	sans objet
+	croissance de plus de 1 000%

THE ENERGY - CLIMATE CHALLENGE

Energy and climate change

In the *Fourth Assessment Report*[1], the Intergovernmental Panel on Climate Change (IPCC)[2] concluded, "Most of the observed increase in global average temperatures since the mid-20th century is *very likely* due to the observed increase in anthropogenic greenhouse gas concentrations". The language "very likely" has been upgraded from the "likely" that was referred to in the *Third Assessment Report*, thus confirming the increasing acceptance by scientists of the link between GHG emissions and global climate change. Energy production and use has various environmental implications. In particular, fuel combustion is responsible for the largest share of global anthropogenic greenhouse gas emissions.

Greenhouse gases and global warming

The increased concentrations of key greenhouse gases are a direct consequence of human activities. Since anthropogenic greenhouse gases accumulate in the atmosphere, they produce net warming by strengthening the natural "greenhouse effect".

Carbon dioxide (CO$_2$) has been increasing compared to the rather steady level of the pre-industrial era (about 280 parts per million in volume, or ppmv). The 2005 concentration of CO$_2$ (379 ppmv) was about 35% higher than a century and a half ago, with the fastest growth occurring in the last ten years (1.9 ppmv/year in the period 1995-2005). Comparable growth has occurred in levels of methane (CH$_4$) and nitrous oxide (N$_2$O).

Some impacts of the increased greenhouse gas concentrations may be slow to become apparent since stability is an inherent characteristic of the interacting climate, ecological, and socio-economic systems. Even after stabilization of the atmospheric concentration of CO$_2$, anthropogenic warming and sea level rise would continue for centuries due to the time scales associated with climate processes and feedbacks. Some changes in the climate system would be effectively irreversible.

Given the long lifetime of CO$_2$ in the atmosphere, stabilizing concentrations of greenhouse gases at any level would require large reductions of global CO$_2$ emissions from current levels. The lower the chosen level for stabilization, the sooner the decline in global CO$_2$ emissions would need to begin, or the deeper the emission reduction would need to be on the longer term.

The 1992 U.N. Framework Convention on Climate Change (UNFCCC)[3] sets an overall framework for intergovernmental efforts to tackle the challenge posed by climate change. The Convention's ultimate objective is to stabilise GHG concentrations in the atmosphere at a level that would prevent dangerous anthropogenic interference with the climate system. This would require significant reductions in global greenhouse gas emissions.

---

1. *IPCC Fourth Assessment Report – Climate Change 2007*, available at http://www.ipcc.ch. In the summary for Policymakers, the following terms have been used to indicate the assessed likelihood, using expert judgement, of an outcome or a result: *Virtually certain* > 99% probability of occurrence, *Extremely likely* > 95%, *Very likely* > 90%, *Likely* > 66%, *More likely than not* > 50%, *Unlikely* < 33%, *Very unlikely* < 10%, *Extremely unlikely* < 5%.

2. The IPCC was created in 1988 by the World Meteorological Organization and the United Nations Environment Programme to assess scientific, technical and socio-economic information relevant for the understanding of climate change, its potential impacts, and options for adaptation and mitigation.

---

3. See http://unfccc.int.

Energy use and greenhouse gases

Among the many human activities that produce greenhouse gases the use of energy represents by far the largest source of emissions. As seen in Figure 1, energy accounts for over 80% of the anthropogenic greenhouse gases in Annex I countries, with emissions resulting from the production, transformation, handling and consumption of all kinds of energy commodities. Smaller shares correspond to agriculture, producing mainly CH_4 and N_2O from domestic livestock and rice cultivation, and to industrial processes not related to energy, producing mainly fluorinated gases and N_2O.

Figure 1. Shares of anthropogenic greenhouse gas emissions in Annex I countries, 2005*

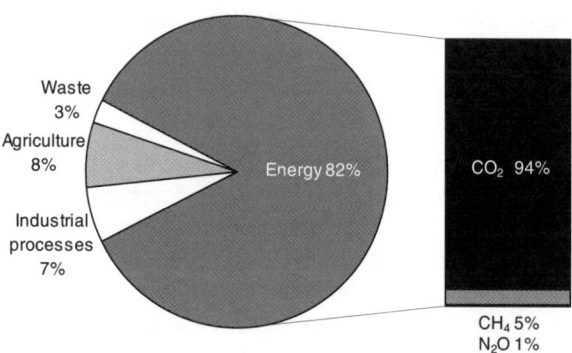

Source: UNFCCC.

* Based on Annex I data for 2005; without Land Use, Land Use Change and Forestry, and with Solvent Use included in Industrial Processes.

Key point: Accounting for the largest share of global greenhouse gas emissions, energy emissions are predominently CO_2.

The energy sector is dominated by the direct combustion of fuels[4], a process leading to large emissions of CO_2. A by-product of fuel combustion, CO_2 results from the oxidation of carbon in fuels (in perfect combustion conditions, the total carbon content of fuels would be converted to CO_2).

CO_2 from energy represents about 80% of the anthropogenic greenhouse gas emissions for the Annex I

countries[5] and about 60% of global emissions. This percentage varies greatly by country, due to diverse national energy structures.

Worldwide economic stability and development require energy. As illustrated in Figure 2, the total primary energy supply (TPES) of the world doubled between 1971 and 2006, mainly relying on fossil fuels.

Figure 2. World primary energy supply*

Gigatonnes of oil equivalent

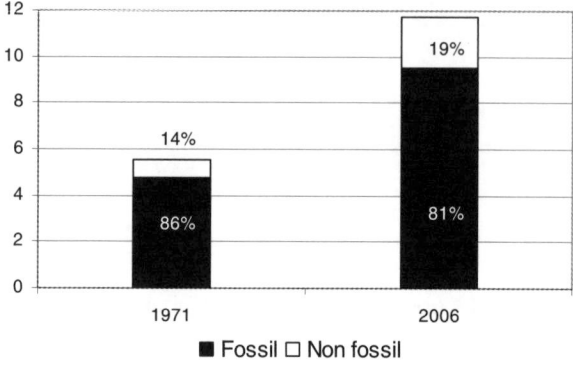

* World primary energy supply includes international bunkers.

Key point: Fossil fuels still satisfy most of the world energy supply.

Despite the growth of non-fossil energy (such as nuclear and hydropower) considered as non-emitting[6], fossil fuels have maintained their shares of the world energy supply relatively unchanged over the course of the past 35 years. In 2006, fossil sources accounted for 81% of the global TPES.

Still dependent upon fossil fuels, the growing world energy demand clearly plays a key role in the observed upward trends in CO_2 emissions illustrated in Figure 3. Since the industrial revolution, annual CO_2 emissions from fuel combustion dramatically increased from near zero to 28 Gt CO_2 in 2006.

---

4. Energy includes emissions from "fuel combustion" (the large majority) and "fugitive emissions", which are intentional or unintentional releases of gases resulting from production, processes, transmission, storage and use of fuels (e.g. CH_4 emissions from coal mining or oil and gas systems).

5. Based on Annex I countries. The Annex I Parties to the UNFCCC are: Australia, Austria, Belarus, Belgium, Bulgaria, Canada, Croatia, Czech Republic, Denmark, Estonia, European Economic Community, Finland, France, Germany, Greece, Hungary, Iceland, Ireland, Italy, Japan, Latvia, Lichtenstein, Lithuania, Luxembourg, Monaco, the Netherlands, New Zealand, Norway, Poland, Portugal, Romania, Russia, the Slovak Republic, Slovenia, Spain, Sweden, Switzerland, Turkey, Ukraine, United Kingdom and United States.

6. Excluding the life cycle of all non-emitting sources and excluding combustion of biomass (considered as non-emitting CO_2, based on the assumption that the released carbon will be reabsorbed by biomass regrowth, under balanced conditions).

Figure 3. Trend in CO_2 emissions from fossil fuel combustion

Gigatonnes of CO_2

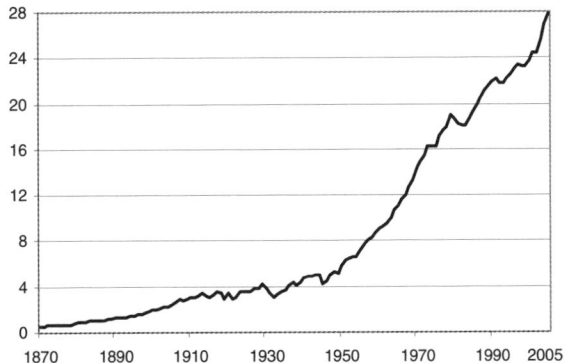

Source: Carbon Dioxide Information Analysis Center, Oak Ridge National Laboratory, U.S. Department of Energy, Oak Ridge, Tenn., United States.

Key point: Since 1870, CO_2 emissions from fuel combustion have risen exponentially.

The *World Energy Outlook*[7] projects that world energy supply will rise by 45% between 2006 and 2030. With fossil fuels remaining at 80% of TPES, CO_2 emissions are consequently expected to continue their growth unabated, reaching 40.6 Gt CO_2 by 2030.

IPCC projections of climate impacts are consistent with this growth in energy demand. Based on the IPCC report[8], by 2100, temperatures are projected to rise by between 1.8 and 4.0°C, depending on the scenario.

The link between climate change and energy is a part of the larger challenge of sustainable development. The socio-economic and technological characteristics of development paths will strongly affect emissions, the rate and magnitude of climate change, climate change impacts, the capability to adapt, and the capacity to mitigate the emissions themselves.

Scrutinizing the sources of CO_2 emissions

Trends in CO_2 emissions from fuel combustion illustrate the need for the global economy to shape a more sustainable energy future, with special emphasis first

---

7. Unless otherwise specified, projections from the *World Energy Outlook* refer to the Reference Scenario from the 2008 edition.

8. *IPCC Fourth Assessment Report – Climate Change 2007.*

on the industrialised nations, with the highest per capita incomes and that are responsible for the bulk of cumulative emissions. However, with the rapidly growing energy demand of developing countries, it is important that they also strive to use energy in a rational way. *Energy Technology Perspectives 2008* shows that enhancing energy efficiency and reducing the carbon intensity of a supply largely reliant on fossil fuels are fundamental steps towards a global low-carbon energy system.

Annual snapshot: 2005-2006

The most recent annual changes in CO_2 emissions by fuel type are illustrated in Figure 4. The global increase between 2005 and 2006 was 0.9 Gt CO_2 and was primarily due to an increase in the coal demand of developing countries (Non-Annex I Parties to the UNFCCC). This represented a growth rate of 3% in CO_2 emissions, identical to that of the previous year.

Figure 4. Global change in CO_2 emissions (2005-2006)

Million tonnes of CO_2

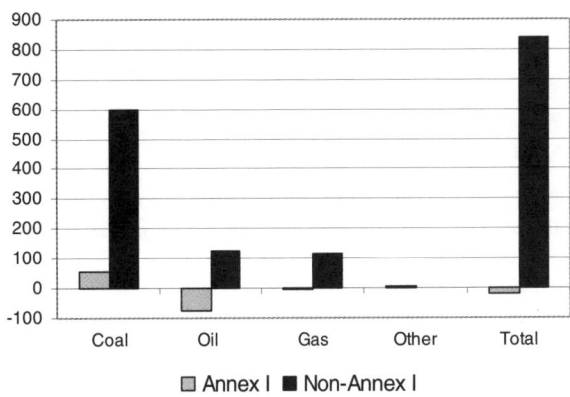

Key point: Combustion of coal in developing countries drove the growth in global emissions between 2005 and 2006.

In the future, coal is expected to satisfy much of the growing energy demand of those developing countries, such as China and India, where energy-intensive industrial production is growing rapidly and large coal reserves exist with limited reserves of other energy sources. *Energy Technology Perspectives 2008* shows that intensified use of coal would substantially increase the emissions of CO_2 unless there was very widespread deployment of carbon capture and storage.

Fuel contribution to CO$_2$ emissions

Though coal represented only a quarter of the world TPES in 2006, as shown in Figure 5, it accounted for 42% of the global CO$_2$ emissions due to its heavy carbon content per unit of energy released. As compared to gas, coal is on average nearly twice as emission intensive[9]. Without additional measures, the *World Energy Outlook* projects that coal supply will grow from 3 053 million tonnes of oil equivalent (Mtoe) in 2006 to 4 908 Mtoe in 2030.

Figure 5. World primary energy supply and CO$_2$ emissions: shares by fuel in 2006

Percent share

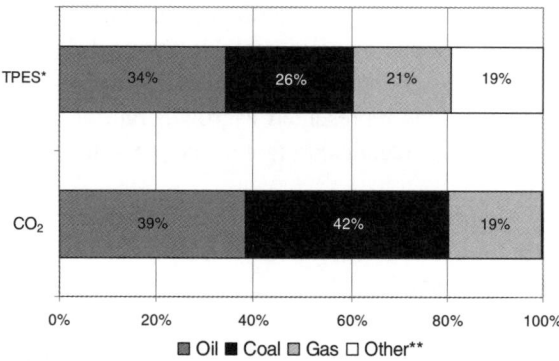

* TPES includes international bunkers.

** Other includes nuclear, hydro, geothermal, solar, tide, wind, combustible renewables and waste.

Key point: Coal generates about twice the CO$_2$ emissions of gas, despite having a comparable share in the world energy supply.

Oil still dominates TPES, with a share of 34% in 2006. However, the share of oil in TPES decreased by about ten percentage points since 1971, largely counterbalanced by the penetration of gas. The supply of gas in 2006 was more than two and a half times higher than in 1971 and its share in emissions increased by five percentage points over that period.

Observed and projected trends in TPES and CO$_2$ emissions vary greatly by country, depending on stages of economic development and related energy choices, as illustrated in the next section.

Emissions by region

The dramatic increase of Non-Annex I emissions between 2005 and 2006, seen in Figure 4 above, corroborated the growth already observed over the last decade. Figure 6 shows trends over the period 1971-2006, highlighting changes in the relative contributions from major world regions.

Figure 6. Trends in regional CO$_2$ emissions

Gigatonnes of CO$_2$

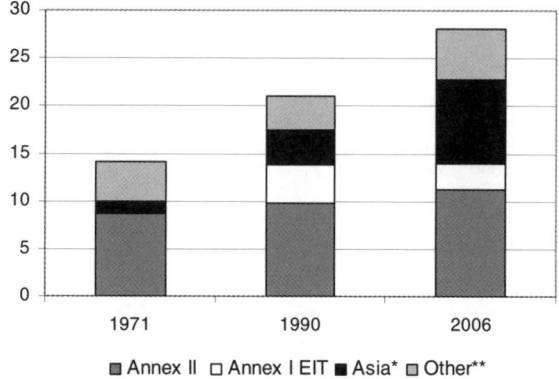

* Asia includes Korea and excludes Japan (which is included in Annex II).

** Other includes Africa, Latin America, Middle East, Non-Annex I EIT, Turkey, international bunkers, and, for 1971, Annex I EIT.

Key point: Asian emissions will soon rival those of Annex II.

Between 1971 and 2006, global emissions nearly doubled, with industrialized countries (Annex II Parties to the UNFCCC[10]) dominating historical totals. However, the share of Annex II progressively shrank (61% in 1971, 47% in 1990 and 40% in 2006), as developing countries, led by Asia, increased at a much faster rate. Between 1990 and 2006, CO$_2$ emissions rose by 95% for Non-Annex I countries as a whole and more than doubled for Asia. This is in contrast to the 14% growth which occurred in the Annex II countries. The growth in Asian emissions reflects a striking rate of economic development, particularly within China and India.

---

9. IPCC default carbon emission factors from the *1996 IPCC Guidelines*: 15.3 t C/TJ for gas, 16.8 to 27.5 t C/TJ for oil products, 25.8 to 29.1 t C/TJ for primary coal products.

10. The original Annex II Parties to the UNFCCC are Australia, Austria, Belgium, Canada, Denmark, European Economic Community, Finland, France, Germany, Greece, Iceland, Ireland, Italy, Japan, Liechtenstein, Luxembourg, Monaco, Netherlands, New Zealand, Norway, Portugal, Spain, Sweden, Switzerland, Turkey, United Kingdom and United States. Turkey was removed from Annex II on 28 June 2002.

Emissions from the group of countries with economies in transition (Annex I EIT[11]) followed a peculiar path due to a rapid decline in industrial productivity subsequent to the 1989 collapse of their centrally planned economies. Between 1990 and 2000, the EIT emissions declined by 36%. Emissions in the former USSR alone fell by over 1.4 Gt CO_2, or 39%, between 1990 and 2000. However, this trend was reversed in recent years.

Regional differences in contributions to global emissions conceal even larger differences among individual countries, as illustrated in Figure 7. Two-thirds of world emissions for 2006 originated from just ten countries, with the shares of the United States and China far surpassing those of all others. Combined, these two countries alone produced 11.3 Gt CO_2, about 40% of 2006 world CO_2 emissions.

Figure 7. Top-10 emitting countries in 2006

Gigatonnes of CO₂

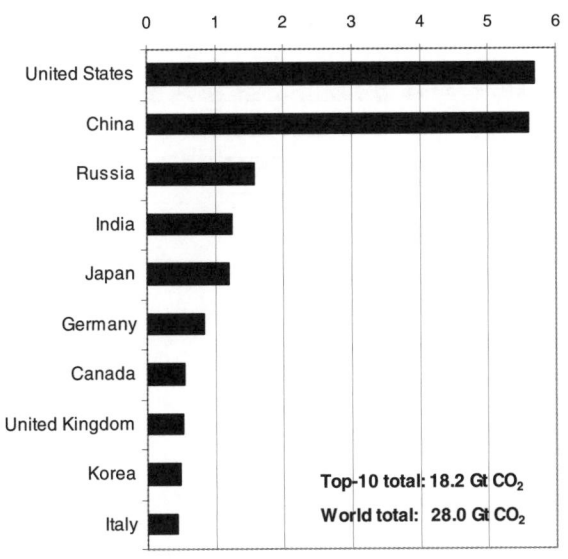

Key point: The top-10 emitting countries account for about two-thirds of the world CO_2 emissions.

This top-ten group, which includes countries of very diverse economic structures, also produced 63% of the global GDP[12]. As detailed in the following section, economic output and CO_2 emissions are generally strongly linked.

---

11. Annex I EIT Parties include: Belarus, Bulgaria, Croatia, Czech Republic, Slovak Republic, Estonia, Hungary, Latvia, Lithuania, Poland, Romania, Russia, Slovenia and Ukraine.

12. In this discussion, GDP refers to GDP using purchasing power parities.

Coupling emissions with socio-economic indicators[13]

In 2006, the United States, China, Russia, India and Japan, the largest five emitters, produced together 55% of the global CO_2 emissions, 50% of the world GDP and comprised 46% of the total population. However, for all three variables, the relative shares of these five countries within the subtotal of the group were very diverse, as illustrated in Figure 8.

Figure 8. Top-5 emitting countries: relative shares in 2006

Percent share

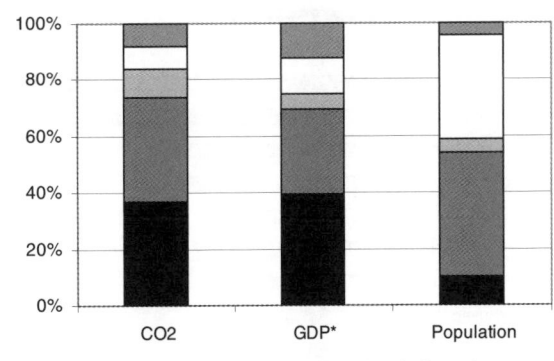

* GDP using purchasing power parities.

Note: this is not "world shares", but "relative shares" within the top-five.

Key point: Within the top-5 emitting countries, the relative share of CO_2 emissions does not necessarily follow those of GDP and population.

In 2006, the United States alone generated 20% of world CO_2 emissions, despite a population of less than 5% of the global total. Conversely, China and India together, contributing to a comparable share of world emissions (20% and 4%), accounted for almost 40% of the world population. Thus, the levels of per capita emissions were very diverse, ranging from 1 tonne of CO_2 per capita for India and 4 for China to 19 for the United States.

In the United States, the large share of global emissions is associated with a commensurate share of economic output (GDP), the largest in the world. While the high per capita emissions of the United

---

13. No single indicator can provide a complete picture of a country's CO_2 emissions performance or its relative capacity to reduce emissions. The indicators discussed here provide some guidance but are certainly incomplete.

States in 2006 were comparable to those of 1971, its emissions intensity in terms of economic output (CO_2/GDP) was about half, due to energy efficiency improvements and to economic growth in less-CO_2-intensive sectors over the 35-year period.

With a GDP about two and a half times larger than that of Russia, Japan emits 24% less. As illustrated for major world regions in Figure 9, economies can achieve quite diverse emission efficiencies.

Figure 9. CO₂ emissions per GDP* by major world regions in 2006

Kilogrammes of CO_2 per 2000 US$ PPP

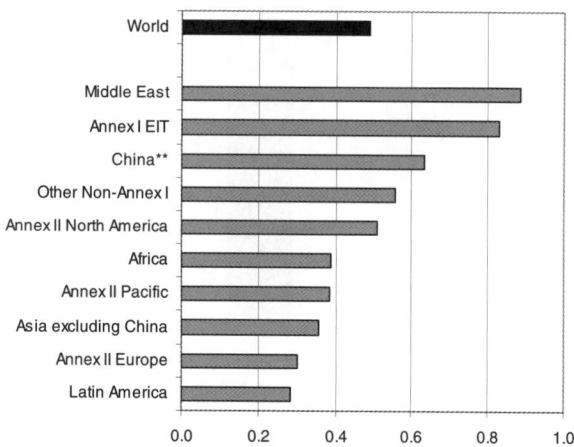

* GDP using purchasing power parities.

** China includes Hong Kong.

Key point: Emissions intensity in economic terms varies greatly around the world.

Worldwide, the highest levels of emissions per GDP are observed for the oil and gas exporting region of the Middle East, for the relatively energy-intensive EITs and for China. The rapid decoupling of emissions from economic growth that characterized the Chinese economy during the 1980s and 1990s has recently slowed and reversed, as noted in subsequent sections.

Relatively high values of emissions per GDP indicate a potential for decoupling CO_2 emissions from economic growth. Possible improvements can derive from fuel switching away from carbon-intensive sources or from energy efficiency at all stages of the energy supply chain (from fuel extraction to energy end-use)[14].

The ratio of CO_2 emissions per GDP responds to changes in energy intensity (energy per unit of GDP) and in the CO_2 intensity of the fuel mix (CO_2 per unit of energy)[15]. For example, industrialized countries witnessed a rapid reduction in emissions per unit of GDP between 1973 and 1990, following the oil price shocks of the 1970s, through a decline in their energy intensity. On the contrary, even on a global scale, the CO_2 intensity of the fuel mix (as measured for example by the ratio of CO_2/TPES) has remained rather constant between 1971 and 2006 as fossil fuels continued to dominate the global energy supply.

As compared to emissions per unit of GDP, the range of per capita emissions levels across the world is even larger, highlighting wide divergences between living standards of different regions, as illustrated in Figure 10.

Figure 10. CO₂ emissions per population by major world regions in 2006

Tonnes of CO_2 per capita

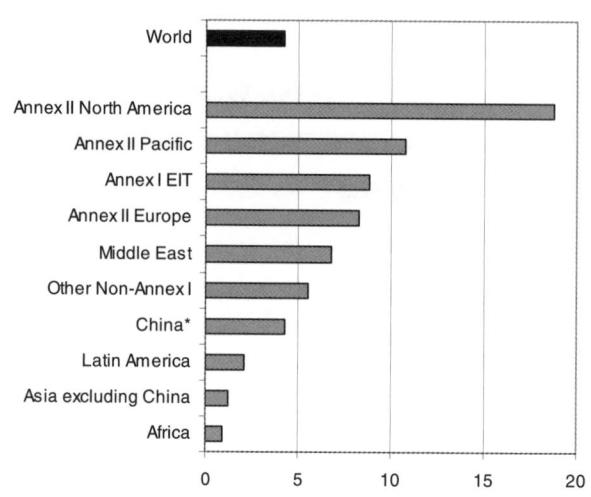

* China includes Hong Kong.

Key point: Emissions per capita vary even more widely across world regions than GDP per capita.

Industrialized countries emit far larger amounts of CO_2 per capita than the world average. However, some rapidly expanding economies are significantly increasing their emissions per capita. For example, between 1990 and 2006, China more than doubled its per capita emissions and India increased them by almost two-thirds. Clearly, these two countries contributed much to the 7% increase of global per capita emissions over the period.

---

14. Since 1999, the IEA has collected and classified energy efficiency policies and measures of its member countries. The online database is available at: http://www.iea.org/textbase/effi/index.asp.

15. See discussion in *Energy Technology Perspectives 2008*, IEA, 2008, p. 71.

Indicators such as those briefly discussed in this section strongly reflect energy constraints and choices made to supply the economic activities of each country. They also reflect the sectors that predominate in different countries' economies. The major sectors driving the observed growth in global emissions are discussed in the next section.

Emissions by sector

In 2006, two sectors, electricity and heat generation and transport, produced nearly two-thirds of the global CO_2 emissions, as illustrated in Figure 11. The emissions of these same sectors also increased at faster rates than global emissions (53% and 41%, respectively, versus the average 33%, between 1990 and 2006).

Figure 11. World CO₂ emissions by sector

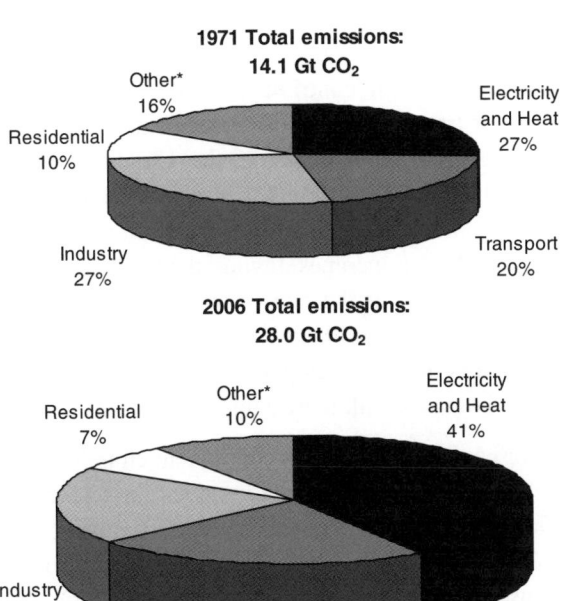

* Other includes commercial/public services, agriculture/forestry, fishing, energy industries other than electricity and heat generation, and other emissions not specified elsewhere.

Key point: Between 1971 and 2006, the combined share of electricity and heat generation and transport shifted from one-half to two-thirds of global emissions.

Generation of electricity and heat was responsible in 2006 for 41% of the world total CO_2 emissions, as compared to 27% in 1971. By 2030, the *World Energy*

Outlook projects that demand for electricity will be almost twice as high as in 2006, driven by rapid growth in population and income in developing countries, by the continuing increase in the number of electrical devices used in homes and commercial buildings, and by the growth in electrically-driven industrial processes.

Worldwide, the generation of electricity and heat relies heavily on coal, amplifying the sector's share in global emissions. Countries such as Australia, China, India, Poland and South Africa produce between 68% and 94% of their electricity and heat through the combustion of coal.

As illustrated in Figure 12, fossil fuels provide over 70% of the world electricity and heat generation. Coal, the dominant source, supplied 40% of the generation in 2006. In Non-Annex I countries, the share of coal in electricity and heat generation increased from 43% in 1992 to 52% in 2006. On the contrary, the share of oil generally decreased across the world (from 12% in 1992 to 6% in 2006 globally). Gas grew significantly in industrialized countries as a result of their fuel switching efforts: Annex II countries increased the share of gas in electricity and heat generation from 12% in 1992 to 21% in 2006. The future development of the emissions intensity of this sector depends strongly on the fuels that are used to generate the electricity. As an indication, Box 1 presents product-specific implied emission factors per unit of electricity produced.

Figure 12. Coal, oil and gas: shares in world electricity and heat generation*

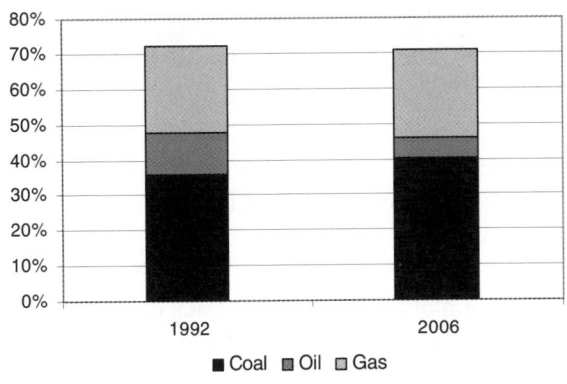

* Refers to main activity producers and autoproducers of electricity and heat.

Key point: World electricity and heat generation increasingly rely on coal.

Box 1: Implied emission factors from electricity and heat generation

Summary tables presenting CO_2 emissions per kWh from electricity and heat generation by country are presented in Part II. However, these values will vary enormously depending on the fuel mix of individual countries. Average implied emission factors by individual product for this sector are presented below. These values represent the average grammes of CO_2 per kWh of electricity and heat produced in the OECD countries between 2004 and 2006. These figures will reflect any problems that may occur in net calorific values or in input/output efficiencies. Consequently, these values are given as an approximation and actual values may vary considerably.

Fuel	Grammes CO₂ / kWh
Anthracite *	920
Coking Coal *	680
Other Bituminous Coal	830
Sub-Bituminous Coal	930
Lignite/Brown Coal	950
Patent Fuel	870
Coke Oven Coke *	500
BKB/Peat Briquettes *	720-1200
Gas Works Gas *	400
Coke Oven Gas *	370
Blast Furnace Gas *	2200
Oxygen Steel Furnace Gas *	1900
Natural Gas	390
Crude Oil *	630
Natural Gas Liquids *	540
Liquefied Petroleum Gases *	470
Kerosene *	580
Gas/Diesel Oil *	750
Residual Fuel Oil	650
Petroleum Coke *	950
Peat *	570
Industrial Waste *	450-1600
Municipal Waste (Non-Renewable) *	450-1900

* These fuels represent less than 1% of electricity and heat output in the OECD. Values will be less reliable and should be used with caution.

Figure 13. CO₂ emissions from oil

Gigatonnes of CO₂

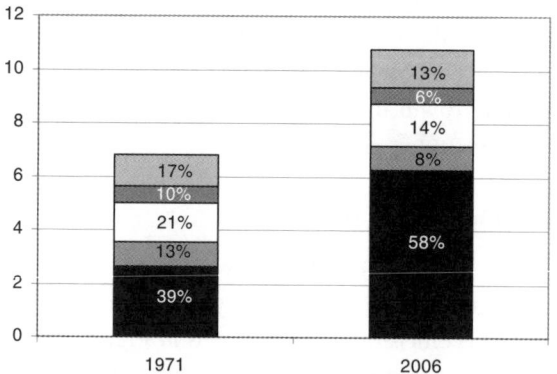

* Other includes commercial/public services, agriculture/forestry, fishing, energy industries other than electricity and heat generation, and other emissions not specified elsewhere.

Key point: With a share that increased by about 50% since 1971, transport dominates emissions from oil.

Economic growth contributes to the increasing demand for transport, both for personal mobility and for shipping goods. For example, the United States has the highest level of travel per capita in the world (more than 25 000 kilometres per person per year). In addition, larger incomes favour the switch to faster modes: air travel is the most rapidly growing mode of transport in industrialized countries, while growth in car travel is first in developing countries. Car ownership generally grows with increasing income per capita.

As for energy intensity and consequent emissions, relatively high fuel prices provide an incentive for more efficient vehicles. In the United States (until recently), lower fuel prices have contributed to a trend towards the use of larger vehicles, while in Europe higher fuel prices have helped encourage improved fuel economy (along with the EU voluntary agreement with manufacturers). As a result, there is more than a 50% variation in the average fuel consumption of new light-duty vehicles across OECD countries[16].

Global demand for transport appears unlikely to decrease in the foreseeable future; the *World Energy Outlook* projects that transport will grow by 42% by 2030. To limit the emissions from this sector, policy

While electricity and heat generation draws from various energy sources, the transport sector relies almost entirely on oil (95% of the energy used for transport came from oil in 2006). The share of transport in global oil emissions was close to 60% in 2006, as shown in Figure 13. While CO_2 emissions from oil consumption in most sectors remained nearly steady in absolute terms since 1971, those of transport more than doubled. Dominated by road traffic, this end-use sector is the strongest driver of world dependence on oil.

---

16. *Energy Technology Perspectives 2008*, IEA, 2008, p. 435.

Box 2: Biofuels*

Compatible with many conventional engines and blendable with current transport fuels, biofuels have the potential to contribute to energy security by diversifying supply sources for transport, and to reduce greenhouse gas emissions. However, the economic, environmental and social benefits of the current generation of biofuels vary enormously.

Though there are important uncertainties about their efficacy in reducing GHG emissions, biofuels can be classified on the basis of their well-to-wheel performance with respect to conventional fossil fuels. When ethanol is derived from corn, the well-to-wheel greenhouse gas reduction with respect to conventional gasoline is typically in the range of 10 to 30%. The reduction is much higher for sugarcane-based ethanol from Brazil, reaching an estimated 90%. Similarly, oilseed-derived biodiesel leads to greenhouse gas reductions, on a well-to-wheel basis, of 40% to 60% when compared to conventional petroleum diesel. "Second generation" biofuels, derived from non-food crops such as trees and perennial grasses, have the potential to dramatically expand the scope for very low CO$_2$ biofuels production. However these biofuels are still under development. None of these estimates takes into account the possibility that changes in land use from starting biofuels production can result in one-time releases of CO$_2$ that could be quite large; more research is needed into the impacts of both direct and indirect land use change and how to minimize adverse impacts.

For both current and second generation biofuels, production cost is the main barrier to a larger penetration of biofuels in the transport fuel mix. Without subsidies, only ethanol from sugarcane produced in Brazil has been competitive with petroleum fuels, although this may change with the higher oil prices occurring recently. The cost barrier is such that market introduction of biofuels has typically required substantial regulatory intervention and governmental support.

Currently, several countries have mandated or promoted biofuel blending standards to displace oil in domestic transport supply. In Brazil, gasoline contains 20-25% ethanol. Furthermore, 70% of the cars now purchased in Brazil can run on either 100% ethanol or on the gasoline/ethanol blend. With recent high oil prices, most drivers are choosing to operate these vehicles mainly on ethanol. In 2006, the United States introduced mandatory standards and these were extended in 2007 under the EISA law. Blending requirements will reach 9 billion gallons in 2008 and will reach 36 billion gallons by 2022 (of which more than half will be required to be second generation biofuels).

Several years ago the European Union introduced a target for biofuel use equivalent to 2% of the market share of motor fuel by 2005 (although it was not reached) and 5.75% by the end of 2010, while the target for 2020 is now set at 10%. The current legislation also requires "sustainability criteria" in order to prevent mass investment in potentially environmentally harmful biofuels. Australia (New South Wales and Queensland) and Canada are also mandating the use of biofuels, as are a number of non-OECD countries.

For the future, it is crucial that policies foster innovation and support the most sustainable biofuels only, through a continuous monitoring and assessment of their effectiveness in reducing GHG emissions and in providing benefits for rural workers. Suitable land availability and potential influence of biofuel production on global food prices also need to be carefully monitored, taking into account all global food, fibre and energy needs for the growing world population out to 2100. However, barriers to the commercial viability of biofuels shrink as technologies evolve and as prices of conventional fossil fuels remain high.

* See discussions in *Biofuels for Transport*, IEA, 2004; *Focus on Biofuels*, IEA Governing Board and Management Committee, June 2006 (IEA/GB(2006)10/REV1) and *Energy Technology Perspectives*, IEA, 2008.

makers first and foremost should consider measures to encourage or require improved vehicle efficiency, as the United States has recently done and the European Union is currently doing as a follow-up to the voluntary agreement. Policies that encourage a shift from cars to public transportation and to lower-emission modes of transportation can also help. Finally, policies can encourage a shift to new, preferably low CO$_2$ fuels. These include electricity (e.g. electric and plug-in hybrid vehicles), hydrogen (e.g. through the introduction of fuel cell vehicles) and greater use of biofuels (e.g. as a blend in gasoline and diesel fuel – see Box 2).

These policies would both reduce the environmental impact of transport and help to secure domestic fuel supplies sometimes unsettled by the geopolitics of oil trade. As they will ease demand growth, these policies

are also likely to help reduce oil prices below what they otherwise might be.

The importance of electricity generation and transport in shaping global CO$_2$ emissions is apparent in Figures 14 and 15, which detail the contributions from individual sectors to trends of the socio-economic indicators discussed in previous sections such as CO$_2$ emissions per GDP and CO$_2$ emissions per capita.

The world average per capita carbon intensity increased marginally since 1971. However, this nearly flat growth concealed a significant rise in the emissions per capita of electricity generation and transport. Between 1971 and 2006, the emissions per capita for these two sectors grew by 77% and 30%, respectively. The growth in the number of people accessing electricity and the growth in electricity infrastructure contributed significantly to this rise.

Figure 14. Per capita emissions by sector

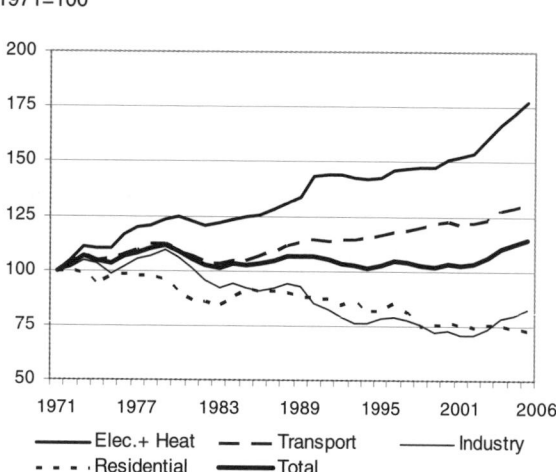

Key point: Relative to the almost-stable average emissions per capita, those of power generation and transport have grown markedly since 1971.

Overall, the emissions intensity of the world economy, in terms of CO_2 per GDP, declined by almost 40% between 1971 and 2006. However, the electricity and heat sector slowed the global decoupling between emissions and economic growth with a decrease in emissions per global unit of GDP of only 7% over that period.

Power generation and transport challenge the sustainability of both the global economy and the environment. This is particularly pronounced for developing countries that increased their emissions from these two sectors, respectively, by three and a half times and by two times faster than the global average between 1990 and 2006. Access to modern energy services is crucial to eradicating poverty and for economic development of these countries and the challenge will be to help developing countries use energy in a rational way.

Strong energy efficiency gains, the increased use of new technologies for road transport and the decarbonisation of electricity supply (both through a shift toward less carbon-intensive fuels such as natural gas and renewables and through the introduction of CO_2 capture and storage) are some of the potential means to achieve a more sustainable energy path[17].

Investment decisions taken over the next few years will have a huge long-term impact, since energy systems could be locked into a fuel mix for about 50 years, and consequently into a CO_2 emissions trajectory, that may be difficult to change.

---

17. *Energy Technology Perspectives 2008*, IEA, 2008.

Figure 15. Per GDP* emissions by sector

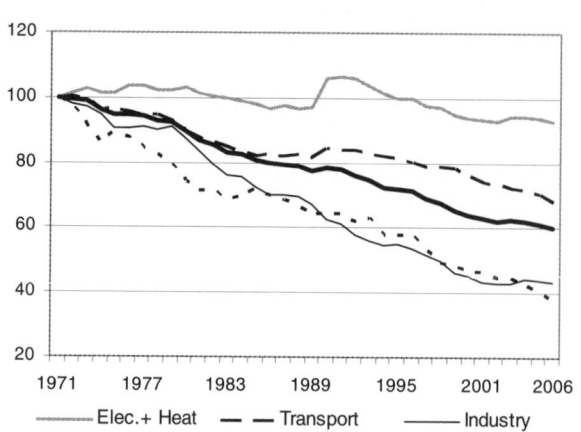

* GDP using purchasing power parities.

Key point: Generation of electricity and heat and to a lesser extent transport have slowed down the global decoupling of emissions from economic growth.

The BRICS countries

One of the most important recent developments in the world economy is the increasing economic integration of large non-OECD countries, in particular Brazil, Russia, India, China and South Africa, the so-called BRICS countries. Already, the BRICS represent over one fourth of world GDP, up from 18% in 1990. In 2006, these five countries represented 30% of global energy use and 33% of CO_2 emissions from fuel combustion (see Figure 16). These shares are likely to rise further in coming years, if the ongoing strong economic performance currently enjoyed by most of these countries continues, as many commentators expect. In fact, China, Russia and India are already three of the four countries that emit the most CO_2 emissions in absolute terms.

This brief discussion focuses on the BRICS countries, of which only Russia is a member of Annex I. Each of these countries has very different endemic resources, energy supply constraints and sectoral consumption patterns. Consequently, the issues relating to CO_2 emissions that these five countries are facing are quite different.

Figure 16. The growing importance of the BRICS countries

Gigatonnes of CO₂

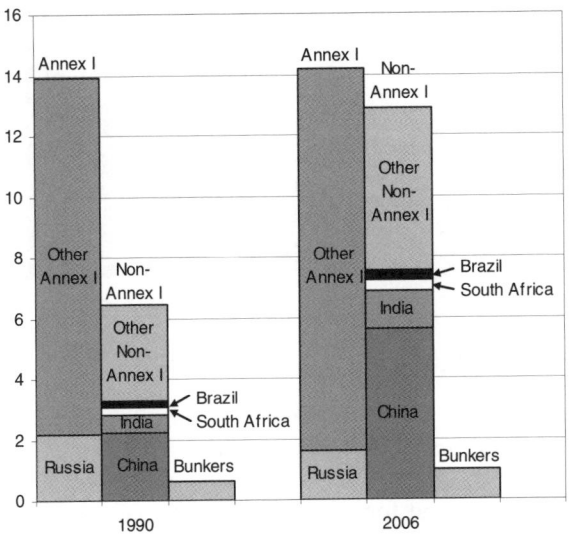

Key point: With the exception of Russia, the BRICS countries represent a growing share of CO₂ emissions in the world.

Russia

Russia is the only one of the BRICS countries where CO₂ emissions fell between 1990 and 2006, with a 27% drop over the period. The economic downturn after the break-up of the former USSR caused emissions to fall by 34% between 1990 and 1998. CO₂ emissions grew in 1999 and 2000 (3% a year) due to Russia's strong economic recovery, stimulated by the increase in world energy prices. CO₂ emissions remained fairly constant for the next five years. However, this temporary levelling off stopped in 2006 when CO₂ emissions grew by 4%. The *World Energy Outlook* projects Russian CO₂ emissions will continue to increase steadily, and in 2015 will represent about 86% of the estimated 1990 level.

CO₂ emissions from fuel combustion in Russia have stabilised following the collapse of the Soviet Union. However, other sources of greenhouse gases, in particular CH₄ emissions from leaks in the oil and gas transmission/distribution system and CO₂ emissions from flaring of associated gas, represent an important share of the Russian GHG emissions. To effectively reduce GHG emissions from energy, these two problems would also need to be addressed[18].

---

18. *Optimising Russian Natural Gas: Reform and Climate Policy*, IEA, 2006.

Figure 17. Russia: CO₂ emissions by sector

Million tonnes of CO₂

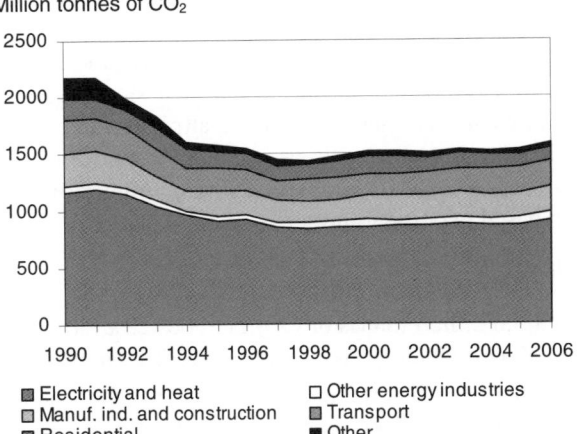

Key point: CO₂ emissions in Russia increased in 2006, after having remained fairly constant for the previous five years.

In 2006, the electricity and heat generation sector represented 58% of Russian CO₂ emissions, compared to a global average of 41%. Within this sector, 46% of the electricity was generated by natural gas, 18% by coal and only 2% by oil.

Figure 18. Russia: Electricity generation by fuel

Terawatt hour

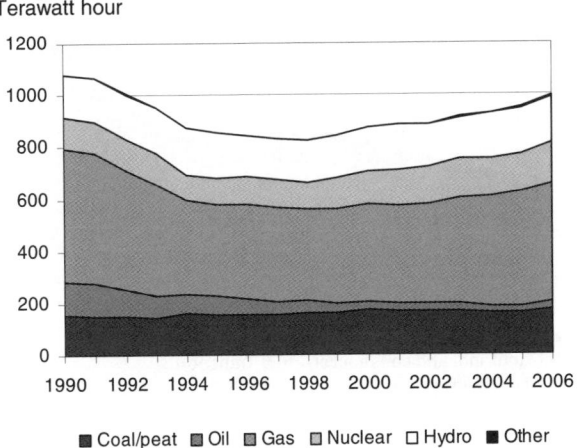

Key point: A large portion of Russia's electricity and heat generation come from non-emitting (nuclear and hydro) or low-emitting (natural gas) sources.

Of the BRICS countries, in 2006, Russia had the highest CO₂ emissions per capita (11.1 t CO₂), which put it close to the average of OECD countries (10.9 t CO₂). In terms of CO₂/GDP, Russia's economy remains CO₂ intensive with 1.1 kg CO₂ per unit of GDP, more than 2.5 times higher than the OECD average.

Canada, whose geography and natural resources are comparable to those of Russia, has a carbon intensity of 0.5 kg CO_2/US\$ – half of Russia's level. However, IEA statistics show a reduction of Russia's energy intensity of GDP of about 5% per year since 1998. It is not clear how much this can be attributed to energy efficiency improvements as opposed to the dramatic increase in GDP due to Russia's much higher oil and gas-based export earnings.

China

With 5.6 billion tonnes of CO_2 in 2006 (20% of global emissions), Chinese emissions surpass by far those of the other BRICS countries – in fact, China overtook the United States in 2007 as the world's largest emitter of energy-related CO_2. Chinese CO_2 emissions have more than doubled between 1990 and 2006. The increase was especially large in the last four years (16% in 2003, 19% in 2004 and 11% in both 2005 and 2006). The *World Energy Outlook* Reference Scenario projects that the growth in Chinese emissions will slow down to 3.1% per year up to 2030. Even with this slower growth, emissions in 2030 will be twice those in 2006.

Figure 19. China: CO₂ emissions by sector

Million tonnes of CO₂

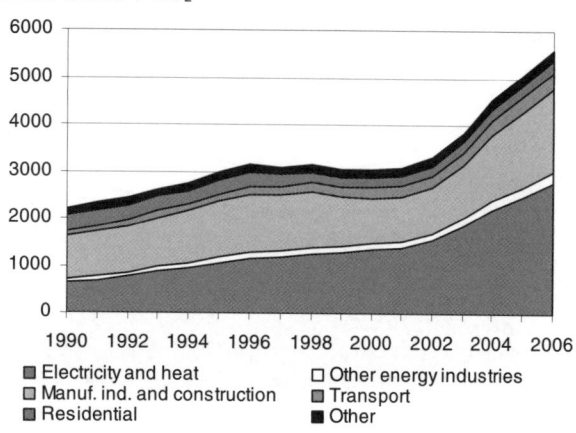

Key point: For the last four years, China showed dramatic growth in CO₂ emissions from electricity and heat generation.

Since 1990, the electricity and heat generation sector grew the most, representing 50% of Chinese CO_2 emissions in 2006. The transport sector also grew rapidly, but from a much smaller base. The *World Energy Outlook* projects that the transport sector will continue to grow and will go from 7% of the energy demand in 2006 to 12% in 2030.

Figure 20. China: Electricity generation by fuel

Terawatt hour

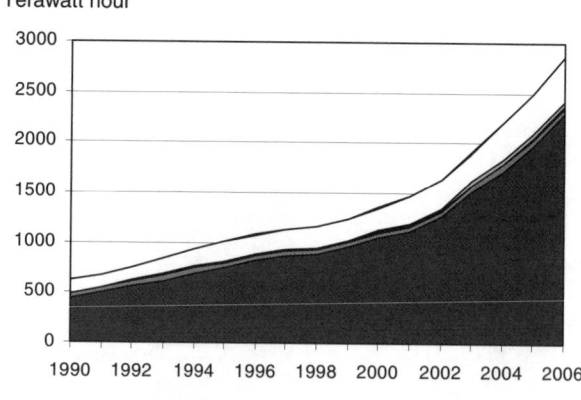

Key point: Coal dominates China's electricity generation, and its very fast growth.

Chinese demand for electricity was the largest driver of the rise in emissions. Increasing capacity at the rate of two large power plants (2 000 MW) per week[19], in 2006 alone China added almost the equivalent of the entire generating capacity of France. Figure 20 illustrates the growing demand for electricity generation and the large role played by coal. Nearly all (99%) of the 1990-2006 emissions growth from power generation derived from coal.

In the past few decades, China had experienced a rapid decoupling of energy consumption and CO_2 emissions from economic growth. During the 1980s, the central government in China could influence industrial energy intensity by establishing standards and quotas for the energy supplied to firms and by simply shutting off the power supply when enterprises exceeded their limits[20]. However, as the Chinese economy has moved towards an open-market operation, investment in energy conservation as a percentage of total energy investment has gradually declined (from 13% in 1983 to 7% in 1995 to 4% in 2003)[21]. More importantly, rapid expansion of heavy industrial sectors to serve huge infrastructure investments and burgeoning demand for Chinese products from domestic and overseas consumers made the Chinese economy less, not more, emissions efficient from 2002 to 2006.

19. *China Electricity Council, Annual Report of Electricity Sector Statistics*, CEC, Beijing, 2007.

20. See the complete discussion in *Trends in Energy Efficiency Investments in China and the US*, Jiang Lin, Lawrence Berkeley National Laboratory, Berkeley, CA, 2005.

21. For a discussion on China's electricity sector, see also *China's Power Sector Reforms*, IEA, 2006.

Despite this recent trend, the 2006 TPES/GDP is 54% less than in 1990, and a recent push by the government to reduce energy intensity has helped to resume the long-term intensity decline, albeit at a much slower rate than in the past. The increasing share of coal in power generation, however, means that a small decline in energy intensity may still be paired with an increase in emissions intensity, as was the case in 2005 and 2006. Although per capita emissions in China in 2006 were only about one third that of the OECD average, they have doubled since 1990, with the largest increases occurring in the last four years.

India

India emits 4% of global CO_2 emissions, and continues to grow. As with China, CO_2 emissions have doubled between 1990 and 2006 and the *World Energy Outlook* is projecting that CO_2 emissions in India will almost triple between 2006 and 2030 (increasing by 4.1% per year). A large share of these emissions is produced by the electricity and heat sector, which represented 56% of CO_2 in 2006, up from 42% in 1990. The transport sector, which was only 8% of CO_2 emissions in 2006, is growing relatively slowly compared to other sectors of the economy.

Figure 21. India: CO₂ emissions by sector

Million tonnes of CO₂

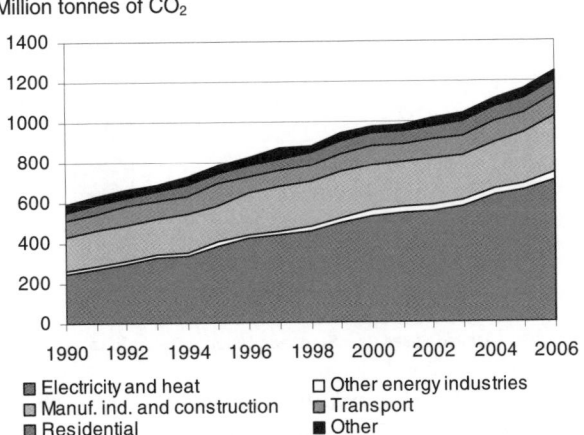

Key point: The bulk of CO₂ emissions in India come from the electricity and heat generation sector, and its share is continuing to grow.

In 2006, 68% of electricity came from coal, another 8% from natural gas and 4% from oil. The share of fossil fuels in the generation mix grew from 73% in 1990 to 85% in 2002. Since then the share of fossil fuels has declined steadily, falling to 81% in 2006. Although electricity produced from hydro has actually

increased during this period, the share fell from 25% in 1990 to 15% in 2006. India is promoting the installation of other renewable power sources into its generation mix. With an installed wind capacity of 9 GW in March 2008[22], India has the fourth largest installed capacity of wind power in the world.

Figure 22. India: Electricity generation by fuel

Terawatt hour

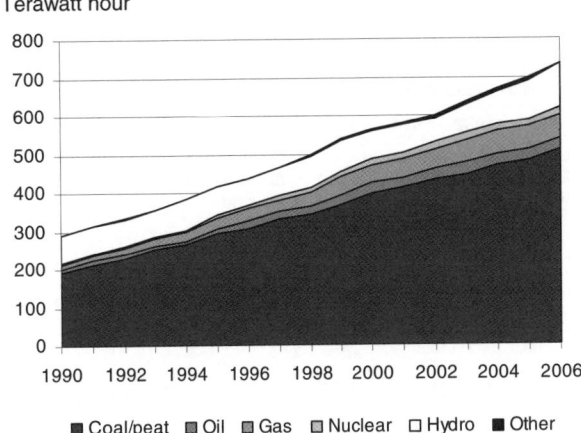

■ Coal/peat   ■ Oil   ■ Gas   ▨ Nuclear   □ Hydro   ■ Other

Key point: About two thirds of India's electricity comes from coal.

Of the BRICS countries, India has the lowest CO_2 emissions per capita (1.1 t CO_2 in 2006), about one fourth that of the world average. However, due to the recent large increases in emissions, the ratio is more than one and a half times that of 1990 and will continue to grow. But India's per capita emissions in 2030 will still be well below those in the OECD countries today.

In terms of CO_2/GDP, India has continuously improved the efficiency of its economy and reduced the CO_2 emissions per unit of GDP by 19% between 1990 and 2006.

Brazil

Brazil is the fifth largest emitter of GHGs in the world, with the particularity that the country's energy system has a relatively minor impact on GHG emissions (only 19%). The bulk of Brazilian GHG emissions (81%) come, instead, from agriculture, land-use and forestry activities, mainly through the expansion of agricultural frontiers in the Amazon region.

---

22. According to the website of the Ministry of New and Renewable Energy of the Government of India (http://mnes.nic.in).

Figure 23. Brazil: CO₂ emissions by sector

Million tonnes of CO₂

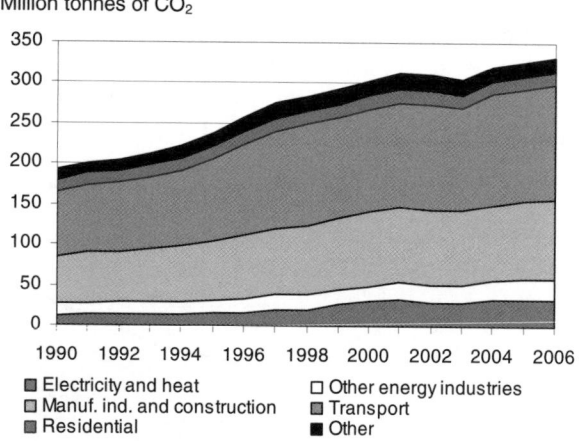

Key point: The transport sector produces the largest share of CO₂ emissions from fuel combustion in Brazil.

Compared to Russia, China and India, CO₂ emissions from fuel combustion in Brazil are small, representing only 1.2% of global CO₂ emissions from fuel combustion. Within the energy sector, the sub-sectors that contribute the most to total GHG emissions - the transport sector (42% in 2006) and the industrial sector (30%) - are also the ones that are likely to grow the most over the next years.

Electricity generation relies heavily on hydropower, as illustrated in Figure 24. Over the last three decades, the number of major dams has grown steadily and hydropower accounted for 83% of the total in 2006. Droughts in recent years have led to a wider diversification in the electricity production mix, increasing the use of gas. However, lack of investment in electricity infrastructure and unclear regulation of the power sector remain an issue. Among the smaller sources of electricity generation, the share of biomass is larger than that of coal. Indeed, the overall energy supply of Brazil is remarkable for the prominence of renewable sources in both electricity generation and transport.

In 2007, the Brazilian government announced the development of five new nuclear power plants amid concerns about the risk of power-supply shortages beyond 2012 unless Brazil builds new capacity. The government's 2030 National Energy Plan anticipates 5 300 MW of additional installed generation capacity from new nuclear plants (Angra 3 and four other plants) by 2030.

Figure 24. Brazil: Electricity generation by fuel

Terawatt hour

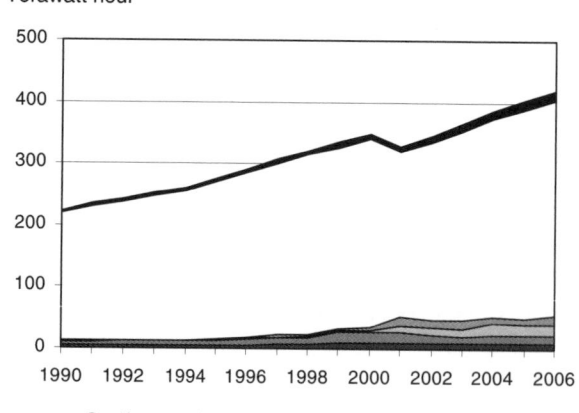

Key point: Brazilian electricity generation draws heavily on hydropower.

As Figure 25 illustrates, biofuels supply a comparatively significant share of the energy consumed for road transport. As such, Brazilian transport has a relatively low CO₂ emissions intensity[23]. CO₂ emissions per unit of fuel consumed in road traffic are 10% lower than the world average (2.6 versus 2.9 t CO₂ per toe).

Figure 25: Share of biofuels energy in road transport (2006)

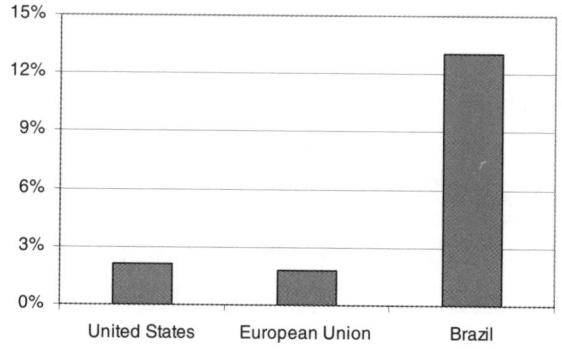

Key point: Brazil's relative consumption of biofuels far outstrips that of any other country.

Brazil is the world's largest exporter and consumer of fuel ethanol from sugarcane[24], which substituted 230 billion litres of gasoline between 1975 and 2004.

23. Box 2 provides a more complete discussion on the advantages and limitations of using biofuels to replace oil. Note: CO₂ emissions intensity considers the tank-to-wheel emissions and assumes that the CO₂ emissions derived from the combustion of biomass are zero.

24. In 2005, the United States displaced Brazil as the largest ethanol producer, although mainly derived from corn and not sugarcane.

Currently, cars that can run on either 100% ethanol or a gasoline-anhydrous ethanol blend represent more than 80% of the new cars purchased in Brazil (an estimated 1.3 million in 2006) and cost the same as cars that can only run on conventional fuel. The commercial viability of biofuels in Brazil reflects both an economy well-suited to large-scale sugarcane production and several decades of government intervention through the Brazilian Alcohol Programme (Proalcool) launched in the 1970s. The government offered a variety of incentives, including low-interest loans to build distilleries and favourable pricing relative to gasoline. Mandatory ethanol blending targets were set up for 1977 (4.5% of the gasoline, by volume) and during the 1980s (20-25%). After experiencing severe problems in the 1990s[25], the program has now become the largest commercial application of biomass for energy production and use in the world.

South Africa

South Africa currently relies almost completely on fossil fuels as a primary energy source (87% in 2006); with coal providing most of that. Although South Africa accounted for 40% of CO₂ emissions from fuel combustion in Africa in 2006, it represented only 1.2% of the global total. The electricity and heat sector produced 64% of South Africa's CO₂ emissions in 2006.

Coal dominates the South African energy system, accounting for more than 72% of primary energy supply and nearly a quarter of final energy consumption. In 2006, South Africa generated 94% of its electricity using coal. It follows that the major climate change issue facing South Africa is to reduce its greenhouse gas emissions, primarily by reducing its reliance on fossil fuels.

---

25. By the mid-1980s more than three quarters of the 800 000 cars could run on ethanol. However, when sugar prices rose sharply in 1989, sugarcane growers diverted crops to the export market, and a severe shortage of ethanol occurred in the second quarter of 1989. This shortage resulted in a loss of consumer confidence in the security of ethanol supply and discredited ProAlcool. In response, the government authorized ethanol imports, and Brazil became the world's largest importer of ethanol. Brazilian drivers as well as Brazilian car makers were left in disarray for lack of fuel and, as a result, ethanol fell into discredit for some time. By the end of the 1990s, the sales of ethanol-fuelled cars amounted to less than 1% of total annual auto sales because fuel manufacturers could not assure hydrous-ethanol consumers security of supply. The turning point took place in 2003 when car manufacturers, beginning with Volkswagen, introduced the "flex fuel" car, which gave consumers the choice and resilience to buy any combination of the cheapest fuel while protecting them from any fuel shortages.

Figure 26. South Africa: CO₂ emissions by sector

Million tonnes of CO₂

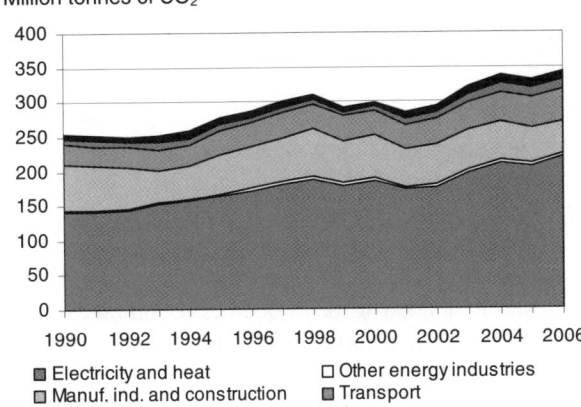

■ Electricity and heat   □ Other energy industries
□ Manuf. ind. and construction ■ Transport
■ Residential   ■ Other

Key point: The largest share of CO₂ emissions in South Africa comes from the electricity and heat sector, but growth remains moderate compared to some of the other BRICS countries.

Prices of commercial forms of energy in South Africa are in general quite low by international standards. Given the relatively lower rate of electrification (about 66%), the direct use of commercial forms of energy by households is more limited. Biomass, and especially wood, dominates energy use by rural households, generating health and safety problems as well as concerns about the sustainability of wood supplies. Over the last 16 years, per capita CO₂ emissions in South Africa have remained fairly constant while emissions per unit of GDP have decreased by 12%.

Figure 27. South Africa: Electricity generation by fuel

Terawatt hour

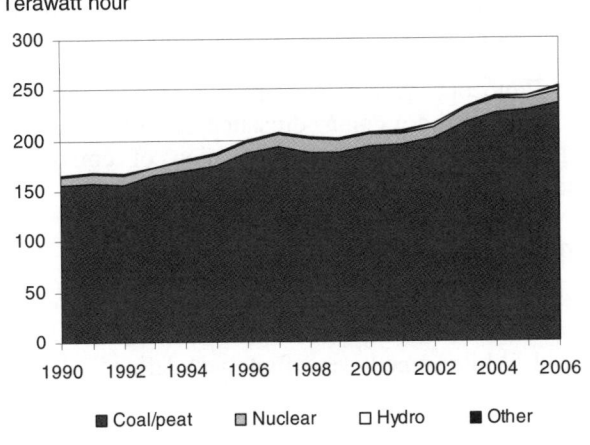

■ Coal/peat   ■ Nuclear   □ Hydro   ■ Other

Key point: South Africa relies almost solely on coal to produce its electricity.

Development of a carbon-constrained world

Until now, industrialized countries have emitted the large majority of anthropogenic greenhouse gases. However, shares of developing countries are rising very rapidly and are projected to continue to do so. To shift towards a carbon-constrained world, mitigation measures now taking shape within industrialized countries will need to be refined and complemented by comprehensive efforts worldwide.

International mitigation measures

Complementing various national policies and measures[26], the Kyoto Protocol of the UNFCCC is by far the most comprehensive multinational effort to mitigate climate change, both politically and geographically. Having entered into force in February 2005, the Protocol commits industrialized countries to curb domestic emissions by about 5% as a group relative to 1990 by the 2008-2012 first commitment period. The Protocol also creates "flexible mechanisms" by which industrialized countries can transfer emission allowances among themselves and earn emission credits from emissions reductions of developing countries and countries with economies in transition.

Despite its possible worldwide influence, the Protocol is limited in its potential to address global emissions since not all the major emitters are included. The United States remains outside of its jurisdiction and though most of the developing countries (i.e. non-Annex I countries) signed the Protocol, they committed to no emissions targets. As illustrated in Table 1, the Kyoto Protocol implies action on less than a third of global CO$_2$ emissions (as measured in 2006).

The Protocol's quantitative emissions reductions further engendered a commoditisation of carbon, as detailed in the following examination of emissions trading schemes.

Emissions trading schemes

Emissions trading schemes are developing or being proposed in several regions and countries around the world. While some have definite and defined rules in the short term (e.g. EU ETS, 10 Northeastern and Mid-Atlantic US states, Norway), others have not yet finalised their precise rules of functioning (e.g. Australia, Canada, New Zealand). Nonetheless, even for those schemes in which trading has commenced, policy makers have allowed flexibility in the changing design options over the longer term. Indeed, lessons from the first years of existing schemes are helping the elaboration of others[27].

In the European Union, the largest scheme in operation, the ETS, is learning the lessons from its first phase to shape the scheme's post-2012 design[28]. Reviews of the first trading period have led to a growing consensus on key strategic issues such as:

- the need for establishing a stable carbon regime for a longer period to provide visibility for investors and set investment incentives for low-carbon technologies;

- an allocation approach based on more auctioning, particularly for power generation, to send a strong economic signal to carbon-intensive generators, and prevent the use of allocation to meet other policy purposes;

- further harmonisation of the cap-setting approach on a sectoral level;

- harmonisation of new entrants/closures provisions.

In addition, since December 2006, the Commission has adopted legislation to broaden the scheme to the aviation sector. In July 2008, the European Parliament backed the proposal to include aviation in the EU ETS from January 2012, based on a deal struck by negotiators from the European Council and the European Parliament in June 2008.

Several other ETS are being developed, including in countries that are not Parties to the Kyoto Protocol. In the United States, the first regional scheme (i.e. in the North Eastern States) is set to start in the fourth quarter of 2008. Others may follow. Further, the U.S. Congress is considering a set of bills designed to limit the nation's GHG emissions, whereby several of these proposals call for adoption of some form of a cap-and-trade system.

---

26. Since 1999, the IEA has collected and classified information on the climate change policies and measures of its member countries. The database is available at: http://www.iea.org/textbase/envissu/pamsdb/index.html.

27. Reinaud, J. and C. Philibert, 2007: *Emissions Trading: Updates and Trends*, OECD/IEA information paper.

28. Convery, F., Ellerman, A.D. and C. de Perthuis. 2008: *The European Carbon Market in Action: Lessons from the First Trading Period*, APREC research program on the ex-post evaluation of the European CO$_2$ market, Paris. Downloadable at www.aprec.net

Table 1. World CO$_2$ emissions from fuel combustion and Kyoto targets

Million tonnes of CO$_2$

	1990	2006	% change 90-06	Kyoto Target [1]		1990	2006	% change 90-06	Kyoto Target [1]
KYOTO PARTIES	**8 802.1**	**8 157.5**	**-7.3%**	**-4.7% e**	**NON-KYOTO PARTIES**	**11 572.2**	**18 865.6**	**63.0%**	
North America	*432.2*	*538.8*	*24.7%*		*Non-participating*				
Canada	432.2	538.8	24.7%	-6%	*Annex I Parties*	*5 105.0*	*6 000.6*	*17.5%*	
					Belarus	114.8	64.1	-44.2%	none
Europe	*3 161.6*	*3 341.3*	*5.7%*		Turkey	126.9	239.7	88.9%	none
Austria	56.6	72.8	28.8%	-13%	United States	4 863.3	5 696.8	17.1%	-7%
Belgium	110.3	117.2	6.3%	-7.5%					
Denmark	50.4	55.2	9.5%	-21%	*Other Regions*	*6 467.2*	*12 865.0*	*98.9%*	
Finland	54.4	66.8	22.9%	0%	Africa	549.3	854.2	55.5%	none
France [2]	352.1	377.5	7.2%	0%	Middle East	587.9	1 291.0	119.6%	none
Germany	950.4	823.5	-13.4%	-21%	Non-OECD Europe [3]	106.7	92.8	-13.0%	none
Greece	70.1	94.0	34.0%	+25%	Other Former USSR [3]	579.3	396.2	-31.6%	none
Iceland	1.9	2.2	16.1%	+10%	Latin America [3]	896.1	1 388.4	54.9%	none
Ireland	30.6	44.9	46.7%	+13%	Asia (excl. China) [3]	1 503.9	3 193.9	112.4%	none
Italy	397.8	448.0	12.6%	-6.5%	China	2 244.0	5 648.5	151.7%	none
Luxembourg	10.5	11.2	6.8%	-28%					
Netherlands	156.6	178.3	13.9%	-6%	**INTL. MARINE BUNKERS**	**357.9**	**582.6**	**62.8%**	
Norway	28.4	36.8	29.5%	+1%	**INTL. AVIATION**	**255.4**	**397.1**	**55.5%**	
Portugal	39.3	56.3	43.4%	+27%					
Spain	205.8	327.6	59.2%	+15%	**WORLD**	**20 987.6**	**28 002.7**	**33.4%**	
Sweden	52.8	48.3	-8.5%	+4%					
Switzerland	40.7	44.1	8.2%	-8%					
United Kingdom	553.0	536.5	-3.0%	-12.5%					
Pacific	*1 352.6*	*1 643.9*	*21.5%*						
Australia	259.8	394.4	51.8%	+8%					
Japan	1 071.4	1 212.7	13.2%	-6%					
New Zealand	21.4	36.8	72.2%	0%					
Economies in Transition	*3 855.7*	*2 633.5*	*-31.7%*						
Bulgaria	74.9	47.5	-36.6%	-8%					
Croatia	21.6	20.7	-4.1%	-5%					
Czech Republic	155.1	121.0	-22.0%	-8%					
Estonia	36.2	15.1	-58.2%	-8%					
Hungary	68.5	56.4	-17.7%	-6%					
Latvia	18.4	8.0	-56.3%	-8%					
Lithuania	33.1	13.7	-58.7%	-8%					
Poland	343.9	306.0	-11.0%	-6%					
Romania	167.1	94.7	-43.3%	-8%					
Russia	2 179.9	1 587.2	-27.2%	0%					
Slovak Republic	56.7	37.5	-34.0%	-8%					
Slovenia	12.5	15.5	24.4%	-8%					
Ukraine	687.9	310.3	-54.9%	0%					

Gigatonnes CO$_2$

Note: Changes made this year to the net calorific values used for coal and petroleum products will affect the emissions estimates for the entire time series, including the base year. More information on the changes to the net calorific values are available in Chapter 1.

(1) The targets apply to a basket of six greenhouse gases and take sinks into account. The overall EU target under the Protocol is 8%, but the member countries have agreed on a burden-sharing arrangement as listed. Because of lack of data and information on base years and gases, an overall "Kyoto target" cannot be precisely calculated for total Kyoto Parties: estimates applying the targets to IEA energy data suggest the target is equivalent to about 4.7% on an aggregate basis for CO$_2$ emissions from fuel combustion.

(2) Emissions from Monaco are included with France.

(3) Composition of regions differs from elsewhere in this publication to take into account countries that are not Kyoto Parties.

(4) The Kyoto target is calculated as percentage of the 1990 CO$_2$ emissions from fuel combustion only, therefore it does not represent the total target for the six-gas basket. This assumes that the reduction targets are spread equally across all gases.

Key point: The Kyoto Protocol is limited in its potential to reduce emissions as not all major emitters are included.

In New Zealand, the government announced an emission trading system (NZ ETS) in September 2007, proposing a staged introduction with the aim of having all the major sectors included in the scheme by 2013. In addition, unlimited use of Kyoto Protocol project credits is foreseen. Only recently, in September 2008, the parliament passed legislation to enact the NZ ETS.

In Australia, the federal government published its revised climate change policy in July 2007, announcing a plan to establish an emission trading scheme (the so-called "Carbon Pollution Reduction Scheme") as part of an effective framework for meeting the climate change challenge. Details of this envisaged emissions trading scheme, which is scheduled to start in 2010, have recently been revealed by the government in a Green Paper, and are currently under discussion. The proposal includes broad coverage of GHG emissions and sectors and assistance to help households and business adjust.

In April 2007, the new Canadian government presented its "Regulatory Framework for Air Emissions", announcing that emissions trading will be one of the instruments permitted to comply with this regulation. The proposal includes a cap-and-trade scheme based on intensity targets for large emitters, who will have the ability to trade emissions through three channels: internal abatements[29] beyond the baseline; a domestic offsets system; and Certified Emissions Reductions (CERs) from projects under the Clean Development Mechanisms (CDMs) to meet 10% of their compliance obligation.

In September 2008, Japan unveiled an outline of a GHG emissions trading scheme to be launched on a trial basis in October 2008. Initially, the system will be voluntary and Japanese companies will be allowed to set their own emission reduction targets. In addition to allowance trading, companies will be able to use CDM credits, national offset credits and credits from Japan's voluntary emissions trading scheme.

Steps for future action

Held in late 2005, the first Meeting of the Parties to the Kyoto Protocol (COP/MOP1) witnessed the official opening of talks on post-2012 climate change policy. Parties organized two official fora: the Ad Hoc Working Group (AWG) on Further Commitments for Annex I Parties and the UNFCCC "Dialogue on long-term cooperative action to address climate change by enhancing implementation of the Convention" (UNFCCC Dialogue).

The AWG focuses on the design of post-2012 commitments for Annex I Parties under the Protocol. Ideally, it would also provide some certainty to carbon-constrained investments in infrastructure and to the carbon market itself. However, the AWG has no mandate to encourage participation from Non-Annex I Parties or from non-participating Annex I Parties.

The broader UNFCCC Dialogue was instead designed to explore worldwide climate change mitigation and adaptation through an "open and non-binding exchange of views, information and ideas". Participants in its first meeting discussed strategic adaptation to climate change, sustainable development, and the mitigation potential of technology and market mechanisms. The Bali Road Map adopted at COP/MOP3 in Bali established a two-track process, i.e. both for the Convention and Kyoto Protocol strands, aiming at the identification of a post-2012 global climate regime to be adopted by COP15 and COP/MOP5 in Copenhagen in 2009. While the Bali Action Plan, adopted under the Convention track, did not introduce binding commitments to reduce GHG emissions, it included the request for developed countries to contribute to the mitigation of global warming in the context of sustainable development. In addition, the plan envisaged enhanced actions on adaptation, technology development and on the provision financial resources, as well as measures against deforestation.

The challenge of post-2012 discussions is the need to engage developing countries with approaches, possibly including the carbon market, that suit their capacity and their legitimate aspiration for economic and social development. Both the Asia Pacific Partnership for Clean Development and Climate (APP or AP6) and the G8 2005 Gleneagles Plan of Action seek to involve developed and developing nations in common measures to address climate change.

The AP6, which groups Australia, China, India, Japan, Korea and the United States, is one of many initiatives. AP6 focuses on the emissions of specific sectors: iron and steel, cement, aluminium, mining, buildings and appliances; and the methods of clean

---

29. Internal abatement means that emitters reduce their GHG emissions through in-house measures, e.g. by making changes to improve the functioning of their plants.

fossil energy use, renewable energy generation, and more efficient power generation and transmission.

Canada, France, Germany, Italy, Japan, Russia, the United Kingdom and the United States launched the July 2005 Gleneagles Plan of Action to, in part, promote clean energy and sustainable development while mitigating climate change. Through the Plan of Action the G8 members committed to: 1) transform the way they use energy, namely through means of energy efficiency; 2) foster research and development of lower-emission technology; 3) finance the economic transition to cleaner energy and 4) manage the effects of climate change. The IEA was tasked under the Plan of Action to develop concrete recommendations to help the G8 achieve these four objectives. Additionally, the G8 sought to engage South Africa, India, Brazil, China and Mexico in an official Dialogue to address climate change, clean energy, and sustainable development worldwide. This commitment by the G8 was reiterated at the St. Petersburg summit in July 2006 and subsequently at the 2007 summit in Heiligendamm and the 2008 summit in Hokkaido.

In all these efforts, timely and accurate CO$_2$ and other GHG statistics will prove essential to ascertain compliance to international agreements and to inform carbon market participants. The ability of countries to monitor and review emissions from their sources is essential in their engagement towards global GHG mitigation.

Conclusion

Fossil fuel combustion is the single largest human influence on climate. Over the past two decades, the global community has recognized the pressing need to address and reduce CO$_2$ emissions from fuel combustion that enter the atmosphere.

Two sectors, both growing rapidly, represent the bulk of CO$_2$ emissions from fuel combustion: the electricity and heat generation sector and the transport sector. Improving the energy efficiency and reducing the carbon intensity of both sectors could significantly diminish their contribution to global climate change.

Since the industrial revolution, most of the CO$_2$ emissions have originated from the industrialized countries. However, this dominance appears short-lived due to the size of some of the developing economies and the growth in their energy needs. Effective emissions mitigation will require all countries, regardless of energy demand and infrastructure, to use energy in a sustainable manner.

This analysis is based on energy statistics collected from various sources. Although quality and completeness of these statistics have increased over the last years, up-to-date and accurate information on energy use and GHG emissions will be more and more essential for monitoring progress towards addressing the energy-climate challenge.

PART I:

METHODOLOGY

PARTIE I :

METHODOLOGIE

1. IEA EMISSIONS ESTIMATES

The estimates of CO_2 emissions from fuel combustion presented in this publication are calculated using the IEA energy data[1] and the default methods and emission factors from the *Revised 1996 IPCC Guidelines for National Greenhouse Gas Inventories*, IPCC/OECD/IEA Paris, 1997 (*1996 IPCC Guidelines*).

Although the IPCC approved the *2006 Guidelines* at the 25th session of the IPCC in April 2006 in Mauritius, most countries (as well as the IEA) are still calculating their inventories using the *1996 IPCC Guidelines*.

The IEA Secretariat reviews its energy databases each year. In the light of new assessments, important revisions may be made to the time series of individual countries. Therefore, certain data in this publication may have been revised with respect to previous editions.

Changes made this year to the net calorific values used for coal and petroleum products will affect the emissions estimates for the entire time series, including the base year. More information on the changes to the net calorific values are available in *Energy Balances of OECD Countries*.

Up until this year, petroleum products have been converted using a single set of net calorific values for all countries. This year the IEA has decided to apply regional conversion factors (in conjunction with Eurostat for the European countries) for the petroleum products.

In prior years the inputs of coal to main activity electricity, CHP and heat only plants were converted to energy units using an average net calorific value from the Annual Coal Questionnaire. Coal inputs to auto-producer plants were converted to energy units using the same value as coal used in industry. Starting this year, coal inputs to each type of plant (i.e. main activity electricity plant, autoproducer electricity plant, main activity CHP plant, autoproducer CHP plant, main activity heat plant, autoproducer heat plant) are converted to energy units using average factors calculated from the Annual Electricity Questionnaire.

Inventory quality

The *IPCC Guidelines* allow Parties under the UNFCCC to prepare and periodically update national inventories that are accurate, complete, comparable and transparent. Inventory quality is an important issue since countries are now implementing legally-binding commitments.

One way to assess inventory quality is to do comparisons among inventories, methodologies and input data. The *IPCC Guidelines* recommend that countries which have used a detailed Sectoral Approach for CO_2 emissions from energy combustion also use the Reference Approach for verification purposes. This will identify areas where a full accounting of emissions may not have been made (see Chapter 5, IPCC methodologies).

Reference Approach vs. Sectoral Approach

The Reference Approach and the Sectoral Approach often give different results because the Reference Approach is a top-down approach using a country's energy supply data and has no detailed information on how the individual fuels are used in each sector.

---

1. Published in *Energy Statistics of OECD Countries, Energy Balances of OECD Countries, Energy Statistics of Non-OECD Countries* and *Energy Balances of Non-OECD Countries*, IEA/OECD Paris, 2008.

The Reference Approach provides estimates of CO_2 to compare with estimates derived using a Sectoral Approach. Theoretically, it indicates an upper bound to the Sectoral Approach "1A fuel combustion", because some of the carbon in the fuel is not combusted but will be emitted as fugitive emissions (as leakage or evaporation in the production and/or transformation stage).

Calculating CO_2 emissions inventories with the two approaches can lead to different results for some countries. In general the gap between the two approaches is relatively small (5 per cent or less) when compared to the total carbon flows involved. In cases where 1) fugitive emissions are proportional to the mass flows entering production and/or transformation processes, 2) stock changes at the level of the final consumer are not significant and 3) statistical differences in the energy data are limited, the Reference Approach and the Sectoral Approach should lead to similar evaluations of the CO_2 emissions trends.

When significant discrepancies and/or large time-series deviations do occur, they may be due to various reasons such as:

Large statistical differences between the energy supply and the energy consumption in the basic energy data. Statistical differences arise from the collection of data from different parts of the fuel flow from its supply origins to the various stages of downstream conversion and use. They are a normal part of a fuel balance. Large random statistical differences must always be examined to determine the reason for the difference, but equally importantly smaller statistical differences which systematically show an excess of supply over demand (or vice versa) should be pursued.

Significant mass imbalances between crude oil and other feedstock entering refineries and the (gross) petroleum products manufactured.

The use of aggregate net calorific and carbon content values for primary fuels which are converted rather than combusted. For example, it may appear that there is not conservation of energy or carbon depending on the calorific value and/or the carbon content chosen for the crude oil entering refineries and for the mix of products produced from the refinery for a particular year. This may cause an overestimation or underestimation of the emissions associated with the Reference Approach.

The misallocation of the quantities of fuels used for conversion into derived products (other than power or heat) *or quantities combusted in the energy sector*. When reconciling differences between the Reference Approach and a Sectoral Approach it is important to ensure that the quantities reported in the transformation and energy sectors (e.g. for coke ovens) reflect correctly the quantities used for conversion and for fuel use, respectively, and that no misallocation has occurred. Note that the quantities of fuels converted to derived products should have been reported in the transformation sector of the energy balance. If any derived products are used to fuel the conversion process, the amounts involved should have been reported in the energy sector of the energy balance. In a Sectoral Approach the inputs to the transformation sector should not be included in the activity data used to estimate emissions.

Missing information on certain transformation outputs. Emissions from combustion of secondary fuels produced in integrated processes (for example, coke oven gas) may be overlooked in a Tier 1 Sectoral Approach if data are poor or unavailable. The use of secondary fuels (the output from the transformation process) should be included in the Sectoral Approach. Failure to do so will result in an underestimation of the Sectoral Approach.

Simplifications in the Reference Approach. Certain quantities of carbon should be included in the Reference Approach because their emissions fall under fuel combustion. These quantities have been excluded where the flows are small or not represented by a major statistic available within energy data. Examples of quantities not accounted for in the Reference Approach include lubricants used in two-stroke engines, blast furnace and other by-product gases which are used for fuel combustion outside their source category of production and combustion of waxed products in waste plants with heat recovery. On the other hand, certain flows of carbon should be excluded from the Reference Approach, but for reasons similar to the above no practical means can be found to exclude them without over complicating the calculations. These include coals and other hydrocarbons injected into blast furnaces as well as cokes used as reductants in the manufacture of inorganic chemicals. These simplifications will determine discrepancies between the Reference Approach and a Sectoral Approach. If data are available, the magnitudes of these effects can be estimated.

Missing information on stock changes that may occur at the final consumer level. The relevance of consumer stocks depends on the method used for the Sectoral Approach. If delivery figures are used (this is often the case) then changes in consumers' stocks are irrelevant. If, however, the Sectoral Approach is using actual consumption of the fuel, then this could cause either an overestimation or an underestimation of the Reference Approach.

High distribution losses or unrecorded consumption for gas may mean that the emissions are overestimated by the Reference Approach or underestimated by the Sectoral Approach.

The treatment of transfers and reclassifications of energy products may cause a difference in the Sectoral Approach estimation since different net calorific values and emission factors may be used depending on how the fuel is classified.

Differences between IEA estimates and UNFCCC submissions

It is possible to use the IEA CO_2 estimates for comparison with the greenhouse gas inventories reported by countries to the UNFCCC Secretariat. In this way, problems in methods, input data or emission factors may become apparent. However, care should be used in interpreting the results of any comparison since the IEA estimates may differ from a country's official submission for many reasons.

A recent comparison of the IEA estimates with the inventories submitted to the UNFCCC showed that for most Annex II countries, the two calculations were within 5%. For some EIT and Non-Annex I countries, differences between the IEA estimates and national inventories were larger. In some of the countries the underlying energy data were different; suggesting that more work is needed on the collecting and reporting of energy statistics for those countries.

Some countries have incorrectly defined bunkers as fuel used abroad by their own ships and planes. Still other countries have made calculation errors for carbon oxidation or have included international bunkers in their totals. Since all of the above will affect the national totals of CO_2 emissions from fuel combustion, a systematic comparison with the IEA estimates

would allow countries to verify their calculations and produce more internationally comparable inventories.

In addition, the main bias in the energy data and emission factors will probably be systematic and not random. This means that the emission trends will usually be more reliable than the absolute emission levels. By comparing trends in the IEA estimates with trends in emissions as reported to the UNFCCC, it should be possible to identify definition problems or changes in the calculations, which were not reflected in the base year.

For many reasons the IEA estimates may differ from the numbers that a country submits to the UNFCCC, even if a country has accounted for all of its energy use and correctly applied the *IPCC Guidelines*. No attempt has been made to quantify the effects of these differences. In most cases these differences will be relatively small. Some of the reasons for these differences are:

- **The IEA uses a Tier 1 method.**

The IEA uses a Tier 1 Sectoral Approach based on the *1996 IPCC Guidelines*. Countries may be using a Tier 2 or Tier 3 method that takes into account different technologies.

- **The IEA is using the *1996 IPCC Guidelines*.**

The IEA is still using the *1996 IPCC Guidelines*. Some countries may have already started using the *2006 IPCC Guidelines*.

- **Energy activity data are extracted from the IEA energy balances and may differ from those used for the UNFCCC calculations.**

Countries often have several "official" sources of data such as a Ministry, a Central Bureau of Statistics, a nationalised electricity company, etc. Data can also be collected from the energy suppliers, the energy consumers or customs statistics. The IEA tries to collect the most accurate data, but does not necessarily have access to the complete data set that may be available to national experts calculating emission inventories for the UNFCCC. In addition to different sources, the methodology used by the national bodies providing the data to the IEA and to the UNFCCC may differ. For example, general surveys, specific surveys, questionnaires, estimations, combined methods and classifications of data used in national statistics and in their subsequent reclassification according to international standards may result in different series.

- **The IEA uses average net calorific values.**

The IEA uses an average net calorific value (NCV) for each secondary oil product. These NCVs are region-specific and constant over time. Country-specific NCVs that can vary over time are used for NGL, refinery feedstocks and additives. Crude oil NCVs are further split into production, imports, exports and average. Different coal types have specific NCVs for production, imports, exports, inputs to public power plants and coal used in coke ovens, blast furnaces and industry, and can vary over time for each country.

Country experts may have the possibility of going into much more detail when calculating the heat content of the fuels. This in turn could produce different values than the IEA.

- **The IEA uses average emission factors.**

The IEA uses the default emission factors which are given in the *1996 IPCC Guidelines*. Country experts may have better information available.

- **The IEA does not have detailed information for the stored carbon calculation.**

The IEA does not have complete information on the non-energy use of fuels. The amount of carbon stored is estimated using the default values given in the *1996 IPCC Guidelines*. For "other products" in the stored carbon calculation, the IEA assumes that 100% of kerosene, white spirit and petroleum coke that is reported as non-energy use in the energy balance is also stored. Country experts calculating the inventories may have more detailed information.

- **The IEA cannot allocate emissions from auto-producers into the end-use sectors.**

The *1996 IPCC Guidelines* recommend that emissions from autoproduction should be included with emissions from other fuel use by end-consumers. At the same time, the emissions from the autoproduction of electricity and heat should be excluded from the energy transformation source category to avoid double counting. The IEA is not able to allocate the fuel use from autoproducers between the industrial and "other" sectors. Therefore, this publication shows a category called "Unallocated autoproducers". However, this should not affect the total emissions for a country.

- **Military emissions may be treated differently.**

According to the *1996 IPCC Guidelines*, military emissions should be reported in Source/Sink Category 1 A 5, *Other (not elsewhere specified)*. Before

last year, the IEA questionnaires requested that warships be included in international marine bunkers and that the military use of aviation fuels be included in domestic air. All other military use should have been reported in *non-specified other sector*.

At the IEA/Eurostat/UNECE Energy Statistics Working Group meeting (Paris, November 2004), participants decided to harmonise the definitions used to collect energy data on the joint IEA/Eurostat/UNECE questionnaires with those used by the IPCC to report greenhouse gas inventories. As a result, starting in the 2006 edition of this publication, all military consumption should be reported in non-specified other sectors. Sea-going versus coastal is no longer a criterion for splitting international and domestic navigation. For more information on the changes, please consult the Energy Statistics Working Group meeting report on our website at http://www.iea.org/Textbase/stats/questionnaire/index.asp.

However, it is not clear whether countries are reporting on the new basis, and if they are, whether they will be able to revise their historical data. The IEA has found that in practice most countries consider information on military consumption as confidential and therefore either combine it with other information or do not include it at all.

- **The IEA estimates include emissions from coke inputs into blast furnaces. Countries may have included these emissions in the IPCC category Industrial processes.**

National greenhouse gas inventories submitted to the UNFCCC divide emissions according to source categories. Two of these IPCC Source/Sink Categories are energy and industrial processes. The IPCC Reference Approach estimates national emissions from fuel combustion based on the supply of fuel to a country and by implication includes emissions from coke inputs to blast furnaces in the energy sector. However, within detailed sectoral calculations certain non-energy processes can be distinguished. In the reduction of iron in a blast furnace through the combustion of coke, the primary purpose of coke oxidation is to produce pig iron and the emissions can be considered as an industrial process. Care must be taken not to double count these emissions in both energy and industrial processes. The IEA estimates of emissions from fuel combustion in this publication include the coke inputs to blast furnaces.

• **The units may be different.**

The *1996 IPCC Guidelines* and the UNFCCC *Reporting Guidelines on Annual Inventories* both ask that CO_2 emissions be reported in Gg of CO_2. A million tonnes of CO_2 is equal to 1 000 Gg of CO_2, so to compare the numbers in this publication with national inventories expressed in Gg, the IEA emissions must be multiplied by 1 000.

Key sources

In May 2000, the IPCC Plenary accepted the report on *Good Practice Guidance and Uncertainty Management in National Greenhouse Gas Inventories*. The report provides good practice guidance to assist countries in determining their key source categories. By identifying these key sources in the national inventory, inventory agencies can prioritise their efforts and improve their overall estimates.

The *Good Practice Guidance* identifies a key source category as one that is prioritised within the national inventory system because its estimate has a significant influence on a country's total inventory of direct greenhouse gases in terms of the absolute level of emissions, the trend in emissions, or both.

For a more complete description of the IPCC methodology for determining key sources, see Chapter 5, IPCC methodologies.

In the *Good Practice Guidance*, the recommendation for choosing the level of the key source analysis is to "disaggregate to the level where emission factors are distinguished. In most inventories, this will be the main fuel types. If emission factors are determined independently for some sub-source categories, these should be distinguished in the analysis."

Since the emission estimates in this publication were produced using the default emission factors from the *1996 IPCC Guidelines*, this means that the fuel combustion categories would have been divided into:

    stationary combustion – coal
    stationary combustion – oil
    stationary combustion – gas
    mobile combustion – coal
    mobile combustion – oil
    mobile combustion – gas

Clearly this level of aggregation is not particularly useful in identifying where additional work is needed in refining the inventory. It does not take into account the possibility of improving data collection methods, improving emission factors or using a higher tier calculation for certain key sectors within the energy from fuel combustion source category. For this reason the IEA has disaggregated the key source analysis to the same level of detail presented in the country tables of this publication. For each country, the 11 largest sources, split by coal, oil, gas and other, are shown in the key sources table.

To calculate the level assessment, the IEA has started with the CO_2 emissions from fuel combustion as calculated by the IEA. To supplement this, where possible, the IEA has used the emissions that were submitted by the Annex I Parties to the UNFCCC in the 2008 submission of the Common Reporting Format for CO_2 (only fugitive), CH_4, N_2O, HFCs, PFCs and SF_6, not taking into account CO_2 emissions/removals from land use, land use change and forestry[2]. This was possible for Australia, Austria, Belarus, Belgium, Bulgaria, Canada, Croatia, the Czech Republic, Denmark, Estonia, Finland, France, Germany, Greece, Hungary, Iceland, Ireland, Italy, Japan, Latvia, Lithuania, Luxembourg, the Netherlands, New Zealand, Norway, Poland, Portugal, Romania, the Slovak Republic, Slovenia, Spain, Sweden, Switzerland, the United Kingdom and the United States.

At the time of preparation of this book, Russia, Turkey and Ukraine had not yet submitted their 2008 inventories to the UNFCCC. Therefore, non-CO_2 data for those countries were taken from the inventories submitted previously.

For the Non-Annex I Parties, CO_2 emissions from fuel combustion were from the IEA and the rest of the 2006 emissions were estimated by PBL.

The cumulative contribution only includes the 11 largest key sources of CO_2 from fuel combustion. As a result, in most cases the cumulative contribution will not be 95% as recommended in the *Good Practice Guidance* and key sources from fugitive emissions, industrial processes, solvents, agriculture and waste will not be shown. The percentage of CO_2 emissions from fuel combustion in total GHG emissions has been included as a memo item at the bottom of the table.

---

2. As recommended in the *Good Practice Guidance*.

Notes on tables and graphs

Table of CO$_2$ emissions by sector

Row 1: *Sectoral Approach* contains total CO$_2$ emissions from fuel combustion as calculated using the IPCC Tier 1 Sectoral Approach and corresponds to IPCC Source/Sink Category 1 A. Emissions calculated using a Sectoral Approach include emissions only when the fuel is actually combusted.

Row 2: *Main activity producer electricity and heat* contains the sum of emissions from main activity producer electricity generation, combined heat and power generation and heat plants. Main activity producers (formerly known as public utilities) are defined as those undertakings whose primary activity is to supply the public. They may be publicly or privately owned. Emissions from own on-site use of fuel are included. This corresponds to IPCC Source/Sink Category 1 A 1 a.

Row 3: *Unallocated autoproducers* contains the emissions from the generation of electricity and/or heat by autoproducers. Autoproducers are defined as undertakings that generate electricity and/or heat, wholly or partly for their own use as an activity which supports their primary activity. They may be privately or publicly owned. In the *1996 IPCC Guidelines*, these emissions would normally be distributed between industry, transport and "other" sectors.

Row 4: *Other energy industries* contains emissions from fuel combusted in petroleum refineries, for the manufacture of solid fuels, coal mining, oil and gas extraction and other energy-producing industries. This corresponds to the IPCC Source/Sink Categories 1 A 1 b and 1 A 1 c. According to the *1996 IPCC Guidelines*, emissions from coke inputs to blast furnaces can either be counted here or in the industrial processes source/sink category. Within detailed sectoral calculations, certain non-energy processes can be distinguished. In the reduction of iron in a blast furnace through the combustion of coke, the primary purpose of the coke oxidation is to produce pig iron and the emissions can be considered as an industrial process. Care must be taken not to double count these emissions in both energy and industrial processes. In the IEA estimations, these emissions have been included in this category.

Row 5: *Manufacturing industries and construction* contains the emissions from combustion of fuels in industry. The IPCC Source/Sink Category 1 A 2 includes these emissions. However, in the *1996 IPCC Guidelines,* the IPCC category also includes emissions from industry autoproducers that generate electricity and/or heat. The IEA data are not collected in a way that allows the energy consumption to be split by specific end-use and therefore, this publication shows autoproducers as a separate item. See Row 3, *Unallocated autoproducers. Manufacturing industries and construction* also includes emissions from coke inputs into blast furnaces, which may be reported either in the transformation sector, the industry sector or the separate IPCC Source/Sink Category 2, Industrial processes.

Row 6: *Transport* contains emissions from the combustion of fuel for all transport activity, regardless of the sector, except for international marine bunkers and international aviation. This includes domestic aviation, domestic navigation, road, rail and pipeline transport, and corresponds to IPCC Source/Sink Category 1 A 3. In addition, the IEA data are not collected in a way that allows the autoproducer consumption to be split by specific end-use and therefore, this publication shows autoproducers as a separate item. See Row 3, *Unallocated autoproducers.*

Note: Starting in the 2006 edition, military consumption previously included in *domestic aviation* and in *road* should be in *non-specified other sectors*. See the section on Differences between IEA estimates and UNFCCC submissions, for further details.

Row 7: *Road* contains the emissions arising from fuel use in road vehicles, including the use of agricultural vehicles on highways. This corresponds to the IPCC Source/Sink Category 1 A 3 b.

Row 8: *Other Sectors* contains the emissions from commercial/institutional activities, agriculture/forestry, fishing, residential and other emissions not specified elsewhere that are included in the IPCC Source/Sink Categories 1 A 4 and 1 A 5. In the *1996 IPCC Guidelines,* the category also includes emissions from autoproducers in the commercial/residential/agricultural sectors that generate electricity and/or heat. The IEA data are not collected in a way that allows the energy consumption to be split by specific end-use and therefore, this publication shows autoproducers as a separate item. See Row 3, *Unallocated autoproducers.*

Row 9: *Residential* contains all emissions from fuel combustion in households. This corresponds to IPCC Source/Sink Category 1 A 4 b.

Row 10: *Reference Approach* contains total CO_2 emissions from fuel combustion as calculated using the IPCC Reference Approach. The Reference Approach is based on the supply of energy in a country and as a result, all inventories calculated using this method include fugitive emissions from energy transformation (e.g. from oil refineries) which are normally included in Category 1 B. For this reason, Reference Approach estimates are likely to overestimate national CO_2 emissions. In these tables, the difference between the Sectoral Approach and the Reference Approach includes statistical differences, product transfers, transformation losses and distribution losses.

Row 11: *Differences due to losses and/or transformation* contains emissions that result from the transformation of energy from a primary fuel to a secondary or tertiary fuel. Included here are solid fuel transformation, oil refineries, gas works and other fuel transformation industries. These emissions are normally reported as fugitive emissions in the IPCC Source/Sink Category 1 B, but will be included in 1 A in inventories that are calculated using the IPCC Reference Approach. Theoretically, this category should show relatively small emissions representing the loss of carbon by other ways than combustion, such as evaporation or leakage.

Negative emissions for one product and positive emissions for another product would imply a change in the classification of the emission source as a result of an energy transformation between coal and gas, between coal and oil, etc. In practice, however, it often proves difficult to correctly account for all inputs and outputs in energy transformation industries, and to separate energy that is transformed from energy that is combusted. Therefore, the row *Differences due to losses and/or transformation* sometimes shows quite large positive emissions or even negative ones due to problems in the underlying energy data.

Row 12: *Statistical differences* can be due to unexplained discrepancies in the underlying energy data. They can also be caused by differences between emissions calculated using the Reference Approach and the Sectoral Approach.

Row 13: *International marine bunkers* contains emissions from fuels burned by ships of all flags that are engaged in international navigation. The international navigation may take place at sea, on inland lakes and waterways, and in coastal waters. Consumption by ships engaged in domestic navigation is excluded. The domestic/international split is determined on the basis of port of departure and port of arrival, and not by the flag or nationality of the ship. Consumption by fishing vessels and by military forces is also excluded. Emissions from international marine bunkers should be excluded from the national totals. This corresponds to IPCC Source/Sink Category 1 A 3 d i.

Row 14: *International aviation* contains emissions from fuels used by aircraft for international aviation. Fuels used by airlines for their road vehicles are excluded. The domestic/international split should be determined on the basis of departure and landing locations and not by the nationality of the airline. Emissions from international aviation should be excluded from the national totals. This corresponds to IPCC Source/Sink Category 1 A 3 a i.

Figures 2 and 3: Emissions by sector

The sector *Other* includes emissions from commercial and public services, agriculture/forestry and fishing. Emissions from unallocated autoproducers are included in *Electricity and heat*.

Figure 5: Electricity generation by fuel

The product *Other* includes geothermal, solar, wind, combustible renewables and waste, etc. Electricity generation includes both main activity producer and autoproducer electricity.

Country notes

Belgium

In this edition, the increases in CO_2 emissions are largely due to the revision of the industrial waste time series back to 1990. The revisions concern production and consumption in the chemical sector.

Cuba

International marine bunkers for residual fuel oil in the period 1971-1983 were estimated on the basis of 1984 figures and the data reported as domestic navigation in the energy balance.

Cyprus

Note by Turkey:

With respect to Cyprus, Turkey reserves its position as stated in its declaration of 1 May 2004. The information in the report under the heading Cyprus relates to the southern part of the Island. There is no single authority representing both Turkish and Greek Cypriot people on the Island. Turkey recognises the Turkish Republic of Northern Cyprus (TRNC).

Note by all the European Union Member States of the OECD and the European Commission:

The Republic of Cyprus is recognised by all members of the United Nations with the exception of Turkey. The information in this report relates to the area under the effective control of the Government of the Republic of Cyprus.

Estonia

The data reported as lignite in the energy balance have been *considered* as oil shale for the calculation of CO₂ emissions.

France

The *methodology* for calculating main activity electricity and heat production from gas changed in 2000.

Italy

Prior to 1990, gas use in commercial/public services was included in residential.

Japan

For four consecutive years, the IEA has received revisions from the Japanese Administration. The first set of revisions received in 2004 increased the 1990 supply by 5% for coal, 2% for natural gas and 0.7% for oil compared to the previous data. This led to an increase of 2.5% in 1990 CO₂ emissions calculated using the Reference Approach while the Sectoral Approach remained fairly constant. For the 2006 edition, the IEA received revisions to the coal and oil data which had a significant impact on both the energy data and the CO₂ emissions. The most significant revisions occurred for coke oven coke, naphtha, blast furnace gas and petroleum coke. These revisions affected consumption rather than supply in the years concerned. As a result, the sectoral approach CO₂ emissions increased for all the years, however at different

rates. For example, the sectoral approach CO₂ emissions for 1990 were 4.6% higher than those calculated for the 2005 edition while the 2003 emissions were 1.1% higher than those of the previous edition. Due to the impact these successive revisions have had on the final energy balance as well as on CO₂ emissions, the IEA was in close contact with the Japanese Administration to better understand the reasons be-hind these changes. These changes are mainly due to the Government of Japan's efforts to improve the input-output balances in the production of oil products and coal products in response to inquiries from the UNFCCC Secretariat. To cope with this issue, the Japanese Administration established a working group in March 2004. The working group completed its work in April 2006. Many of its conclusions were incorporated in the 2006 edition but some further revisions to the time series (especially in industry and other sectors) were submitted for the 2007 edition.

Netherlands Antilles

Prior to 1992, the Reference Approach overstates emissions since data for lubricants and bitumen (which store carbon) are not available.

Norway

Discrepancies between Reference and Sectoral Approach estimates and the difference in the resulting growth rates arise from statistical differences between supply and consumption data for oil and natural gas. For Norway, supply of these fuels is the residual of two very large and opposite terms, production and exports.

Switzerland

The sectoral breakdown for gas/diesel oil used in the residential sector before 1978 was estimated on the basis of commercial and residential consumption in 1978 and the data reported as commercial consumption in the energy balance in previous years.

United Kingdom

For reasons of confidentiality, gas for main activity electricity is included in autoproducers for 1990.

Vietnam

A detailed sectoral breakdown is available starting in 1980.

2. UNITS AND CONVERSIONS

General conversion factors for energy

To:	TJ	Gcal	Mtoe	MBtu	GWh
From:	multiply by:				
TJ	1	238.8	2.388×10^{-5}	947.8	0.2778
Gcal	4.1868×10^{-3}	1	10^{-7}	3.968	1.163×10^{-3}
Mtoe	4.1868×10^{4}	10^{7}	1	3.968×10^{7}	11630
MBtu	1.0551×10^{-3}	0.252	2.52×10^{-8}	1	2.931×10^{-4}
GWh	3.6	860	8.6×10^{-5}	3412	1

Conversion factors for mass

To:	kg	T	Lt	st	lb
From:	multiply by:				
kilogramme (kg)	1	0.001	9.84×10^{-4}	1.102×10^{-3}	2.2046
tonne (t)	1000	1	0.984	1.1023	2204.6
long ton (lt)	1016	1.016	1	1.120	2240.0
short ton (st)	907.2	0.9072	0.893	1	2000.0
pound (lb)	0.454	4.54×10^{-4}	4.46×10^{-4}	5.0×10^{-4}	1

Conversion factors for volume

To:	gal U.S.	gal U.K.	bbl	ft^3	l	m^3
From:	multiply by:					
U.S. gallon (gal)	1	0.8327	0.02381	0.1337	3.785	0.0038
U.K. gallon (gal)	1.201	1	0.02859	0.1605	4.546	0.0045
Barrel (bbl)	42.0	34.97	1	5.615	159.0	0.159
Cubic foot (ft^3)	7.48	6.229	0.1781	1	28.3	0.0283
Litre (l)	0.2642	0.220	0.0063	0.0353	1	0.001
Cubic metre (m^3)	264.2	220.0	6.289	35.3147	1000.0	1

Decimal prefixes

10^1	deca (da)	10^{-1}	deci (d)
10^2	hecto (h)	10^{-2}	centi (c)
10^3	kilo (k)	10^{-3}	milli (m)
10^6	mega (M)	10^{-6}	micro (μ)
10^9	giga (G)	10^{-9}	nano (n)
10^{12}	tera (T)	10^{-12}	pico (p)
10^{15}	peta (P)	10^{-15}	femto (f)
10^{18}	exa (E)	10^{-18}	atto (a)

Tonne of CO$_2$

The *1996 IPCC Guidelines* and the UNFCCC *Reporting Guidelines on Annual Inventories* both ask that CO$_2$ emissions be reported in Gg of CO$_2$. A million tonnes of CO$_2$ is equal to 1 000 Gg of CO$_2$, so to compare the numbers in this publication with national inventories expressed in Gg, multiply the IEA emissions by 1 000.

Other organisations may present CO$_2$ emissions in tonnes of carbon instead of tonnes of CO$_2$. To convert from tonnes of carbon, multiply by 44/12, which is the molecular weight ratio of CO$_2$ to C.

3. INDICATORS

Population

The main source of the 1970 to 2006 population data for the OECD countries is *National Accounts of OECD Countries, Volume 1*, OECD Paris, 2008. Data for 1960 to 1969 have been estimated using the growth rates from the population series published in the *OECD Economic Outlook No. 76*. For the **Czech Republic**, **Hungary** and **Poland** (1960 to 1969) and **Mexico** (1960 to 1962), the data are estimated using the growth rates from the population series from the World Bank published in the *World Development Indicators CD-ROM*. For the **Slovak Republic**, population data for 1960 to 1989 are from the Demographic Research Centre, Infostat, Slovak Republic.

The main source of the population data for the Non-OECD countries is *World Development Indicators*, World Bank, Washington D.C., 2008. Population data for **Chinese Taipei**, **Gibraltar**, **Iraq** and a few countries within the regions[3] **Other Africa**, **Other Latin America** and **Other Asia** are based on the CHELEM-CEPII online database, 2008.

GDP

The main source of the 1970 to 2006 GDP series for the OECD countries is *National Accounts of OECD Countries, Volume 1*, 2008. GDP data for 1960 to 1969 have been estimated using the growth rates from

the series in the *OECD Economic Outlook No 76* and data previously published by the OECD. Data prior to 1990 for the **Czech Republic** and **Poland**, prior to 1991 for **Hungary**, and prior to 1992 for the **Slovak Republic** are IEA Secretariat estimates based on GDP growth rates from the World Bank.

The main source of the GDP series for the Non-OECD countries is *World Development Indicators*, World Bank Washington D.C., 2008. GDP figures for **Bosnia and Herzegovina**, **Brunei Darussalam**, **Chinese Taipei**, **Cuba**, **Gibraltar**, **Iraq**, **Democratic People's Republic of Korea**, **Libya**, **Myanmar**, **Netherlands Antilles** (available from 1980), **Qatar**, **Former USSR** (before 1990), **Former Yugoslavia** (before 1990) and a few countries within the regions **Other Africa**, **Other Latin America** and **Other Asia** are from the CHELEM-CEPII online database, 2008. GDP figures for **Albania** (1971-1979), **Angola** (1971-1979), **Bahrain** (1971-1979), **Bulgaria** (1971-1979), **Cyprus** (2005-2006), **Ethiopia** (1971-1980), **Israel** (2006), **Jordan** (1971-1974), **Kuwait** (2006), **Lebanon** (1971-1987), **Malta** (2006), **Mongolia** (1985-1995), **Mozambique** (1971-1979), **Namibia** (1971-1979), **Oman** (2005-2006), **Romania** (1971-1979), **Saudi Arabia** (2006), **Serbia**[4] (1990-1998), **Slovenia** (1992), **United Republic of Tanzania** (1971-1987), the **United Arab Emirates** (1971-1972 and 2006), **Vietnam** (1971-1983) and **Yemen** (1971-1989) have been estimated based on the growth rates of the CHELEM-CEPII online database, 2008.

The GDP data have been compiled for individual countries at market prices in local currency and annual rates. These data have been scaled up/down to the price levels of 2000 and then converted to US dollars

---

3. Due to lack of complete time series, figures for population and for GDP of Other Latin America do not include British Virgin Islands, Cayman Islands, Falkland Islands, Martinique, Montserrat, Saint Pierre and Miquelon, and Turks and Caicos Islands; and figures for population and GDP of Other Asia do not include Cook Islands.

---

4. Data for GDP for Serbia include Montenegro until 2004 and Kosovo until 1999.

using the yearly average 2000 exchange rates or purchasing power parities (PPPs).

Purchasing power parities are the rates of currency conversion that equalise the purchasing power of different currencies. A given sum of money, when converted into different currencies at the PPP rates, buys the same basket of goods and services in all countries. In other words, PPPs are the rates of currency conversion which eliminate the differences in price levels between different countries. For the OECD countries, the PPPs selected to convert the GDP from national currencies to US dollars come from the OECD and were aggregated using the Geary-Khamis (GK) method and rebased on the United States. For a more detailed description of the methodology please see *Purchasing Power Parities and Real Expenditures, GK Results, Volume II, 1990*, OECD 1993. The PPPs for the other countries come from the World Bank and CHELEM-CEPII.

Note that GDP and GDP PPP time series were significantly revised compared to last year's edition for the following countries: **Brunei Darussalam**, **Cuba**, **Gibraltar**, **Libya**, **Myanmar**, **Netherlands Antilles** and **Qatar**. These time series should be used with special caution.

CO_2 emissions

The estimates of CO_2 emissions in this publication are based on the *1996 IPCC Guidelines* and represent the total emissions from fuel combustion. Emissions have been calculated using both the IPCC Reference Approach and the IPCC Sectoral Approach (which corresponds to IPCC Source/Sink Category 1 A). Reference Approach totals may include certain fugitive emissions from energy transformation which should normally be included in Category 1 B. National totals do not include emissions from international marine bunkers and international aviation. See Chapter 1, IEA emissions estimates for further details.

Electricity and heat output

Total output (shown in the summary tables section) includes electricity and heat generated in the transformation sector using fossil fuels, nuclear, hydro (excluding pumped storage), geothermal, solar, biomass, etc.

Both **main activity**[5] **producer** (formerly known as public) and **autoproducer**[6] **plants** have been included where available.

For electricity, data include the total number of TWh generated by both **electricity plants** and **CHP plants**.

For heat, data include the total amount of TJ generated by both **CHP plants** and **heat plants**.

To calculate the total electricity and heat output, the heat generated in TJ has been converted to TWh using the relationship 1 TWh = 3 600 TJ and added to electricity generated.

Ratios

CO_2 / TPES: This ratio is expressed in tonnes of CO_2 per terajoule. It has been calculated using the Sectoral Approach CO_2 emissions and total primary energy supply (including biomass and other non-fossil forms of energy).

CO_2 / GDP: This ratio is expressed in kilogrammes of CO_2 per 2000 US dollar. It has been calculated using the Sectoral Approach CO_2 emissions and is shown with both GDP calculated using exchange rates and GDP calculated using purchasing power parities.

CO_2 / population: This ratio is expressed in tonnes of CO_2 per capita. It has been calculated using the Sectoral Approach CO_2 emissions.

Per capita CO_2 emissions by sector: These ratios are expressed in kilogrammes of CO_2 per capita. They have been calculated in two different ways. In the first ratio, the emissions from electricity and heat production are shown separately. In the second ratio, the emissions from electricity and heat have been allocated to final consuming sectors in proportion to the electricity and heat consumed by those sectors.

CO_2 emissions per kWh: These ratios are expressed in grammes of CO_2 per kWh. They have been calculated using CO_2 emissions from electricity and heat as shown in the country tables in the rows "main activity producer

---

5. Main activity producers (formerly known as public supply undertakings) generate electricity and/or heat for sale to third parties, *as their primary activity*. They may be privately or publicly owned. Note that the sale need not take place through the public grid.

6. Autoproducer undertakings generate electricity and/or heat, wholly or partly for their own use as an activity which supports their primary activity. They may be privately or publicly owned.

electricity and heat" and "unallocated autoproducers", and electricity and heat output as described above.

In the first table on CO$_2$ emissions per kWh, the CO$_2$ emissions include emissions from fossil fuels, industrial waste and non-renewable municipal waste that are consumed for electricity and heat generation in the transformation sector and output includes electricity and heat generated from fossil fuels, nuclear, hydro (excluding pumped storage), geothermal, solar, biomass, etc. As a result, the emissions per kWh can vary from year to year depending on the generation mix.

In the ratios of CO$_2$ emissions per kWh **by fuel**:

- **Coal** includes primary and secondary coal, peat and manufactured gases (excluding gas works gas).

- **Oil** includes petroleum products (and small amounts of crude oil for some countries).

- **Gas** includes natural gas and gas works gas.

Note: Emissions per kWh should be used with caution due to data quality problems relating to electricity efficiencies for some countries.

4. GEOGRAPHICAL COVERAGE

Africa includes Algeria, Angola, Benin, Botswana (from 1981), Cameroon, Congo, Democratic Republic of Congo, Côte d'Ivoire, Egypt, Eritrea, Ethiopia, Gabon, Ghana, Kenya, Libya, Morocco, Mozambique, Namibia (from 1991), Nigeria, Senegal, South Africa, Sudan, United Republic of Tanzania, Togo, Tunisia, Zambia, Zimbabwe and **Other Africa**.

Other Africa includes Botswana (until 1980), Burkina Faso, Burundi, Cape Verde, Central African Republic, Chad, Comoros, Djibouti, Equatorial Guinea, Gambia, Guinea, Guinea-Bissau, Lesotho, Liberia, Madagascar, Malawi, Mali, Mauritania, Mauritius, Namibia (until 1990), Niger, Reunion, Rwanda, Sao Tome and Principe, Seychelles, Sierra Leone, Somalia, Swaziland and Uganda.

Middle East includes Bahrain, Islamic Republic of Iran, Iraq, Israel, Jordan, Kuwait, Lebanon, Oman, Qatar, Saudi Arabia, Syria, United Arab Emirates and Yemen.

Non-OECD Europe includes Albania, Bosnia and Herzegovina, Bulgaria, Croatia, Cyprus[7], Gibraltar, Former Yugoslav Republic of Macedonia (FYROM), Malta, Romania, Serbia[8], and Slovenia.

Former USSR includes Armenia, Azerbaijan, Belarus, Estonia, Georgia, Kazakhstan, Kyrgyzstan, Latvia, Lithuania, Republic of Moldova, Russia, Tajikistan, Turkmenistan, Ukraine and Uzbekistan.

Latin America includes Argentina, Bolivia, Brazil, Chile, Colombia, Costa Rica, Cuba, Dominican Republic, Ecuador, El Salvador, Guatemala, Haiti, Honduras, Jamaica, Netherlands Antilles, Nicaragua, Panama, Paraguay, Peru, Trinidad and Tobago, Uruguay, Venezuela and **Other Latin America**.

Other Latin America includes Antigua and Barbuda, Aruba, Bahamas, Barbados, Belize, Bermuda, British Virgin Islands, Cayman Islands, Dominica, Falkland Islands, French Guyana, Grenada, Guadeloupe, Guyana, Martinique, Montserrat, St. Kitts and Nevis, Saint Lucia, Saint Pierre et Miquelon, St. Vincent and the Grenadines, Suriname and Turks/Caicos Islands.

China includes the People's Republic of China and Hong Kong (China).

Asia includes Bangladesh, Brunei Darussalam, Cambodia (from 1995), Chinese Taipei, India, Indonesia, DPR of Korea, Malaysia, Mongolia (from 1985), Myanmar, Nepal, Pakistan, Philippines, Singapore, Sri Lanka, Thailand, Vietnam and **Other Asia**.

Other Asia includes Afghanistan, Bhutan, Fiji, French Polynesia, Kiribati, Laos, Macau, Maldives, New Caledonia, Papua New Guinea, Samoa, Solomon Islands, Tonga and Vanuatu.

The **Organisation for Economic Co-Operation and Development (OECD)** includes Australia, Austria, Belgium, Canada, the Czech Republic, Denmark, Finland, France, Germany, Greece, Hungary, Iceland, Ireland, Italy, Japan, Korea, Luxembourg, Mexico, the Netherlands, New Zealand, Norway, Poland, Portugal, the Slovak Republic, Spain, Sweden, Switzerland, Turkey, the United Kingdom and the United States.

Within OECD:

Australia excludes the overseas territories.

Denmark excludes Greenland and the Danish Faroes, except prior to 1990, where data on oil for Greenland

---

7. See the note concerning Cyprus in Chapter 1.
8. Serbia includes Montenegro until 2004 and Kosovo until 1999.

were included with the Danish statistics. The Administration is planning to revise the series back to 1974 to exclude these amounts.

France includes Monaco, and excludes the following overseas departments and territories (Guadeloupe, Guyana, Martinique, New Caledonia, French Polynesia, Reunion and St.-Pierre and Miquelon).

Germany includes the new federal states of Germany from 1970 onwards.

Italy includes San Marino and the Vatican.

Japan includes Okinawa.

The **Netherlands** excludes Suriname and the Netherlands Antilles.

Portugal includes the Azores and Madeira.

Spain includes the Canary Islands.

Switzerland does not include Liechtenstein.

United States includes the 50 states and the District of Columbia. Oil statistics as well as coal trade statistics also include Puerto Rico, Guam, the Virgin Islands, American Samoa, Johnston Atoll, Midway Islands, Wake Island and the Northern Mariana Islands.

The **European Union - 27 (EU-27)** includes Austria, Belgium, Bulgaria, Cyprus, the Czech Republic, Denmark, Estonia, Finland, France, Germany, Greece, Hungary, Ireland, Italy, Latvia, Lithuania, Luxembourg, Malta, Netherlands, Poland, Portugal, Romania, the Slovak Republic, Slovenia, Spain, Sweden and the United Kingdom.

The **International Energy Agency (IEA)** includes Australia, Austria, Belgium, Canada, the Czech Republic, Denmark, Finland, France, Germany, Greece, Hungary, Ireland, Italy, Japan, Korea, Luxembourg, the Netherlands, New Zealand, Norway, Poland, Portugal, the Slovak Republic, Spain, Sweden, Switzerland, Turkey, the United Kingdom and the United States.

Annex I Parties include Australia, Austria, Belarus, Belgium, Bulgaria, Canada, Croatia, the Czech Republic[9], Denmark, Estonia, Finland, France, Germany, Greece, Hungary, Iceland, Ireland, Italy, Japan, Latvia, Liechtenstein (not available in this publication),

Lithuania, Luxembourg, Monaco (included with France), the Netherlands, New Zealand, Norway, Poland, Portugal, Romania, Russia, the Slovak Republic[9], Slovenia, Spain, Sweden, Switzerland, Turkey, Ukraine, the United Kingdom and the United States.

The countries that are listed above are included in Annex I of the United Nations Framework Convention on Climate Change as amended on 11 December 1997 by the 12th Plenary meeting of the Third Conference of the Parties in Decision 4/CP.3. This includes the countries that were members of the OECD at the time of the signing of the Convention, the EEC, and fourteen countries in Central and Eastern Europe and the former USSR that are undergoing the process of transition to market economies.

Annex II Parties include Australia, Austria, Belgium, Canada, Denmark, Finland, France, Germany, Greece, Iceland, Ireland, Italy, Japan, Liechtenstein (not available in this publication), Luxembourg, Monaco (included with France), the Netherlands, New Zealand, Norway, Portugal, Spain, Sweden, Switzerland, the United Kingdom and the United States.

According to Decision 26/CP.7 in document FCCC/CP/2001/13/Add.4, Turkey has been deleted from the list of Annex II countries to the Convention. This amendment entered into force on 28 June 2002.

Economies in Transition (EITs) are those countries in Annex I that are undergoing the process of transition to a market economy. This includes Belarus, Bulgaria, Croatia, the Czech Republic[9], Estonia, Hungary, Latvia, Lithuania, Poland, Romania, Russia, the Slovak Republic[9], Slovenia and Ukraine.

Annex I Kyoto Parties include Australia, Austria, Belgium, Bulgaria, Canada, Croatia, the Czech Republic, Denmark, Estonia, Finland, France, Germany, Greece, Hungary, Iceland, Ireland, Italy, Japan, Latvia, Liechtenstein (not available in this publication), Lithuania, Luxembourg, Monaco (included with France), the Netherlands, New Zealand, Norway, Poland, Portugal, Romania, Russia, the Slovak Republic, Slovenia, Spain, Sweden, Switzerland, Ukraine and the United Kingdom.

Membership in the Kyoto Protocol is almost identical to that of Annex I, except for Turkey and Belarus which did not agree to a target under the Protocol and the United States which has expressed the intention

---

9. Czechoslovakia was in the original list of Annex I countries.

not to ratify the Protocol. Australia ratified the Protocol on 12 December 2007 and has been included in the Kyoto aggregate in this edition.

Please note that the following countries have not been considered due to lack of data:

Africa: Saint Helena and Western Sahara.

America: Anguilla.

Asia and Oceania: Christmas Island, Nauru, Niue and Palau.

Non-OECD Europe: Montenegro[10] (after 2004).

---

10. Data for Montenegro are included under Serbia until 2004.

5. IPCC METHODOLOGIES

General notes

The ultimate objective of the UNFCCC (the Convention) is the stabilisation of greenhouse gas (GHG) concentrations in the atmosphere at a level that would prevent dangerous anthropogenic interference with the climate system. The Convention also calls for all Parties to commit themselves to the following objectives:

- to develop, update periodically, publish and make available to the Conference of the Parties (COP) their national inventories of anthropogenic emissions by sources and removals by sinks, of all GHGs not controlled by the Montreal Protocol.

- to use comparable methodologies for inventories of GHG emissions and removals, to be agreed upon by the COP.

As a response to the objectives of the UNFCCC, the IEA, together with the IPCC, the OECD and numerous international experts, has helped to develop and refine an internationally-agreed methodology for the calculation and reporting of national GHG emissions from fuel combustion. This methodology was published in 1995 in the *IPCC Guidelines for National Greenhouse Gas Inventories*. After the initial dissemination of the methodology, revisions were added to several chapters, and published as the *Revised 1996 IPCC Guidelines for National Greenhouse Gas Inventories* (*1996 IPCC Guidelines*). In April 2006, the IPCC approved the *2006 Guidelines* at the 25th session of the IPCC in Mauritius. For now, most countries (as well as the IEA) are still calculating their inventories using the *1996 IPCC Guidelines*[11].

---

11. Both the *1996 IPCC Guidelines* and the *2006 IPCC Guidelines* are available from the IPCC Greenhouse Gas Inventories Programme (http://www.ipcc-nggip.iges.or.jp).

Since the IPCC methodology for fuel combustion is largely based on energy balances, the IEA estimates for CO$_2$ from fuel combustion published in this document have been calculated using the IEA energy balances and the default IPCC methodology. However, other possibly more detailed methodologies may be used by Parties to calculate their inventories. This may lead to different estimates of emissions. See Chapter 1, IEA emissions estimates, for further details.

The calculation of CO$_2$ emissions from fuel combustion may be done at three different levels referred to as Tiers 1, 2 and 3. The Tier 1 methods estimate the emissions from the carbon content of fuels supplied to the country as a whole (the Reference Approach) or to the main fuel combustion activities (Sectoral Approach). The following chapter summarises the IPCC Tier 1 methodology from the *1996 IPCC Guidelines*.

Reference Approach

Introduction

Carbon dioxide emissions are produced when carbon-based fuels are burned. National emissions estimates are based on the amounts of fuels used and on the carbon content of fuels.

Fuel combustion is widely dispersed throughout most activities in national economies and a complete record of the quantities of each fuel type consumed in each end-use activity is a considerable task, which some countries have not undertaken. Fortunately, it is possible to obtain a relatively accurate estimate of national CO$_2$ emissions by accounting for the carbon in fuels supplied to the economy. The supply of fuels is simple to record and the statistics are more likely to be available in many countries.

In accounting for fuels supplied[12] it is important to distinguish between *primary fuels* (i.e. fuels which are found in nature such as coal, crude oil, natural gas), and *secondary fuels* or fuel products, such as gasoline and lubricants, which are derived from primary fuels.

Accounting for carbon is based mainly on the supply of primary fuels and the net quantities of secondary fuels brought into the country.

To calculate supply of fuels to the country necessitates the following data for each fuel and year chosen:

- the amounts of primary fuels produced (production of secondary fuels is excluded);

- the amounts of primary and secondary fuels imported;

- the amounts of primary and secondary fuels exported;

- the amounts of fuel used for international marine bunkers and international aviation (hereafter referred to as bunkers);

- the net increases or decreases in stocks of the fuels.

For each fuel, the production (where appropriate) and imports are added together and the exports, bunkers, and stock changes are subtracted to calculate the apparent consumption of the fuels. In cases where exports of secondary fuels exceed imports or stock increases exceed net imports, negative numbers will result.

The manufacture of secondary fuels is ignored in the main calculation, as the carbon in these fuels has already been accounted for in the supply of primary fuels from which they are derived. However, information on production of some secondary fuel products is required to adjust for carbon stored in these products.

Three other important points influence the accounting methodology:

---

12. The following discussion excludes all non-carbon energy sources such as nuclear, hydro, geothermal, solar, etc.

- *Stored carbon*

Not all fuel supplied to an economy is burned for heat energy. Some is used as a raw material (or feedstock) for manufacture of products such as plastics or in a non-energy use (e.g. bitumen for road construction), without oxidation (emissions) of the carbon. This is called *stored carbon*, and is deducted from the carbon emissions calculation. Estimation of the stored carbon requires data for fuel use by activities using the fuel as raw material.

- *International bunker fuels*

The procedures given for calculating emissions ensure that emissions from the use of fuels for **international** marine and air transport are excluded from national emissions totals. However, for information purposes, the quantities and types of fuels delivered and the corresponding emissions from international marine bunkers and international aviation should be separately reported.

- *Biomass fuels*

In the IPCC methodology, biomass fuels are not included in the CO₂ emissions from fuel combustion and are only shown for informational purposes. This is because for CO₂ emissions, biomass consumption for fuel is assumed to equal its regrowth. Any departures from this hypothesis are counted within the land use, land use change and forestry module of the *1996 IPCC Guidelines*. For this reason, emissions from the burning of biomass for energy are not included in the CO₂ emissions from fuel combustion in this publication.

Methodology

The IPCC methodology breaks the calculation of carbon dioxide emissions from fuel combustion into six steps:

Step 1: Estimate apparent fuel consumption in original units

Step 2: Convert to a common energy unit

Step 3: Multiply by emission factors to compute the carbon content

Step 4: Compute carbon stored

Step 5: Correct for carbon unoxidised

Step 6: Convert carbon oxidised to CO₂ emissions

Completing Worksheet 1

This section is from the Workbook of the *1996 IPCC Guidelines* and provides step-by-step instructions for calculating emissions at the detailed fuels and fuel products level. Worksheet 1 can be consulted at the end of this chapter.

NOTE: The main worksheet allows CO_2 emissions from biomass fuels to be calculated but it does not include them in the national total.

Step 1	Estimating apparent fuel consumption

1 Apparent consumption is the basis for calculating the carbon supply for the country. To calculate apparent consumption (or total fuel supplied) for each fuel, the following data for primary fuels are entered:

- Production (Column A)
- Imports (Column B)
- Exports (Column C)
- International bunkers (Column D)
- Stock change (Column E)

For secondary fuels and products, the only figures entered are:

- Imports (Column B)
- Exports (Column C)
- International bunkers (Column D)
- Stock change (Column E)

These allow the overall calculation to account for all consumption.

Amounts of all fuels can be expressed in joules (J), megajoules (MJ), gigajoules (GJ), terajoules (TJ) or thousands of tonnes of oil equivalent (ktoe). Solid or liquid fuels can be expressed as thousands of tonnes (kt) and dry natural gas can be expressed as tera-calories (Tcal) or cubic metres (m³).

NOTE: The figure for production of natural gas, used in Worksheet 1, **does not** include quantities of gas vented, flared or re-injected into the well.

Quantities are expressed in terms of the net calorific values (NCV) of the fuels concerned. NCV is sometimes referred to as the lower heating value (LHV). NCVs are approximately 95% of the gross calorific value (GCV) for liquid fossil, solid fossil and biomass fuels, and 90% of the GCV for natural gas.

2 Apparent consumption is calculated for each fuel using this formula:

Apparent consumption =
Production + Imports - Exports - International bunkers - stock Change

The results are entered in Column F.

Particular attention is given to the algebraic sign of "stock change" as it is entered in Column E. When more fuel is added to stock than is taken from it during the year there is a net stock build and the quantity is entered in Column E with a plus sign. In the converse case (a stock draw) the quantity is entered in Column E with a minus sign.

Step 2	Converting to a common energy unit (TJ)

1 The conversion factor used for each fuel is entered in Column G.

2 The Apparent consumption is multiplied by the relevant conversion factor (NCV or scaling factor) to give apparent consumption in terajoules. The result is entered in Column H.

TABLE 1 CONVERSION FACTORS	
Unit	*Conversion factor*
J, MJ or GJ	Number is divided by the appropriate factor, 10^{12}, 10^6 or 10^3 respectively, to convert to TJ.
10^6 toe	Number is multiplied by the conversion factor, 41868 TJ/10^6 toe, to convert to TJ.
Tcal	Number is multiplied by the conversion factor, 4.1868 TJ/Tcal.
10^3 t	The net calorific value of each fuel is used (see Table 2).

TABLE 2
SELECTED NET CALORIFIC VALUES

	Factors (TJ/10³ tonnes)
Refined petroleum products	
Gasoline	44.80
Jet kerosene	44.59
Other kerosene	44.75
Shale oil	36.00
Gas/diesel oil	43.33
Residual fuel oil	40.19
LPG	47.31
Ethane	47.49
Naphtha	45.01
Bitumen	40.19
Lubricants	40.19
Petroleum coke	31.00
Refinery feedstocks	44.80
Refinery gas	48.15
Other oil products	40.19
Other products	
Coal oils and tars derived from coking coals	28.00
Oil shale	9.40
Orimulsion	27.50

NOTE: When converting from 10^3 t, for anthracite, coking coal, other bituminous coal, sub-bituminous coal and lignite, separate country specific net calorific values are used for production (Column A), imports (Column B), and exports (Column C). For these fuels, apparent consumption is calculated by converting production, imports, exports, and stock changes to TJ first. For international bunkers (Column D) and stock change (Column E), either a weighted average net calorific value or a factor appropriate to the dominant source of supply is used.

Step 3   Multiplying by carbon emission factors

1   The carbon emission factor (CEF) used to convert apparent consumption into carbon content is entered in Column I.

Table 3 shows the default values used in this publication.

TABLE 3
CARBON EMISSION FACTORS (CEF)

Fuel	Carbon emission factor (t C/TJ)
LIQUID FOSSIL	
Primary fuels	
Crude oil	20.0
Orimulsion	22.0
Natural gas liquids	17.2
Secondary fuels/products	
Gasoline	18.9
Jet kerosene	19.5
Other kerosene	19.6
Shale oil	20.0
Gas/diesel oil	20.2
Residual fuel oil	21.1
LPG	17.2
Ethane	16.8
Naphtha	(20.0) [a]
Bitumen	22.0
Lubricants	(20.0) [a]
Petroleum coke	27.5
Refinery feedstocks	(20.0) [a]
Refinery gas	18.2 [b]
Other oil	(20.0) [a]
SOLID FOSSIL	
Primary fuels	
Anthracite	26.8
Coking coal	25.8
Other bituminous coal	25.8
Sub-bituminous coal	26.2
Lignite	27.6
Oil shale	29.1
Peat	28.9
Secondary fuels/products	
BKB & patent fuel	(25.8) [a]
Coke oven / gas coke	29.5
Coke oven gas	13.0 [b]
Blast furnace gas	66.0 [b]
GASEOUS FOSSIL	
Natural gas (dry)	15.3
BIOMASS [c]	
Solid biomass	29.9
Liquid biomass	(20.0) [a]
Gas biomass	(30.6) [a]

2 The apparent consumption in TJ (in Column H) is multiplied by the carbon emission factor (in Column I) to give the carbon content in tonnes of C. The result is entered in Column J.

3 The carbon content in tonnes C is divided by 10^3 to give gigagrammes of carbon. The result is entered in Column K.

Step 4   Calculating carbon stored

1 Estimating fuel quantities

Bitumen and lubricants

Domestic production for bitumen and lubricants is added to the apparent consumption (shown in Column F of the main Worksheet 1) for these products and the sum is entered in Column A of Auxiliary Worksheet 1.

Coal oils and tars

For coking coal, the default assumption is that 6% of the carbon in coking coal consumed is converted to oils and tars. The apparent consumption for coking coal (from Worksheet 1, Column F) is multiplied by 0.06.

Starting with the 2006 edition, the IEA has requested coal tar data on its annual coal questionnaire. In cases where this information has been provided, to be consistent with the *1996 IPCC Guidelines*, 75% of the part reported as non-energy was considered to be stored and the default 6% of coking coal was not applied.

Natural gas, LPG, ethane, naphtha and gas/diesel oil

The amount of these fuels used as a feedstock for non-energy purposes is entered in Column A.

2 Converting to TJ

The appropriate conversion factors are inserted in Column B of Auxiliary Worksheet 1. The estimated fuel quantities (Column A) are multiplied by the relevant conversion factor to give the estimated fuel quantities in TJ. The result is entered in Column C.

3 Calculating carbon content

The estimated fuel quantities in TJ (Column C of Auxiliary Worksheet 1) are multiplied by the emission factor in tonnes of carbon per terajoule (Column D) to give the carbon content in tonnes of C (Column E). The figures are divided by 10^3 to express the amount as gigagrammes of carbon. The results are entered in Column F.

4 Calculating actual carbon stored

The carbon content (Column F of Auxiliary Worksheet 1) is multiplied by the fraction of carbon stored (Column G) to give the carbon stored. The result is entered in Column H.

When Auxiliary Worksheet 1 is completed

5 The values for carbon stored for the relevant fuels/products are entered in Column L of the main Worksheet 1.

6 The values for carbon stored (Column L) are subtracted from carbon content (Column K) to give net carbon emissions. The results are entered in Column M.

Step 5   Correcting for carbon unoxidised

1 The values for fraction of carbon oxidised are entered in Column N of Worksheet 1. Table 4 provides information on typical values measured from various facilities and suggests global default values for solid, liquid and gaseous fuels.

2 Net carbon emissions (Column M) are multiplied by the fraction of carbon oxidised (Column N) and the results are entered in Column O, actual carbon emissions.

TABLE 4 FRACTION OF CARBON OXIDISED	
Coal[1]	0.98
Oil and oil products	0.99
Gas	0.995
Peat for electricity generation[2]	0.99
1 This figure is a global average but varies for different types of coal, and can be as low as 0.91. 2 The fraction for peat used in households may be much lower.	

Step 6   Converting to CO_2 emissions

1   Actual carbon emissions (Column O) are multiplied by 44/12 (which is the molecular weight ratio of CO_2 to C) to find total carbon dioxide (CO_2) emitted from fuel combustion. The results are entered in Column P.

2   The sum is total national emissions of carbon dioxide from fuel combustion. These are the numbers shown for total CO_2 emissions from fuel combustion in this publication.

Sectoral Approach

Introduction

A sectoral breakdown of national CO_2 emissions using the defined IPCC Source/Sink Categories is needed for monitoring and abatement policy discussions. The IPCC Reference Approach provides a rapid estimate of the total CO_2 emissions from fuels supplied to the country but it does not break down the emissions by sector.

The more detailed calculations used for the Sectoral Approach are essentially similar in content to those used for the Reference Approach.

Completing Worksheet 2

This section is from the Workbook of the *1996 IPCC Guidelines* and provides step-by-step instructions for calculating emissions by fuels for each of the main source categories using the IPCC Tier 1 Sectoral Approach. A sample sheet of Worksheet 2 can be consulted at the end of this chapter.

Step 1   Estimating sectoral fuel consumption

The amount of each fuel consumed by sector is entered in Column A.

Energy and transformation sector

Special care needs to be taken when considering the fuel use of the energy and transformation sector so that double counting is avoided.

Fuel use in the energy and transformation sector can be divided into three groups:

Transformation sector

1   Fuels transformed into secondary fuels by physical or chemical processes not involving combustion (e.g. crude oil to petroleum products in refineries, coal to coke and coke oven gas in coke ovens);

2   Fuels combusted to generate electricity and/or heat (excluding fuels used for autoproduction of electricity and heat, which are reported in the sector where they are used);

Energy sector

3   Fuels combusted by the energy (energy extraction and transformation) industries for heating, pumping, traction and lighting purposes (e.g. refinery gas for heating distillation columns, use of colliery methane at mines for heating purposes).

In this worksheet, only fuel use by Groups 2 and 3 (fuels that are combusted) is included. However, see Step 4 for the reporting of lubricants used by the energy industries. For emissions resulting from fuel use by Group 1, no worksheets are available. They should be reported under the IPCC Source/Sink Category 1B: Fugitive emissions from fuels. It is most important that this distinction be appreciated. The quantities of *primary* fuels reported in Column A will understate the quantities used for Group 1 activities. The reported quantities cover only the combustion needs of these industries.

Step 2   Converting to a common energy unit (TJ)

1   The conversion factor (NCV or scaling factor) to convert to terajoules is entered in Column B.

2   The consumption is multiplied by the relevant conversion factor to give consumption in terajoules. The result is entered in Column C.

Step 3   Multiplying by carbon emission factors

1   The carbon emission factor used to convert consumption into carbon content is entered in Column D.

2   The consumption in TJ (in Column C) is multiplied by the carbon emission factor (in Column D) to give the carbon content in tonnes of carbon. The result is entered in Column E.

3 The carbon content in tonnes of carbon is divided by 10^3 to be expressed as gigagrammes of carbon. The result is entered in Column F.

Step 4 Calculating carbon stored

For the calculation of carbon stored, fuels are distinguished into four groups:
- Fuels used as feedstocks, such as naphtha, natural gas, gas/diesel oil, LPG or ethane;
- Lubricants;
- Bitumen and coal tars;
- Fuels for which no carbon is stored.

Fuels used as feedstocks, such as naphtha, natural gas, gas/diesel oil, LPG or ethane:

This subsection on feedstocks applies only to the industry source category.

1 **Estimating fuel quantities**

The amount of fuel used as a feedstock for non-energy purposes is entered in Column A of Auxiliary Worksheet 2.

2 **Converting to TJ**

The appropriate conversion factor is inserted in Column B. Feedstock use (Column A) is multiplied by the relevant conversion factor to give the feedstock use in TJ. The result is entered in Column C of Auxiliary Worksheet 2.

3 **Calculating carbon content**

The feedstock use in TJ (Column C) is multiplied by the emission factor in tonnes of carbon per terajoule (Column D) to give the carbon content in tonnes C (Column E). The figures are divided by 10^3 to express the amount as gigagrammes of carbon. The results are entered in Column F of Auxiliary Worksheet 2.

4 **Calculating actual carbon stored**

The carbon content (Column F) is multiplied by the fraction of carbon stored (Column G) to give the carbon stored. The result is entered in Column H of Auxiliary Worksheet 2.

After completion of Auxiliary Worksheet 2

5 The amount of carbon stored for the relevant fuel/product is entered in Column H of Worksheet 2 for the industry source category.

6 The amount of carbon stored (Column H) is subtracted from the carbon content (Column F) to give net carbon emissions. The results are entered in Column I.

Lubricants:

It has been estimated that during the first use, recycling and final disappearance of lubricants, approximately half of the production is oxidised as CO_2.

1 For each sector where lubricants are used, the fraction of carbon stored for lubricants is entered in Column G. The default value of 0.5 is used for this publication.

2 The carbon content (Column F) is multiplied by the fraction of carbon stored (Column G) to obtain the amount of carbon stored. The result is entered in Column H.

3 The amount of carbon stored (Column H) is subtracted from the carbon content (Column F) to obtain the net carbon emissions. The result is entered in Column I.

Bitumen and coal tars:

Bitumen and coal tars are usually not combusted but used in a manner that stores almost all of the carbon. Emissions of non-methane volatile organic compounds (NMVOCs) from the use of bitumen for road paving are estimated in the industrial processes chapter.

Fuels for which no carbon is stored:

Step 4 is skipped and the values from Column F are entered in Column I before continuing with Step 5.

Step 5 Correcting for carbon unoxidised

1 Values for fraction of carbon oxidised are entered in Column J of Worksheet 2. Table 4 provides information on typical values measured from coal facilities and suggests global default values for solid, liquid and gaseous fuels.

2 Net carbon emissions (Column I) are multiplied by fraction of carbon oxidised (Column J) and the results are entered in Column K, actual carbon emissions.

Step 6 Converting to CO₂ emissions

1 Actual carbon emissions (Column K) are multiplied by 44/12 (which is the molecular weight ratio of CO_2 to C) to find actual carbon dioxide (CO_2) emissions. The results are entered in Column L and correspond to the sectoral emissions included in the present publication.

MODULE	ENERGY					
SUBMODULE	CO_2 FROM ENERGY SOURCES (REFERENCE APPROACH)					
WORKSHEET	1					
SHEET	1 OF 5					

			STEP 1					
			A Production	B Imports	C Exports	D International Bunkers	E Stock Change	F Apparent Consumption
FUEL TYPES								F=(A+B -C-D-E)
Liquid Fossil	Primary Fuels	Crude Oil						
		Orimulsion						
		Natural Gas Liquids						
	Secondary Fuels	Gasoline						
		Jet Kerosene						
		Other Kerosene						
		Shale Oil						
		Gas / Diesel Oil						
		Residual Fuel Oil						
		LPG						
		Ethane						
		Naphtha						
		Bitumen						
		Lubricants						
		Petroleum Coke						
		Refinery Feedstocks						
		Other Oil						
Liquid Fossil Totals								
Solid Fossil	Primary Fuels	Anthracite[a]						
		Coking Coal						
		Other Bit. Coal						
		Sub-Bit. Coal						
		Lignite						
		Oil Shale						
		Peat						
	Secondary Fuels	BKB & Patent Fuel						
		Coke Oven/Gas Coke						
Solid Fossil Totals								
Gaseous Fossil		Natural Gas (Dry)						
Total								
Biomass Total								
		Solid biomass						
		Liquid biomass						
		Gas biomass						

(a) If anthracite is not separately available, include with other bituminous coal.

MODULE	ENERGY				
SUBMODULE	CO$_2$ FROM ENERGY SOURCES (REFERENCE APPROACH)				
WORKSHEET	1				
SHEET	2 OF 5				

			STEP 2		STEP 3	
			G(a) Conversion Factor (TJ/Unit)	H Apparent Consumption (TJ)	I Carbon Emission Factor (t C/TJ)	J Carbon Content (t C)	K Carbon Content (Gg C)
FUEL TYPES				H=(FxG)		J=(HxI)	K=(Jx10^{-3})
Liquid Fossil	Primary Fuels	Crude Oil					
		Orimulsion					
		Natural Gas Liquids					
	Secondary Fuels	Gasoline					
		Jet Kerosene					
		Other Kerosene					
		Shale Oil					
		Gas / Diesel Oil					
		Residual Fuel Oil					
		LPG					
		Ethane					
		Naphtha					
		Bitumen					
		Lubricants					
		Petroleum Coke					
		Refinery Feedstocks					
		Other Oil					
Liquid Fossil Totals							
Solid Fossil	Primary Fuels	Anthracite(b)					
		Coking Coal					
		Other Bit. Coal					
		Sub-Bit. Coal					
		Lignite					
		Oil Shale					
		Peat					
	Secondary Fuels	BKB & Patent Fuel					
		Coke Oven/Gas Coke					
Solid Fossil Totals							
Gaseous Fossil		Natural Gas (Dry)					
Total							
Biomass Total							
		Solid biomass					
		Liquid biomass					
		Gas biomass					

(a) Please specify units.
(b) If anthracite is not separately available, include with other bituminous coal.

				STEP 4		STEP 5		STEP 6
MODULE			**ENERGY**					
SUBMODULE			**CO₂ FROM ENERGY SOURCES (REFERENCE APPROACH)**					
WORKSHEET			**1**					
SHEET			**3 OF 5**					

			L Carbon Stored (Gg C)	M Net Carbon Emissions (Gg C)	N Fraction of Carbon Oxidised	O Actual Carbon Emissions (Gg C)	P Actual CO₂ Emissions (Gg CO₂)
FUEL TYPES				M=(K-L)		O=(MxN)	P=(Ox[44/12])
Liquid Fossil	Primary Fuels	Crude Oil					
		Orimulsion					
		Natural Gas Liquids					
	Secondary Fuels	Gasoline					
		Jet Kerosene					
		Other Kerosene					
		Shale Oil					
		Gas / Diesel Oil					
		Residual Fuel Oil					
		LPG					
		Ethane					
		Naphtha					
		Bitumen					
		Lubricants					
		Petroleum Coke					
		Refinery Feedstocks					
		Other Oil					
Liquid Fossil Totals							
Solid Fossil	Primary Fuels	Anthracite[a]					
		Coking Coal					
		Other Bit. Coal					
		Sub-Bit. Coal					
		Lignite					
		Oil Shale					
		Peat					
	Secondary Fuels	BKB & Patent Fuel					
		Coke Oven/Gas Coke					
Solid Fossil Totals							
Gaseous Fossil		Natural Gas (Dry)					
Total							
Biomass Total							
		Solid biomass					
		Liquid biomass					
		Gas biomass					

(a) If anthracite is not separately available, include with other bituminous coal.

MODULE	ENERGY					
SUBMODULE	CO₂ FROM ENERGY SOURCES (REFERENCE APPROACH)					
WORKSHEET	1					
SHEET	4 OF 5 EMISSIONS FROM INTERNATIONAL BUNKERS (INTERNATIONAL MARINE AND AIR TRANSPORT)					

		STEP 1	STEP 2		STEP 3		
		A	B	C	D	E	F
		Quantities Delivered[a]	Conversion Factor (TJ/unit)	Quantities Delivered (TJ)	Carbon Emission Factor (t C/TJ)	Carbon Content (t C)	Carbon Content (Gg C)
FUEL TYPES				C=(AxB)		E=(CxD)	F=(E x 10⁻³)
Solid Fossil	Other Bituminous Coal						
	Sub-Bituminous Coal						
Liquid Fossil	Gasoline						
	Jet Kerosene						
	Gas/Diesel Oil						
	Residual Fuel Oil						
	Lubricants						
			Total				

(a) Enter the quantities from Worksheet 1, Sheet 1, Column D: "International Bunkers".

MODULE	ENERGY					
SUBMODULE	CO₂ FROM ENERGY SOURCES (REFERENCE APPROACH)					
WORKSHEET	1					
SHEET	5 OF 5 EMISSIONS FROM INTERNATIONAL BUNKERS (INTERNATIONAL MARINE AND AIR TRANSPORT)					

		STEP 4			STEP 5		STEP 6
		G	H	I	J	K	L
		Fraction of Carbon Stored	Carbon Stored (Gg C)	Net Carbon Emissions (Gg C)	Fraction of Carbon Oxidised	Actual Carbon Emissions (Gg C)	Actual CO₂ Emissions (Gg CO₂)
FUEL TYPES			H=(FxG)	I=(F-H)		K=(IxJ)	L=(Kx44/12)
Solid Fossil	Other Bituminous Coal	0	0				
	Sub-Bituminous Coal	0	0				
Liquid Fossil	Gasoline	0	0				
	Jet Kerosene	0	0				
	Gas/Diesel Oil	0	0				
	Residual Fuel Oil	0	0				
	Lubricants	0.5					
							Total[a]

(a) The bunker emissions are not to be added to national totals.

	MODULE	ENERGY
	SUBMODULE	CO$_2$ FROM ENERGY
	WORKSHEET	AUXILIARY WORKSHEET 1: ESTIMATING CARBON STORED IN PRODUCTS
	SHEET	1 OF 1

	A	B	C	D	E	F	G	H
	Estimated Fuel Quantities	Conversion Factor (TJ/Units)	Estimated Fuel Quantities (TJ)	Carbon Emission Factor (t C/TJ)	Carbon Content (t C)	Carbon Content (Gg C)	Fraction of Carbon Stored	Carbon Stored (Gg C)
FUEL TYPES			C=(AxB)		E=(CxD)	F=(Ex10^{-3})		H=(FxG)
Naphtha[a]							0.80	
Lubricants							0.50	
Bitumen							1.0	
Coal Oils and Tars (from Coking Coal)							0.75	
Natural Gas[a]							0.33	
Gas/Diesel Oil[a]							0.50	
LPG[a]							0.80	
Ethane[a]							0.80	
Other fuels[b]								

(a) Enter these fuels when they are used as feedstocks.
(b) Use the other fuels rows to enter any other products in which carbon may be stored.

MODULE	ENERGY					
SUBMODULE	CO₂ FROM FUEL COMBUSTION (TIER I SECTORAL APPROACH)					
WORKSHEET	2 STEP BY STEP CALCULATIONS					
SHEET	SAMPLE SHEET - FILLED OUT FOR EACH SECTOR					

Energy Industries	A Consumption	B Conversion Factor (TJ/unit)	C Consumption (TJ)	D Carbon Emission Factor (t C/TJ)	E Carbon Content (t C)	F Carbon Content (Gg C)
specific fuels listed for each sector (a)			C=(AxB)		E=(CxD)	F=(E x 10⁻³)
		Total				
Memo items:						
Wood/Wood Waste						
Charcoal						
Other Solid Biomass						
Liquid Biomass						
Gaseous Biomass						
		Total Biomass				

(a) Certain sectors have specific calculations for some products. See the *Revised 1996 IPCC Guidelines for National Greenhouse Gas Inventories* for further details.

MODULE	ENERGY					
SUBMODULE	CO₂ FROM FUEL COMBUSTION (TIER I SECTORAL APPROACH)					
WORKSHEET	2 STEP BY STEP CALCULATIONS					
SHEET	SAMPLE SHEET - FILLED OUT FOR EACH SECTOR					

Energy Industries	G Fraction of Carbon Stored	H Carbon Stored (Gg C)	I Net Carbon Emissions (Gg C)	J Fraction of Carbon Oxidised	K Actual Carbon Emissions (Gg C)	L Actual CO₂ Emissions (Gg CO₂)
specific fuels listed for each sector (a)		H=(FxG)	I=(F-H)		K=(IxJ)	L=(K x [44/12])
					Total	
Memo items:						
Wood/Wood Waste						
Charcoal						
Other Solid Biomass						
Liquid Biomass						
Gaseous Biomass						
					Total Biomass	

(a) Certain sectors have specific calculations for some products. See the *Revised 1996 IPCC Guidelines for National Greenhouse Gas Inventories* for further details.

MODULE	ENERGY
SUBMODULE	CO$_2$ FROM FUEL COMBUSTION BY (TIER I SECTORAL APPROACH)
WORKSHEET	AUXILIARY WORKSHEET 2: ESTIMATING CARBON STORED IN PRODUCTS
SHEET	1

	A Feedstock Use	B Conversion Factor (TJ/Units)	C Feedstock Use (TJ)	D Carbon Emission Factor (t C/TJ)	E Carbon Content (t C)	F Carbon Content (Gg C)	G Fraction of Carbon Stored	H Carbon Stored[a] (Gg C)
FUEL TYPES			C=(AxB)		E=(CxD)	F=(Ex10^{-3})		H=(FxG)
Gas/Diesel Oil							0.5	
LPG							0.8	
Ethane							0.8	
Naphtha							0.8	
Natural Gas							0.33	
Other Fuels[b]								

(a) Enter the result of this calculation in Worksheet 2 Step by Step Calculation, in the m*anufacturing industries and construction* sector.
(b) Please specify.

Key sources

In May 2000, the IPCC Plenary, at its 16th session held in Montreal, accepted the report on *Good Practice Guidance and Uncertainty Management in National Greenhouse Gas Inventories*[13]. The report provides good practice guidance to assist countries in producing inventories that are neither over nor underestimates so far as can be judged, and in which uncertainties are reduced as far as practicable. It supports the development of inventories that are transparent, documented, consistent over time, complete, comparable, assessed for uncertainties, subject to quality control and quality assurance, and efficient in the use of resources. The report does not revise or replace the *Revised 1996 IPCC Guidelines for National Greenhouse Gas Inventories*, but provides a reference that complements and is consistent with those guidelines.

Methodological choice for individual source categories is important in managing overall inventory uncertainty. Generally, inventory uncertainty is lower when emissions are estimated using the most rigorous methods, but due to finite resources, this may not be feasible for every source category. To make the most efficient use of available resources, it is good practice to identify those source categories that have the greatest contribution to overall inventory uncertainty. By identifying these key source categories in the national inventory, inventory agencies can prioritise their efforts and improve their overall estimates. Such a process will lead to improved inventory quality, as well as greater confidence in the resulting emissions estimates. It is good practice for each inventory agency to identify its national key source categories in a systematic and objective manner.

A key source category is one that is prioritised within the national inventory system because its estimate has a significant influence on a country's total inventory of direct greenhouse gases in terms of the absolute level of emissions, the trend in emissions, or both.

Any inventory agency that has prepared an emissions inventory will be able to identify key source categories in terms of their contribution to the absolute level of national emissions. For those inventory agencies that have prepared a time series, the quantitative determination of key source categories should include evaluation of both the absolute level and the trend in emissions. Evaluating only the influence of a source category on the overall level of emissions provides limited information about why the source category is key. Some key source categories may not be identified if the influence of their trend is not taken into account.

The *Good Practice Guidance* describes both a basic Tier 1 approach and a Tier 2 approach. The basic difference between the two approaches is that the Tier 2 approach accounts for uncertainty.

In each country's national inventory, certain source categories are particularly significant in terms of their contribution to the overall uncertainty of the inventory. It is important to identify these key source categories so that the resources available for inventory preparation may be prioritised and the best possible estimates prepared for the most significant source categories.

The results of the key source category determination will be most useful if the analysis is done at the appropriate level of detail. The *Good Practice Guidance* suggests at which levels of details the various IPCC Source Categories should be analysed. For example, the combustion of fossil fuels is a large emission source category that can be broken down into sub-source categories, and even to the level of individual plants or boilers. The following guidance describes good practice in determining the appropriate level of analysis to identify key source categories:

- The analysis should be performed at the level of IPCC source categories (i.e. at the level at which the IPCC methods are described). The analysis should be performed using CO$_2$-equivalent emissions calculated using the global warming potentials (GWPs) specified for the preparation of national greenhouse gas inventories by Parties included in Annex I to the Convention, Part I: UNFCCC reporting guidelines on annual inventories (UNFCCC Guidelines).

- Each greenhouse gas emitted from a single source category should be considered separately, unless there are specific methodological reasons for treating gases collectively. For example, carbon dioxide (CO$_2$), methane (CH$_4$) and nitrous oxide (N$_2$O) are

---

13. The report on *IPCC Good Practice Guidance and Uncertainty Management in National Greenhouse Gas Inventories* is available from the IPCC Greenhouse Gas Inventories Programme (http://www.ipcc-nggip.iges.or.jp).

emitted from mobile sources. The key source category evaluation should be performed for each of these gases separately because methods, emission factors and related uncertainties differ for each gas. In contrast, a collective evaluation of hydro-fluorocarbons (HFCs) and perfluorocarbons (PFCs) may be appropriate for some source categories, such as emissions from substitutes for Ozone Depleting Substances (ODS substitutes).

- Source categories that use the same emission factors based on common assumptions should be aggregated before analysis. This approach can also help deal with cross-correlations between source categories in the uncertainty analysis. The same pattern of aggregation should be used both to quantify uncertainties and to identify key source categories unless the associated activity data uncertainties are very different.

Quantitative approaches to identify key source categories

It is good practice for each inventory agency to identify its national key source categories in a systematic and objective manner, by performing a quantitative analysis of the relationships between the level and the trend of each source category's emissions and total national emissions.

Any inventory agency that has developed an emissions inventory will be able to perform the Tier 1 Level Assessment and identify the source categories whose level has a significant effect on total national emissions. Those inventory agencies that have developed emissions inventories for more than one year will also be able to perform the Tier 1 Trend Assessment and identify sources that are key because of their contribution to the total trend of national emissions. Both assessments are described in detail in the *Good Practice Guidance*.

For CO$_2$ emissions from stationary combustion, the *Good Practice Guidance* suggests that the emissions be disaggregated to the level where emission factors are distinguished. In most inventories, this will be the main fuel types. If emission factors are determined independently for some sub-source categories, these should be distinguished in the analysis.

When using the Tier 1 approach, key source categories are identified using a pre-determined cumulative emissions threshold. The pre-determined threshold is based on an evaluation of several inventories, and is aimed at establishing a general level where 90% of inventory uncertainty will be covered by key source categories.

The Tier 1 method to identify key source categories of the national emissions inventory assesses the impacts of various source categories on the level and, if possible, on the trend. When national inventory estimates are available for several years, it is good practice to assess the contribution of each source category to both the level and trend of the national inventory. If only a single year's inventory is available, only a Level Assessment can be performed.

For the **Tier 1 Level Assessment**, the contribution of each source category to the total national inventory level is calculated according to Equation 1:

EQUATION 1

**Source Category Level Assessment =
Source Category Estimate / Total Estimate**

$$L_{x,t} = E_{x,t} / E_t$$

Where:

$L_{x,t}$ is the Level Assessment for source x in year t

Source category estimate ($E_{x,t}$) is the emission estimate of source category x in year t

Total estimate (E_t) is the total inventory estimate in year t

The value of the source category Level Assessment should be calculated separately for each source category, and the cumulative sum of all the entries is calculated. Key source categories are those that, when summed together in descending order of magnitude, add up to over 95% of the total. Any source category that meets the 95% threshold in any year should be identified as a key source category.

The **Tier 1 Trend Assessment** calculates the contribution of each source category trend to the trend in the total national inventory. This assessment will identify source categories that have a different trend to the trend of the overall inventory. As differences in trend are more significant to the overall inventory level for larger source categories, the result of the trend difference (i.e. the source category trend minus total trend) is multiplied by the result of the level assessment (L$_{x,t}$ from Equation 1) to provide appropriate weighting. Thus, key source categories will be those where the source category trend diverges significantly from the total trend, weighted by the emission level of the source category.

If nationally derived source-level uncertainties are available, inventory agencies can use **Tier 2** to identify key source categories. The Tier 2 approach is a more detailed analysis that builds on the Tier 1 approach, and it is likely to reduce the number of key source categories. Under Tier 2, the results of the Tier 1 analysis are multiplied by the relative uncertainty of each source category. In this case, the pre-determined threshold applies to the cumulative uncertainty and not to the cumulative emissions. Key source categories are those that together represent 90% of total uncertainty.

PART II:

CO$_2$ EMISSIONS FROM FUEL COMBUSTION

PARTIE II :

EMISSIONS DE CO$_2$ DUES A LA COMBUSTION D'ENERGIE

INTERNATIONAL ENERGY AGENCY

SUMMARY TABLES

TABLEAUX RECAPITULATIFS

CO$_2$ emissions: Sectoral Approach

Emissions de CO$_2$: Méthode sectorielle

million tonnes of CO$_2$

	1971	1975	1980	1985	1990	1995	2000	2003	2004	2005	2006	% change 90-06
World *	14 094.8	15 689.2	18 053.9	18 628.5	20 987.6	21 829.0	23 508.5	25 107.8	26 331.8	27 146.3	28 002.7	33.4%
Annex I Parties	..	..	..	..	*13 907.1*	*13 194.6*	*13 778.8*	*14 088.6*	*14 156.9*	*14 179.6*	*14 158.1*	*1.8%*
Annex II Parties	*8 607.3*	*8 884.2*	*9 530.9*	*9 163.5*	*9 809.8*	*10 213.9*	*11 018.7*	*11 238.7*	*11 332.8*	*11 345.1*	*11 220.8*	*14.4%*
North America	*4 630.7*	*4 738.0*	*5 088.5*	*4 948.0*	*5 295.5*	*5 598.4*	*6 225.6*	*6 243.0*	*6 322.8*	*6 340.8*	*6 235.6*	*17.8%*
Europe	*3 059.9*	*3 092.8*	*3 337.3*	*3 099.0*	*3 161.6*	*3 149.2*	*3 229.7*	*3 376.2*	*3 382.5*	*3 353.2*	*3 341.3*	*5.7%*
Pacific	*916.7*	*1 053.4*	*1 105.1*	*1 116.5*	*1 352.6*	*1 466.3*	*1 563.3*	*1 619.6*	*1 627.5*	*1 651.1*	*1 643.9*	*21.5%*
Annex I EIT	..	..	..	..	*3 970.5*	*2 828.0*	*2 559.6*	*2 647.8*	*2 616.8*	*2 618.1*	*2 697.6*	*-32.1%*
Non-Annex I Parties	..	..	..	..	*6 467.2*	*7 946.5*	*8 922.0*	*10 211.3*	*11 288.5*	*12 026.2*	*12 865.0*	*98.9%*
Annex I Kyoto Parties	..	..	..	..	*8 802.1*	*7 849.1*	*7 830.0*	*8 140.6*	*8 117.5*	*8 117.8*	*8 157.5*	*-7.3%*
Intl. marine bunkers	344.5	328.6	344.0	291.7	357.9	403.5	466.7	465.7	521.0	551.6	582.6	62.8%
International aviation	167.9	171.3	199.6	223.6	255.4	284.4	341.1	342.2	365.5	388.8	397.1	55.5%
Non-OECD Total	4 245.8	5 423.4	6 853.2	7 725.5	9 291.2	9 545.5	10 187.3	11 521.4	12 541.1	13 264.1	14 149.4	52.3%
OECD Total	9 336.6	9 765.8	10 657.0	10 387.6	11 083.2	11 595.5	12 513.5	12 778.6	12 904.3	12 941.7	12 873.7	16.2%
Canada	339.4	377.1	426.9	402.2	432.2	465.1	532.6	554.3	550.4	556.3	538.8	24.7%
Mexico	97.1	138.8	212.1	251.6	292.9	309.6	356.8	371.0	374.3	402.2	416.3	42.1%
United States	4 291.3	4 360.8	4 661.6	4 545.7	4 863.3	5 133.3	5 693.0	5 688.6	5 772.4	5 784.5	5 696.8	17.1%
OECD N. America	**4 727.8**	**4 876.8**	**5 300.5**	**5 199.6**	**5 588.5**	**5 908.0**	**6 582.4**	**6 613.9**	**6 697.2**	**6 743.0**	**6 651.8**	**19.0%**
Australia	144.1	180.0	208.0	221.0	259.8	285.2	338.7	360.9	369.6	387.2	394.4	51.8%
Japan	758.8	856.3	880.7	876.0	1 071.4	1 156.7	1 192.4	1 222.8	1 222.4	1 227.7	1 212.7	13.2%
Korea	52.1	76.8	124.4	153.3	229.3	364.8	431.3	458.6	478.9	468.9	476.1	107.6%
New Zealand	13.7	17.1	16.4	19.6	21.4	24.4	32.3	35.9	35.5	36.3	36.8	72.2%
OECD Pacific	**968.7**	**1 130.1**	**1 229.5**	**1 269.8**	**1 581.9**	**1 831.1**	**1 994.6**	**2 078.2**	**2 106.3**	**2 120.0**	**2 120.0**	**34.0%**
Austria	48.7	50.2	55.7	54.3	56.6	59.2	62.0	73.5	73.6	75.0	72.8	28.8%
Belgium	116.8	115.6	125.7	101.9	110.3	120.9	127.3	127.0	124.4	120.4	117.2	6.3%
Czech Republic	151.0	152.6	165.1	168.6	155.1	123.5	121.6	120.9	122.0	119.9	121.0	-22.0%
Denmark	55.0	52.5	62.5	60.5	50.4	57.6	49.9	56.2	50.7	47.4	55.2	9.5%
Finland	39.8	44.4	55.2	48.6	54.4	56.0	53.9	72.2	66.9	55.1	66.8	22.9%
France	431.9	430.6	461.4	360.3	352.1	353.7	375.8	384.3	383.8	386.6	377.5	7.2%
Germany	978.6	975.5	1 055.6	1 014.6	950.4	869.3	827.1	842.1	843.4	811.3	823.5	-13.4%
Greece	25.2	34.5	45.3	54.6	70.1	75.8	87.4	93.7	93.3	95.0	94.0	34.0%
Hungary	62.1	72.3	85.3	82.1	68.5	58.8	55.3	57.7	56.6	56.9	56.4	-17.7%
Iceland	1.4	1.6	1.7	1.6	1.9	1.9	2.1	2.2	2.2	2.2	2.2	16.1%
Ireland	21.7	21.1	25.9	26.4	30.6	33.0	41.2	41.6	41.8	43.4	44.9	46.7%
Italy	292.9	319.6	359.8	347.5	397.8	409.7	424.7	452.4	450.0	453.8	448.0	12.6%
Luxembourg	15.4	12.1	11.9	9.9	10.5	8.2	8.0	9.8	11.0	11.2	11.2	6.8%
Netherlands	129.6	140.8	153.2	146.7	156.6	171.3	173.1	183.9	185.1	182.6	178.3	13.9%
Norway	23.5	24.1	28.0	27.2	28.4	32.8	33.8	35.4	35.9	36.7	36.8	29.5%
Poland	286.7	338.2	413.1	419.5	343.9	331.5	292.0	291.2	295.2	294.2	306.0	-11.0%
Portugal	14.4	18.1	23.8	24.6	39.3	48.3	59.5	58.4	59.8	62.7	56.3	43.4%
Slovak Republic	39.1	43.8	55.3	54.4	56.7	40.8	37.4	38.4	37.3	38.1	37.5	-34.0%
Spain	120.0	156.6	187.9	175.5	205.8	233.7	283.9	309.6	327.4	339.5	327.6	59.2%
Sweden	82.4	79.4	73.4	58.8	52.8	57.5	52.8	54.9	53.6	50.4	48.3	-8.5%
Switzerland	38.9	36.7	39.2	41.4	40.7	41.0	41.6	43.1	43.9	44.4	44.1	8.2%
Turkey	41.4	59.2	70.9	94.6	126.9	152.7	200.6	202.1	207.2	216.4	239.7	88.9%
United Kingdom	623.5	579.5	571.1	544.5	553.0	519.1	525.6	535.9	535.6	535.4	536.5	-3.0%
OECD Europe	**3 640.1**	**3 758.9**	**4 127.0**	**3 918.2**	**3 912.8**	**3 856.4**	**3 936.5**	**4 086.5**	**4 100.8**	**4 078.7**	**4 101.8**	**4.8%**
European Union - 27	..	..	..	..	*4 063.1*	*3 857.9*	*3 841.6*	*4 004.9*	*4 009.9*	*3 978.7*	*3 983.0*	*-2.0%*

* Total world includes Non-OECD total, OECD total as well as international marine bunkers and international aviation.

CO$_2$ emissions: Sectoral Approach

Emissions de CO$_2$: Méthode sectorielle

million tonnes of CO$_2$

	1971	1975	1980	1985	1990	1995	2000	2003	2004	2005	2006	% change 90-06
Non-OECD Total	4 245.8	5 423.4	6 853.2	7 725.5	9 291.2	9 545.5	10 187.3	11 521.4	12 541.1	13 264.1	14 149.4	**52.3%**
Algeria	8.9	14.5	29.9	45.6	54.8	59.3	66.6	77.7	78.6	83.8	85.9	56.9%
Angola	1.7	2.1	2.7	2.9	4.1	4.0	5.2	7.6	7.4	7.8	8.6	109.9%
Benin	0.3	0.5	0.4	0.5	0.3	0.2	1.4	2.3	2.4	2.5	3.0	+
Botswana	..	..	..	1.6	2.9	3.3	4.2	3.9	4.1	4.3	4.5	54.7%
Cameroon	0.7	1.0	1.7	2.4	2.7	2.5	2.8	3.0	3.0	2.9	3.1	16.6%
Congo	0.6	0.7	0.8	0.8	0.7	0.5	0.6	0.8	0.9	1.0	1.2	69.6%
Dem. Rep. of Congo	2.5	2.6	3.1	3.2	3.0	2.1	2.1	2.2	2.2	2.3	2.3	-21.5%
Côte d'Ivoire	2.4	3.0	3.4	3.0	2.6	3.2	6.1	5.1	5.7	6.3	6.1	132.9%
Egypt	20.4	25.9	42.3	65.5	79.2	84.0	110.2	130.5	138.0	149.3	152.7	92.8%
Eritrea	..	..	..	..	..	0.8	0.6	0.7	0.7	0.6	0.5	..
Ethiopia	1.3	1.2	1.4	1.4	2.2	2.3	3.2	4.5	4.7	4.8	5.3	138.4%
Gabon	0.5	0.7	1.3	1.7	0.9	1.3	1.4	1.6	1.7	2.1	2.1	132.3%
Ghana	1.9	2.3	2.3	2.2	2.7	3.3	5.1	7.1	6.2	6.7	8.6	218.9%
Kenya	3.8	4.4	5.6	5.5	6.3	7.3	8.9	7.7	8.8	9.9	11.0	73.6%
Libya	3.7	9.2	18.6	22.5	27.4	35.1	39.7	41.9	43.7	42.5	42.4	55.2%
Morocco	6.8	9.9	14.0	16.5	19.6	25.4	29.5	33.1	35.7	39.3	39.8	102.6%
Mozambique	2.9	2.3	2.3	1.5	1.1	1.1	1.3	1.7	1.7	1.5	1.6	50.0%
Namibia	..	..	..	..	..	1.8	1.9	2.6	2.7	2.9	3.0	..
Nigeria	5.9	11.7	26.7	32.4	29.2	30.4	41.1	48.3	48.6	55.6	51.4	76.3%
Senegal	1.2	1.6	2.0	2.1	2.0	2.5	3.6	3.8	4.5	4.6	4.5	121.6%
South Africa	173.8	209.2	214.5	229.0	254.6	276.8	298.6	320.8	337.5	330.4	342.0	34.3%
Sudan	3.3	3.3	3.7	4.2	5.5	4.6	5.5	8.9	10.3	10.3	11.4	107.7%
United Rep. of Tanzania	1.5	1.5	1.6	1.5	1.7	2.5	2.6	3.3	3.8	4.5	4.8	180.6%
Togo	0.3	0.3	0.4	0.3	0.6	0.6	1.0	1.1	1.0	1.0	0.9	57.3%
Tunisia	3.7	4.8	7.8	9.6	12.1	14.3	18.0	19.1	19.7	19.3	19.7	63.0%
Zambia	3.4	4.4	3.4	2.8	2.6	2.0	1.7	2.0	2.0	2.1	2.3	-13.3%
Zimbabwe	7.2	7.2	8.0	9.6	16.0	14.8	12.7	10.5	9.7	10.4	9.9	-38.2%
Other Africa	7.6	9.2	13.3	11.8	14.7	17.0	18.9	21.3	22.4	23.1	25.5	73.7%
Africa	**266.6**	**333.6**	**410.9**	**480.1**	**549.3**	**603.2**	**694.4**	**773.1**	**807.8**	**831.8**	**854.2**	**55.5%**
Bahrain	3.0	5.3	7.4	10.4	11.7	11.6	14.1	16.2	16.9	18.3	20.0	70.7%
Islamic Rep. of Iran	41.4	74.9	92.3	146.3	175.3	249.4	304.8	351.9	380.6	396.7	432.8	146.9%
Iraq	12.3	15.6	32.3	43.8	52.8	71.8	75.9	67.5	79.9	82.1	86.5	63.8%
Israel	14.4	17.1	19.6	24.5	33.6	46.3	55.5	61.6	61.4	61.5	62.6	86.6%
Jordan	1.3	2.1	4.2	7.4	9.2	12.1	14.3	14.8	16.7	17.9	18.3	98.8%
Kuwait	23.2	22.9	30.8	37.8	24.3	41.0	50.2	59.8	67.0	74.3	66.7	173.9%
Lebanon	4.6	5.7	6.6	7.7	6.4	12.6	14.2	17.0	15.3	15.8	13.3	108.7%
Oman	0.3	0.7	2.2	5.5	9.9	14.4	19.8	25.2	25.3	26.9	29.4	196.7%
Qatar	2.2	4.9	7.7	12.2	14.2	18.8	26.5	30.2	33.8	35.2	39.7	179.6%
Saudi Arabia	13.3	23.7	101.3	129.0	161.4	204.5	251.1	287.5	303.6	321.9	340.0	110.7%
Syria	6.8	10.3	15.1	23.6	31.0	38.6	45.8	46.5	47.7	50.1	51.5	66.2%
United Arab Emirates	2.4	4.9	19.1	35.4	51.6	70.0	86.1	102.1	104.8	107.3	110.3	113.7%
Yemen	1.2	1.7	3.4	4.8	6.4	9.3	13.3	16.4	17.5	19.2	19.8	207.9%
Middle East	**126.5**	**189.6**	**342.1**	**488.3**	**587.9**	**800.4**	**971.5**	**1 096.6**	**1 170.6**	**1 227.2**	**1 291.0**	**119.6%**
Albania	3.9	4.5	7.6	7.2	6.2	1.9	3.2	3.9	3.5	4.6	4.2	-32.3%
Bosnia and Herzegovina *	..	..	..	..	23.6	3.3	13.7	14.4	14.9	15.7	17.2	-27.4%
Bulgaria	62.8	72.2	83.8	81.1	74.9	53.4	42.0	46.4	45.3	46.0	47.5	-36.6%
Croatia *	..	..	..	..	21.6	15.8	17.7	20.9	20.4	20.7	20.7	-4.1%
Cyprus	1.8	1.7	2.6	2.8	3.8	5.2	6.3	7.0	6.9	7.0	7.0	83.3%
Gibraltar	0.1	0.1	0.1	0.1	0.2	0.3	0.4	0.4	0.4	0.4	0.4	152.3%
FYR of Macedonia *	..	..	..	..	9.1	8.8	8.4	8.3	8.2	8.3	8.0	-12.1%
Malta	0.6	0.6	1.0	1.1	2.3	2.4	2.2	2.5	2.6	2.6	2.5	9.3%
Romania	114.9	140.6	176.1	173.3	167.1	117.1	86.3	94.4	91.5	91.7	94.7	-43.3%
Serbia *	..	..	..	..	61.4	44.0	42.5	51.8	56.0	50.2	53.4	-13.0%
Slovenia *	..	..	..	..	12.5	13.0	14.0	15.2	15.3	15.3	15.5	24.4%
Former Yugoslavia *	63.2	75.2	87.6	121.7	-	-	-	-	-	-	-	-
Non-OECD Europe	**247.3**	**294.8**	**358.8**	**387.3**	**382.8**	**265.1**	**236.6**	**265.2**	**265.1**	**262.4**	**271.2**	**-29.1%**

* Data for individual countries of the Former Yugoslavia are not available prior to 1990.

CO$_2$ emissions: Sectoral Approach
Emissions de CO$_2$: Méthode sectorielle

million tonnes of CO$_2$

	1971	1975	1980	1985	1990	1995	2000	2003	2004	2005	2006	% change 90-06
Armenia	..	..	..	..	20.5	3.4	3.4	3.3	3.5	4.1	4.1	-79.8%
Azerbaijan	..	..	..	..	62.7	30.9	28.2	28.1	29.2	31.1	30.2	-51.8%
Belarus	..	..	..	..	114.8	59.4	55.2	57.3	59.7	61.0	64.1	-44.2%
Estonia	..	..	..	..	36.2	16.0	14.5	16.3	16.5	15.9	15.1	-58.2%
Georgia	..	..	..	..	28.7	7.1	4.4	3.1	3.3	3.9	4.6	-83.9%
Kazakhstan	..	..	..	..	236.4	167.0	130.2	149.6	155.8	168.2	182.0	-23.0%
Kyrgyzstan	..	..	..	..	22.7	4.6	4.6	5.2	5.6	5.4	5.2	-77.0%
Latvia	..	..	..	..	18.4	8.8	6.8	7.4	7.5	7.6	8.0	-56.3%
Lithuania	..	..	..	..	33.1	14.2	11.2	12.1	12.8	13.6	13.7	-58.7%
Republic of Moldova	..	..	..	..	30.2	10.9	6.5	7.3	7.5	7.9	7.4	-75.4%
Russia	..	..	..	..	2 179.9	1 582.9	1 513.8	1 540.0	1 524.1	1 531.2	1 587.2	-27.2%
Tajikistan	..	..	..	..	11.7	5.3	4.2	4.9	5.3	5.6	6.1	-47.3%
Turkmenistan	..	..	..	..	46.6	34.4	36.2	42.9	39.3	41.4	43.6	-6.6%
Ukraine	..	..	..	..	687.9	392.8	292.0	329.6	312.6	306.0	310.3	-54.9%
Uzbekistan	..	..	..	..	119.8	101.6	116.5	118.6	115.7	109.8	112.9	-5.8%
Former USSR *	**1 995.8**	**2 567.9**	**3 056.0**	**3 197.5**	**3 649.5**	**2 439.3**	**2 227.5**	**2 325.7**	**2 298.3**	**2 312.7**	**2 394.6**	**-34.4%**
Argentina	83.1	85.9	95.9	88.6	100.4	115.3	132.9	122.8	136.2	139.1	148.7	48.2%
Bolivia	2.1	3.2	4.3	4.5	5.4	8.2	7.6	9.1	10.4	11.9	12.7	134.1%
Brazil	90.7	136.2	178.0	167.0	192.7	238.4	303.4	304.1	321.0	327.1	332.4	72.5%
Chile	20.8	17.0	21.2	19.4	31.9	39.1	53.2	52.9	58.6	58.8	59.8	87.3%
Colombia	26.2	28.3	33.8	38.3	45.0	58.0	60.7	57.0	59.8	59.7	59.4	32.1%
Costa Rica	1.3	1.7	2.2	2.0	2.6	4.4	4.6	5.3	5.5	5.4	5.9	127.1%
Cuba	18.4	25.4	28.5	30.6	27.6	22.1	24.8	26.2	25.4	24.4	26.6	-3.5%
Dominican Republic	3.4	5.1	6.2	6.1	7.6	11.4	17.4	17.9	17.9	17.5	18.6	144.0%
Ecuador	3.7	6.2	10.6	12.1	13.2	16.3	18.5	21.9	21.8	23.5	25.0	89.6%
El Salvador	1.3	2.0	1.7	1.7	2.2	4.7	5.2	5.7	5.8	5.9	5.8	169.2%
Guatemala	2.3	3.0	4.2	3.3	3.3	6.0	8.8	9.9	10.3	10.9	11.0	233.5%
Haiti	0.4	0.4	0.6	0.8	0.9	0.9	1.4	1.6	1.6	1.7	1.7	82.1%
Honduras	1.1	1.3	1.7	1.7	2.1	3.9	4.4	5.8	6.4	6.4	7.1	232.6%
Jamaica	5.5	7.4	6.5	4.6	7.2	8.4	9.8	10.3	10.4	9.8	11.5	60.5%
Netherlands Antilles	14.6	10.3	8.9	4.7	2.9	3.0	3.2	3.7	3.7	3.8	3.9	37.3%
Nicaragua	1.5	1.8	1.8	1.8	1.8	2.5	3.5	4.0	4.1	4.1	4.0	117.1%
Panama	2.5	3.2	2.9	2.6	2.5	4.1	4.7	5.9	5.5	5.7	6.0	144.6%
Paraguay	0.6	0.7	1.4	1.4	1.9	3.4	3.3	3.7	3.7	3.4	3.6	86.1%
Peru	15.6	18.4	20.5	18.2	19.2	23.7	26.4	25.0	28.9	28.5	27.9	45.4%
Trinidad and Tobago	6.1	5.8	7.9	9.6	11.4	12.3	17.9	21.2	22.2	23.3	26.9	136.9%
Uruguay	5.2	5.5	5.6	3.1	3.7	4.5	5.3	4.1	5.4	5.2	6.1	63.8%
Venezuela	52.1	62.8	92.4	95.2	105.1	118.3	128.3	120.5	129.9	139.1	149.2	42.0%
Other Latin America	7.8	10.8	10.2	9.2	12.4	13.4	14.4	16.3	16.4	16.8	17.9	44.1%
Latin America	**366.3**	**442.7**	**547.1**	**526.5**	**603.1**	**722.3**	**859.8**	**855.0**	**910.9**	**931.9**	**972.1**	**61.2%**
Bangladesh	3.2	4.7	7.2	8.8	13.6	20.5	25.2	32.2	33.5	36.3	38.1	180.7%
Brunei Darussalam	0.4	1.4	2.6	2.9	3.4	4.7	4.6	5.5	5.2	5.1	5.8	71.5%
Cambodia	..	..	..	..	..	1.4	2.4	3.1	3.5	3.7	4.1	..
Chinese Taipei	31.0	42.5	72.2	72.3	113.9	158.7	215.0	246.4	255.4	262.1	270.3	137.4%
India	199.3	240.2	292.5	419.5	589.3	782.6	976.5	1 042.9	1 114.1	1 160.7	1 249.7	112.1%
Indonesia	25.1	38.0	69.1	84.8	140.2	192.2	264.6	298.8	316.3	331.0	334.6	138.6%
DPR of Korea	67.5	76.7	105.6	126.4	114.0	74.9	68.8	69.5	71.1	74.3	75.4	-33.8%
Malaysia	12.7	16.1	23.4	32.7	49.0	78.7	112.7	121.5	133.0	145.8	154.0	214.3%
Mongolia	..	..	..	11.6	12.7	10.1	8.8	9.0	9.2	9.6	10.1	-19.8%
Myanmar	4.5	3.9	5.1	5.8	4.0	6.7	8.1	8.9	9.4	10.1	9.8	146.9%
Nepal	0.2	0.3	0.5	0.5	0.9	1.7	3.1	2.9	2.7	3.0	3.1	250.5%
Pakistan	16.6	20.9	26.4	39.5	59.0	80.1	97.8	103.3	116.0	118.3	125.7	113.0%
Philippines	22.8	28.2	32.2	26.9	36.1	59.5	68.9	70.4	72.3	72.4	66.5	84.5%
Singapore	6.0	8.4	12.7	16.3	28.8	38.0	38.1	38.6	39.2	43.1	43.1	49.8%
Sri Lanka	2.8	2.7	3.7	3.6	3.7	5.5	10.8	11.4	12.4	12.3	11.4	204.2%
Thailand	17.2	21.9	34.2	40.5	78.6	141.3	159.5	196.0	213.4	214.1	217.0	176.1%
Vietnam	16.1	16.7	14.4	16.8	17.0	27.5	43.8	60.6	78.8	80.4	82.6	387.4%
Other Asia	8.4	10.2	16.6	10.1	10.5	9.3	11.1	13.6	15.6	15.3	16.4	55.3%
Asia	**433.7**	**532.7**	**718.3**	**918.9**	**1 274.6**	**1 693.4**	**2 120.0**	**2 334.7**	**2 501.0**	**2 597.7**	**2 717.8**	**113.2%**
People's Rep. of China	800.4	1 051.2	1 405.3	1 704.5	2 211.0	2 985.9	3 037.9	3 830.0	4 547.0	5 059.8	5 606.5	153.6%
Hong Kong, China	9.2	10.8	14.7	22.3	33.1	35.9	39.7	41.1	40.3	40.7	41.9	26.8%
China	**809.6**	**1 062.0**	**1 420.0**	**1 726.8**	**2 244.0**	**3 021.8**	**3 077.6**	**3 871.1**	**4 587.3**	**5 100.5**	**5 648.5**	**151.7%**

* Data for individual countries of the Former USSR are not available prior to 1990.

CO$_2$ emissions: Sectoral Approach - Coal/peat

Emissions de CO$_2$: Méthode sectorielle - Charbon/tourbe

million tonnes of CO$_2$

	1971	1975	1980	1985	1990	1995	2000	2003	2004	2005	2006	% change 90-06
World *	5 201.3	5 608.9	6 569.1	7 371.8	8 308.8	8 546.0	8 833.9	9 740.1	10 487.9	11 033.3	11 686.3	40.6%
Annex I Parties	..	..	..	..	*5 111.7*	*4 601.2*	*4 717.4*	*4 765.6*	*4 762.7*	*4 769.0*	*4 824.6*	*-5.6%*
Annex II Parties	*2 645.9*	*2 604.8*	*2 962.8*	*3 316.3*	*3 485.2*	*3 397.5*	*3 654.2*	*3 688.3*	*3 727.1*	*3 740.9*	*3 727.3*	*6.9%*
North America	*1 140.5*	*1 253.0*	*1 481.2*	*1 725.0*	*1 890.8*	*1 994.3*	*2 247.0*	*2 192.2*	*2 210.2*	*2 233.6*	*2 197.2*	*16.2%*
Europe	*1 234.0*	*1 059.0*	*1 182.9*	*1 224.1*	*1 155.8*	*926.1*	*842.9*	*873.7*	*876.8*	*847.8*	*860.8*	*-25.5%*
Pacific	*271.5*	*292.9*	*298.7*	*367.3*	*438.6*	*477.1*	*564.2*	*622.5*	*640.1*	*659.5*	*669.3*	*52.6%*
Annex I EIT	..	..	..	..	*1 568.6*	*1 143.0*	*974.4*	*995.4*	*950.5*	*941.8*	*995.6*	*-36.5%*
Non-Annex I Parties	..	..	..	..	*3 197.2*	*3 944.8*	*4 116.5*	*4 974.6*	*5 725.2*	*6 264.3*	*6 861.7*	*114.6%*
Annex I Kyoto Parties	..	..	..	..	*3 253.8*	*2 645.1*	*2 505.7*	*2 607.3*	*2 576.8*	*2 559.8*	*2 630.6*	*-19.2%*
Intl. marine bunkers	0.1	..	..	..	..	-	-	-	-	-	-	..
International aviation	..	..	..	..	..	-	-	-	-	-	-	..
Non-OECD Total	2 071.0	2 476.7	2 974.4	3 358.1	4 201.1	4 568.4	4 573.7	5 429.5	6 129.9	6 660.8	7 294.2	73.6%
OECD Total	3 130.2	3 132.2	3 594.7	4 013.8	4 107.8	3 977.6	4 260.2	4 310.6	4 358.0	4 372.5	4 392.1	6.9%
Canada	61.7	56.6	80.5	99.4	98.8	103.3	127.0	117.7	111.3	113.2	107.3	8.5%
Mexico	5.2	6.6	7.2	11.6	14.2	21.5	27.0	36.2	29.7	38.4	35.7	150.7%
United States	1 078.7	1 196.4	1 400.7	1 625.5	1 792.0	1 891.0	2 120.0	2 074.4	2 098.9	2 120.4	2 090.0	16.6%
OECD N. America	1 145.6	1 259.6	1 488.5	1 736.6	1 905.1	2 015.8	2 274.1	2 228.3	2 239.9	2 272.0	2 232.9	17.2%
Australia	73.2	90.3	104.0	116.7	137.1	152.3	189.3	201.1	208.1	220.7	226.6	65.3%
Japan	194.1	197.7	190.8	246.7	297.6	320.8	368.5	411.0	421.1	427.5	431.4	44.9%
Korea	21.2	30.6	48.1	80.2	86.3	101.6	156.9	180.7	195.4	195.0	204.8	137.2%
New Zealand	4.2	4.8	3.8	3.9	3.9	3.9	6.4	10.4	10.8	11.4	11.3	188.3%
OECD Pacific	292.7	323.5	346.8	447.4	525.0	578.8	721.1	803.2	835.4	854.5	874.1	66.5%
Austria	15.9	13.5	13.7	16.9	15.8	13.2	14.2	16.3	16.4	15.5	15.4	-2.7%
Belgium	42.2	37.0	40.2	37.8	39.0	33.4	29.0	22.1	21.4	19.1	17.7	-54.5%
Czech Republic	129.2	121.7	128.8	131.6	120.7	88.4	83.6	80.1	79.6	76.4	78.1	-35.3%
Denmark	6.0	8.0	23.8	28.4	23.7	25.3	15.4	22.3	17.1	14.4	21.6	-8.8%
Finland	8.4	9.3	19.6	19.8	21.1	23.2	20.9	34.1	30.4	20.0	30.7	45.2%
France	135.3	104.2	121.2	91.3	73.3	57.3	56.7	51.1	49.6	53.3	50.4	-31.2%
Germany	554.1	494.5	552.2	580.7	504.6	370.1	337.2	340.1	348.9	331.9	339.3	-32.8%
Greece	6.8	11.0	13.4	24.9	33.4	36.4	37.6	37.7	38.3	37.8	34.6	3.5%
Hungary	36.7	34.4	37.9	35.9	25.9	18.5	16.2	15.2	14.6	12.7	12.4	-52.3%
Iceland	0.0	-	0.1	0.3	0.3	0.2	0.4	0.4	0.4	0.4	0.3	20.2%
Ireland	8.8	7.1	8.0	10.5	14.5	12.3	10.6	10.3	9.6	10.6	9.7	-33.3%
Italy	31.7	30.2	43.0	58.1	55.1	44.9	43.3	54.7	62.4	62.8	62.4	13.4%
Luxembourg	11.3	7.5	7.9	6.3	5.0	2.1	0.5	0.3	0.4	0.3	0.4	-91.3%
Netherlands	14.4	11.5	13.8	23.1	31.8	33.5	29.9	32.6	31.7	30.3	28.9	-9.3%
Norway	3.7	3.9	3.9	4.4	3.4	4.1	4.2	3.1	3.5	3.0	2.6	-23.4%
Poland	252.5	289.7	350.9	359.8	286.9	268.3	217.3	211.2	210.0	207.1	215.9	-24.7%
Portugal	2.4	1.6	1.6	2.9	10.6	13.9	14.7	12.7	12.9	13.1	13.0	22.2%
Slovak Republic	23.5	23.7	32.0	33.3	30.6	21.1	16.0	17.2	16.5	15.6	16.2	-47.2%
Spain	36.9	37.5	47.9	69.4	74.1	71.8	81.5	77.3	79.9	80.0	66.6	-10.1%
Sweden	5.4	6.9	5.4	10.6	10.4	9.4	8.1	10.5	10.9	9.8	9.0	-14.0%
Switzerland	2.0	1.0	1.4	2.0	1.4	0.8	0.6	0.6	0.5	0.6	0.6	-55.7%
Turkey	16.0	20.7	26.8	45.1	57.9	60.7	88.9	81.8	85.2	86.3	101.7	75.8%
United Kingdom	348.4	274.2	266.1	236.8	238.1	174.1	138.2	147.6	142.5	144.6	157.6	-33.8%
OECD Europe	1 691.9	1 549.1	1 759.5	1 829.8	1 677.8	1 383.0	1 265.0	1 279.1	1 282.7	1 245.9	1 285.1	-23.4%
European Union - 27	..	..	..	..	*1 737.5*	*1 405.7*	*1 241.8*	*1 275.9*	*1 273.5*	*1 234.9*	*1 262.5*	*-27.3%*

* Total world includes Non-OECD total, OECD total as well as international marine bunkers and international aviation.

CO$_2$ emissions: Sectoral Approach - Coal/peat

Emissions de CO$_2$: Méthode sectorielle - Charbon/tourbe

million tonnes of CO$_2$

	1971	1975	1980	1985	1990	1995	2000	2003	2004	2005	2006	% change 90-06
Non-OECD Total	2 071.0	2 476.7	2 974.4	3 358.1	4 201.1	4 568.4	4 573.7	5 429.5	6 129.9	6 660.8	7 294.2	73.6%
Algeria	0.4	0.3	0.2	1.0	1.3	1.4	0.7	0.9	1.0	1.1	1.0	-23.0%
Angola	-	-	-	-	-	-	-	-	-	-	-	-
Benin	-	-	-	-	-	-	-	-	-	-	-	-
Botswana	..	..	..	1.1	1.9	2.2	2.5	2.0	2.2	2.3	2.5	26.7%
Cameroon	-	-	-	-	-	-	-	-	-	-	-	-
Congo	-	-	-	-	-	-	-	-	-	-	-	-
Dem. Rep. of Congo	1.0	0.8	0.8	0.8	0.9	1.0	0.8	0.9	0.9	1.0	1.0	19.6%
Côte d'Ivoire	-	-	-	-	-	-	-	-	-	-	-	-
Egypt	1.3	2.1	2.1	2.7	2.7	2.8	3.3	3.4	3.3	3.2	3.1	13.5%
Eritrea	..	..	..	..	..	-	-	-	-	-	-	..
Ethiopia	-	-	-	-	-	-	-	-	-	-	-	-
Gabon	-	-	-	-	-	-	-	-	-	-	-	-
Ghana	-	-	-	-	-	-	-	-	-	-	-	-
Kenya	0.2	0.1	0.0	0.2	0.4	0.2	0.2	0.2	0.3	0.2	0.3	-20.5%
Libya	-	-	-	-	-	-	-	-	-	-	-	-
Morocco	1.2	1.7	1.6	2.7	4.1	6.1	9.2	11.2	12.7	13.5	13.5	225.9%
Mozambique	1.5	1.2	0.7	0.2	0.1	0.1	-	-	-	-	-	..
Namibia	..	..	..	..	..	0.0	0.0	0.1	0.1	0.1	0.1	..
Nigeria	0.5	0.6	0.4	0.2	0.2	0.0	0.0	0.1	0.0	0.0	0.0	-89.5%
Senegal	-	-	-	-	-	-	-	-	0.3	0.4	0.4	x
South Africa	146.3	175.1	179.4	189.5	208.3	227.3	248.1	266.1	280.0	271.0	280.5	34.7%
Sudan	-	-	0.0	-	-	-	-	-	-	-	-	-
United Rep. of Tanzania	-	-	0.0	0.0	0.0	0.1	0.2	0.1	0.2	0.2	0.2	+
Togo	-	-	-	-	-	-	-	-	-	-	-	-
Tunisia	0.3	0.3	0.3	0.3	0.3	0.3	0.3	0.1	-	-	-	..
Zambia	2.0	1.9	1.4	1.1	0.9	0.3	0.3	0.3	0.4	0.4	0.4	-54.4%
Zimbabwe	5.6	5.0	6.1	7.5	13.4	11.2	9.7	8.1	7.8	8.3	7.9	-41.1%
Other Africa	0.5	0.7	0.7	0.9	1.1	1.1	2.1	2.1	2.4	2.4	2.5	126.4%
Africa	160.7	190.0	193.7	208.3	235.6	254.2	277.3	295.7	311.5	303.9	313.3	33.0%
Bahrain	-	-	-	-	-	-	-	-	-	-	-	-
Islamic Rep. of Iran	0.8	4.1	3.8	3.1	2.3	3.3	4.1	3.9	3.4	3.9	4.2	85.5%
Iraq	-	-	-	-	-	-	-	-	-	-	-	-
Israel	0.0	0.0	0.0	7.2	9.3	16.2	25.1	31.0	31.4	31.0	31.0	232.7%
Jordan	-	-	-	-	-	-	-	-	-	-	-	-
Kuwait	-	-	-	-	-	-	-	-	-	-	-	-
Lebanon	0.0	0.0	0.0	-	-	0.5	0.5	0.5	0.5	0.5	0.5	x
Oman	-	-	-	-	-	-	-	-	-	-	-	-
Qatar	-	-	-	-	-	-	-	-	-	-	-	-
Saudi Arabia	-	-	-	-	-	-	-	-	-	-	-	-
Syria	0.0	0.0	0.0	0.0	-	0.0	0.0	0.0	0.0	0.0	0.0	x
United Arab Emirates	-	-	-	-	-	-	-	-	-	-	-	-
Yemen	-	-	-	-	-	-	-	-	-	-	-	-
Middle East	0.8	4.2	3.9	10.3	11.6	20.0	29.7	35.4	35.3	35.5	35.7	208.2%
Albania	1.2	1.6	2.5	3.7	2.4	0.1	0.1	0.1	0.1	0.1	0.1	-95.7%
Bosnia and Herzegovina *	..	..	..	..	17.3	1.4	9.9	10.9	11.1	11.7	13.0	-24.8%
Bulgaria	33.2	35.0	37.8	42.2	36.8	29.7	25.3	29.4	28.4	27.8	28.4	-22.8%
Croatia *	..	..	..	..	3.4	0.8	1.7	2.6	2.7	2.6	2.5	-27.4%
Cyprus	-	-	-	0.2	0.2	0.2	0.1	0.1	0.1	0.1	0.1	-43.8%
Gibraltar	-	-	-	-	-	-	-	-	-	-	-	-
FYR of Macedonia *	..	..	..	..	6.1	6.5	5.6	5.7	5.5	5.5	5.2	-15.4%
Malta	-	-	-	0.5	0.7	0.1	-	-	-	-	-	..
Romania	31.2	38.0	48.9	57.6	49.7	40.5	28.7	33.9	32.9	33.2	36.5	-26.5%
Serbia *	..	..	..	..	41.3	36.2	35.0	38.3	39.9	34.4	36.6	-11.4%
Slovenia *	..	..	..	..	5.7	4.7	5.4	6.1	6.2	6.0	6.0	4.2%
Former Yugoslavia *	35.8	40.5	42.6	72.4	-	-	-	-	-	-	-	-
Non-OECD Europe	101.4	115.0	131.7	176.5	163.7	120.1	111.8	127.2	127.0	121.5	128.4	-21.5%

* Data for individual countries of the Former Yugoslavia are not available prior to 1990.

CO$_2$ emissions: Sectoral Approach - Coal/peat

Emissions de CO$_2$: Méthode sectorielle - Charbon/tourbe

million tonnes of CO$_2$

	1971	1975	1980	1985	1990	1995	2000	2003	2004	2005	2006	% change 90-06
Armenia	..	..	..	..	1.0	0.0	-	0.0	-	-	0.0	-99.8%
Azerbaijan	..	..	..	..	0.3	0.0	-	-	-	-	-	..
Belarus	..	..	..	..	8.0	4.4	2.9	2.0	1.9	2.5	2.3	-71.2%
Estonia	..	..	..	..	24.0	11.3	10.4	11.9	11.8	11.0	10.3	-57.2%
Georgia	..	..	..	..	2.2	0.1	0.0	0.1	0.0	0.1	0.0	-97.9%
Kazakhstan	..	..	..	..	153.3	111.1	86.2	97.1	99.0	101.3	109.7	-28.5%
Kyrgyzstan	..	..	..	..	10.0	1.3	1.9	2.5	2.4	2.2	2.0	-79.6%
Latvia	..	..	..	..	2.5	1.0	0.5	0.3	0.3	0.3	0.3	-86.2%
Lithuania	..	..	..	..	3.1	1.0	0.4	0.7	0.7	0.8	1.1	-65.5%
Republic of Moldova	..	..	..	..	7.8	2.3	0.4	0.6	0.3	0.3	0.3	-95.7%
Russia	..	..	..	..	688.2	492.3	449.7	441.9	417.5	422.4	444.6	-35.4%
Tajikistan	..	..	..	..	2.5	0.1	0.0	0.1	0.1	0.2	0.2	-92.5%
Turkmenistan	..	..	..	..	1.2	-	-	-	-	-	-	..
Ukraine	..	..	..	..	283.0	161.2	116.3	142.8	127.4	123.3	141.0	-50.2%
Uzbekistan	..	..	..	..	13.7	4.4	3.6	2.7	3.8	4.2	4.4	-68.0%
Former USSR *	**875.2**	**1 028.9**	**1 141.8**	**982.9**	**1 200.8**	**790.4**	**672.4**	**702.9**	**665.2**	**668.6**	**716.3**	**-40.4%**
Argentina	3.5	3.7	3.3	3.7	3.9	4.9	4.5	3.3	4.6	5.2	4.8	22.0%
Bolivia	-	-	-	0.2	-	-	-	-	-	-	-	-
Brazil	7.2	8.6	17.6	29.9	28.7	35.9	43.6	44.6	47.9	47.8	47.0	64.0%
Chile	5.0	3.5	4.7	4.8	10.3	9.5	12.4	10.7	14.2	14.2	15.3	49.1%
Colombia	5.6	6.6	7.5	8.8	10.7	12.4	13.4	11.6	11.2	11.5	10.2	-4.0%
Costa Rica	0.0	0.0	0.0	0.0	0.0	-	-	0.2	0.2	0.1	0.2	+
Cuba	0.4	0.3	0.4	0.7	0.7	0.6	0.4	0.4	0.4	0.4	0.4	-42.2%
Dominican Republic	-	-	-	0.5	0.0	0.2	0.2	2.5	1.9	1.1	2.0	+
Ecuador	-	-	-	-	-	-	-	-	-	-	-	..
El Salvador	-	-	0.0	-	-	0.0	0.0	0.0	0.0	0.0	0.0	x
Guatemala	-	-	0.1	-	-	-	0.5	0.9	1.1	1.4	1.5	x
Haiti	-	-	-	0.1	0.0	-	-	-	-	-	-	..
Honduras	-	-	-	-	0.0	0.0	0.3	0.4	0.4	0.4	0.5	+
Jamaica	-	-	-	-	0.1	0.1	0.2	0.2	0.2	0.1	0.1	-38.5%
Netherlands Antilles	-	-	-	-	-	-	-	-	-	-	-	..
Nicaragua	-	-	-	-	-	-	-	-	-	-	-	..
Panama	0.0	0.0	-	0.1	0.1	0.1	0.1	-	-	-	-	..
Paraguay	-	-	-	-	-	-	-	-	-	-	-	..
Peru	0.5	0.6	0.6	0.7	0.6	1.4	2.4	2.9	3.3	3.5	3.0	412.2%
Trinidad and Tobago	-	-	-	-	-	-	-	-	-	-	-	..
Uruguay	0.1	0.1	0.0	0.0	0.0	0.0	0.0	0.0	0.0	0.0	0.0	-55.8%
Venezuela	0.6	1.0	0.6	0.7	1.8	0.0	0.5	0.2	-	0.1	0.1	-91.8%
Other Latin America	0.1	0.1	0.1	-	0.0	0.0	0.0	0.0	0.0	0.0	0.0	199.9%
Latin America	**22.9**	**24.4**	**34.9**	**50.3**	**57.0**	**65.2**	**78.6**	**78.0**	**85.3**	**86.0**	**85.1**	**49.4%**
Bangladesh	0.4	0.5	0.5	0.2	1.1	1.2	1.3	1.4	1.4	1.4	1.4	24.3%
Brunei Darussalam	-	-	-	-	-	-	-	-	-	-	-	..
Cambodia	..	..	..	..	..	-	-	..	..	-	-	..
Chinese Taipei	10.0	8.4	14.7	26.7	41.3	64.3	109.6	134.9	140.6	145.8	152.6	269.5%
India	142.6	176.1	206.0	294.6	406.3	528.0	635.1	682.6	745.3	782.1	844.4	107.8%
Indonesia	0.5	0.5	0.8	1.5	11.7	17.5	49.1	66.0	79.2	90.2	108.3	824.5%
DPR of Korea	64.9	72.5	97.5	119.0	106.1	70.9	65.7	66.2	67.7	71.4	73.3	-31.0%
Malaysia	0.0	0.0	0.2	1.1	4.0	4.8	6.9	15.9	22.2	26.7	31.8	690.4%
Mongolia	..	..	..	9.4	10.2	9.0	7.5	7.5	7.5	7.9	8.3	-19.0%
Myanmar	0.6	0.6	0.6	0.6	0.3	0.1	0.2	0.3	0.4	0.4	0.4	66.3%
Nepal	0.0	0.1	0.2	0.0	0.2	0.3	1.0	0.7	0.6	1.0	1.0	500.0%
Pakistan	2.5	2.2	2.9	5.2	7.5	8.4	7.2	12.0	15.2	15.0	15.3	104.2%
Philippines	0.1	0.2	1.4	4.7	4.3	7.7	19.5	19.4	20.6	24.2	22.8	426.7%
Singapore	0.0	0.1	0.1	0.1	0.1	0.2	0.2	0.2	0.2	0.2	0.2	71.2%
Sri Lanka	0.0	0.0	0.0	0.0	0.0	0.0	0.0	0.3	0.3	0.3	0.3	+
Thailand	0.5	0.6	1.9	6.5	16.1	29.4	31.4	38.5	43.5	46.9	49.8	209.9%
Vietnam	5.6	10.0	8.8	10.9	8.6	12.9	17.0	22.6	32.4	31.5	34.2	296.2%
Other Asia	4.1	4.3	7.7	0.9	0.8	0.5	1.3	1.7	1.6	1.7	1.8	117.1%
Asia	**231.9**	**276.2**	**343.2**	**481.5**	**618.8**	**755.3**	**952.9**	**1 069.8**	**1 178.7**	**1 246.5**	**1 345.8**	**117.5%**
People's Rep. of China	677.9	837.9	1 125.0	1 435.4	1 889.3	2 538.9	2 433.3	3 094.6	3 700.0	4 171.6	4 641.0	145.6%
Hong Kong, China	0.1	0.1	0.2	12.8	24.4	24.4	17.7	25.9	26.9	27.2	28.6	17.3%
China	**678.0**	**838.1**	**1 125.2**	**1 448.1**	**1 913.7**	**2 563.3**	**2 451.0**	**3 120.5**	**3 726.9**	**4 198.8**	**4 669.6**	**144.0%**

* Data for individual countries of the Former USSR are not available prior to 1990.

CO$_2$ emissions: Sectoral Approach - Oil

Emissions de CO$_2$: Méthode sectorielle - Pétrole

million tonnes of CO$_2$

	1971	1975	1980	1985	1990	1995	2000	2003	2004	2005	2006	% change 90-06
World *	**6 834.1**	**7 794.6**	**8 710.9**	**8 085.0**	**8 824.2**	**9 092.3**	**9 857.3**	**10 182.1**	**10 533.9**	**10 680.4**	**10 768.3**	**22.0%**
Annex I Parties	..	..	..	..	*5 685.5*	*5 342.0*	*5 492.9*	*5 622.2*	*5 669.4*	*5 672.4*	*5 595.1*	*-1.6%*
Annex II Parties	*4 522.9*	*4 773.7*	*4 901.2*	*4 225.5*	*4 493.1*	*4 637.1*	*4 860.7*	*4 991.5*	*5 036.5*	*5 043.7*	*4 948.4*	*10.1%*
North America	*2 232.9*	*2 341.6*	*2 427.9*	*2 164.8*	*2 251.2*	*2 265.8*	*2 517.9*	*2 636.0*	*2 707.4*	*2 721.3*	*2 674.5*	*18.8%*
Europe	*1 657.7*	*1 700.3*	*1 736.7*	*1 423.8*	*1 482.8*	*1 565.6*	*1 566.6*	*1 598.2*	*1 581.4*	*1 572.1*	*1 556.7*	*5.0%*
Pacific	*632.3*	*731.8*	*736.6*	*636.9*	*759.2*	*805.7*	*776.2*	*757.3*	*747.7*	*750.3*	*717.2*	*-5.5%*
Annex I EIT	..	..	..	..	*1 129.9*	*625.9*	*549.5*	*551.5*	*554.2*	*551.6*	*569.3*	*-49.6%*
Non-Annex I Parties	..	..	..	..	*2 525.4*	*3 062.3*	*3 556.7*	*3 752.1*	*3 978.0*	*4 067.6*	*4 193.6*	*66.1%*
Annex I Kyoto Parties	..	..	..	..	*3 501.4*	*3 180.1*	*3 109.9*	*3 146.6*	*3 131.1*	*3 126.8*	*3 084.7*	*-11.9%*
Intl. marine bunkers	**344.4**	**328.6**	**344.0**	**291.7**	**357.9**	**403.5**	**466.7**	**465.7**	**521.0**	**551.6**	**582.6**	**62.8%**
International aviation	**167.9**	**171.3**	**199.6**	**223.6**	**255.4**	**284.4**	**341.1**	**342.2**	**365.5**	**388.8**	**397.1**	**55.5%**
Non-OECD Total	**1 597.9**	**2 226.0**	**2 862.9**	**2 926.8**	**3 198.1**	**3 129.2**	**3 524.4**	**3 738.1**	**3 960.4**	**4 047.3**	**4 197.6**	**31.3%**
OECD Total	**4 723.9**	**5 068.7**	**5 304.4**	**4 642.9**	**5 012.8**	**5 275.1**	**5 525.1**	**5 636.2**	**5 687.1**	**5 692.7**	**5 591.0**	**11.5%**
Canada	209.8	233.2	246.7	188.8	209.4	212.2	237.1	259.6	267.4	272.4	263.6	25.9%
Mexico	71.7	106.5	161.6	186.5	226.6	230.4	255.9	243.5	249.3	259.1	257.7	13.7%
United States	2 023.0	2 108.4	2 181.2	1 976.0	2 041.8	2 053.5	2 280.8	2 376.4	2 440.1	2 449.0	2 410.9	18.1%
OECD N. America	**2 304.6**	**2 448.1**	**2 589.5**	**2 351.3**	**2 477.8**	**2 496.1**	**2 773.8**	**2 879.6**	**2 956.7**	**2 980.4**	**2 932.2**	**18.3%**
Australia	66.8	80.8	87.3	79.9	89.1	94.4	104.6	107.0	107.0	110.1	112.3	26.0%
Japan	556.2	639.4	638.6	547.4	658.3	697.4	656.0	633.1	623.0	622.3	586.8	-10.9%
Korea	30.9	46.2	76.2	73.1	135.3	240.2	229.9	221.4	216.9	203.6	195.7	44.6%
New Zealand	9.3	11.6	10.7	9.6	11.8	14.0	15.5	17.2	17.7	17.9	18.1	53.2%
OECD Pacific	**663.2**	**778.0**	**812.9**	**710.0**	**894.5**	**1 045.9**	**1 006.0**	**978.7**	**964.6**	**953.9**	**912.9**	**2.1%**
Austria	27.2	29.2	33.0	26.9	28.1	30.3	31.6	38.0	37.8	38.6	38.0	35.2%
Belgium	63.3	60.4	65.0	46.7	48.7	55.4	56.9	61.6	58.7	57.9	54.9	12.9%
Czech Republic	19.9	27.9	30.6	27.9	23.0	20.5	20.2	22.3	23.8	25.0	24.7	7.7%
Denmark	49.0	44.2	38.5	30.2	22.0	24.4	23.4	22.1	21.8	21.6	22.0	-0.3%
Finland	31.4	33.6	33.9	26.9	28.2	26.2	24.0	27.1	26.9	26.2	26.7	-5.1%
France	277.3	293.5	292.8	214.5	220.1	227.3	233.7	239.6	239.2	236.7	233.0	5.8%
Germany	385.7	392.4	385.9	326.6	323.1	345.7	324.0	309.1	304.0	295.7	297.7	-7.9%
Greece	18.4	23.5	32.0	29.6	36.5	39.1	45.7	51.3	49.7	51.7	53.1	45.5%
Hungary	18.6	27.2	29.8	27.0	22.7	19.8	17.3	15.8	15.9	16.8	17.8	-21.5%
Iceland	1.4	1.6	1.7	1.4	1.6	1.7	1.7	1.8	1.8	1.8	1.9	15.3%
Ireland	12.9	14.0	16.2	11.4	12.1	15.7	22.9	22.8	23.8	24.9	26.0	114.4%
Italy	237.3	248.6	267.5	229.6	252.7	261.3	246.0	246.7	232.2	224.8	222.3	-12.0%
Luxembourg	4.1	3.8	3.0	2.9	4.4	4.7	5.9	6.9	7.7	8.0	7.8	75.1%
Netherlands	68.1	56.8	70.0	48.3	52.7	57.8	60.7	65.8	66.0	68.5	67.8	28.6%
Norway	19.8	19.8	22.0	19.8	20.2	20.4	21.1	23.0	22.4	21.9	22.4	11.4%
Poland	21.9	33.5	42.8	39.2	35.1	41.0	51.6	53.8	57.4	58.2	60.2	71.2%
Portugal	12.0	16.5	22.2	21.8	28.7	34.4	39.9	39.2	38.8	40.5	34.6	20.7%
Slovak Republic	12.6	15.2	18.1	14.3	14.4	7.1	6.8	8.6	8.6	9.1	9.1	-36.5%
Spain	82.4	117.3	136.9	101.6	121.0	143.4	166.8	182.8	190.0	191.4	190.3	57.3%
Sweden	77.1	72.5	67.6	47.3	40.1	45.4	41.5	40.6	39.0	36.7	35.0	-12.8%
Switzerland	36.9	34.8	36.0	35.8	34.2	33.5	33.2	33.8	34.0	34.2	33.8	-1.1%
Turkey	25.4	38.5	44.1	49.4	62.5	78.9	82.7	79.2	78.7	77.1	77.3	23.7%
United Kingdom	253.5	238.0	212.7	202.5	208.4	198.8	187.5	186.2	187.5	191.1	189.6	-9.1%
OECD Europe	**1 756.2**	**1 842.6**	**1 902.0**	**1 581.6**	**1 640.5**	**1 733.1**	**1 745.3**	**1 778.0**	**1 765.8**	**1 758.4**	**1 745.9**	**6.4%**
European Union - 27	..	..	..	..	*1 647.7*	*1 676.1*	*1 671.4*	*1 708.6*	*1 698.3*	*1 694.7*	*1 681.7*	*2.1%*

* Total world includes Non-OECD total, OECD total as well as international marine bunkers and international aviation.

CO$_2$ emissions: Sectoral Approach - Oil
Emissions de CO$_2$: Méthode sectorielle - Pétrole

million tonnes of CO$_2$

	1971	1975	1980	1985	1990	1995	2000	2003	2004	2005	2006	% change 90-06
Non-OECD Total	1 597.9	2 226.0	2 862.9	2 926.8	3 198.1	3 129.2	3 524.4	3 738.1	3 960.4	4 047.3	4 197.6	31.3%
Algeria	5.9	9.1	14.8	20.5	23.0	21.8	24.1	27.8	29.7	30.7	30.5	32.8%
Angola	1.6	1.9	2.6	2.7	3.0	3.0	4.1	6.4	6.0	6.4	7.0	130.8%
Benin	0.3	0.5	0.4	0.5	0.3	0.2	1.4	2.3	2.4	2.5	3.0	+
Botswana	..	..	..	0.5	1.0	1.2	1.7	1.9	1.9	2.0	2.1	110.1%
Cameroon	0.7	1.0	1.7	2.4	2.7	2.5	2.8	3.0	3.0	2.9	3.1	16.6%
Congo	0.6	0.7	0.8	0.8	0.7	0.5	0.6	0.8	0.8	1.0	1.1	63.0%
Dem. Rep. of Congo	1.5	1.8	2.3	2.4	2.1	1.1	1.3	1.3	1.3	1.3	1.3	-38.4%
Côte d'Ivoire	2.4	3.0	3.4	3.0	2.6	3.1	3.2	2.4	2.8	3.0	2.9	11.5%
Egypt	18.9	23.6	36.9	54.8	61.6	58.2	66.9	69.3	77.6	83.0	86.7	40.8%
Eritrea	..	..	..	..	..	0.8	0.6	0.7	0.7	0.6	0.5	..
Ethiopia	1.3	1.2	1.4	1.4	2.2	2.3	3.2	4.5	4.7	4.8	5.3	138.4%
Gabon	0.5	0.7	1.3	1.6	0.7	1.1	1.1	1.4	1.4	1.8	1.8	163.8%
Ghana	1.9	2.3	2.3	2.2	2.7	3.3	5.1	7.1	6.2	6.7	8.6	218.9%
Kenya	3.6	4.3	5.5	5.3	6.0	7.0	8.7	7.5	8.5	9.7	10.7	79.2%
Libya	1.6	6.7	13.1	15.5	18.3	26.6	30.9	32.0	31.7	32.1	31.2	70.2%
Morocco	5.6	8.1	12.3	13.6	15.4	19.3	20.2	21.8	22.9	25.0	25.2	63.7%
Mozambique	1.4	1.1	1.6	1.2	0.9	1.0	1.3	1.7	1.7	1.5	1.6	64.3%
Namibia	..	..	..	..	..	1.8	1.9	2.5	2.6	2.8	2.9	..
Nigeria	5.0	10.1	23.4	25.2	22.1	21.2	28.6	33.2	32.3	38.5	32.3	46.3%
Senegal	1.2	1.6	2.0	2.1	2.0	2.4	3.6	3.8	4.1	4.2	4.0	101.7%
South Africa	27.6	34.1	35.1	39.5	46.3	49.5	50.5	54.7	57.5	59.4	61.4	32.6%
Sudan	3.3	3.3	3.7	4.2	5.5	4.6	5.5	8.9	10.3	10.3	11.4	107.7%
United Rep. of Tanzania	1.5	1.5	1.6	1.5	1.7	2.4	2.4	3.2	3.4	3.7	3.9	127.7%
Togo	0.3	0.3	0.4	0.3	0.6	0.6	1.0	1.1	1.0	1.0	0.9	57.3%
Tunisia	3.4	4.0	6.7	7.1	9.0	9.5	11.3	11.5	11.9	12.1	11.6	30.0%
Zambia	1.5	2.5	1.9	1.7	1.7	1.7	1.4	1.6	1.7	1.8	1.9	6.9%
Zimbabwe	1.6	2.1	1.8	2.0	2.6	3.6	3.0	2.4	1.9	2.1	2.0	-23.5%
Other Africa	7.1	8.5	12.6	10.9	13.6	15.9	16.8	18.2	19.1	19.8	20.5	51.2%
Africa	100.4	134.2	189.5	223.1	248.3	266.2	303.1	332.9	349.3	370.4	375.7	51.3%
Bahrain	1.2	1.2	1.7	1.8	2.1	2.4	2.5	2.9	3.2	3.7	4.5	116.5%
Islamic Rep. of Iran	35.2	62.7	80.0	126.4	136.0	166.0	181.9	193.1	205.2	207.9	225.7	65.9%
Iraq	10.5	12.4	29.8	42.1	49.1	65.7	69.9	64.5	75.0	77.0	79.9	62.8%
Israel	14.2	17.0	19.4	17.3	24.2	30.1	30.4	30.6	27.7	27.4	27.4	13.2%
Jordan	1.3	2.1	4.2	7.4	9.0	11.6	13.8	14.3	13.9	14.7	13.6	51.8%
Kuwait	13.3	13.0	17.6	28.2	12.5	23.0	32.3	41.5	47.4	52.3	44.1	252.0%
Lebanon	4.6	5.6	6.6	7.7	6.4	12.1	13.7	16.5	14.8	15.3	12.8	100.6%
Oman	0.3	0.7	1.5	3.3	5.0	7.7	8.4	11.2	10.9	11.9	12.7	153.8%
Qatar	0.3	0.7	1.5	1.7	2.0	2.5	3.0	4.2	4.6	5.5	6.6	225.3%
Saudi Arabia	10.6	18.3	80.1	95.0	114.6	143.1	176.2	194.2	204.3	212.2	226.7	97.8%
Syria	6.8	10.3	15.0	23.3	27.8	33.8	35.3	34.4	35.4	39.3	40.3	45.1%
United Arab Emirates	0.4	1.6	9.4	15.6	18.5	21.4	21.9	28.3	28.8	30.1	31.4	69.9%
Yemen	1.2	1.7	3.4	4.8	6.4	9.3	13.3	16.4	17.5	19.2	19.8	207.9%
Middle East	99.9	147.4	270.3	374.5	413.6	528.8	602.4	652.2	688.7	716.5	745.5	80.2%
Albania	2.4	2.3	4.4	2.8	3.4	1.7	3.1	3.8	3.4	4.4	4.1	20.4%
Bosnia and Herzegovina *	..	..	..	..	5.4	1.6	3.3	3.1	3.3	3.2	3.4	-37.2%
Bulgaria	29.1	34.9	38.6	28.0	26.1	13.7	10.4	11.6	11.5	12.0	12.6	-51.6%
Croatia *	..	..	..	..	13.4	11.0	11.3	13.3	12.4	12.9	13.2	-2.2%
Cyprus	1.8	1.7	2.6	2.6	3.6	5.0	6.1	6.8	6.7	6.8	6.9	91.3%
Gibraltar	0.1	0.1	0.1	0.1	0.2	0.3	0.4	0.4	0.4	0.4	0.4	152.3%
FYR of Macedonia *	..	..	..	..	3.0	2.3	2.7	2.5	2.5	2.6	2.7	-10.5%
Malta	0.6	0.6	1.0	0.7	1.6	2.2	2.2	2.5	2.6	2.6	2.5	59.4%
Romania	31.5	40.0	51.6	41.1	50.0	32.0	26.5	27.3	27.2	27.8	26.9	-46.3%
Serbia *	..	..	..	..	14.1	4.8	4.1	9.4	10.9	11.5	12.5	-11.6%
Slovenia *	..	..	..	..	5.0	6.7	6.7	6.9	7.1	7.2	7.4	47.7%
Former Yugoslavia *	25.5	31.8	39.2	38.3	-	-	-	-	-	-	-	-
Non-OECD Europe	91.1	111.4	137.4	113.7	125.8	81.3	76.9	87.7	88.1	91.6	92.6	-26.4%

* Data for individual countries of the Former Yugoslavia are not available prior to 1990.

CO$_2$ emissions: Sectoral Approach - Oil

Emissions de CO$_2$: Méthode sectorielle - Pétrole

million tonnes of CO$_2$

	1971	1975	1980	1985	1990	1995	2000	2003	2004	2005	2006	% change 90-06
Armenia	..	..	..	..	11.2	0.7	0.8	0.9	0.9	1.0	0.9	-91.6%
Azerbaijan	..	..	..	..	30.8	18.1	17.4	11.6	11.2	13.1	10.5	-65.8%
Belarus	..	..	..	..	79.9	29.5	19.5	20.0	19.6	19.5	22.1	-72.3%
Estonia	..	..	..	..	9.3	3.5	2.6	2.8	3.1	3.1	3.1	-66.7%
Georgia	..	..	..	..	15.8	4.8	2.1	1.6	1.6	2.0	2.0	-87.3%
Kazakhstan	..	..	..	..	58.3	32.5	23.4	24.6	24.7	26.3	28.7	-50.8%
Kyrgyzstan	..	..	..	..	9.1	1.6	1.3	1.3	1.7	1.8	1.7	-81.6%
Latvia	..	..	..	..	10.3	5.5	3.8	4.0	4.1	4.1	4.4	-57.4%
Lithuania	..	..	..	..	19.7	9.0	6.5	6.5	7.1	7.6	7.4	-62.6%
Republic of Moldova	..	..	..	..	14.8	3.1	1.2	1.7	1.9	1.9	1.9	-87.3%
Russia	..	..	..	..	625.4	351.2	332.4	320.2	318.0	309.9	321.0	-48.7%
Tajikistan	..	..	..	..	5.9	3.5	2.7	3.8	4.0	4.3	4.8	-18.9%
Turkmenistan	..	..	..	..	16.9	8.2	10.7	12.9	12.4	12.7	14.8	-12.1%
Ukraine	..	..	..	..	195.5	75.4	33.7	38.3	38.5	38.2	39.3	-79.9%
Uzbekistan	..	..	..	..	30.6	19.8	19.5	20.9	19.7	16.1	15.0	-50.8%
Former USSR *	**688.9**	**1 018.6**	**1 210.0**	**1 193.3**	**1 133.6**	**566.5**	**477.7**	**471.2**	**468.5**	**461.7**	**477.7**	**-57.9%**
Argentina	67.3	65.1	70.9	54.4	53.1	59.2	59.9	50.2	57.6	58.7	64.9	22.3%
Bolivia	2.0	2.9	3.7	3.4	3.9	5.7	5.3	7.1	7.6	8.3	9.0	127.1%
Brazil	83.2	126.9	158.8	132.8	157.7	194.0	242.5	230.4	237.7	241.2	245.5	55.7%
Chile	14.5	12.4	15.1	13.0	18.3	26.3	28.4	26.7	28.7	29.1	30.0	63.6%
Colombia	18.0	18.5	20.6	22.2	26.8	37.4	34.6	32.4	35.0	34.0	34.8	30.1%
Costa Rica	1.3	1.7	2.2	2.0	2.6	4.4	4.6	5.1	5.3	5.3	5.8	121.4%
Cuba	18.0	25.1	28.0	29.9	26.8	21.4	23.3	24.5	23.7	22.5	24.1	-9.9%
Dominican Republic	3.4	5.1	6.2	5.6	7.6	11.2	17.2	15.2	15.8	15.8	16.0	110.5%
Ecuador	3.5	5.9	10.5	11.7	12.7	15.6	17.9	21.0	21.0	22.5	23.7	87.1%
El Salvador	1.3	2.0	1.7	1.7	2.2	4.7	5.2	5.7	5.8	5.9	5.8	169.1%
Guatemala	2.3	3.0	4.2	3.3	3.3	6.0	8.3	9.0	9.2	9.5	9.5	188.3%
Haiti	0.4	0.4	0.6	0.6	0.9	0.9	1.4	1.6	1.6	1.7	1.7	87.8%
Honduras	1.1	1.3	1.7	1.7	2.1	3.9	4.1	5.4	6.0	6.0	6.7	211.7%
Jamaica	5.5	7.4	6.5	4.6	7.1	8.2	9.6	10.1	10.2	9.7	11.5	62.4%
Netherlands Antilles	14.6	10.3	8.9	4.7	2.9	3.0	3.2	3.7	3.7	3.8	3.9	37.3%
Nicaragua	1.5	1.8	1.8	1.8	1.8	2.5	3.5	4.0	4.1	4.1	4.0	117.1%
Panama	2.5	3.2	2.9	2.6	2.4	4.0	4.6	5.9	5.5	5.7	6.0	152.5%
Paraguay	0.6	0.7	1.4	1.4	1.9	3.4	3.3	3.7	3.7	3.4	3.6	86.1%
Peru	14.4	17.0	18.9	16.2	17.6	21.8	23.0	20.7	23.5	21.4	21.1	19.8%
Trinidad and Tobago	2.7	3.0	2.8	2.5	2.1	2.2	2.7	2.7	2.8	3.1	3.9	85.9%
Uruguay	5.1	5.4	5.5	3.1	3.7	4.5	5.2	4.0	5.2	5.0	5.9	58.9%
Venezuela	30.7	37.5	59.1	56.0	57.0	59.9	64.5	67.5	77.8	86.1	94.4	65.6%
Other Latin America	7.7	10.7	10.1	9.2	12.4	13.3	13.6	14.9	14.9	15.4	16.4	32.5%
Latin America	**301.7**	**367.5**	**442.1**	**384.3**	**426.8**	**513.7**	**585.9**	**571.5**	**606.1**	**618.2**	**648.1**	**51.9%**
Bangladesh	2.2	3.3	4.6	4.6	5.2	8.4	9.4	11.7	11.6	12.9	12.7	145.2%
Brunei Darussalam	0.2	0.2	0.5	0.6	0.9	1.3	1.4	1.6	1.6	1.6	1.8	112.6%
Cambodia	..	..	..	..	..	1.4	2.4	3.1	3.5	3.7	4.1	..
Chinese Taipei	19.0	31.3	54.2	43.4	69.2	86.6	92.7	93.1	94.7	95.2	96.2	39.0%
India	55.5	62.3	84.1	117.8	164.1	221.7	299.2	310.9	313.2	315.0	338.7	106.4%
Indonesia	24.4	36.4	61.0	69.7	91.2	116.5	153.5	165.2	176.3	179.5	163.6	79.5%
DPR of Korea	2.6	4.2	8.0	7.4	7.9	3.9	3.1	3.4	3.4	2.8	2.2	-72.4%
Malaysia	12.6	16.0	23.1	26.7	37.3	48.3	55.2	58.5	62.6	63.1	63.0	69.0%
Mongolia	..	..	..	2.2	2.4	1.0	1.3	1.5	1.7	1.7	1.9	-23.4%
Myanmar	3.8	3.0	3.8	3.4	2.0	3.9	5.2	5.5	5.6	5.8	5.3	165.8%
Nepal	0.2	0.2	0.3	0.5	0.7	1.5	2.1	2.2	2.1	2.1	2.1	194.0%
Pakistan	8.8	11.0	13.2	20.9	30.6	43.7	56.1	43.2	47.0	47.3	54.3	77.2%
Philippines	22.6	27.9	30.8	22.2	31.7	51.7	49.4	46.0	47.0	42.0	37.9	19.5%
Singapore	5.9	8.3	12.6	16.1	28.7	34.4	35.1	27.9	26.6	29.0	27.9	-2.7%
Sri Lanka	2.8	2.7	3.7	3.6	3.7	5.5	10.8	11.1	12.2	12.1	11.1	198.7%
Thailand	16.8	21.3	32.3	28.3	52.6	93.7	90.8	108.2	117.4	113.4	112.1	113.4%
Vietnam	10.6	6.7	5.6	5.8	8.3	14.2	24.2	31.7	35.6	37.3	36.8	342.0%
Other Asia	3.8	5.4	8.7	8.0	9.1	8.3	9.3	11.6	13.7	13.4	14.3	56.4%
Asia	**191.7**	**240.3**	**346.6**	**381.1**	**545.5**	**746.0**	**901.3**	**936.4**	**976.0**	**978.0**	**985.9**	**80.7%**
People's Rep. of China	115.2	195.9	252.4	247.2	295.8	415.3	560.8	674.4	775.5	802.5	864.4	192.2%
Hong Kong, China	9.0	10.7	14.5	9.6	8.7	11.5	16.3	11.7	8.3	8.4	7.7	-11.2%
China	**124.2**	**206.6**	**267.0**	**256.8**	**304.5**	**426.7**	**577.1**	**686.2**	**783.8**	**810.9**	**872.1**	**186.4%**

* Data for individual countries of the Former USSR are not available prior to 1990.

CO$_2$ emissions: Sectoral Approach - Gas

Emissions de CO $_2$: Méthode sectorielle - Gaz

million tonnes of CO$_2$

	1971	1975	1980	1985	1990	1995	2000	2003	2004	2005	2006	% change 90-06
World *	**2 058.5**	**2 281.6**	**2 768.6**	**3 163.7**	**3 812.3**	**4 112.6**	**4 716.0**	**5 081.3**	**5 206.5**	**5 334.9**	**5 444.7**	**42.8%**
Annex I Parties	..	..	..	..	*3 068.9*	*3 176.8*	*3 471.7*	*3 604.4*	*3 630.2*	*3 649.2*	*3 644.5*	*18.8%*
Annex II Parties	*1 438.5*	*1 503.1*	*1 663.5*	*1 616.2*	*1 794.0*	*2 121.9*	*2 426.3*	*2 478.2*	*2 495.6*	*2 492.0*	*2 473.8*	*37.9%*
North America	*1 257.4*	*1 143.4*	*1 179.4*	*1 058.1*	*1 135.1*	*1 309.4*	*1 423.0*	*1 381.8*	*1 378.0*	*1 359.9*	*1 336.8*	*17.8%*
Europe	*168.1*	*331.0*	*414.3*	*446.1*	*505.8*	*631.3*	*784.1*	*861.1*	*882.4*	*895.5*	*884.5*	*74.9%*
Pacific	*12.9*	*28.7*	*69.8*	*112.0*	*153.1*	*181.3*	*219.1*	*235.3*	*235.2*	*236.6*	*252.5*	*65.0%*
Annex I EIT	..	..	..	..	*1 268.4*	*1 041.9*	*1 016.6*	*1 085.1*	*1 091.3*	*1 104.4*	*1 110.1*	*-12.5%*
Non-Annex I Parties	..	..	..	..	*743.4*	*935.8*	*1 244.3*	*1 477.0*	*1 576.3*	*1 685.7*	*1 800.3*	*142.2%*
Annex I Kyoto Parties	..	..	..	..	*2 024.2*	*1 978.1*	*2 155.7*	*2 323.4*	*2 342.5*	*2 368.4*	*2 375.7*	*17.4%*
Intl. marine bunkers	..	..	..	..	..	-	-	-	-	-	-	..
International aviation	..	..	..	..	..	-	-	-	-	-	-	..
Non-OECD Total	**576.9**	**720.7**	**1 015.9**	**1 440.7**	**1 892.0**	**1 835.7**	**2 074.4**	**2 339.0**	**2 430.7**	**2 537.0**	**2 637.0**	**39.4%**
OECD Total	**1 481.6**	**1 560.9**	**1 752.7**	**1 723.1**	**1 920.3**	**2 276.9**	**2 641.6**	**2 742.4**	**2 775.8**	**2 798.0**	**2 807.8**	**46.2%**
Canada	67.9	87.3	99.7	113.9	123.8	149.1	168.1	176.5	171.2	170.2	167.4	35.3%
Mexico	20.2	25.6	43.2	53.6	52.1	57.7	73.8	91.2	95.3	104.7	122.9	136.0%
United States	1 189.5	1 056.1	1 079.7	944.2	1 011.3	1 160.2	1 254.9	1 205.3	1 206.8	1 189.7	1 169.4	15.6%
OECD N. America	**1 277.6**	**1 169.0**	**1 222.6**	**1 111.7**	**1 187.2**	**1 367.1**	**1 496.8**	**1 473.0**	**1 473.3**	**1 464.6**	**1 459.7**	**23.0%**
Australia	4.1	8.9	16.7	24.4	32.8	37.7	43.9	52.1	53.8	55.9	55.1	67.9%
Japan	8.5	19.2	51.2	81.5	114.6	137.1	164.8	174.9	174.4	173.7	190.0	65.8%
Korea	-	-	-	-	6.4	19.4	39.9	50.9	60.0	63.8	68.2	971.1%
New Zealand	0.2	0.6	1.8	6.1	5.7	6.5	10.4	8.3	7.0	7.0	7.5	31.6%
OECD Pacific	**12.9**	**28.7**	**69.8**	**112.0**	**159.4**	**200.6**	**259.0**	**286.2**	**295.2**	**300.4**	**320.7**	**101.2%**
Austria	5.6	7.5	9.0	10.1	11.8	14.7	15.0	17.4	17.2	18.9	17.2	45.6%
Belgium	11.3	18.2	20.5	16.9	18.9	24.5	30.7	33.2	33.9	33.3	34.1	80.4%
Czech Republic	1.9	3.1	5.6	9.1	11.5	14.5	17.0	17.9	18.0	17.8	17.4	52.3%
Denmark	-	0.0	0.0	1.5	4.2	7.3	10.3	10.9	10.9	10.4	10.6	156.0%
Finland	-	1.5	1.7	1.9	5.1	6.6	7.9	9.5	9.2	8.4	9.0	77.2%
France	19.2	33.0	47.4	54.5	56.1	65.8	81.1	89.2	90.9	92.5	90.1	60.7%
Germany	38.8	86.4	114.9	105.3	118.1	147.0	158.4	184.6	182.3	179.8	182.2	54.2%
Greece	-	-	-	0.1	0.2	0.1	3.9	4.6	5.1	5.4	6.3	+
Hungary	6.8	10.7	17.6	19.2	19.8	20.3	21.6	26.6	26.0	27.0	25.8	30.4%
Iceland	-	-	-	-	-	-	-	-	-	-	-	
Ireland	-	-	1.7	4.5	4.0	5.0	7.7	8.5	8.3	7.9	9.2	132.3%
Italy	23.9	40.8	49.3	59.8	89.2	102.8	134.0	147.2	152.4	163.2	159.8	79.1%
Luxembourg	0.0	0.8	1.0	0.7	1.0	1.3	1.6	2.5	2.8	2.8	2.9	187.2%
Netherlands	47.0	72.5	69.4	75.3	71.0	78.6	79.8	82.5	84.2	80.6	78.5	10.6%
Norway	-	0.4	2.0	2.8	4.6	8.1	8.2	8.8	9.6	11.2	11.3	144.1%
Poland	11.4	13.5	17.6	18.2	18.4	18.3	21.0	24.0	25.6	26.7	27.0	46.8%
Portugal	-	-	-	-	-	-	4.6	6.1	7.7	8.6	8.3	x
Slovak Republic	2.9	4.9	5.1	6.7	11.7	11.7	13.1	12.5	12.0	13.2	12.0	2.5%
Spain	0.7	1.8	3.1	4.5	10.5	17.4	34.7	49.0	56.9	67.2	70.0	564.0%
Sweden	-	-	-	0.2	1.2	1.6	1.6	1.9	1.9	1.7	2.0	59.2%
Switzerland	0.0	1.0	1.9	2.9	3.8	5.1	5.6	6.1	6.3	6.5	6.3	66.8%
Turkey	-	-	-	0.1	6.5	13.0	28.9	41.1	43.3	52.8	60.5	826.3%
United Kingdom	21.6	67.2	92.3	105.2	106.0	145.4	199.0	199.0	203.0	197.1	186.7	76.1%
OECD Europe	**191.1**	**363.2**	**460.3**	**499.4**	**573.7**	**709.2**	**885.7**	**983.1**	**1 007.3**	**1 033.0**	**1 027.3**	**79.1%**
European Union - 27	..	..	..	..	*658.6*	*745.5*	*890.0*	*976.8*	*996.0*	*1 010.9*	*998.7*	*51.6%*

* Total world includes Non-OECD total, OECD total as well as international marine bunkers and international aviation.

CO$_2$ emissions: Sectoral Approach - Gas

Emissions de CO$_2$: Méthode sectorielle - Gaz

million tonnes of CO$_2$

	1971	1975	1980	1985	1990	1995	2000	2003	2004	2005	2006	% change 90-06
Non-OECD Total	576.9	720.7	1 015.9	1 440.7	1 892.0	1 835.7	2 074.4	2 339.0	2 430.7	2 537.0	2 637.0	39.4%
Algeria	2.6	5.1	14.9	24.1	30.5	36.1	41.8	49.0	47.8	52.1	54.4	78.5%
Angola	0.1	0.1	0.2	0.2	1.0	1.1	1.1	1.2	1.4	1.4	1.5	48.1%
Benin	-	-	-	-	-	-	-	-	-	-	-	-
Botswana	..	..	..	-	-	-	-	-	-	-	-	-
Cameroon	-	-	-	-	-	-	-	-	-	-	-	-
Congo	0.0	0.0	-	0.0	-	-	-	0.0	0.0	0.0	0.0	x
Dem. Rep. of Congo	-	-	-	-	-	-	-	-	-	-	-	-
Côte d'Ivoire	-	-	-	-	-	0.1	3.0	2.7	2.9	3.3	3.2	x
Egypt	0.2	0.1	3.4	7.9	14.9	22.9	40.1	57.7	57.1	63.0	63.0	321.8%
Eritrea	..	..	..	..	..	-	-	-	-	-	-	..
Ethiopia	-	-	-	-	-	-	-	-	-	-	-	-
Gabon	-	-	0.0	0.1	0.2	0.3	0.2	0.3	0.3	0.3	0.3	27.5%
Ghana	-	-	-	-	-	-	-	-	-	-	-	-
Kenya	-	-	-	-	-	-	-	-	-	-	-	-
Libya	2.1	2.5	5.5	7.0	9.0	8.5	8.8	9.9	12.0	10.4	11.2	24.6%
Morocco	0.1	0.1	0.1	0.2	0.1	0.0	0.1	0.1	0.1	0.9	1.1	+
Mozambique	-	-	-	-	-	0.0	0.0	0.0	0.0	0.0	0.1	x
Namibia	..	..	..	..	..	-	-	-	-	-	-	..
Nigeria	0.4	1.0	2.9	6.9	6.9	9.2	12.5	15.1	16.3	17.1	19.1	177.4%
Senegal	-	-	-	-	0.0	0.1	0.0	0.0	0.0	0.0	0.0	86.5%
South Africa	-	-	-	-	-	-	-	0.0	0.0	0.0	0.1	x
Sudan	-	-	-	-	-	-	-	-	-	-	-	-
United Rep. of Tanzania	-	-	-	-	-	-	-	-	0.2	0.7	0.7	x
Togo	-	-	-	-	-	-	-	-	-	-	-	-
Tunisia	0.0	0.5	0.8	2.2	2.8	4.6	6.4	7.5	7.8	7.2	8.1	187.7%
Zambia	-	-	-	-	-	-	-	-	-	-	-	-
Zimbabwe	-	-	-	-	-	-	-	-	-	-	-	-
Other Africa	-	-	-	-	-	-	0.0	1.0	0.9	0.9	2.5	x
Africa	5.5	9.5	27.8	48.7	65.4	82.8	114.0	144.5	147.0	157.4	165.2	152.5%
Bahrain	1.8	4.1	5.7	8.6	9.6	9.3	11.6	13.2	13.7	14.6	15.5	60.7%
Islamic Rep. of Iran	5.5	8.1	8.5	16.8	37.0	80.0	118.9	154.8	172.0	184.8	202.9	448.4%
Iraq	1.8	3.1	2.4	1.6	3.8	6.0	6.0	3.0	5.0	5.1	6.7	76.8%
Israel	0.2	0.1	0.2	0.1	0.0	0.0	0.0	0.0	2.3	3.1	4.2	+
Jordan	-	-	-	-	0.2	0.5	0.5	0.5	2.8	3.2	4.7	+
Kuwait	9.9	9.9	13.2	9.7	11.8	18.0	17.9	18.3	19.6	22.0	22.6	91.3%
Lebanon	-	-	-	-	-	-	-	-	-	-	-	-
Oman	-	-	0.7	2.1	4.9	6.7	11.4	14.0	14.3	15.0	16.7	240.3%
Qatar	1.9	4.2	6.3	10.5	12.2	16.2	23.6	26.1	29.2	29.7	33.1	172.0%
Saudi Arabia	2.7	5.4	21.2	34.1	46.8	61.5	75.0	93.3	99.3	109.8	113.3	142.2%
Syria	-	-	0.1	0.3	3.2	4.8	10.4	12.1	12.3	10.8	11.2	249.8%
United Arab Emirates	2.0	3.3	9.6	19.8	33.1	48.6	64.2	73.7	76.0	77.2	78.9	138.1%
Yemen	-	-	-	-	-	-	-	-	-	-	-	-
Middle East	25.8	38.1	67.9	103.6	162.7	251.6	339.4	409.0	446.6	475.2	509.8	213.3%
Albania	0.2	0.6	0.8	0.8	0.5	0.1	0.0	0.0	0.0	0.0	0.0	-92.9%
Bosnia and Herzegovina *	..	..	..	..	0.9	0.3	0.5	0.4	0.6	0.7	0.7	-19.0%
Bulgaria	0.6	2.3	7.4	10.8	12.0	10.0	6.2	5.3	5.2	5.9	6.2	-48.3%
Croatia *	..	..	..	..	4.7	4.1	4.7	5.0	5.3	5.1	5.1	7.2%
Cyprus	-	-	-	-	-	-	-	-	-	-	-	-
Gibraltar	-	-	-	-	-	-	-	-	-	-	-	-
FYR of Macedonia *	..	..	..	..	-	-	0.1	0.2	0.1	0.1	0.2	x
Malta	-	-	-	-	-	-	-	-	-	-	-	-
Romania	52.1	62.6	75.7	74.6	67.4	43.1	30.6	32.8	30.9	30.2	30.9	-54.1%
Serbia *	..	..	..	..	6.0	3.0	3.4	4.1	5.2	4.3	4.4	-28.0%
Slovenia *	..	..	..	..	1.7	1.6	1.8	2.0	2.0	2.1	2.0	19.2%
Former Yugoslavia *	1.9	2.9	5.8	11.0	-	-	-	-	-	-	-	-
Non-OECD Europe	54.8	68.4	89.6	97.1	93.2	62.2	47.4	49.7	49.4	48.6	49.5	-46.9%

* Data for individual countries of the Former Yugoslavia are not available prior to 1990.

CO₂ emissions: Sectoral Approach - Gas

Emissions de CO₂ : Méthode sectorielle - Gaz

million tonnes of CO₂

	1971	1975	1980	1985	1990	1995	2000	2003	2004	2005	2006	% change 90-06
Armenia	..	..	..	..	8.3	2.7	2.6	2.3	2.5	3.1	3.2	-61.5%
Azerbaijan	..	..	..	..	31.5	12.7	10.8	16.5	18.0	18.0	19.7	-37.5%
Belarus	..	..	..	..	26.9	25.5	32.2	34.6	37.6	38.3	38.9	45.0%
Estonia	..	..	..	..	2.9	1.2	1.4	1.5	1.7	1.7	1.8	-38.5%
Georgia	..	..	..	..	10.6	2.2	2.2	1.4	1.7	1.8	2.6	-76.0%
Kazakhstan	..	..	..	..	24.8	23.5	20.6	27.8	32.1	40.5	43.6	75.8%
Kyrgyzstan	..	..	..	..	3.6	1.7	1.3	1.4	1.6	1.4	1.5	-57.6%
Latvia	..	..	..	..	5.6	2.3	2.5	3.1	3.1	3.2	3.3	-41.1%
Lithuania	..	..	..	..	10.3	4.3	4.3	4.9	5.0	5.3	5.2	-49.3%
Republic of Moldova	..	..	..	..	7.6	5.5	4.8	5.0	5.2	5.6	5.2	-31.7%
Russia	..	..	..	..	866.3	728.8	718.1	766.4	772.2	783.4	804.5	-7.1%
Tajikistan	..	..	..	..	3.2	1.7	1.5	1.1	1.1	1.1	1.1	-64.8%
Turkmenistan	..	..	..	..	28.6	26.2	25.5	30.0	26.8	28.7	28.8	0.5%
Ukraine	..	..	..	..	209.4	156.1	141.9	148.4	146.7	144.5	130.0	-37.9%
Uzbekistan	..	..	..	..	75.5	77.4	93.4	95.0	92.2	89.4	93.4	23.7%
Former USSR *	**431.8**	**520.4**	**704.2**	**1 021.2**	**1 315.1**	**1 071.8**	**1 063.1**	**1 139.4**	**1 147.6**	**1 166.1**	**1 182.8**	**-10.1%**
Argentina	12.3	17.1	21.7	30.5	43.4	51.2	68.4	69.2	74.1	75.3	79.0	82.3%
Bolivia	0.1	0.3	0.6	0.8	1.5	2.5	2.3	2.1	2.9	3.6	3.8	152.5%
Brazil	0.2	0.7	1.7	4.3	6.4	8.5	17.3	29.1	35.5	38.0	39.9	524.9%
Chile	1.3	1.1	1.4	1.6	3.3	3.2	12.4	15.5	15.7	15.5	14.5	336.8%
Colombia	2.6	3.2	5.7	7.3	7.5	8.3	12.8	13.0	13.6	14.3	14.3	90.6%
Costa Rica	-	-	-	-	-	-	-	-	-	-	-	-
Cuba	0.0	0.0	0.0	0.0	0.1	0.0	1.1	1.3	1.3	1.4	2.1	+
Dominican Republic	-	-	-	-	-	-	-	0.2	0.3	0.5	0.6	x
Ecuador	0.1	0.3	0.1	0.4	0.5	0.6	0.7	0.9	0.9	1.0	1.3	148.8%
El Salvador	-	-	-	-	-	-	-	-	-	-	-	-
Guatemala	-	-	-	-	-	-	-	-	-	-	-	-
Haiti	-	-	-	-	-	-	-	-	-	-	-	-
Honduras	-	-	-	-	-	-	-	-	-	-	-	-
Jamaica	-	-	-	-	-	-	-	-	-	-	-	-
Netherlands Antilles	-	-	-	-	-	-	-	-	-	-	-	-
Nicaragua	-	-	-	-	-	-	-	-	-	-	-	-
Panama	-	-	-	-	-	-	-	-	-	-	-	-
Paraguay	-	-	-	-	-	-	-	-	-	-	-	-
Peru	0.6	0.8	1.0	1.3	1.0	0.6	1.1	1.3	2.0	3.5	3.9	272.8%
Trinidad and Tobago	3.4	2.8	5.1	7.1	9.3	10.0	15.3	18.5	19.4	20.2	23.0	148.4%
Uruguay	-	-	-	-	-	-	0.1	0.1	0.2	0.2	0.2	x
Venezuela	20.8	24.3	32.6	38.5	46.3	58.4	63.3	52.8	52.2	52.8	54.7	18.1%
Other Latin America	0.0	0.0	0.0	0.0	0.0	0.0	0.7	1.5	1.5	1.5	1.5	+
Latin America	**41.6**	**50.8**	**70.0**	**91.9**	**119.4**	**143.4**	**195.3**	**205.4**	**219.5**	**227.7**	**238.9**	**100.1%**
Bangladesh	0.6	0.9	2.1	4.0	7.3	10.8	14.5	19.1	20.6	22.1	24.0	229.3%
Brunei Darussalam	0.2	1.2	2.1	2.3	2.5	3.4	3.2	3.9	3.6	3.5	4.0	57.6%
Cambodia	..	..	..	..	..	-	-	-	-	-	-	..
Chinese Taipei	1.9	2.7	3.3	2.1	3.4	7.8	12.7	16.3	17.8	19.1	19.5	475.5%
India	1.2	1.8	2.4	7.2	18.9	32.8	42.3	49.4	55.5	63.6	66.7	252.7%
Indonesia	0.3	1.0	7.3	13.5	37.3	58.2	62.1	67.6	60.7	61.3	62.7	68.0%
DPR of Korea	-	-	-	-	-	-	-	-	-	-	-	-
Malaysia	0.0	0.1	0.2	4.9	7.7	25.7	50.6	47.2	48.1	55.9	59.1	669.5%
Mongolia	..	..	..	-	-	-	-	-	-	-	-	-
Myanmar	0.1	0.3	0.6	1.8	1.7	2.8	2.7	3.0	3.5	3.9	4.1	137.0%
Nepal	-	-	-	-	-	-	-	-	-	-	-	-
Pakistan	5.3	7.7	10.3	13.4	20.9	28.0	34.5	48.2	53.7	56.0	56.1	168.4%
Philippines	-	-	-	-	-	0.0	0.0	5.1	4.7	6.2	5.8	x
Singapore	-	-	-	-	-	3.5	2.8	10.5	12.4	13.9	15.0	x
Sri Lanka	-	-	-	-	-	-	-	-	-	-	-	-
Thailand	-	-	-	5.7	10.0	18.2	37.3	49.3	52.5	53.9	55.1	452.7%
Vietnam	-	-	-	0.1	0.0	0.4	2.6	6.3	10.8	11.5	11.7	+
Other Asia	0.5	0.5	0.2	1.2	0.6	0.5	0.5	0.3	0.2	0.3	0.3	-52.0%
Asia	**10.1**	**16.2**	**28.5**	**56.3**	**110.3**	**192.1**	**265.7**	**326.4**	**344.0**	**371.1**	**384.0**	**248.2%**
People's Rep. of China	7.3	17.3	27.8	21.9	25.8	31.7	43.7	60.9	71.5	85.7	101.2	291.5%
Hong Kong, China	-	-	-	-	-	0.1	5.7	3.5	5.1	5.1	5.6	x
China	**7.3**	**17.3**	**27.8**	**21.9**	**25.8**	**31.8**	**49.5**	**64.5**	**76.6**	**90.8**	**106.8**	**313.2%**

* Data for individual countries of the Former USSR are not available prior to 1990.

CO$_2$ emissions: Reference Approach

Emissions de CO$_2$: Méthode de référence

million tonnes of CO$_2$

	1971	1975	1980	1985	1990	1995	2000	2003	2004	2005	2006	% change 90-06
World *	14 617.0	16 160.0	18 648.4	19 299.9	21 475.4	22 089.9	23 786.4	25 460.4	26 802.0	27 622.0	28 408.2	**32.3%**
Annex I Parties	..	..	..	..	14 110.9	13 287.2	13 888.4	14 172.8	14 294.0	14 345.0	14 291.9	1.3%
Annex II Parties	8 638.1	8 951.2	9 721.8	9 300.4	9 846.5	10 241.4	11 080.0	11 265.3	11 406.5	11 445.9	11 303.2	14.8%
North America	4 612.3	4 775.0	5 191.6	5 009.7	5 277.2	5 587.4	6 232.9	6 246.8	6 353.5	6 408.7	6 306.9	19.5%
Europe	3 098.9	3 118.9	3 387.8	3 152.0	3 207.0	3 178.5	3 263.2	3 402.9	3 415.4	3 396.1	3 357.3	4.7%
Pacific	927.0	1 057.4	1 142.4	1 138.6	1 362.3	1 475.4	1 583.8	1 615.5	1 637.7	1 641.1	1 639.0	20.3%
Annex I EIT	..	..	..	..	4 126.3	2 888.5	2 605.0	2 704.1	2 678.0	2 679.5	2 746.1	-33.4%
Non-Annex I Parties	..	..	..	..	6 751.2	8 114.8	9 090.2	10 479.7	11 621.5	12 336.5	13 136.7	94.6%
Annex I Kyoto Parties	..	..	..	..	9 001.5	7 931.8	7 909.9	8 195.4	8 202.5	8 200.9	8 201.3	-8.9%
Intl. marine bunkers	344.5	328.6	344.0	291.7	357.9	403.5	466.7	465.7	521.0	551.6	582.6	**62.8%**
International aviation	167.9	171.3	199.6	223.6	255.4	284.4	341.1	342.2	365.5	388.8	397.1	**55.5%**
Non-OECD Total	4 681.9	5 774.6	7 196.3	8 212.4	9 709.1	9 766.2	10 385.2	11 808.5	12 899.1	13 604.1	14 449.8	**48.8%**
OECD Total	9 422.7	9 885.4	10 908.5	10 572.1	11 153.0	11 635.8	12 593.5	12 844.0	13 016.4	13 077.4	12 978.7	**16.4%**
Canada	337.2	392.3	428.6	399.9	423.4	452.5	517.8	535.3	536.4	548.0	526.9	24.4%
Mexico	100.8	145.1	242.2	265.7	294.3	307.4	355.8	382.0	394.5	426.0	426.2	44.8%
United States	4 275.1	4 382.7	4 763.0	4 609.9	4 853.7	5 134.9	5 715.2	5 711.5	5 817.0	5 860.7	5 780.1	19.1%
OECD N. America	4 713.0	4 920.1	5 433.8	5 275.4	5 571.5	5 894.8	6 588.7	6 628.8	6 747.9	6 834.6	6 733.1	**20.8%**
Australia	156.9	182.7	212.1	220.5	260.9	278.6	330.4	337.0	337.8	363.4	370.4	42.0%
Japan	755.6	857.1	913.0	896.4	1 078.4	1 169.8	1 222.9	1 246.0	1 267.8	1 245.6	1 235.5	14.6%
Korea	54.8	77.9	125.7	157.7	238.6	361.4	441.1	470.6	485.9	464.1	471.4	97.6%
New Zealand	14.4	17.7	17.3	21.7	23.0	27.1	30.5	32.5	32.1	32.1	33.0	43.6%
OECD Pacific	981.8	1 135.3	1 268.1	1 296.3	1 600.9	1 836.8	2 025.0	2 086.1	2 123.6	2 105.2	2 110.4	**31.8%**
Austria	51.2	52.3	58.3	55.9	57.1	60.1	62.4	73.4	73.1	75.4	73.3	28.4%
Belgium	120.0	119.5	129.8	103.9	111.8	122.0	130.1	129.2	126.7	122.7	121.0	8.2%
Czech Republic	168.5	158.9	165.3	169.4	161.0	127.0	125.4	125.8	126.7	125.0	126.6	-21.4%
Denmark	56.2	52.6	61.0	61.0	50.7	57.7	50.4	56.6	51.1	47.4	54.7	8.1%
Finland	39.9	45.5	57.4	50.5	52.1	54.0	54.2	72.3	69.0	56.3	67.5	29.6%
France	434.6	431.8	473.0	374.3	366.7	348.2	360.0	386.1	387.4	388.4	376.5	2.7%
Germany	993.1	976.5	1 076.4	1 022.5	971.7	877.5	843.9	849.0	843.5	820.1	821.3	-15.5%
Greece	25.3	35.4	45.4	55.9	69.2	72.6	85.3	90.2	91.6	93.1	90.9	31.3%
Hungary	58.2	67.4	80.7	78.8	67.7	58.8	55.5	58.3	57.2	57.3	56.5	-16.5%
Iceland	1.4	1.6	1.8	1.6	2.0	1.9	2.1	2.2	2.2	2.2	2.2	11.7%
Ireland	22.5	21.8	26.3	27.2	31.3	31.5	40.1	41.5	41.2	41.5	41.5	32.6%
Italy	280.3	311.2	349.0	339.6	384.8	413.5	431.9	452.1	452.6	455.7	449.9	16.9%
Luxembourg	15.2	13.1	12.0	10.0	10.5	8.3	8.0	9.8	10.9	11.2	11.2	7.0%
Netherlands	130.4	138.0	155.7	147.2	158.5	172.3	174.7	186.7	187.8	182.6	178.7	12.7%
Norway	23.4	24.0	28.6	27.1	28.5	31.8	35.9	39.5	44.6	54.8	34.3	20.4%
Poland	310.3	367.5	438.6	441.2	352.3	340.2	294.8	299.6	297.7	300.6	313.9	-10.9%
Portugal	14.9	18.9	24.6	25.5	38.5	49.5	60.0	59.1	60.9	63.3	57.1	48.2%
Slovak Republic	48.3	55.0	60.9	59.4	54.4	42.3	37.4	39.0	38.4	38.9	38.3	-29.6%
Spain	121.5	162.1	192.0	187.6	212.1	239.2	286.7	313.0	332.1	341.9	335.5	58.2%
Sweden	84.5	80.9	72.0	61.8	51.8	54.7	49.5	54.9	54.4	51.4	50.5	-2.5%
Switzerland	39.7	37.4	39.8	39.5	42.1	39.6	40.1	41.7	42.4	43.5	44.2	5.2%
Turkey	43.7	62.4	73.3	99.7	138.2	157.3	203.5	203.5	209.5	219.7	242.6	75.5%
United Kingdom	644.9	596.3	584.7	560.8	567.7	544.2	548.0	545.5	544.0	544.9	546.8	-3.7%
OECD Europe	3 727.9	3 830.0	4 206.5	4 000.4	3 980.6	3 904.1	3 979.7	4 129.1	4 144.9	4 137.6	4 135.2	**3.9%**
European Union - 27	..	..	..	..	4 126.2	3 919.9	3 884.3	4 050.0	4 047.6	4 019.4	4 022.2	-2.5%

* Total world includes Non-OECD total, OECD total as well as international marine bunkers and international aviation.

CO₂ emissions: Reference Approach

Emissions de CO₂ : Méthode de référence

million tonnes of CO₂

	1971	1975	1980	1985	1990	1995	2000	2003	2004	2005	2006	% change 90-06
Non-OECD Total	4 681.9	5 774.6	7 196.3	8 212.4	9 709.1	9 766.2	10 385.2	11 808.5	12 899.1	13 604.1	14 449.8	**48.8%**
Algeria	10.0	15.6	30.5	48.9	58.4	63.7	71.1	81.1	82.4	84.3	89.7	53.7%
Angola	1.7	2.1	2.8	3.0	4.3	4.1	5.3	7.8	7.7	8.1	8.8	105.3%
Benin	0.3	0.5	0.4	0.5	0.2	0.2	1.5	2.3	2.4	2.5	3.0	+
Botswana	..	..	..	1.6	2.9	3.3	4.2	4.1	4.1	4.3	4.5	55.1%
Cameroon	0.7	1.0	1.7	2.5	2.7	2.6	3.0	3.3	3.5	3.2	3.2	16.9%
Congo	0.6	0.7	0.8	1.0	0.8	0.6	0.6	1.0	1.0	1.4	1.3	59.9%
Dem. Rep. of Congo	2.7	2.9	2.9	3.4	4.1	3.0	2.0	2.1	2.2	2.2	2.3	-45.1%
Côte d'Ivoire	2.4	3.1	3.4	2.5	2.9	3.7	6.6	5.6	6.1	8.6	6.6	130.9%
Egypt	20.6	26.3	39.6	67.1	82.0	87.6	109.8	131.8	135.6	147.9	151.3	84.6%
Eritrea	..	..	..	..	..	0.8	0.6	0.8	0.8	0.8	0.5	..
Ethiopia	1.4	1.2	1.4	1.4	2.4	2.6	3.2	4.6	4.7	4.9	5.4	123.4%
Gabon	1.7	2.1	2.2	1.9	1.1	1.2	1.3	1.5	1.5	1.9	1.8	74.1%
Ghana	1.9	2.5	2.2	2.5	2.8	3.6	5.5	7.0	6.2	7.1	8.5	198.0%
Kenya	3.8	4.3	5.4	5.4	6.5	6.8	9.9	7.4	9.5	10.1	11.2	70.8%
Libya	3.8	9.9	17.2	24.7	28.0	40.6	42.6	44.6	46.4	45.1	45.0	60.8%
Morocco	6.8	9.9	13.9	16.4	20.2	25.2	30.0	32.7	35.5	39.1	40.0	98.5%
Mozambique	3.0	2.4	2.4	1.5	1.0	1.1	1.5	1.7	1.7	1.5	1.6	62.7%
Namibia	..	..	..	..	..	1.8	1.9	2.6	2.7	2.9	3.0	..
Nigeria	5.9	11.8	26.9	33.2	38.2	41.5	42.9	51.4	51.3	60.8	54.4	42.2%
Senegal	1.2	1.6	2.0	1.9	2.2	2.5	3.7	3.9	4.6	4.7	4.7	115.6%
South Africa	148.8	175.6	214.5	288.3	291.1	337.7	351.8	375.3	415.0	405.6	412.4	41.7%
Sudan	4.1	3.9	3.9	4.3	5.6	4.7	6.7	9.9	11.4	11.3	11.2	100.6%
United Rep. of Tanzania	2.1	1.9	2.2	2.0	2.0	3.0	2.3	3.3	3.8	4.5	4.8	134.5%
Togo	0.3	0.3	0.4	0.3	0.6	0.6	1.0	1.1	1.0	1.0	0.9	50.1%
Tunisia	3.7	5.0	8.0	10.1	12.3	14.0	17.4	18.8	19.8	19.2	19.7	59.9%
Zambia	3.4	3.3	3.4	2.9	2.7	2.1	1.7	2.0	2.1	2.2	2.4	-13.7%
Zimbabwe	7.9	7.7	8.0	9.6	15.4	15.3	12.8	10.5	9.8	10.6	10.1	-34.6%
Other Africa	7.3	8.7	11.2	12.0	14.7	17.1	18.9	21.6	22.8	23.4	25.6	74.2%
Africa	**246.3**	**304.5**	**407.5**	**548.9**	**605.2**	**691.0**	**759.4**	**840.0**	**895.7**	**919.2**	**933.8**	**54.3%**
Bahrain	3.1	4.8	6.4	9.8	10.2	11.6	13.8	15.9	16.5	17.9	19.6	91.9%
Islamic Rep. of Iran	45.1	73.9	106.8	150.7	183.3	243.9	304.3	354.0	381.6	393.4	422.9	130.7%
Iraq	12.4	15.0	29.9	45.2	50.8	74.6	72.9	72.3	81.2	83.4	89.0	75.4%
Israel	17.2	21.0	23.1	23.5	35.3	48.6	56.3	62.9	60.7	63.0	63.5	79.7%
Jordan	1.4	2.1	4.3	7.5	9.4	12.4	14.3	14.8	17.2	18.5	18.5	98.1%
Kuwait	13.6	13.5	39.7	38.5	19.7	41.9	54.5	60.7	68.7	76.5	67.2	241.7%
Lebanon	4.6	5.5	6.5	7.6	6.4	12.6	14.2	17.0	15.3	15.8	13.3	108.0%
Oman	0.3	0.7	2.2	7.5	11.0	15.9	23.9	30.9	29.2	34.5	38.0	245.9%
Qatar	2.2	5.0	7.7	12.4	14.0	17.9	26.4	30.7	33.8	35.4	39.9	185.3%
Saudi Arabia	18.4	24.1	87.7	125.4	141.9	215.2	258.3	289.8	304.0	324.4	337.6	137.8%
Syria	8.0	10.3	14.2	24.4	32.4	39.6	46.9	47.6	47.4	49.8	51.2	57.9%
United Arab Emirates	2.4	4.9	18.8	34.4	49.9	67.6	82.1	97.3	100.0	102.7	105.6	111.7%
Yemen	1.9	1.8	3.4	4.8	7.1	9.9	14.0	16.7	18.7	20.0	20.5	187.3%
Middle East	**130.6**	**182.7**	**350.8**	**491.9**	**571.4**	**811.8**	**982.0**	**1 110.7**	**1 174.4**	**1 235.1**	**1 286.8**	**125.2%**
Albania	4.1	4.7	7.9	7.4	6.5	1.9	3.1	3.9	3.8	4.4	4.1	-36.8%
Bosnia and Herzegovina *	..	..	..	..	23.9	3.5	13.7	14.2	15.2	15.8	17.4	-27.5%
Bulgaria	63.8	73.0	84.2	85.1	76.2	57.5	43.4	48.4	46.5	47.7	49.1	-35.6%
Croatia *	..	..	..	..	21.7	16.1	17.9	21.1	20.6	20.8	20.9	-3.9%
Cyprus	1.8	1.7	2.6	2.8	4.1	5.2	6.3	7.0	6.5	6.6	6.9	68.5%
Gibraltar	0.1	0.1	0.1	0.1	0.2	0.3	0.4	0.4	0.4	0.4	0.4	152.3%
FYR of Macedonia *	..	..	..	..	9.6	9.1	8.6	8.5	8.3	8.4	8.3	-13.8%
Malta	0.6	0.6	1.0	1.1	2.3	2.2	2.1	2.5	2.6	2.6	2.5	9.3%
Romania	111.6	138.9	177.8	178.9	171.8	127.2	87.7	97.7	92.9	91.9	98.6	-42.6%
Serbia *	..	..	..	..	61.6	44.4	41.9	51.4	56.4	50.7	54.3	-11.7%
Slovenia *	..	..	..	..	12.8	13.5	14.0	15.3	15.4	15.4	15.6	21.7%
Former Yugoslavia *	65.5	77.1	101.5	127.2	-	-	-	-	-	-	-	-
Non-OECD Europe	**247.4**	**296.1**	**375.1**	**402.7**	**390.7**	**281.0**	**239.1**	**270.5**	**268.6**	**265.0**	**278.1**	**-28.8%**

* Data for individual countries of the Former Yugoslavia are not available prior to 1990.

CO$_2$ emissions: Reference Approach

Emissions de CO$_2$: Méthode de référence

million tonnes of CO$_2$

	1971	1975	1980	1985	1990	1995	2000	2003	2004	2005	2006	% change 90-06
Armenia	..	..	..	..	20.5	3.4	3.4	3.3	3.5	4.1	4.1	-79.8%
Azerbaijan	..	..	..	..	66.5	33.3	29.3	29.1	30.4	32.4	33.4	-49.9%
Belarus	..	..	..	..	117.4	63.2	59.9	62.4	65.0	63.8	68.0	-42.1%
Estonia	..	..	..	..	37.1	17.2	15.3	17.4	17.6	17.0	16.3	-56.1%
Georgia	..	..	..	..	29.2	7.2	4.4	3.6	3.7	4.5	5.2	-82.3%
Kazakhstan	..	..	..	..	237.0	169.3	137.4	158.8	165.9	179.2	194.3	-18.0%
Kyrgyzstan	..	..	..	..	22.7	4.6	4.6	5.2	5.7	5.4	5.2	-77.0%
Latvia	..	..	..	..	18.4	9.0	6.4	7.1	6.9	6.9	7.6	-58.7%
Lithuania	..	..	..	..	33.7	14.5	11.0	12.3	12.9	13.7	13.8	-59.2%
Republic of Moldova	..	..	..	..	30.2	11.4	6.5	7.4	7.6	8.0	7.5	-75.1%
Russia	..	..	..	..	2 302.6	1 573.1	1 510.7	1 544.3	1 540.6	1 545.0	1 595.3	-30.7%
Tajikistan	..	..	..	..	11.9	5.3	4.2	4.9	5.3	5.6	6.2	-48.4%
Turkmenistan	..	..	..	..	52.4	34.7	36.3	43.0	39.4	41.5	43.7	-16.5%
Ukraine	..	..	..	..	699.1	428.8	325.7	355.3	339.7	335.4	325.7	-53.4%
Uzbekistan	..	..	..	..	120.6	103.8	120.9	121.9	118.8	112.9	116.2	-3.6%
Former USSR *	**2 368.9**	**2 842.6**	**3 242.5**	**3 448.3**	**3 799.4**	**2 478.9**	**2 276.0**	**2 375.8**	**2 362.9**	**2 375.3**	**2 442.5**	**-35.7%**
Argentina	86.0	89.8	101.2	92.7	106.8	119.9	136.9	126.6	140.0	140.4	152.5	42.8%
Bolivia	2.3	3.4	4.5	4.6	5.3	8.4	11.2	9.8	12.2	12.1	13.5	154.7%
Brazil	93.7	144.2	189.4	179.5	202.4	250.2	311.6	309.4	324.2	330.2	334.2	65.1%
Chile	21.5	17.5	21.7	19.8	32.0	41.0	57.3	57.1	63.3	63.5	62.8	96.3%
Colombia	27.0	31.9	38.3	42.7	48.9	57.9	57.6	56.2	56.8	60.2	63.0	28.9%
Costa Rica	1.4	1.8	2.2	2.0	2.8	4.2	4.7	5.5	5.2	5.2	6.0	112.6%
Cuba	21.6	28.0	32.1	30.6	31.8	22.3	24.5	23.7	23.0	23.8	27.0	-15.2%
Dominican Republic	3.4	5.6	6.5	7.1	9.3	13.5	18.9	19.9	18.5	18.4	18.9	102.7%
Ecuador	3.4	6.5	10.9	12.3	13.0	16.0	19.1	23.0	24.2	24.8	27.4	110.4%
El Salvador	1.5	2.1	1.8	1.9	2.3	4.8	5.3	6.0	5.7	5.9	6.0	154.8%
Guatemala	2.4	2.7	4.3	3.4	3.7	6.0	9.3	9.8	10.3	11.1	11.1	203.7%
Haiti	0.4	0.4	0.6	0.8	0.9	0.9	1.4	1.6	1.6	1.7	1.7	82.7%
Honduras	1.1	1.3	1.7	1.7	2.2	3.9	4.4	5.8	6.4	6.4	7.1	226.7%
Jamaica	5.2	7.4	6.4	4.5	7.1	8.5	10.1	10.5	10.5	9.8	11.8	66.2%
Netherlands Antilles	13.8	9.8	10.2	5.0	4.1	3.5	3.5	4.2	4.2	4.0	4.5	9.3%
Nicaragua	1.5	1.9	1.9	1.9	1.7	2.6	3.4	4.0	4.1	4.2	4.0	129.7%
Panama	3.8	3.7	2.5	2.8	2.6	4.1	5.4	5.8	5.4	5.7	6.0	135.1%
Paraguay	0.6	0.7	1.4	1.4	1.9	3.5	3.2	3.7	3.7	3.4	3.6	83.4%
Peru	16.1	19.4	21.8	18.4	18.2	22.8	26.0	23.4	26.9	28.3	25.9	42.0%
Trinidad and Tobago	5.0	4.8	8.3	11.0	12.7	13.3	19.6	21.5	24.7	25.1	27.8	118.6%
Uruguay	5.8	5.9	6.0	3.4	4.0	4.7	6.1	4.2	5.5	5.5	6.6	63.5%
Venezuela	43.6	60.3	88.8	99.1	105.0	116.7	125.7	121.2	128.5	135.7	136.6	30.1%
Other Latin America	11.5	15.5	15.1	9.3	12.5	13.4	13.8	16.2	16.2	16.6	18.4	46.8%
Latin America	**372.6**	**464.5**	**577.5**	**556.0**	**631.4**	**741.9**	**879.1**	**869.2**	**921.2**	**941.9**	**976.3**	**54.6%**
Bangladesh	3.4	4.7	7.2	9.3	14.1	21.3	26.7	33.5	35.0	38.2	39.7	181.1%
Brunei Darussalam	0.4	1.7	3.2	4.3	4.1	5.5	6.0	6.3	6.3	6.2	6.6	59.8%
Cambodia	..	..	..	..	..	1.4	2.3	3.2	3.5	3.8	4.1	..
Chinese Taipei	31.2	43.2	75.1	73.6	112.8	161.3	216.8	252.9	267.0	273.9	281.7	149.8%
India	197.8	237.5	292.8	427.9	597.8	797.1	978.1	1 056.9	1 140.1	1 190.2	1 269.7	112.4%
Indonesia	25.5	39.3	73.3	90.0	146.1	215.4	264.4	301.5	326.8	337.9	344.8	136.0%
DPR of Korea	69.4	79.6	108.6	129.8	117.6	75.8	68.9	69.6	71.2	74.4	75.5	-35.8%
Malaysia	13.8	16.9	29.1	37.6	55.4	94.1	121.7	143.4	138.2	165.6	172.3	211.0%
Mongolia	..	..	..	11.6	12.7	10.1	8.8	9.0	9.2	9.6	10.1	-19.8%
Myanmar	4.6	4.1	5.2	6.0	4.1	6.7	8.8	9.4	9.6	10.3	9.8	139.1%
Nepal	0.2	0.3	0.5	0.5	0.9	1.8	3.1	2.9	2.6	3.0	3.1	240.2%
Pakistan	17.1	21.2	27.1	40.4	61.4	82.9	101.0	105.1	117.1	118.9	127.3	107.4%
Philippines	24.2	29.3	33.7	26.7	39.6	58.5	69.3	68.6	72.6	71.6	66.3	67.7%
Singapore	7.0	9.7	14.1	16.2	29.3	50.9	52.0	46.4	50.6	62.3	59.9	104.7%
Sri Lanka	2.9	2.9	3.9	3.7	4.0	5.8	10.7	10.9	12.5	11.8	11.4	187.3%
Thailand	17.3	21.8	34.3	42.0	81.4	143.5	162.9	204.7	222.3	227.9	232.1	185.3%
Vietnam	16.1	16.7	14.4	16.8	17.0	27.5	43.8	60.5	78.7	79.7	81.7	381.8%
Other Asia	8.3	10.1	16.5	10.0	10.4	9.3	11.1	13.7	15.7	15.4	16.5	58.1%
Asia	**439.2**	**539.2**	**739.1**	**946.5**	**1 308.5**	**1 768.8**	**2 156.5**	**2 398.3**	**2 579.1**	**2 700.6**	**2 812.9**	**115.0%**
People's Rep. of China	867.6	1 133.9	1 489.2	1 794.7	2 371.2	2 957.9	3 054.8	3 901.1	4 656.1	5 125.6	5 676.9	139.4%
Hong Kong, China	9.1	11.1	14.5	23.5	31.3	35.0	38.4	42.8	41.0	41.4	42.6	36.2%
China	**876.7**	**1 145.0**	**1 503.7**	**1 818.1**	**2 402.5**	**2 992.9**	**3 093.1**	**3 943.9**	**4 697.1**	**5 167.0**	**5 719.5**	**138.1%**

* Data for individual countries of the Former USSR are not available prior to 1990.

CO$_2$ emissions from international marine bunkers
Emissions de CO$_2$ imputables aux soutes maritimes internationales

million tonnes of CO$_2$

	1971	1975	1980	1985	1990	1995	2000	2003	2004	2005	2006	% change 90-06
World	344.47	328.58	343.95	291.72	357.86	403.55	466.67	465.68	520.98	551.63	582.55	62.8%
Annex I Parties	..	..	..	..	233.61	230.93	252.32	230.14	258.91	273.56	287.39	23.0%
Annex II Parties	202.63	216.81	234.71	171.25	223.46	227.78	249.27	225.54	253.12	267.11	281.20	25.8%
North America	26.41	36.12	93.91	56.43	93.55	93.68	92.24	62.06	78.69	83.63	89.86	-3.9%
Europe	120.20	110.37	97.05	87.88	109.06	112.25	136.38	143.39	153.29	160.02	168.54	54.5%
Pacific	56.02	70.31	43.75	26.94	20.84	21.85	20.65	20.09	21.13	23.46	22.80	9.4%
Annex I EIT	..	..	..	..	9.78	2.58	1.80	2.67	2.69	3.14	3.13	-68.0%
Non-Annex I Parties	..	..	..	..	124.25	172.61	214.36	235.53	262.07	278.07	295.16	137.6%
Annex I Kyoto Parties	..	..	..	..	142.55	139.85	162.16	167.73	179.03	188.50	196.18	37.6%
Non-OECD Total	138.16	108.73	105.71	115.57	125.49	157.66	190.89	213.66	238.28	244.25	261.36	108.3%
OECD Total	206.31	219.85	238.24	176.15	232.36	245.88	275.79	252.02	282.70	307.38	321.20	38.2%
Canada	3.07	2.58	4.71	1.18	2.87	3.17	3.34	1.57	1.91	1.88	1.70	-40.6%
Mexico	0.26	0.38	1.00	1.33	2.03	1.89	4.16	2.51	2.38	2.70	2.71	33.8%
United States	23.34	33.54	89.20	55.26	90.68	90.51	88.90	60.49	76.78	81.76	88.16	-2.8%
OECD N. America	26.67	36.51	94.91	57.76	95.58	95.57	96.39	64.57	81.07	86.34	92.57	-3.1%
Australia	5.10	5.03	3.68	2.28	2.14	2.79	2.96	2.40	2.75	2.81	3.21	50.2%
Japan	49.88	64.20	38.90	23.92	17.66	17.92	16.93	16.84	17.63	19.81	18.64	5.5%
Korea	1.53	0.17	0.31	1.69	5.27	15.20	20.21	21.14	23.29	33.24	33.30	532.0%
New Zealand	1.04	1.08	1.18	0.74	1.04	1.13	0.75	0.85	0.75	0.84	0.95	-8.8%
OECD Pacific	57.55	70.48	44.06	28.63	26.11	37.04	40.86	41.23	44.43	56.71	56.10	114.8%
Austria	-	-	-	-	-	-	-	-	-	-	-	-
Belgium	8.06	8.64	7.52	7.30	12.97	12.36	17.03	21.93	24.65	24.40	26.40	103.6%
Czech Republic	-	-	-	-	-	-	-	-	-	-	-	-
Denmark	2.09	1.67	1.32	1.34	3.02	4.96	4.18	3.06	2.49	2.57	3.34	10.7%
Finland	0.24	0.30	1.84	1.45	1.78	1.04	2.10	2.01	1.62	1.59	1.75	-1.8%
France	12.71	14.53	12.52	7.52	7.96	7.94	9.42	8.37	9.48	8.65	8.97	12.7%
Germany	12.93	10.52	11.00	10.85	7.79	6.43	6.85	8.17	8.36	7.83	8.11	4.1%
Greece	1.78	2.70	2.63	3.51	7.97	11.17	11.28	10.07	10.16	9.02	9.74	22.2%
Hungary	-	-	-		-	-	-	-	-	-	-	-
Iceland	..	..	..	0.02	0.10	0.14	0.21	0.21	0.22	0.20	0.11	12.7%
Ireland	0.24	0.20	0.23	0.09	0.06	0.36	0.47	0.53	0.47	0.32	0.38	590.3%
Italy	22.80	17.97	13.08	10.75	8.37	7.59	8.49	10.08	10.54	10.64	10.95	30.8%
Luxembourg	-	-	-	-	-	-	-	-	-	-	-	-
Netherlands	28.26	32.86	29.39	27.45	34.29	35.59	41.98	42.72	46.39	53.31	55.26	61.1%
Norway	1.90	1.49	0.87	1.03	1.39	2.19	2.56	1.75	1.60	2.16	1.56	12.3%
Poland	1.63	2.21	2.22	1.63	1.24	0.44	0.90	0.89	0.80	1.01	0.93	-25.2%
Portugal	2.32	2.00	1.34	1.48	1.91	1.52	2.08	1.82	2.07	1.82	2.00	4.6%
Slovak Republic	-	-	-	-	-	-	-	-	-	-	-	-
Spain	5.94	3.44	5.07	6.76	11.46	10.00	18.97	22.09	22.78	25.00	26.11	127.9%
Sweden	3.58	3.45	2.66	1.76	2.09	3.30	4.28	5.09	5.99	6.12	6.57	214.1%
Switzerland	..	..	..	..	0.06	0.05	0.03	0.03	0.03	0.04	0.03	-50.0%
Turkey	0.26	0.29	..	0.25	0.37	0.58	1.25	1.93	3.11	3.31	3.06	722.0%
United Kingdom	17.37	10.60	7.57	6.56	7.84	7.62	6.44	5.46	6.45	6.34	7.26	-7.5%
OECD Europe	122.10	112.87	99.26	89.76	110.68	113.27	138.53	146.22	157.20	164.34	172.53	55.9%
European Union - 27	..	..	..	..	111.56	112.70	136.04	144.46	154.30	161.66	170.90	53.2%

CO$_2$ emissions from international marine bunkers
Emissions de CO$_2$ imputables aux soutes maritimes internationales

million tonnes of CO$_2$

	1971	1975	1980	1985	1990	1995	2000	2003	2004	2005	2006	% change 90-06
Non-OECD Total	138.16	108.73	105.71	115.57	125.49	157.66	190.89	213.66	238.28	244.25	261.36	108.3%
Algeria	0.61	0.77	1.29	1.16	1.36	1.17	0.77	0.67	1.03	1.17	0.98	-27.6%
Angola	0.77	0.48	0.83	0.10	0.02	0.03	..	..	..	0.00	0.00	-80.0%
Benin	..	..	..	..	..	..	..	..	..	..	..	..
Botswana	..	..	..	..	..	..	..	..	..	..	..	..
Cameroon	..	..	0.12	0.03	0.04	0.09	0.06	0.06	0.05	0.04	0.13	221.2%
Congo	..	..	..	..	..	..	..	..	..	..	..	..
Dem. Rep. of Congo	0.40	0.22	0.08	0.09	0.10	0.01	0.01	0.01	0.01	0.01	0.01	-94.1%
Côte d'Ivoire	0.06	0.01	1.35	0.73	0.12	0.27	0.29	0.28	0.28	0.23	0.20	67.3%
Egypt	0.06	1.08	3.19	4.71	5.25	7.73	8.58	8.97	5.73	4.51	3.36	-35.9%
Eritrea	..	..	..	..	..	0.42	..	..	..	..	..	..
Ethiopia	0.07	0.01	0.01	0.03	0.04	0.52	..	..	..	..	..	..
Gabon	0.20	0.14	0.19	0.22	0.08	0.44	0.60	0.45	0.46	0.48	0.48	506.9%
Ghana	0.16	0.14	0.10	..	..	..	..	..	..	..	..	..
Kenya	1.47	1.05	0.56	0.45	0.55	0.17	0.26	0.04	0.12	0.13	0.15	-73.4%
Libya	0.01	0.01	0.02	0.04	0.25	0.28	0.28	0.28	0.28	0.28	0.28	12.5%
Morocco	0.24	0.18	0.21	0.04	0.06	0.04	0.04	0.04	0.04	0.04	0.04	-34.9%
Mozambique	0.76	0.35	0.27	0.10	0.09	0.01	0.00	0.14	0.13	0.01	0.01	-89.3%
Namibia	..	..	..	..	..	..	..	..	..	..	..	..
Nigeria	0.02	0.11	0.25	0.34	0.58	1.42	0.86	1.97	1.64	1.95	1.91	228.0%
Senegal	2.99	2.09	0.84	0.33	0.11	0.09	0.30	0.27	0.26	0.36	0.24	115.0%
South Africa	10.81	7.15	5.25	3.41	5.95	10.28	8.51	8.37	7.69	8.52	8.38	40.7%
Sudan	..	0.01	0.02	0.02	0.02	0.03	0.03	0.03	0.03	0.03	0.03	14.3%
United Rep. of Tanzania	0.05	0.05	0.12	0.08	0.08	0.07	0.07	0.07	0.07	0.07	0.07	-11.5%
Togo	..	..	..	..	..	..	0.01	0.02	0.02	0.01	0.01	..
Tunisia	0.06	0.02	0.02	0.01	0.07	0.06	0.03	0.03	0.03	0.03	0.03	-58.3%
Zambia	-	-	-	-	-	-	-	-	-	-	-	-
Zimbabwe	..	..	..	..	..	..	..	..	..	..	..	..
Other Africa	3.02	2.08	1.77	1.82	1.99	2.11	2.77	2.47	2.53	2.71	2.81	41.5%
Africa	21.76	15.95	16.48	13.70	16.77	25.23	23.47	24.17	20.39	20.57	19.12	14.0%
Bahrain	3.27	1.95	1.50	0.64	..	..	..	..	..	..	..	..
Islamic Rep. of Iran	1.29	1.57	1.55	1.15	1.56	2.34	1.98	1.82	1.92	1.73	1.43	-8.7%
Iraq	0.26	0.29	0.37	0.46	0.40	..	..	..	..	..	..	..
Israel	..	..	..	0.35	0.38	0.65	0.58	0.85	0.71	0.87	0.81	114.2%
Jordan	..	..	..	..	..	0.03	0.13	0.04	0.15	0.25	0.13	..
Kuwait	5.60	5.63	5.00	2.12	0.55	1.82	1.50	1.73	1.72	1.64	1.97	256.2%
Lebanon	0.71	0.03	..	..	..	0.04	0.04	0.05	0.05	0.05	0.05	..
Oman	3.85	2.54	0.71	0.35	0.06	0.08	0.19	0.00	..	0.00	..	..
Qatar	..	..	..	..	..	..	..	..	..	..	..	..
Saudi Arabia	40.05	25.86	13.62	28.01	5.74	5.96	6.60	6.87	6.99	7.09	8.27	44.1%
Syria	..	..	..	..	..	..	..	..	..	..	..	..
United Arab Emirates	..	..	5.53	9.69	18.99	33.16	29.30	28.99	33.65	37.44	40.83	115.0%
Yemen	1.13	0.91	2.13	1.24	1.24	0.31	0.30	0.39	0.39	0.39	0.39	-68.2%
Middle East	56.17	38.79	30.42	44.02	28.93	44.39	40.63	40.74	45.58	49.46	53.88	86.3%
Albania	..	..	..	..	..	..	..	..	..	..	..	..
Bosnia and Herzegovina *	..	..	..	..	..	..	..	..	..	..	..	..
Bulgaria	..	..	..	0.71	0.18	0.85	0.20	0.43	0.36	0.34	0.33	83.2%
Croatia *	..	..	..	..	0.15	0.10	0.06	0.07	0.07	0.08	0.06	-57.5%
Cyprus	0.01	0.06	0.05	0.11	0.18	0.21	0.60	0.38	0.17	0.90	0.91	410.6%
Gibraltar	0.55	0.58	0.41	0.88	1.38	2.69	3.22	3.45	3.56	3.63	3.73	171.4%
FYR of Macedonia *	-	-	-	-	-	-	-	-	-	-	-	-
Malta	0.19	0.08	0.09	0.06	0.09	0.14	0.13	0.07	0.07	0.07	0.07	-24.3%
Romania	..	..	..	..	..	..	..	..	..	..	..	..
Serbia *	..	..	..	..	..	..	..	..	..	..	..	..
Slovenia *	..	..	..	..	..	..	..	..	..	0.07	0.09	..
Former Yugoslavia *	..	..	..	..	..	..	..	..	..	..	..	..
Non-OECD Europe	0.75	0.72	0.55	1.75	1.97	3.99	4.20	4.40	4.23	5.09	5.20	163.6%

* Data for individual countries of the Former Yugoslavia are not available prior to 1990.

CO$_2$ emissions from international marine bunkers
Emissions de CO$_2$ imputables aux soutes maritimes internationales

million tonnes of CO$_2$

	1971	1975	1980	1985	1990	1995	2000	2003	2004	2005	2006	% change 90-06
Armenia	..	..	..	..	-	-	-	-	-	-	-	-
Azerbaijan	..	..	..	..	..	..	..	..	..	..	..	..
Belarus	..	..	..	..	-	-	-	-	-	-	-	-
Estonia	..	..	..	..	0.57	0.28	0.33	0.35	0.47	0.38	0.67	17.4%
Georgia	..	..	..	..	..	0.16	..	..	..	..	..	..
Kazakhstan	..	..	..	..	..	..	..	..	..	..	..	..
Kyrgyzstan	..	..	..	..	-	-	-	-	-	-	-	-
Latvia	..	..	..	..	1.48	0.47	0.02	0.59	0.63	0.81	0.62	-58.4%
Lithuania	..	..	..	..	0.30	0.44	0.29	0.34	0.36	0.45	0.44	46.7%
Republic of Moldova	..	..	..	..	..	..	..	..	..	..	..	..
Russia	..	..	..	..	5.87	..	..	..	..	..	..	..
Tajikistan	..	..	..	..	-	..	..	..	..	..	..	..
Turkmenistan	..	..	..	..	..	..	..	..	..	..	..	..
Ukraine	..	..	..	..	..	..	..	..	..	..	..	..
Uzbekistan	..	..	..	..	..	..	-	-	-	-	-	..
Former USSR *	**13.17**	**14.09**	**14.09**	**13.79**	**8.21**	**1.35**	**0.64**	**1.28**	**1.46**	**1.64**	**1.72**	**-79.1%**
Argentina	0.66	0.28	1.32	2.00	2.22	1.77	1.48	1.85	1.62	2.19	2.34	5.3%
Bolivia	-	-	-	-	-	-	-	-	-	-	-	-
Brazil	1.00	1.17	1.42	1.71	1.72	3.64	9.27	10.08	10.08	10.96	10.63	519.6%
Chile	0.60	0.37	0.27	0.09	0.56	1.18	2.10	2.74	2.99	3.87	4.36	673.8%
Colombia	0.95	0.49	0.31	0.22	0.33	0.58	0.72	0.70	0.94	1.05	1.21	267.3%
Costa Rica	..	..	..	..	..	..	..	..	..	..	..	..
Cuba	0.49	0.55	0.56	0.68	0.75	0.26	0.32	0.21	0.22	0.23	0.20	-73.6%
Dominican Republic	..	..	..	..	..	..	..	..	..	..	..	..
Ecuador	0.28	..	0.34	0.11	0.57	1.05	0.87	0.80	0.70	0.69	0.77	34.7%
El Salvador	..	..	..	..	..	..	..	..	..	..	..	..
Guatemala	0.18	0.27	0.40	0.38	0.38	0.38	0.38	0.38	0.38	0.38	0.38	-
Haiti	..	..	..	..	..	..	..	..	..	..	..	..
Honduras	..	..	..	..	..	..	..	..	..	..	..	..
Jamaica	0.16	0.26	0.10	0.04	0.09	0.09	0.09	0.09	0.09	0.09	0.09	-
Netherlands Antilles	7.71	7.34	7.27	6.13	5.18	5.32	5.31	5.31	5.31	5.32	5.34	3.1%
Nicaragua	..	..	..	..	..	..	..	..	..	..	..	..
Panama	..	..	..	..	..	..	..	..	..	..	..	..
Paraguay	-	-	-	-	-	-	-	-	-	-	-	..
Peru	0.04	0.05	0.38	0.53	0.03	0.41	0.13	0.14	0.18	0.71	0.31	800.0%
Trinidad and Tobago	5.12	3.54	1.42	0.31	0.11	0.16	0.87	2.32	2.80	0.82	0.85	680.6%
Uruguay	0.27	0.20	0.24	0.33	0.37	1.21	0.90	0.99	1.06	1.11	0.77	109.7%
Venezuela	9.13	4.82	1.99	1.76	2.50	2.30	2.06	1.69	2.17	2.12	2.19	-12.2%
Other Latin America	3.08	2.04	2.79	1.87	0.86	0.71	0.76	0.97	1.00	1.04	1.07	24.3%
Latin America	**29.66**	**21.38**	**18.83**	**16.16**	**15.68**	**19.04**	**25.27**	**28.26**	**29.55**	**30.60**	**30.52**	**94.7%**
Bangladesh	0.06	0.05	0.19	0.07	0.06	0.11	0.11	0.11	0.11	0.11	0.11	78.6%
Brunei Darussalam	..	..	..	..	..	..	..	..	..	..	..	..
Cambodia	..	..	..	..	..	..	..	..	..	..	..	..
Chinese Taipei	0.39	0.33	0.66	1.62	4.86	7.56	11.00	9.44	7.63	7.71	7.38	52.0%
India	0.71	0.57	0.72	0.34	0.47	0.39	0.27	0.19	0.09	0.08	0.09	-81.5%
Indonesia	0.70	1.09	0.79	0.68	1.68	1.28	0.36	1.53	1.12	1.17	1.12	-33.3%
DPR of Korea	..	..	..	..	..	..	..	..	..	..	..	..
Malaysia	0.11	0.22	0.18	0.31	0.28	0.52	0.67	0.22	0.31	0.26	0.16	-42.2%
Mongolia	..	..	..	..	..	..	..	..	..	..	..	..
Myanmar	0.01	0.00	-	-	-	0.01	0.01	0.01	0.01	0.01	0.01	x
Nepal	-	-	-	-	-	-	-	-	-	-	-	..
Pakistan	0.29	0.21	0.47	0.08	0.11	0.05	0.08	0.05	0.20	0.25	0.32	203.8%
Philippines	1.27	0.44	0.59	0.49	0.37	0.35	0.58	0.67	0.43	0.37	0.40	8.3%
Singapore	8.89	10.43	14.96	15.14	33.87	35.28	57.58	64.22	72.71	78.60	86.35	155.0%
Sri Lanka	1.19	1.29	1.10	1.01	1.21	1.09	0.50	0.36	0.38	0.53	0.43	-64.1%
Thailand	0.21	0.25	0.50	0.65	1.70	3.02	2.46	3.77	4.53	5.18	5.26	208.9%
Vietnam	..	..	..	..	..	..	..	..	..	..	..	..
Other Asia	0.57	0.53	0.46	0.20	0.21	0.25	0.24	0.35	0.41	0.38	0.40	93.6%
Asia	**14.39**	**15.42**	**20.61**	**20.58**	**44.82**	**49.90**	**73.96**	**80.82**	**87.91**	**94.66**	**102.05**	**127.7%**
People's Rep. of China	0.30	0.69	1.87	2.47	4.59	6.62	12.13	17.19	25.17	24.47	26.10	468.5%
Hong Kong, China	1.96	1.69	2.86	3.10	4.52	7.15	10.58	16.80	23.98	17.76	22.76	404.0%
China	**2.26**	**2.37**	**4.72**	**5.57**	**9.11**	**13.77**	**22.71**	**33.99**	**49.15**	**42.23**	**48.86**	**436.5%**

* Data for individual countries of the Former USSR are not available prior to 1990.

CO$_2$ emissions from international aviation

Emissions de CO$_2$ imputables à l'aviation internationale

million tonnes of CO$_2$

	1971	1975	1980	1985	1990	1995	2000	2003	2004	2005	2006	% change 90-06
World	167.91	171.35	199.63	223.63	255.41	284.43	341.06	342.18	365.48	388.82	397.10	55.5%
Annex I Parties	..	..	..	..	*163.45*	*174.68*	*218.83*	*211.69*	*221.78*	*232.06*	*230.43*	*41.0%*
Annex II Parties	*58.57*	*61.75*	*70.77*	*81.47*	*126.28*	*155.41*	*200.17*	*190.14*	*199.87*	*208.15*	*205.65*	*62.8%*
North America	*16.61*	*17.53*	*21.18*	*21.83*	*41.50*	*48.54*	*60.20*	*51.65*	*53.10*	*54.63*	*50.42*	*21.5%*
Europe	*35.96*	*37.67*	*42.70*	*48.59*	*65.82*	*82.93*	*111.48*	*108.82*	*116.05*	*121.41*	*125.70*	*91.0%*
Pacific	*6.01*	*6.55*	*6.90*	*11.05*	*18.96*	*23.94*	*28.49*	*29.67*	*30.72*	*32.12*	*29.52*	*55.7%*
Annex I EIT	..	..	..	..	*36.64*	*18.50*	*17.12*	*18.88*	*19.03*	*20.69*	*21.87*	*-40.3%*
Non-Annex I Parties	..	..	..	..	*91.96*	*109.75*	*122.23*	*130.49*	*143.70*	*156.75*	*166.67*	*81.2%*
Annex I Kyoto Parties	..	..	..	..	*124.12*	*127.95*	*160.17*	*159.51*	*168.52*	*176.77*	*179.62*	*44.7%*
Non-OECD Total	**106.49**	**105.40**	**121.80**	**134.01**	**120.46**	**117.06**	**127.51**	**135.69**	**148.72**	**159.50**	**168.08**	**39.5%**
OECD Total	**61.42**	**65.95**	**77.83**	**89.62**	**134.95**	**167.37**	**213.56**	**206.49**	**216.76**	**229.31**	**229.02**	**69.7%**
Canada	1.25	1.93	1.35	1.22	2.71	2.58	3.08	2.14	2.71	2.55	2.53	-6.7%
Mexico	1.39	2.40	4.23	4.53	5.48	7.10	8.07	7.93	7.62	7.89	8.45	54.3%
United States	15.35	15.60	19.83	20.61	38.79	45.96	57.11	49.51	50.39	52.07	47.90	23.5%
OECD N. America	**17.99**	**19.92**	**25.41**	**26.36**	**46.98**	**55.64**	**68.27**	**59.58**	**60.72**	**62.52**	**58.87**	**25.3%**
Australia	1.57	1.89	2.40	2.76	4.29	5.75	7.15	6.86	6.92	8.10	7.29	69.7%
Japan	3.80	4.32	3.92	7.63	13.31	16.61	19.57	20.52	21.22	21.37	19.84	49.0%
Korea	..	0.36	0.83	1.69	0.84	2.05	1.70	3.59	3.92	7.25	8.83	949.4%
New Zealand	0.64	0.34	0.57	0.66	1.35	1.58	1.77	2.30	2.58	2.65	2.40	77.6%
OECD Pacific	**6.01**	**6.91**	**7.72**	**12.74**	**19.80**	**25.99**	**30.19**	**33.26**	**34.65**	**39.36**	**38.35**	**93.7%**
Austria	0.28	0.24	0.38	0.65	0.82	1.29	1.63	1.26	1.48	1.67	1.75	113.8%
Belgium	1.21	1.05	1.22	1.62	2.82	2.61	4.37	4.36	4.01	3.80	3.49	23.9%
Czech Republic	0.69	0.58	0.85	0.63	0.65	0.56	0.48	0.60	0.86	0.94	0.99	52.1%
Denmark	1.92	1.56	1.59	1.56	1.70	1.84	2.32	2.12	2.42	2.55	2.56	50.4%
Finland	0.18	0.40	0.46	0.48	0.97	0.86	1.02	1.07	1.23	1.24	1.38	41.6%
France	4.57	5.71	5.62	6.43	9.32	11.44	15.22	14.98	16.01	16.20	16.86	80.8%
Germany	7.57	8.16	8.22	9.46	12.58	14.13	17.39	16.92	18.29	19.69	20.69	64.5%
Greece	1.29	1.31	2.23	2.33	2.34	2.52	2.41	2.32	2.39	2.30	2.76	18.1%
Hungary	0.15	0.20	0.36	0.44	0.49	0.54	0.69	0.60	0.69	0.79	0.80	65.0%
Iceland	0.22	0.13	0.09	0.18	0.22	0.20	0.39	0.30	0.35	0.40	0.53	143.7%
Ireland	0.96	0.73	0.60	0.57	1.03	1.11	1.73	2.15	2.04	2.35	2.40	132.7%
Italy	3.47	2.44	4.15	4.33	4.07	5.55	7.75	7.97	7.98	8.45	9.00	121.2%
Luxembourg	0.11	0.15	0.19	0.22	0.39	0.56	0.95	1.16	1.26	1.28	1.20	207.8%
Netherlands	2.01	2.26	2.72	3.47	4.29	7.38	9.65	9.70	10.38	10.67	10.81	151.8%
Norway	0.70	0.51	0.67	0.92	1.24	1.09	1.05	0.62	0.72	0.80	1.11	-10.5%
Poland	0.52	0.53	0.67	0.67	0.68	0.82	0.82	0.86	0.84	0.96	1.27	87.5%
Portugal	0.70	0.80	0.88	1.27	1.49	1.49	1.69	1.87	2.05	2.13	2.28	53.0%
Slovak Republic	..	..	..	..	..	0.12	0.08	0.10	0.08	0.12	0.12	..
Spain	1.74	2.77	2.58	2.67	3.32	6.01	8.03	8.25	9.15	9.18	9.57	188.3%
Sweden	0.33	0.33	0.49	0.51	1.07	1.76	2.06	1.51	1.85	1.87	1.96	82.2%
Switzerland	1.63	1.80	2.02	2.41	3.00	3.63	4.57	3.57	3.41	3.48	3.68	22.6%
Turkey	0.09	0.14	0.12	0.18	0.53	0.78	1.54	2.67	2.87	3.21	2.91	446.3%
United Kingdom	7.08	7.32	8.59	9.53	15.14	19.45	29.24	28.67	31.02	33.36	33.66	122.4%
OECD Europe	**37.41**	**39.12**	**44.70**	**50.51**	**68.17**	**85.74**	**115.09**	**113.65**	**121.39**	**127.43**	**131.79**	**93.3%**
European Union - 27	..	..	..	..	*66.31*	*82.89*	*109.51*	*108.87*	*116.48*	*122.07*	*126.15*	*90.3%*

CO$_2$ emissions from international aviation

Emissions de CO$_2$ imputables à l'aviation internationale

million tonnes of CO$_2$

	1971	1975	1980	1985	1990	1995	2000	2003	2004	2005	2006	% change 90-06
Non-OECD Total	106.49	105.40	121.80	134.01	120.46	117.06	127.51	135.69	148.72	159.50	168.08	39.5%
Algeria	0.29	0.66	0.93	1.31	1.09	0.96	1.17	1.20	1.13	1.16	1.14	4.3%
Angola	0.23	0.31	0.25	0.99	1.03	1.17	1.42	0.92	1.05	0.87	1.04	1.2%
Benin	0.02	0.01	0.03	0.06	0.05	0.07	0.07	0.08	0.08	0.07	0.08	50.0%
Botswana	..	..	..	0.01	0.03	0.02	0.02	0.02	0.03	0.03	0.03	-9.1%
Cameroon	0.17	0.10	0.15	0.15	0.15	0.17	0.18	0.23	0.20	0.20	0.22	45.0%
Congo	..	..	..	..	..	..	..	..	..	..	..	..
Dem. Rep. of Congo	0.28	0.24	0.37	0.40	0.32	0.35	0.36	0.36	0.37	0.36	0.36	13.6%
Côte d'Ivoire	0.13	0.21	0.27	0.29	0.27	0.26	0.37	0.28	0.28	0.28	0.28	4.7%
Egypt	0.21	0.27	0.51	0.12	0.44	0.79	1.71	1.82	2.18	2.23	2.45	454.3%
Eritrea	..	..	..	..	..	0.02	0.03	0.03	0.03	0.03	0.02	..
Ethiopia	0.14	0.16	0.20	0.34	0.53	0.20	0.24	0.27	0.37	0.46	0.56	5.4%
Gabon	0.03	0.04	0.07	0.08	0.20	0.19	0.24	0.25	0.21	0.21	0.20	1.4%
Ghana	0.13	0.15	0.12	0.10	0.14	0.18	0.32	0.42	0.35	0.39	0.50	257.4%
Kenya	..	..	..	..	..	..	..	..	..	..	..	..
Libya	0.27	0.53	0.89	1.05	0.63	0.91	1.33	0.65	0.66	0.58	0.55	-13.5%
Morocco	0.35	0.44	0.78	0.70	0.79	0.73	0.90	0.92	1.01	1.16	1.32	67.5%
Mozambique	0.12	0.05	0.08	0.09	0.13	0.06	0.13	0.12	0.13	0.14	0.17	31.7%
Namibia	..	..	..	..	..	..	..	..	..	..	..	..
Nigeria	0.24	0.70	1.14	1.33	0.95	1.36	1.74	1.21	0.60	0.71	0.71	-25.2%
Senegal	0.30	0.37	0.58	0.43	0.45	0.45	0.75	0.66	0.74	0.74	0.80	75.9%
South Africa	0.51	0.71	0.87	0.99	1.15	1.72	2.73	2.47	2.17	2.13	2.21	91.5%
Sudan	0.34	0.14	0.20	0.21	0.09	0.10	0.34	0.47	0.54	0.62	0.69	631.3%
United Rep. of Tanzania	0.08	0.20	0.17	0.13	0.22	0.19	0.18	0.23	0.24	0.26	0.28	26.0%
Togo	..	..	..	..	0.10	0.12	0.03	0.08	0.12	0.15	0.11	3.0%
Tunisia	0.39	0.38	0.56	0.30	0.57	0.74	0.85	0.61	0.70	0.65	0.65	14.4%
Zambia	0.04	0.14	0.23	0.12	0.19	0.10	0.13	0.14	0.15	0.16	0.17	-14.3%
Zimbabwe	0.08	0.19	0.21	0.33	0.25	0.35	0.36	0.11	0.03	0.03	0.03	-89.9%
Other Africa	..	..	0.90	0.89	0.81	0.89	1.20	1.24	1.25	1.31	1.35	67.7%
Africa	**4.33**	**6.00**	**9.51**	**10.43**	**10.60**	**12.08**	**16.78**	**14.80**	**14.62**	**14.94**	**15.90**	**50.1%**
Bahrain	0.43	0.84	1.53	1.21	1.43	1.15	1.12	1.46	1.62	1.72	1.76	23.4%
Islamic Rep. of Iran	7.02	7.01	2.15	1.64	1.48	1.97	2.70	2.43	2.47	2.69	3.14	111.7%
Iraq	0.24	0.81	1.05	1.12	2.89	1.34	1.49	1.24	1.77	2.37	2.48	-14.1%
Israel	1.79	1.88	2.21	1.99	1.56	2.10	2.35	1.98	1.84	1.75	1.91	21.9%
Jordan	0.14	0.22	0.62	0.68	0.71	0.77	0.76	0.84	0.63	0.98	0.94	32.9%
Kuwait	0.34	0.34	1.04	0.97	0.51	1.12	1.15	2.26	1.69	1.82	1.75	242.0%
Lebanon	0.83	0.76	0.58	0.38	0.19	0.66	0.40	0.40	0.40	0.46	0.33	71.7%
Oman	0.01	0.15	0.38	0.57	0.93	0.46	0.65	1.13	1.17	1.23	1.25	34.1%
Qatar	..	0.16	0.23	0.24	0.34	0.43	0.57	1.88	1.75	1.46	1.82	430.3%
Saudi Arabia	0.47	1.40	3.45	4.57	6.14	5.71	5.70	5.43	5.19	5.22	5.43	-11.7%
Syria	0.24	0.65	0.72	0.87	0.87	0.62	0.41	0.31	0.37	0.33	0.32	-62.9%
United Arab Emirates	0.02	0.34	0.80	1.80	9.79	10.08	9.87	10.46	10.02	11.04	11.33	15.7%
Yemen	0.09	0.18	0.21	0.46	0.17	0.28	0.38	0.29	0.33	0.36	0.35	103.7%
Middle East	**11.63**	**14.75**	**14.98**	**16.50**	**27.03**	**26.70**	**27.53**	**30.10**	**29.24**	**31.44**	**32.82**	**21.4%**
Albania	..	..	..	..	..	..	0.12	0.14	0.17	0.21	0.25	..
Bosnia and Herzegovina *	..	..	..	..	0.08	..	..	..	..	..	..	..
Bulgaria	0.61	0.61	0.91	1.11	0.71	0.98	0.24	0.47	0.45	0.56	0.53	-24.6%
Croatia *	..	..	..	..	0.15	0.17	0.10	0.07	0.09	0.12	0.12	-18.8%
Cyprus	0.15	0.02	0.23	0.44	0.72	0.79	0.82	0.98	0.90	0.89	0.91	27.1%
Gibraltar	0.02	0.02	0.01	0.01	0.02	0.01	0.01	0.01	0.01	0.01	0.01	-42.9%
FYR of Macedonia *	..	..	..	..	0.02	0.09	0.09	0.02	0.02	0.02	0.02	-
Malta	0.17	0.18	0.23	0.14	0.21	0.22	0.26	0.23	0.30	0.27	0.23	7.1%
Romania	0.06	0.05	..	..	0.69	0.54	0.37	0.35	0.40	0.33	0.40	-41.4%
Serbia *	..	..	..	..	0.43	0.11	0.09	0.19	0.14	0.15	0.16	-62.9%
Slovenia *	..	..	..	..	0.08	0.06	0.07	0.08	0.06	0.07	0.07	-7.7%
Former Yugoslavia *	0.64	0.88	1.00	0.99	..	..	..	..	..	..	..	..
Non-OECD Europe	**1.65**	**1.76**	**2.39**	**2.70**	**3.09**	**2.98**	**2.16**	**2.55**	**2.54**	**2.61**	**2.71**	**-12.4%**

* Data for individual countries of the Former Yugoslavia are not available prior to 1990.

CO$_2$ emissions from international aviation

Emissions de CO$_2$ imputables à l'aviation internationale

million tonnes of CO$_2$

	1971	1975	1980	1985	1990	1995	2000	2003	2004	2005	2006	% change 90-06
Armenia	..	..	..	..	0.59	0.10	0.19	0.08	0.12	0.13	0.12	-79.9%
Azerbaijan	..	..	..	..	0.71	1.27	0.36	1.00	1.01	1.45	1.48	108.2%
Belarus	..	..	..	..	..	..	..	..	..	..	..	..
Estonia	..	..	..	..	0.11	0.05	0.06	0.05	0.08	0.12	0.09	-20.0%
Georgia	..	..	..	..	0.60	0.01	0.05	0.08	0.11	0.11	0.11	-81.2%
Kazakhstan	..	..	..	..	2.68	0.78	0.34	0.52	0.65	0.70	0.75	-71.8%
Kyrgyzstan	..	..	..	..	..	..	..	..	..	..	..	..
Latvia	..	..	..	..	0.22	0.08	0.08	0.12	0.14	0.17	0.19	-9.9%
Lithuania	..	..	..	..	0.40	0.12	0.08	0.09	0.10	0.14	0.16	-61.1%
Republic of Moldova	..	..	..	..	0.22	0.03	0.06	0.04	0.03	0.04	0.04	-83.3%
Russia	..	..	..	..	26.36	13.98	13.26	14.38	14.13	15.27	16.13	-38.8%
Tajikistan	..	..	..	..	..	0.02	0.01	0.01	0.01	0.01	0.01	..
Turkmenistan	..	..	..	..	..	..	..	..	..	..	..	..
Ukraine	..	..	..	..	6.11	0.47	0.78	1.10	1.11	1.11	0.99	-83.8%
Uzbekistan	..	..	..	..	..	..	..	..	..	..	..	..
Former USSR *	**66.66**	**62.09**	**70.62**	**76.70**	**37.99**	**16.92**	**15.26**	**17.47**	**17.50**	**19.26**	**20.07**	**-47.2%**
Argentina	..	..	..	..	..	..	..	..	..	..	..	..
Bolivia	..	..	..	..	..	..	..	..	..	..	..	..
Brazil	..	..	0.61	0.74	1.41	2.06	2.03	3.35	3.35	3.35	3.87	173.9%
Chile	0.43	0.35	0.54	0.49	0.89	1.27	1.73	1.66	1.84	1.96	2.09	134.0%
Colombia	0.77	1.03	1.42	1.39	1.56	2.15	1.89	1.78	1.78	1.83	1.75	12.0%
Costa Rica	0.02	0.03	0.07	0.04	0.13	0.32	0.37	0.30	0.29	0.59	0.58	340.3%
Cuba	0.28	0.45	0.49	0.67	1.02	0.56	0.65	0.46	0.56	0.54	0.57	-43.6%
Dominican Republic	0.08	0.10	0.17	0.16	0.11	0.17	0.22	0.28	0.31	0.31	0.30	166.7%
Ecuador	0.27	0.14	0.45	0.45	0.39	0.55	0.66	0.46	0.85	0.96	1.00	158.5%
El Salvador	0.03	0.05	0.05	0.10	0.11	0.15	0.22	0.21	0.23	0.24	0.23	114.7%
Guatemala	0.15	0.11	0.13	0.12	0.13	0.14	0.15	0.13	0.14	0.12	0.12	-9.5%
Haiti	0.02	0.03	0.05	0.04	0.07	0.07	0.09	0.06	0.07	0.07	0.08	4.3%
Honduras	0.02	0.03	0.06	0.12	0.09	0.07	0.11	0.08	0.09	0.07	0.09	-
Jamaica	0.42	0.33	0.30	0.39	0.43	0.49	0.50	0.60	0.51	0.56	0.72	68.4%
Netherlands Antilles	..	..	..	..	..	..	..	..	..	..	..	..
Nicaragua	0.05	0.06	0.06	0.04	0.08	0.06	0.08	0.07	0.06	0.05	0.05	-34.6%
Panama	0.03	0.02	0.01	0.01	0.01	0.01	0.01	0.01	0.01	0.01	0.01	-
Paraguay	0.03	0.04	0.06	0.06	0.03	0.03	0.04	0.07	0.05	0.05	0.07	125.2%
Peru	0.51	0.74	0.92	0.71	0.64	1.10	1.06	0.43	1.35	0.96	1.43	121.6%
Trinidad and Tobago	0.21	0.12	0.17	0.22	0.20	0.17	0.18	0.03	0.03	0.18	0.22	14.5%
Uruguay	..	..	..	..	..	..	..	..	..	..	..	..
Venezuela	0.29	0.37	0.73	0.81	1.02	1.00	0.94	0.76	1.92	2.31	2.13	108.1%
Other Latin America	1.19	0.63	0.90	0.86	1.01	1.07	1.70	1.13	1.15	1.18	1.21	20.3%
Latin America	**4.81**	**4.63**	**7.17**	**7.43**	**9.33**	**11.43**	**12.61**	**11.87**	**14.58**	**15.33**	**16.53**	**77.1%**
Bangladesh	0.06	0.08	0.15	0.22	0.27	0.30	0.38	0.72	0.74	0.85	0.84	209.3%
Brunei Darussalam	0.00	0.06	0.07	0.05	0.11	0.21	0.21	0.24	0.24	0.25	0.23	105.6%
Cambodia	..	..	..	..	..	0.03	0.06	0.07	0.06	0.06	0.08	..
Chinese Taipei	1.48	1.62	1.66	1.64	2.85	5.38	6.77	6.50	7.33	7.62	7.76	172.7%
India	2.39	2.83	3.55	4.59	5.29	6.57	7.10	7.84	8.87	10.40	12.55	137.0%
Indonesia	0.16	0.32	0.73	0.65	0.96	1.78	1.52	2.48	2.43	2.23	2.19	127.9%
DPR of Korea	..	..	..	..	..	..	..	..	..	..	..	..
Malaysia	0.42	0.74	0.80	0.89	1.94	3.44	4.67	5.50	6.10	5.96	5.96	207.4%
Mongolia	..	..	..	..	0.01	0.06	0.06	0.08	0.07	0.06	0.13	925.0%
Myanmar	0.09	0.08	0.13	0.13	0.09	0.14	0.20	0.21	0.20	0.15	0.24	167.9%
Nepal	0.01	0.02	0.04	0.06	0.05	0.11	0.17	0.13	0.17	0.19	0.19	293.3%
Pakistan	1.13	1.08	1.69	1.41	1.39	1.70	2.28	2.39	2.70	2.84	2.72	94.9%
Philippines	0.75	0.88	0.69	1.08	1.58	1.31	1.60	1.80	2.15	2.39	2.53	59.8%
Singapore	0.70	1.32	2.71	3.19	5.63	7.81	8.60	7.40	9.12	9.74	10.54	87.2%
Sri Lanka	..	0.00	0.00	..	..	..	..	0.35	0.40	0.40	0.37	..
Thailand	1.26	2.17	2.39	3.12	5.59	7.51	8.27	8.91	10.05	10.17	10.70	91.4%
Vietnam	6.88	2.60	..	..	..	0.12	0.30	0.47	0.79	0.79	0.73	..
Other Asia	0.66	0.52	0.30	0.47	0.51	0.26	0.56	1.08	0.90	0.92	0.98	90.0%
Asia	**16.00**	**14.33**	**14.90**	**17.49**	**26.29**	**36.76**	**42.72**	**46.16**	**52.32**	**55.03**	**58.74**	**123.4%**
People's Rep. of China	..	..	..	0.22	0.50	0.99	2.13	2.86	4.55	6.19	7.29	+
Hong Kong, China	1.41	1.83	2.24	2.55	5.62	9.22	8.31	9.87	13.38	14.71	14.02	149.4%
China	**1.41**	**1.83**	**2.24**	**2.77**	**6.12**	**10.20**	**10.43**	**12.73**	**17.93**	**20.90**	**21.31**	**248.3%**

* Data for individual countries of the Former USSR are not available prior to 1990.

Total primary energy supply
Approvisionnements totaux en énergie primaire

petajoules

	1971	1975	1980	1985	1990	1995	2000	2003	2004	2005	2006	% change 90-06
World *	**231 638**	**259 287**	**302 443**	**324 406**	**366 714**	**386 463**	**420 154**	**445 687**	**466 559**	**479 703**	**491 529**	**34.0%**
Annex I Parties	*..*	*..*	*..*	*..*	*235 303*	*231 558*	*244 672*	*248 614*	*252 732*	*254 732*	*254 592*	*8.2%*
Annex II Parties	*131 186*	*139 295*	*154 296*	*155 204*	*169 722*	*182 783*	*198 303*	*199 878*	*203 757*	*204 934*	*203 455*	*19.9%*
North America	*72 617*	*76 426*	*83 921*	*82 666*	*89 420*	*97 071*	*106 958*	*106 482*	*108 728*	*109 507*	*108 457*	*21.3%*
Europe	*44 833*	*47 111*	*52 563*	*53 702*	*57 469*	*60 127*	*63 911*	*66 420*	*67 334*	*67 524*	*67 049*	*16.7%*
Pacific	*13 736*	*15 759*	*17 812*	*18 836*	*22 833*	*25 585*	*27 435*	*26 976*	*27 695*	*27 902*	*27 950*	*22.4%*
Annex I EIT	*..*	*..*	*..*	*..*	*63 365*	*46 187*	*43 150*	*45 440*	*45 549*	*46 220*	*47 201*	*-25.5%*
Non-Annex I Parties	*..*	*..*	*..*	*..*	*126 689*	*149 585*	*169 333*	*190 940*	*206 969*	*217 715*	*229 276*	*81.0%*
Annex I Kyoto Parties	*..*	*..*	*..*	*..*	*150 666*	*140 561*	*144 017*	*148 725*	*150 712*	*151 980*	*152 296*	*1.1%*
Intl. marine bunkers	**4 521**	**4 313**	**4 517**	**3 840**	**4 721**	**5 319**	**6 149**	**6 133**	**6 858**	**7 256**	**7 660**	**62.2%**
International aviation	**2 374**	**2 421**	**2 821**	**3 160**	**3 609**	**4 019**	**4 819**	**4 834**	**5 164**	**5 493**	**5 610**	**55.5%**
Non-OECD Total	**85 662**	**103 194**	**127 381**	**147 484**	**172 674**	**176 386**	**191 040**	**213 455**	**229 081**	**239 912**	**252 028**	**46.0%**
OECD Total	**141 455**	**151 780**	**170 545**	**173 081**	**189 318**	**204 758**	**222 965**	**226 099**	**230 619**	**232 535**	**231 841**	**22.5%**
Canada	5 936	6 975	8 083	8 097	8 772	9 700	10 555	10 978	11 261	11 457	11 294	28.8%
Mexico	1 819	2 511	4 042	4 611	5 150	5 499	6 287	6 689	6 918	7 395	7 429	44.2%
United States	66 681	69 451	75 838	74 569	80 649	87 371	96 403	95 504	97 467	98 050	97 163	20.5%
OECD N. America	**74 436**	**78 936**	**87 963**	**87 277**	**94 571**	**102 570**	**113 245**	**113 171**	**115 646**	**116 903**	**115 885**	**22.5%**
Australia	2 183	2 555	2 948	3 094	3 671	3 956	4 629	4 723	4 733	5 055	5 128	39.7%
Japan	11 255	12 833	14 480	15 264	18 586	20 966	22 049	21 528	22 225	22 122	22 088	18.8%
Korea	711	1 029	1 737	2 265	3 909	6 170	7 931	8 658	8 888	8 899	9 064	131.9%
New Zealand	298	371	384	478	576	662	758	724	737	724	734	27.5%
OECD Pacific	**14 447**	**16 788**	**19 549**	**21 101**	**26 742**	**31 755**	**35 366**	**35 634**	**36 583**	**36 801**	**37 015**	**38.4%**
Austria	792	846	975	976	1 049	1 136	1 216	1 373	1 381	1 425	1 433	36.6%
Belgium	1 678	1 787	1 975	1 869	2 082	2 340	2 591	2 611	2 603	2 584	2 554	22.7%
Czech Republic	1 910	1 837	1 977	2 069	2 051	1 720	1 692	1 867	1 917	1 893	1 928	-6.0%
Denmark	802	754	824	830	750	839	811	870	846	825	876	16.8%
Finland	763	830	1 036	1 088	1 202	1 223	1 359	1 549	1 559	1 439	1 567	30.4%
France	6 704	6 987	8 108	8 624	9 529	10 099	10 811	11 364	11 532	11 564	11 416	19.8%
Germany	12 879	13 241	15 070	15 089	14 890	14 311	14 367	14 545	14 627	14 456	14 593	-2.0%
Greece	382	510	659	768	931	985	1 168	1 253	1 277	1 299	1 303	40.0%
Hungary	799	962	1 192	1 253	1 196	1 075	1 047	1 103	1 105	1 165	1 155	-3.4%
Iceland	41	48	64	77	90	97	135	141	146	151	181	100.1%
Ireland	295	289	353	369	432	450	594	623	629	635	647	49.8%
Italy	4 462	4 923	5 537	5 475	6 200	6 744	7 255	7 586	7 675	7 776	7 711	24.4%
Luxembourg	172	160	152	131	148	140	152	176	193	197	197	33.0%
Netherlands	2 158	2 503	2 733	2 588	2 810	3 058	3 199	3 409	3 461	3 449	3 354	19.4%
Norway	567	618	776	849	897	996	1 076	1 137	1 219	1 384	1 092	21.8%
Poland	3 613	4 322	5 151	5 163	4 181	4 176	3 743	3 827	3 840	3 881	4 091	-2.2%
Portugal	273	333	431	477	722	867	1 057	1 079	1 111	1 137	1 065	47.5%
Slovak Republic	597	702	831	868	892	746	744	782	770	790	782	-12.4%
Spain	1 808	2 447	2 871	3 007	3 819	4 306	5 219	5 694	5 952	6 068	6 052	58.5%
Sweden	1 514	1 639	1 702	1 985	1 991	2 132	2 020	2 141	2 228	2 185	2 148	7.9%
Switzerland	709	745	867	959	1 038	1 040	1 088	1 119	1 130	1 130	1 181	13.7%
Turkey	820	1 122	1 318	1 649	2 216	2 588	3 218	3 296	3 426	3 578	3 936	77.6%
United Kingdom	8 837	8 450	8 429	8 541	8 888	9 364	9 791	9 749	9 764	9 819	9 677	8.9%
OECD Europe	**52 572**	**56 056**	**63 032**	**64 703**	**68 005**	**70 433**	**74 355**	**77 295**	**78 390**	**78 831**	**78 941**	**16.1%**
European Union - 27	*..*	*..*	*..*	*..*	*69 329*	*69 767*	*72 191*	*75 269*	*76 103*	*76 245*	*76 304*	*10.1%*

* Total world includes Non-OECD total, OECD total as well as international marine bunkers. In TPES, international aviation is included in country totals.

Total primary energy supply

Approvisionnements totaux en énergie primaire

petajoules

	1971	1975	1980	1985	1990	1995	2000	2003	2004	2005	2006	% change 90-06
Non-OECD Total	85 662	103 194	127 381	147 484	172 674	176 386	191 040	213 455	229 081	239 912	252 028	46.0%
Algeria	154	250	510	805	1 001	1 091	1 227	1 397	1 404	1 452	1 537	53.4%
Angola	164	177	196	225	263	287	333	384	395	408	430	63.3%
Benin	46	52	57	65	70	78	84	101	105	108	118	67.7%
Botswana	..	..	..	37	53	63	77	78	76	79	82	53.9%
Cameroon	115	128	155	189	211	233	266	285	292	292	297	40.8%
Congo	21	24	27	33	33	33	36	43	45	51	50	51.2%
Dem. Rep. of Congo	284	316	360	422	499	553	618	670	690	711	733	47.1%
Côte d'Ivoire	105	127	153	159	185	217	287	279	290	329	305	65.1%
Egypt	328	414	642	1 078	1 339	1 489	1 916	2 316	2 371	2 565	2 617	95.5%
Eritrea	..	..	..	..	..	42	30	36	31	32	29	..
Ethiopia	362	397	456	523	630	690	784	859	882	906	934	48.3%
Gabon	45	55	59	58	52	59	65	70	71	75	76	46.6%
Ghana	127	155	170	184	223	273	330	357	354	372	398	78.0%
Kenya	235	272	331	384	470	535	630	651	700	721	751	60.0%
Libya	70	161	301	433	483	674	713	734	772	743	744	53.9%
Morocco	107	150	215	244	302	370	441	474	513	564	585	93.9%
Mozambique	290	280	283	268	250	264	302	339	353	358	369	47.6%
Namibia	..	..	..	..	..	38	43	52	56	59	62	..
Nigeria	1 514	1 757	2 212	2 591	2 969	3 367	3 738	4 096	4 177	4 398	4 399	48.2%
Senegal	56	63	74	71	77	84	111	116	125	127	126	63.9%
South Africa	1 898	2 261	2 739	3 632	3 820	4 416	4 659	4 945	5 413	5 344	5 435	42.3%
Sudan	299	315	353	399	446	503	564	670	708	725	742	66.1%
United Rep. of Tanzania	318	324	338	369	411	464	563	687	741	804	871	112.1%
Togo	30	33	37	41	54	67	89	98	99	101	101	85.2%
Tunisia	75	96	145	179	215	254	318	345	364	354	366	70.1%
Zambia	147	165	191	208	229	245	263	284	291	298	306	33.7%
Zimbabwe	229	250	275	315	393	417	419	400	389	407	401	2.1%
Other Africa	1 102	1 201	1 386	1 547	1 764	1 982	2 340	2 673	2 752	2 788	2 854	61.8%
Africa	**8 123**	**9 425**	**11 665**	**14 459**	**16 441**	**18 788**	**21 244**	**23 440**	**24 461**	**25 171**	**25 718**	**56.4%**
Bahrain	65	101	139	191	202	223	261	303	315	341	367	81.6%
Islamic Rep. of Iran	799	1 228	1 638	2 291	2 882	3 964	4 974	5 840	6 324	6 618	7 155	148.3%
Iraq	189	249	456	677	798	1 106	1 089	1 059	1 212	1 253	1 341	68.0%
Israel	265	320	359	345	507	685	805	866	860	888	891	75.7%
Jordan	22	34	72	118	146	191	217	228	269	293	300	104.8%
Kuwait	249	246	636	611	335	688	855	960	1 063	1 179	1 059	216.3%
Lebanon	83	94	106	117	97	190	212	249	226	233	199	106.0%
Oman	4	12	42	125	191	263	405	523	495	587	646	238.1%
Qatar	39	90	147	239	273	347	506	590	654	672	758	178.0%
Saudi Arabia	323	405	1 371	2 022	2 568	3 721	4 471	5 150	5 524	5 883	6 117	138.2%
Syria	113	154	224	375	489	596	735	745	753	769	792	62.0%
United Arab Emirates	43	86	311	584	971	1 284	1 550	1 819	1 860	1 913	1 963	102.3%
Yemen	32	32	56	79	107	147	205	244	271	289	297	176.5%
Middle East	**2 226**	**3 051**	**5 556**	**7 775**	**9 566**	**13 403**	**16 285**	**18 577**	**19 826**	**20 917**	**21 885**	**128.8%**
Albania	71	82	128	113	111	55	76	89	87	100	95	-14.8%
Bosnia and Herzegovina *	..	..	..	..	295	64	182	184	202	211	226	-23.4%
Bulgaria	805	982	1 201	1 299	1 206	981	785	823	794	840	867	-28.2%
Croatia *	..	..	..	..	381	300	327	369	370	373	375	-1.6%
Cyprus	27	24	39	45	67	84	101	112	104	105	110	63.1%
Gibraltar	2	2	2	2	3	5	6	6	6	6	6	129.8%
FYR of Macedonia *	..	..	..	..	114	116	113	113	113	115	116	1.6%
Malta	11	11	17	16	32	33	32	37	39	38	37	14.1%
Romania	1 765	2 170	2 731	2 719	2 616	1 946	1 520	1 635	1 612	1 608	1 681	-35.7%
Serbia *	..	..	..	..	816	570	559	678	738	673	715	-12.4%
Slovenia *	..	..	..	..	234	248	270	292	298	304	304	30.2%
Former Yugoslavia *	927	1 080	1 426	1 736	..	..	..	..	..	..	..	..
Non-OECD Europe	**3 607**	**4 351**	**5 544**	**5 930**	**5 875**	**4 401**	**3 971**	**4 338**	**4 364**	**4 373**	**4 530**	**-22.9%**

* Data for individual countries of the Former Yugoslavia are not available prior to 1990.

Total primary energy supply
Approvisionnements totaux en énergie primaire

petajoules

	1971	1975	1980	1985	1990	1995	2000	2003	2004	2005	2006	% change 90-06
Armenia	..	..	..	..	331	70	86	84	89	107	108	-67.2%
Azerbaijan	..	..	..	..	1 092	552	484	516	544	581	589	-46.0%
Belarus	..	..	..	..	1 772	1 038	1 033	1 089	1 127	1 124	1 198	-32.4%
Estonia	..	..	..	..	402	202	190	209	216	211	205	-49.1%
Georgia	..	..	..	..	515	156	121	114	118	134	140	-72.8%
Kazakhstan	..	..	..	..	3 084	2 187	1 767	2 048	2 156	2 374	2 572	-16.6%
Kyrgyzstan	..	..	..	..	317	102	102	114	117	117	118	-62.9%
Latvia	..	..	..	..	329	193	156	179	184	187	193	-41.3%
Lithuania	..	..	..	..	680	368	300	382	386	364	358	-47.4%
Republic of Moldova	..	..	..	..	416	184	120	139	141	149	142	-65.9%
Russia	..	..	..	..	36 798	26 329	25 732	26 814	26 892	27 483	28 311	-23.1%
Tajikistan	..	..	..	..	233	137	119	131	137	143	152	-34.8%
Turkmenistan	..	..	..	..	822	582	607	719	655	692	723	-12.0%
Ukraine	..	..	..	..	10 627	6 865	5 612	6 070	6 039	5 998	5 754	-45.9%
Uzbekistan	..	..	..	..	1 941	1 782	2 109	2 129	2 069	1 968	2 029	4.5%
Former USSR *	**33 110**	**40 228**	**47 450**	**53 332**	**59 358**	**40 747**	**38 539**	**40 736**	**40 870**	**41 630**	**42 591**	**-28.2%**
Argentina	1 409	1 505	1 751	1 731	1 929	2 281	2 592	2 499	2 643	2 659	2 893	50.0%
Bolivia	43	63	102	109	116	166	207	184	225	222	245	110.9%
Brazil	2 913	3 815	4 772	5 416	5 861	6 735	7 948	8 370	8 829	9 065	9 384	60.1%
Chile	371	324	405	408	589	789	1 087	1 103	1 205	1 237	1 247	111.7%
Colombia	588	659	796	896	1 036	1 222	1 148	1 141	1 154	1 198	1 265	22.1%
Costa Rica	47	55	64	70	85	110	138	154	155	173	191	125.9%
Cuba	461	552	627	611	705	437	482	438	422	411	445	-36.8%
Dominican Republic	99	130	146	155	173	249	327	337	325	327	328	89.5%
Ecuador	100	139	217	248	257	295	347	401	423	431	471	83.4%
El Salvador	74	95	106	112	106	145	171	190	188	194	197	85.9%
Guatemala	117	142	161	160	188	226	299	305	317	339	343	82.7%
Haiti	63	72	88	79	66	72	85	94	92	105	107	61.9%
Honduras	58	65	79	86	101	124	126	151	162	162	181	79.2%
Jamaica	90	117	100	78	123	142	164	170	171	161	192	55.8%
Netherlands Antilles	231	163	167	77	63	58	59	67	68	64	72	15.5%
Nicaragua	53	63	65	82	89	99	115	131	138	140	145	62.9%
Panama	70	71	59	65	62	84	108	109	107	108	116	86.5%
Paraguay	58	62	88	96	129	165	162	167	168	166	166	28.8%
Peru	390	444	484	453	417	475	525	491	553	580	567	36.2%
Trinidad and Tobago	113	98	162	216	253	266	413	466	519	533	599	136.9%
Uruguay	101	102	111	84	94	108	129	105	120	121	134	41.7%
Venezuela	822	1 051	1 492	1 662	1 839	2 174	2 375	2 225	2 386	2 530	2 605	41.7%
Other Latin America	213	260	263	175	217	233	259	289	289	296	321	47.9%
Latin America	**8 485**	**10 048**	**12 305**	**13 067**	**14 498**	**16 653**	**19 265**	**19 587**	**20 656**	**21 223**	**22 216**	**53.2%**
Bangladesh	239	283	354	420	537	670	783	920	954	1 013	1 049	95.2%
Brunei Darussalam	7	32	58	75	75	100	106	111	112	110	117	55.8%
Cambodia	..	..	..	..	..	142	167	187	195	201	209	..
Chinese Taipei	443	625	1 194	1 416	2 008	2 711	3 455	4 116	4 352	4 418	4 517	124.9%
India	6 573	7 467	8 736	10 816	13 394	16 224	19 250	20 569	21 745	22 529	23 690	76.9%
Indonesia	1 514	1 760	2 408	2 842	4 304	5 529	6 340	6 879	7 203	7 368	7 497	74.2%
DPR of Korea	813	932	1 271	1 507	1 391	920	828	843	862	898	907	-34.8%
Malaysia	252	310	518	679	976	1 654	2 146	2 434	2 329	2 760	2 861	193.0%
Mongolia	..	..	..	131	143	114	100	103	106	109	117	-18.4%
Myanmar	331	351	395	461	447	495	526	574	582	598	598	33.7%
Nepal	153	169	192	214	243	283	342	366	372	385	394	62.0%
Pakistan	729	867	1 066	1 376	1 818	2 274	2 678	2 898	3 110	3 192	3 320	82.6%
Philippines	612	705	855	887	1 095	1 422	1 776	1 762	1 844	1 827	1 799	64.2%
Singapore	124	174	253	328	559	900	931	934	1 080	1 297	1 284	129.6%
Sri Lanka	159	172	190	209	231	249	338	360	397	380	393	70.3%
Thailand	591	757	955	1 100	1 839	2 720	3 141	3 783	4 092	4 214	4 329	135.5%
Vietnam	829	813	820	907	1 018	1 260	1 556	1 847	2 101	2 147	2 189	115.0%
Other Asia	194	229	313	256	266	273	305	352	378	377	398	49.3%
Asia	**13 565**	**15 646**	**19 576**	**23 625**	**30 347**	**37 939**	**44 769**	**49 038**	**51 815**	**53 824**	**55 667**	**83.4%**
People's Rep. of China	16 400	20 266	25 057	28 976	36 142	43 877	46 301	57 034	66 355	72 016	78 659	117.6%
Hong Kong, China	146	178	228	319	447	577	666	703	734	757	762	70.4%
China	**16 546**	**20 444**	**25 285**	**29 295**	**36 589**	**44 454**	**46 967**	**57 738**	**67 090**	**72 773**	**79 421**	**117.1%**

* Data for individual countries of the Former USSR are not available prior to 1990.

Total primary energy supply
Approvisionnements totaux en énergie primaire

million tonnes of oil equivalent

	1971	1975	1980	1985	1990	1995	2000	2003	2004	2005	2006	% change 90-06
World *	5 532.6	6 193.0	7 223.7	7 748.3	8 758.8	9 230.5	10 035.2	10 645.0	11 143.6	11 457.5	11 740.0	34.0%
Annex I Parties	..	..	..	..	5 620.1	5 530.7	5 843.9	5 938.0	6 036.4	6 084.2	6 080.8	8.2%
Annex II Parties	3 133.3	3 327.0	3 685.3	3 707.0	4 053.7	4 365.7	4 736.4	4 774.0	4 866.6	4 894.8	4 859.5	19.9%
North America	1 734.4	1 825.4	2 004.4	1 974.4	2 135.8	2 318.5	2 554.6	2 543.3	2 596.9	2 615.5	2 590.4	21.3%
Europe	1 070.8	1 125.2	1 255.4	1 282.6	1 372.6	1 436.1	1 526.5	1 586.4	1 608.2	1 612.8	1 601.4	16.7%
Pacific	328.1	376.4	425.4	449.9	545.4	611.1	655.3	644.3	661.5	666.4	667.6	22.4%
Annex I EIT	..	..	..	..	1 513.4	1 103.2	1 030.6	1 085.3	1 087.9	1 104.0	1 127.4	-25.5%
Non-Annex I Parties	..	..	..	..	3 025.9	3 572.8	4 044.5	4 560.5	4 943.4	5 200.0	5 476.2	81.0%
Annex I Kyoto Parties	..	..	..	..	3 598.6	3 357.3	3 439.8	3 552.2	3 599.7	3 630.0	3 637.5	1.1%
Intl. marine bunkers	108.0	103.0	107.9	91.7	112.8	127.1	146.9	146.5	163.8	173.3	183.0	62.2%
International aviation	56.7	57.8	67.4	75.5	86.2	96.0	115.1	115.5	123.3	131.2	134.0	55.5%
Non-OECD Total	2 046.0	2 464.7	3 042.4	3 522.6	4 124.3	4 212.9	4 562.9	5 098.3	5 471.5	5 730.2	6 019.6	46.0%
OECD Total	3 378.6	3 625.2	4 073.4	4 134.0	4 521.8	4 890.6	5 325.4	5 400.3	5 508.3	5 554.0	5 537.4	22.5%
Canada	141.8	166.6	193.1	193.4	209.5	231.7	252.1	262.2	269.0	273.7	269.7	28.8%
Mexico	43.5	60.0	96.5	110.1	123.0	131.3	150.2	159.8	165.2	176.6	177.4	44.2%
United States	1 592.7	1 658.8	1 811.4	1 781.1	1 926.3	2 086.8	2 302.6	2 281.1	2 328.0	2 341.9	2 320.7	20.5%
OECD N. America	1 777.9	1 885.4	2 101.0	2 084.6	2 258.8	2 449.8	2 704.8	2 703.0	2 762.2	2 792.2	2 767.9	22.5%
Australia	52.1	61.0	70.4	73.9	87.7	94.5	110.6	112.8	113.1	120.7	122.5	39.7%
Japan	268.8	306.5	345.8	364.6	443.9	500.8	526.6	514.2	530.8	528.4	527.6	18.8%
Korea	17.0	24.6	41.5	54.1	93.4	147.4	189.4	206.8	212.3	212.5	216.5	131.9%
New Zealand	7.1	8.9	9.2	11.4	13.8	15.8	18.1	17.3	17.6	17.3	17.5	27.5%
OECD Pacific	345.1	401.0	466.9	504.0	638.7	758.5	844.7	851.1	873.8	879.0	884.1	38.4%
Austria	18.9	20.2	23.3	23.3	25.1	27.1	29.0	32.8	33.0	34.0	34.2	36.6%
Belgium	40.1	42.7	47.2	44.6	49.7	55.9	61.9	62.4	62.2	61.7	61.0	22.7%
Czech Republic	45.6	43.9	47.2	49.4	49.0	41.1	40.4	44.6	45.8	45.2	46.1	-6.0%
Denmark	19.2	18.0	19.7	19.8	17.9	20.1	19.4	20.8	20.2	19.7	20.9	16.8%
Finland	18.2	19.8	24.8	26.0	28.7	29.2	32.5	37.0	37.2	34.4	37.4	30.4%
France	160.1	166.9	193.7	206.0	227.6	241.2	258.2	271.4	275.4	276.2	272.7	19.8%
Germany	307.6	316.3	359.9	360.4	355.6	341.8	343.2	347.4	349.4	345.3	348.6	-2.0%
Greece	9.1	12.2	15.7	18.3	22.2	23.5	27.9	29.9	30.5	31.0	31.1	40.0%
Hungary	19.1	23.0	28.5	29.9	28.6	25.7	25.0	26.3	26.4	27.8	27.6	-3.4%
Iceland	1.0	1.2	1.5	1.8	2.2	2.3	3.2	3.4	3.5	3.6	4.3	100.1%
Ireland	7.0	6.9	8.4	8.8	10.3	10.7	14.2	14.9	15.0	15.2	15.5	49.8%
Italy	106.6	117.6	132.2	130.8	148.1	161.1	173.3	181.2	183.3	185.7	184.2	24.4%
Luxembourg	4.1	3.8	3.6	3.1	3.5	3.3	3.6	4.2	4.6	4.7	4.7	33.0%
Netherlands	51.5	59.8	65.3	61.8	67.1	73.0	76.4	81.4	82.7	82.4	80.1	19.4%
Norway	13.5	14.8	18.5	20.3	21.4	23.8	25.7	27.2	29.1	33.1	26.1	21.8%
Poland	86.3	103.2	123.0	123.3	99.9	99.7	89.4	91.4	91.7	92.7	97.7	-2.2%
Portugal	6.5	8.0	10.3	11.4	17.2	20.7	25.2	25.8	26.5	27.2	25.4	47.5%
Slovak Republic	14.3	16.8	19.8	20.7	21.3	17.8	17.8	18.7	18.4	18.9	18.7	-12.4%
Spain	43.2	58.4	68.6	71.8	91.2	102.8	124.7	136.0	142.2	144.9	144.6	58.5%
Sweden	36.2	39.1	40.7	47.4	47.6	50.9	48.3	51.1	53.2	52.2	51.3	7.9%
Switzerland	16.9	17.8	20.7	22.9	24.8	24.8	26.0	26.7	27.0	27.0	28.2	13.7%
Turkey	19.6	26.8	31.5	39.4	52.9	61.8	76.9	78.7	81.8	85.5	94.0	77.6%
United Kingdom	211.1	201.8	201.3	204.0	212.3	223.7	233.9	232.9	233.2	234.5	231.1	8.9%
OECD Europe	1 255.7	1 338.9	1 505.5	1 545.4	1 624.3	1 682.3	1 775.9	1 846.2	1 872.3	1 882.9	1 885.5	16.1%
European Union - 27	..	..	..	..	1 655.9	1 666.3	1 724.2	1 797.8	1 817.7	1 821.1	1 822.5	10.1%

* Total world includes Non-OECD total, OECD total as well as international marine bunkers. In TPES, international aviation is included in country totals.

Total primary energy supply
Approvisionnements totaux en énergie primaire

million tonnes of oil equivalent

	1971	1975	1980	1985	1990	1995	2000	2003	2004	2005	2006	% change 90-06
Non-OECD Total	2 046.0	2 464.7	3 042.4	3 522.6	4 124.3	4 212.9	4 562.9	5 098.3	5 471.5	5 730.2	6 019.6	46.0%
Algeria	3.7	6.0	12.2	19.2	23.9	26.0	29.3	33.4	33.5	34.7	36.7	53.4%
Angola	3.9	4.2	4.7	5.4	6.3	6.8	8.0	9.2	9.4	9.7	10.3	63.3%
Benin	1.1	1.2	1.4	1.6	1.7	1.9	2.0	2.4	2.5	2.6	2.8	67.7%
Botswana	..	..	..	0.9	1.3	1.5	1.8	1.9	1.8	1.9	2.0	53.9%
Cameroon	2.8	3.1	3.7	4.5	5.0	5.6	6.4	6.8	7.0	7.0	7.1	40.8%
Congo	0.5	0.6	0.7	0.8	0.8	0.8	0.8	1.0	1.1	1.2	1.2	51.2%
Dem. Rep. of Congo	6.8	7.6	8.6	10.1	11.9	13.2	14.8	16.0	16.5	17.0	17.5	47.1%
Côte d'Ivoire	2.5	3.0	3.7	3.8	4.4	5.2	6.9	6.7	6.9	7.8	7.3	65.1%
Egypt	7.8	9.9	15.3	25.8	32.0	35.6	45.8	55.3	56.6	61.3	62.5	95.5%
Eritrea	..	..	..	..	..	1.0	0.7	0.9	0.7	0.8	0.7	..
Ethiopia	8.7	9.5	10.9	12.5	15.0	16.5	18.7	20.5	21.1	21.6	22.3	48.3%
Gabon	1.1	1.3	1.4	1.4	1.2	1.4	1.5	1.7	1.7	1.8	1.8	46.6%
Ghana	3.0	3.7	4.1	4.4	5.3	6.5	7.9	8.5	8.5	8.9	9.5	78.0%
Kenya	5.6	6.5	7.9	9.2	11.2	12.8	15.0	15.6	16.7	17.2	17.9	60.0%
Libya	1.7	3.8	7.2	10.3	11.5	16.1	17.0	17.5	18.4	17.7	17.8	53.9%
Morocco	2.5	3.6	5.1	5.8	7.2	8.8	10.5	11.3	12.3	13.5	14.0	93.9%
Mozambique	6.9	6.7	6.7	6.4	6.0	6.3	7.2	8.1	8.4	8.5	8.8	47.6%
Namibia	..	..	..	..	..	0.9	1.0	1.2	1.3	1.4	1.5	..
Nigeria	36.2	42.0	52.8	61.9	70.9	80.4	89.3	97.8	99.8	105.0	105.1	48.2%
Senegal	1.3	1.5	1.8	1.7	1.8	2.0	2.7	2.8	3.0	3.0	3.0	63.9%
South Africa	45.3	54.0	65.4	86.7	91.2	105.5	111.3	118.1	129.3	127.6	129.8	42.3%
Sudan	7.1	7.5	8.4	9.5	10.7	12.0	13.5	16.0	16.9	17.3	17.7	66.1%
United Rep. of Tanzania	7.6	7.7	8.1	8.8	9.8	11.1	13.4	16.4	17.7	19.2	20.8	112.1%
Togo	0.7	0.8	0.9	1.0	1.3	1.6	2.1	2.3	2.4	2.4	2.4	85.2%
Tunisia	1.8	2.3	3.5	4.3	5.1	6.1	7.6	8.2	8.7	8.5	8.7	70.1%
Zambia	3.5	4.0	4.6	5.0	5.5	5.9	6.3	6.8	6.9	7.1	7.3	33.8%
Zimbabwe	5.5	6.0	6.6	7.5	9.4	10.0	10.0	9.6	9.3	9.7	9.6	2.1%
Other Africa	26.3	28.7	33.1	37.0	42.1	47.3	55.9	63.8	65.7	66.6	68.2	61.8%
Africa	**194.0**	**225.1**	**278.6**	**345.4**	**392.7**	**448.7**	**507.4**	**559.9**	**584.2**	**601.2**	**614.3**	**56.4%**
Bahrain	1.6	2.4	3.3	4.6	4.8	5.3	6.2	7.2	7.5	8.1	8.8	81.6%
Islamic Rep. of Iran	19.1	29.3	39.1	54.7	68.8	94.7	118.8	139.5	151.0	158.1	170.9	148.3%
Iraq	4.5	5.9	10.9	16.2	19.1	26.4	26.0	25.3	29.0	29.9	32.0	68.0%
Israel	6.3	7.7	8.6	8.2	12.1	16.4	19.2	20.7	20.5	21.2	21.3	75.7%
Jordan	0.5	0.8	1.7	2.8	3.5	4.6	5.2	5.4	6.4	7.0	7.2	104.8%
Kuwait	5.9	5.9	15.2	14.6	8.0	16.4	20.4	22.9	25.4	28.1	25.3	216.3%
Lebanon	2.0	2.2	2.5	2.8	2.3	4.5	5.1	6.0	5.4	5.6	4.8	106.0%
Oman	0.1	0.3	1.0	3.0	4.6	6.3	9.7	12.5	11.8	14.0	15.4	238.1%
Qatar	0.9	2.1	3.5	5.7	6.5	8.3	12.1	14.1	15.6	16.0	18.1	178.0%
Saudi Arabia	7.7	9.7	32.8	48.3	61.3	88.9	106.8	123.0	131.9	140.5	146.1	138.2%
Syria	2.7	3.7	5.3	8.9	11.7	14.2	17.6	17.8	18.0	18.4	18.9	62.0%
United Arab Emirates	1.0	2.1	7.4	14.0	23.2	30.7	37.0	43.5	44.4	45.7	46.9	102.3%
Yemen	0.8	0.8	1.3	1.9	2.6	3.5	4.9	5.8	6.5	6.9	7.1	176.5%
Middle East	**53.2**	**72.9**	**132.7**	**185.7**	**228.5**	**320.1**	**389.0**	**443.7**	**473.5**	**499.6**	**522.7**	**128.8%**
Albania	1.7	2.0	3.1	2.7	2.7	1.3	1.8	2.1	2.1	2.4	2.3	-14.8%
Bosnia and Herzegovina *	..	..	..	..	7.0	1.5	4.4	4.4	4.8	5.0	5.4	-23.4%
Bulgaria	19.2	23.5	28.7	31.0	28.8	23.4	18.7	19.7	19.0	20.1	20.7	-28.2%
Croatia *	..	..	..	..	9.1	7.2	7.8	8.8	8.8	8.9	9.0	-1.6%
Cyprus	0.6	0.6	0.9	1.1	1.6	2.0	2.4	2.7	2.5	2.5	2.6	63.1%
Gibraltar	0.0	0.0	0.0	0.0	0.1	0.1	0.1	0.1	0.1	0.1	0.2	129.8%
FYR of Macedonia *	..	..	..	..	2.7	2.8	2.7	2.7	2.7	2.7	2.8	1.6%
Malta	0.3	0.3	0.4	0.4	0.8	0.8	0.8	0.9	0.9	0.9	0.9	14.2%
Romania	42.1	51.8	65.2	64.9	62.5	46.5	36.3	39.1	38.5	38.4	40.1	-35.7%
Serbia *	..	..	..	..	19.5	13.6	13.3	16.2	17.6	16.1	17.1	-12.4%
Slovenia *	..	..	..	..	5.6	5.9	6.4	7.0	7.1	7.3	7.3	30.2%
Former Yugoslavia *	22.1	25.8	34.1	41.5	..	..	..	..	..	..	..	..
Non-OECD Europe	**86.2**	**103.9**	**132.4**	**141.6**	**140.3**	**105.1**	**94.8**	**103.6**	**104.2**	**104.5**	**108.2**	**-22.9%**

* Data for individual countries of the Former Yugoslavia are not available prior to 1990.

Total primary energy supply

Approvisionnements totaux en énergie primaire

million tonnes of oil equivalent

	1971	1975	1980	1985	1990	1995	2000	2003	2004	2005	2006	% change 90-06
Armenia	..	..	..	..	7.9	1.7	2.1	2.0	2.1	2.6	2.6	-67.2%
Azerbaijan	..	..	..	..	26.1	13.2	11.6	12.3	13.0	13.9	14.1	-46.0%
Belarus	..	..	..	..	42.3	24.8	24.7	26.0	26.9	26.8	28.6	-32.4%
Estonia	..	..	..	..	9.6	4.8	4.5	5.0	5.2	5.0	4.9	-49.1%
Georgia	..	..	..	..	12.3	3.7	2.9	2.7	2.8	3.2	3.3	-72.8%
Kazakhstan	..	..	..	..	73.6	52.2	42.2	48.9	51.5	56.7	61.4	-16.6%
Kyrgyzstan	..	..	..	..	7.6	2.4	2.4	2.7	2.8	2.8	2.8	-62.9%
Latvia	..	..	..	..	7.9	4.6	3.7	4.3	4.4	4.5	4.6	-41.3%
Lithuania	..	..	..	..	16.2	8.8	7.2	9.1	9.2	8.7	8.5	-47.4%
Republic of Moldova	..	..	..	..	9.9	4.4	2.9	3.3	3.4	3.5	3.4	-65.9%
Russia	..	..	..	..	878.9	628.9	614.6	640.4	642.3	656.4	676.2	-23.1%
Tajikistan	..	..	..	..	5.6	3.3	2.8	3.1	3.3	3.4	3.6	-34.8%
Turkmenistan	..	..	..	..	19.6	13.9	14.5	17.2	15.7	16.5	17.3	-12.0%
Ukraine	..	..	..	..	253.8	164.0	134.0	145.0	144.2	143.3	137.4	-45.9%
Uzbekistan	..	..	..	..	46.4	42.6	50.4	50.8	49.4	47.0	48.5	4.5%
Former USSR *	**790.8**	**960.8**	**1 133.3**	**1 273.8**	**1 417.7**	**973.2**	**920.5**	**973.0**	**976.2**	**994.3**	**1 017.3**	**-28.2%**
Argentina	33.7	35.9	41.8	41.3	46.1	54.5	61.9	59.7	63.1	63.5	69.1	50.0%
Bolivia	1.0	1.5	2.4	2.6	2.8	4.0	4.9	4.4	5.4	5.3	5.8	110.9%
Brazil	69.6	91.1	114.0	129.4	140.0	160.9	189.8	199.9	210.9	216.5	224.1	60.1%
Chile	8.9	7.7	9.7	9.7	14.1	18.8	26.0	26.4	28.8	29.5	29.8	111.7%
Colombia	14.1	15.7	19.0	21.4	24.7	29.2	27.4	27.3	27.6	28.6	30.2	22.1%
Costa Rica	1.1	1.3	1.5	1.7	2.0	2.6	3.3	3.7	3.7	4.1	4.6	125.8%
Cuba	11.0	13.2	15.0	14.6	16.8	10.4	11.5	10.5	10.1	9.8	10.6	-36.8%
Dominican Republic	2.4	3.1	3.5	3.7	4.1	6.0	7.8	8.1	7.8	7.8	7.8	89.5%
Ecuador	2.4	3.3	5.2	5.9	6.1	7.0	8.3	9.6	10.1	10.3	11.2	83.4%
El Salvador	1.8	2.3	2.5	2.7	2.5	3.5	4.1	4.5	4.5	4.6	4.7	85.9%
Guatemala	2.8	3.4	3.8	3.8	4.5	5.4	7.1	7.3	7.6	8.1	8.2	82.7%
Haiti	1.5	1.7	2.1	1.9	1.6	1.7	2.0	2.2	2.2	2.5	2.6	61.9%
Honduras	1.4	1.6	1.9	2.0	2.4	3.0	3.0	3.6	3.9	3.9	4.3	79.1%
Jamaica	2.2	2.8	2.4	1.9	2.9	3.4	3.9	4.1	4.1	3.8	4.6	55.8%
Netherlands Antilles	5.5	3.9	4.0	1.8	1.5	1.4	1.4	1.6	1.6	1.5	1.7	15.5%
Nicaragua	1.3	1.5	1.6	2.0	2.1	2.4	2.7	3.1	3.3	3.3	3.5	62.9%
Panama	1.7	1.7	1.4	1.6	1.5	2.0	2.6	2.6	2.5	2.6	2.8	86.5%
Paraguay	1.4	1.5	2.1	2.3	3.1	3.9	3.9	4.0	4.0	4.0	4.0	28.8%
Peru	9.3	10.6	11.6	10.8	10.0	11.3	12.5	11.7	13.2	13.9	13.6	36.2%
Trinidad and Tobago	2.7	2.3	3.9	5.1	6.0	6.4	9.9	11.1	12.4	12.7	14.3	136.9%
Uruguay	2.4	2.4	2.6	2.0	2.3	2.6	3.1	2.5	2.9	2.9	3.2	41.7%
Venezuela	19.6	25.1	35.6	39.7	43.9	51.9	56.7	53.1	57.0	60.4	62.2	41.7%
Other Latin America	5.1	6.2	6.3	4.2	5.2	5.6	6.2	6.9	6.9	7.1	7.7	47.9%
Latin America	**202.7**	**240.0**	**293.9**	**312.1**	**346.3**	**397.8**	**460.1**	**467.8**	**493.4**	**506.9**	**530.6**	**53.2%**
Bangladesh	5.7	6.8	8.5	10.0	12.8	16.0	18.7	22.0	22.8	24.2	25.0	95.2%
Brunei Darussalam	0.2	0.8	1.4	1.8	1.8	2.4	2.5	2.7	2.7	2.6	2.8	55.8%
Cambodia	..	..	..	..	..	3.4	4.0	4.5	4.7	4.8	5.0	..
Chinese Taipei	10.6	14.9	28.5	33.8	48.0	64.8	82.5	98.3	103.9	105.5	107.9	124.9%
India	157.0	178.4	208.6	258.3	319.9	387.5	459.8	491.3	519.4	538.1	565.8	76.9%
Indonesia	36.2	42.0	57.5	67.9	102.8	132.1	151.4	164.3	172.0	176.0	179.1	74.2%
DPR of Korea	19.4	22.3	30.4	36.0	33.2	22.0	19.8	20.1	20.6	21.4	21.7	-34.8%
Malaysia	6.0	7.4	12.4	16.2	23.3	39.5	51.3	58.1	55.6	65.9	68.3	193.0%
Mongolia	..	..	..	3.1	3.4	2.7	2.4	2.5	2.5	2.6	2.8	-18.4%
Myanmar	7.9	8.4	9.4	11.0	10.7	11.8	12.6	13.7	13.9	14.3	14.3	33.7%
Nepal	3.7	4.0	4.6	5.1	5.8	6.8	8.2	8.8	8.9	9.2	9.4	62.0%
Pakistan	17.4	20.7	25.5	32.9	43.4	54.3	64.0	69.2	74.3	76.2	79.3	82.6%
Philippines	14.6	16.8	20.4	21.2	26.2	34.0	42.4	42.1	44.0	43.6	43.0	64.2%
Singapore	3.0	4.2	6.0	7.8	13.4	21.5	22.2	22.3	25.8	31.0	30.7	129.6%
Sri Lanka	3.8	4.1	4.5	5.0	5.5	5.9	8.1	8.6	9.5	9.1	9.4	70.3%
Thailand	14.1	18.1	22.8	26.3	43.9	65.0	75.0	90.3	97.7	100.6	103.4	135.5%
Vietnam	19.8	19.4	19.6	21.7	24.3	30.1	37.2	44.1	50.2	51.3	52.3	115.0%
Other Asia	4.6	5.5	7.5	6.1	6.4	6.5	7.3	8.4	9.0	9.0	9.5	49.3%
Asia	**324.0**	**373.7**	**467.6**	**564.3**	**724.8**	**906.2**	**1 069.3**	**1 171.3**	**1 237.6**	**1 285.6**	**1 329.6**	**83.4%**
People's Rep. of China	391.7	484.0	598.5	692.1	863.2	1 048.0	1 105.9	1 362.2	1 584.9	1 720.1	1 878.7	117.6%
Hong Kong, China	3.5	4.2	5.4	7.6	10.7	13.8	15.9	16.8	17.5	18.1	18.2	70.4%
China	**395.2**	**488.3**	**603.9**	**699.7**	**873.9**	**1 061.8**	**1 121.8**	**1 379.0**	**1 602.4**	**1 738.2**	**1 896.9**	**117.1%**

* Data for individual countries of the Former USSR are not available prior to 1990.

GDP using exchange rates
PIB selon les taux de change

billion 2000 US$ using exchange rates

	1971	1975	1980	1985	1990	1995	2000	2003	2004	2005	2006	% change 90-06
World	**12 865.4**	**14 901.1**	**18 033.8**	**20 412.3**	**24 080.6**	**27 001.2**	**31 802.2**	**33 780.0**	**35 146.2**	**36 352.4**	**37 759.4**	**56.8%**
Annex I Parties	*..*	*..*	*..*	*..*	*19 815.1*	*21 547.3*	*25 000.0*	*26 142.0*	*26 964.3*	*27 639.1*	*28 432.1*	*43.5%*
Annex II Parties	*10 320.2*	*11 697.6*	*13 928.7*	*15 817.2*	*18 836.7*	*20 755.1*	*24 088.4*	*25 118.2*	*25 868.0*	*26 479.4*	*27 197.4*	*44.4%*
North America	*4 138.8*	*4 620.2*	*5 540.0*	*6 482.7*	*7 598.6*	*8 564.9*	*10 489.7*	*11 023.5*	*11 421.4*	*11 772.5*	*12 109.8*	*59.4%*
Europe	*4 094.6*	*4 602.4*	*5 345.1*	*5 790.3*	*6 794.9*	*7 368.3*	*8 478.9*	*8 836.0*	*9 043.3*	*9 196.4*	*9 455.5*	*39.2%*
Pacific	*2 086.8*	*2 475.0*	*3 043.6*	*3 544.2*	*4 443.2*	*4 821.9*	*5 119.8*	*5 258.7*	*5 403.3*	*5 510.5*	*5 632.1*	*26.8%*
Annex I EIT	*..*	*..*	*..*	*..*	*838.2*	*628.0*	*712.3*	*813.3*	*867.0*	*913.5*	*973.5*	*16.1%*
Non-Annex I Parties	*..*	*..*	*..*	*..*	*4 265.5*	*5 453.9*	*6 802.3*	*7 638.0*	*8 181.9*	*8 713.3*	*9 327.3*	*118.7%*
Annex I Kyoto Parties	*..*	*..*	*..*	*..*	*12 605.5*	*13 400.9*	*15 023.1*	*15 666.7*	*16 094.4*	*16 424.0*	*16 885.6*	*34.0%*
Non-OECD Total	**2 063.3**	**2 584.7**	**3 329.2**	**3 697.1**	**4 170.5**	**4 982.6**	**6 125.7**	**6 951.1**	**7 479.9**	**7 999.8**	**8 590.7**	**106.0%**
OECD Total	**10 802.2**	**12 316.4**	**14 704.7**	**16 715.2**	**19 910.1**	**22 018.6**	**25 676.5**	**26 828.9**	**27 666.3**	**28 352.6**	**29 168.7**	**46.5%**
Canada	288.3	343.3	412.0	471.7	543.6	592.1	724.9	773.7	797.5	¯821.9	844.6	55.4%
Mexico	189.7	250.1	345.1	379.9	412.8	445.3	580.8	593.2	617.9	635.2	665.5	61.2%
United States	3 850.5	4 276.9	5 128.0	6 011.0	7 055.0	7 972.8	9 764.8	10 249.8	10 623.9	10 950.6	11 265.2	59.7%
OECD N. America	**4 328.5**	**4 870.3**	**5 885.1**	**6 862.6**	**8 011.4**	**9 010.2**	**11 070.5**	**11 616.7**	**12 039.3**	**12 407.7**	**12 775.3**	**59.5%**
Australia	163.1	181.1	210.0	243.6	281.0	330.1	399.6	445.1	457.0	469.8	481.4	71.3%
Japan	1 894.9	2 259.9	2 800.6	3 261.9	4 122.4	4 445.4	4 667.5	4 754.6	4 885.1	4 978.3	5 087.1	23.4%
Korea	66.1	87.8	122.8	179.0	283.6	413.0	511.7	585.9	613.6	639.4	671.3	136.7%
New Zealand	28.8	34.0	33.0	38.7	39.8	46.4	52.7	59.0	61.2	62.4	63.6	59.8%
OECD Pacific	**2 152.9**	**2 562.8**	**3 166.4**	**3 723.2**	**4 726.8**	**5 234.9**	**5 631.5**	**5 844.6**	**6 016.9**	**6 149.9**	**6 303.4**	**33.4%**
Austria	88.8	102.5	120.4	129.6	150.7	167.7	193.8	199.5	204.1	208.3	215.2	42.8%
Belgium	114.5	131.5	153.7	161.1	187.5	203.0	231.9	239.7	246.8	250.9	258.1	37.7%
Czech Republic	38.3	43.7	48.7	51.1	55.3	52.7	56.7	61.3	64.1	68.2	72.5	31.1%
Denmark	83.2	88.1	101.0	115.5	123.9	139.1	160.1	162.6	166.0	171.1	177.2	43.0%
Finland	53.0	64.1	74.5	85.1	100.3	96.5	121.9	129.4	134.2	138.1	145.0	44.6%
France	630.8	727.7	861.1	929.8	1 091.8	1 156.3	1 328.0	1 381.3	1 415.5	1 439.7	1 468.3	34.5%
Germany	950.5	1 038.9	1 225.9	1 311.9	1 543.2	1 720.5	1 900.2	1 919.6	1 939.9	1 955.1	2 011.2	30.3%
Greece	64.8	76.8	94.2	94.8	100.8	107.3	127.1	144.9	151.6	157.4	164.0	62.7%
Hungary	25.9	33.2	39.6	43.2	44.4	39.4	47.9	54.3	56.9	59.2	61.5	38.6%
Iceland	3.1	3.8	5.1	5.8	6.7	6.8	8.7	9.3	10.0	10.7	10.9	62.7%
Ireland	22.3	27.4	34.3	38.9	48.9	61.3	96.4	113.8	118.8	126.0	133.2	172.4%
Italy	518.1	594.4	739.0	803.3	937.4	998.5	1 097.3	1 121.3	1 134.8	1 135.8	1 157.0	23.4%
Luxembourg	6.1	6.8	7.6	8.6	12.4	15.1	20.3	22.1	23.2	24.3	25.8	108.1%
Netherlands	173.6	196.5	223.9	237.6	282.0	315.8	385.1	394.1	402.9	409.0	421.3	49.4%
Norway	61.0	73.1	91.2	107.5	117.0	140.5	168.3	176.0	182.8	187.8	191.8	63.9%
Poland	89.2	114.1	119.0	120.1	118.2	131.6	171.3	182.6	192.4	199.4	211.6	79.0%
Portugal	41.3	48.0	61.5	64.3	84.7	92.2	112.7	114.9	116.6	117.5	118.9	40.4%
Slovak Republic	12.9	14.7	16.4	17.7	19.0	17.3	20.4	22.9	24.1	25.6	27.7	46.2%
Spain	241.9	299.4	330.0	353.6	440.6	474.9	580.7	637.3	658.1	681.9	708.2	60.7%
Sweden	134.7	151.6	162.0	177.8	201.3	208.4	245.6	259.0	269.7	278.6	290.0	44.1%
Switzerland	166.1	166.2	180.7	194.7	224.8	225.9	249.9	253.4	259.8	266.1	274.7	22.2%
Turkey	59.8	75.1	84.4	107.0	140.2	164.2	199.3	210.5	229.3	246.2	261.2	86.3%
United Kingdom	740.8	805.6	879.0	970.4	1 140.9	1 238.5	1 450.9	1 557.8	1 608.5	1 638.1	1 684.7	47.7%
OECD Europe	**4 320.8**	**4 883.3**	**5 653.2**	**6 129.4**	**7 171.9**	**7 773.5**	**8 974.5**	**9 367.6**	**9 610.1**	**9 795.0**	**10 090.0**	**40.7%**
European Union - 27	*..*	*..*	*..*	*..*	*6 799.4*	*7 334.6*	*8 455.2*	*8 842.0*	*9 060.1*	*9 223.4*	*9 500.6*	*39.7%*

GDP using exchange rates

PIB selon les taux de change

billion 2000 US$ using exchange rates

	1971	1975	1980	1985	1990	1995	2000	2003	2004	2005	2006	% change 90-06
Non-OECD Total	**2 063.3**	**2 584.7**	**3 329.2**	**3 697.1**	**4 170.5**	**4 982.6**	**6 125.7**	**6 951.1**	**7 479.9**	**7 999.8**	**8 590.7**	**106.0%**
Algeria	17.5	26.1	35.3	44.6	46.4	47.0	54.8	62.9	66.2	69.7	71.8	54.8%
Angola	6.7	6.7	6.7	7.2	8.5	6.7	9.1	11.1	12.4	14.9	17.1	102.2%
Benin	0.8	0.9	1.1	1.4	1.4	1.7	2.3	2.6	2.7	2.7	2.8	101.1%
Botswana	..	..	..	1.9	3.4	4.1	6.2	7.3	7.7	8.0	8.4	147.1%
Cameroon	3.5	4.7	6.3	9.9	8.8	8.0	10.1	11.4	11.8	12.1	12.5	42.5%
Congo	1.0	1.4	1.7	2.8	2.8	2.9	3.2	3.6	3.7	4.0	4.2	51.3%
Dem. Rep. of Congo	7.1	7.6	7.0	7.7	7.7	5.3	4.3	4.6	4.9	5.2	5.5	-28.1%
Côte d'Ivoire	5.0	6.3	7.7	7.8	8.3	8.9	10.4	10.1	10.3	10.2	10.6	28.7%
Egypt	21.0	24.1	38.5	53.3	65.6	77.4	99.8	110.0	114.6	119.7	127.9	95.0%
Eritrea	..	..	..	..	..	0.6	0.6	0.7	0.8	0.8	0.7	..
Ethiopia	4.4	4.8	5.3	5.0	6.3	6.3	7.9	8.3	9.4	10.4	11.3	79.6%
Gabon	1.9	3.9	3.6	4.1	4.3	5.0	5.1	5.3	5.4	5.5	5.6	30.0%
Ghana	2.7	2.5	2.6	2.6	3.3	4.0	5.0	5.7	6.0	6.4	6.8	106.9%
Kenya	4.0	5.2	7.1	8.0	10.6	11.4	12.7	13.7	14.3	15.2	16.0	51.7%
Libya	34.4	27.8	43.8	37.7	29.8	31.8	34.5	40.6	42.5	44.0	46.5	56.0%
Morocco	11.6	14.0	18.3	21.5	26.7	28.0	33.3	38.6	40.2	40.9	43.9	64.3%
Mozambique	2.6	2.2	2.2	1.7	2.3	2.6	3.8	5.0	5.4	5.7	6.2	171.1%
Namibia	..	..	..	..	..	2.9	3.4	3.9	4.1	4.3	4.5	..
Nigeria	22.6	26.0	31.5	27.0	35.0	39.5	46.0	53.3	56.5	60.0	63.5	81.6%
Senegal	2.0	2.3	2.4	2.8	3.3	3.5	4.4	4.9	5.2	5.5	5.6	72.5%
South Africa	71.5	82.0	95.5	102.2	110.9	115.8	132.9	145.8	153.0	160.8	168.8	52.2%
Sudan	4.0	4.9	5.6	5.7	7.1	9.1	12.4	14.7	15.5	16.7	18.9	166.6%
United Rep. of Tanzania	3.6	4.3	4.9	5.2	6.8	7.4	9.1	10.9	11.7	12.5	13.2	94.1%
Togo	0.6	0.8	1.0	0.9	1.1	1.1	1.3	1.4	1.5	1.5	1.5	40.2%
Tunisia	4.7	6.3	8.6	10.6	12.2	14.8	19.4	21.9	23.2	24.2	25.5	108.0%
Zambia	2.4	2.7	2.7	2.8	3.0	2.8	3.2	3.7	3.9	4.1	4.3	43.2%
Zimbabwe	3.5	4.1	4.4	5.4	6.7	7.1	7.4	6.2	5.9	5.6	5.3	-20.6%
Other Africa	24.2	26.3	30.9	32.5	37.5	38.4	48.2	55.8	59.0	61.9	64.3	71.5%
Africa	**263.4**	**297.7**	**374.9**	**412.4**	**459.6**	**494.2**	**590.8**	**663.8**	**697.6**	**732.4**	**773.3**	**68.3%**
Bahrain	1.3	2.4	4.0	3.7	4.6	6.5	8.0	9.4	9.9	10.6	11.4	145.7%
Islamic Rep. of Iran	46.6	66.1	57.3	69.4	70.3	83.1	101.3	120.9	127.1	132.6	140.3	99.6%
Iraq	50.5	64.2	96.6	61.8	33.0	12.6	25.9	13.1	19.1	19.8	19.9	-39.7%
Israel	30.3	39.2	47.3	54.7	67.6	92.6	115.5	115.8	120.9	127.2	133.7	97.7%
Jordan	2.1	2.0	4.2	5.4	5.1	7.2	8.5	9.8	10.6	11.4	12.1	136.9%
Kuwait	31.9	26.4	27.9	22.0	25.3	34.3	37.7	45.3	48.1	52.2	54.8	116.2%
Lebanon	12.7	12.4	10.6	14.8	8.4	14.9	16.8	18.9	20.3	20.5	20.5	143.9%
Oman	3.2	4.1	5.4	10.9	12.7	16.8	19.9	22.0	22.7	24.4	26.2	107.2%
Qatar	9.0	9.1	10.6	9.0	8.8	10.2	17.8	20.3	24.6	26.1	28.4	221.5%
Saudi Arabia	52.9	110.0	153.7	121.8	144.1	166.0	188.4	204.2	215.0	229.1	239.6	66.3%
Syria	4.0	6.9	9.5	10.9	11.8	17.3	19.3	21.5	22.5	23.6	24.8	110.5%
United Arab Emirates	8.8	22.7	47.3	41.3	46.4	54.8	70.6	87.5	96.0	104.2	114.3	146.3%
Yemen	1.3	1.9	3.3	4.7	5.5	7.2	9.4	10.6	11.0	11.5	11.9	115.7%
Middle East	**254.5**	**367.5**	**477.6**	**430.4**	**443.6**	**523.5**	**639.1**	**699.4**	**747.8**	**793.1**	**837.8**	**88.8%**
Albania	1.7	2.1	2.8	3.1	3.2	2.8	3.7	4.3	4.5	4.8	5.0	56.5%
Bosnia and Herzegovina *	..	..	..	..	1.4	1.5	5.1	5.8	6.1	6.4	6.8	388.3%
Bulgaria	6.4	8.8	11.8	13.9	15.0	13.1	12.6	14.4	15.4	16.4	17.4	15.8%
Croatia *	..	..	..	..	21.5	15.6	18.4	21.4	22.2	23.2	24.2	12.7%
Cyprus	2.1	1.9	3.3	4.4	6.1	7.6	9.1	9.9	10.3	10.7	11.1	81.7%
Gibraltar	0.4	0.4	0.4	0.5	0.6	0.6	0.7	0.8	0.8	0.8	0.9	47.5%
FYR of Macedonia *	..	..	..	..	3.9	3.1	3.6	3.6	3.7	3.8	4.0	0.5%
Malta	0.6	0.9	1.6	1.8	2.4	3.1	3.9	3.8	3.8	3.9	4.0	67.1%
Romania	18.8	28.4	40.9	48.2	44.0	39.5	37.1	43.3	46.9	48.9	52.6	19.6%
Serbia *	..	..	..	..	10.2	9.9	9.9	11.0	11.9	11.6	12.2	20.4%
Slovenia *	..	..	..	..	16.1	15.6	19.3	21.1	22.0	22.9	24.1	49.4%
Former Yugoslavia *	33.7	41.3	55.6	56.6	..	..	..	..	..	..	..	..
Non-OECD Europe	**63.7**	**83.9**	**116.6**	**128.4**	**124.4**	**112.5**	**123.4**	**139.4**	**147.7**	**153.3**	**162.2**	**30.5%**

* Data for individual countries of the Former Yugoslavia are not available prior to 1990.

GDP using exchange rates

PIB selon les taux de change

billion 2000 US$ using exchange rates

	1971	1975	1980	1985	1990	1995	2000	2003	2004	2005	2006	% change 90-06
Armenia	..	..	..	..	2.8	1.5	1.9	2.7	3.0	3.4	3.9	37.1%
Azerbaijan	..	..	..	..	9.0	3.7	5.3	7.1	7.9	9.9	13.4	49.1%
Belarus	..	..	..	..	14.4	9.4	12.7	15.0	16.7	18.3	20.1	40.0%
Estonia	..	..	..	..	6.1	4.3	5.6	7.0	7.6	8.4	9.3	52.5%
Georgia	..	..	..	..	8.2	2.3	3.1	3.8	4.0	4.3	4.8	-41.7%
Kazakhstan	..	..	..	..	26.3	16.2	18.3	24.9	27.3	30.0	33.1	25.7%
Kyrgyzstan	..	..	..	..	2.1	1.0	1.4	1.5	1.7	1.6	1.7	-17.7%
Latvia	..	..	..	..	10.4	5.9	7.8	9.7	10.5	11.6	13.0	24.7%
Lithuania	..	..	..	..	16.0	9.3	11.4	14.4	15.4	16.6	17.8	11.1%
Republic of Moldova	..	..	..	..	3.6	1.5	1.3	1.6	1.7	1.8	1.9	-47.9%
Russia	..	..	..	..	385.9	239.7	259.7	306.6	328.7	349.8	373.2	-3.3%
Tajikistan	..	..	..	..	2.6	1.0	1.0	1.3	1.4	1.5	1.6	-36.3%
Turkmenistan	..	..	..	..	3.7	2.3	2.9	4.7	5.3	5.8	6.3	69.5%
Ukraine	..	..	..	..	72.0	34.5	31.3	39.3	44.0	45.2	48.4	-32.7%
Uzbekistan	..	..	..	..	14.0	11.4	13.8	15.5	16.7	17.9	19.2	36.8%
Former USSR *	**404.4**	**505.6**	**616.9**	**685.7**	**577.1**	**344.1**	**377.4**	**455.1**	**491.9**	**526.2**	**567.7**	**-1.6%**
Argentina	167.5	184.7	212.1	186.6	182.2	250.3	284.2	263.5	287.3	313.6	340.1	86.7%
Bolivia	4.1	5.2	5.7	5.2	5.8	7.1	8.4	9.0	9.4	9.7	10.2	75.7%
Brazil	212.6	311.5	430.2	454.1	501.6	583.4	644.5	678.0	716.7	737.8	765.1	52.5%
Chile	23.0	19.7	28.0	29.2	40.5	61.4	75.2	82.6	87.5	92.5	96.2	137.7%
Colombia	28.5	35.4	46.0	51.4	65.4	80.0	83.8	90.0	94.4	98.8	105.6	61.5%
Costa Rica	4.6	5.8	7.5	7.5	9.6	12.5	15.9	17.6	18.4	19.5	21.0	119.6%
Cuba	15.5	18.5	21.8	32.8	32.5	22.5	28.2	30.4	31.7	35.5	39.9	22.8%
Dominican Republic	4.9	6.8	8.8	9.6	11.1	13.6	19.8	21.0	21.4	23.4	25.9	133.7%
Ecuador	5.9	8.4	10.9	11.7	13.3	15.2	15.9	18.1	19.6	20.5	21.4	60.7%
El Salvador	7.2	8.7	8.7	7.6	8.4	11.3	13.1	14.0	14.2	14.6	15.2	81.4%
Guatemala	7.2	8.9	11.8	11.2	12.9	15.9	19.3	20.6	21.2	21.9	22.9	77.3%
Haiti	3.3	3.5	4.6	4.4	4.4	3.4	3.8	3.8	3.7	3.7	3.8	-12.8%
Honduras	2.1	2.4	3.4	3.7	4.3	5.1	6.0	6.5	6.8	7.1	7.5	74.6%
Jamaica	5.6	6.0	5.1	5.2	6.6	8.0	8.0	8.5	8.6	8.7	9.0	35.5%
Netherlands Antilles	..	..	1.0	1.0	1.0	1.2	1.2	1.2	1.2	1.3	1.3	22.6%
Nicaragua	3.2	4.0	3.2	3.3	2.8	3.1	3.9	4.2	4.4	4.6	4.7	68.3%
Panama	4.5	5.2	6.2	7.3	7.1	9.3	11.6	12.5	13.4	14.3	15.5	118.2%
Paraguay	2.0	2.7	4.5	4.9	5.9	7.1	7.1	7.5	7.8	8.0	8.3	40.8%
Peru	28.5	34.9	39.1	39.7	36.1	47.1	53.3	58.3	61.4	65.4	70.6	95.6%
Trinidad and Tobago	4.5	5.1	7.5	6.7	6.0	6.4	8.2	10.4	11.1	11.9	13.4	125.1%
Uruguay	11.4	12.3	15.4	12.7	15.4	18.6	20.7	18.2	20.3	21.6	23.2	50.9%
Venezuela	68.3	77.8	87.8	83.8	95.3	112.9	117.1	101.8	120.5	132.9	146.6	53.9%
Other Latin America	10.1	10.4	13.9	15.0	19.6	20.8	24.8	25.8	26.6	27.5	28.5	45.8%
Latin America	**624.6**	**777.9**	**983.2**	**994.4**	**1 087.6**	**1 316.3**	**1 474.1**	**1 503.5**	**1 607.5**	**1 694.9**	**1 796.0**	**65.1%**
Bangladesh	17.8	16.7	20.4	24.5	29.5	36.5	47.1	54.5	57.9	61.4	65.5	122.2%
Brunei Darussalam	2.2	2.7	4.4	3.7	3.8	4.1	4.3	4.8	4.8	4.8	5.0	34.2%
Cambodia	..	..	..	..	..	2.6	3.7	4.6	5.0	5.7	6.3	..
Chinese Taipei	35.1	47.7	79.4	109.9	170.9	242.4	321.2	340.4	361.3	376.0	393.6	130.3%
India	116.2	131.6	153.4	199.2	269.4	347.2	460.2	544.4	589.7	644.1	703.3	161.0%
Indonesia	29.5	40.2	58.8	77.4	109.2	159.4	165.0	187.3	196.7	207.9	219.3	100.9%
DPR of Korea	3.0	4.7	8.2	13.1	15.6	12.2	10.9	10.9	11.1	11.3	11.5	-26.1%
Malaysia	12.7	16.9	25.4	32.6	45.5	71.5	90.3	99.7	106.9	112.5	119.1	162.0%
Mongolia	..	..	..	0.7	0.9	0.8	0.9	1.1	1.2	1.3	1.4	42.8%
Myanmar	2.6	2.9	4.0	5.0	4.5	5.9	8.9	12.6	14.4	16.2	17.4	286.8%
Nepal	1.7	1.9	2.1	2.7	3.4	4.3	5.5	6.0	6.2	6.3	6.5	92.6%
Pakistan	17.2	20.1	27.1	37.6	49.8	62.5	73.3	80.9	86.9	93.2	99.0	98.8%
Philippines	28.2	35.4	47.6	44.6	56.2	62.6	75.9	84.7	89.9	94.4	99.4	76.8%
Singapore	10.5	14.5	21.8	29.7	44.7	68.2	92.7	97.2	105.7	112.7	121.6	172.3%
Sri Lanka	4.3	5.0	6.5	8.3	9.8	12.8	16.3	17.7	18.7	19.8	21.3	116.6%
Thailand	20.1	25.4	37.3	48.6	79.4	120.0	122.7	141.5	150.4	157.1	165.0	107.9%
Vietnam	8.1	8.2	8.6	11.9	15.0	22.3	31.2	38.3	41.3	44.8	48.4	222.4%
Other Asia	10.4	11.6	13.6	15.4	17.7	21.6	23.6	27.5	30.5	32.2	35.1	98.2%
Asia	**319.7**	**385.5**	**518.7**	**664.8**	**925.1**	**1 257.0**	**1 553.8**	**1 753.8**	**1 878.6**	**2 001.7**	**2 138.6**	**131.2%**
People's Rep. of China	107.1	133.4	182.9	304.5	444.6	792.8	1 198.5	1 557.7	1 715.0	1 889.9	2 092.2	370.6%
Hong Kong, China	25.8	33.1	58.3	76.6	108.4	142.2	168.8	178.5	193.8	208.4	222.8	105.5%
China	**132.9**	**166.5**	**241.3**	**381.1**	**553.0**	**935.0**	**1 367.2**	**1 736.2**	**1 908.8**	**2 098.3**	**2 315.0**	**318.6%**

* Data for individual countries of the Former USSR are not available prior to 1990.

GDP using purchasing power parities
PIB selon les parités de pouvoir d'achat

billion 2000 US$ using PPPs

	1971	1975	1980	1985	1990	1995	2000	2003	2004	2005	2006	% change 90-06
World	17 400.4	20 474.0	24 889.5	28 422.9	33 070.4	37 504.6	45 240.0	49 647.5	52 222.8	54 690.8	57 564.5	74.1%
Annex I Parties	..	..	..	..	*22 257.3*	*23 355.1*	*27 164.2*	*28 650.3*	*29 636.1*	*30 448.1*	*31 421.4*	*41.2%*
Annex II Parties	*10 521.9*	*11 911.5*	*14 139.3*	*15 977.3*	*18 940.6*	*20 882.4*	*24 392.0*	*25 491.0*	*26 244.2*	*26 862.7*	*27 599.7*	*45.7%*
North America	*4 197.7*	*4 690.3*	*5 624.1*	*6 579.0*	*7 709.6*	*8 685.7*	*10 637.7*	*11 181.5*	*11 584.2*	*11 940.3*	*12 282.2*	*59.3%*
Europe	*4 748.2*	*5 359.8*	*6 241.3*	*6 751.0*	*7 934.4*	*8 600.9*	*9 903.3*	*10 328.6*	*10 569.4*	*10 748.2*	*11 050.7*	*39.3%*
Pacific	*1 576.0*	*1 861.3*	*2 273.9*	*2 647.3*	*3 296.6*	*3 595.8*	*3 851.0*	*3 980.9*	*4 090.6*	*4 174.1*	*4 266.8*	*29.4%*
Annex I EIT	..	..	..	..	*3 007.1*	*2 110.1*	*2 332.2*	*2 694.5*	*2 885.5*	*3 041.7*	*3 244.9*	*7.9%*
Non-Annex I Parties	..	..	..	..	*10 813.1*	*14 149.5*	*18 075.9*	*20 997.2*	*22 586.7*	*24 242.7*	*26 143.0*	*141.8%*
Annex I Kyoto Parties	..	..	..	..	*14 838.5*	*14 984.3*	*16 911.3*	*17 879.2*	*18 442.8*	*18 884.9*	*19 503.5*	*31.4%*
Non-OECD Total	5 933.4	7 359.6	9 280.3	10 764.8	12 153.5	14 340.1	17 993.8	21 083.1	22 742.7	24 451.3	26 406.9	117.3%
OECD Total	11 467.0	13 114.3	15 609.2	17 658.1	20 916.9	23 164.5	27 246.3	28 564.4	29 480.1	30 239.5	31 157.5	49.0%
Canada	347.2	413.4	496.1	568.0	654.6	712.9	872.9	931.7	960.3	989.7	1 017.0	55.4%
Mexico	293.8	387.2	534.4	588.2	639.2	689.5	899.3	918.5	956.7	983.5	1 030.5	61.2%
United States	3 850.5	4 276.9	5 128.0	6 011.0	7 055.0	7 972.8	9 764.8	10 249.8	10 623.9	10 950.6	11 265.2	59.7%
OECD N. America	4 491.5	5 077.5	6 158.4	7 167.2	8 348.8	9 375.3	11 537.0	12 100.0	12 540.9	12 923.9	13 312.7	59.5%
Australia	214.2	237.8	275.7	319.8	368.9	433.4	524.6	584.3	599.9	616.8	631.9	71.3%
Japan	1 317.9	1 571.8	1 947.9	2 268.7	2 867.2	3 091.8	3 246.3	3 306.9	3 397.6	3 462.5	3 538.1	23.4%
Korea	99.8	132.7	185.5	270.3	428.3	623.8	772.8	884.9	926.8	965.7	1 013.9	136.7%
New Zealand	43.9	51.8	50.3	58.8	60.6	70.6	80.1	89.8	91.8	93.1	94.9	96.7	59.7%
OECD Pacific	1 675.8	1 994.0	2 459.4	2 917.6	3 724.9	4 219.6	4 623.8	4 865.9	5 017.4	5 139.8	5 280.7	41.8%
Austria	107.0	123.4	145.0	156.0	181.4	202.0	233.4	240.2	245.8	250.8	259.1	42.8%
Belgium	139.3	160.0	187.0	196.0	228.2	246.9	282.2	291.6	300.3	305.3	314.0	37.6%
Czech Republic	104.0	118.7	132.1	138.7	150.0	142.9	153.8	166.4	173.9	184.9	196.7	31.1%
Denmark	79.9	84.6	97.0	110.9	118.9	133.5	153.7	156.1	159.4	164.3	170.1	43.0%
Finland	57.7	69.9	81.1	92.7	109.3	105.2	132.8	141.0	146.2	150.5	158.0	44.6%
France	728.2	840.1	994.0	1 073.4	1 260.4	1 334.8	1 533.0	1 594.6	1 634.0	1 661.9	1 695.0	34.5%
Germany	1 065.6	1 164.7	1 374.4	1 470.8	1 730.1	1 928.8	2 130.3	2 152.0	2 174.8	2 191.9	2 254.7	30.3%
Greece	102.3	121.3	148.7	149.8	159.3	169.5	200.8	229.0	239.4	248.6	259.0	62.6%
Hungary	67.8	86.9	103.5	113.0	116.0	102.9	125.2	141.7	148.5	154.7	160.7	38.6%
Iceland	2.9	3.5	4.8	5.4	6.3	6.4	8.1	8.6	9.3	9.9	10.2	62.4%
Ireland	25.2	30.9	38.6	43.8	55.1	69.1	108.6	128.3	133.9	142.0	150.1	172.4%
Italy	687.3	788.6	980.3	1 065.7	1 243.6	1 324.6	1 455.8	1 487.5	1 505.4	1 506.8	1 535.0	23.4%
Luxembourg	7.0	7.9	8.8	10.0	14.3	17.4	23.4	25.5	26.7	28.1	29.8	108.2%
Netherlands	210.8	238.6	271.9	288.6	342.4	383.5	467.7	478.6	489.3	496.7	511.7	49.4%
Norway	58.7	70.4	87.9	103.5	112.6	135.3	162.1	169.5	176.0	180.8	184.7	64.0%
Poland	210.5	269.2	280.8	283.3	278.6	310.3	403.8	430.6	453.6	470.0	498.8	79.0%
Portugal	64.0	74.3	95.3	99.7	131.3	142.9	174.5	178.0	180.7	182.0	184.2	40.3%
Slovak Republic	37.3	42.5	47.3	51.1	54.8	50.1	59.4	66.5	70.1	74.3	80.4	46.8%
Spain	357.1	442.1	487.3	522.2	650.7	701.2	857.5	941.1	971.8	1 007.0	1 045.8	60.7%
Sweden	135.0	151.9	162.3	178.1	201.6	208.7	246.0	259.5	270.2	279.1	290.5	44.1%
Switzerland	151.4	151.4	164.6	177.4	204.8	205.8	227.7	230.9	236.7	242.4	250.3	22.2%
Turkey	132.0	165.7	186.3	236.2	309.6	362.6	440.0	464.8	506.3	543.7	576.8	86.3%
United Kingdom	768.9	836.2	912.3	1 007.2	1 184.2	1 285.4	1 505.9	1 616.8	1 669.5	1 700.2	1 748.6	47.7%
OECD Europe	5 299.8	6 042.8	6 991.4	7 573.3	8 843.3	9 569.7	11 085.5	11 598.6	11 921.8	12 175.8	12 564.2	42.1%
European Union - 27	..	..	..	..	*8 548.3*	*9 144.3*	*10 544.8*	*11 071.0*	*11 364.5*	*11 590.4*	*11 962.6*	*39.9%*

GDP using purchasing power parities
PIB selon les parités de pouvoir d'achat

billion 2000 US$ using PPPs

	1971	1975	1980	1985	1990	1995	2000	2003	2004	2005	2006	% change 90-06
Non-OECD Total	5 933.4	7 359.6	9 280.3	10 764.8	12 153.5	14 340.1	17 993.8	21 083.1	22 742.7	24 451.3	26 406.9	117.3%
Algeria	51.8	77.4	104.5	132.2	137.3	139.1	162.3	186.3	196.0	206.4	212.6	54.8%
Angola	14.8	14.9	15.0	16.0	18.8	14.9	20.2	24.7	27.5	33.1	37.9	102.2%
Benin	2.5	2.8	3.4	4.2	4.4	5.4	7.0	8.0	8.2	8.5	8.8	101.1%
Botswana	..	..	..	4.6	8.1	9.8	14.7	17.3	18.4	19.1	19.9	147.0%
Cameroon	9.7	12.9	17.6	27.4	24.4	22.1	27.9	31.6	32.7	33.4	34.7	42.5%
Congo	1.1	1.6	2.0	3.2	3.1	3.2	3.6	4.0	4.2	4.5	4.8	51.3%
Dem. Rep. of Congo	49.9	52.9	49.1	53.8	53.6	36.8	30.1	32.3	34.4	36.6	38.5	-28.1%
Côte d'Ivoire	12.9	16.0	19.7	19.9	21.1	22.7	26.6	25.8	26.2	26.1	27.2	28.7%
Egypt	50.0	57.3	91.5	126.8	155.9	183.9	237.3	261.4	272.3	284.6	303.9	95.0%
Eritrea	..	..	..	..	..	3.5	3.6	4.2	4.3	4.3	4.3	..
Ethiopia	29.0	31.6	35.3	33.3	41.7	41.9	52.4	55.1	62.4	68.7	74.9	79.6%
Gabon	2.8	5.7	5.3	6.0	6.3	7.3	7.4	7.8	7.9	8.1	8.2	30.0%
Ghana	20.6	19.3	20.2	19.8	25.0	30.9	38.2	43.6	46.1	48.8	51.8	106.9%
Kenya	10.0	13.0	17.7	20.0	26.3	28.5	31.7	34.1	35.7	37.8	40.0	51.7%
Libya	46.7	37.8	59.6	51.2	40.5	43.2	46.9	55.2	57.8	59.8	63.1	56.0%
Morocco	35.2	42.4	55.3	65.0	80.7	84.5	100.7	116.5	121.5	123.6	132.5	64.3%
Mozambique	9.8	8.3	8.5	6.6	8.6	9.8	14.3	18.9	20.3	21.6	23.4	171.2%
Namibia	..	..	..	..	..	9.3	11.1	12.5	13.2	13.8	14.4	..
Nigeria	51.9	59.6	72.2	61.9	80.3	90.8	105.6	122.4	129.8	137.8	145.9	81.7%
Senegal	6.9	7.7	8.1	9.4	11.1	11.9	14.8	16.6	17.5	18.5	19.1	72.6%
South Africa	207.5	238.0	277.2	296.5	322.0	336.1	385.6	423.0	444.0	466.7	489.9	52.2%
Sudan	16.1	19.8	22.3	23.0	28.5	36.5	49.6	59.1	62.2	67.1	75.9	166.6%
United Rep. of Tanzania	6.9	8.3	9.5	10.0	13.2	14.4	17.6	21.2	22.7	24.2	25.6	94.2%
Togo	3.5	4.2	5.3	5.2	5.9	5.9	7.3	7.8	8.0	8.1	8.2	40.3%
Tunisia	14.5	19.6	26.6	32.7	37.8	45.7	60.1	67.6	71.7	74.7	78.6	108.0%
Zambia	6.2	7.0	7.1	7.3	7.9	7.3	8.4	9.6	10.1	10.6	11.3	43.2%
Zimbabwe	14.9	17.3	18.6	22.9	28.6	30.4	31.5	26.2	25.2	23.9	22.8	-20.6%
Other Africa	95.9	102.4	117.5	124.3	140.5	141.6	176.0	199.8	209.5	219.2	229.1	63.1%
Africa	771.0	877.9	1 068.9	1 183.2	1 331.5	1 417.4	1 692.4	1 892.5	1 989.8	2 089.6	2 207.4	65.8%
Bahrain	1.7	3.2	5.2	4.9	6.1	8.5	10.4	12.3	13.0	13.9	15.0	145.7%
Islamic Rep. of Iran	170.0	241.3	209.1	253.3	256.5	303.2	369.7	441.3	463.8	484.0	512.1	99.6%
Iraq	69.0	87.8	132.0	84.5	45.1	17.2	35.4	17.9	26.1	27.1	27.2	-39.7%
Israel	37.9	49.2	59.3	68.6	84.7	116.0	144.7	145.1	151.5	159.4	167.5	97.7%
Jordan	4.9	4.8	9.9	12.8	12.1	17.1	20.0	23.2	25.1	26.9	28.9	139.0%
Kuwait	36.3	30.0	31.7	25.1	28.8	39.1	42.9	51.5	54.7	59.4	62.3	116.2%
Lebanon	12.2	12.0	10.2	14.3	8.1	14.4	16.2	18.2	19.6	19.8	19.8	143.9%
Oman	4.9	6.4	8.3	16.8	19.6	26.1	30.8	34.1	35.2	37.8	40.6	107.2%
Qatar	8.1	8.2	9.5	8.0	7.9	9.1	15.9	18.2	22.0	23.3	25.4	221.5%
Saudi Arabia	78.8	164.0	229.1	181.5	214.8	247.4	280.8	304.4	320.4	341.4	357.1	66.3%
Syria	11.1	18.9	26.1	30.1	32.4	47.5	53.2	59.1	62.0	64.9	68.2	110.5%
United Arab Emirates	8.7	22.4	46.7	40.8	45.8	54.2	69.7	86.4	94.8	102.9	112.9	146.2%
Yemen	2.1	2.9	5.1	7.3	8.6	11.3	14.7	16.5	17.2	18.0	18.6	115.7%
Middle East	445.7	651.0	782.3	747.9	770.6	911.0	1 104.6	1 228.4	1 305.5	1 378.8	1 455.5	88.9%
Albania	5.3	6.6	8.8	9.7	9.9	8.7	11.4	13.3	14.0	14.8	15.5	56.5%
Bosnia and Herzegovina *	..	..	..	..	5.7	6.1	20.5	23.5	24.9	26.2	27.8	388.2%
Bulgaria	24.9	34.0	45.8	54.0	58.2	51.0	48.9	56.1	59.8	63.5	67.4	15.8%
Croatia *	..	..	..	..	47.9	34.7	41.0	47.7	49.5	51.6	54.0	12.7%
Cyprus	3.1	2.8	4.8	6.3	8.9	11.1	13.3	14.4	14.9	15.5	16.1	81.7%
Gibraltar	0.4	0.4	0.5	0.5	0.6	0.7	0.8	0.8	0.9	0.9	0.9	47.4%
FYR of Macedonia *	..	..	..	..	13.3	10.5	12.2	12.0	12.5	13.0	13.4	0.5%
Malta	1.1	1.7	2.9	3.1	4.2	5.5	6.9	6.8	6.7	6.9	7.1	67.2%
Romania	67.0	101.4	146.2	172.0	157.0	141.0	132.3	154.6	167.6	174.5	187.9	19.6%
Serbia *	..	..	..	..	37.4	36.6	36.5	40.6	43.8	42.6	45.0	20.4%
Slovenia *	..	..	..	..	27.9	27.0	33.5	36.5	38.1	39.7	41.7	49.4%
Former Yugoslavia *	73.0	89.6	120.6	122.7	..	..	..	..	..	..	..	..
Non-OECD Europe	174.8	236.5	329.5	368.4	371.1	333.0	357.2	406.2	432.8	449.1	476.8	28.5%

* Data for individual countries of the Former Yugoslavia are not available prior to 1990.

GDP using purchasing power parities
PIB selon les parités de pouvoir d'achat

billion 2000 US$ using PPPs

	1971	1975	1980	1985	1990	1995	2000	2003	2004	2005	2006	% change 90-06
Armenia	..	..	..	..	11.0	5.8	7.5	10.5	11.7	13.3	15.1	37.1%
Azerbaijan	..	..	..	..	33.8	14.2	19.9	26.9	29.7	37.5	50.5	49.1%
Belarus	..	..	..	..	54.2	35.4	48.1	56.6	63.1	68.9	75.9	40.0%
Estonia	..	..	..	..	14.0	9.8	12.9	16.0	17.3	19.1	21.3	52.5%
Georgia	..	..	..	..	25.1	7.1	9.4	11.6	12.3	13.4	14.7	-41.7%
Kazakhstan	..	..	..	..	93.2	57.2	64.7	88.1	96.5	105.9	117.1	25.7%
Kyrgyzstan	..	..	..	..	11.0	5.6	7.4	8.3	8.9	8.9	9.1	-17.6%
Latvia	..	..	..	..	25.2	14.4	18.9	23.3	25.4	28.0	31.4	24.7%
Lithuania	..	..	..	..	42.9	24.9	30.5	38.4	41.2	44.3	47.6	11.1%
Republic of Moldova	..	..	..	..	15.8	6.3	5.6	6.9	7.4	7.9	8.3	-47.7%
Russia	..	..	..	..	1 523.6	946.5	1 025.4	1 210.7	1 297.9	1 381.0	1 473.5	-3.3%
Tajikistan	..	..	..	..	13.1	5.0	5.0	6.6	7.3	7.8	8.4	-36.2%
Turkmenistan	..	..	..	..	20.2	12.6	15.4	25.1	28.8	31.4	34.2	69.7%
Ukraine	..	..	..	..	456.9	219.3	198.5	249.5	279.7	287.2	307.6	-32.7%
Uzbekistan	..	..	..	..	37.7	30.6	36.9	41.7	44.9	48.0	51.6	36.8%
Former USSR *	**1 665.5**	**2 082.2**	**2 540.8**	**2 823.8**	**2 377.6**	**1 394.5**	**1 506.0**	**1 820.2**	**1 971.9**	**2 102.7**	**2 266.1**	**-4.7%**
Argentina	263.1	290.0	333.1	292.9	286.1	392.9	446.3	413.7	451.0	492.4	534.1	86.7%
Bolivia	9.7	12.2	13.6	12.3	13.7	16.8	19.9	21.3	22.1	23.0	24.1	75.7%
Brazil	410.3	601.2	830.3	876.4	968.1	1 126.0	1 243.8	1 308.5	1 383.2	1 424.0	1 476.7	52.5%
Chile	43.0	36.8	52.3	54.7	75.7	114.8	140.7	154.5	163.7	173.1	180.0	137.7%
Colombia	84.7	105.2	136.6	152.7	194.3	237.9	249.0	267.5	280.5	293.7	313.7	61.5%
Costa Rica	9.3	11.7	15.0	15.0	19.3	25.2	32.1	35.5	37.0	39.2	42.3	119.5%
Cuba	35.7	42.8	50.3	75.7	75.0	52.0	65.1	70.1	73.2	81.8	92.1	22.8%
Dominican Republic	13.8	19.2	24.8	27.3	31.3	38.4	55.9	59.4	60.5	66.2	73.2	133.7%
Ecuador	14.7	21.0	27.1	29.0	33.2	37.9	39.7	45.2	48.8	51.1	53.4	60.7%
El Salvador	15.9	19.2	19.1	16.6	18.4	24.8	28.9	30.7	31.3	32.2	33.4	81.4%
Guatemala	16.9	21.0	27.7	26.2	30.2	37.2	45.2	48.3	49.6	51.2	53.5	77.3%
Haiti	10.9	11.6	15.3	14.5	14.7	11.4	12.9	12.7	12.3	12.5	12.8	-12.8%
Honduras	6.5	7.4	10.5	11.4	13.4	15.9	18.4	20.1	21.1	22.0	23.3	74.6%
Jamaica	6.5	7.0	5.9	6.0	7.7	9.3	9.3	9.9	10.0	10.1	10.4	35.4%
Netherlands Antilles	..	..	2.3	2.2	2.4	2.7	2.7	2.8	2.8	2.8	2.9	22.6%
Nicaragua	12.6	15.7	12.7	13.1	11.0	12.1	15.4	16.4	17.2	17.9	18.6	68.3%
Panama	7.0	8.0	9.5	11.3	10.9	14.2	17.8	19.1	20.6	22.0	23.8	118.2%
Paraguay	6.4	8.4	14.2	15.4	18.7	22.5	22.3	23.6	24.6	25.3	26.3	40.8%
Peru	65.6	80.3	89.9	91.4	83.0	108.4	122.6	134.2	141.2	150.3	162.4	95.6%
Trinidad and Tobago	6.5	7.3	10.7	9.6	8.6	9.2	11.7	14.9	15.9	17.1	19.2	125.1%
Uruguay	16.2	17.5	21.8	18.0	21.7	26.4	29.3	25.7	28.8	30.6	32.8	50.8%
Venezuela	81.6	93.0	105.0	100.2	113.8	134.9	140.0	121.7	144.0	158.8	175.2	53.9%
Other Latin America	15.5	16.3	20.7	21.4	27.1	29.4	34.7	36.2	37.4	38.6	40.3	48.9%
Latin America	**1 152.2**	**1 452.6**	**1 848.4**	**1 893.3**	**2 078.2**	**2 500.4**	**2 803.7**	**2 891.9**	**3 076.9**	**3 236.2**	**3 424.5**	**64.8%**
Bangladesh	75.3	70.4	86.4	103.7	124.5	154.3	199.0	230.2	244.6	259.2	276.6	122.2%
Brunei Darussalam	2.7	3.3	5.3	4.4	4.5	4.9	5.2	5.7	5.8	5.8	6.0	34.2%
Cambodia	..	..	..	..	..	15.5	22.1	27.4	30.1	34.1	37.7	..
Chinese Taipei	53.6	73.0	121.4	168.1	261.4	370.8	491.4	520.6	552.6	575.1	602.0	130.3%
India	606.3	686.9	800.8	1 039.8	1 406.3	1 812.3	2 402.1	2 841.4	3 077.9	3 362.1	3 671.2	161.0%
Indonesia	107.2	145.9	213.6	280.9	396.4	578.8	599.3	680.1	714.3	754.9	796.3	100.9%
DPR of Korea	10.6	16.7	28.7	45.9	54.8	43.0	38.2	38.4	39.1	39.8	40.5	-26.1%
Malaysia	27.6	36.9	55.5	71.2	99.2	156.0	197.2	217.7	233.5	245.5	260.0	162.0%
Mongolia	..	..	..	2.6	3.7	3.2	3.7	4.1	4.5	4.9	5.3	42.9%
Myanmar	15.8	17.6	23.9	30.3	27.2	35.9	53.9	76.4	86.8	98.2	105.1	286.8%
Nepal	10.1	11.1	12.5	15.9	19.8	25.6	32.4	35.2	36.5	37.4	38.1	92.5%
Pakistan	61.0	71.0	96.0	133.2	176.5	221.3	259.7	286.7	307.8	330.2	350.8	98.8%
Philippines	113.6	142.6	191.5	179.6	226.3	251.9	305.5	340.7	361.8	379.8	400.2	76.8%
Singapore	10.8	14.8	22.3	30.4	45.7	69.8	94.8	99.4	108.1	115.3	124.4	172.3%
Sri Lanka	17.5	20.6	26.6	33.9	40.1	52.1	66.7	72.3	76.3	80.9	86.8	116.6%
Thailand	63.8	80.4	118.0	153.8	251.1	379.8	388.4	447.7	475.8	497.2	522.0	107.9%
Vietnam	41.0	41.4	43.8	60.4	76.3	113.2	158.4	194.6	209.7	227.4	246.0	222.4%
Other Asia	36.0	39.0	44.3	51.1	52.8	57.3	62.5	74.3	80.8	86.0	91.9	74.1%
Asia	**1 252.9**	**1 471.6**	**1 890.5**	**2 405.1**	**3 266.5**	**4 345.6**	**5 380.0**	**6 192.7**	**6 645.9**	**7 133.7**	**7 660.9**	**134.5%**
People's Rep. of China	444.5	553.6	759.4	1 263.9	1 845.6	3 291.0	4 975.2	6 466.3	7 119.3	7 845.5	8 685.0	370.6%
Hong Kong, China	26.7	34.3	60.4	79.3	112.3	147.2	174.7	184.8	200.6	215.7	230.7	105.5%
China	**471.2**	**587.9**	**819.8**	**1 343.2**	**1 957.9**	**3 438.3**	**5 149.9**	**6 651.0**	**7 320.0**	**8 061.2**	**8 915.7**	**355.4%**

* Data for individual countries of the Former USSR are not available prior to 1990.

Population

Population

millions

	1971	1975	1980	1985	1990	1995	2000	2003	2004	2005	2006	% change 90-06
World	3 759.3	4 064.8	4 438.4	4 831.1	5 262.4	5 675.9	6 072.8	6 305.8	6 383.0	6 459.7	6 536.0	24.2%
Annex I Parties	*827.8*	*858.5*	*891.8*	*920.9*	*1 176.5*	*1 208.8*	*1 234.4*	*1 250.9*	*1 256.5*	*1 261.4*	*1 266.7*	*7.7%*
Annex II Parties	*705.1*	*729.1*	*754.8*	*775.7*	*799.2*	*827.7*	*853.1*	*870.9*	*876.7*	*882.5*	*888.1*	*11.1%*
North America	*229.7*	*239.1*	*252.2*	*264.3*	*277.9*	*295.9*	*313.1*	*323.0*	*326.1*	*329.3*	*332.5*	*19.6%*
Europe	*354.6*	*361.4*	*367.8*	*371.3*	*377.3*	*384.4*	*390.0*	*396.2*	*398.6*	*400.9*	*403.0*	*6.8%*
Pacific	*120.8*	*128.6*	*134.8*	*140.0*	*144.0*	*147.3*	*150.0*	*151.7*	*152.0*	*152.3*	*152.6*	*6.0%*
Annex I EIT	*86.6*	*89.3*	*92.7*	*94.9*	*321.1*	*319.5*	*313.9*	*309.3*	*308.0*	*306.8*	*305.6*	*-4.8%*
Non-Annex I Parties	*2 931.4*	*3 206.2*	*3 546.6*	*3 910.2*	*4 085.9*	*4 467.1*	*4 838.4*	*5 054.9*	*5 126.5*	*5 198.4*	*5 269.3*	*29.0%*
Annex I Kyoto Parties	*583.9*	*602.5*	*619.7*	*632.1*	*859.9*	*870.3*	*874.5*	*879.0*	*880.8*	*882.6*	*884.1*	*2.8%*
Non-OECD Total	2 877.7	3 144.2	3 473.8	3 827.6	4 218.8	4 586.1	4 942.9	5 150.6	5 219.8	5 289.3	5 358.1	27.0%
OECD Total	881.6	920.6	964.6	1 003.6	1 043.6	1 089.8	1 129.9	1 155.2	1 163.2	1 170.4	1 177.9	12.9%
Canada	22.0	23.1	24.5	25.8	27.7	29.3	30.7	31.7	32.0	32.3	32.6	17.8%
Mexico	49.9	56.7	65.7	73.5	81.3	91.1	98.3	101.9	102.9	103.8	104.7	28.9%
United States	207.7	216.0	227.7	238.5	250.2	266.6	282.5	291.3	294.1	297.0	299.8	19.8%
OECD N. America	**279.5**	**295.9**	**317.9**	**337.9**	**359.1**	**387.0**	**411.4**	**424.9**	**429.0**	**433.1**	**437.2**	**21.7%**
Australia	13.2	14.0	14.8	15.9	17.2	18.2	19.3	20.0	20.2	20.5	20.7	20.8%
Japan	104.8	111.5	116.8	120.8	123.5	125.5	126.8	127.7	127.8	127.8	127.8	3.5%
Korea	32.9	35.3	38.1	40.8	42.9	45.1	47.0	47.9	48.0	48.1	48.3	12.7%
New Zealand	2.9	3.1	3.1	3.3	3.4	3.7	3.9	4.0	4.1	4.1	4.1	23.2%
OECD Pacific	**153.7**	**163.9**	**172.9**	**180.8**	**186.9**	**192.4**	**197.0**	**199.6**	**200.1**	**200.5**	**200.9**	**7.5%**
Austria	7.5	7.6	7.5	7.6	7.7	7.9	8.0	8.1	8.2	8.2	8.3	7.9%
Belgium	9.7	9.8	9.9	9.9	10.0	10.1	10.2	10.4	10.4	10.5	10.5	5.8%
Czech Republic	9.8	10.1	10.3	10.3	10.4	10.3	10.3	10.2	10.2	10.2	10.3	-0.9%
Denmark	5.0	5.1	5.1	5.1	5.1	5.2	5.3	5.4	5.4	5.4	5.4	5.8%
Finland	4.6	4.7	4.8	4.9	5.0	5.1	5.2	5.2	5.2	5.2	5.3	5.6%
France	52.4	53.9	55.1	56.6	58.2	59.4	60.8	62.0	62.4	62.8	63.2	8.6%
Germany	78.3	78.7	78.3	77.7	79.4	81.7	82.2	82.5	82.5	82.5	82.4	3.8%
Greece	9.0	9.2	9.8	10.1	10.3	10.6	10.9	11.0	11.1	11.1	11.1	7.9%
Hungary	10.4	10.5	10.7	10.6	10.4	10.3	10.2	10.1	10.1	10.1	10.1	-2.8%
Iceland	0.2	0.2	0.2	0.2	0.3	0.3	0.3	0.3	0.3	0.3	0.3	19.2%
Ireland	3.0	3.2	3.4	3.5	3.5	3.6	3.8	4.0	4.1	4.1	4.3	21.3%
Italy	54.1	55.4	56.4	56.6	56.7	56.8	56.9	57.6	58.2	58.6	58.9	3.8%
Luxembourg	0.3	0.4	0.4	0.4	0.4	0.4	0.4	0.5	0.5	0.5	0.5	23.8%
Netherlands	13.2	13.7	14.1	14.5	14.9	15.5	15.9	16.2	16.3	16.3	16.3	9.3%
Norway	3.9	4.0	4.1	4.2	4.2	4.4	4.5	4.6	4.6	4.6	4.7	9.9%
Poland	32.8	34.0	35.6	37.2	38.0	38.3	38.3	38.2	38.2	38.2	38.1	0.3%
Portugal	8.7	9.2	9.9	10.1	10.0	10.0	10.2	10.4	10.5	10.5	10.6	5.9%
Slovak Republic	4.6	4.7	5.0	5.2	5.3	5.4	5.4	5.4	5.4	5.4	5.4	1.8%
Spain	34.3	35.7	37.7	38.6	39.0	39.4	40.3	42.0	42.7	43.4	44.1	13.0%
Sweden	8.1	8.2	8.3	8.4	8.6	8.8	8.9	9.0	9.0	9.0	9.1	6.1%
Switzerland	6.3	6.4	6.4	6.5	6.8	7.1	7.2	7.4	7.5	7.5	7.6	11.2%
Turkey	36.2	40.1	44.4	50.3	56.2	61.6	67.5	70.7	71.8	72.1	73.0	29.8%
United Kingdom	55.9	56.2	56.3	56.6	57.2	58.0	58.9	59.6	59.8	60.2	60.5	5.8%
OECD Europe	**448.4**	**460.9**	**473.8**	**484.9**	**497.6**	**510.4**	**521.6**	**530.8**	**534.2**	**536.8**	**539.8**	**8.5%**
European Union - 27	*431.7*	*441.0*	*450.6*	*456.2*	*472.9*	*478.7*	*482.9*	*487.6*	*489.8*	*492.0*	*493.8*	*4.4%*

Population

Population

millions

	1971	1975	1980	1985	1990	1995	2000	2003	2004	2005	2006	% change 90-06
Non-OECD Total	2 877.7	3 144.2	3 473.8	3 827.6	4 218.8	4 586.1	4 942.9	5 150.6	5 219.8	5 289.3	5 358.1	27.0%
Algeria	14.2	16.0	18.8	22.1	25.3	28.3	30.5	31.9	32.4	32.9	33.4	31.9%
Angola	6.2	6.8	7.8	9.3	10.5	12.3	13.9	15.2	15.6	16.1	16.6	57.2%
Benin	2.9	3.2	3.7	4.4	5.2	6.2	7.2	8.0	8.2	8.5	8.8	69.1%
Botswana	..	..	..	1.2	1.4	1.6	1.7	1.8	1.8	1.8	1.9	35.9%
Cameroon	7.0	7.8	9.1	10.5	12.2	14.1	15.9	17.0	17.4	17.8	18.2	48.5%
Congo	1.4	1.5	1.8	2.1	2.4	2.8	3.2	3.4	3.5	3.6	3.7	52.3%
Dem. Rep. of Congo	21.2	24.0	28.1	32.4	37.9	45.3	50.7	55.2	56.9	58.7	60.6	59.8%
Côte d'Ivoire	5.5	6.6	8.3	10.5	12.8	15.0	17.0	18.0	18.3	18.6	18.9	48.0%
Egypt	36.0	39.2	43.7	49.2	55.1	60.6	66.5	70.3	71.6	72.9	74.2	34.5%
Eritrea	..	..	..	..	..	3.2	3.7	4.2	4.4	4.5	4.7	..
Ethiopia	31.6	35.1	40.2	46.2	54.3	56.6	65.8	71.4	73.2	75.2	77.2	42.0%
Gabon	0.5	0.6	0.7	0.8	0.9	1.1	1.2	1.2	1.3	1.3	1.3	42.8%
Ghana	9.3	10.3	11.4	13.5	15.6	17.9	20.1	21.6	22.1	22.5	23.0	47.7%
Kenya	11.7	13.5	16.3	19.7	23.4	27.4	31.3	33.8	34.7	35.6	36.6	55.9%
Libya	2.1	2.5	3.1	3.9	4.4	4.8	5.3	5.7	5.8	5.9	6.0	38.4%
Morocco	15.4	17.1	19.4	21.8	24.2	26.4	28.5	29.5	29.8	30.1	30.5	26.2%
Mozambique	9.7	10.6	12.1	13.3	13.5	15.9	18.2	19.6	20.1	20.5	21.0	54.8%
Namibia	..	..	..	..	..	1.7	1.9	2.0	2.0	2.0	2.0	..
Nigeria	55.1	61.2	71.1	81.6	94.5	109.0	124.8	134.7	138.0	141.4	144.7	53.2%
Senegal	4.5	5.1	5.9	6.8	7.9	9.1	10.3	11.2	11.5	11.8	12.1	52.9%
South Africa	22.6	24.7	27.6	31.3	35.2	39.1	44.0	45.8	46.3	46.9	47.4	34.6%
Sudan	14.9	16.8	19.6	23.1	25.9	29.5	33.3	35.4	36.1	36.9	37.7	45.4%
United Rep. of Tanzania	14.0	16.0	18.7	21.8	25.5	29.9	33.8	36.6	37.5	38.5	39.5	54.8%
Togo	2.2	2.4	2.8	3.4	4.0	4.5	5.4	5.9	6.1	6.2	6.4	61.8%
Tunisia	5.2	5.6	6.4	7.3	8.2	9.0	9.6	9.8	9.9	10.0	10.1	24.2%
Zambia	4.4	5.0	5.9	7.0	8.1	9.3	10.5	11.1	11.3	11.5	11.7	44.0%
Zimbabwe	5.4	6.2	7.3	8.9	10.5	11.8	12.7	12.9	13.0	13.1	13.2	26.1%
Other Africa	68.9	75.9	88.7	99.8	116.0	127.0	148.1	161.7	166.4	171.3	176.3	52.0%
Africa	371.8	413.8	478.3	551.6	634.9	719.3	815.2	874.8	895.2	916.2	937.5	47.6%
Bahrain	0.2	0.3	0.3	0.4	0.5	0.6	0.7	0.7	0.7	0.7	0.7	49.9%
Islamic Rep. of Iran	29.4	33.2	39.1	47.1	54.4	59.0	63.9	67.0	68.1	69.1	70.1	28.9%
Iraq	9.7	11.1	13.2	15.7	18.1	19.6	22.7	24.7	25.4	26.1	26.8	47.7%
Israel	3.1	3.5	3.9	4.2	4.7	5.5	6.3	6.7	6.8	6.9	7.0	51.3%
Jordan	1.6	1.8	2.2	2.6	3.2	4.2	4.8	5.2	5.3	5.4	5.5	74.7%
Kuwait	0.8	1.0	1.4	1.7	2.1	1.8	2.2	2.4	2.5	2.5	2.6	22.3%
Lebanon	2.5	2.7	2.8	2.9	3.0	3.5	3.8	3.9	4.0	4.0	4.1	36.3%
Oman	0.8	0.9	1.2	1.5	1.8	2.2	2.4	2.5	2.5	2.5	2.5	38.1%
Qatar	0.1	0.2	0.2	0.4	0.5	0.5	0.6	0.7	0.8	0.8	0.8	75.8%
Saudi Arabia	6.0	7.3	9.6	12.9	16.4	18.5	20.7	22.1	22.5	23.1	23.7	44.6%
Syria	6.6	7.5	9.0	10.8	12.7	14.6	16.5	17.9	18.4	18.9	19.4	52.6%
United Arab Emirates	0.3	0.5	1.0	1.4	1.8	2.4	3.2	3.8	3.9	4.1	4.2	139.6%
Yemen	6.5	7.1	8.4	10.1	12.3	15.5	18.2	19.9	20.5	21.1	21.7	76.5%
Middle East	67.5	77.1	92.3	111.8	131.5	147.9	165.9	177.4	181.3	185.3	189.3	44.0%
Albania	2.2	2.4	2.7	3.0	3.3	3.2	3.1	3.1	3.1	3.2	3.2	-3.6%
Bosnia and Herzegovina *	..	..	..	..	4.3	3.4	3.8	3.9	3.9	3.9	3.9	-8.9%
Bulgaria	8.5	8.7	8.9	8.9	8.7	8.4	8.1	7.8	7.8	7.7	7.7	-11.8%
Croatia *	..	..	..	..	4.8	4.7	4.5	4.4	4.4	4.4	4.4	-7.1%
Cyprus	0.6	0.5	0.5	0.5	0.6	0.7	0.7	0.7	0.7	0.8	0.8	32.9%
Gibraltar	0.0	0.0	0.0	0.0	0.0	0.0	0.0	0.0	0.0	0.0	0.0	-3.4%
FYR of Macedonia *	..	..	..	..	1.9	2.0	2.0	2.0	2.0	2.0	2.0	6.7%
Malta	0.3	0.3	0.4	0.3	0.4	0.4	0.4	0.4	0.4	0.4	0.4	12.8%
Romania	20.5	21.2	22.2	22.7	23.2	22.7	22.4	21.7	21.7	21.6	21.6	-7.0%
Serbia *	..	..	..	..	9.9	10.9	8.2	8.1	8.1	7.4	7.4	-25.1%
Slovenia *	..	..	..	..	2.0	2.0	2.0	2.0	2.0	2.0	2.0	0.5%
Former Yugoslavia *	20.0	20.7	21.6	22.2	..	..	..	..	..	..	..	..
Non-OECD Europe	52.2	54.0	56.3	57.7	59.1	58.2	55.2	54.3	54.2	53.6	53.5	-9.5%

* Data for individual countries of the Former Yugoslavia are not available prior to 1990.

Population

Population

millions

	1971	1975	1980	1985	1990	1995	2000	2003	2004	2005	2006	% change 90-06
Armenia	..	..	..	..	3.5	3.2	3.1	3.0	3.0	3.0	3.0	-15.1%
Azerbaijan	..	..	..	..	7.2	7.7	8.0	8.2	8.3	8.4	8.5	18.5%
Belarus	..	..	..	..	10.2	10.2	10.0	9.9	9.8	9.8	9.7	-4.5%
Estonia	..	..	..	..	1.6	1.4	1.4	1.4	1.3	1.3	1.3	-14.5%
Georgia	..	..	..	..	5.5	5.0	4.6	4.5	4.5	4.5	4.4	-18.8%
Kazakhstan	..	..	..	..	16.3	15.8	14.9	14.9	15.0	15.1	15.3	-6.4%
Kyrgyzstan	..	..	..	..	4.4	4.6	4.9	5.0	5.1	5.1	5.2	17.4%
Latvia	..	..	..	..	2.7	2.5	2.4	2.3	2.3	2.3	2.3	-14.3%
Lithuania	..	..	..	..	3.7	3.6	3.5	3.5	3.4	3.4	3.4	-8.2%
Republic of Moldova	..	..	..	..	4.4	4.4	4.1	4.0	3.9	3.9	3.8	-12.7%
Russia	..	..	..	..	148.3	148.1	146.3	144.6	143.9	143.2	142.5	-3.9%
Tajikistan	..	..	..	..	5.3	5.8	6.2	6.4	6.5	6.6	6.6	25.2%
Turkmenistan	..	..	..	..	3.7	4.2	4.5	4.7	4.8	4.8	4.9	33.6%
Ukraine	..	..	..	..	51.9	51.5	49.2	47.8	47.5	47.1	46.8	-9.8%
Uzbekistan	..	..	..	..	20.5	22.8	24.7	25.6	25.9	26.2	26.5	29.4%
Former USSR *	**244.9**	**254.5**	**265.9**	**277.8**	**289.1**	**290.9**	**287.8**	**285.8**	**285.2**	**284.7**	**284.4**	**-1.6%**
Argentina	24.4	26.0	28.1	30.3	32.6	34.8	36.9	38.0	38.4	38.7	39.1	20.1%
Bolivia	4.3	4.8	5.4	6.0	6.7	7.5	8.3	8.8	9.0	9.2	9.4	40.3%
Brazil	98.4	108.1	121.6	136.1	149.5	161.6	174.2	181.8	184.3	186.8	189.3	26.6%
Chile	9.7	10.4	11.2	12.1	13.2	14.4	15.4	16.0	16.1	16.3	16.4	24.7%
Colombia	23.1	25.3	28.4	31.6	34.9	38.3	41.7	43.7	44.3	44.9	45.6	30.6%
Costa Rica	1.9	2.1	2.3	2.7	3.1	3.5	3.9	4.2	4.3	4.3	4.4	43.0%
Cuba	8.9	9.4	9.8	10.1	10.6	10.9	11.1	11.2	11.2	11.3	11.3	6.2%
Dominican Republic	4.7	5.3	5.9	6.6	7.3	8.0	8.7	9.2	9.3	9.5	9.6	31.8%
Ecuador	6.1	6.9	8.0	9.1	10.3	11.4	12.3	12.8	12.9	13.1	13.2	28.5%
El Salvador	3.7	4.1	4.6	4.8	5.1	5.6	6.2	6.5	6.6	6.7	6.8	32.3%
Guatemala	5.6	6.2	7.0	7.9	8.9	10.0	11.2	12.1	12.4	12.7	13.0	46.3%
Haiti	4.8	5.1	5.7	6.4	7.1	7.8	8.6	9.0	9.1	9.3	9.4	32.9%
Honduras	2.8	3.1	3.6	4.2	4.9	5.6	6.2	6.6	6.7	6.8	7.0	42.5%
Jamaica	1.9	2.0	2.1	2.3	2.4	2.5	2.6	2.6	2.6	2.7	2.7	11.6%
Netherlands Antilles	0.2	0.2	0.2	0.2	0.2	0.2	0.2	0.2	0.2	0.2	0.2	-1.0%
Nicaragua	2.5	2.8	3.3	3.7	4.1	4.7	5.1	5.3	5.4	5.5	5.5	33.6%
Panama	1.5	1.7	1.9	2.2	2.4	2.7	3.0	3.1	3.2	3.2	3.3	36.4%
Paraguay	2.4	2.7	3.1	3.6	4.2	4.8	5.3	5.7	5.8	5.9	6.0	42.6%
Peru	13.6	15.2	17.3	19.5	21.8	23.9	25.7	26.6	27.0	27.3	27.6	26.8%
Trinidad and Tobago	1.0	1.0	1.1	1.2	1.2	1.3	1.3	1.3	1.3	1.3	1.3	8.5%
Uruguay	2.8	2.8	2.9	3.0	3.1	3.2	3.3	3.3	3.3	3.3	3.3	6.7%
Venezuela	11.1	12.7	15.1	17.5	19.8	22.0	24.3	25.7	26.1	26.6	27.0	36.8%
Other Latin America	2.6	2.7	2.7	2.9	3.0	3.2	3.3	3.5	3.5	3.6	3.6	19.5%
Latin America	**237.8**	**260.6**	**291.4**	**323.9**	**356.3**	**387.8**	**418.9**	**437.1**	**443.1**	**449.1**	**455.0**	**27.7%**
Bangladesh	71.6	79.0	88.9	100.5	113.0	126.3	139.4	147.7	150.5	153.3	156.0	38.0%
Brunei Darussalam	0.1	0.2	0.2	0.2	0.3	0.3	0.3	0.4	0.4	0.4	0.4	48.6%
Cambodia	..	..	..	..	..	11.4	12.8	13.5	13.7	14.0	14.2	..
Chinese Taipei	14.9	16.1	17.8	19.3	20.3	21.3	22.2	22.5	22.6	22.7	22.8	12.3%
India	560.3	613.5	687.3	765.1	849.5	932.2	1 015.9	1 064.4	1 079.7	1 094.6	1 109.8	30.6%
Indonesia	120.4	132.6	148.3	163.0	178.2	192.8	206.3	214.7	217.6	220.6	223.0	25.1%
DPR of Korea	14.6	16.1	17.2	18.7	20.1	21.7	22.9	23.4	23.5	23.6	23.7	17.7%
Malaysia	11.1	12.3	13.8	15.7	18.1	20.6	23.3	24.7	25.2	25.7	26.1	44.3%
Mongolia	..	..	..	1.9	2.1	2.3	2.4	2.5	2.5	2.6	2.6	22.7%
Myanmar	27.0	29.8	33.3	36.8	40.1	43.1	45.9	47.2	47.6	48.0	48.4	20.5%
Nepal	12.4	13.5	15.2	17.0	19.1	21.7	24.4	26.0	26.6	27.1	27.6	44.6%
Pakistan	62.5	71.0	82.7	94.8	108.0	122.4	138.1	148.4	152.1	155.8	159.0	47.3%
Philippines	37.6	42.0	48.1	54.3	61.2	68.6	76.2	81.2	82.9	84.6	86.3	40.9%
Singapore	2.1	2.3	2.4	2.7	3.0	3.5	4.0	4.2	4.2	4.3	4.5	47.2%
Sri Lanka	12.6	13.5	14.7	15.8	17.0	18.1	19.4	19.3	19.5	19.7	19.9	16.9%
Thailand	38.2	42.2	46.8	50.8	54.3	57.5	60.7	62.1	62.6	63.0	63.4	16.9%
Vietnam	43.7	48.0	53.7	58.9	66.2	73.0	77.6	80.9	82.0	83.1	84.1	27.1%
Other Asia	28.9	31.3	32.8	32.4	36.3	34.3	38.8	42.9	44.7	46.4	47.9	31.8%
Asia	**1 058.3**	**1 163.4**	**1 303.3**	**1 448.2**	**1 607.0**	**1 771.0**	**1 930.6**	**2 026.0**	**2 057.8**	**2 089.2**	**2 119.7**	**31.9%**
People's Rep. of China	841.1	916.4	981.2	1 051.0	1 135.2	1 204.9	1 262.6	1 288.4	1 296.2	1 304.5	1 311.8	15.6%
Hong Kong, China	4.0	4.5	5.1	5.5	5.7	6.2	6.7	6.8	6.8	6.8	6.9	20.2%
China	**845.2**	**920.9**	**986.3**	**1 056.5**	**1 140.9**	**1 211.0**	**1 269.3**	**1 295.2**	**1 302.9**	**1 311.3**	**1 318.7**	**15.6%**

* Data for individual countries of the Former USSR are not available prior to 1990.

CO$_2$ emissions / TPES

Emissions de CO$_2$ / ATEP

tonnes CO$_2$ / terajoule

	1971	1975	1980	1985	1990	1995	2000	2003	2004	2005	2006	% change 90-06
World *	**60.8**	**60.5**	**59.7**	**57.4**	**57.2**	**56.5**	**56.0**	**56.3**	**56.4**	**56.6**	**57.0**	**-0.5%**
Annex I Parties	..	..	..	..	*59.1*	*57.0*	*56.3*	*56.7*	*56.0*	*55.7*	*55.6*	*-5.9%*
Annex II Parties	*65.6*	*63.8*	*61.8*	*59.0*	*57.8*	*55.9*	*55.6*	*56.2*	*55.6*	*55.4*	*55.2*	*-4.6%*
North America	*63.8*	*62.0*	*60.6*	*59.9*	*59.2*	*57.7*	*58.2*	*58.6*	*58.2*	*57.9*	*57.5*	*-2.9%*
Europe	*68.2*	*65.6*	*63.5*	*57.7*	*55.0*	*52.4*	*50.5*	*50.8*	*50.2*	*49.7*	*49.8*	*-9.4%*
Pacific	*66.7*	*66.8*	*62.0*	*59.3*	*59.2*	*57.3*	*57.0*	*60.0*	*58.8*	*59.2*	*58.8*	*-0.7%*
Annex I EIT	..	..	..	..	*62.7*	*61.2*	*59.3*	*58.3*	*57.4*	*56.6*	*57.2*	*-8.8%*
Non-Annex I Parties	..	..	..	..	*51.0*	*53.1*	*52.7*	*53.5*	*54.5*	*55.2*	*56.1*	*9.9%*
Annex I Kyoto Parties	..	..	..	..	*58.4*	*55.8*	*54.4*	*54.7*	*53.9*	*53.4*	*53.6*	*-8.3%*
Non-OECD Total	**49.6**	**52.6**	**53.8**	**52.4**	**53.8**	**54.1**	**53.3**	**54.0**	**54.7**	**55.3**	**56.1**	**4.3%**
OECD Total	**66.0**	**64.3**	**62.5**	**60.0**	**58.5**	**56.6**	**56.1**	**56.5**	**56.0**	**55.7**	**55.5**	**-5.1%**
Canada	57.2	54.1	52.8	49.7	49.3	47.9	50.5	50.5	48.9	48.6	47.7	-3.2%
Mexico	53.4	55.3	52.5	54.6	56.9	56.3	56.7	55.5	54.1	54.4	56.0	-1.5%
United States	64.4	62.8	61.5	61.0	60.3	58.8	59.1	59.6	59.2	59.0	58.6	-2.8%
OECD N. America	**63.5**	**61.8**	**60.3**	**59.6**	**59.1**	**57.6**	**58.1**	**58.4**	**57.9**	**57.7**	**57.4**	**-2.9%**
Australia	66.0	70.5	70.6	71.4	70.8	72.1	73.2	76.4	78.1	76.6	76.9	8.7%
Japan	67.4	66.7	60.8	57.4	57.6	55.2	54.1	56.8	55.0	55.5	54.9	-4.8%
Korea	73.3	74.6	71.6	67.7	58.7	59.1	54.4	53.0	53.9	52.7	52.5	-10.5%
New Zealand	46.0	45.9	42.7	41.0	37.1	36.9	42.6	49.6	48.2	50.1	50.1	35.1%
OECD Pacific	**67.1**	**67.3**	**62.9**	**60.2**	**59.2**	**57.7**	**56.4**	**58.3**	**57.6**	**57.6**	**57.3**	**-3.2%**
Austria	61.5	59.3	57.1	55.6	53.9	52.1	51.0	53.5	53.2	52.6	50.8	-5.7%
Belgium	69.6	64.7	63.6	54.5	53.0	51.7	49.1	48.7	47.8	46.6	45.9	-13.3%
Czech Republic	79.0	83.1	83.5	81.5	75.6	71.8	71.9	64.7	63.7	63.3	62.7	-17.0%
Denmark	68.6	69.7	75.9	72.9	67.2	68.6	61.5	64.6	59.9	57.4	63.0	-6.2%
Finland	52.1	53.4	53.2	44.7	45.3	45.8	39.7	46.6	42.9	38.2	42.6	-5.8%
France	64.4	61.6	56.9	41.8	37.0	35.0	34.8	33.8	33.3	33.4	33.1	-10.5%
Germany	76.0	73.7	70.0	67.2	63.8	60.7	57.6	57.9	57.7	56.1	56.4	-11.6%
Greece	65.9	67.7	68.8	71.1	75.3	77.0	74.8	74.8	73.0	73.2	72.1	-4.3%
Hungary	77.8	75.1	71.5	65.6	57.3	54.6	52.8	52.3	51.2	48.9	48.8	-14.8%
Iceland	34.2	33.3	27.2	21.1	20.8	20.1	15.8	15.3	15.3	14.4	12.0	-42.0%
Ireland	73.7	73.1	73.3	71.4	70.9	73.4	69.4	66.8	66.5	68.3	69.4	-2.1%
Italy	65.7	64.9	65.0	63.5	64.2	60.7	58.5	59.6	58.6	58.4	58.1	-9.4%
Luxembourg	89.9	75.6	78.6	75.6	70.5	58.4	52.7	55.5	56.6	56.8	56.7	-19.7%
Netherlands	60.0	56.2	56.0	56.7	55.7	56.0	54.1	53.9	53.5	53.0	53.2	-4.6%
Norway	41.5	39.0	36.0	32.0	31.7	32.9	31.4	31.1	29.5	26.5	33.7	6.3%
Poland	79.3	78.3	80.2	81.3	82.3	79.4	78.0	76.1	76.9	75.8	74.8	-9.1%
Portugal	53.0	54.4	55.3	51.7	54.4	55.7	56.3	54.2	53.9	55.2	52.9	-2.8%
Slovak Republic	65.4	62.4	66.6	62.7	63.6	54.7	50.2	49.2	48.5	48.2	47.9	-24.7%
Spain	66.3	64.0	65.5	58.4	53.9	54.3	54.4	54.4	55.0	55.9	54.1	0.4%
Sweden	54.5	48.4	43.1	29.6	26.5	27.0	26.1	25.6	24.0	23.1	22.5	-15.2%
Switzerland	54.9	49.3	45.2	43.2	39.2	39.5	38.3	38.5	38.9	39.3	37.3	-4.9%
Turkey	50.5	52.8	53.8	57.4	57.3	59.0	62.3	61.3	60.5	60.5	60.9	6.4%
United Kingdom	70.6	68.6	67.8	63.8	62.2	55.4	53.7	55.0	54.9	54.5	55.4	-10.9%
OECD Europe	**69.2**	**67.1**	**65.5**	**60.6**	**57.5**	**54.8**	**52.9**	**52.9**	**52.3**	**51.7**	**52.0**	**-9.7%**
European Union - 27	..	..	..	..	*58.6*	*55.3*	*53.2*	*53.2*	*52.7*	*52.2*	*52.2*	*-10.9%*

* The ratio for the world has been calculated to include emissions from international marine bunkers and international aviation. The ratios for individual countries and regions do not include these emissions. For information, the world ratio excluding emissions from international marine bunkers and international aviation is 56.5 t CO$_2$ per terajoule in 2006.

CO$_2$ emissions / TPES

Emissions de CO$_2$ / ATEP

tonnes CO$_2$ / terajoule

	1971	1975	1980	1985	1990	1995	2000	2003	2004	2005	2006	% change 90-06
Non-OECD Total	**49.6**	**52.6**	**53.8**	**52.4**	**53.8**	**54.1**	**53.3**	**54.0**	**54.7**	**55.3**	**56.1**	**4.3%**
Algeria	57.9	58.1	58.7	56.6	54.7	54.4	54.3	55.6	55.9	57.7	55.9	2.3%
Angola	10.4	11.7	13.9	13.1	15.5	14.1	15.5	19.8	18.8	19.2	19.9	28.5%
Benin	6.5	8.8	6.8	7.2	3.6	2.8	16.8	22.2	22.9	23.3	25.5	607.4%
Botswana	..	..	..	42.4	55.1	53.0	54.3	50.4	53.8	54.3	55.4	0.6%
Cameroon	6.3	8.1	10.6	12.9	12.7	10.7	10.5	10.5	10.3	10.0	10.5	-17.2%
Congo	27.1	27.6	29.2	25.4	20.9	16.0	16.6	19.1	19.6	19.7	23.5	12.2%
Dem. Rep. of Congo	8.9	8.1	8.6	7.6	5.9	3.8	3.4	3.3	3.2	3.2	3.2	-46.6%
Côte d'Ivoire	22.7	23.8	22.0	19.1	14.3	14.8	21.3	18.1	19.7	19.1	20.1	41.1%
Egypt	62.2	62.4	65.9	60.7	59.2	56.4	57.5	56.4	58.2	58.2	58.4	-1.4%
Eritrea	..	..	..	..	..	18.4	20.0	19.6	22.0	19.0	18.1	..
Ethiopia	3.7	3.0	3.0	2.7	3.5	3.4	4.1	5.2	5.3	5.3	5.6	60.7%
Gabon	10.4	13.7	21.8	29.1	17.3	22.3	21.3	23.5	23.7	27.8	27.4	58.5%
Ghana	15.2	15.1	13.3	11.8	12.1	12.1	15.5	19.9	17.6	18.1	21.7	79.2%
Kenya	16.2	16.1	16.8	14.2	13.5	13.6	14.1	11.8	12.6	13.7	14.6	8.5%
Libya	53.7	57.0	61.6	52.0	56.6	52.1	55.7	57.1	56.6	57.1	57.0	0.8%
Morocco	64.1	66.5	64.9	67.7	65.1	68.7	66.9	69.8	69.5	69.8	68.0	4.5%
Mozambique	9.9	8.3	8.2	5.5	4.3	4.3	4.4	4.9	4.8	4.2	4.4	1.6%
Namibia	..	..	..	..	..	47.7	43.4	49.7	48.8	48.3	48.3	..
Nigeria	3.9	6.7	12.1	12.5	9.8	9.0	11.0	11.8	11.6	12.6	11.7	19.0%
Senegal	21.5	25.4	27.1	29.6	26.1	29.3	32.4	32.7	35.7	36.4	35.3	35.2%
South Africa	91.6	92.5	78.3	63.1	66.7	62.7	64.1	64.9	62.4	61.8	62.9	-5.6%
Sudan	10.9	10.5	10.5	10.5	12.3	9.1	9.7	13.3	14.5	14.2	15.4	25.0%
United Rep. of Tanzania	4.8	4.7	4.7	4.1	4.2	5.4	4.6	4.8	5.2	5.6	5.5	32.3%
Togo	11.2	9.6	9.8	7.1	10.5	8.5	10.8	11.2	10.5	9.6	8.9	-15.0%
Tunisia	49.2	49.8	54.2	53.6	56.1	56.5	56.7	55.3	54.1	54.5	53.8	-4.1%
Zambia	23.3	26.6	17.5	13.5	11.4	8.3	6.5	6.9	7.0	7.2	7.4	-35.2%
Zimbabwe	31.6	28.7	29.0	30.5	40.7	35.6	30.3	26.2	24.9	25.5	24.7	-39.5%
Other Africa	6.9	7.7	9.6	7.6	8.3	8.6	8.1	8.0	8.2	8.3	8.9	7.4%
Africa	**32.8**	**35.4**	**35.2**	**33.2**	**33.4**	**32.1**	**32.7**	**33.0**	**33.0**	**33.0**	**33.2**	**-0.6%**
Bahrain	46.3	52.5	53.1	54.3	57.8	52.2	54.1	53.4	53.5	53.7	54.4	-6.0%
Islamic Rep. of Iran	51.9	61.0	56.4	63.8	60.8	62.9	61.3	60.3	60.2	59.9	60.5	-0.6%
Iraq	65.2	62.6	70.8	64.6	66.2	64.9	69.7	63.7	65.9	65.5	64.6	-2.5%
Israel	54.2	53.2	54.7	71.1	66.2	67.7	68.9	71.1	71.4	69.3	70.3	6.2%
Jordan	59.0	61.3	58.7	62.2	62.8	63.6	65.8	65.0	62.1	61.1	61.0	-2.9%
Kuwait	93.4	92.9	48.4	61.9	72.7	59.6	58.7	62.3	63.0	63.1	63.0	-13.4%
Lebanon	56.0	60.2	62.3	65.4	66.0	66.1	66.9	68.3	67.7	67.7	66.9	1.3%
Oman	68.0	58.9	53.6	43.7	52.0	54.8	48.8	48.2	51.0	45.8	45.6	-12.3%
Qatar	57.3	54.7	52.8	51.1	52.0	54.2	52.5	51.2	51.8	52.4	52.3	0.6%
Saudi Arabia	41.1	58.5	73.9	63.8	62.9	55.0	56.2	55.8	55.0	54.7	55.6	-11.6%
Syria	59.9	66.7	67.5	63.0	63.4	64.7	62.2	62.3	63.3	65.1	65.0	2.6%
United Arab Emirates	57.4	56.8	61.3	60.6	53.2	54.5	55.5	56.1	56.4	56.1	56.2	5.7%
Yemen	37.2	55.0	61.1	60.7	59.9	63.6	64.9	67.0	64.8	66.4	66.7	11.4%
Middle East	**56.9**	**62.2**	**61.6**	**62.8**	**61.5**	**59.7**	**59.7**	**59.0**	**59.0**	**58.7**	**59.0**	**-4.0%**
Albania	54.5	54.0	59.4	63.5	56.0	33.5	41.7	44.3	40.2	45.7	44.5	-20.5%
Bosnia and Herzegovina *	..	..	..	..	80.2	52.2	74.9	77.9	74.1	74.1	76.0	-5.2%
Bulgaria	78.0	73.5	69.8	62.4	62.1	54.4	53.5	56.3	57.1	54.8	54.9	-11.7%
Croatia *	..	..	..	..	56.6	52.8	54.0	56.7	55.0	55.4	55.2	-2.5%
Cyprus	66.5	69.9	66.0	62.3	57.2	61.9	62.0	62.5	65.9	66.2	64.3	12.4%
Gibraltar	62.3	57.7	68.1	65.7	64.7	70.2	70.7	70.8	70.9	70.9	71.0	9.8%
FYR of Macedonia *	..	..	..	..	80.2	76.0	74.4	73.2	72.2	72.0	69.4	-13.4%
Malta	57.5	56.8	59.4	69.8	71.2	71.8	68.6	67.9	67.4	67.4	68.2	-4.2%
Romania	65.1	64.8	64.5	63.7	63.9	60.2	56.7	57.8	56.8	57.0	56.3	-11.8%
Serbia *	..	..	..	..	75.3	77.2	76.2	76.4	75.9	74.6	74.8	-0.7%
Slovenia *	..	..	..	..	53.3	52.2	51.7	52.0	51.3	50.5	51.0	-4.4%
Former Yugoslavia *	68.2	69.6	61.5	70.1	..	..	..	..	..	..	..	..
Non-OECD Europe	**68.6**	**67.8**	**64.7**	**65.3**	**65.2**	**60.2**	**59.6**	**61.1**	**60.7**	**60.0**	**59.9**	**-8.1%**

* Data for individual countries of the Former Yugoslavia are not available prior to 1990.

CO$_2$ emissions / TPES

Emissions de CO$_2$ / ATEP

tonnes CO$_2$ / terajoule

	1971	1975	1980	1985	1990	1995	2000	2003	2004	2005	2006	% change 90-06
Armenia	..	..	..	..	61.9	49.0	39.3	38.9	38.9	38.6	38.3	-38.2%
Azerbaijan	..	..	..	..	57.4	55.9	58.2	54.5	53.7	53.6	51.3	-10.7%
Belarus	..	..	..	..	64.8	57.3	53.4	52.6	53.0	54.2	53.5	-17.4%
Estonia	..	..	..	..	90.0	79.4	76.4	77.8	76.7	75.4	74.0	-17.8%
Georgia	..	..	..	..	55.7	45.3	36.2	27.0	27.9	29.3	32.9	-40.9%
Kazakhstan	..	..	..	..	76.7	76.4	73.7	73.0	72.3	70.8	70.8	-7.7%
Kyrgyzstan	..	..	..	..	71.6	45.0	44.7	45.8	48.4	46.4	44.4	-38.0%
Latvia	..	..	..	..	55.8	45.6	43.5	41.6	40.6	40.4	41.6	-25.5%
Lithuania	..	..	..	..	48.7	38.5	37.4	31.8	33.1	37.5	38.2	-21.5%
Republic of Moldova	..	..	..	..	72.5	59.3	54.0	52.7	53.2	52.9	52.4	-27.8%
Russia	..	..	..	..	59.2	60.1	58.8	57.4	56.7	55.7	56.1	-5.4%
Tajikistan	..	..	..	..	50.0	38.4	35.2	37.6	38.4	38.9	40.4	-19.2%
Turkmenistan	..	..	..	..	56.7	59.2	59.6	59.6	59.9	59.8	60.3	6.2%
Ukraine	..	..	..	..	64.7	57.2	52.0	54.3	51.8	51.0	53.9	-16.7%
Uzbekistan	..	..	..	..	61.7	57.0	55.2	55.7	55.9	55.8	55.6	-9.9%
Former USSR *	**60.3**	**63.8**	**64.4**	**60.0**	**61.5**	**59.9**	**57.8**	**57.1**	**56.2**	**55.6**	**56.2**	**-8.6%**
Argentina	58.9	57.1	54.8	51.2	52.0	50.6	51.3	49.1	51.5	52.3	51.4	-1.2%
Bolivia	49.4	50.8	42.2	41.0	46.9	49.2	36.9	49.7	46.3	53.4	52.0	11.0%
Brazil	31.1	35.7	37.3	30.8	32.9	35.4	38.2	36.3	36.4	36.1	35.4	7.7%
Chile	56.2	52.3	52.5	47.6	54.2	49.5	49.0	48.0	48.6	47.5	48.0	-11.5%
Colombia	44.5	42.9	42.5	42.8	43.4	47.5	52.9	50.0	51.9	49.9	47.0	8.2%
Costa Rica	26.5	31.7	34.1	28.6	30.8	40.2	32.9	34.7	35.4	31.4	30.9	0.6%
Cuba	40.0	46.1	45.4	50.0	39.1	50.5	51.4	59.8	60.1	59.3	59.7	52.7%
Dominican Republic	34.8	39.3	42.7	39.6	44.1	45.7	53.3	53.1	55.0	53.4	56.8	28.8%
Ecuador	36.8	44.7	49.0	48.8	51.4	55.3	53.4	54.7	51.6	54.5	53.2	3.4%
El Salvador	17.7	20.9	15.8	15.0	20.4	32.5	30.6	30.2	30.7	30.6	29.5	44.8%
Guatemala	19.5	21.5	26.3	20.4	17.6	26.6	29.5	32.3	32.2	32.2	32.1	82.5%
Haiti	5.9	5.7	7.0	9.9	14.2	12.6	16.5	17.5	17.2	16.0	16.0	12.5%
Honduras	19.1	20.3	21.2	19.5	21.1	31.3	35.0	38.8	39.6	39.6	39.2	85.7%
Jamaica	61.2	63.4	65.3	59.7	58.3	58.9	59.5	60.7	60.9	61.0	60.0	3.0%
Netherlands Antilles	63.1	63.2	53.5	61.2	45.7	52.3	54.3	54.3	55.3	58.3	54.3	18.9%
Nicaragua	28.0	29.0	27.5	22.0	20.6	25.2	30.7	30.2	29.9	29.4	27.5	33.2%
Panama	36.2	45.7	49.4	40.3	39.5	49.4	43.5	53.7	51.3	52.3	51.8	31.2%
Paraguay	9.9	11.1	15.4	14.7	14.8	20.9	20.1	22.0	22.2	20.7	21.4	44.5%
Peru	40.0	41.5	42.4	40.2	46.1	49.9	50.4	50.9	52.2	49.1	49.2	6.8%
Trinidad and Tobago	54.5	59.3	49.0	44.6	45.0	46.1	43.5	45.5	42.7	43.6	45.0	-0.0%
Uruguay	51.6	53.3	50.2	37.3	39.8	42.0	41.1	39.3	44.7	43.3	46.0	15.6%
Venezuela	63.3	59.8	61.9	57.2	57.2	54.4	54.0	54.2	54.4	55.0	57.3	0.2%
Other Latin America	36.6	41.6	38.9	52.7	57.3	57.5	55.5	56.7	56.7	56.9	55.8	-2.6%
Latin America	**43.2**	**44.1**	**44.5**	**40.3**	**41.6**	**43.4**	**44.6**	**43.6**	**44.1**	**43.9**	**43.8**	**5.2%**
Bangladesh	13.3	16.5	20.3	21.0	25.3	30.5	32.2	35.0	35.2	35.9	36.3	43.8%
Brunei Darussalam	53.4	44.3	45.7	39.0	44.6	47.1	44.0	49.2	46.3	46.4	49.1	10.1%
Cambodia	..	..	..	..	..	9.9	14.4	16.7	18.0	18.6	19.4	..
Chinese Taipei	69.9	68.0	60.5	51.0	56.7	58.5	62.2	59.9	58.7	59.3	59.9	5.6%
India	30.3	32.2	33.5	38.8	44.0	48.2	50.7	50.7	51.2	51.5	52.8	19.9%
Indonesia	16.6	21.6	28.7	29.8	32.6	34.8	41.7	43.4	43.9	44.9	44.6	37.0%
DPR of Korea	83.1	82.3	83.0	83.8	82.0	81.3	83.1	82.5	82.4	82.7	83.2	1.5%
Malaysia	50.3	51.8	45.1	48.1	50.2	47.6	52.5	49.9	57.1	52.8	53.8	7.3%
Mongolia	..	..	..	88.5	88.4	88.1	88.3	87.3	87.1	87.8	86.8	-1.7%
Myanmar	13.6	11.2	12.9	12.5	8.9	13.6	15.5	15.5	16.2	17.0	16.4	84.7%
Nepal	1.2	1.9	2.7	2.5	3.6	6.2	8.9	7.8	7.2	7.9	7.9	116.3%
Pakistan	22.8	24.1	24.7	28.7	32.5	35.2	36.5	35.6	37.3	37.1	37.9	16.6%
Philippines	37.2	40.0	37.7	30.3	32.9	41.8	38.8	40.0	39.2	39.6	37.0	12.3%
Singapore	48.0	48.3	50.1	49.5	51.5	42.3	41.0	41.4	36.3	33.3	33.6	-34.8%
Sri Lanka	17.4	15.7	19.6	17.1	16.2	22.2	32.0	31.7	31.3	32.4	29.0	78.6%
Thailand	29.2	28.9	35.8	36.8	42.7	51.9	50.8	51.8	52.2	50.8	50.1	17.3%
Vietnam	19.5	20.5	17.6	18.5	16.6	21.8	28.2	32.8	37.5	37.4	37.7	126.7%
Other Asia	43.1	44.5	52.9	39.5	39.5	34.2	36.5	38.7	41.2	40.6	41.1	4.0%
Asia	**32.0**	**34.0**	**36.7**	**38.9**	**42.0**	**44.6**	**47.4**	**47.6**	**48.3**	**48.3**	**48.8**	**16.2%**
People's Rep. of China	48.8	51.9	56.1	58.8	61.2	68.1	65.6	67.2	68.5	70.3	71.3	16.5%
Hong Kong, China	62.9	60.8	64.6	70.0	73.9	62.1	59.7	58.5	54.9	53.8	55.0	-25.6%
China	**48.9**	**51.9**	**56.2**	**58.9**	**61.3**	**68.0**	**65.5**	**67.0**	**68.4**	**70.1**	**71.1**	**16.0%**

* Data for individual countries of the Former USSR are not available prior to 1990.

CO$_2$ emissions / GDP using exchange rates

Emissions de CO$_2$ / PIB selon les taux de change

kilogrammes CO$_2$ / US$ using 2000 prices and exchange rates

	1971	1975	1980	1985	1990	1995	2000	2003	2004	2005	2006	% change 90-06
World *	**1.09**	**1.05**	**1.00**	**0.91**	**0.87**	**0.81**	**0.74**	**0.74**	**0.75**	**0.75**	**0.74**	**-14.9%**
Annex I Parties	..	..	..	..	*0.70*	*0.61*	*0.55*	*0.54*	*0.53*	*0.51*	*0.50*	*-29.0%*
Annex II Parties	*0.83*	*0.76*	*0.68*	*0.58*	*0.52*	*0.49*	*0.46*	*0.45*	*0.44*	*0.43*	*0.41*	*-20.8%*
North America	*1.12*	*1.03*	*0.92*	*0.76*	*0.70*	*0.65*	*0.59*	*0.57*	*0.55*	*0.54*	*0.51*	*-26.1%*
Europe	*0.75*	*0.67*	*0.62*	*0.54*	*0.47*	*0.43*	*0.38*	*0.38*	*0.37*	*0.36*	*0.35*	*-24.0%*
Pacific	*0.44*	*0.43*	*0.36*	*0.32*	*0.30*	*0.30*	*0.31*	*0.31*	*0.30*	*0.30*	*0.29*	*-4.1%*
Annex I EIT	..	..	..	..	*4.74*	*4.50*	*3.59*	*3.26*	*3.02*	*2.87*	*2.77*	*-41.5%*
Non-Annex I Parties	..	..	..	..	*1.52*	*1.46*	*1.31*	*1.34*	*1.38*	*1.38*	*1.38*	*-9.0%*
Annex I Kyoto Parties	..	..	..	..	*0.70*	*0.59*	*0.52*	*0.52*	*0.50*	*0.49*	*0.48*	*-30.8%*
Non-OECD Total	**2.05**	**2.09**	**2.06**	**2.09**	**2.23**	**1.92**	**1.66**	**1.66**	**1.68**	**1.66**	**1.65**	**-26.1%**
OECD Total	**0.86**	**0.79**	**0.72**	**0.62**	**0.56**	**0.53**	**0.49**	**0.48**	**0.47**	**0.46**	**0.44**	**-20.7%**
Canada	1.18	1.10	1.04	0.85	0.80	0.79	0.73	0.72	0.69	0.68	0.64	-19.8%
Mexico	0.51	0.56	0.61	0.66	0.71	0.70	0.61	0.63	0.61	0.63	0.63	-11.9%
United States	1.11	1.02	0.91	0.76	0.69	0.64	0.58	0.56	0.54	0.53	0.51	-26.6%
OECD N. America	**1.09**	**1.00**	**0.90**	**0.76**	**0.70**	**0.66**	**0.59**	**0.57**	**0.56**	**0.54**	**0.52**	**-25.4%**
Australia	0.88	0.99	0.99	0.91	0.92	0.86	0.85	0.81	0.81	0.82	0.82	-11.4%
Japan	0.40	0.38	0.31	0.27	0.26	0.26	0.26	0.26	0.25	0.25	0.24	-8.3%
Korea	0.79	0.87	1.01	0.86	0.81	0.88	0.84	0.78	0.78	0.73	0.71	-12.3%
New Zealand	0.48	0.50	0.50	0.51	0.54	0.53	0.61	0.61	0.58	0.58	0.58	7.7%
OECD Pacific	**0.45**	**0.44**	**0.39**	**0.34**	**0.33**	**0.35**	**0.35**	**0.36**	**0.35**	**0.34**	**0.34**	**0.5%**
Austria	0.55	0.49	0.46	0.42	0.38	0.35	0.32	0.37	0.36	0.36	0.34	-9.8%
Belgium	1.02	0.88	0.82	0.63	0.59	0.60	0.55	0.53	0.50	0.48	0.45	-22.8%
Czech Republic	3.94	3.49	3.39	3.30	2.80	2.34	2.14	1.97	1.90	1.76	1.67	-40.5%
Denmark	0.66	0.60	0.62	0.52	0.41	0.41	0.31	0.35	0.31	0.28	0.31	-23.4%
Finland	0.75	0.69	0.74	0.57	0.54	0.58	0.44	0.56	0.50	0.40	0.46	-15.0%
France	0.68	0.59	0.54	0.39	0.32	0.31	0.28	0.28	0.27	0.27	0.26	-20.3%
Germany	1.03	0.94	0.86	0.77	0.62	0.51	0.44	0.44	0.43	0.42	0.41	-33.5%
Greece	0.39	0.45	0.48	0.58	0.70	0.71	0.69	0.65	0.62	0.60	0.57	-17.7%
Hungary	2.40	2.17	2.15	1.90	1.54	1.49	1.15	1.06	0.99	0.96	0.92	-40.6%
Iceland	0.45	0.42	0.34	0.28	0.28	0.29	0.25	0.23	0.22	0.20	0.20	-28.6%
Ireland	0.97	0.77	0.76	0.68	0.63	0.54	0.43	0.37	0.35	0.34	0.34	-46.2%
Italy	0.57	0.54	0.49	0.43	0.42	0.41	0.39	0.40	0.40	0.40	0.39	-8.8%
Luxembourg	2.53	1.78	1.57	1.15	0.84	0.54	0.40	0.44	0.47	0.46	0.43	-48.7%
Netherlands	0.75	0.72	0.68	0.62	0.56	0.54	0.45	0.47	0.46	0.45	0.42	-23.8%
Norway	0.39	0.33	0.31	0.25	0.24	0.23	0.20	0.20	0.20	0.20	0.19	-21.0%
Poland	3.21	2.96	3.47	3.49	2.91	2.52	1.70	1.59	1.53	1.48	1.45	-50.3%
Portugal	0.35	0.38	0.39	0.38	0.46	0.52	0.53	0.51	0.51	0.53	0.47	2.2%
Slovak Republic	3.03	2.98	3.38	3.08	2.99	2.36	1.83	1.68	1.55	1.49	1.35	-54.8%
Spain	0.50	0.52	0.57	0.50	0.47	0.49	0.49	0.49	0.50	0.50	0.46	-1.0%
Sweden	0.61	0.52	0.45	0.33	0.26	0.28	0.21	0.21	0.20	0.18	0.17	-36.5%
Switzerland	0.23	0.22	0.22	0.21	0.18	0.18	0.17	0.17	0.17	0.17	0.16	-11.4%
Turkey	0.69	0.79	0.84	0.88	0.91	0.93	1.01	0.96	0.90	0.88	0.92	1.4%
United Kingdom	0.84	0.72	0.65	0.56	0.48	0.42	0.36	0.34	0.33	0.33	0.32	-34.3%
OECD Europe	**0.84**	**0.77**	**0.73**	**0.64**	**0.55**	**0.50**	**0.44**	**0.44**	**0.43**	**0.42**	**0.41**	**-25.5%**
European Union - 27	..	..	..	..	*0.60*	*0.53*	*0.45*	*0.45*	*0.44*	*0.43*	*0.42*	*-29.9%*

* The ratio for the world has been calculated to include emissions from international marine bunkers and international aviation. The ratios for individual countries and regions do not include these emissions. For information, the world ratio excluding emissions from international marine bunkers and international aviation is 0.72 kg CO$_2$ per US$ 2000 in 2006.

CO$_2$ emissions / GDP using exchange rates

Emissions de CO$_2$ / PIB selon les taux de change

kilogrammes CO$_2$ / US\$ using 2000 prices and exchange rates

	1971	1975	1980	1985	1990	1995	2000	2003	2004	2005	2006	% change 90-06
Non-OECD Total	**2.05**	**2.09**	**2.06**	**2.09**	**2.23**	**1.92**	**1.66**	**1.66**	**1.68**	**1.66**	**1.65**	**-26.1%**
Algeria	0.51	0.56	0.85	1.02	1.18	1.26	1.22	1.23	1.19	1.20	1.20	1.3%
Angola	0.26	0.31	0.40	0.41	0.48	0.60	0.57	0.68	0.60	0.52	0.50	3.8%
Benin	0.37	0.52	0.36	0.35	0.18	0.13	0.63	0.88	0.91	0.92	1.06	490.3%
Botswana	..	..	..	0.81	0.86	0.81	0.68	0.54	0.53	0.54	0.54	-37.4%
Cameroon	0.21	0.22	0.26	0.25	0.30	0.31	0.28	0.26	0.25	0.24	0.25	-18.2%
Congo	0.57	0.48	0.46	0.30	0.25	0.18	0.18	0.23	0.24	0.25	0.28	12.1%
Dem. Rep. of Congo	0.35	0.34	0.44	0.42	0.39	0.40	0.49	0.47	0.45	0.43	0.42	9.3%
Côte d'Ivoire	0.47	0.48	0.44	0.39	0.32	0.36	0.59	0.50	0.56	0.61	0.58	81.1%
Egypt	0.97	1.07	1.10	1.23	1.21	1.09	1.10	1.19	1.20	1.25	1.19	-1.1%
Eritrea	..	..	..	..	..	1.27	0.95	0.95	0.92	0.81	0.71	..
Ethiopia	0.30	0.25	0.26	0.28	0.35	0.37	0.40	0.54	0.50	0.46	0.47	32.8%
Gabon	0.25	0.19	0.36	0.42	0.21	0.27	0.27	0.31	0.31	0.38	0.37	78.7%
Ghana	0.72	0.93	0.86	0.84	0.83	0.82	1.03	1.25	1.04	1.06	1.28	54.1%
Kenya	0.95	0.84	0.78	0.68	0.60	0.64	0.70	0.56	0.61	0.65	0.69	14.4%
Libya	0.11	0.33	0.42	0.60	0.92	1.11	1.15	1.03	1.03	0.97	0.91	-0.5%
Morocco	0.59	0.71	0.76	0.77	0.74	0.91	0.89	0.86	0.89	0.96	0.91	23.4%
Mozambique	1.11	1.07	1.03	0.85	0.48	0.44	0.35	0.33	0.31	0.27	0.26	-44.7%
Namibia	..	..	..	..	..	0.63	0.55	0.67	0.67	0.67	0.67	..
Nigeria	0.26	0.45	0.85	1.20	0.83	0.77	0.89	0.91	0.86	0.93	0.81	-2.9%
Senegal	0.60	0.70	0.83	0.76	0.61	0.70	0.82	0.78	0.86	0.85	0.79	28.4%
South Africa	2.43	2.55	2.25	2.24	2.29	2.39	2.25	2.20	2.21	2.05	2.03	-11.7%
Sudan	0.82	0.67	0.67	0.73	0.78	0.50	0.44	0.61	0.66	0.61	0.60	-22.1%
United Rep. of Tanzania	0.43	0.35	0.32	0.30	0.25	0.34	0.28	0.30	0.33	0.36	0.36	44.5%
Togo	0.53	0.41	0.38	0.31	0.53	0.53	0.72	0.77	0.71	0.66	0.60	12.2%
Tunisia	0.79	0.76	0.91	0.90	0.99	0.97	0.93	0.87	0.85	0.80	0.77	-21.6%
Zambia	1.44	1.64	1.23	1.00	0.86	0.73	0.52	0.53	0.53	0.52	0.52	-39.5%
Zimbabwe	2.07	1.77	1.82	1.78	2.38	2.08	1.72	1.70	1.63	1.84	1.85	-22.2%
Other Africa	0.31	0.35	0.43	0.36	0.39	0.44	0.39	0.38	0.38	0.37	0.40	1.3%
Africa	**1.01**	**1.12**	**1.10**	**1.16**	**1.20**	**1.22**	**1.18**	**1.16**	**1.16**	**1.14**	**1.10**	**-7.6%**
Bahrain	2.29	2.18	1.86	2.80	2.52	1.80	1.77	1.72	1.70	1.73	1.75	-30.5%
Islamic Rep. of Iran	0.89	1.13	1.61	2.11	2.49	3.00	3.01	2.91	2.99	2.99	3.08	23.7%
Iraq	0.24	0.24	0.33	0.71	1.60	5.69	2.93	5.15	4.19	4.14	4.36	171.7%
Israel	0.48	0.43	0.41	0.45	0.50	0.50	0.48	0.53	0.51	0.48	0.47	-5.6%
Jordan	0.64	1.03	1.00	1.36	1.80	1.68	1.69	1.51	1.57	1.57	1.51	-16.1%
Kuwait	0.73	0.87	1.10	1.72	0.96	1.19	1.33	1.32	1.39	1.42	1.22	26.7%
Lebanon	0.37	0.45	0.62	0.52	0.76	0.84	0.84	0.90	0.75	0.77	0.65	-14.5%
Oman	0.08	0.17	0.42	0.50	0.78	0.86	0.99	1.15	1.11	1.10	1.12	43.1%
Qatar	0.25	0.54	0.73	1.36	1.61	1.85	1.49	1.49	1.38	1.35	1.40	-13.0%
Saudi Arabia	0.25	0.22	0.66	1.06	1.12	1.23	1.33	1.41	1.41	1.41	1.42	26.7%
Syria	1.68	1.50	1.59	2.16	2.63	2.24	2.37	2.16	2.12	2.12	2.08	-21.0%
United Arab Emirates	0.28	0.22	0.40	0.86	1.11	1.28	1.22	1.17	1.09	1.03	0.97	-13.2%
Yemen	0.90	0.93	1.05	1.03	1.17	1.29	1.41	1.55	1.60	1.67	1.67	42.7%
Middle East	**0.50**	**0.52**	**0.72**	**1.13**	**1.33**	**1.53**	**1.52**	**1.57**	**1.57**	**1.55**	**1.54**	**16.3%**
Albania	2.27	2.07	2.68	2.29	1.94	0.66	0.86	0.92	0.77	0.95	0.84	-56.8%
Bosnia and Herzegovina *	..	..	..	..	16.90	2.22	2.71	2.49	2.44	2.43	2.51	-85.1%
Bulgaria	9.78	8.24	7.10	5.82	5.00	4.06	3.33	3.21	2.94	2.81	2.74	-45.2%
Croatia *	..	..	..	..	1.00	1.01	0.96	0.98	0.92	0.89	0.85	-14.9%
Cyprus	0.83	0.88	0.78	0.64	0.63	0.69	0.68	0.70	0.67	0.65	0.64	0.9%
Gibraltar	0.26	0.24	0.26	0.24	0.31	0.51	0.53	0.52	0.52	0.52	0.53	71.1%
FYR of Macedonia *	..	..	..	..	2.32	2.83	2.35	2.34	2.21	2.15	2.03	-12.5%
Malta	1.05	0.69	0.61	0.65	0.96	0.76	0.57	0.65	0.69	0.67	0.63	-34.6%
Romania	6.12	4.95	4.30	3.60	3.80	2.96	2.33	2.18	1.95	1.88	1.80	-52.6%
Serbia *	..	..	..	..	6.05	4.43	4.29	4.70	4.71	4.35	4.37	-27.8%
Slovenia *	..	..	..	..	0.77	0.83	0.72	0.72	0.70	0.67	0.64	-16.7%
Former Yugoslavia *	1.88	1.82	1.58	2.15	..	..	..	..	..	..	..	..
Non-OECD Europe	**3.88**	**3.51**	**3.08**	**3.01**	**3.08**	**2.36**	**1.92**	**1.90**	**1.79**	**1.71**	**1.67**	**-45.7%**

* Data for individual countries of the Former Yugoslavia are not available prior to 1990.

CO$_2$ emissions / GDP using exchange rates

Emissions de CO $_2$ / PIB selon les taux de change

kilogrammes CO $_2$ / US$ using 2000 prices and exchange rates

	1971	1975	1980	1985	1990	1995	2000	2003	2004	2005	2006	% change 90-06
Armenia	..	..	..	..	7.27	2.30	1.78	1.20	1.16	1.21	1.07	-85.2%
Azerbaijan	..	..	..	..	7.00	8.23	5.34	3.95	3.72	3.14	2.26	-67.7%
Belarus	..	..	..	..	7.99	6.34	4.33	3.82	3.57	3.34	3.19	-60.1%
Estonia	..	..	..	..	5.93	3.73	2.57	2.32	2.18	1.90	1.63	-72.6%
Georgia	..	..	..	..	3.52	3.07	1.43	0.82	0.83	0.90	0.97	-72.5%
Kazakhstan	..	..	..	..	8.97	10.32	7.12	6.00	5.71	5.61	5.49	-38.8%
Kyrgyzstan	..	..	..	..	11.05	4.42	3.34	3.38	3.42	3.29	3.09	-72.1%
Latvia	..	..	..	..	1.76	1.48	0.87	0.77	0.71	0.65	0.62	-64.9%
Lithuania	..	..	..	..	2.06	1.53	0.98	0.84	0.83	0.82	0.77	-62.9%
Republic of Moldova	..	..	..	..	8.34	7.52	5.03	4.66	4.45	4.33	3.94	-52.8%
Russia	..	..	..	..	5.65	6.60	5.83	5.02	4.64	4.38	4.25	-24.7%
Tajikistan	..	..	..	..	4.53	5.37	4.28	3.79	3.66	3.64	3.75	-17.3%
Turkmenistan	..	..	..	..	12.47	14.77	12.70	9.22	7.36	7.11	6.87	-44.9%
Ukraine	..	..	..	..	9.56	11.37	9.34	8.39	7.10	6.77	6.41	-33.0%
Uzbekistan	..	..	..	..	8.53	8.92	8.46	7.63	6.91	6.13	5.87	-31.2%
Former USSR *	**4.94**	**5.08**	**4.95**	**4.66**	**6.32**	**7.09**	**5.90**	**5.11**	**4.67**	**4.40**	**4.22**	**-33.3%**
Argentina	0.50	0.47	0.45	0.47	0.55	0.46	0.47	0.47	0.47	0.44	0.44	-20.6%
Bolivia	0.52	0.62	0.75	0.86	0.94	1.15	0.91	1.02	1.12	1.22	1.25	33.2%
Brazil	0.43	0.44	0.41	0.37	0.38	0.41	0.47	0.45	0.45	0.44	0.43	13.1%
Chile	0.91	0.86	0.76	0.67	0.79	0.64	0.71	0.64	0.67	0.64	0.62	-21.2%
Colombia	0.92	0.80	0.74	0.75	0.69	0.73	0.72	0.63	0.63	0.60	0.56	-18.2%
Costa Rica	0.27	0.30	0.29	0.27	0.27	0.35	0.29	0.30	0.30	0.28	0.28	3.5%
Cuba	1.19	1.37	1.31	0.93	0.85	0.98	0.88	0.86	0.80	0.69	0.67	-21.4%
Dominican Republic	0.71	0.76	0.71	0.64	0.69	0.84	0.88	0.85	0.84	0.75	0.72	4.4%
Ecuador	0.62	0.74	0.98	1.04	0.99	1.07	1.16	1.21	1.12	1.15	1.17	18.0%
El Salvador	0.18	0.23	0.19	0.22	0.26	0.42	0.40	0.41	0.40	0.40	0.38	48.4%
Guatemala	0.32	0.34	0.36	0.29	0.26	0.38	0.46	0.48	0.49	0.50	0.48	88.1%
Haiti	0.12	0.12	0.13	0.18	0.22	0.26	0.37	0.43	0.43	0.45	0.45	108.8%
Honduras	0.53	0.55	0.50	0.45	0.50	0.76	0.74	0.90	0.94	0.90	0.94	90.5%
Jamaica	0.98	1.23	1.28	0.89	1.09	1.04	1.22	1.22	1.21	1.12	1.29	18.5%
Netherlands Antilles	..	..	8.57	4.74	2.73	2.48	2.66	2.96	3.01	2.97	3.06	12.0%
Nicaragua	0.46	0.46	0.55	0.54	0.65	0.81	0.90	0.94	0.94	0.90	0.84	29.0%
Panama	0.56	0.62	0.47	0.36	0.35	0.44	0.40	0.47	0.41	0.40	0.39	12.1%
Paraguay	0.28	0.26	0.30	0.29	0.32	0.48	0.46	0.49	0.48	0.43	0.43	32.2%
Peru	0.55	0.53	0.53	0.46	0.53	0.50	0.50	0.43	0.47	0.44	0.40	-25.7%
Trinidad and Tobago	1.36	1.14	1.06	1.44	1.90	1.92	2.20	2.04	2.00	1.95	2.00	5.2%
Uruguay	0.46	0.44	0.36	0.25	0.24	0.24	0.26	0.23	0.26	0.24	0.27	8.6%
Venezuela	0.76	0.81	1.05	1.14	1.10	1.05	1.05	1.10	1.18	1.08	1.05	1.02	-7.8%
Other Latin America	0.77	1.04	0.73	0.62	0.64	0.64	0.58	0.63	0.62	0.61	0.63	-1.2%
Latin America	**0.56**	**0.56**	**0.56**	**0.53**	**0.55**	**0.55**	**0.58**	**0.57**	**0.57**	**0.55**	**0.54**	**-2.4%**
Bangladesh	0.18	0.28	0.35	0.36	0.46	0.56	0.53	0.59	0.58	0.59	0.58	26.4%
Brunei Darussalam	0.18	0.52	0.59	0.80	0.90	1.16	1.08	1.15	1.07	1.05	1.15	27.8%
Cambodia	..	..	..	..	..	0.55	0.66	0.69	0.70	0.66	0.65	..
Chinese Taipei	0.88	0.89	0.91	0.66	0.67	0.65	0.67	0.72	0.71	0.70	0.69	3.1%
India	1.72	1.83	1.91	2.11	2.19	2.25	2.12	1.92	1.89	1.80	1.78	-18.8%
Indonesia	0.85	0.94	1.17	1.10	1.28	1.21	1.60	1.60	1.61	1.59	1.53	18.8%
DPR of Korea	22.35	16.20	12.93	9.67	7.32	6.12	6.34	6.37	6.40	6.57	6.55	-10.5%
Malaysia	1.00	0.95	0.92	1.00	1.08	1.10	1.25	1.22	1.24	1.30	1.29	19.9%
Mongolia	..	..	..	17.63	13.34	12.22	9.37	8.53	7.90	7.69	7.49	-43.8%
Myanmar	1.72	1.35	1.28	1.15	0.89	1.13	0.91	0.70	0.66	0.62	0.57	-36.2%
Nepal	0.11	0.17	0.24	0.20	0.26	0.40	0.56	0.48	0.43	0.48	0.48	82.0%
Pakistan	0.96	1.04	0.97	1.05	1.19	1.28	1.33	1.28	1.33	1.27	1.27	7.1%
Philippines	0.81	0.79	0.68	0.60	0.64	0.95	0.91	0.83	0.80	0.77	0.67	4.3%
Singapore	0.57	0.58	0.58	0.55	0.64	0.56	0.41	0.40	0.37	0.38	0.35	-45.0%
Sri Lanka	0.64	0.53	0.57	0.43	0.38	0.43	0.66	0.64	0.67	0.62	0.54	40.5%
Thailand	0.86	0.86	0.92	0.83	0.99	1.18	1.30	1.39	1.42	1.36	1.32	32.8%
Vietnam	2.00	2.05	1.68	1.41	1.13	1.24	1.41	1.58	1.91	1.80	1.71	51.2%
Other Asia	0.80	0.88	1.22	0.66	0.60	0.43	0.47	0.50	0.51	0.48	0.47	-21.7%
Asia	**1.36**	**1.38**	**1.38**	**1.38**	**1.38**	**1.35**	**1.36**	**1.33**	**1.33**	**1.30**	**1.27**	**-7.8%**
People's Rep. of China	7.47	7.88	7.68	5.60	4.97	3.77	2.53	2.46	2.65	2.68	2.68	-46.1%
Hong Kong, China	0.36	0.33	0.25	0.29	0.30	0.25	0.24	0.23	0.21	0.20	0.19	-38.3%
China	**6.09**	**6.38**	**5.89**	**4.53**	**4.06**	**3.23**	**2.25**	**2.23**	**2.40**	**2.43**	**2.44**	**-39.9%**

* Data for individual countries of the Former USSR are not available prior to 1990.

CO$_2$ Emissions / GDP using purchasing power parities

Emissions de CO$_2$ / PIB selon les parités de pouvoir d'achat

kilogrammes CO$_2$ / US$ using 2000 prices and purchasing power parities

	1971	1975	1980	1985	1990	1995	2000	2003	2004	2005	2006	% change 90-06
World *	0.81	0.77	0.73	0.66	0.63	0.58	0.52	0.51	0.50	0.50	0.49	**-23.3%**
Annex I Parties	..	..	..	..	0.62	0.57	0.51	0.49	0.48	0.47	0.45	-27.9%
Annex II Parties	0.82	0.75	0.67	0.57	0.52	0.49	0.45	0.44	0.43	0.42	0.41	-21.5%
North America	1.10	1.01	0.90	0.75	0.69	0.64	0.59	0.56	0.55	0.53	0.51	-26.1%
Europe	0.64	0.58	0.53	0.46	0.40	0.37	0.33	0.33	0.32	0.31	0.30	-24.1%
Pacific	0.58	0.57	0.49	0.42	0.41	0.41	0.41	0.41	0.40	0.40	0.39	-6.1%
Annex I EIT	..	..	..	..	1.32	1.34	1.10	0.98	0.91	0.86	0.83	-37.0%
Non-Annex I Parties	..	..	..	..	0.60	0.56	0.49	0.49	0.50	0.50	0.49	-17.7%
Annex I Kyoto Parties	..	..	..	..	0.59	0.52	0.46	0.46	0.44	0.43	0.42	-29.5%
Non-OECD Total	0.71	0.74	0.74	0.72	0.76	0.67	0.57	0.55	0.55	0.54	0.54	**-29.9%**
OECD Total	0.81	0.74	0.68	0.59	0.53	0.50	0.46	0.45	0.44	0.43	0.41	**-22.0%**
Canada	0.98	0.91	0.86	0.71	0.66	0.65	0.61	0.60	0.57	0.56	0.53	-19.8%
Mexico	0.33	0.36	0.40	0.43	0.46	0.45	0.40	0.40	0.39	0.41	0.40	-11.8%
United States	1.11	1.02	0.91	0.76	0.69	0.64	0.58	0.56	0.54	0.53	0.51	-26.6%
OECD N. America	1.05	0.96	0.86	0.73	0.67	0.63	0.57	0.55	0.53	0.52	0.50	**-25.4%**
Australia	0.67	0.76	0.75	0.69	0.70	0.66	0.65	0.62	0.62	0.63	0.62	-11.4%
Japan	0.58	0.54	0.45	0.39	0.37	0.37	0.37	0.37	0.36	0.35	0.34	-8.3%
Korea	0.52	0.58	0.67	0.57	0.54	0.58	0.56	0.52	0.52	0.49	0.47	-12.3%
New Zealand	0.31	0.33	0.33	0.33	0.35	0.35	0.40	0.40	0.38	0.38	0.38	7.8%
OECD Pacific	0.58	0.57	0.50	0.44	0.42	0.43	0.43	0.43	0.42	0.41	0.40	**-5.5%**
Austria	0.46	0.41	0.38	0.35	0.31	0.29	0.27	0.31	0.30	0.30	0.28	-9.8%
Belgium	0.84	0.72	0.67	0.52	0.48	0.49	0.45	0.44	0.41	0.39	0.37	-22.8%
Czech Republic	1.45	1.29	1.25	1.22	1.03	0.86	0.79	0.73	0.70	0.65	0.62	-40.5%
Denmark	0.69	0.62	0.65	0.55	0.42	0.43	0.32	0.36	0.32	0.29	0.32	-23.4%
Finland	0.69	0.64	0.68	0.52	0.50	0.53	0.41	0.51	0.46	0.37	0.42	-15.0%
France	0.59	0.51	0.46	0.34	0.28	0.27	0.25	0.24	0.23	0.23	0.22	-20.3%
Germany	0.92	0.84	0.77	0.69	0.55	0.45	0.39	0.39	0.39	0.37	0.37	-33.5%
Greece	0.25	0.28	0.30	0.36	0.44	0.45	0.44	0.41	0.39	0.38	0.36	-17.6%
Hungary	0.92	0.83	0.82	0.73	0.59	0.57	0.44	0.41	0.38	0.37	0.35	-40.6%
Iceland	0.48	0.45	0.36	0.30	0.30	0.31	0.26	0.25	0.24	0.22	0.21	-28.5%
Ireland	0.86	0.68	0.67	0.60	0.56	0.48	0.38	0.32	0.31	0.31	0.30	-46.1%
Italy	0.43	0.41	0.37	0.33	0.32	0.31	0.29	0.30	0.30	0.30	0.29	-8.8%
Luxembourg	2.20	1.53	1.35	0.99	0.73	0.47	0.34	0.38	0.41	0.40	0.38	-48.7%
Netherlands	0.61	0.59	0.56	0.51	0.46	0.45	0.37	0.38	0.38	0.37	0.35	-23.8%
Norway	0.40	0.34	0.32	0.26	0.25	0.24	0.21	0.21	0.20	0.20	0.20	-21.0%
Poland	1.36	1.26	1.47	1.48	1.23	1.07	0.72	0.68	0.65	0.63	0.61	-50.3%
Portugal	0.23	0.24	0.25	0.25	0.30	0.34	0.34	0.33	0.33	0.34	0.31	2.2%
Slovak Republic	1.05	1.03	1.17	1.06	1.04	0.81	0.63	0.58	0.53	0.51	0.47	-55.0%
Spain	0.34	0.35	0.39	0.34	0.32	0.33	0.33	0.33	0.34	0.34	0.31	-1.0%
Sweden	0.61	0.52	0.45	0.33	0.26	0.28	0.21	0.21	0.20	0.18	0.17	-36.5%
Switzerland	0.26	0.24	0.24	0.23	0.20	0.20	0.18	0.19	0.19	0.18	0.18	-11.5%
Turkey	0.31	0.36	0.38	0.40	0.41	0.42	0.46	0.43	0.41	0.40	0.42	1.4%
United Kingdom	0.81	0.69	0.63	0.54	0.47	0.40	0.35	0.33	0.32	0.31	0.31	-34.3%
OECD Europe	0.69	0.62	0.59	0.52	0.44	0.40	0.36	0.35	0.34	0.34	0.33	**-26.2%**
European Union - 27	..	..	..	..	0.48	0.42	0.36	0.36	0.35	0.34	0.33	-29.9%

* The ratio for the world has been calculated to include emissions from international marine bunkers and international aviation. The ratios for individual countries and regions do not include these emissions. For information, the world ratio excluding emissions from international marine bunkers and international aviation is 0.47 kg CO$_2$ per US$ using 2000 prices and purchasing power parities in 2006.

CO$_2$ Emissions / GDP using purchasing power parities

Emissions de CO$_2$ / PIB selon les parités de pouvoir d'achat

kilogrammes CO$_2$ / US$ using 2000 prices and purchasing power parities

	1971	1975	1980	1985	1990	1995	2000	2003	2004	2005	2006	% change 90-06
Non-OECD Total	0.71	0.74	0.74	0.72	0.76	0.67	0.57	0.55	0.55	0.54	0.54	**-29.9%**
Algeria	0.17	0.19	0.29	0.34	0.40	0.43	0.41	0.42	0.40	0.41	0.40	1.3%
Angola	0.12	0.14	0.18	0.18	0.22	0.27	0.26	0.31	0.27	0.24	0.23	3.9%
Benin	0.12	0.17	0.12	0.11	0.06	0.04	0.20	0.28	0.29	0.30	0.34	489.8%
Botswana	..	..	..	0.34	0.36	0.34	0.29	0.23	0.22	0.23	0.23	-37.4%
Cameroon	0.08	0.08	0.09	0.09	0.11	0.11	0.10	0.09	0.09	0.09	0.09	-18.2%
Congo	0.51	0.42	0.41	0.26	0.22	0.16	0.16	0.21	0.21	0.22	0.25	12.1%
Dem. Rep. of Congo	0.05	0.05	0.06	0.06	0.06	0.06	0.07	0.07	0.07	0.06	0.06	9.2%
Côte d'Ivoire	0.19	0.19	0.17	0.15	0.12	0.14	0.23	0.20	0.22	0.24	0.23	81.0%
Egypt	0.41	0.45	0.46	0.52	0.51	0.46	0.46	0.50	0.51	0.52	0.50	-1.1%
Eritrea	..	..	..	..	..	0.22	0.17	0.17	0.16	0.14	0.12	..
Ethiopia	0.05	0.04	0.04	0.04	0.05	0.06	0.06	0.08	0.07	0.07	0.07	32.6%
Gabon	0.17	0.13	0.24	0.28	0.14	0.18	0.19	0.21	0.21	0.26	0.26	78.7%
Ghana	0.09	0.12	0.11	0.11	0.11	0.11	0.13	0.16	0.14	0.14	0.17	54.2%
Kenya	0.38	0.34	0.31	0.27	0.24	0.25	0.28	0.23	0.25	0.26	0.28	14.4%
Libya	0.08	0.24	0.31	0.44	0.68	0.81	0.85	0.76	0.76	0.71	0.67	-0.5%
Morocco	0.19	0.23	0.25	0.25	0.24	0.30	0.29	0.28	0.29	0.32	0.30	23.4%
Mozambique	0.29	0.28	0.27	0.22	0.13	0.12	0.09	0.09	0.08	0.07	0.07	-44.7%
Namibia	..	..	..	..	..	0.19	0.17	0.21	0.21	0.21	0.21	..
Nigeria	0.11	0.20	0.37	0.52	0.36	0.33	0.39	0.40	0.37	0.40	0.35	-2.9%
Senegal	0.18	0.21	0.25	0.22	0.18	0.21	0.24	0.23	0.26	0.25	0.23	28.4%
South Africa	0.84	0.88	0.77	0.77	0.79	0.82	0.77	0.76	0.76	0.71	0.70	-11.7%
Sudan	0.20	0.17	0.17	0.18	0.19	0.12	0.11	0.15	0.17	0.15	0.15	-22.1%
United Rep. of Tanzania	0.22	0.18	0.17	0.15	0.13	0.17	0.15	0.16	0.17	0.19	0.19	44.5%
Togo	0.10	0.08	0.07	0.06	0.10	0.10	0.13	0.14	0.13	0.12	0.11	12.2%
Tunisia	0.25	0.24	0.29	0.29	0.32	0.31	0.30	0.28	0.28	0.26	0.25	-21.6%
Zambia	0.55	0.63	0.47	0.39	0.33	0.28	0.20	0.20	0.20	0.20	0.20	-39.5%
Zimbabwe	0.49	0.42	0.43	0.42	0.56	0.49	0.40	0.40	0.38	0.43	0.43	-22.2%
Other Africa	0.08	0.09	0.11	0.10	0.10	0.12	0.11	0.11	0.11	0.11	0.11	6.5%
Africa	0.35	0.38	0.38	0.41	0.41	0.43	0.41	0.41	0.41	0.40	0.39	**-6.2%**
Bahrain	1.74	1.66	1.42	2.14	1.92	1.37	1.35	1.31	1.30	1.32	1.33	-30.5%
Islamic Rep. of Iran	0.24	0.31	0.44	0.58	0.68	0.82	0.82	0.80	0.82	0.82	0.85	23.7%
Iraq	0.18	0.18	0.24	0.52	1.17	4.16	2.14	3.77	3.06	3.03	3.19	171.7%
Israel	0.38	0.35	0.33	0.36	0.40	0.40	0.38	0.42	0.41	0.39	0.37	-5.6%
Jordan	0.27	0.44	0.42	0.57	0.76	0.71	0.72	0.64	0.67	0.66	0.63	-16.8%
Kuwait	0.64	0.76	0.97	1.51	0.84	1.05	1.17	1.16	1.22	1.25	1.07	26.7%
Lebanon	0.38	0.47	0.65	0.54	0.79	0.87	0.87	0.93	0.78	0.80	0.67	-14.5%
Oman	0.05	0.11	0.27	0.32	0.51	0.55	0.64	0.74	0.72	0.71	0.72	43.1%
Qatar	0.28	0.60	0.81	1.52	1.80	2.06	1.67	1.66	1.54	1.51	1.56	-13.0%
Saudi Arabia	0.17	0.14	0.44	0.71	0.75	0.83	0.89	0.94	0.95	0.94	0.95	26.7%
Syria	0.61	0.54	0.58	0.78	0.96	0.81	0.86	0.79	0.77	0.77	0.76	-21.0%
United Arab Emirates	0.28	0.22	0.41	0.87	1.13	1.29	1.23	1.18	1.11	1.04	0.98	-13.2%
Yemen	0.58	0.60	0.67	0.66	0.75	0.83	0.90	0.99	1.02	1.07	1.07	42.8%
Middle East	0.28	0.29	0.44	0.65	0.76	0.88	0.88	0.89	0.90	0.89	0.89	**16.3%**
Albania	0.73	0.67	0.87	0.74	0.63	0.21	0.28	0.30	0.25	0.31	0.27	-56.8%
Bosnia and Herzegovina *	..	..	..	..	4.16	0.55	0.67	0.61	0.60	0.60	0.62	-85.1%
Bulgaria	2.52	2.12	1.83	1.50	1.29	1.05	0.86	0.83	0.76	0.72	0.71	-45.2%
Croatia *	..	..	..	..	0.45	0.46	0.43	0.44	0.41	0.40	0.38	-14.9%
Cyprus	0.57	0.61	0.54	0.44	0.43	0.47	0.47	0.48	0.46	0.45	0.44	0.9%
Gibraltar	0.25	0.23	0.25	0.23	0.29	0.49	0.51	0.50	0.50	0.50	0.50	71.1%
FYR of Macedonia *	..	..	..	..	0.68	0.84	0.69	0.69	0.65	0.63	0.60	-12.5%
Malta	0.59	0.39	0.34	0.37	0.54	0.43	0.32	0.37	0.39	0.37	0.35	-34.6%
Romania	1.71	1.39	1.20	1.01	1.06	0.83	0.65	0.61	0.55	0.53	0.50	-52.6%
Serbia *	..	..	..	..	1.64	1.20	1.17	1.28	1.28	1.18	1.19	-27.8%
Slovenia *	..	..	..	..	0.45	0.48	0.42	0.42	0.40	0.39	0.37	-16.7%
Former Yugoslavia *	0.87	0.84	0.73	0.99	..	..	..	..	..	..	..	..
Non-OECD Europe	1.41	1.25	1.09	1.05	1.03	0.80	0.66	0.65	0.61	0.58	0.57	**-44.8%**

* Data for individual countries of the Former Yugoslavia are not available prior to 1990.

CO$_2$ Emissions / GDP using purchasing power parities

Emissions de CO$_2$ / PIB selon les parités de pouvoir d'achat

kilogrammes CO$_2$ / US$ using 2000 prices and purchasing power parities

	1971	1975	1980	1985	1990	1995	2000	2003	2004	2005	2006	% change 90-06
Armenia	..	..	..	..	1.86	0.59	0.46	0.31	0.30	0.31	0.27	-85.2%
Azerbaijan	..	..	..	..	1.85	2.18	1.41	1.04	0.98	0.83	0.60	-67.7%
Belarus	..	..	..	..	2.12	1.68	1.15	1.01	0.95	0.88	0.84	-60.1%
Estonia	..	..	..	..	2.59	1.63	1.13	1.02	0.96	0.83	0.71	-72.6%
Georgia	..	..	..	..	1.14	0.99	0.46	0.27	0.27	0.29	0.31	-72.5%
Kazakhstan	..	..	..	..	2.54	2.92	2.01	1.70	1.61	1.59	1.55	-38.8%
Kyrgyzstan	..	..	..	..	2.06	0.82	0.62	0.63	0.64	0.61	0.57	-72.1%
Latvia	..	..	..	..	0.73	0.61	0.36	0.32	0.29	0.27	0.26	-64.9%
Lithuania	..	..	..	..	0.77	0.57	0.37	0.32	0.31	0.31	0.29	-62.8%
Republic of Moldova	..	..	..	..	1.91	1.72	1.15	1.07	1.02	0.99	0.90	-52.9%
Russia	..	..	..	..	1.43	1.67	1.48	1.27	1.17	1.11	1.08	-24.7%
Tajikistan	..	..	..	..	0.89	1.06	0.84	0.74	0.72	0.72	0.74	-17.4%
Turkmenistan	..	..	..	..	2.31	2.74	2.35	1.71	1.36	1.32	1.27	-44.9%
Ukraine	..	..	..	..	1.51	1.79	1.47	1.32	1.12	1.07	1.01	-33.0%
Uzbekistan	..	..	..	..	3.18	3.32	3.15	2.85	2.58	2.28	2.19	-31.2%
Former USSR *	**1.20**	**1.23**	**1.20**	**1.13**	**1.53**	**1.75**	**1.48**	**1.28**	**1.17**	**1.10**	**1.06**	**-31.2%**
Argentina	0.32	0.30	0.29	0.30	0.35	0.29	0.30	0.30	0.30	0.28	0.28	-20.6%
Bolivia	0.22	0.26	0.32	0.36	0.40	0.49	0.38	0.43	0.47	0.52	0.53	33.2%
Brazil	0.22	0.23	0.21	0.19	0.20	0.21	0.24	0.23	0.23	0.23	0.23	13.1%
Chile	0.48	0.46	0.41	0.36	0.42	0.34	0.38	0.34	0.36	0.34	0.33	-21.2%
Colombia	0.31	0.27	0.25	0.25	0.23	0.24	0.24	0.21	0.21	0.20	0.19	-18.2%
Costa Rica	0.14	0.15	0.14	0.13	0.14	0.18	0.14	0.15	0.15	0.14	0.14	3.4%
Cuba	0.52	0.59	0.57	0.40	0.37	0.42	0.38	0.37	0.35	0.30	0.29	-21.4%
Dominican Republic	0.25	0.27	0.25	0.23	0.24	0.30	0.31	0.30	0.30	0.26	0.25	4.4%
Ecuador	0.25	0.30	0.39	0.42	0.40	0.43	0.47	0.49	0.45	0.46	0.47	18.0%
El Salvador	0.08	0.10	0.09	0.10	0.12	0.19	0.18	0.19	0.18	0.18	0.17	48.5%
Guatemala	0.14	0.15	0.15	0.12	0.11	0.16	0.20	0.20	0.21	0.21	0.21	88.0%
Haiti	0.03	0.04	0.04	0.05	0.06	0.08	0.11	0.13	0.13	0.13	0.13	108.9%
Honduras	0.17	0.18	0.16	0.15	0.16	0.24	0.24	0.29	0.30	0.29	0.30	90.4%
Jamaica	0.84	1.06	1.10	0.77	0.94	0.90	1.05	1.05	1.04	0.97	1.11	18.5%
Netherlands Antilles	..	..	3.81	2.11	1.21	1.10	1.18	1.32	1.34	1.32	1.36	12.0%
Nicaragua	0.12	0.12	0.14	0.14	0.17	0.21	0.23	0.24	0.24	0.23	0.21	29.0%
Panama	0.37	0.41	0.31	0.23	0.23	0.29	0.26	0.31	0.27	0.26	0.25	12.1%
Paraguay	0.09	0.08	0.10	0.09	0.10	0.15	0.15	0.16	0.15	0.14	0.14	32.2%
Peru	0.24	0.23	0.23	0.20	0.23	0.22	0.22	0.19	0.20	0.19	0.17	-25.7%
Trinidad and Tobago	0.95	0.79	0.74	1.00	1.33	1.34	1.54	1.42	1.40	1.36	1.40	5.3%
Uruguay	0.32	0.31	0.25	0.17	0.17	0.17	0.18	0.16	0.19	0.17	0.19	8.6%
Venezuela	0.64	0.68	0.88	0.95	0.92	0.88	0.92	0.99	0.90	0.88	0.85	-7.8%
Other Latin America	0.50	0.67	0.50	0.43	0.46	0.46	0.42	0.45	0.44	0.44	0.45	-3.2%
Latin America	**0.31**	**0.30**	**0.30**	**0.28**	**0.29**	**0.29**	**0.31**	**0.30**	**0.30**	**0.29**	**0.28**	**-2.2%**
Bangladesh	0.04	0.07	0.08	0.09	0.11	0.13	0.13	0.14	0.14	0.14	0.14	26.4%
Brunei Darussalam	0.15	0.43	0.50	0.67	0.75	0.97	0.90	0.97	0.90	0.88	0.96	27.8%
Cambodia	..	..	..	..	..	0.09	0.11	0.11	0.12	0.11	0.11	..
Chinese Taipei	0.58	0.58	0.59	0.43	0.44	0.43	0.44	0.47	0.46	0.46	0.45	3.1%
India	0.33	0.35	0.37	0.40	0.42	0.43	0.41	0.37	0.36	0.35	0.34	-18.8%
Indonesia	0.23	0.26	0.32	0.30	0.35	0.33	0.44	0.44	0.44	0.44	0.42	18.8%
DPR of Korea	6.35	4.61	3.68	2.75	2.08	1.74	1.80	1.81	1.82	1.87	1.86	-10.5%
Malaysia	0.46	0.44	0.42	0.46	0.49	0.50	0.57	0.56	0.57	0.59	0.59	19.9%
Mongolia	..	..	..	4.55	3.44	3.15	2.41	2.20	2.04	1.98	1.93	-43.9%
Myanmar	0.28	0.22	0.21	0.19	0.15	0.19	0.15	0.12	0.11	0.10	0.09	-36.2%
Nepal	0.02	0.03	0.04	0.03	0.04	0.07	0.09	0.08	0.07	0.08	0.08	82.1%
Pakistan	0.27	0.29	0.27	0.30	0.33	0.36	0.38	0.36	0.38	0.36	0.36	7.1%
Philippines	0.20	0.20	0.17	0.15	0.16	0.24	0.23	0.21	0.20	0.19	0.17	4.3%
Singapore	0.55	0.57	0.57	0.53	0.63	0.55	0.40	0.39	0.36	0.37	0.35	-45.0%
Sri Lanka	0.16	0.13	0.14	0.11	0.09	0.11	0.16	0.16	0.16	0.15	0.13	40.4%
Thailand	0.27	0.27	0.29	0.26	0.31	0.37	0.41	0.44	0.45	0.43	0.42	32.9%
Vietnam	0.39	0.40	0.33	0.28	0.22	0.24	0.28	0.31	0.38	0.35	0.34	51.1%
Other Asia	0.23	0.26	0.37	0.20	0.20	0.16	0.18	0.18	0.19	0.18	0.18	-10.8%
Asia	**0.35**	**0.36**	**0.38**	**0.38**	**0.39**	**0.39**	**0.39**	**0.38**	**0.38**	**0.36**	**0.35**	**-9.1%**
People's Rep. of China	1.80	1.90	1.85	1.35	1.20	0.91	0.61	0.59	0.64	0.64	0.65	-46.1%
Hong Kong, China	0.34	0.32	0.24	0.28	0.29	0.24	0.23	0.22	0.20	0.19	0.18	-38.3%
China	**1.72**	**1.81**	**1.73**	**1.29**	**1.15**	**0.88**	**0.60**	**0.58**	**0.63**	**0.63**	**0.63**	**-44.7%**

* Data for individual countries of the Former USSR are not available prior to 1990.

CO$_2$ emissions / population

Emissions de CO$_2$ / population

tonnes CO$_2$ / capita

	1971	1975	1980	1985	1990	1995	2000	2003	2004	2005	2006	% change 90-06
World *	3.75	3.86	4.07	3.86	3.99	3.85	3.87	3.98	4.13	4.20	4.28	7.4%
Annex I Parties	..	..	..	..	11.82	10.92	11.16	11.26	11.27	11.24	11.18	-5.4%
Annex II Parties	12.21	12.18	12.63	11.81	12.27	12.34	12.92	12.91	12.93	12.86	12.64	2.9%
North America	20.16	19.81	20.17	18.72	19.06	18.92	19.88	19.33	19.39	19.26	18.76	-1.6%
Europe	8.63	8.56	9.08	8.35	8.38	8.19	8.28	8.52	8.49	8.36	8.29	-1.0%
Pacific	7.59	8.19	8.20	7.97	9.39	9.95	10.42	10.68	10.71	10.84	10.77	14.7%
Annex I EIT	..	..	..	..	12.37	8.85	8.16	8.56	8.50	8.53	8.83	-28.6%
Non-Annex I Parties	..	..	..	..	1.58	1.78	1.84	2.02	2.20	2.31	2.44	54.3%
Annex I Kyoto Parties	..	..	..	..	10.24	9.02	8.95	9.26	9.22	9.20	9.23	-9.9%
Non-OECD Total	1.48	1.72	1.97	2.02	2.20	2.08	2.06	2.24	2.40	2.51	2.64	19.9%
OECD Total	10.59	10.61	11.05	10.35	10.62	10.64	11.07	11.06	11.09	11.06	10.93	2.9%
Canada	15.46	16.30	17.41	15.56	15.60	15.87	17.36	17.50	17.21	17.22	16.52	5.8%
Mexico	1.95	2.45	3.23	3.42	3.61	3.40	3.63	3.64	3.64	3.87	3.97	10.2%
United States	20.66	20.19	20.47	19.06	19.44	19.26	20.16	19.53	19.63	19.48	19.00	-2.3%
OECD N. America	16.91	16.48	16.67	15.39	15.56	15.27	16.00	15.57	15.61	15.57	15.21	-2.2%
Australia	10.92	12.89	14.05	13.90	15.13	15.68	17.57	18.07	18.29	18.91	19.02	25.7%
Japan	7.24	7.68	7.54	7.25	8.68	9.22	9.40	9.57	9.57	9.61	9.49	9.4%
Korea	1.58	2.18	3.26	3.76	5.35	8.09	9.17	9.58	9.97	9.74	9.86	84.3%
New Zealand	4.80	5.52	5.22	5.99	6.36	6.64	8.36	8.95	8.75	8.84	8.88	39.7%
OECD Pacific	6.30	6.90	7.11	7.02	8.46	9.52	10.13	10.41	10.53	10.57	10.55	24.6%
Austria	6.49	6.62	7.37	7.18	7.37	7.45	7.74	9.06	9.00	9.11	8.80	19.4%
Belgium	12.09	11.82	12.75	10.34	11.06	11.93	12.42	12.25	11.94	11.50	11.12	0.5%
Czech Republic	15.35	15.17	15.98	16.31	14.97	11.96	11.84	11.85	11.95	11.71	11.78	-21.3%
Denmark	11.09	10.37	12.21	11.83	9.80	11.02	9.34	10.43	9.38	8.74	10.15	3.6%
Finland	8.62	9.42	11.54	9.91	10.91	10.97	10.42	13.84	12.81	10.50	12.69	16.3%
France	8.24	7.99	8.37	6.37	6.05	5.95	6.19	6.19	6.15	6.15	5.97	-1.3%
Germany	12.49	12.40	13.48	13.06	11.98	10.65	10.06	10.20	10.22	9.84	10.00	-16.5%
Greece	2.80	3.75	4.62	5.41	6.78	7.13	8.01	8.50	8.43	8.56	8.43	24.2%
Hungary	6.00	6.86	7.97	7.77	6.61	5.69	5.41	5.69	5.60	5.64	5.60	-15.3%
Iceland	6.79	7.37	7.62	6.71	7.37	7.30	7.60	7.51	7.62	7.36	7.18	-2.6%
Ireland	7.29	6.64	7.62	7.45	8.74	9.17	10.84	10.43	10.30	10.46	10.56	20.9%
Italy	5.42	5.76	6.38	6.14	7.01	7.21	7.46	7.85	7.74	7.74	7.61	8.5%
Luxembourg	45.11	33.69	32.75	27.03	27.40	19.92	18.27	21.64	23.92	24.11	23.64	-13.7%
Netherlands	9.82	10.31	10.82	10.13	10.48	11.08	10.87	11.33	11.37	11.19	10.91	4.2%
Norway	6.02	6.01	6.85	6.54	6.71	7.53	7.52	7.75	7.83	7.94	7.91	17.9%
Poland	8.74	9.94	11.61	11.28	9.04	8.66	7.63	7.62	7.73	7.71	8.02	-11.3%
Portugal	1.66	1.97	2.41	2.44	3.93	4.82	5.82	5.60	5.70	5.94	5.32	35.4%
Slovak Republic	8.57	9.25	11.10	10.54	10.71	7.61	6.92	7.15	6.93	7.07	6.95	-35.1%
Spain	3.49	4.39	4.99	4.55	5.28	5.93	7.05	7.37	7.67	7.82	7.44	40.9%
Sweden	10.18	9.69	8.84	7.04	6.16	6.52	5.95	6.13	5.96	5.58	5.32	-13.8%
Switzerland	6.14	5.73	6.14	6.34	5.99	5.80	5.78	5.82	5.89	5.92	5.83	-2.7%
Turkey	1.14	1.48	1.60	1.88	2.26	2.48	2.97	2.86	2.89	3.00	3.29	45.5%
United Kingdom	11.15	10.31	10.14	9.63	9.66	8.95	8.93	9.00	8.95	8.89	8.86	-8.3%
OECD Europe	8.12	8.16	8.71	8.08	7.86	7.56	7.55	7.70	7.68	7.60	7.60	-3.4%
European Union - 27	..	..	..	..	8.59	8.06	7.95	8.21	8.19	8.09	8.07	-6.1%

* The ratio for the world has been calculated to include emissions from international marine bunkers and international aviation. The ratios for individual countries and regions do not include these emissions. For information, the world ratio excluding emissions from international marine bunkers and international aviation is 4.13 t CO$_2$ per capita in 2006.

CO$_2$ emissions / population

Emissions de CO$_2$ / population

tonnes CO$_2$ / capita

	1971	1975	1980	1985	1990	1995	2000	2003	2004	2005	2006	% change 90-06
Non-OECD Total	**1.48**	**1.72**	**1.97**	**2.02**	**2.20**	**2.08**	**2.06**	**2.24**	**2.40**	**2.51**	**2.64**	**19.9%**
Algeria	0.63	0.91	1.59	2.06	2.17	2.10	2.18	2.44	2.43	2.55	2.58	18.9%
Angola	0.28	0.30	0.35	0.32	0.39	0.33	0.37	0.50	0.47	0.49	0.52	33.5%
Benin	0.10	0.14	0.11	0.11	0.05	0.04	0.20	0.28	0.29	0.30	0.34	601.4%
Botswana	..	..	..	1.34	2.15	2.13	2.42	2.19	2.26	2.35	2.44	13.8%
Cameroon	0.10	0.13	0.18	0.23	0.22	0.18	0.18	0.18	0.17	0.16	0.17	-21.5%
Congo	0.42	0.43	0.45	0.40	0.29	0.19	0.18	0.24	0.25	0.28	0.32	11.4%
Dem. Rep. of Congo	0.12	0.11	0.11	0.10	0.08	0.05	0.04	0.04	0.04	0.04	0.04	-50.8%
Côte d'Ivoire	0.43	0.46	0.40	0.29	0.21	0.21	0.36	0.28	0.31	0.34	0.32	57.4%
Egypt	0.57	0.66	0.97	1.33	1.44	1.38	1.66	1.86	1.93	2.05	2.06	43.4%
Eritrea	..	..	..	..	..	0.24	0.16	0.17	0.16	0.14	0.11	..
Ethiopia	0.04	0.03	0.03	0.03	0.04	0.04	0.05	0.06	0.06	0.06	0.07	67.8%
Gabon	0.87	1.26	1.87	2.14	0.98	1.26	1.17	1.32	1.32	1.63	1.60	62.7%
Ghana	0.21	0.23	0.20	0.16	0.17	0.19	0.25	0.33	0.28	0.30	0.38	116.0%
Kenya	0.32	0.32	0.34	0.28	0.27	0.27	0.29	0.23	0.25	0.28	0.30	11.3%
Libya	1.79	3.72	6.06	5.84	6.27	7.27	7.42	7.38	7.54	7.18	7.03	12.1%
Morocco	0.45	0.58	0.72	0.76	0.81	0.96	1.04	1.12	1.20	1.30	1.31	60.6%
Mozambique	0.30	0.22	0.19	0.11	0.08	0.07	0.07	0.08	0.08	0.07	0.08	-3.3%
Namibia	..	..	..	..	..	1.09	1.00	1.32	1.38	1.42	1.46	..
Nigeria	0.11	0.19	0.38	0.40	0.31	0.28	0.33	0.36	0.35	0.39	0.36	15.1%
Senegal	0.27	0.31	0.34	0.31	0.25	0.27	0.35	0.34	0.39	0.39	0.37	44.9%
South Africa	7.69	8.46	7.78	7.31	7.23	7.07	6.79	7.00	7.28	7.05	7.22	-0.2%
Sudan	0.22	0.20	0.19	0.18	0.21	0.15	0.16	0.25	0.28	0.28	0.30	42.9%
United Rep. of Tanzania	0.11	0.09	0.09	0.07	0.07	0.08	0.08	0.09	0.10	0.12	0.12	81.3%
Togo	0.15	0.13	0.13	0.09	0.14	0.13	0.18	0.19	0.17	0.16	0.14	-2.8%
Tunisia	0.71	0.85	1.23	1.32	1.48	1.60	1.88	1.94	1.99	1.92	1.95	31.3%
Zambia	0.78	0.87	0.56	0.40	0.32	0.22	0.16	0.18	0.18	0.19	0.19	-39.8%
Zimbabwe	1.34	1.17	1.09	1.08	1.53	1.26	1.00	0.81	0.74	0.79	0.75	-51.0%
Other Africa	0.11	0.12	0.15	0.12	0.13	0.13	0.13	0.13	0.13	0.13	0.14	14.3%
Africa	**0.72**	**0.81**	**0.86**	**0.87**	**0.87**	**0.84**	**0.85**	**0.88**	**0.90**	**0.91**	**0.91**	**5.3%**
Bahrain	13.21	19.53	21.31	25.16	23.73	20.11	21.74	23.30	23.74	25.26	27.02	13.9%
Islamic Rep. of Iran	1.41	2.26	2.36	3.11	3.22	4.23	4.77	5.25	5.59	5.74	6.17	91.6%
Iraq	1.26	1.40	2.44	2.79	2.91	3.67	3.35	2.73	3.15	3.15	3.23	10.9%
Israel	4.69	4.94	5.05	5.79	7.20	8.35	8.83	9.21	9.02	8.88	8.89	23.4%
Jordan	0.83	1.15	1.93	2.78	2.90	2.89	2.98	2.87	3.16	3.31	3.30	13.8%
Kuwait	29.21	22.74	22.40	22.09	11.46	22.76	22.90	24.94	27.24	29.33	25.66	123.9%
Lebanon	1.85	2.06	2.36	2.65	2.15	3.60	3.76	4.35	3.85	3.94	3.29	53.0%
Oman	0.33	0.78	1.88	3.57	5.39	6.63	8.23	10.26	10.19	10.72	11.57	114.7%
Qatar	18.26	28.64	33.80	33.85	30.38	35.71	42.99	41.59	44.30	44.22	48.32	59.1%
Saudi Arabia	2.22	3.26	10.55	10.02	9.85	11.05	12.15	13.03	13.48	13.92	14.36	45.7%
Syria	1.03	1.36	1.68	2.18	2.44	2.64	2.77	2.60	2.60	2.65	2.65	9.0%
United Arab Emirates	9.71	9.67	18.28	25.67	29.11	29.03	26.50	27.01	26.56	26.14	25.96	-10.8%
Yemen	0.18	0.24	0.41	0.47	0.52	0.60	0.73	0.82	0.86	0.91	0.91	74.5%
Middle East	**1.87**	**2.46**	**3.70**	**4.37**	**4.47**	**5.41**	**5.85**	**6.18**	**6.46**	**6.62**	**6.82**	**52.5%**
Albania	1.78	1.85	2.84	2.43	1.90	0.59	1.03	1.26	1.12	1.45	1.33	-29.8%
Bosnia and Herzegovina *	..	..	..	..	5.49	0.98	3.61	3.69	3.83	4.00	4.37	-20.3%
Bulgaria	7.36	8.28	9.46	9.07	8.60	6.36	5.21	5.93	5.83	5.95	6.18	-28.1%
Croatia *	..	..	..	..	4.51	3.39	3.92	4.71	4.59	4.65	4.66	3.3%
Cyprus	2.86	3.39	5.07	5.13	6.62	8.01	9.03	9.64	9.26	9.21	9.13	37.9%
Gibraltar	3.51	3.37	3.99	4.17	6.13	11.97	13.94	14.71	15.26	15.48	16.02	161.3%
FYR of Macedonia *	..	..	..	..	4.78	4.47	4.20	4.10	4.02	4.06	3.94	-17.6%
Malta	2.00	1.97	2.71	3.34	6.35	6.22	5.71	6.29	6.53	6.40	6.15	-3.0%
Romania	5.61	6.62	7.93	7.63	7.20	5.16	3.84	4.34	4.22	4.24	4.39	-39.1%
Serbia *	..	..	..	..	6.19	4.05	5.20	6.38	6.93	6.75	7.18	16.1%
Slovenia *	..	..	..	..	6.23	6.51	7.02	7.59	7.66	7.66	7.72	23.8%
Former Yugoslavia *	3.16	3.63	4.05	5.48	..	..	..	..	..	..	..	..
Non-OECD Europe	**4.74**	**5.46**	**6.38**	**6.71**	**6.48**	**4.56**	**4.29**	**4.88**	**4.89**	**4.90**	**5.07**	**-21.7%**

* Data for individual countries of the Former Yugoslavia are not available prior to 1990.

CO$_2$ emissions / population
Emissions de CO$_2$ / population

tonnes CO$_2$ / capita

	1971	1975	1980	1985	1990	1995	2000	2003	2004	2005	2006	% change 90-06
Armenia	..	..	..	..	5.77	1.06	1.10	1.07	1.14	1.37	1.38	-76.2%
Azerbaijan	..	..	..	..	8.76	4.01	3.50	3.42	3.51	3.71	3.56	-59.3%
Belarus	..	..	..	..	11.27	5.83	5.52	5.80	6.07	6.24	6.58	-41.6%
Estonia	..	..	..	..	23.06	11.14	10.57	12.01	12.26	11.82	11.28	-51.1%
Georgia	..	..	..	..	5.25	1.40	0.93	0.68	0.73	0.88	1.04	-80.2%
Kazakhstan	..	..	..	..	14.46	10.56	8.75	10.03	10.38	11.10	11.89	-17.8%
Kyrgyzstan	..	..	..	..	5.14	1.01	0.93	1.04	1.11	1.05	1.01	-80.4%
Latvia	..	..	..	..	6.87	3.49	2.87	3.20	3.23	3.29	3.51	-48.9%
Lithuania	..	..	..	..	8.95	3.91	3.21	3.51	3.72	3.99	4.03	-55.0%
Republic of Moldova	..	..	..	..	6.88	2.49	1.56	1.84	1.91	2.03	1.94	-71.8%
Russia	..	..	..	..	14.70	10.69	10.35	10.65	10.60	10.70	11.14	-24.2%
Tajikistan	..	..	..	..	2.20	0.91	0.68	0.77	0.81	0.85	0.93	-57.9%
Turkmenistan	..	..	..	..	12.71	8.21	8.04	9.13	8.24	8.56	8.90	-30.0%
Ukraine	..	..	..	..	13.26	7.63	5.94	6.89	6.59	6.50	6.63	-50.0%
Uzbekistan	..	..	..	..	5.84	4.46	4.72	4.64	4.47	4.20	4.25	-27.2%
Former USSR *	**8.15**	**10.09**	**11.49**	**11.51**	**12.62**	**8.39**	**7.74**	**8.14**	**8.06**	**8.12**	**8.42**	**-33.3%**
Argentina	3.41	3.30	3.41	2.92	3.08	3.31	3.60	3.23	3.55	3.59	3.80	23.4%
Bolivia	0.50	0.67	0.81	0.75	0.82	1.09	0.92	1.03	1.16	1.29	1.36	66.9%
Brazil	0.92	1.26	1.46	1.23	1.29	1.48	1.74	1.67	1.74	1.75	1.76	36.2%
Chile	2.14	1.63	1.90	1.61	2.42	2.71	3.45	3.32	3.63	3.61	3.64	50.2%
Colombia	1.13	1.12	1.19	1.21	1.29	1.52	1.46	1.31	1.35	1.33	1.30	1.1%
Costa Rica	0.68	0.85	0.93	0.74	0.85	1.28	1.16	1.28	1.29	1.25	1.35	58.8%
Cuba	2.08	2.70	2.90	3.03	2.60	2.02	2.22	2.33	2.26	2.16	2.36	-9.2%
Dominican Republic	0.73	0.97	1.05	0.93	1.05	1.42	1.99	1.95	1.92	1.84	1.94	85.2%
Ecuador	0.60	0.90	1.33	1.33	1.28	1.43	1.51	1.72	1.69	1.80	1.89	47.5%
El Salvador	0.35	0.48	0.37	0.35	0.42	0.83	0.84	0.88	0.88	0.89	0.86	103.4%
Guatemala	0.41	0.49	0.60	0.41	0.37	0.60	0.79	0.81	0.83	0.86	0.84	128.0%
Haiti	0.08	0.08	0.11	0.12	0.13	0.12	0.16	0.18	0.17	0.18	0.18	37.1%
Honduras	0.40	0.42	0.46	0.39	0.44	0.70	0.71	0.89	0.95	0.94	1.02	133.4%
Jamaica	2.91	3.68	3.05	2.01	3.01	3.37	3.78	3.93	3.93	3.69	4.33	43.9%
Netherlands Antilles	90.60	61.92	51.21	25.72	15.00	15.83	17.69	20.07	20.34	20.19	20.81	38.8%
Nicaragua	0.60	0.65	0.55	0.48	0.44	0.53	0.69	0.74	0.76	0.75	0.72	62.5%
Panama	1.64	1.88	1.49	1.21	1.02	1.54	1.59	1.88	1.72	1.75	1.83	79.4%
Paraguay	0.24	0.26	0.44	0.39	0.45	0.72	0.61	0.65	0.64	0.58	0.59	30.5%
Peru	1.15	1.22	1.19	0.93	0.88	0.99	1.03	0.94	1.07	1.04	1.01	14.7%
Trinidad and Tobago	6.26	5.76	7.33	8.15	9.29	9.66	13.79	16.11	16.79	17.57	20.28	118.3%
Uruguay	1.85	1.93	1.91	1.04	1.21	1.41	1.61	1.25	1.62	1.59	1.85	53.5%
Venezuela	4.70	4.93	6.12	5.45	5.32	5.37	5.28	4.69	4.97	5.23	5.52	3.8%
Other Latin America	3.00	4.06	3.72	3.20	4.16	4.22	4.32	4.70	4.66	4.74	5.02	20.6%
Latin America	**1.54**	**1.70**	**1.88**	**1.63**	**1.69**	**1.86**	**2.05**	**1.96**	**2.06**	**2.08**	**2.14**	**26.2%**
Bangladesh	0.04	0.06	0.08	0.09	0.12	0.16	0.18	0.22	0.22	0.24	0.24	103.3%
Brunei Darussalam	2.93	8.74	13.64	13.16	13.08	15.94	13.96	15.32	14.18	13.62	15.10	15.4%
Cambodia	..	..	..	..	0.12	0.19	0.23	0.26	0.27	0.29	..	
Chinese Taipei	2.08	2.63	4.04	3.74	5.62	7.45	9.69	10.93	11.29	11.55	11.87	111.3%
India	0.36	0.39	0.43	0.55	0.69	0.84	0.96	0.98	1.03	1.06	1.13	62.3%
Indonesia	0.21	0.29	0.47	0.52	0.79	1.00	1.28	1.39	1.45	1.50	1.50	90.7%
DPR of Korea	4.61	4.77	6.12	6.75	5.66	3.45	3.00	2.97	3.02	3.14	3.18	-43.8%
Malaysia	1.14	1.31	1.70	2.09	2.71	3.82	4.84	4.91	5.28	5.68	5.90	117.9%
Mongolia	..	..	..	6.08	6.01	4.42	3.68	3.62	3.66	3.76	3.93	-34.7%
Myanmar	0.17	0.13	0.15	0.16	0.10	0.16	0.18	0.19	0.20	0.21	0.20	104.8%
Nepal	0.02	0.02	0.03	0.03	0.05	0.08	0.13	0.11	0.10	0.11	0.11	142.1%
Pakistan	0.27	0.29	0.32	0.42	0.55	0.65	0.71	0.70	0.76	0.76	0.79	44.6%
Philippines	0.61	0.67	0.67	0.50	0.59	0.87	0.90	0.87	0.87	0.86	0.77	30.9%
Singapore	2.82	3.71	5.25	5.94	9.45	10.79	9.47	9.23	9.26	9.93	9.62	1.8%
Sri Lanka	0.22	0.20	0.25	0.23	0.22	0.30	0.56	0.59	0.64	0.63	0.57	160.3%
Thailand	0.45	0.52	0.73	0.80	1.45	2.46	2.63	3.15	3.41	3.40	3.42	136.3%
Vietnam	0.37	0.35	0.27	0.29	0.26	0.38	0.56	0.75	0.96	0.97	0.98	283.6%
Other Asia	0.29	0.33	0.51	0.31	0.29	0.27	0.29	0.32	0.35	0.33	0.34	17.8%
Asia	**0.41**	**0.46**	**0.55**	**0.63**	**0.79**	**0.96**	**1.10**	**1.15**	**1.22**	**1.24**	**1.28**	**61.7%**
People's Rep. of China	0.95	1.15	1.43	1.62	1.95	2.48	2.41	2.97	3.51	3.88	4.27	119.4%
Hong Kong, China	2.27	2.42	2.91	4.09	5.79	5.83	5.96	6.08	5.94	5.98	6.11	5.5%
China	**0.96**	**1.15**	**1.44**	**1.63**	**1.97**	**2.50**	**2.42**	**2.99**	**3.52**	**3.89**	**4.28**	**117.8%**

* Data for individual countries of the Former USSR are not available prior to 1990.

Per capita emissions by sector* in 2006
*Emissions 2006 par habitant ventilées par secteur**

kg CO$_2$ / capita

	Total CO$_2$ emissions from fuel combustion	Main activity producer electricity and heat	Unallocated auto-producers	Other energy industries**	Manuf. industries and construction	Transport	of which: road	Other sectors
World	**4 284**	**1 591**	**170**	**205**	**838**	**987**	**721**	**494**
Annex I Parties	*11 177*	*4 026*	*599*	*531*	*1 691*	*2 841*	*2 411*	*1 489*
Annex II Parties	*12 635*	*4 522*	*373*	*630*	*1 835*	*3 579*	*3 110*	*1 698*
North America	*18 756*	*7 339*	*288*	*1 004*	*2 201*	*5 922*	*4 967*	*2 002*
Europe	*8 292*	*2 386*	*361*	*408*	*1 370*	*2 162*	*2 010*	*1 605*
Pacific	*10 770*	*4 022*	*590*	*402*	*2 263*	*2 214*	*1 967*	*1 279*
Annex I EIT	*8 826*	*3 312*	*1 365*	*349*	*1 475*	*1 239*	*835*	*1 086*
Non-Annex I Parties	*2 441*	*1 006*	*66*	*126*	*633*	*356*	*315*	*254*
Annex I Kyoto Parties	*9 227*	*3 020*	*737*	*447*	*1 622*	*1 970*	*1 680*	*1 430*
Non-OECD Total	**2 641**	**1 080**	**129**	**128**	**663**	**364**	**305**	**277**
OECD Total	**10 929**	**3 918**	**356**	**554**	**1 636**	**2 989**	**2 615**	**1 476**
Canada	16 516	3 361	151	1 982	3 041	4 891	3 801	3 090
Mexico	3 974	1 083	207	439	577	1 334	1 267	333
United States	19 000	7 772	303	897	2 110	6 034	5 093	1 883
OECD N. America	**15 215**	**5 840**	**268**	**868**	**1 812**	**4 823**	**4 080**	**1 602**
Australia	19 018	10 765	389	886	2 329	3 761	3 253	887
Japan	9 492	2 989	605	326	2 286	1 921	1 720	1 365
Korea	9 858	3 638	734	450	1 958	1 783	1 624	1 295
New Zealand	8 884	2 118	1 141	305	1 219	3 501	3 136	601
OECD Pacific	**10 551**	**3 930**	**625**	**413**	**2 190**	**2 110**	**1 884**	**1 283**
Austria	8 795	1 450	600	917	1 767	2 495	2 373	1 566
Belgium	11 120	2 164	151	430	3 342	2 392	2 310	2 640
Czech Republic	11 783	5 408	753	330	2 252	1 709	1 646	1 330
Denmark	10 149	4 894	232	467	983	2 445	2 288	1 128
Finland	12 693	5 601	717	483	2 427	2 516	2 271	948
France	5 973	506	321	253	1 141	2 080	1 982	1 673
Germany	9 998	3 658	528	329	1 433	1 867	1 768	2 184
Greece	8 428	3 926	30	372	868	1 994	1 672	1 238
Hungary	5 598	1 785	23	169	812	1 283	1 258	1 526
Iceland	7 176	23	-	-	2 186	2 931	2 678	2 036
Ireland	10 565	3 364	121	142	1 311	3 196	3 100	2 432
Italy	7 611	2 234	273	294	1 342	2 044	1 969	1 425
Luxembourg	23 642	2 414	532	-	3 583	14 191	14 105	2 922
Netherlands	10 912	2 837	486	982	2 239	2 156	2 084	2 212
Norway	7 905	153	32	2 465	1 497	2 960	2 183	800
Poland	8 024	4 124	290	211	1 020	1 001	961	1 378
Portugal	5 323	1 810	252	119	841	1 793	1 729	507
Slovak Republic	6 947	1 519	315	1 018	1 786	1 123	941	1 187
Spain	7 435	2 154	220	343	1 436	2 549	2 217	733
Sweden	5 315	941	82	264	1 208	2 471	2 324	349
Switzerland	5 828	12	216	156	864	2 179	2 152	2 401
Turkey	3 285	979	147	92	859	579	502	631
United Kingdom	8 863	2 922	498	571	1 056	2 157	1 950	1 659
OECD Europe	**7 599**	**2 356**	**328**	**351**	**1 286**	**1 831**	**1 701**	**1 446**
European Union - 27	*8 066*	*2 614*	*344*	*367*	*1 328*	*1 928*	*1 801*	*1 485*

* This table shows per capita emissions for the same sectors which are present throughout this publication. In particular, the emissions from electricity and heat production are shown separately and not reallocated as in the table on pages II.55-II.57. Total CO$_2$ has been calculated using the Sectoral Approach.
** Includes emissions from own use in petroleum refining, the manufacture of solid fuels, coal mining, oil and gas extraction and other energy-producing industries.

Per capita emissions by sector in 2006

Emissions 2006 par habitant ventilées par secteur

kg CO$_2$ / capita

	Total CO$_2$ emissions from fuel combustion	Main activity producer electricity and heat	Unallocated auto-producers	Other energy industries	Manuf. industries and construction	Transport	*of which: road*	Other sectors
Non-OECD Total	**2 641**	**1 080**	**129**	**128**	**663**	**364**	**305**	**277**
Algeria	2 576	715	12	376	348	557	450	569
Angola	517	16	2	22	185	209	209	84
Benin	344	8	2	-	18	208	208	108
Botswana	2 444	799	239	-	468	839	817	99
Cameroon	171	9	-	4	14	117	117	27
Congo	321	13	-	1	15	276	217	16
Dem. Rep. of Congo	38	-	-	-	13	8	8	17
Côte d'Ivoire	324	128	-	7	28	73	62	88
Egypt	2 059	731	-	143	511	436	397	238
Eritrea	114	38	2	-	6	29	29	39
Ethiopia	68	-	-	-	18	41	41	10
Gabon	1 598	290	167	17	621	329	329	175
Ghana	376	101	-	4	61	155	145	55
Kenya	301	56	-	16	39	151	87	38
Libya	7 027	3 491	-	538	1 018	1 578	1 576	402
Morocco	1 305	468	70	12	204	61	39	489
Mozambique	77	1	-	-	15	53	48	9
Namibia	1 458	59	-	-	124	878	787	396
Nigeria	355	62	-	67	31	158	157	38
Senegal	369	137	15	2	48	127	121	40
South Africa	7 216	4 394	225	96	1 011	937	864	553
Sudan	303	69	-	10	31	174	173	19
United Rep. of Tanzania	121	19	3	-	13	71	71	15
Togo	140	14	1	-	14	89	89	20
Tunisia	1 945	670	91	20	333	445	445	385
Zambia	193	2	3	6	82	82	74	18
Zimbabwe	747	423	-	4	121	94	87	106
Other Africa	145	29	9	-	9	53	46	44
Africa	**911**	**387**	**18**	**46**	**144**	**197**	**180**	**119**
Bahrain	27 020	8 991	1 972	5 134	6 940	3 662	3 662	320
Islamic Rep. of Iran	6 175	1 399	76	221	1 088	1 531	1 531	1 860
Iraq	3 231	834	-	215	724	1 142	1 142	317
Israel	8 887	5 614	72	388	242	1 434	1 434	1 136
Jordan	3 304	1 182	75	117	535	847	840	548
Kuwait	25 661	11 777	-	5 411	4 728	3 580	3 580	165
Lebanon	3 286	1 591	-	-	354	938	938	403
Oman	11 566	4 568	-	2 838	2 071	1 595	1 595	494
Qatar	48 318	3 506	8 173	16 909	12 686	6 809	6 809	234
Saudi Arabia	14 360	4 739	996	1 703	3 344	3 423	3 347	155
Syria	2 653	1 105	56	96	463	734	702	200
United Arab Emirates	25 962	12 888	-	456	6 546	5 435	5 435	638
Yemen	911	177	25	87	89	296	296	238
Middle East	**6 820**	**2 203**	**209**	**579**	**1 335**	**1 600**	**1 587**	**893**
Albania	1 333	8	44	47	273	634	573	327
Bosnia and Herzegovina	4 370	2 878	65	32	291	623	613	480
Bulgaria	6 180	3 288	177	256	1 111	1 045	955	302
Croatia	4 660	1 053	66	435	968	1 329	1 234	809
Cyprus	9 132	4 546	28	-	1 321	2 379	2 375	858
Gibraltar	16 023	3 939	-	-	2 129	9 954	9 954	-
FYR of Macedonia	3 939	2 482	129	3	575	502	492	247
Malta	6 154	4 717	-	-	-	1 281	1 281	157
Romania	4 385	1 769	156	334	970	576	554	580
Serbia	7 183	4 321	390	-	1 105	944	943	422
Slovenia	7 721	2 892	48	4	1 422	2 245	2 225	1 110
Non-OECD Europe	**5 069**	**2 393**	**163**	**213**	**918**	**860**	**825**	**522**

Per capita emissions by sector in 2006

Emissions 2006 par habitant ventilées par secteur

kg CO$_2$ / capita

	Total CO$_2$ emissions from fuel combustion	Main activity producer electricity and heat	Unallocated auto-producers	Other energy industries	Manuf. industries and construction	Transport	*of which:* road	Other sectors
Armenia	1 376	299	-	-	481	172	172	424
Azerbaijan	3 563	1 652	30	313	279	565	527	724
Belarus	6 585	2 777	656	158	1 326	604	431	1 063
Estonia	11 281	8 050	168	109	808	1 696	1 570	450
Georgia	1 039	251	-	69	136	349	346	234
Kazakhstan	11 886	6 165	-	554	2 391	675	593	2 102
Kyrgyzstan	1 007	292	-	-	286	209	134	220
Latvia	3 509	914	55	-	514	1 452	1 335	575
Lithuania	4 026	1 061	31	491	780	1 267	1 166	394
Republic of Moldova	1 937	914	74	-	155	247	189	546
Russia	11 138	3 841	2 569	460	1 559	1 595	840	1 115
Tajikistan	926	76	-	-	-	581	581	270
Turkmenistan	8 896	2 513	-	1 305	-	556	556	4 522
Ukraine	6 632	2 315	396	175	2 013	643	463	1 090
Uzbekistan	4 253	1 329	3	163	777	325	173	1 655
Former USSR	**8 420**	**3 034**	**1 378**	**349**	**1 399**	**1 081**	**643**	**1 179**
Argentina	3 801	713	179	303	680	1 121	970	805
Bolivia	1 363	276	10	215	119	418	366	325
Brazil	1 756	107	74	131	519	743	677	181
Chile	3 641	990	41	142	1 185	1 020	955	265
Colombia	1 304	132	46	112	388	453	434	173
Costa Rica	1 347	62	32	17	239	904	903	91
Cuba	2 361	1 441	49	14	426	186	186	245
Dominican Republic	1 939	716	202	17	145	590	480	269
Ecuador	1 895	322	139	22	297	874	783	240
El Salvador	860	173	6	7	175	408	408	91
Guatemala	845	183	21	-	171	380	376	91
Haiti	182	18	-	-	43	91	39	29
Honduras	1 020	355	-	-	290	321	321	54
Jamaica	4 326	1 165	1 160	2	103	1 039	599	858
Netherlands Antilles	20 812	2 362	2 460	1 868	3 296	9 144	7 795	1 681
Nicaragua	719	294	-	-	95	264	256	65
Panama	1 832	372	45	-	326	916	400	174
Paraguay	592	-	-	-	29	532	523	31
Peru	1 012	150	21	67	292	373	370	109
Trinidad and Tobago	20 283	3 825	17	2 562	12 072	1 607	1 607	200
Uruguay	1 853	502	-	108	215	706	702	321
Venezuela	5 522	814	37	1 250	1 460	1 689	1 678	271
Other Latin America	5 021	1 513	177	-	352	1 491	1 435	1 488
Latin America	**2 137**	**333**	**76**	**190**	**546**	**743**	**682**	**249**
Bangladesh	244	91	-	1	67	29	22	55
Brunei Darussalam	15 097	6 426	663	4 640	492	2 673	2 673	205
Cambodia	286	87	-	-	10	83	82	105
Chinese Taipei	11 866	4 963	1 731	355	2 766	1 596	1 551	455
India	11 866	4 963	1 731	355	2 766	1 596	1 551	455
Indonesia	1 126	563	70	37	256	91	84	109
DPR of Korea	1 500	403	1	176	431	324	294	165
Malaysia	3 182	505	-	1	2 018	42	42	616
Mongolia	5 895	2 189	109	433	1 503	1 483	1 472	178
Myanmar	203	43	-	11	40	77	75	32
Nepal	112	-	-	-	37	31	31	44
Pakistan	791	255	1	12	266	169	146	88
Philippines	771	286	-	34	132	259	208	59
Singapore	9 619	4 715	-	2 230	1 130	1 520	1 520	23
Sri Lanka	573	148	-	9	80	273	234	62
Thailand	3 421	990	128	218	999	842	834	244
Vietnam	982	240	26	-	337	236	220	142
Other Asia	342	68	37	-	82	101	61	53
Asia	**1 282**	**519**	**62**	**62**	**331**	**190**	**175**	**119**
People's Rep. of China	4 274	2 081	50	156	1 345	280	190	363
Hong Kong, China	6 113	4 813	-	-	293	644	644	363
China	**4 283**	**2 096**	**50**	**155**	**1 339**	**281**	**192**	**363**

Per capita emissions with electricity and heat allocated to consuming sectors* in 2006

*Emissions 2006 par habitant avec allocation de l'électricité et de la chaleur aux secteurs de consommation**

kg CO$_2$ / capita

	Total CO$_2$ emissions from fuel combustion	Other energy industries**	Manufacturing industries and construction	Transport	of which: road	Other sectors
World	**4 284**	**290**	**1 539**	**1 011**	**721**	**1 445**
Annex I Parties	*11 177*	*780*	*3 234*	*2 919*	*2 411*	*4 244*
Annex II Parties	*12 635*	*761*	*3 384*	*3 635*	*3 110*	*4 855*
North America	*18 756*	*1 232*	*4 207*	*5 943*	*4 967*	*7 375*
Europe	*8 292*	*478*	*2 413*	*2 220*	*2 010*	*3 181*
Pacific	*10 770*	*489*	*3 835*	*2 295*	*1 967*	*4 152*
Annex I EIT	*8 826*	*939*	*3 204*	*1 386*	*835*	*3 297*
Non-Annex I Parties	*2 441*	*168*	*1 179*	*364*	*315*	*731*
Kyoto Parties	*9 227*	*699*	*3 016*	*2 060*	*1 680*	*3 451*
Non-OECD Total	**2 641**	**211**	**1 226**	**383**	**305**	**821**
OECD Total	**10 929**	**677**	**3 059**	**3 038**	**2 615**	**4 155**
Canada	16 516	2 170	4 433	4 921	3 801	4 993
Mexico	3 974	482	1 303	1 342	1 267	847
United States	19 000	1 112	4 083	6 050	5 093	7 755
OECD N. America	**15 215**	**1 052**	**3 497**	**4 840**	**4 080**	**5 825**
Australia	19 018	1 401	7 095	3 893	3 253	6 628
Japan	9 492	374	3 437	1 989	1 720	3 692
Korea	9 858	450	4 262	1 809	1 624	3 337
New Zealand	8 884	343	2 445	3 542	3 136	2 554
OECD Pacific	**10 551**	**478**	**3 955**	**2 177**	**1 884**	**3 941**
Austria	8 795	951	2 488	2 581	2 373	2 774
Belgium	11 120	574	4 447	2 432	2 310	3 667
Czech Republic	11 783	766	4 422	1 860	1 646	4 735
Denmark	10 149	539	1 976	2 475	2 288	5 159
Finland	12 693	527	5 672	2 547	2 271	3 946
France	5 973	280	1 374	2 101	1 982	2 218
Germany	9 998	421	3 210	1 958	1 768	4 409
Greece	8 428	538	1 877	2 010	1 672	4 003
Hungary	5 598	370	1 277	1 323	1 258	2 626
Iceland	7 176	-	2 200	2 931	2 678	2 045
Ireland	10 565	161	2 513	3 208	3 100	4 683
Italy	7 611	352	2 326	2 112	1 969	2 821
Luxembourg	23 642	-	5 445	14 236	14 105	3 961
Netherlands	10 912	1 159	3 621	2 193	2 084	3 938
Norway	7 905	2 470	1 577	2 962	2 183	896
Poland	8 024	819	2 365	1 074	961	3 766
Portugal	5 323	150	1 680	1 813	1 729	1 679
Slovak Republic	6 947	1 117	2 443	1 154	941	2 233
Spain	7 435	408	2 424	2 598	2 217	2 004
Sweden	5 315	279	1 555	2 488	2 324	993
Switzerland	5 828	156	940	2 191	2 152	2 542
Turkey	3 285	104	1 424	584	502	1 173
United Kingdom	8 863	658	2 230	2 237	1 950	3 737
OECD Europe	**7 599**	**443**	**2 300**	**1 885**	**1 701**	**2 971**
European Union - 27	*8 066*	*479*	*2 419*	*1 988*	*1 801*	*3 181*

* Emissions from electricity and heat generation have been allocated to final consuming sectors in proportion to the electricity and heat consumed. The detailed unallocated emissions are shown in the table on pages II.52-II.54. Total CO$_2$ has been calculated using the Sectoral Approach.

** Includes emissions from own use in petroleum refining, the manufacture of solid fuels, coal mining, oil and gas extraction and other energy-producing industries.

Per capita emissions with electricity and heat allocated to consuming sectors in 2006

Emissions 2006 par habitant avec allocation de l'électricité et de la chaleur aux secteurs de consommation

kg CO$_2$ / capita

	Total CO$_2$ emissions from fuel combustion	Other energy industries	Manufacturing industries and construction	Transport	of which: road	Other sectors
Non-OECD Total	**2 641**	**211**	**1 226**	**383**	**305**	**821**
Algeria	2 576	389	599	572	450	1 017
Angola	517	22	190	209	209	96
Benin	344	-	20	208	208	116
Botswana	2 444	-	1 008	839	817	597
Cameroon	171	4	18	117	117	33
Congo	321	1	22	276	217	22
Dem. Rep. of Congo	38	-	13	8	8	18
Côte d'Ivoire	324	7	80	73	62	164
Egypt	2 059	143	768	436	397	712
Eritrea	114	-	17	29	29	68
Ethiopia	68	-	18	41	41	10
Gabon	1 598	27	741	330	329	500
Ghana	376	4	116	155	145	100
Kenya	301	16	74	151	87	59
Libya	7 027	538	1 565	1 578	1 576	3 346
Morocco	1 305	28	422	76	39	780
Mozambique	77	-	15	53	48	9
Namibia	1 458	-	136	878	787	443
Nigeria	355	67	45	158	157	85
Senegal	369	2	94	127	121	146
South Africa	7 216	346	3 506	1 061	864	2 303
Sudan	303	10	52	174	173	67
United Rep. of Tanzania	121	1	24	71	71	25
Togo	140	-	19	89	89	31
Tunisia	1 945	20	702	445	445	777
Zambia	193	6	86	82	74	19
Zimbabwe	747	4	311	94	87	339
Other Africa	145	1	16	53	46	74
Africa	**911**	**59**	**324**	**203**	**180**	**325**
Bahrain	27 020	5 134	8 600	3 662	3 662	9 624
Islamic Rep. of Iran	6 175	238	1 598	1 531	1 531	2 808
Iraq	3 231	215	724	1 142	1 142	1 151
Israel	8 887	388	1 723	1 434	1 434	5 341
Jordan	3 304	130	883	847	840	1 443
Kuwait	25 661	7 206	4 728	3 580	3 580	10 147
Lebanon	3 286	-	772	938	938	1 577
Oman	11 566	2 838	2 531	1 595	1 595	4 602
Qatar	48 318	16 909	16 097	6 809	6 809	8 503
Saudi Arabia	14 360	2 394	3 797	3 423	3 347	4 746
Syria	2 653	96	917	734	702	907
United Arab Emirates	25 962	456	8 166	5 435	5 435	11 905
Yemen	911	87	89	296	296	440
Middle East	**6 820**	**694**	**1 785**	**1 600**	**1 587**	**2 741**
Albania	1 333	49	286	634	573	364
Bosnia and Herzegovina	4 370	32	1 092	623	613	2 623
Bulgaria	6 180	472	2 306	1 081	955	2 320
Croatia	4 660	463	1 230	1 348	1 234	1 620
Cyprus	9 132	8	1 939	2 414	2 375	4 771
Gibraltar	16 023	-	2 129	9 954	9 954	3 939
FYR of Macedonia	3 939	108	1 499	511	492	1 821
Malta	6 154	-	1 349	1 281	1 281	3 524
Romania	4 385	554	1 721	612	554	1 498
Serbia	7 183	106	2 612	975	943	3 490
Slovenia	7 721	34	2 959	2 283	2 225	2 445
Non-OECD Europe	**5 069**	**367**	**1 814**	**891**	**825**	**1 997**

Per capita emissions with electricity and heat allocated to consuming sectors in 2006

Emissions 2006 par habitant avec allocation de l'électricité et de la chaleur aux secteurs de consommation

kg CO$_2$ / capita

	Total CO$_2$ emissions from fuel combustion	Other energy industries	Manufacturing industries and construction	Transport	of which: road	Other sectors
Armenia	1 376	-	557	179	172	640
Azerbaijan	3 563	447	791	605	527	1 719
Belarus	6 585	356	2 583	672	431	2 974
Estonia	11 281	445	2 702	1 747	1 570	6 387
Georgia	1 039	105	165	361	346	408
Kazakhstan	11 886	744	5 539	761	593	4 842
Kyrgyzstan	1 007	3	368	212	134	423
Latvia	3 509	22	656	1 463	1 335	1 369
Lithuania	4 026	572	1 043	1 272	1 166	1 139
Republic of Moldova	1 937	44	405	257	189	1 231
Russia	11 138	1 382	3 909	1 818	840	4 029
Tajikistan	926	-	32	581	581	313
Turkmenistan	8 896	1 627	640	602	556	6 027
Ukraine	6 632	313	3 387	741	463	2 191
Uzbekistan	4 253	189	1 065	350	173	2 649
Former USSR	**8 420**	**884**	**3 066**	**1 224**	**643**	**3 247**
Argentina	3 801	303	1 106	1 127	970	1 264
Bolivia	1 363	215	220	418	366	510
Brazil	1 756	131	607	744	677	273
Chile	3 641	156	1 869	1 026	955	589
Colombia	1 304	112	446	453	434	293
Costa Rica	1 347	17	262	904	903	163
Cuba	2 361	14	856	199	186	1 293
Dominican Republic	1 939	17	536	590	480	796
Ecuador	1 895	22	386	874	783	612
El Salvador	860	7	270	408	408	175
Guatemala	845	-	250	380	376	214
Haiti	182	-	52	91	39	39
Honduras	1 020	-	387	321	321	312
Jamaica	4 326	2	1 807	1 039	599	1 479
Netherlands Antilles	20 812	1 868	5 951	9 144	7 795	3 848
Nicaragua	719	-	165	264	256	290
Panama	1 832	-	365	916	400	551
Paraguay	592	-	29	532	523	31
Peru	1 012	67	383	373	370	190
Trinidad and Tobago	20 283	2 562	14 503	1 607	1 607	1 612
Uruguay	1 853	108	352	706	702	687
Venezuela	5 522	1 274	1 879	1 692	1 678	676
Other Latin America	5 021	-	934	1 491	1 435	2 596
Latin America	**2 137**	**192**	**740**	**744**	**682**	**461**
Bangladesh	244	1	105	29	22	108
Brunei	15 097	4 640	1 817	2 673	2 673	5 967
Cambodia	286	-	24	83	82	179
Chinese Taipei	11 866	491	5 988	1 629	1 551	3 758
India	1 126	37	541	104	84	443
Indonesia	1 500	176	587	324	294	413
DPR of Korea	3 182	1	2 270	42	42	868
Malaysia	5 895	433	2 663	1 485	1 472	1 314
Mongolia	3 925	-	1 316	529	353	2 080
Myanmar	203	11	58	77	75	57
Nepal	112	-	37	31	31	44
Pakistan	791	12	340	169	146	269
Philippines	771	34	232	260	208	245
Singapore	9 619	2 531	2 804	1 569	1 520	2 715
Sri Lanka	573	9	130	273	234	160
Thailand	3 421	218	1 517	843	834	843
Vietnam	982	-	463	239	220	281
Other Asia	342	-	117	101	61	123
Asia	**1 282**	**65**	**585**	**195**	**175**	**437**
People's Rep. of China	4 274	302	2 698	295	190	979
Hong Kong, China	6 113	-	758	644	644	4 711
China	**4 283**	**301**	**2 686**	**297**	**192**	**1 000**

Electricity and heat output *

*Production d'électricité et de chaleur *

terawatt hours

	1990	1995	1998	1999	2000	2001	2002	2003	2004	2005	2006	% change 90-06
World	..	17 054.4	17 601.4	18 005.0	18 755.0	18 899.2	19 512.8	20 266.8	21 083.5	22 018.4	22 796.3	..
Annex I Parties	..	*12 726.4*	*12 637.2*	*12 798.6*	*13 131.4*	*13 022.2*	*13 250.5*	*13 478.4*	*13 706.2*	*14 004.8*	*14 134.5*	..
Annex II Parties	..	*8 182.8*	*8 674.6*	*8 868.7*	*9 153.3*	*9 007.7*	*9 279.9*	*9 454.6*	*9 679.8*	*9 939.3*	*9 966.2*	..
North America	..	*4 240.3*	*4 485.0*	*4 567.1*	*4 730.5*	*4 522.5*	*4 740.2*	*4 756.6*	*4 823.9*	*4 974.5*	*4 955.8*	..
Europe	*2 547.1*	*2 769.4*	*2 942.0*	*3 026.3*	*3 121.0*	*3 192.9*	*3 217.4*	*3 384.8*	*3 504.2*	*3 580.8*	*3 617.9*	*42.0%*
Pacific	*1 025.1*	*1 173.1*	*1 247.7*	*1 275.2*	*1 301.8*	*1 292.2*	*1 322.3*	*1 313.2*	*1 351.7*	*1 384.1*	*1 392.5*	*35.8%*
Annex I EIT	..	*4 457.3*	*3 851.5*	*3 813.5*	*3 848.7*	*3 888.3*	*3 836.4*	*3 878.9*	*3 870.4*	*3 893.6*	*3 980.9*	..
Non-Annex I Parties	..	*4 328.0*	*4 964.2*	*5 206.4*	*5 623.6*	*5 877.0*	*6 262.3*	*6 788.4*	*7 377.3*	*8 013.6*	*8 661.8*	..
Annex I Kyoto Parties	..	*8 862.6*	*8 500.0*	*8 591.7*	*8 782.8*	*8 865.8*	*8 881.4*	*9 070.0*	*9 225.8*	*9 384.0*	*9 500.7*	..
Non-OECD Total	..	7 984.5	7 955.7	8 136.9	8 496.4	8 741.9	9 058.7	9 592.7	10 136.5	10 753.8	11 465.5	..
OECD Total	..	9 069.9	9 645.7	9 868.2	10 258.6	10 157.3	10 454.1	10 674.1	10 946.9	11 264.5	11 330.9	..
Canada	489.3	568.1	569.5	588.0	614.9	599.6	611.0	600.3	610.6	636.7	622.2	27.1%
Mexico	124.1	157.5	181.2	189.9	203.6	209.1	214.6	217.8	224.1	242.0	249.6	101.1%
United States	..	3 672.2	3 915.5	3 979.1	4 115.6	3 922.9	4 129.2	4 156.2	4 213.3	4 337.8	4 333.7	..
OECD N. America	..	4 397.8	4 666.2	4 757.0	4 934.2	4 731.6	4 954.8	4 974.4	5 047.9	5 216.5	5 205.5	..
Australia	155.0	173.0	195.6	203.0	207.4	216.5	226.2	227.9	234.3	245.1	251.3	62.2%
Japan	837.9	964.8	1 015.8	1 034.0	1 055.1	1 036.3	1 055.0	1 044.1	1 074.3	1 095.7	1 097.5	31.0%
Korea	105.4	190.8	225.7	248.5	327.4	347.6	369.9	382.4	418.1	441.3	454.8	331.6%
New Zealand	32.3	35.3	36.3	38.2	39.2	39.4	41.1	41.2	43.2	43.3	43.7	35.3%
OECD Pacific	1 130.5	1 364.0	1 473.3	1 523.8	1 629.2	1 639.9	1 692.2	1 695.7	1 769.8	1 825.4	1 847.2	63.4%
Austria	57.2	66.1	69.1	73.2	73.2	75.4	74.1	72.1	77.6	79.7	79.1	38.4%
Belgium	73.0	76.3	86.3	88.4	89.2	85.2	87.3	90.0	90.8	91.9	93.9	28.6%
Czech Republic	105.3	109.4	108.5	104.8	111.6	115.7	115.6	123.7	123.9	120.6	120.1	14.1%
Denmark	51.6	69.7	76.4	73.2	69.2	73.4	74.6	82.4	76.5	72.3	81.7	58.1%
Finland	78.5	91.2	102.3	104.0	104.8	112.5	115.1	131.6	133.1	115.9	137.7	75.4%
France	422.8	497.5	513.9	528.0	573.7	591.3	601.4	608.7	617.1	620.0	615.1	45.5%
Germany	672.2	648.5	659.5	658.0	660.1	671.1	669.8	799.8	810.9	839.8	854.0	27.1%
Greece	34.8	41.3	46.5	49.7	53.8	53.4	54.3	58.4	59.3	60.0	60.8	74.9%
Hungary	49.0	51.1	56.9	58.0	54.4	56.3	53.4	51.9	51.1	53.4	52.9	8.1%
Iceland	6.0	7.2	8.2	9.6	9.9	10.2	11.3	11.2	11.4	11.3	12.8	113.7%
Ireland	14.2	17.6	20.9	21.8	23.7	24.6	24.8	24.9	25.2	25.6	27.7	94.5%
Italy	213.1	237.4	253.7	259.3	269.9	271.9	277.5	286.3	348.4	350.5	365.7	71.6%
Luxembourg	0.6	0.6	0.6	0.6	0.7	0.9	3.2	3.3	4.0	4.1	4.3	584.9%
Netherlands	76.1	100.5	120.1	117.9	121.9	125.6	127.6	128.5	135.7	147.7	137.7	80.9%
Norway	123.4	124.2	118.4	124.8	141.9	122.0	133.2	110.1	113.6	140.8	125.0	1.3%
Poland	339.9	253.9	249.5	243.2	237.8	246.6	240.1	252.3	248.6	250.0	255.5	-24.8%
Portugal	28.7	33.6	39.8	43.9	44.9	48.0	48.0	49.1	47.8	50.0	52.4	82.7%
Slovak Republic	34.8	38.1	38.1	38.7	41.0	48.1	46.4	46.4	45.4	45.9	44.2	27.1%
Spain	151.2	165.8	194.2	206.7	222.2	233.2	241.6	257.9	277.2	288.9	299.1	97.8%
Sweden	167.7	193.6	204.7	201.1	189.1	209.9	194.9	184.2	201.0	208.7	193.6	15.5%
Switzerland	58.2	65.9	66.3	72.8	70.2	75.4	69.7	69.9	68.5	62.6	67.0	15.1%
Turkey	57.5	86.2	111.0	116.4	129.4	126.2	134.2	144.8	155.9	171.8	187.4	225.8%
United Kingdom	317.8	332.5	361.1	393.4	402.7	408.9	408.9	416.6	406.0	411.1	410.1	29.1%
OECD Europe	3 133.6	3 308.2	3 506.1	3 587.4	3 695.3	3 785.8	3 807.0	4 004.0	4 129.2	4 222.6	4 278.1	36.5%
European Union - 27	..	*3 327.2*	*3 476.4*	*3 506.0*	*3 578.6*	*3 697.0*	*3 696.3*	*3 908.9*	*4 017.4*	*4 073.5*	*4 124.2*	..

* Includes electricity, CHP and heat only from both main activity producer and autoproducer plants. Due to missing data for heat in 1990, the output for some countries and regions is not available.

Electricity and heat output
Production d'électricité et de chaleur

terawatt hours

	1990	1995	1998	1999	2000	2001	2002	2003	2004	2005	2006	% change 90-06
Non-OECD Total	..	**7 984.5**	**7 955.7**	**8 136.9**	**8 496.4**	**8 741.9**	**9 058.7**	**9 592.7**	**10 136.5**	**10 753.8**	**11 465.5**	..
Algeria	..	19.7	23.3	24.8	25.4	26.6	27.6	29.6	31.3	33.9	35.2	..
Angola	..	1.0	1.3	1.3	1.4	1.6	1.8	2.0	2.2	2.6	3.0	..
Benin	..	0.0	0.1	0.1	0.1	0.1	0.1	0.1	0.1	0.1	0.1	..
Botswana	..	1.0	1.1	1.1	0.9	1.0	1.1	1.1	1.0	1.0	1.0	..
Cameroon	..	2.8	3.2	3.4	3.5	3.5	3.3	3.7	4.1	4.1	4.0	..
Congo	..	0.4	0.3	0.1	0.3	0.3	0.4	0.4	0.5	0.4	0.5	..
Dem. Rep. of Congo	..	6.2	4.7	5.3	6.0	5.9	6.1	6.4	6.9	7.4	7.9	..
Côte d'Ivoire	..	2.9	4.0	4.8	4.8	4.9	5.3	5.1	5.4	5.6	5.5	..
Egypt	..	52.0	63.0	68.5	78.1	83.3	89.2	95.2	101.3	108.7	115.4	..
Eritrea	..	0.2	0.2	0.2	0.2	0.2	0.3	0.3	0.3	0.3	0.3	..
Ethiopia	..	1.5	1.7	1.6	1.7	2.0	2.0	2.3	2.5	2.8	3.3	..
Gabon	..	1.1	1.3	1.3	1.3	1.4	1.5	1.5	1.5	1.6	1.7	..
Ghana	..	6.1	5.0	5.9	7.2	7.9	7.3	5.9	6.0	6.8	8.4	..
Kenya	..	4.2	4.7	4.5	4.1	4.6	4.8	5.2	5.6	6.0	6.5	..
Libya	..	11.4	13.5	14.4	15.5	16.1	17.5	18.9	20.2	22.3	24.0	..
Morocco	..	12.3	13.8	13.5	13.7	15.6	16.7	18.1	19.3	22.5	23.2	..
Mozambique	..	0.4	6.9	7.7	9.7	11.9	12.7	10.9	11.7	13.3	14.7	..
Namibia	..	1.2	1.0	1.2	1.4	1.4	1.4	1.4	1.4	1.7	1.6	..
Nigeria	..	15.9	15.1	16.1	14.7	15.5	19.7	20.2	24.2	23.5	23.1	..
Senegal	..	1.1	1.4	1.4	1.9	2.2	2.5	2.6	2.7	3.0	2.5	..
South Africa	..	186.6	203.0	200.4	207.8	208.2	215.7	232.3	242.5	242.9	251.9	..
Sudan	..	1.9	2.0	2.4	2.5	2.6	2.9	3.4	3.9	4.1	4.2	..
United Rep. of Tanzania	..	1.9	2.2	2.4	2.5	2.8	2.9	2.7	2.9	3.0	2.8	..
Togo	..	0.3	0.3	0.2	0.2	0.1	0.2	0.2	0.2	0.2	0.2	..
Tunisia	..	7.7	9.1	10.0	10.6	11.4	11.8	12.4	13.1	13.8	14.1	..
Zambia	..	7.9	7.6	7.8	7.8	7.9	8.2	8.3	8.5	8.9	9.4	..
Zimbabwe	..	7.8	6.6	7.1	7.0	7.9	8.6	8.8	9.7	10.3	9.8	..
Other Africa	..	8.8	10.3	10.4	11.1	11.5	11.8	12.2	12.8	13.0	13.5	..
Africa	..	**364.3**	**406.5**	**418.0**	**441.6**	**458.4**	**483.2**	**511.1**	**541.8**	**563.9**	**587.8**	..
Bahrain	..	4.6	5.8	6.0	6.3	6.8	7.3	7.8	8.4	8.7	9.8	..
Islamic Rep. of Iran	..	85.0	103.4	112.7	121.4	130.1	140.8	152.6	166.0	180.4	201.0	..
Iraq	..	29.0	30.9	31.6	31.9	32.3	33.9	28.3	32.3	30.4	31.9	..
Israel	..	30.4	38.0	39.2	43.0	43.8	45.4	47.0	48.5	49.8	51.8	..
Jordan	..	5.6	6.7	7.1	7.4	7.5	8.1	8.0	9.0	10.1	11.6	..
Kuwait	..	24.1	30.5	32.1	32.9	34.8	36.9	39.8	41.3	43.7	47.6	..
Lebanon	..	5.5	8.3	8.2	7.8	8.2	9.7	10.5	10.2	10.1	9.3	..
Oman	..	6.5	8.2	8.4	9.1	9.7	10.3	10.7	11.5	12.6	13.6	..
Qatar	..	6.0	8.1	8.6	9.1	10.0	10.9	12.0	13.2	14.4	15.3	..
Saudi Arabia	..	97.8	114.6	119.0	126.2	133.7	141.7	153.0	159.4	175.0	179.8	..
Syria	..	16.6	21.2	22.8	25.2	26.7	28.0	29.5	32.1	34.9	37.3	..
United Arab Emirates	..	25.0	33.4	37.1	39.9	43.2	46.9	49.5	52.4	60.7	66.8	..
Yemen	..	2.4	2.9	3.1	3.4	3.6	3.8	4.1	4.4	4.8	5.3	..
Middle East	..	**338.6**	**412.1**	**435.9**	**463.6**	**490.4**	**523.6**	**552.9**	**588.7**	**635.7**	**681.1**	..
Albania	..	4.5	5.1	5.6	5.0	3.9	3.9	5.3	5.6	5.5	5.2	..
Bosnia and Herzegovina	..	4.5	9.7	10.8	10.9	11.1	11.3	11.9	13.5	13.6	14.4	..
Bulgaria	..	78.9	57.8	53.4	54.7	58.0	56.0	57.3	55.5	58.4	59.5	..
Croatia	..	12.5	14.4	15.8	13.8	15.6	15.5	16.2	16.7	16.1	15.6	..
Cyprus	..	2.5	3.0	3.1	3.4	3.6	3.8	4.1	4.2	4.4	4.7	..
Gibraltar	..	0.1	0.1	0.1	0.1	0.1	0.1	0.1	0.1	0.1	0.2	..
FYR of Macedonia	..	7.7	9.2	9.0	8.9	8.2	7.9	8.5	8.3	8.6	8.6	..
Malta	..	1.6	1.7	1.9	1.9	1.9	2.1	2.2	2.2	2.2	2.3	..
Romania	..	139.0	127.8	110.6	104.9	107.1	98.2	97.0	94.1	94.9	97.0	..
Serbia	..	39.8	43.3	38.3	39.0	40.6	40.9	41.3	45.0	50.0	49.0	..
Slovenia	..	14.3	15.4	14.7	16.2	17.1	17.1	16.5	18.0	17.9	17.8	..
Non-OECD Europe	..	**305.4**	**287.5**	**263.3**	**258.9**	**267.3**	**256.8**	**260.4**	**263.3**	**271.9**	**274.1**	..

Electricity and heat output

Production d'électricité et de chaleur

terawatt hours

	1990	1995	1998	1999	2000	2001	2002	2003	2004	2005	2006	% change 90-06
Armenia	..	6.5	6.9	6.4	6.8	6.3	6.0	5.9	6.4	6.8	6.5	..
Azerbaijan	..	28.4	25.8	23.7	23.4	24.4	25.6	27.8	28.1	27.5	30.1	..
Belarus	..	105.4	110.7	111.4	103.6	107.2	105.7	107.3	111.1	111.2	112.7	..
Estonia	..	17.4	16.7	16.4	16.0	16.0	16.1	17.4	17.8	17.6	17.2	..
Georgia	..	8.9	7.7	7.7	7.4	6.9	8.1	8.1	7.9	8.0	7.7	..
Kazakhstan	..	163.0	126.9	121.1	130.2	137.2	150.6	163.3	168.8	174.1	181.5	..
Kyrgyzstan	..	17.2	14.6	16.5	18.7	17.3	15.2	17.5	18.4	18.5	19.1	..
Latvia	..	16.8	17.7	14.2	13.0	13.7	13.2	13.3	13.3	13.6	13.2	..
Lithuania	..	32.1	34.1	27.9	24.5	27.6	31.3	33.1	32.5	28.3	26.6	..
Republic of Moldova	..	10.2	8.8	7.4	5.4	5.9	5.1	5.3	7.2	7.7	8.0	..
Russia	..	3 095.9	2 589.3	2 604.5	2 678.4	2 674.9	2 638.5	2 665.9	2 665.1	2 683.1	2 780.0	..
Tajikistan	..	16.2	15.5	16.8	15.1	15.3	16.2	17.5	17.5	18.1	18.0	..
Turkmenistan	..	9.8	11.7	11.0	11.2	12.0	12.1	12.2	13.5	14.5	15.5	..
Ukraine	..	492.5	414.5	400.0	378.7	384.4	389.4	380.5	377.2	382.5	368.4	..
Uzbekistan	..	77.6	75.6	75.9	77.7	77.7	79.5	79.5	80.0	77.7	79.2	..
Former USSR	..	**4 097.9**	**3 476.5**	**3 461.0**	**3 510.1**	**3 527.0**	**3 512.7**	**3 554.8**	**3 564.9**	**3 589.2**	**3 683.7**	..
Argentina	..	67.0	74.0	80.5	88.9	90.1	84.5	92.0	100.2	105.5	115.0	..
Bolivia	..	3.0	3.7	3.9	3.9	4.0	4.2	4.3	4.5	4.9	5.3	..
Brazil	..	275.6	321.9	335.6	350.1	328.9	346.6	366.0	388.7	404.1	421.0	..
Chile	..	28.0	35.5	38.4	41.3	43.9	45.5	48.8	52.0	54.5	57.6	..
Colombia	..	42.7	45.6	44.2	44.6	44.1	45.9	47.6	51.0	51.6	54.3	..
Costa Rica	..	4.9	5.4	6.2	6.9	6.9	7.5	7.6	8.2	8.3	8.7	..
Cuba	..	12.5	14.1	14.5	15.0	15.3	15.7	15.8	15.6	15.3	16.5	..
Dominican Republic	..	5.5	7.7	7.7	8.5	10.3	11.5	13.5	13.8	12.9	14.2	..
Ecuador	..	8.4	10.9	10.3	10.6	11.1	11.9	11.5	12.6	13.4	15.4	..
El Salvador	..	3.4	3.8	3.8	3.9	3.9	4.1	4.4	4.4	4.8	5.6	..
Guatemala	..	3.4	4.5	5.2	6.0	5.9	6.2	6.6	7.0	7.6	7.9	..
Haiti	..	0.5	0.7	0.7	0.5	0.6	0.5	0.5	0.5	0.6	0.6	..
Honduras	..	2.7	3.4	3.2	3.7	3.9	4.2	4.5	4.9	5.6	6.0	..
Jamaica	..	5.8	6.5	6.6	6.6	6.7	6.9	7.1	7.2	7.4	7.5	..
Netherlands Antilles	..	1.0	1.1	1.1	1.1	1.1	1.1	1.2	1.2	1.2	1.3	..
Nicaragua	..	1.8	2.2	2.1	2.3	2.5	2.7	2.7	2.8	2.9	3.0	..
Panama	..	3.5	4.2	4.6	4.9	5.1	5.3	5.6	5.8	5.8	6.0	..
Paraguay	..	42.2	50.9	52.0	53.5	45.3	48.2	51.8	51.9	51.2	53.8	..
Peru	..	16.1	18.6	19.0	19.9	20.8	22.0	22.9	24.3	25.5	27.4	..
Trinidad and Tobago	..	4.3	5.2	5.2	5.5	5.6	5.6	6.4	6.4	7.1	7.0	..
Uruguay	..	6.3	9.6	7.2	7.6	9.3	9.6	8.6	5.9	7.7	5.6	..
Venezuela	..	73.4	80.9	80.6	85.2	90.1	89.0	91.8	98.5	105.8	110.4	..
Other Latin America	..	9.0	10.0	10.3	10.6	10.8	11.1	11.2	11.3	11.6	11.9	..
Latin America	..	**621.2**	**720.4**	**742.9**	**781.1**	**766.1**	**789.8**	**832.6**	**878.8**	**915.1**	**961.7**	..
Bangladesh	..	10.8	12.9	14.5	15.8	17.4	18.7	19.7	21.5	22.6	24.3	..
Brunei Darussalam	..	2.0	2.5	2.4	2.5	2.6	2.7	3.2	3.3	3.3	3.3	..
Cambodia	..	0.2	0.4	0.4	0.5	0.5	0.6	0.6	0.8	0.9	1.2	..
Chinese Taipei	..	129.1	158.8	165.6	180.5	184.5	195.2	205.2	215.1	223.6	231.5	..
India	..	417.6	496.9	537.4	562.2	581.0	598.4	635.2	667.6	699.2	744.1	..
Indonesia	..	58.9	77.3	84.3	92.6	101.6	108.2	112.9	120.2	127.4	133.1	..
DPR of Korea	..	23.0	17.0	18.6	19.4	20.2	19.8	21.0	22.0	22.9	22.4	..
Malaysia	..	45.5	60.7	65.2	69.3	71.4	74.2	78.5	82.0	84.8	91.6	..
Mongolia	..	10.6	10.3	10.8	11.0	10.7	11.2	11.5	12.4	12.6	12.8	..
Myanmar	..	4.1	4.1	4.6	5.1	4.7	5.1	5.4	5.6	6.0	6.2	..
Nepal	..	1.2	1.3	1.5	1.7	1.9	2.1	2.3	2.4	2.6	2.7	..
Pakistan	..	57.0	65.4	65.8	68.1	72.4	75.7	80.8	85.7	93.8	98.4	..
Philippines	..	33.6	38.4	41.3	45.3	47.0	48.5	52.9	56.0	56.5	56.7	..
Singapore	..	22.2	28.4	29.5	31.7	33.1	34.7	35.3	36.8	38.2	39.4	..
Sri Lanka	..	4.8	5.7	6.2	6.7	6.5	6.8	7.6	8.0	8.8	9.4	..
Thailand	..	80.1	90.1	90.0	96.0	102.4	109.0	117.0	125.7	132.2	138.7	..
Vietnam	..	14.6	21.7	23.6	26.6	30.6	35.8	40.9	46.0	53.5	56.5	..
Other Asia	..	8.4	10.0	11.3	12.7	13.7	14.2	14.3	15.1	15.3	16.4	..
Asia	..	**923.6**	**1 101.7**	**1 173.0**	**1 247.6**	**1 302.3**	**1 360.8**	**1 444.4**	**1 526.0**	**1 604.3**	**1 688.7**	..
People's Rep. of China	..	1 305.6	1 519.6	1 613.3	1 762.2	1 898.0	2 097.5	2 401.0	2 736.0	3 135.4	3 549.8	..
Hong Kong, China	..	27.9	31.4	29.5	31.3	32.4	34.3	35.5	37.1	38.5	38.6	..
China	..	**1 333.5**	**1 551.0**	**1 642.8**	**1 793.5**	**1 930.4**	**2 131.8**	**2 436.5**	**2 773.1**	**3 173.8**	**3 588.4**	..

CO$_2$ emissions per kWh from electricity and heat generation *

Emissions de CO$_2$ par kWh pour le secteur de l'électricité et de la chaleur *

grammes CO$_2$ / kilowatt hour

	1990	1995	1998	1999	2000	2001	2002	2003	2004	2005	2006	Average 04-06
World	..	472	494	489	486	492	488	496	502	501	505	502
Annex I Parties	..	419	435	430	428	435	426	429	421	418	414	418
Annex II Parties	..	459	467	458	456	468	454	455	447	443	436	442
North America	..	526	555	542	539	566	522	527	526	522	512	520
Europe	399	357	338	328	326	325	332	326	316	306	306	309
Pacific	482	461	452	467	469	480	505	522	507	511	506	508
Annex I EIT	..	342	360	360	357	355	357	366	355	355	359	356
Non-Annex I Parties	..	627	643	633	622	618	619	630	651	646	652	650
Annex I Kyoto Parties	..	352	357	355	354	355	361	366	353	349	350	351
Non-OECD Total	..	474	515	514	512	511	518	535	552	555	565	557
OECD Total	..	470	476	467	465	476	461	462	454	450	444	450
Canada	203	184	221	212	222	231	217	226	209	196	184	196
Mexico	538	507	572	561	566	568	570	576	528	555	541	541
United States	..	579	604	591	586	617	567	571	572	570	559	567
OECD N. America	..	526	556	543	540	566	524	529	526	523	513	521
Australia	813	808	861	867	863	890	938	919	914	922	921	919
Japan	434	411	381	397	401	402	422	445	428	427	418	424
Korea	520	540	497	482	447	477	454	449	475	460	464	466
New Zealand	128	113	216	239	230	278	250	295	275	312	309	299
OECD Pacific	486	472	459	469	465	479	494	506	499	499	495	498
Austria	245	214	208	193	180	203	196	234	228	223	214	222
Belgium	344	357	315	278	284	272	266	274	281	271	260	271
Czech Republic	597	602	589	580	596	584	561	524	525	525	527	526
Denmark	476	430	390	363	339	336	332	357	308	282	341	310
Finland	227	247	212	212	211	242	253	293	254	193	242	229
France	109	76	100	86	83	71	76	80	78	92	85	85
Germany	553	522	506	489	494	506	508	434	436	405	404	415
Greece	990	946	797	779	817	831	814	778	776	776	725	759
Hungary	433	444	432	412	410	394	391	425	392	341	344	359
Iceland	1	2	3	4	1	1	1	1	1	1	1	1
Ireland	740	727	703	697	642	668	635	600	574	582	535	564
Italy	575	545	513	494	499	483	506	516	416	413	404	411
Luxembourg	2 588	1 340	249	258	255	240	329	330	334	328	326	329
Netherlands	588	530	470	468	447	460	458	463	440	387	394	407
Norway	3	4	5	6	4	6	5	8	7	6	7	6
Poland	641	670	663	664	671	660	662	662	664	657	659	660
Portugal	516	569	471	539	479	442	512	413	452	501	416	456
Slovak Republic	376	375	351	340	267	241	215	255	240	229	223	231
Spain	427	453	379	443	430	382	434	378	382	396	350	376
Sweden	48	50	53	49	42	42	52	59	51	44	48	48
Switzerland	22	22	28	22	22	21	22	23	24	26	26	25
Turkey	568	512	530	549	519	544	472	444	419	426	438	428
United Kingdom	672	529	477	441	461	474	460	478	485	484	505	491
OECD Europe	435	394	377	367	364	362	364	358	347	338	339	341
European Union - 27	..	416	392	383	382	378	382	376	363	355	354	357

* CO$_2$ emissions from fossil fuels consumed for electricity, combined heat and power and main activity heat plants divided by the output of electricity and heat generated from fossil fuels, nuclear, hydro (excluding pumped storage), geothermal, solar and biomass. Both main activity producers and autoproducers have been included in the calculation of the emissions. Due to missing data for heat in 1990, the ratio for some countries and regions is not available.

CO$_2$ emissions per kWh from electricity and heat generation
Emissions de CO$_2$ par kWh pour le secteur de l'électricité et de la chaleur

grammes CO$_2$ / kilowatt hour

	1990	1995	1998	1999	2000	2001	2002	2003	2004	2005	2006	Average 04-06
Non-OECD Total	..	**474**	**515**	**514**	**512**	**511**	**518**	**535**	**552**	**555**	**565**	**557**
Algeria	..	699	706	693	686	687	699	700	700	671	688	686
Angola	..	177	202	341	382	381	354	373	216	154	98	156
Benin	..	951	678	659	601	955	950	752	740	709	696	715
Botswana	..	1 800	1 248	1 575	1 876	1 318	1 323	1 320	1 739	1 851	1 851	1 814
Cameroon	..	10	15	11	10	16	27	31	28	39	43	36
Congo	..	9	9	114	-	-	-	96	83	103	102	96
Dem. Rep. of Congo	..	4	5	4	4	4	4	3	3	3	3	3
Côte d'Ivoire	..	275	517	414	379	394	409	384	404	445	436	428
Egypt	..	443	467	455	412	381	437	432	473	471	470	471
Eritrea	..	1 463	687	700	713	749	659	694	722	677	690	697
Ethiopia	..	42	25	10	11	9	8	6	6	3	3	4
Gabon	..	255	344	326	326	272	282	306	322	376	347	348
Ghana	..	3	231	187	68	115	255	277	84	147	276	169
Kenya	..	72	282	412	562	392	271	200	280	307	317	301
Libya	..	1 131	1 069	1 056	1 022	996	971	978	888	907	879	891
Morocco	..	869	730	758	770	764	766	737	750	724	708	727
Mozambique	..	64	3	3	5	4	3	3	3	1	1	2
Namibia	..	37	45	30	21	29	75	74	75	76	76	75
Nigeria	..	292	338	350	407	340	354	340	400	383	386	390
Senegal	..	881	878	908	782	799	645	520	555	634	726	638
South Africa	..	878	927	890	893	829	819	845	866	848	869	861
Sudan	..	465	466	428	533	533	632	743	828	637	614	693
United Rep. of Tanzania	..	284	42	126	192	70	57	51	138	268	316	241
Togo	..	185	454	399	561	1 493	333	216	442	352	459	418
Tunisia	..	588	608	598	574	584	564	554	532	476	546	518
Zambia	..	7	10	7	7	7	7	7	7	7	7	7
Zimbabwe	..	920	908	812	740	848	717	515	572	572	573	572
Other Africa	..	381	398	414	469	478	481	486	480	489	489	486
Africa	..	**687**	**710**	**680**	**669**	**623**	**626**	**638**	**652**	**636**	**645**	**644**
Bahrain	..	815	822	852	868	840	835	883	881	890	825	865
Islamic Rep. of Iran	..	605	562	582	568	578	560	534	532	528	514	525
Iraq	..	698	678	678	731	813	751	787	702	700	701	701
Israel	..	821	766	767	761	773	823	818	809	798	774	794
Jordan	..	834	807	747	708	702	741	680	683	631	602	638
Kuwait	..	638	650	673	689	670	624	663	754	808	643	735
Lebanon	..	654	783	815	733	751	722	709	565	667	695	642
Oman	..	830	751	809	796	817	829	853	885	854	856	865
Qatar	..	1 131	865	823	771	781	782	779	649	618	626	631
Saudi Arabia	..	815	815	811	810	778	751	739	762	752	755	756
Syria	..	586	596	598	567	559	554	563	556	590	604	584
United Arab Emirates	..	737	710	708	728	746	764	805	913	844	820	859
Yemen	..	946	995	921	930	930	919	884	874	841	823	846
Middle East	..	**728**	**705**	**709**	**706**	**706**	**691**	**687**	**697**	**692**	**670**	**686**
Albania	..	37	17	39	49	60	58	30	32	34	32	33
Bosnia and Herzegovina	..	173	802	709	797	767	825	849	741	752	802	765
Bulgaria	..	429	480	446	431	463	433	470	471	450	448	456
Croatia	..	272	322	306	303	313	357	380	300	311	318	310
Cyprus	..	822	843	856	838	777	756	833	773	789	758	773
Gibraltar	..	766	766	766	760	754	760	755	766	740	730	745
FYR of Macedonia	..	839	751	685	680	778	722	665	679	644	619	647
Malta	..	957	932	903	862	1 022	815	809	896	855	834	862
Romania	..	440	351	360	396	412	412	451	418	400	429	416
Serbia	..	900	864	730	807	764	795	825	781	664	716	720
Slovenia	..	339	394	367	330	340	372	367	337	328	332	332
Non-OECD Europe	..	**492**	**486**	**457**	**485**	**497**	**502**	**530**	**504**	**478**	**499**	**494**

CO$_2$ emissions per kWh from electricity and heat generation
Emissions de CO$_2$ par kWh pour le secteur de l'électricité et de la chaleur

grammes CO$_2$ / kilowatt hour

	1990	1995	1998	1999	2000	2001	2002	2003	2004	2005	2006	Average 04-06
Armenia	..	214	258	225	236	243	153	148	120	138	138	132
Azerbaijan	..	502	540	614	648	561	490	523	511	504	473	496
Belarus	..	323	304	297	306	297	297	292	301	296	296	298
Estonia	..	680	715	700	691	678	663	717	701	665	640	669
Georgia	..	487	162	154	193	133	72	76	100	103	145	116
Kazakhstan	..	448	439	438	480	422	465	465	457	449	520	475
Kyrgyzstan	..	127	123	104	106	101	106	94	90	82	79	83
Latvia	..	238	198	218	200	189	188	183	166	162	167	165
Lithuania	..	175	177	178	161	149	125	114	116	139	139	131
Republic of Moldova	..	514	685	631	739	767	738	755	515	519	476	503
Russia	..	292	326	327	321	321	327	329	325	325	329	326
Tajikistan	..	50	45	41	41	41	27	27	28	27	28	28
Turkmenistan	..	931	610	791	795	795	795	795	795	795	795	795
Ukraine	..	383	332	339	347	330	325	381	316	331	344	330
Uzbekistan	..	433	485	483	458	467	475	454	448	442	446	446
Former USSR	**..**	**315**	**334**	**336**	**334**	**330**	**334**	**342**	**332**	**333**	**341**	**335**
Argentina	..	273	344	365	338	267	258	275	317	307	303	309
Bolivia	..	480	448	312	304	507	469	448	525	513	505	514
Brazil	..	55	62	82	88	104	86	79	85	84	81	84
Chile	..	261	418	459	331	261	262	279	341	328	294	321
Colombia	..	205	213	177	201	191	187	176	163	163	150	159
Costa Rica	..	156	68	21	8	14	15	20	17	27	47	31
Cuba	..	1 137	1 170	1 032	1 024	991	1 090	1 138	1 075	1 012	1 019	1 035
Dominican Republic	..	876	831	850	759	658	734	661	605	590	624	606
Ecuador	..	314	287	236	215	272	281	299	302	369	396	356
El Salvador	..	403	369	273	288	302	310	296	275	263	217	252
Guatemala	..	306	450	338	392	421	484	404	434	384	334	384
Haiti	..	327	379	289	346	340	399	320	301	307	305	304
Honduras	..	327	381	261	280	329	282	352	451	411	413	425
Jamaica	..	888	831	823	821	824	803	795	785	734	830	783
Netherlands Antilles	..	717	718	719	717	717	718	717	718	718	717	718
Nicaragua	..	484	632	605	610	613	563	558	557	539	550	549
Panama	..	317	446	224	231	399	270	356	266	275	229	256
Paraguay	..	2	0	0	-	-	-	-	-	-	-	-
Peru	..	186	195	171	152	120	143	148	206	198	172	192
Trinidad and Tobago	..	711	709	708	691	694	772	731	759	709	724	731
Uruguay	..	53	33	187	57	3	4	2	150	103	296	183
Venezuela	..	219	237	218	210	282	278	245	245	189	208	214
Other Latin America	..	691	579	510	496	486	501	514	507	509	509	508
Latin America	**..**	**183**	**201**	**204**	**196**	**205**	**197**	**193**	**204**	**193**	**194**	**197**
Bangladesh	..	601	588	592	556	602	604	574	628	557	584	590
Brunei Darussalam	..	880	865	831	795	799	818	801	802	782	821	801
Cambodia	..	1 816	2 074	1 764	1 798	1 940	1 970	1 880	1 301	1 205	1 005	1 170
Chinese Taipei	..	530	575	593	618	629	617	650	644	651	659	651
India	..	927	922	920	939	935	920	904	943	936	944	941
Indonesia	..	552	607	626	596	679	655	711	690	694	677	687
DPR of Korea	..	481	500	552	584	583	568	542	528	522	533	528
Malaysia	..	556	539	528	517	541	591	525	538	641	655	611
Mongolia	..	610	595	560	587	585	613	554	526	533	523	528
Myanmar	..	508	600	572	457	405	376	426	414	365	338	372
Nepal	..	26	73	34	12	7	2	1	6	4	4	4
Pakistan	..	405	411	468	479	463	443	371	397	380	413	397
Philippines	..	509	591	501	498	530	482	460	457	495	435	462
Singapore	..	939	774	656	664	635	595	574	556	544	536	545
Sri Lanka	..	51	204	229	427	406	435	378	429	398	314	380
Thailand	..	606	608	596	564	562	548	528	539	535	511	528
Vietnam	..	294	468	397	420	392	424	375	407	406	396	403
Other Asia	..	353	289	261	243	223	254	287	310	308	308	308
Asia	**..**	**713**	**724**	**723**	**729**	**733**	**719**	**708**	**726**	**726**	**729**	**727**
People's Rep. of China	..	803	823	798	765	740	748	776	805	787	788	793
Hong Kong, China	..	854	741	716	712	720	725	795	831	809	855	832
China	**..**	**804**	**821**	**796**	**764**	**739**	**748**	**776**	**806**	**788**	**788**	**794**

CO$_2$ emissions per kWh from electricity and heat generation using coal/peat*

Emissions de CO$_2$ par kWh pour le secteur de l'électricité et de la chaleur - Charbon/tourbe*

grammes CO$_2$ / kilowatt hour

	1990	1995	1998	1999	2000	2001	2002	2003	2004	2005	2006	Average 04-06
World	..	**884**	**910**	**901**	**879**	**899**	**881**	**891**	**913**	**910**	**913**	**912**
Annex I Parties	..	*839*	*860*	*857*	*840*	*874*	*851*	*854*	*858*	*864*	*866*	*863*
Annex II Parties	..	*924*	*918*	*909*	*911*	*959*	*919*	*910*	*914*	*905*	*906*	*908*
North America	..	*941*	*927*	*914*	*917*	*984*	*919*	*917*	*923*	*912*	*911*	*915*
Europe	*858*	*861*	*855*	*847*	*847*	*867*	*868*	*847*	*850*	*844*	*852*	*849*
Pacific	*1 033*	*992*	*1 004*	*1 007*	*1 003*	*1 004*	*1 012*	*993*	*987*	*974*	*976*	*979*
Annex I EIT	..	*614*	*663*	*675*	*613*	*616*	*627*	*666*	*660*	*711*	*717*	*696*
Non-Annex I Parties	..	*985*	*1 008*	*984*	*950*	*939*	*928*	*942*	*983*	*962*	*963*	*969*
Annex I Kyoto Parties	..	*759*	*796*	*802*	*768*	*778*	*789*	*798*	*800*	*819*	*822*	*814*
Non-OECD Total	..	**849**	**915**	**904**	**857**	**852**	**855**	**884**	**922**	**925**	**928**	**925**
OECD Total	..	**910**	**906**	**900**	**897**	**939**	**905**	**898**	**904**	**894**	**895**	**898**
Canada	1 010	992	944	935	934	916	897	899	927	873	864	888
Mexico	921	919	930	1 084	1 090	1 058	1 063	1 011	1 004	979	897	960
United States	..	938	926	913	916	988	921	918	923	914	913	917
OECD N. America	..	**940**	**927**	**915**	**919**	**985**	**921**	**918**	**924**	**913**	**911**	**916**
Australia	963	968	1 021	1 044	1 046	1 064	1 101	1 073	1 062	1 065	1 061	1 063
Japan	1 099	1 006	976	966	961	950	940	930	925	903	906	912
Korea	2 017	1 250	1 107	1 105	891	940	898	943	987	971	980	979
New Zealand	2 056	2 055	2 748	2 476	2 753	2 471	2 663	1 878	1 854	1 634	1 681	1 723
OECD Pacific	**1 101**	**1 028**	**1 023**	**1 025**	**977**	**988**	**984**	**981**	**987**	**973**	**977**	**979**
Austria	866	922	954	898	845	840	865	846	926	940	941	936
Belgium	990	1 024	1 013	1 104	992	1 072	1 088	1 092	1 136	1 180	1 237	1 184
Czech Republic	736	777	775	777	782	777	787	773	790	780	787	785
Denmark	577	555	544	521	519	517	538	600	556	536	602	565
Finland	504	536	566	556	546	567	572	622	613	532	590	578
France	1 053	1 111	1 069	1 036	921	881	899	886	905	895	923	908
Germany	825	854	821	813	814	873	871	820	818	803	839	820
Greece	1 137	1 126	916	923	986	981	987	989	1 006	1 000	1 003	1 003
Hungary	910	905	953	893	871	931	940	955	987	962	916	955
Iceland	-	-	-	-	-	-	-	-	-	-	-	-
Ireland	917	923	950	964	898	897	912	908	877	868	866	870
Italy	963	987	997	1 006	974	963	976	967	942	970	976	963
Luxembourg	3 170	3 701	-	-	-	-	-	-	-	-	-	-
Netherlands	859	907	918	961	951	960	962	965	958	788	756	834
Norway	1 100	574	637	663	612	721	663	664	583	654	662	633
Poland	666	682	679	682	689	681	686	687	692	687	689	689
Portugal	886	854	869	851	865	849	842	838	843	857	859	853
Slovak Republic	745	795	843	811	760	700	788	838	778	786	790	785
Spain	936	911	910	899	917	915	912	910	891	883	859	878
Sweden	467	473	579	624	638	621	608	616	585	638	619	614
Switzerland	495	908	-	-	-	-	-	-	-	-	-	-
Turkey	1 199	1 132	1 142	1 131	1 080	1 082	1 102	1 068	1 045	916	1 015	992
United Kingdom	910	880	943	916	906	898	890	901	927	934	917	926
OECD Europe	**810**	**825**	**824**	**818**	**819**	**830**	**834**	**818**	**823**	**813**	**822**	**819**
European Union - 27	..	*821*	*817*	*811*	*813*	*824*	*828*	*815*	*821*	*814*	*819*	*818*

* CO$_2$ emissions from coal consumed for electricity, combined heat and power and main activity heat plants divided by output of electricity and heat generated from coal. Both main activity producers and autoproducers have been included in the calculation of the emissions. Due to missing data for heat in 1990, the ratio for some countries and regions is not available.

CO$_2$ emissions per kWh from electricity and heat generation using coal/peat

Emissions de CO$_2$ par kWh pour le secteur de l'électricité et de la chaleur - Charbon/tourbe

grammes CO$_2$ / kilowatt hour

	1990	1995	1998	1999	2000	2001	2002	2003	2004	2005	2006	Average 04-06
Non-OECD Total	..	849	915	904	857	852	855	884	922	925	928	925
Algeria	..	-	-	-	-	-	-	-	-	-	-	-
Angola	..	-	-	-	-	-	-	-	-	-	-	-
Benin	..	-	-	-	-	-	-	-	-	-	-	-
Botswana	..	1 815	1 252	1 588	1 900	1 325	1 329	1 326	1 776	1 856	1 856	1 830
Cameroon	..	-	-	-	-	-	-	-	-	-	-	-
Congo	..	-	-	-	-	-	-	-	-	-	-	-
Dem. Rep. of Congo	..	-	-	-	-	-	-	-	-	-	-	-
Côte d'Ivoire	..	-	-	-	-	-	-	-	-	-	-	-
Egypt	..	-	-	-	-	-	-	-	-	-	-	-
Eritrea	..	-	-	-	-	-	-	-	-	-	-	-
Ethiopia	..	-	-	-	-	-	-	-	-	-	-	-
Gabon	..	-	-	-	-	-	-	-	-	-	-	-
Ghana	..	-	-	-	-	-	-	-	-	-	-	-
Kenya	..	-	-	-	-	-	-	-	-	-	-	-
Libya	..	-	-	-	-	-	-	-	-	-	-	-
Morocco	..	912	880	856	839	821	821	817	839	860	851	850
Mozambique	..	-	-	-	-	-	-	-	-	-	-	-
Namibia	..	1 346	2 384	1 148	1 262	1 403	1 346	1 336	1 344	1 330	1 327	1 334
Nigeria	..	-	-	-	-	-	-	-	-	-	-	-
Senegal	..	-	-	-	-	-	-	-	-	-	-	-
South Africa	..	938	1 004	955	960	884	882	905	930	902	929	920
Sudan	..	-	-	-	-	-	-	-	-	-	-	-
United Rep. of Tanzania	..	1 116	1 120	1 111	1 107	1 116	1 116	1 114	1 113	1 111	1 106	1 110
Togo	..	-	-	-	-	-	-	-	-	-	-	-
Tunisia	..	-	-	-	-	-	-	-	-	-	-	-
Zambia	..	1 718	1 693	1 636	1 636	1 527	1 527	1 575	1 617	1 654	1 688	1 653
Zimbabwe	..	1 287	1 270	1 379	1 383	1 362	1 287	1 311	1 321	1 321	1 321	1 321
Other Africa	..	957	957	956	956	956	956	955	955	955	956	956
Africa	..	**952**	**1 007**	**964**	**966**	**894**	**890**	**908**	**935**	**911**	**936**	**927**
Bahrain	..	-	-	-	-	-	-	-	-	-	-	-
Islamic Rep. of Iran	..	-	-	-	-	-	-	-	-	-	-	-
Iraq	..	-	-	-	-	-	-	-	-	-	-	-
Israel	..	849	855	848	844	858	851	855	859	855	863	859
Jordan	..	-	-	-	-	-	-	-	-	-	-	-
Kuwait	..	-	-	-	-	-	-	-	-	-	-	-
Lebanon	..	-	-	-	-	-	-	-	-	-	-	-
Oman	..	-	-	-	-	-	-	-	-	-	-	-
Qatar	..	-	-	-	-	-	-	-	-	-	-	-
Saudi Arabia	..	-	-	-	-	-	-	-	-	-	-	-
Syria	..	-	-	-	-	-	-	-	-	-	-	-
United Arab Emirates	..	-	-	-	-	-	-	-	-	-	-	-
Yemen	..	-	-	-	-	-	-	-	-	-	-	-
Middle East	..	**849**	**855**	**848**	**844**	**858**	**851**	**855**	**859**	**855**	**863**	**859**
Albania	..	-	-	799	920	967	759	1 898	1 898	1 898	1 898	1 898
Bosnia and Herzegovina	..	977	1 686	1 622	1 615	1 554	1 686	1 479	1 436	1 445	1 450	1 444
Bulgaria	..	892	929	875	853	882	870	897	934	960	946	947
Croatia	..	1 038	1 061	1 017	894	938	907	859	913	874	850	879
Cyprus	..	-	-	-	-	-	-	-	-	-	-	-
Gibraltar	..	-	-	-	-	-	-	-	-	-	-	-
FYR of Macedonia	..	1 080	1 007	984	956	1 012	964	942	976	916	905	932
Malta	..	1 382	-	-	-	-	-	-	-	-	-	-
Romania	..	861	793	827	823	826	830	824	845	822	853	840
Serbia	..	1 568	1 444	1 354	1 367	1 308	1 335	1 277	1 261	1 120	1 152	1 178
Slovenia	..	694	847	830	817	827	878	839	828	784	783	798
Non-OECD Europe	..	**1 030**	**1 058**	**1 019**	**1 013**	**1 000**	**1 020**	**1 000**	**1 020**	**976**	**991**	**995**

CO$_2$ emissions per kWh from electricity and heat generation using coal/peat

Emissions de CO $_2$ par kWh pour le secteur de l'électricité et de la chaleur - Charbon/tourbe

grammes CO $_2$ / kilowatt hour

	1990	1995	1998	1999	2000	2001	2002	2003	2004	2005	2006	Average 04-06
Armenia	..	-	-	-	-	-	-	-	-	-	-	-
Azerbaijan	..	-	-	-	-	-	-	-	-	-	-	-
Belarus	..	498	509	414	425	501	489	499	530	511	487	510
Estonia	..	931	1 009	1 016	1 002	984	954	963	986	952	922	953
Georgia	..	967		-	-	-	-	-	-	-	-	-
Kazakhstan	..	450	443	453	494	433	477	483	480	455	535	490
Kyrgyzstan	..	517	535	531	527	509	508	668	608	474	475	519
Latvia	..	498	583	580	697	608	564	537	508	533	474	505
Lithuania	..	525	460	441	468	500	487	526	477	435	433	448
Republic of Moldova	..	804	1 025	1 011	1 011	1 010	1 058	1 013	400	398	390	396
Russia	..	471	557	592	501	509	523	565	558	634	645	612
Tajikistan	..	-	-	-	-	-	-	-	-	-	-	-
Turkmenistan	..	-	-	-	-	-	-	-	-	-	-	-
Ukraine	..	1 222	1 130	1 024	1 042	939	953	1 120	1 091	1 166	1 085	1 114
Uzbekistan	..	1 140	1 121	1 019	1 019	1 019	1 019	1 018	1 018	1 018	1 018	1 018
Former USSR	**..**	**535**	**589**	**612**	**541**	**533**	**551**	**596**	**583**	**640**	**666**	**630**
Argentina	..	2 026	1 435	1 149	1 246	1 370	1 945	1 709	1 420	1 372	1 235	1 342
Bolivia	..	-	-	-	-	-	-	-	-	-	-	-
Brazil	..	1 565	1 432	1 348	1 474	1 496	1 524	1 576	1 484	1 627	1 665	1 592
Chile	..	960	971	1 018	1 026	1 068	1 130	1 243	1 242	1 235	1 158	1 212
Colombia	..	1 167	1 054	1 208	1 246	1 095	1 191	1 110	1 266	1 100	1 086	1 151
Costa Rica	..	-	-	-	-	-	-	-	-	-	-	-
Cuba	..	-	-	-	-	-	-	-	-	-	-	-
Dominican Republic	..	886	887	887	886	886	886	886	886	886	886	886
Ecuador	..	-	-	-	-	-	-	-	-	-	-	-
El Salvador	..	-	-	-	-	-	-	-	-	-	-	-
Guatemala	..	-	-	1 055	1 029	957	957	925	919	929	948	932
Haiti	..	-	-	-	-	-	-	-	-	-	-	-
Honduras	..	-	-	-	-	-	-	-	-	-	-	-
Jamaica	..	-	-	-	-	-	-	-	-	-	-	-
Netherlands Antilles	..	-	-	-	-	-	-	-	-	-	-	-
Nicaragua	..	-	-	-	-	-	-	-	-	-	-	-
Panama	..	-	-	-	-	-	-	-	-	-	-	-
Paraguay	..	-	-	-	-	-	-	-	-	-	-	-
Peru	..	-	-	-	1 112	1 113	1 112	1 112	1 112	1 112	1 112	1 112
Trinidad and Tobago	..	-	-	-	-	-	-	-	-	-	-	-
Uruguay	..	-	-	-	-	-	-	-	-	-	-	-
Venezuela	..	-	-	-	-	-	-	-	-	-	-	-
Other Latin America	..	-	-	-	-	-	-	-	-	-	-	-
Latin America	**..**	**1 313**	**1 144**	**1 165**	**1 262**	**1 294**	**1 320**	**1 306**	**1 300**	**1 334**	**1 300**	**1 312**
Bangladesh	..	-	-	-	-	-	-	-	-	-	-	-
Brunei Darussalam	..	-	-	-	-	-	-	-	-	-	-	-
Cambodia	..	-	-	-	-	-	-	-	-	-	-	-
Chinese Taipei	..	842	894	924	920	910	890	947	962	970	961	965
India	..	1 213	1 215	1 220	1 203	1 199	1 153	1 161	1 224	1 244	1 270	1 246
Indonesia	..	806	981	1 038	836	1 072	967	1 025	983	1 027	980	997
DPR of Korea	..	1 253	1 226	1 218	1 217	1 208	1 208	1 208	1 208	1 208	1 208	1 208
Malaysia	..	855	901	855	975	771	856	1 083	793	930	1 134	952
Mongolia	..	613	598	560	586	585	612	552	523	530	519	524
Myanmar	..	-	-	-	-	-	-	-	-	-	-	-
Nepal	..	-	-	-	-	-	-	-	-	-	-	-
Pakistan	..	1 575	1 439	1 474	1 484	1 544	1 604	1 855	1 993	2 247	2 346	2 195
Philippines	..	1 436	684	919	936	892	921	971	909	1 151	1 031	1 030
Singapore	..	-	-	-	-	-	-	-	-	-	-	-
Sri Lanka	..	-	-	-	-	-	-	-	-	-	-	-
Thailand	..	986	1 003	970	959	955	976	989	989	980	812	927
Vietnam	..	1 362	1 422	1 414	1 423	1 545	1 193	922	925	926	925	925
Other Asia	..	-	-	-	-	-	-	-	-	-	-	-
Asia	**..**	**1 128**	**1 126**	**1 138**	**1 111**	**1 114**	**1 075**	**1 094**	**1 124**	**1 149**	**1 159**	**1 144**
People's Rep. of China	..	987	1 001	952	911	901	902	918	969	937	931	945
Hong Kong, China	..	855	845	879	868	875	879	889	998	957	1 025	993
China	**..**	**984**	**998**	**951**	**911**	**901**	**902**	**917**	**969**	**938**	**931**	**946**

CO$_2$ emissions per kWh from electricity and heat generation using oil *

Emissions de CO$_2$ par kWh pour le secteur de l'électricité et de la chaleur - Pétrole *

grammes CO$_2$ / kilowatt hour

	1990	1995	1998	1999	2000	2001	2002	2003	2004	2005	2006	Average 04-06
World	..	593	654	660	667	657	659	663	651	664	648	655
Annex I Parties	..	485	555	560	573	558	563	578	558	576	531	555
Annex II Parties	..	605	659	652	659	643	635	654	625	638	589	617
North America	..	506	771	766	789	705	743	741	761	738	776	758
Europe	635	611	582	581	589	600	575	596	503	561	497	520
Pacific	630	652	643	633	630	631	624	623	620	615	574	603
Annex I EIT	..	352	397	394	403	400	410	401	385	401	394	393
Non-Annex I Parties	..	770	786	779	756	751	749	744	732	737	732	734
Annex I Kyoto Parties	..	487	509	514	526	524	530	537	498	528	487	504
Non-OECD Total	..	575	642	653	672	666	676	671	678	685	679	680
OECD Total	..	620	672	669	660	645	636	652	615	636	596	616
Canada	701	624	651	613	613	687	688	705	668	685	709	687
Mexico	734	690	756	765	756	756	795	851	733	813	821	789
United States	..	491	786	784	811	707	750	747	777	744	784	768
OECD N. America	..	582	766	766	775	724	763	772	753	760	793	768
Australia	652	743	623	552	557	634	742	1 111	1 643	1 247	1 144	1 344
Japan	630	651	644	634	631	631	620	615	607	606	563	592
Korea	765	682	645	689	482	484	410	400	404	420	415	413
New Zealand	1 223	1 087	-	-	-	-	-	986	744	781	679	734
OECD Pacific	640	658	643	639	589	583	568	565	553	561	528	547
Austria	500	422	472	449	378	413	388	421	420	391	384	398
Belgium	403	341	464	907	729	536	511	825	828	747	749	775
Czech Republic	430	351	480	551	550	473	456	440	406	398	406	403
Denmark	413	551	560	589	624	562	531	407	400	389	395	394
Finland	341	323	318	319	322	358	344	382	361	344	372	359
France	603	506	565	538	238	201	191	275	320	585	575	493
Germany	497	363	320	334	438	564	473	496	376	718	411	502
Greece	746	737	746	761	731	730	743	749	721	714	694	710
Hungary	457	574	592	577	599	637	555	574	779	751	827	786
Iceland	520	490	340	327	296	327	270	270	781	624	781	728
Ireland	756	736	723	712	696	736	759	792	766	740	825	777
Italy	672	663	655	665	704	706	640	690	489	472	451	471
Luxembourg	1 021	1 226	-	-	-	-	-	-	-	-	-	-
Netherlands	693	534	534	386	536	563	536	530	534	383	403	440
Norway	1 640	1 035	370	372	400	383	281	316	299	401	321	341
Poland	385	451	450	444	463	452	456	456	484	492	510	495
Portugal	693	709	637	624	593	623	621	616	596	600	550	582
Slovak Republic	381	753	688	926	757	405	414	410	382	400	403	395
Spain	802	795	583	650	630	657	654	645	660	696	603	653
Sweden	297	301	340	339	333	326	316	324	345	329	331	335
Switzerland	498	556	656	460	349	342	339	342	351	363	368	361
Turkey	899	951	921	889	852	735	672	668	688	654	740	694
United Kingdom	660	672	534	460	431	563	553	641	668	609	573	617
OECD Europe	616	610	590	589	598	602	575	593	510	561	504	525
European Union - 27	..	560	551	559	572	578	561	583	508	559	504	524

* CO$_2$ emissions from oil consumed for electricity, combined heat and power and main activity heat plants divided by output of electricity and heat generated from oil. Both main activity producers and autoproducers have been included in the calculation of the emissions. Due to missing data for heat in 1990, the ratio for some countries and regions is not available.

CO₂ emissions per kWh from electricity and heat generation using oil

Emissions de CO₂ par kWh pour le secteur de l'électricité et de la chaleur - Pétrole

grammes CO₂ / kilowatt hour

	1990	1995	1998	1999	2000	2001	2002	2003	2004	2005	2006	Average 04-06
Non-OECD Total	..	575	642	653	672	666	676	671	678	685	679	680
Algeria	..	1 178	1 184	1 135	863	840	968	864	869	929	932	910
Angola	..	2 835	1 034	1 034	1 037	1 006	1 004	986	988	984	988	987
Benin	..	951	696	678	616	985	981	771	749	716	696	721
Botswana	..	1 054	1 054	1 051	1 051	1 050	1 085	1 085	1 055	1 026	1 026	1 036
Cameroon	..	893	916	907	919	853	753	733	600	698	716	671
Congo	..	1 587	1 587	794	-	-	-	705	-	-	-	-
Dem. Rep. of Congo	..	1 219	1 155	1 097	1 155	1 155	1 097	1 045	997	954	914	955
Côte d'Ivoire	..	692	665	1 068	970	970	970	1 042	893	635	1 587	1 038
Egypt	..	660	678	768	708	698	773	744	778	791	720	763
Eritrea	..	1 463	691	703	717	752	661	696	725	680	696	700
Ethiopia	..	641	860	836	828	1 003	756	794	882	794	953	876
Gabon	..	803	887	846	777	648	680	676	682	697	702	694
Ghana	..	836	981	1 465	802	720	824	811	665	860	827	784
Kenya	..	728	1 600	1 253	1 083	1 198	1 160	1 124	1 069	1 041	1 040	1 050
Libya	..	1 290	1 194	1 194	1 144	1 111	1 089	1 067	943	1 003	1 078	1 008
Morocco	..	916	767	750	769	820	801	793	793	787	796	792
Mozambique	..	907	762	866	1 058	1 058	1 027	840	814	907	794	838
Namibia	..	833	833	804	804	812	740	740	740	999	999	913
Nigeria	..	693	839	964	966	965	965	963	964	988	1 002	984
Senegal	..	980	931	948	1 045	1 012	993	845	876	917	871	888
South Africa	..	819	-	-	-	-	-	-	-	-	-	-
Sudan	..	972	992	855	1 030	1 031	1 137	1 138	1 137	911	910	986
United Rep. of Tanzania	..	1 495	1 524	1 488	1 488	1 509	1 482	1 459	1 499	1 411	1 494	1 468
Togo	..	1 058	1 058	769	1 309	2 516	780	732	799	589	798	729
Tunisia	..	921	938	934	907	937	919	1 000	953	960	839	917
Zambia	..	917	917	743	922	896	896	896	896	847	847	864
Zimbabwe	..	-	-	2 556	1 539	2 020	3 175	2 963	1 965	2 117	2 117	2 066
Other Africa	..	743	718	742	850	850	856	868	873	869	869	870
Africa	..	**904**	**861**	**927**	**936**	**943**	**947**	**936**	**880**	**893**	**874**	**882**
Bahrain	..	-	-	-	-	-	-	-	-	-	1 216	405
Islamic Rep. of Iran	..	968	1 051	1 020	883	812	830	816	810	840	1 057	902
Iraq	..	712	691	691	745	829	763	799	713	711	712	712
Israel	..	777	557	603	578	518	730	695	721	713	716	717
Jordan	..	860	814	756	717	716	755	686	753	700	675	709
Kuwait	..	734	725	730	746	722	667	700	795	847	693	778
Lebanon	..	753	865	849	778	783	776	814	634	744	751	710
Oman	..	1 056	1 054	1 056	1 056	1 056	1 055	1 055	1 055	1 015	977	1 016
Qatar	..	-	-	-	-	-	-	-	-	-	-	-
Saudi Arabia	..	804	813	830	844	805	743	718	763	744	746	751
Syria	..	777	765	763	729	728	730	714	730	732	776	746
United Arab Emirates	..	968	928	925	953	976	999	1 052	1 194	1 194	1 194	1 194
Yemen	..	946	995	921	930	930	919	884	874	841	823	846
Middle East	..	**811**	**794**	**800**	**793**	**781**	**756**	**748**	**765**	**773**	**787**	**775**
Albania	..	501	504	811	665	658	599	1 115	1 203	1 709	1 189	1 367
Bosnia and Herzegovina	..	583	582	582	288	425	511	499	476	482	474	477
Bulgaria	..	321	504	497	511	635	577	595	524	540	575	546
Croatia	..	456	575	584	582	639	630	622	578	531	547	552
Cyprus	..	822	843	856	838	777	756	833	773	789	758	773
Gibraltar	..	766	766	766	760	754	760	755	766	740	730	745
FYR of Macedonia	..	376	355	344	434	376	382	328	333	324	392	350
Malta	..	932	932	903	862	1 022	815	809	896	855	834	862
Romania	..	378	335	373	374	385	392	406	411	395	389	399
Serbia	..	418	419	419	394	422	676	688	437	381	427	415
Slovenia	..	978	750	406	477	667	523	436	441	463	396	433
Non-OECD Europe	..	**412**	**449**	**485**	**488**	**496**	**516**	**551**	**567**	**537**	**545**	**549**

CO$_2$ emissions per kWh from electricity and heat generation using oil

Emissions de CO $_2$ par kWh pour le secteur de l'électricité et de la chaleur - Pétrole

grammes CO $_2$ / kilowatt hour

	1990	1995	1998	1999	2000	2001	2002	2003	2004	2005	2006	Average 04-06
Armenia	..	306	-	-	-	-	-	-	-	-	-	-
Azerbaijan	..	600	725	725	725	725	725	725	725	725	577	676
Belarus	..	352	359	364	359	353	346	343	370	350	362	361
Estonia	..	349	368	368	365	412	404	419	380	396	408	395
Georgia	..	1 349	1 056	1 055	1 052	2 999	2 603	2 603	2 603	2 603	2 603	2 603
Kazakhstan	..	1 033	850	686	1 102	806	1 277	670	227	476	492	398
Kyrgyzstan	..	-	-	-	-	-	-	-	-	-	-	-
Latvia	..	341	350	372	376	357	339	355	372	350	387	370
Lithuania	..	356	388	382	383	403	415	421	477	527	463	489
Republic of Moldova	..	760	565	875	805	839	835	815	345	402	379	376
Russia	..	328	394	384	398	391	407	392	372	392	383	382
Tajikistan	..	-	-	-	-	-	-	-	-	-	-	-
Turkmenistan	..	-	-	-	-	-	-	-	-	-	-	-
Ukraine	..	481	370	366	372	377	395	433	771	889	940	867
Uzbekistan	..	606	705	698	530	594	730	527	442	380	398	407
Former USSR	..	**369**	**417**	**413**	**429**	**413**	**435**	**419**	**390**	**410**	**397**	**399**
Argentina	..	632	878	896	1 013	1 141	1 059	1 132	922	808	716	815
Bolivia	..	972	1 070	838	925	1 266	1 267	1 272	1 275	1 275	1 275	1 275
Brazil	..	810	805	780	800	790	698	762	701	760	728	730
Chile	..	1 086	893	760	678	720	805	728	769	714	883	789
Colombia	..	891	889	874	864	864	861	874	877	877	874	876
Costa Rica	..	918	830	974	949	980	936	1 119	747	818	772	779
Cuba	..	1 197	1 246	1 099	1 084	1 050	1 156	1 209	1 127	1 057	1 055	1 080
Dominican Republic	..	998	927	1 009	836	687	792	689	653	689	682	675
Ecuador	..	810	714	777	761	756	749	739	698	720	705	707
El Salvador	..	938	788	737	593	672	653	697	602	619	490	570
Guatemala	..	873	924	773	769	769	774	774	775	811	810	798
Haiti	..	669	704	688	716	649	761	611	573	587	582	581
Honduras	..	845	871	787	734	842	690	682	875	618	737	743
Jamaica	..	923	860	851	849	844	826	820	813	760	861	812
Netherlands Antilles	..	717	718	719	717	717	718	717	718	718	717	718
Nicaragua	..	842	820	794	748	748	714	741	741	772	762	758
Panama	..	1 027	922	719	781	787	764	727	782	769	588	713
Paraguay	..	926	1 715	1 467	-	-	-	-	-	-	-	-
Peru	..	964	800	763	854	863	827	793	735	908	649	764
Trinidad and Tobago	..	-	1 058	1 058	1 058	1 058	1 058	1 058	705	794	635	711
Uruguay	..	810	823	814	850	1 126	1 104	1 214	820	821	843	828
Venezuela	..	1 200	925	1 036	889	1 148	1 026	796	1 119	765	769	885
Other Latin America	..	826	681	598	582	568	585	600	593	596	596	595
Latin America	..	**938**	**897**	**854**	**838**	**847**	**845**	**827**	**841**	**784**	**773**	**799**
Bangladesh	..	1 004	1 045	939	1 078	1 182	1 121	1 084	1 017	1 097	1 097	1 070
Brunei Darussalam	..	847	866	722	690	794	762	762	766	766	770	767
Cambodia	..	1 816	2 074	1 764	1 798	1 940	2 076	2 010	1 350	1 269	1 050	1 223
Chinese Taipei	..	701	688	692	695	680	695	720	741	745	729	738
India	..	1 105	1 081	1 003	1 036	1 035	870	915	930	923	865	906
Indonesia	..	685	860	737	786	693	713	775	709	691	606	669
DPR of Korea	..	1 379	1 380	1 380	1 379	1 380	1 379	1 379	1 379	1 379	1 378	1 379
Malaysia	..	778	713	722	742	736	733	731	751	647	679	693
Mongolia	..	481	496	548	606	600	700	682	726	864	906	832
Myanmar	..	894	1 082	917	868	778	747	738	736	735	797	756
Nepal	..	827	771	761	755	755	850	850	971	1 020	1 020	1 004
Pakistan	..	757	751	747	755	758	773	675	795	692	749	746
Philippines	..	736	1 086	891	757	801	825	686	724	689	663	692
Singapore	..	1 201	893	707	707	707	707	707	707	707	707	707
Sri Lanka	..	696	656	703	820	778	720	669	679	656	620	652
Thailand	..	741	741	744	749	805	751	725	715	729	739	728
Vietnam	..	900	899	936	914	936	907	894	891	870	870	877
Other Asia	..	805	698	617	592	498	553	597	621	618	617	619
Asia	..	**812**	**843**	**782**	**794**	**783**	**768**	**777**	**774**	**752**	**728**	**752**
People's Rep. of China	..	619	631	650	637	635	645	667	667	683	648	666
Hong Kong, China	..	813	795	844	942	934	1 011	863	818	935	979	911
China	..	**620**	**631**	**651**	**637**	**636**	**645**	**667**	**667**	**683**	**648**	**666**

CO$_2$ emissions per kWh from electricity and heat generation using gas*

Emissions de CO$_2$ par kWh pour le secteur de l'électricité et de la chaleur - Gaz*

grammes CO$_2$ / kilowatt hour

	1990	1995	1998	1999	2000	2001	2002	2003	2004	2005	2006	Average 04-06
World	..	366	395	396	389	389	391	386	388	390	391	390
Annex I Parties	..	332	359	360	350	348	349	344	342	344	344	343
Annex II Parties	..	457	458	455	415	407	404	390	389	386	388	388
North America	..	502	532	532	459	453	435	426	436	435	433	435
Europe	403	372	367	370	353	340	346	328	320	316	317	318
Pacific	469	455	439	432	428	429	447	447	448	448	463	453
Annex I EIT	..	265	287	288	296	297	298	302	298	301	299	299
Non-Annex I Parties	..	563	558	547	543	543	539	527	531	532	529	531
Annex I Kyoto Parties	..	294	318	320	324	323	326	326	319	320	321	320
Non-OECD Total	..	326	362	363	374	380	385	386	388	393	392	391
OECD Total	..	453	452	449	411	402	400	387	388	386	390	388
Canada	371	360	388	379	407	411	395	424	392	395	398	395
Mexico	555	542	544	536	529	486	461	468	497	512	550	520
United States	..	509	539	541	462	455	437	427	438	437	434	437
OECD N. America	..	504	532	532	463	455	436	430	442	443	446	443
Australia	496	417	383	374	362	392	583	577	560	570	577	569
Japan	465	457	443	436	433	431	432	432	434	432	450	439
Korea	496	389	351	356	336	353	338	325	347	343	349	346
New Zealand	506	533	490	469	471	451	440	439	428	429	438	432
OECD Pacific	470	448	429	423	417	419	431	429	428	426	437	431
Austria	384	404	348	344	314	320	308	315	300	310	290	300
Belgium	454	412	384	346	335	311	310	336	334	348	307	330
Czech Republic	237	227	250	284	271	267	269	266	284	273	283	280
Denmark	222	235	254	255	250	249	250	252	254	249	252	252
Finland	241	274	243	233	238	242	242	244	243	233	247	241
France	337	335	340	325	251	249	246	240	233	242	254	243
Germany	372	314	343	360	345	314	326	259	259	260	257	259
Greece	459	435	481	518	505	482	446	434	416	459	416	430
Hungary	343	359	298	296	305	286	315	335	308	305	312	308
Iceland	-	-	-	-	-	-	-	-	-	-	-	-
Ireland	499	480	490	507	460	473	445	421	407	412	389	403
Italy	475	466	446	439	431	402	435	420	348	344	336	343
Luxembourg	662	307	201	221	206	202	327	322	328	325	326	326
Netherlands	434	363	318	341	300	313	316	317	308	282	297	296
Norway	-	302	257	296	293	328	288	283	288	283	282	284
Poland	289	303	281	296	303	311	327	316	329	333	329	330
Portugal	-	-	436	392	364	346	347	347	339	337	331	335
Slovak Republic	442	429	333	387	333	278	239	240	251	241	236	243
Spain	423	457	302	352	311	281	325	316	324	319	342	328
Sweden	217	218	253	220	227	222	252	219	216	219	217	217
Switzerland	241	232	232	230	230	232	233	237	236	238	242	239
Turkey	488	419	437	408	346	359	357	347	355	357	341	351
United Kingdom	521	426	411	386	382	387	379	379	388	384	390	387
OECD Europe	397	371	364	368	349	337	342	327	321	318	318	319
European Union - 27	..	357	350	357	343	330	336	324	315	312	313	313

* CO$_2$ emissions from gas consumed for electricity, combined heat and power and main activity heat plants divided by output of electricity and heat generated from gas. Both main activity producers and autoproducers have been included in the calculation of the emissions. Due to missing data for heat in 1990, the ratio for some countries and regions is not available.

CO$_2$ emissions per kWh from electricity and heat generation using gas

Emissions de CO$_2$ par kWh pour le secteur de l'électricité et de la chaleur - Gaz

grammes CO$_2$ / kilowatt hour

	1990	1995	1998	1999	2000	2001	2002	2003	2004	2005	2006	Average 04-06
Non-OECD Total	..	326	362	363	374	380	385	386	388	393	392	391
Algeria	..	690	695	687	682	685	695	702	702	677	687	688
Angola	..	-	-	-	-	-	-	-	-	-	-	-
Benin	..	-	-	-	-	-	-	-	-	-	-	-
Botswana	..	-	-	-	-	-	-	-	-	-	-	-
Cameroon	..	-	-	-	-	-	-	-	-	-	-	-
Congo	..	-	-	-	-	-	-	573	576	573	572	574
Dem. Rep. of Congo	..	-	-	-	-	-	-	-	-	-	-	-
Côte d'Ivoire	..	736	813	615	598	622	606	600	596	600	600	599
Egypt	..	529	515	515	467	442	484	484	490	490	490	490
Eritrea	..	-	-	-	-	-	-	-	-	-	-	-
Ethiopia	..	-	-	-	-	-	-	-	-	-	-	-
Gabon	..	876	875	919	929	894	893	899	915	919	910	915
Ghana	..	-	-	-	-	-	-	-	-	-	-	-
Kenya	..	-	-	-	-	-	-	-	-	-	-	-
Libya	..	591	591	591	591	591	529	632	662	662	591	638
Morocco	..	-	-	-	-	-	-	-	-	332	334	222
Mozambique	..	652	527	628	778	1 106	1 155	1 674	775	724	684	728
Namibia	..	-	-	-	-	-	-	-	-	-	-	-
Nigeria	..	410	515	515	628	515	515	515	515	515	515	515
Senegal	..	604	602	611	628	-	518	512	517	519	516	517
South Africa	..	-	-	-	-	804	804	803	803	803	804	803
Sudan	..	-	-	-	-	-	-	-	-	-	-	-
United Rep. of Tanzania	..	-	-	-	-	-	-	-	602	602	603	602
Togo	..	-	-	-	-	-	-	-	-	-	-	-
Tunisia	..	533	568	555	536	550	529	521	502	440	503	482
Zambia	..	-	-	-	-	-	-	-	-	-	-	-
Zimbabwe	..	-	-	-	-	-	-	-	-	-	-	-
Other Africa	..	-	-	-	-	-	-	-	-	-	-	-
Africa	..	563	588	573	545	523	542	544	550	537	543	543
Bahrain	..	815	822	852	868	840	835	883	881	890	799	857
Islamic Rep. of Iran	..	507	507	507	507	529	527	525	511	516	451	493
Iraq	..	-	-	-	-	-	-	-	-	-	-	-
Israel	..	516	524	525	541	529	535	542	548	552	468	522
Jordan	..	681	769	688	671	626	646	667	622	582	576	593
Kuwait	..	539	531	539	553	539	478	516	586	627	510	574
Lebanon	..	-	-	-	-	-	-	-	-	-	-	-
Oman	..	776	690	759	742	765	780	809	848	819	830	832
Qatar	..	1 131	865	823	771	781	782	779	649	618	626	631
Saudi Arabia	..	830	817	784	766	749	759	761	760	761	765	762
Syria	..	543	543	543	543	543	543	543	543	543	543	543
United Arab Emirates	..	730	702	700	721	740	758	798	906	836	812	852
Yemen	..	-	-	-	-	-	-	-	-	-	-	-
Middle East	..	680	645	638	637	651	654	660	668	661	619	650
Albania	..	-	-	-	-	-	-	-	-	-	-	-
Bosnia and Herzegovina	..	-	287	275	287	287	287	287	287	287	287	287
Bulgaria	..	302	296	285	296	283	288	261	232	236	244	237
Croatia	..	423	337	337	339	324	346	313	318	304	323	315
Cyprus	..	-	-	-	-	-	-	-	-	-	-	-
Gibraltar	..	-	-	-	-	-	-	-	-	-	-	-
FYR of Macedonia	..	-	234	238	238	235	236	249	255	243	242	247
Malta	..	-	-	-	-	-	-	-	-	-	-	-
Romania	..	322	288	285	295	292	309	349	313	311	315	313
Serbia	..	241	280	259	260	270	258	268	268	230	229	242
Slovenia	..	-	-	-	237	249	271	278	246	260	244	250
Non-OECD Europe	..	319	294	290	294	290	302	320	293	284	291	289

CO$_2$ emissions per kWh from electricity and heat generation using gas

Emissions de CO$_2$ par kWh pour le secteur de l'électricité et de la chaleur - Gaz

grammes CO$_2$ / kilowatt hour

	1990	1995	1998	1999	2000	2001	2002	2003	2004	2005	2006	Average 04-06
Armenia	..	328	473	457	457	458	454	455	351	404	442	399
Azerbaijan	..	341	305	445	582	521	444	481	496	496	496	496
Belarus	..	299	284	281	298	288	292	289	298	297	297	297
Estonia	..	223	229	227	232	235	236	236	231	233	234	233
Georgia	..	934	923	924	887	616	393	348	369	389	450	403
Kazakhstan	..	559	615	535	591	585	585	585	644	800	737	727
Kyrgyzstan	..	309	309	309	309	309	309	309	309	309	309	309
Latvia	..	247	230	249	240	241	239	236	238	236	234	236
Lithuania	..	255	267	270	268	268	257	257	260	264	257	260
Republic of Moldova	..	402	680	609	734	769	744	752	525	527	483	512
Russia	..	259	288	286	293	298	301	297	299	305	305	303
Tajikistan	..	517	517	517	517	517	338	337	348	342	349	346
Turkmenistan	..	931	610	791	795	795	795	795	795	795	795	795
Ukraine	..	273	282	300	317	308	294	347	293	283	264	280
Uzbekistan	..	422	467	472	465	466	467	468	469	469	469	469
Former USSR	**..**	**272**	**297**	**299**	**308**	**311**	**311**	**314**	**310**	**314**	**313**	**312**
Argentina	..	437	576	520	514	490	482	474	467	448	459	458
Bolivia	..	845	764	563	605	1 043	882	635	898	738	743	793
Brazil	..	740	550	494	496	455	478	445	472	473	451	465
Chile	..	602	452	410	383	387	356	347	382	424	415	407
Colombia	..	646	534	534	534	534	534	534	534	534	535	534
Costa Rica	..	-	-	-	-	-	-	-	-	-	-	-
Cuba	..	377	477	477	477	477	477	-	-	-	-	-
Dominican Republic	..	-	-	-	-	-	-	502	502	502	502	502
Ecuador	..	-	-	-	-	-	937	977	903	965	883	917
El Salvador	..	-	-	-	-	-	-	-	-	-	-	-
Guatemala	..	-	-	-	-	-	-	-	-	-	-	-
Haiti	..	-	-	-	-	-	-	-	-	-	-	-
Honduras	..	-	-	-	-	-	-	-	-	-	-	-
Jamaica	..	-	-	-	-	-	-	-	-	-	-	-
Netherlands Antilles	..	-	-	-	-	-	-	-	-	-	-	-
Nicaragua	..	-	-	-	-	-	-	-	-	-	-	-
Panama	..	-	-	-	-	-	-	-	-	-	-	-
Paraguay	..	-	-	-	-	-	-	-	-	-	-	-
Peru	..	670	670	670	670	646	646	646	646	907	895	816
Trinidad and Tobago	..	716	711	710	693	697	776	732	762	711	727	734
Uruguay	..	-	-	-	-	-	-	451	578	469	536	528
Venezuela	..	675	814	824	753	717	741	652	652	652	719	674
Other Latin America	..	580	714	708	703	711	703	692	659	681	697	679
Latin America	**..**	**572**	**635**	**580**	**552**	**539**	**543**	**503**	**510**	**512**	**524**	**515**
Bangladesh	..	586	588	595	555	597	603	573	639	552	583	591
Brunei Darussalam	..	881	865	832	796	799	819	801	802	782	822	802
Cambodia	..	-	-	-	-	-	-	-	-	-	-	-
Chinese Taipei	..	510	470	443	458	467	434	405	355	362	385	367
India	..	539	554	448	503	493	538	469	480	480	480	480
Indonesia	..	575	487	484	495	560	475	472	507	429	469	468
DPR of Korea	..	-	-	-	-	-	-	-	-	-	-	-
Malaysia	..	569	526	556	532	555	582	457	471	578	544	531
Mongolia	..	-	-	-	-	-	-	-	-	-	-	-
Myanmar	..	843	751	692	686	637	654	725	725	725	725	725
Nepal	..	-	-	-	-	-	-	-	-	-	-	-
Pakistan	..	594	464	545	550	537	529	536	526	537	536	533
Philippines	..	1 051	881	848	1 185	313	380	387	379	368	356	368
Singapore	..	447	443	454	472	449	449	488	488	488	488	488
Sri Lanka	..	-	-	-	-	-	-	-	-	-	-	-
Thailand	..	468	495	486	489	506	503	483	475	472	472	473
Vietnam	..	514	551	601	591	584	643	522	546	546	546	546
Other Asia	..	-	-	-	-	-	-	-	-	-	-	-
Asia	**..**	**545**	**518**	**506**	**514**	**526**	**523**	**482**	**485**	**490**	**491**	**489**
People's Rep. of China	..	516	415	353	334	315	304	326	325	351	370	349
Hong Kong, China	..	859	540	500	468	467	448	457	451	454	472	459
China	**..**	**524**	**477**	**426**	**388**	**375**	**360**	**367**	**365**	**378**	**397**	**380**

GLOBAL AND REGIONAL TOTALS

TOTAUX MONDIAUX ET REGIONAUX

World / Monde

Figure 1. CO₂ emissions by fuel

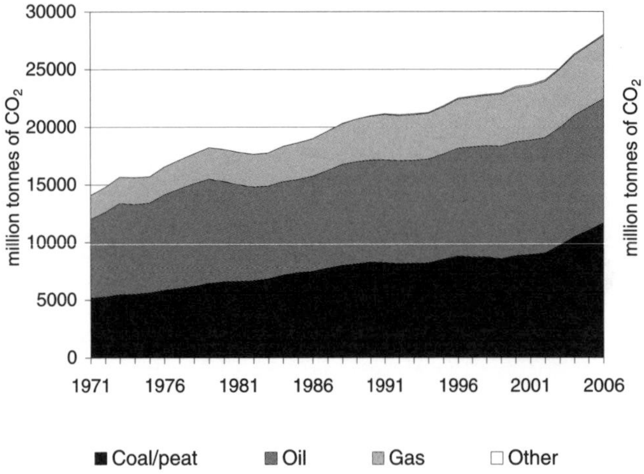

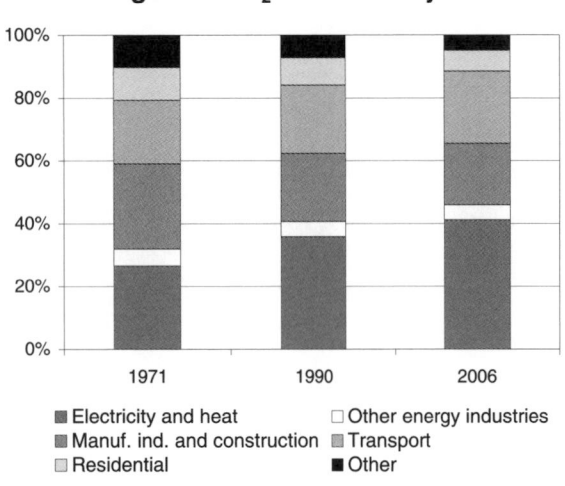

Figure 2. CO₂ emissions by sector

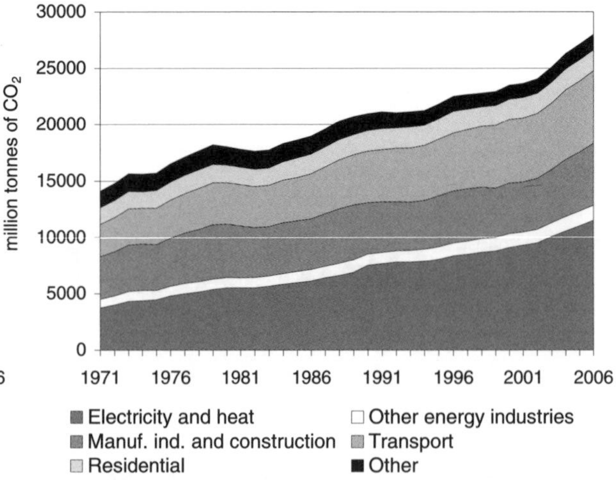

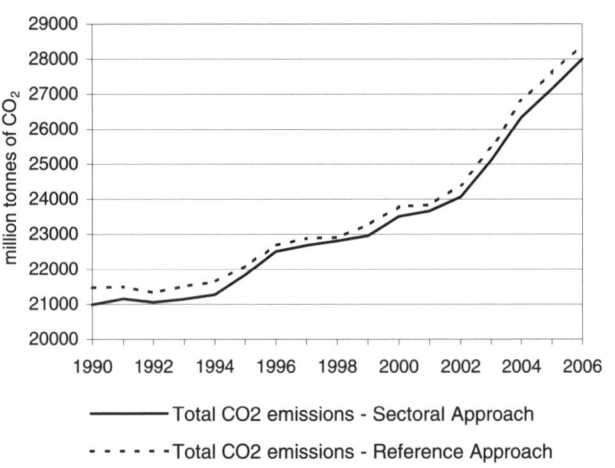

Figure 3. CO₂ emissions by sector

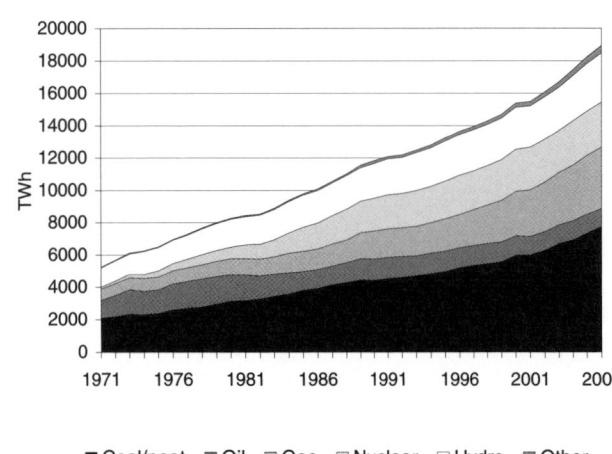

Figure 4. Reference vs Sectoral Approach

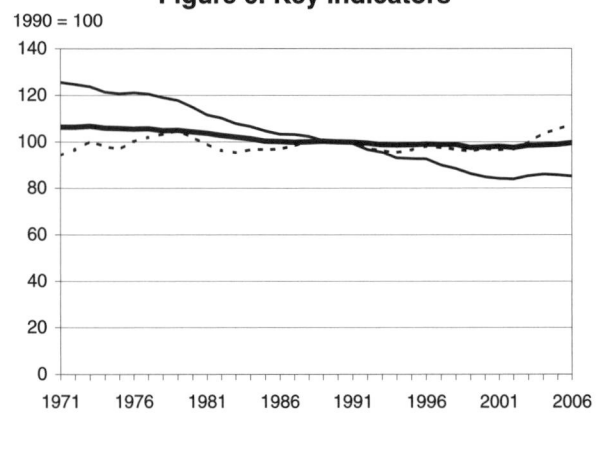

Figure 5. Electricity generation by fuel

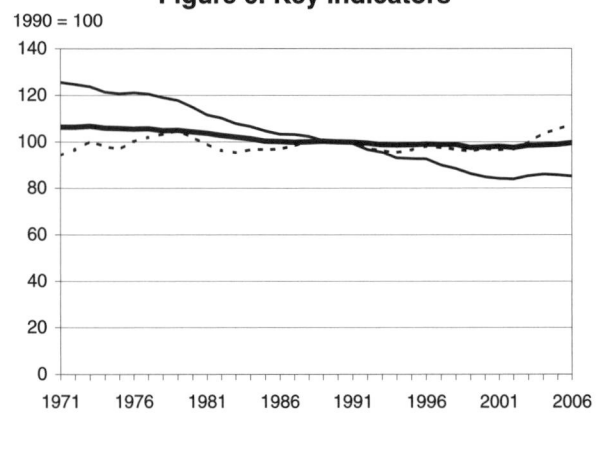

Figure 6. Key indicators

World / Monde

Key indicators

	1990	1995	2000	2003	2004	2005	2006	% change 90-06
CO$_2$ Sectoral Approach (Mt of CO$_2$)	20 987.6	21 829.0	23 508.5	25 107.8	26 331.8	27 146.3	28 002.7	33.4%
CO$_2$ Reference Approach (Mt of CO$_2$)	21 475.4	22 089.9	23 786.4	25 460.4	26 802.0	27 622.0	28 408.2	32.3%
TPES (PJ)	366 714	386 463	420 154	445 687	466 559	479 703	491 529	34.0%
TPES (Mtoe)	8 758.8	9 230.5	10 035.2	10 645.0	11 143.6	11 457.5	11 740.0	34.0%
GDP (billion 2000 US$ using exch. rates)	24 080.6	27 001.2	31 802.2	33 780.0	35 146.2	36 352.4	37 759.4	56.8%
GDP (billion 2000 US$ using PPPs)	33 070.4	37 504.6	45 240.0	49 647.5	52 222.8	54 690.8	57 564.5	74.1%
Population (millions)	5 262.4	5 675.9	6 072.8	6 305.8	6 383.0	6 459.7	6 536.0	24.2%
CO$_2$ / TPES (t CO$_2$ per TJ)	57.2	56.5	56.0	56.3	56.4	56.6	57.0	-0.5%
CO$_2$ / GDP (kg CO$_2$ per 2000 US$)	0.87	0.81	0.74	0.74	0.75	0.75	0.74	-14.9%
CO$_2$ / GDP (kg CO$_2$ per 2000 US$ PPP)	0.63	0.58	0.52	0.51	0.50	0.50	0.49	-23.3%
CO$_2$ / population (t CO$_2$ per capita)	3.99	3.85	3.87	3.98	4.13	4.20	4.28	7.4%

Ratios are based on the Sectoral Approach.

2006 CO$_2$ emissions by sector

million tonnes of CO$_2$	Coal/peat	Oil	Gas	Other *	Total	% change 90-06
Sectoral Approach	**11 686.3**	**10 768.3**	**5 444.7**	**103.4**	**28 002.7**	**33.4%**
Main activity producer elec. and heat	7 842.0	711.9	1 816.2	29.7	10 399.7	49.8%
Unallocated autoproducers	501.3	170.3	400.8	36.7	1 109.1	93.1%
Other energy industries	207.6	665.6	463.5	1.6	1 338.3	32.2%
Manufacturing industries and construction	2 670.6	1 554.0	1 220.3	32.1	5 477.1	20.8%
Transport **	14.7	6 271.5	166.6	-	6 452.8	40.9%
of which: road	-	*4 691.9*	*20.3*	-	*4 712.2*	*43.6%*
Other sectors	450.2	1 394.9	1 377.4	3.3	3 225.8	-3.5%
of which: residential	*279.2*	*650.4*	*930.0*	*0.0*	*1 859.5*	*2.3%*
Reference Approach	**11 892.1**	**10 886.7**	**5 525.1**	**104.3**	**28 408.2**	**32.3%**
Diff. due to losses and/or transformation	218.8	100.2	89.0	0.9	408.9	
Statistical differences	- 13.0	18.2	- 8.6	0.0	- 3.4	
*Memo: international marine bunkers ***	-	*582.6*	-	-	*582.6*	*62.8%*
*Memo: international aviation ***	-	*397.1*	-	-	*397.1*	*55.5%*

* Other includes industrial waste and non-renewable municipal waste.
** World includes international marine bunkers and international aviation.

Key sources for CO$_2$ emissions from fuel combustion in 2006

IPCC source category	CO$_2$ emissions (Mt of CO$_2$)	% change 90-06	Level assessment (%) ***	Cumulative total (%)
Main activity prod. elec. and heat - coal/peat	7 842.0	69.1%	19.1	19.1
Road - oil	4 691.9	43.2%	11.4	30.6
Manufacturing industries - coal/peat	2 670.6	21.5%	6.5	37.1
Main activity prod. elec. and heat - gas	1 816.2	49.8%	4.4	41.5
Other transport - oil	1 579.6	40.1%	3.9	45.4
Manufacturing industries - oil	1 554.0	15.6%	3.8	49.2
Manufacturing industries - gas	1 220.3	24.0%	3.0	52.1
Residential - gas	930.0	45.2%	2.3	54.4
Non-specified other sectors - oil	744.6	1.3%	1.8	56.2
Main activity prod. elec. and heat - oil	711.9	-34.6%	1.7	58.0
Other energy industries - oil	665.6	18.1%	1.6	59.6
Memo: total CO$_2$ from fuel combustion	*28 002.7*	*33.4%*	*68.3*	*68.3*

*** Percent calculated using the total GHG estimate for CO$_2$, CH$_4$, N$_2$O, HFCs, PFCs and SF$_6$ excluding CO$_2$ emissions/removals from land use change and forestry.

Annex I Parties / Parties de l'Annexe I

Figure 1. CO$_2$ emissions by fuel

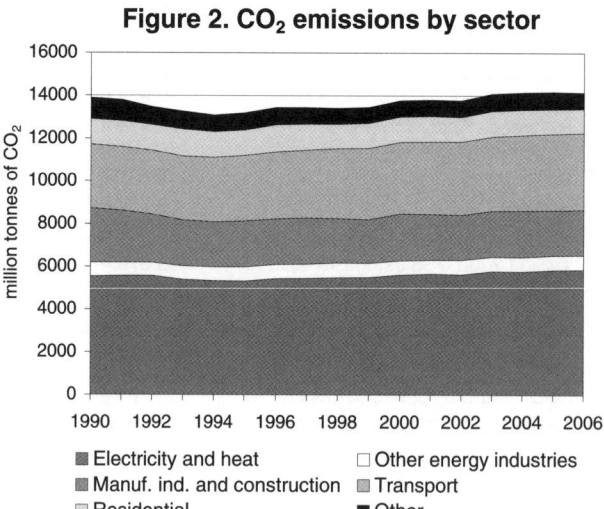

■ Coal/peat   ▨ Oil   ▨ Gas   ☐ Other

Figure 2. CO$_2$ emissions by sector

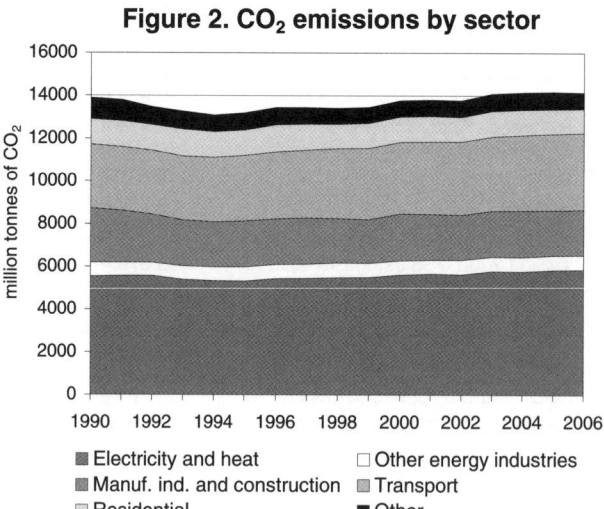

▨ Electricity and heat   ☐ Other energy industries
▨ Manuf. ind. and construction   ▨ Transport
▨ Residential   ■ Other

Figure 3. CO$_2$ emissions by sector

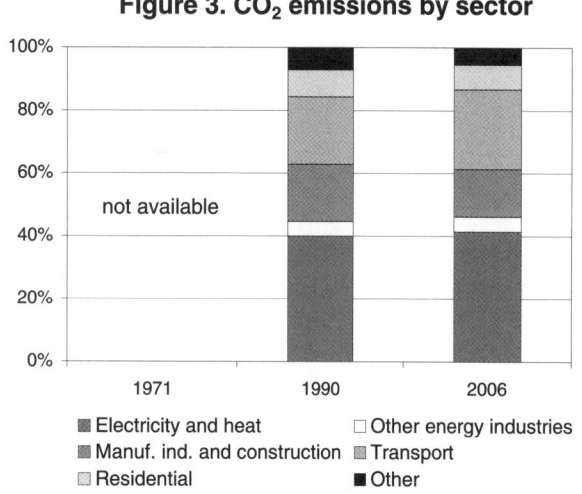

not available

▨ Electricity and heat   ☐ Other energy industries
▨ Manuf. ind. and construction   ▨ Transport
▨ Residential   ■ Other

Figure 4. Reference vs Sectoral Approach

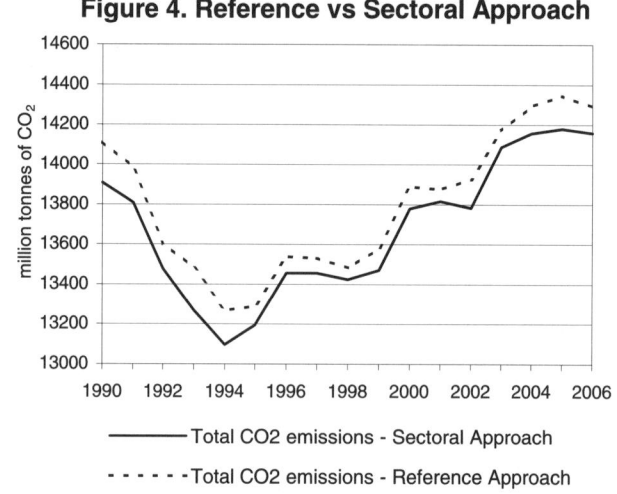

—— Total CO2 emissions - Sectoral Approach

- - - - Total CO2 emissions - Reference Approach

Figure 5. Electricity generation by fuel

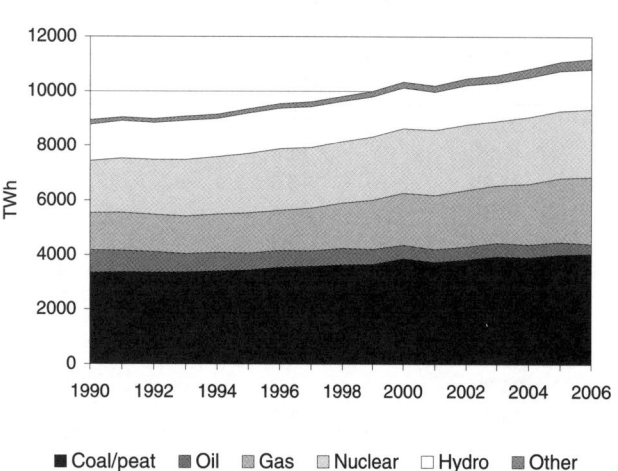

■ Coal/peat   ▨ Oil   ▨ Gas   ▨ Nuclear   ☐ Hydro   ▨ Other

Figure 6. Key indicators

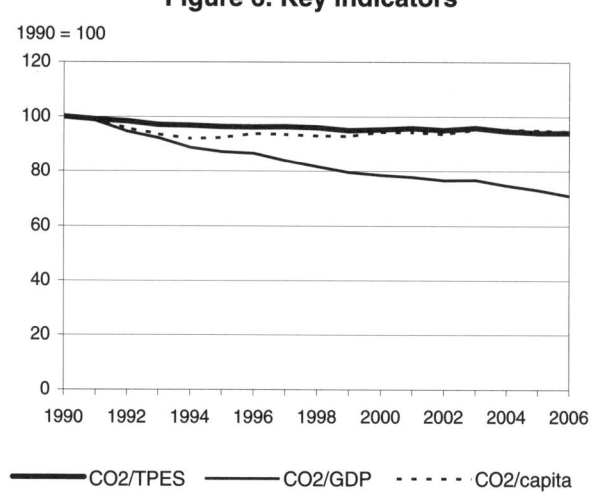

—— CO2/TPES   —— CO2/GDP   - - - - CO2/capita

Annex I Parties / Parties de l'Annexe I
Key indicators

	1990	1995	2000	2003	2004	2005	2006	% change 90-06
CO$_2$ Sectoral Approach (Mt of CO$_2$)	13 907.1	13 194.6	13 778.8	14 088.6	14 156.9	14 179.6	14 158.1	1.8%
CO$_2$ Reference Approach (Mt of CO$_2$)	14 110.9	13 287.2	13 888.4	14 172.8	14 294.0	14 345.0	14 291.9	1.3%
TPES (PJ)	235 303	231 558	244 672	248 614	252 732	254 732	254 592	8.2%
TPES (Mtoe)	5 620.1	5 530.7	5 843.9	5 938.0	6 036.4	6 084.2	6 080.8	8.2%
GDP (billion 2000 US$ using exch. rates)	19 815.1	21 547.3	25 000.0	26 142.0	26 964.3	27 639.1	28 432.1	43.5%
GDP (billion 2000 US$ using PPPs)	22 257.3	23 355.1	27 164.2	28 650.3	29 636.1	30 448.1	31 421.4	41.2%
Population (millions)	1 176.5	1 208.8	1 234.4	1 250.9	1 256.5	1 261.4	1 266.7	7.7%
CO$_2$ / TPES (t CO$_2$ per TJ)	59.1	57.0	56.3	56.7	56.0	55.7	55.6	-5.9%
CO$_2$ / GDP (kg CO$_2$ per 2000 US$)	0.70	0.61	0.55	0.54	0.53	0.51	0.50	-29.0%
CO$_2$ / GDP (kg CO$_2$ per 2000 US$ PPP)	0.62	0.57	0.51	0.49	0.48	0.47	0.45	-27.9%
CO$_2$ / population (t CO$_2$ per capita)	11.82	10.92	11.16	11.26	11.27	11.24	11.18	-5.4%

Ratios are based on the Sectoral Approach.

2006 CO$_2$ emissions by sector

million tonnes of CO$_2$	Coal/peat	Oil	Gas	Other *	Total	% change 90-06
Sectoral Approach	**4 824.6**	**5 595.1**	**3 644.5**	**93.9**	**14 158.1**	**1.8%**
Main activity producer elec. and heat	3 736.3	199.4	1 133.7	29.7	5 099.1	-0.1%
Unallocated autoproducers	300.8	101.3	323.0	34.0	759.1	71.5%
Other energy industries	71.3	390.7	209.4	1.6	672.9	3.7%
Manufacturing industries and construction	615.9	741.3	759.5	25.8	2 142.5	-15.4%
Transport	0.3	3 464.1	134.4	-	3 598.8	20.2%
of which: road	-	*3 050.3*	*3.1*	-	*3 053.4*	*25.5%*
Other sectors	100.0	698.3	1 084.5	2.8	1 885.7	-13.7%
of which: residential	*69.2*	*319.2*	*724.2*	*0.0*	*1 112.7*	*-6.9%*
Reference Approach	**4 884.2**	**5 638.3**	**3 674.6**	**94.8**	**14 291.9**	**1.3%**
Diff. due to losses and/or transformation	16.4	11.3	28.5	0.9	57.0	
Statistical differences	43.2	31.9	1.6	0.0	76.8	
Memo: international marine bunkers	-	*287.4*	-	-	*287.4*	*23.0%*
Memo: international aviation	-	*230.4*	-	-	*230.4*	*41.0%*

* Other includes industrial waste and non-renewable municipal waste.

Key sources for CO$_2$ emissions from fuel combustion in 2006

IPCC source category	CO$_2$ emissions (Mt of CO$_2$)	% change 90-06	Level assessment (%) **	Cumulative total (%)
Main activity prod. elec. and heat - coal/peat	3 736.3	9.2%	20.4	20.4
Road - oil	3 050.3	25.5%	16.6	37.0
Main activity prod. elec. and heat - gas	1 133.7	14.3%	6.2	43.2
Manufacturing industries - gas	759.5	-0.8%	4.1	47.3
Manufacturing industries - oil	741.3	-8.8%	4.0	51.4
Residential - gas	724.2	20.8%	4.0	55.3
Manufacturing industries - coal/peat	615.9	-35.0%	3.4	58.7
Other transport - oil	413.8	-5.6%	2.3	61.0
Other energy industries - oil	390.7	-1.6%	2.1	63.1
Non-specified other sectors - oil	379.0	-20.5%	2.1	65.2
Non-specified other sectors - gas	360.3	24.1%	2.0	67.1
Memo: total CO$_2$ from fuel combustion	*14 158.1*	*1.8%*	*77.2*	*77.2*

** Percent calculated using the total GHG estimate for CO$_2$, CH$_4$, N$_2$O, HFCs, PFCs and SF$_6$ excluding CO$_2$ emissions/removals from land use change and forestry.

Annex II Parties / Parties de l'Annexe II

Figure 1. CO_2 emissions by fuel

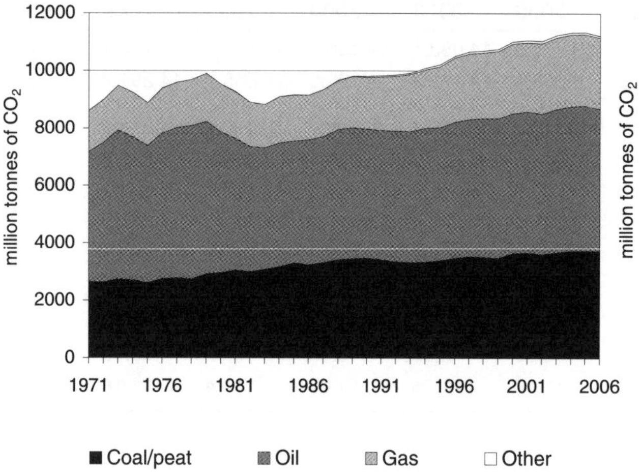
million tonnes of CO2
Coal/peat
Oil
Gas
Other

Figure 2. CO_2 emissions by sector

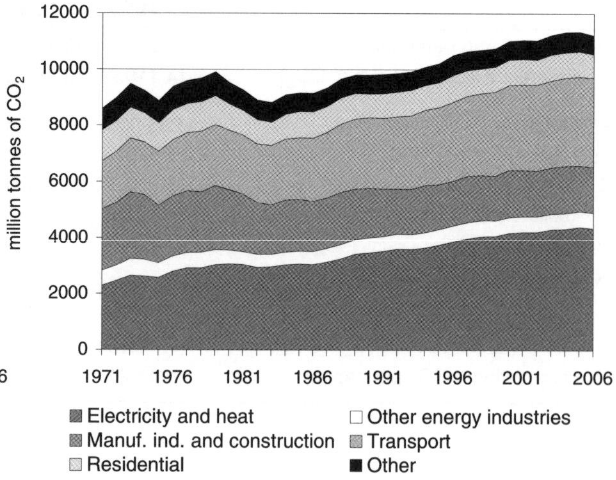
million tonnes of CO2
Electricity and heat
Other energy industries
Manuf. ind. and construction
Transport
Residential
Other

Figure 3. CO_2 emissions by sector

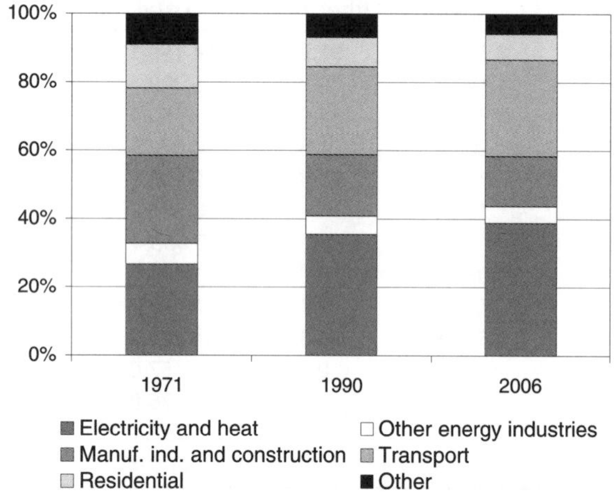
Electricity and heat
Other energy industries
Manuf. ind. and construction
Transport
Residential
Other

Figure 4. Reference vs Sectoral Approach

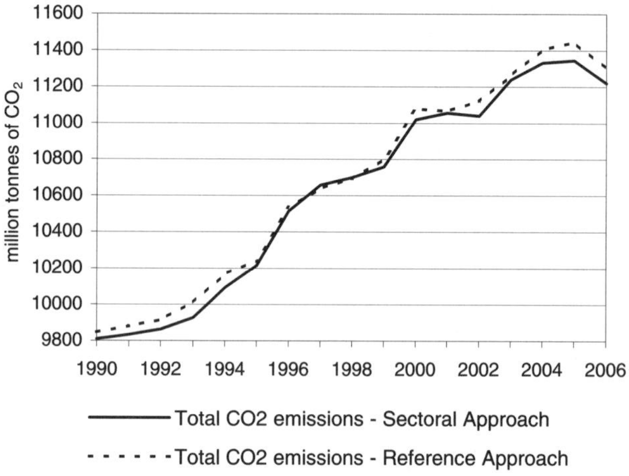
million tonnes of CO2
Total CO2 emissions - Sectoral Approach
Total CO2 emissions - Reference Approach

Figure 5. Electricity generation by fuel

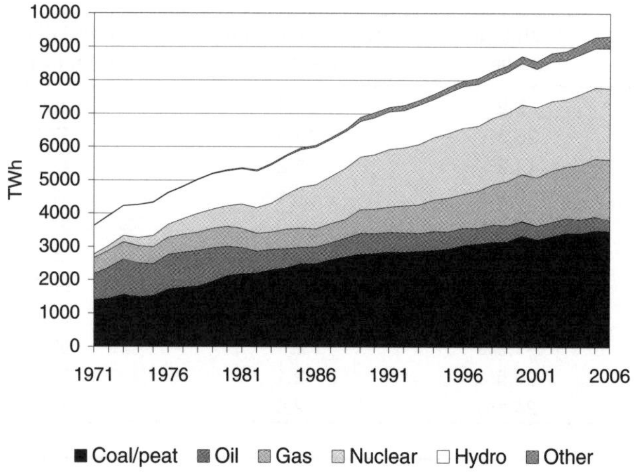
TWh
Coal/peat
Oil
Gas
Nuclear
Hydro
Other

Figure 6. Key indicators

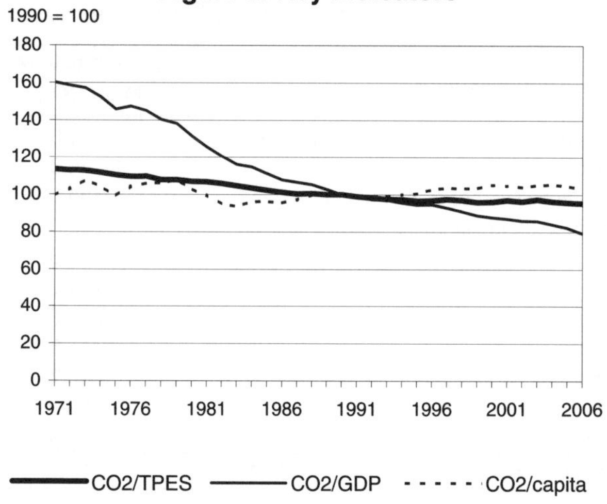
1990 = 100
CO2/TPES
CO2/GDP
CO2/capita

Annex II Parties / Parties de l'Annexe II

Key indicators

	1990	1995	2000	2003	2004	2005	2006	% change 90-06
CO_2 Sectoral Approach (Mt of CO_2)	9 809.8	10 213.9	11 018.7	11 238.7	11 332.8	11 345.1	11 220.8	14.4%
CO_2 Reference Approach (Mt of CO_2)	9 846.5	10 241.4	11 080.0	11 265.3	11 406.5	11 445.9	11 303.2	14.8%
TPES (PJ)	169 722	182 783	198 303	199 878	203 757	204 934	203 455	19.9%
TPES (Mtoe)	4 053.7	4 365.7	4 736.4	4 774.0	4 866.6	4 894.8	4 859.5	19.9%
GDP (billion 2000 US$ using exch. rates)	18 836.7	20 755.1	24 088.4	25 118.2	25 868.0	26 479.4	27 197.4	44.4%
GDP (billion 2000 US$ using PPPs)	18 940.6	20 882.4	24 392.0	25 491.0	26 244.2	26 862.7	27 599.7	45.7%
Population (millions)	799.2	827.7	853.1	870.9	876.7	882.5	888.1	11.1%
CO_2 / TPES (t CO_2 per TJ)	57.8	55.9	55.6	56.2	55.6	55.4	55.2	-4.6%
CO_2 / GDP (kg CO_2 per 2000 US$)	0.52	0.49	0.46	0.45	0.44	0.43	0.41	-20.8%
CO_2 / GDP (kg CO_2 per 2000 US$ PPP)	0.52	0.49	0.45	0.44	0.43	0.42	0.41	-21.5%
CO_2 / population (t CO_2 per capita)	12.27	12.34	12.92	12.91	12.93	12.86	12.64	2.9%

Ratios are based on the Sectoral Approach.

2006 CO_2 emissions by sector

million tonnes of CO_2	Coal/peat	Oil	Gas	Other *	Total	% change 90-06
Sectoral Approach	**3 727.3**	**4 948.4**	**2 473.8**	**71.3**	**11 220.8**	**14.4%**
Main activity producer elec. and heat	3 118.0	167.6	700.6	29.3	4 015.5	26.2%
Unallocated autoproducers	134.4	62.2	116.0	18.7	331.2	13.3%
Other energy industries	52.2	331.4	175.9	-	559.5	5.6%
Manufacturing industries and construction	400.5	642.1	565.9	20.6	1 629.2	-7.2%
Transport	0.3	3 132.2	45.4	-	3 177.9	25.6%
of which: road	-	2 758.7	2.8	-	2 761.5	29.5%
Other sectors	21.9	613.0	870.0	2.7	1 507.6	-0.8%
of which: residential	10.4	283.8	547.1	0.0	841.3	-0.3%
Reference Approach	**3 781.2**	**4 970.9**	**2 479.7**	**71.3**	**11 303.2**	**14.8%**
Diff. due to losses and/or transformation	15.9	- 8.3	5.0	-	12.6	
Statistical differences	38.0	30.8	1.0	0.0	69.8	
Memo: international marine bunkers	-	281.2	-	-	281.2	25.8%
Memo: international aviation	-	205.6	-	-	205.6	62.8%

* Other includes industrial waste and non-renewable municipal waste.

Key sources for CO_2 emissions from fuel combustion in 2006

IPCC source category	CO_2 emissions (Mt of CO_2)	% change 90-06	Level assessment (%) **	Cumulative total (%)
Main activity prod. elec. and heat - coal/peat	3 118.0	23.5%	22.3	22.3
Road - oil	2 758.7	29.4%	19.7	42.0
Main activity prod. elec. and heat - gas	700.6	131.8%	5.0	47.0
Manufacturing industries - oil	642.1	6.0%	4.6	51.6
Manufacturing industries - gas	565.9	8.3%	4.0	55.6
Residential - gas	547.1	22.8%	3.9	59.5
Manufacturing industries - coal/peat	400.5	-35.6%	2.9	62.4
Other transport - oil	373.5	5.7%	2.7	65.1
Other energy industries - oil	331.4	0.2%	2.4	67.4
Non-specified other sectors - oil	329.2	-7.8%	2.4	69.8
Non-specified other sectors - gas	322.9	29.6%	2.3	72.1
Memo: total CO_2 from fuel combustion	11 220.8	14.4%	80.2	80.2

** Percent calculated using the total GHG estimate for CO_2, CH_4, N_2O, HFCs, PFCs and SF_6 excluding CO_2 emissions/removals from land use change and forestry.

Annex II: North America / Annexe II: Amérique du Nord

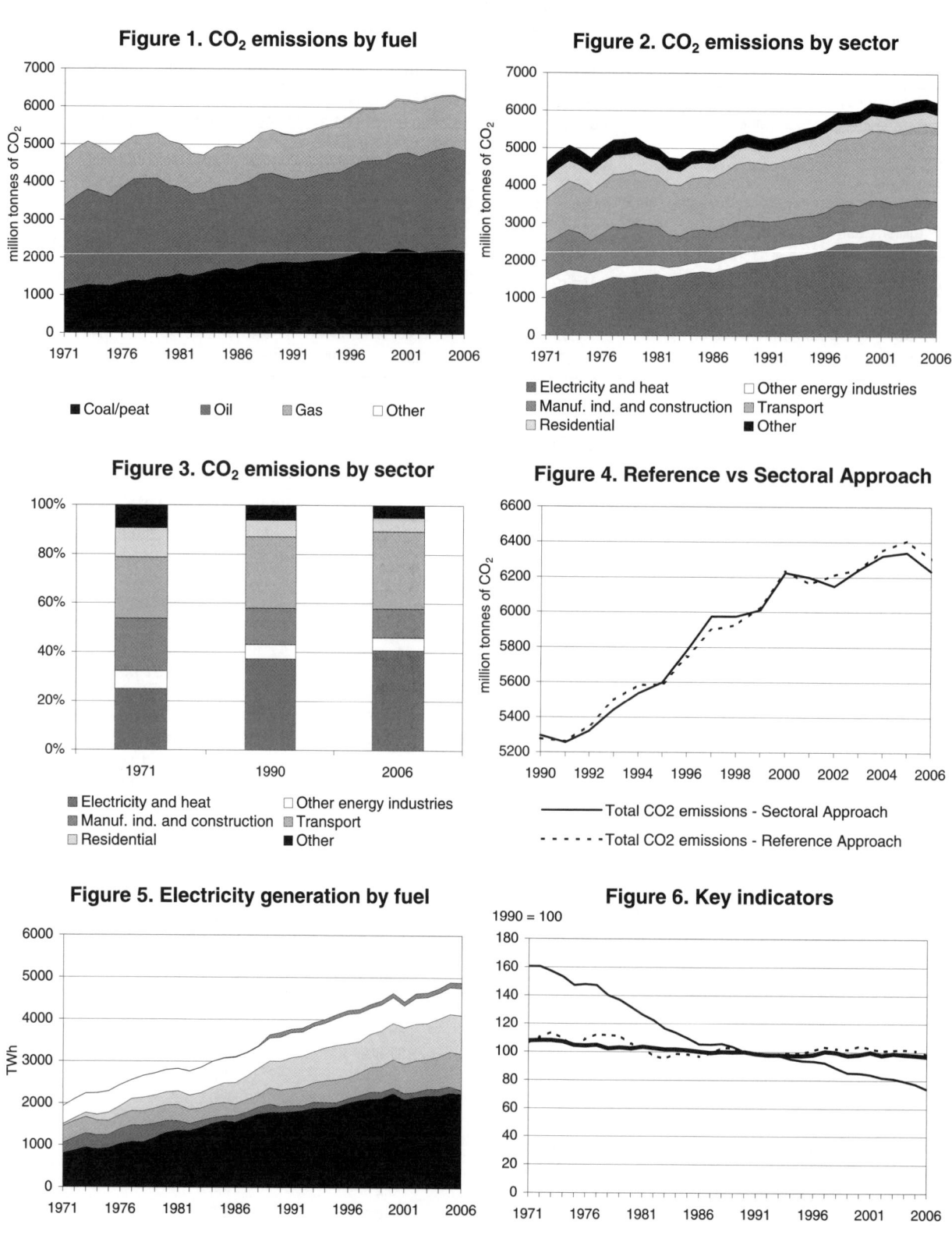

Figure 1. CO$_2$ emissions by fuel

Figure 2. CO$_2$ emissions by sector

Figure 3. CO$_2$ emissions by sector

Figure 4. Reference vs Sectoral Approach

Figure 5. Electricity generation by fuel

Figure 6. Key indicators

Annex II: North America / Annexe II: Amérique du Nord
Key indicators

	1990	1995	2000	2003	2004	2005	2006	% change 90-06
CO$_2$ Sectoral Approach (Mt of CO$_2$)	5 295.5	5 598.4	6 225.6	6 243.0	6 322.8	6 340.8	6 235.6	17.8%
CO$_2$ Reference Approach (Mt of CO$_2$)	5 277.2	5 587.4	6 232.9	6 246.8	6 353.5	6 408.7	6 306.9	19.5%
TPES (PJ)	89 420	97 071	106 958	106 482	108 728	109 507	108 457	21.3%
TPES (Mtoe)	2 135.8	2 318.5	2 554.6	2 543.3	2 596.9	2 615.5	2 590.4	21.3%
GDP (billion 2000 US$ using exch. rates)	7 598.6	8 564.9	10 489.7	11 023.5	11 421.4	11 772.5	12 109.8	59.4%
GDP (billion 2000 US$ using PPPs)	7 709.6	8 685.7	10 637.7	11 181.5	11 584.2	11 940.3	12 282.2	59.3%
Population (millions)	277.9	295.9	313.1	323.0	326.1	329.3	332.5	19.6%
CO$_2$ / TPES (t CO$_2$ per TJ)	59.2	57.7	58.2	58.6	58.2	57.9	57.5	-2.9%
CO$_2$ / GDP (kg CO$_2$ per 2000 US$)	0.70	0.65	0.59	0.57	0.55	0.54	0.51	-26.1%
CO$_2$ / GDP (kg CO$_2$ per 2000 US$ PPP)	0.69	0.64	0.59	0.56	0.55	0.53	0.51	-26.1%
CO$_2$ / population (t CO$_2$ per capita)	19.06	18.92	19.88	19.33	19.39	19.26	18.76	-1.6%

Ratios are based on the Sectoral Approach.

2006 CO$_2$ emissions by sector

million tonnes of CO$_2$	Coal/peat	Oil	Gas	Other *	Total	% change 90-06
Sectoral Approach	**2 197.2**	**2 674.5**	**1 336.8**	**27.0**	**6 235.6**	**17.8%**
Main activity producer elec. and heat	2 015.0	59.9	351.5	13.6	2 440.0	30.5%
Unallocated autoproducers	31.2	13.4	46.3	4.8	95.7	0.5%
Other energy industries	13.3	186.4	134.0	-	333.7	5.8%
Manufacturing industries and construction	132.4	274.7	316.9	7.9	731.9	-6.6%
Transport	-	1 926.0	42.8	-	1 968.8	27.5%
of which: road	*-*	*1 649.8*	*1.5*	*-*	*1 651.2*	*33.9%*
Other sectors	5.4	214.0	445.4	0.8	665.5	-3.2%
of which: residential	*0.2*	*77.9*	*269.0*	*-*	*347.1*	*-4.8%*
Reference Approach	**2 264.7**	**2 670.6**	**1 344.5**	**27.0**	**6 306.9**	**19.5%**
Diff. due to losses and/or transformation	9.4	- 38.4	1.4	-	- 27.6	
Statistical differences	58.1	34.5	6.3	0.0	98.9	
Memo: international marine bunkers	*-*	*89.9*	*-*	*-*	*89.9*	*-3.9%*
Memo: international aviation	*-*	*50.4*	*-*	*-*	*50.4*	*21.5%*

* Other includes industrial waste and non-renewable municipal waste.

Key sources for CO$_2$ emissions from fuel combustion in 2006

IPCC source category	CO$_2$ emissions (Mt of CO$_2$)	% change 90-06	Level assessment (%) **	Cumulative total (%)
Main activity prod. elec. and heat - coal/peat	2 015.0	24.7%	26.3	26.3
Road - oil	1 649.8	33.8%	21.5	47.7
Main activity prod. elec. and heat - gas	351.5	125.9%	4.6	52.3
Manufacturing industries - gas	316.9	-2.0%	4.1	56.5
Other transport - oil	276.3	3.2%	3.6	60.1
Manufacturing industries - oil	274.7	13.3%	3.6	63.6
Residential - gas	269.0	1.1%	3.5	67.1
Other energy industries - oil	186.4	-0.5%	2.4	69.6
Non-specified other sectors - gas	176.4	7.7%	2.3	71.9
Non-specified other sectors - oil	136.1	6.4%	1.8	73.6
Other energy industries - gas	134.0	7.2%	1.7	75.4
Memo: total CO$_2$ from fuel combustion	*6 235.6*	*17.8%*	*81.2*	*81.2*

** Percent calculated using the total GHG estimate for CO$_2$, CH$_4$, N$_2$O, HFCs, PFCs and SF$_6$ excluding CO$_2$ emissions/removals from land use change and forestry.

Annex II: Europe / Annexe II: Europe

Figure 1. CO$_2$ emissions by fuel

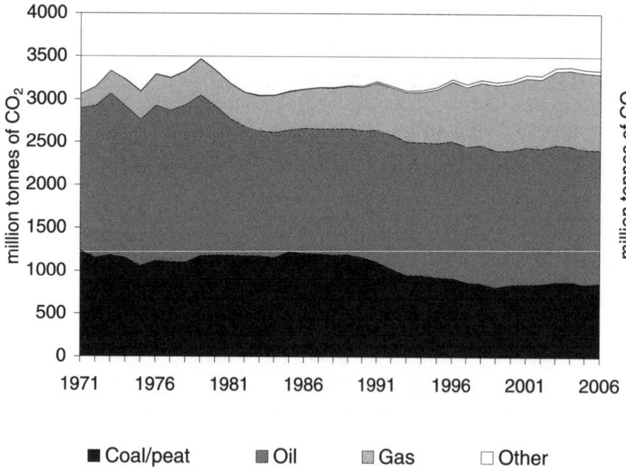

Legend: ■ Coal/peat ■ Oil ■ Gas □ Other

Figure 2. CO$_2$ emissions by sector

Legend: ■ Electricity and heat □ Other energy industries ■ Manuf. ind. and construction ■ Transport □ Residential ■ Other

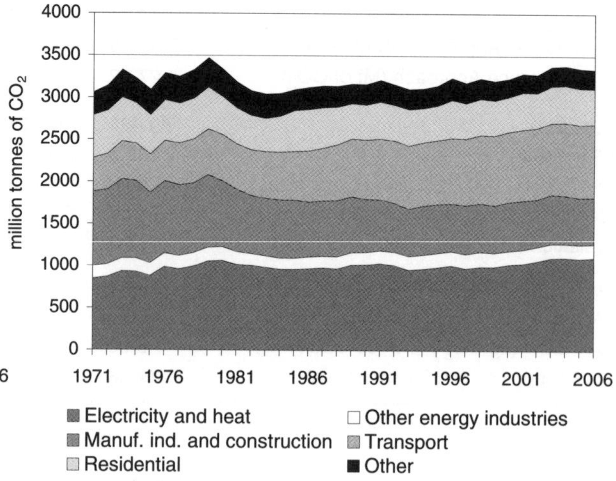

Figure 3. CO$_2$ emissions by sector

Legend: ■ Electricity and heat □ Other energy industries ■ Manuf. ind. and construction ■ Transport □ Residential ■ Other

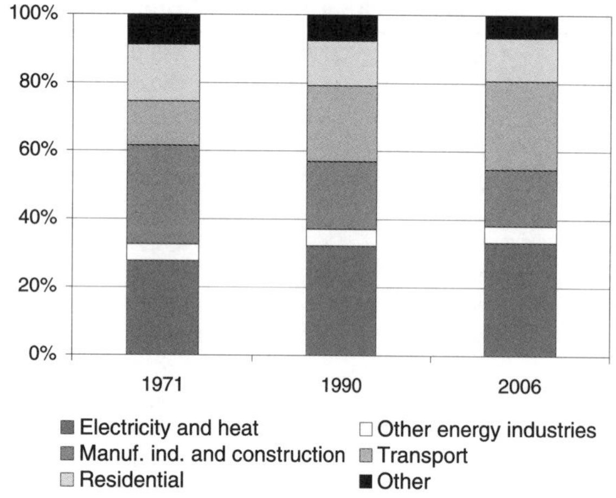

Figure 4. Reference vs Sectoral Approach

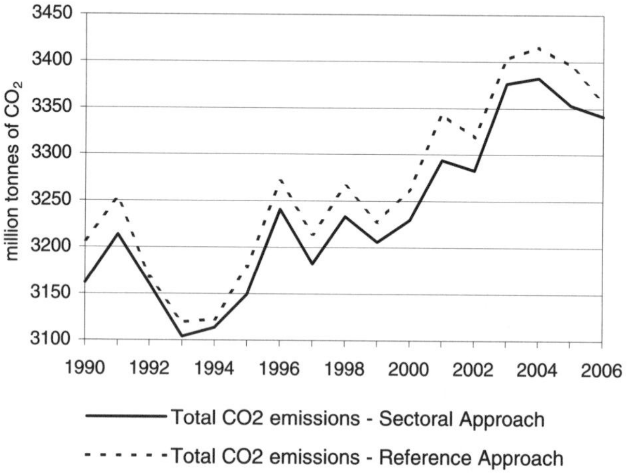

Legend: —— Total CO2 emissions - Sectoral Approach ----- Total CO2 emissions - Reference Approach

Figure 5. Electricity generation by fuel

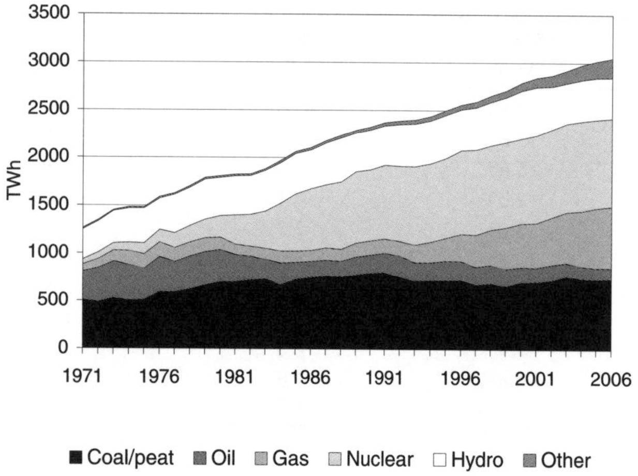

Legend: ■ Coal/peat ■ Oil ■ Gas ■ Nuclear □ Hydro ■ Other

Figure 6. Key indicators

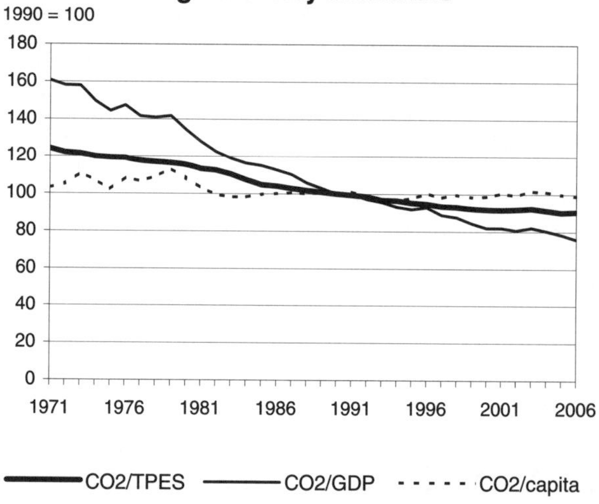

1990 = 100

Legend: —— CO2/TPES —— CO2/GDP ----- CO2/capita

Annex II: Europe / Annexe II: Europe

Key indicators

	1990	1995	2000	2003	2004	2005	2006	% change 90-06
CO$_2$ Sectoral Approach (Mt of CO$_2$)	3 161.6	3 149.2	3 229.7	3 376.2	3 382.5	3 353.2	3 341.3	5.7%
CO$_2$ Reference Approach (Mt of CO$_2$)	3 207.0	3 178.5	3 263.2	3 402.9	3 415.4	3 396.1	3 357.3	4.7%
TPES (PJ)	57 469	60 127	63 911	66 420	67 334	67 524	67 049	16.7%
TPES (Mtoe)	1 372.6	1 436.1	1 526.5	1 586.4	1 608.2	1 612.8	1 601.4	16.7%
GDP (billion 2000 US$ using exch. rates)	6 794.9	7 368.3	8 478.9	8 836.0	9 043.3	9 196.4	9 455.5	39.2%
GDP (billion 2000 US$ using PPPs)	7 934.4	8 600.9	9 903.3	10 328.6	10 569.4	10 748.2	11 050.7	39.3%
Population (millions)	377.3	384.4	390.0	396.2	398.6	400.9	403.0	6.8%
CO$_2$ / TPES (t CO$_2$ per TJ)	55.0	52.4	50.5	50.8	50.2	49.7	49.8	-9.4%
CO$_2$ / GDP (kg CO$_2$ per 2000 US$)	0.47	0.43	0.38	0.38	0.37	0.36	0.35	-24.0%
CO$_2$ / GDP (kg CO$_2$ per 2000 US$ PPP)	0.40	0.37	0.33	0.33	0.32	0.31	0.30	-24.1%
CO$_2$ / population (t CO$_2$ per capita)	8.38	8.19	8.28	8.52	8.49	8.36	8.29	-1.0%

Ratios are based on the Sectoral Approach.

2006 CO$_2$ emissions by sector

million tonnes of CO$_2$	Coal/peat	Oil	Gas	Other *	Total	% change 90-06
Sectoral Approach	**860.8**	**1 556.7**	**884.5**	**39.3**	**3 341.3**	**5.7%**
Main activity producer elec. and heat	664.3	60.7	222.1	14.4	961.5	9.2%
Unallocated autoproducers	50.7	24.9	58.3	11.6	145.5	7.6%
Other energy industries	21.8	109.1	33.5	-	164.4	6.9%
Manufacturing industries and construction	110.9	220.8	208.8	11.3	551.9	-11.9%
Transport	-	869.5	1.7	-	871.2	23.4%
of which: road	-	*808.9*	*1.2*	-	*810.1*	*24.5%*
Other sectors	13.1	271.8	360.0	1.9	646.8	-1.9%
of which: residential	*10.1*	*163.0*	*249.4*	*0.0*	*422.6*	*1.3%*
Reference Approach	**859.4**	**1 565.7**	**893.0**	**39.3**	**3 357.3**	**4.7%**
Diff. due to losses and/or transformation	6.2	20.9	5.9	-	33.1	
Statistical differences	- 7.6	- 11.9	2.5	0.0	- 17.0	
Memo: international marine bunkers	-	*168.5*	-	-	*168.5*	*54.5%*
Memo: international aviation	-	*125.7*	-	-	*125.7*	*91.0%*

* Other includes industrial waste and non-renewable municipal waste.

Key sources for CO$_2$ emissions from fuel combustion in 2006

IPCC source category	CO$_2$ emissions (Mt of CO$_2$)	% change 90-06	Level assessment (%) **	Cumulative total (%)
Road - oil	808.9	24.4%	18.8	18.8
Main activity prod. elec. and heat - coal/peat	664.3	-4.7%	15.4	34.2
Residential - gas	249.4	58.5%	5.8	40.0
Main activity prod. elec. and heat - gas	222.1	274.1%	5.2	45.2
Manufacturing industries - oil	220.8	3.2%	5.1	50.3
Manufacturing industries - gas	208.8	19.8%	4.8	55.1
Residential - oil	163.0	-11.9%	3.8	58.9
Manufacturing industries - coal/peat	110.9	-52.6%	2.6	61.5
Non-specified other sectors - gas	110.5	48.6%	2.6	64.1
Other energy industries - oil	109.1	2.7%	2.5	66.6
Non-specified other sectors - oil	108.7	-19.1%	2.5	69.1
Memo: total CO$_2$ from fuel combustion	*3 341.3*	*5.7%*	*77.6*	*77.6*

** Percent calculated using the total GHG estimate for CO$_2$, CH$_4$, N$_2$O, HFCs, PFCs and SF$_6$ excluding CO$_2$ emissions/removals from land use change and forestry.

Annex II: Pacific / Annexe II: Pacifique

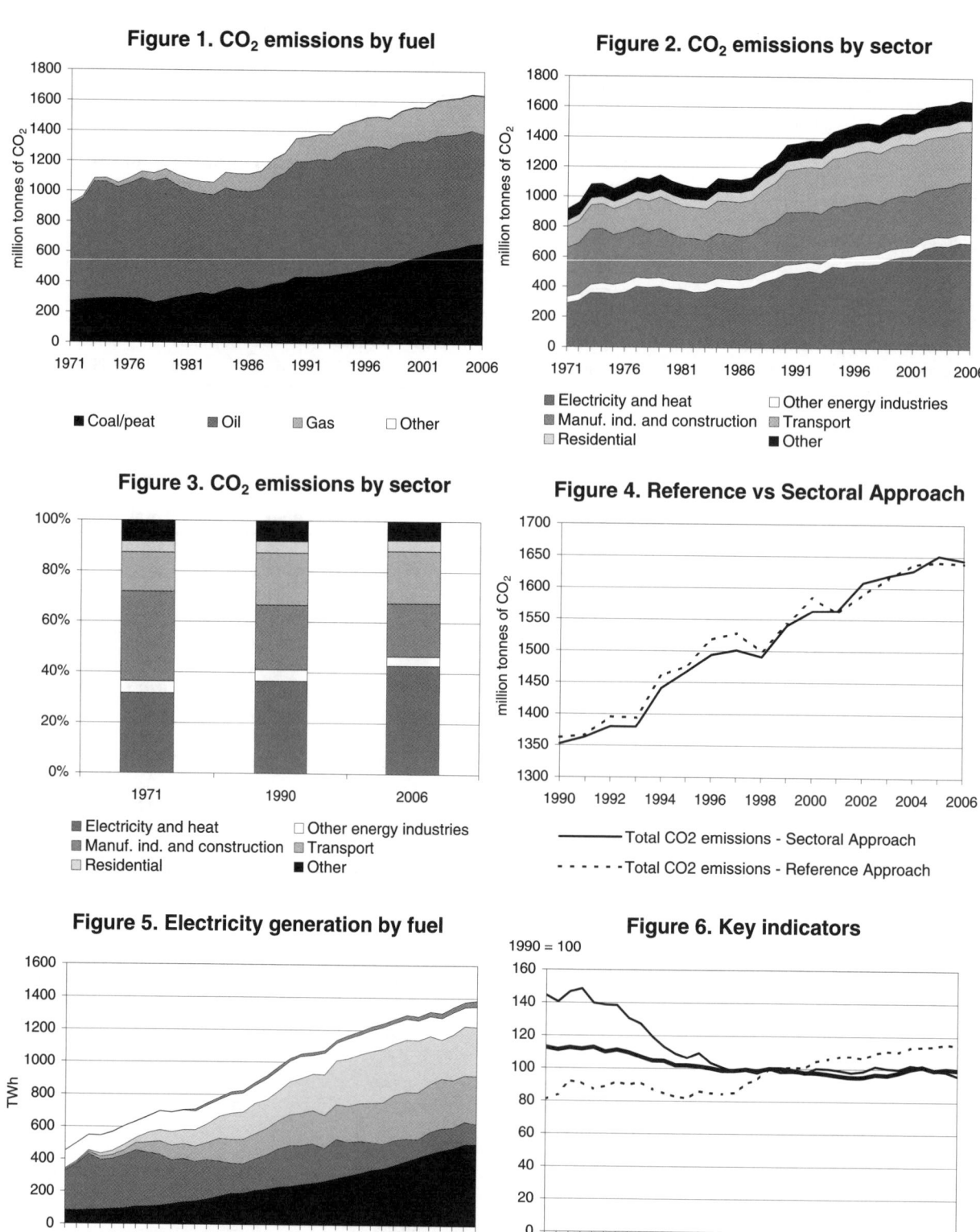

Figure 1. CO$_2$ emissions by fuel

Coal/peat ■   Oil ■   Gas ■   Other □

Figure 2. CO$_2$ emissions by sector

Electricity and heat ■   Other energy industries □
Manuf. ind. and construction ■   Transport ■
Residential □   Other ■

Figure 3. CO$_2$ emissions by sector

Electricity and heat ■   Other energy industries □
Manuf. ind. and construction ■   Transport ■
Residential □   Other ■

Figure 4. Reference vs Sectoral Approach

—— Total CO2 emissions - Sectoral Approach
- - - - Total CO2 emissions - Reference Approach

Figure 5. Electricity generation by fuel

Coal/peat ■   Oil ■   Gas ■   Nuclear □   Hydro □   Other ■

Figure 6. Key indicators

1990 = 100

—— CO2/TPES   —— CO2/GDP   - - - - CO2/capita

Annex II: Pacific / Annexe II: Pacifique
Key indicators

	1990	1995	2000	2003	2004	2005	2006	% change 90-06
CO_2 Sectoral Approach (Mt of CO_2)	1 352.6	1 466.3	1 563.3	1 619.6	1 627.5	1 651.1	1 643.9	21.5%
CO_2 Reference Approach (Mt of CO_2)	1 362.3	1 475.4	1 583.8	1 615.5	1 637.7	1 641.1	1 639.0	20.3%
TPES (PJ)	22 833	25 585	27 435	26 976	27 695	27 902	27 950	22.4%
TPES (Mtoe)	545.4	611.1	655.3	644.3	661.5	666.4	667.6	22.4%
GDP (billion 2000 US$ using exch. rates)	4 443.2	4 821.9	5 119.8	5 258.7	5 403.3	5 510.5	5 632.1	26.8%
GDP (billion 2000 US$ using PPPs)	3 296.6	3 595.8	3 851.0	3 980.9	4 090.6	4 174.1	4 266.8	29.4%
Population (millions)	144.0	147.3	150.0	151.7	152.0	152.3	152.6	6.0%
CO_2 / TPES (t CO_2 per TJ)	59.2	57.3	57.0	60.0	58.8	59.2	58.8	-0.7%
CO_2 / GDP (kg CO_2 per 2000 US$)	0.30	0.30	0.31	0.31	0.30	0.30	0.29	-4.1%
CO_2 / GDP (kg CO_2 per 2000 US$ PPP)	0.41	0.41	0.41	0.41	0.40	0.40	0.39	-6.1%
CO_2 / population (t CO_2 per capita)	9.39	9.95	10.42	10.68	10.71	10.84	10.77	14.7%

Ratios are based on the Sectoral Approach.

2006 CO_2 emissions by sector

million tonnes of CO_2	Coal/peat	Oil	Gas	Other *	Total	% change 90-06
Sectoral Approach	**669.3**	**717.2**	**252.5**	**5.0**	**1 643.9**	**21.5%**
Main activity producer elec. and heat	438.8	47.0	127.0	1.2	614.0	42.1%
Unallocated autoproducers	52.4	23.9	11.4	2.3	90.0	45.0%
Other energy industries	17.1	35.8	8.4	-	61.4	0.8%
Manufacturing industries and construction	157.2	146.6	40.2	1.4	345.4	-0.1%
Transport	0.3	336.7	0.9	-	337.9	20.8%
of which: road	-	*300.1*	*0.1*	-	*300.2*	*20.6%*
Other sectors	3.4	127.2	64.6	-	195.3	13.3%
of which: residential	*0.1*	*42.9*	*28.6*	-	*71.6*	*15.9%*
Reference Approach	**657.1**	**734.6**	**242.2**	**5.0**	**1 639.0**	**20.3%**
Diff. due to losses and/or transformation	0.3	9.2	- 2.4	-	7.1	
Statistical differences	- 12.5	8.2	- 7.8	0.0	- 12.1	
Memo: international marine bunkers	-	*22.8*	-	-	*22.8*	*9.4%*
Memo: international aviation	-	*29.5*	-	-	*29.5*	*55.7%*

* Other includes industrial waste and non-renewable municipal waste.

Key sources for CO_2 emissions from fuel combustion in 2006

IPCC source category	CO_2 emissions (Mt of CO_2)	% change 90-06	Level assessment (%) **	Cumulative total (%)
Main activity prod. elec. and heat - coal/peat	438.8	107.5%	21.7	21.7
Road - oil	300.1	20.6%	14.9	36.6
Manufacturing industries - coal/peat	157.2	-7.8%	7.8	44.4
Manufacturing industries - oil	146.6	-2.0%	7.3	51.7
Main activity prod. elec. and heat - gas	127.0	45.6%	6.3	58.0
Non-specified other sectors - oil	84.3	-11.1%	4.2	62.1
Unallocated autoproducers - coal/peat	52.4	56.7%	2.6	64.7
Main activity prod. elec. and heat - oil	47.0	-64.7%	2.3	67.1
Residential - oil	42.9	8.7%	2.1	69.2
Manufacturing industries - gas	40.2	61.6%	2.0	71.2
Other transport - oil	36.6	20.3%	1.8	73.0
Memo: total CO_2 from fuel combustion	*1 643.9*	*21.5%*	*81.5*	*81.5*

** Percent calculated using the total GHG estimate for CO_2, CH_4, N_2O, HFCs, PFCs and SF_6 excluding CO_2 emissions/removals from land use change and forestry.

Economies in Transition / Economies en transition

Figure 1. CO$_2$ emissions by fuel

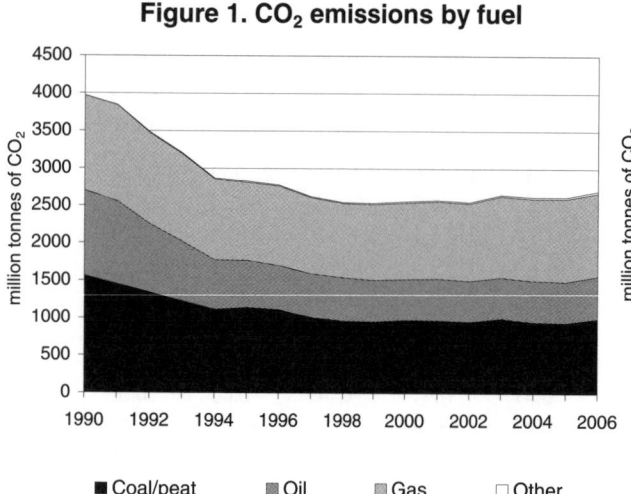

■ Coal/peat   ▨ Oil   ▨ Gas   ☐ Other

Figure 2. CO$_2$ emissions by sector

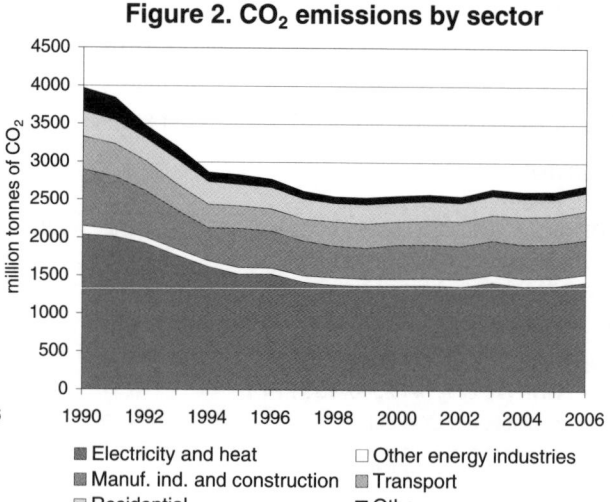

■ Electricity and heat   ☐ Other energy industries
■ Manuf. ind. and construction ▨ Transport
☐ Residential   ■ Other

Figure 3. CO$_2$ emissions by sector

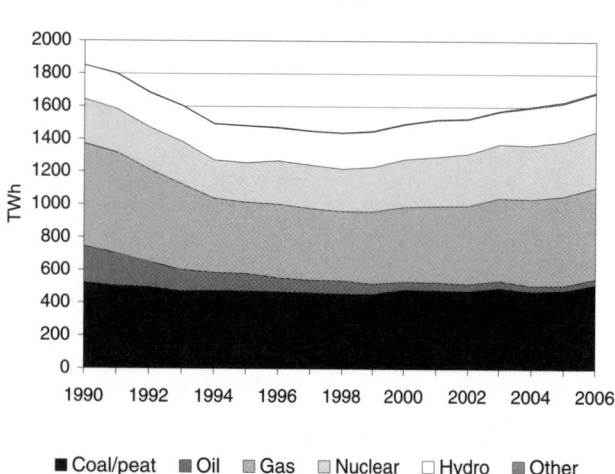

■ Electricity and heat   ☐ Other energy industries
■ Manuf. ind. and construction ▨ Transport
☐ Residential   ■ Other

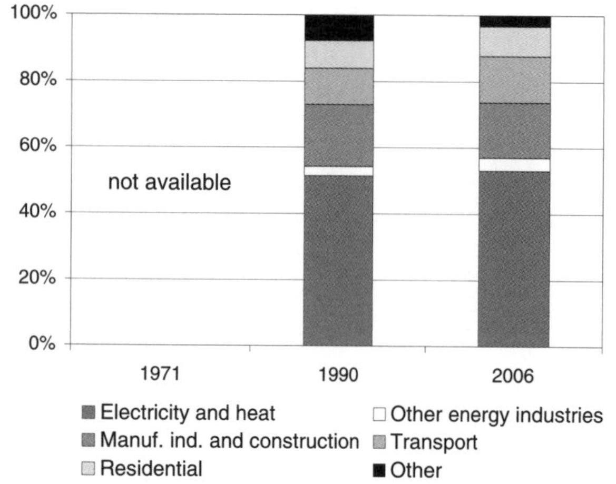

Figure 4. Reference vs Sectoral Approach

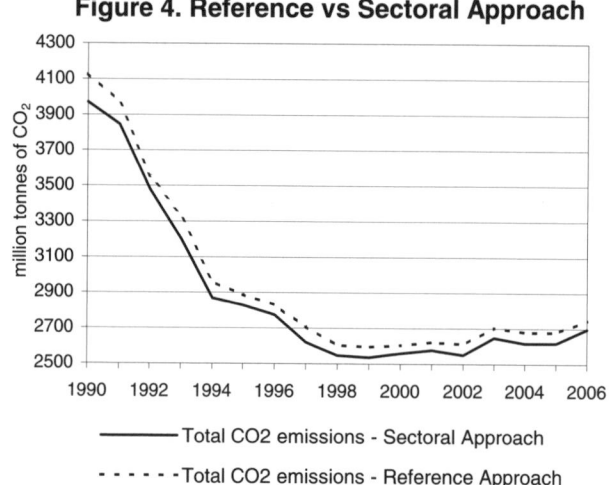

—— Total CO2 emissions - Sectoral Approach

- - - - Total CO2 emissions - Reference Approach

Figure 5. Electricity generation by fuel

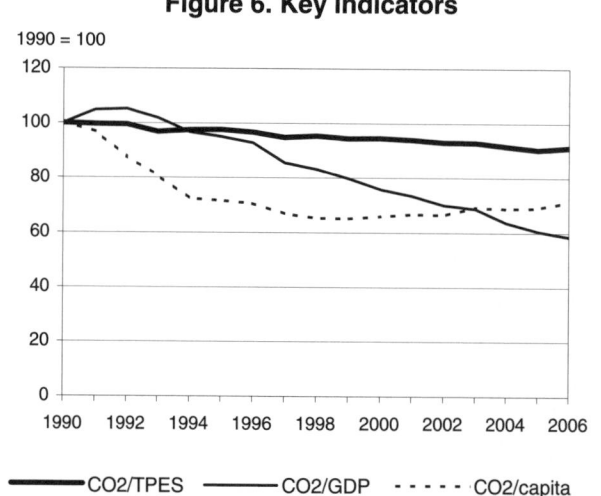

■ Coal/peat ■ Oil ▨ Gas ▨ Nuclear ☐ Hydro ■ Other

Figure 6. Key indicators

1990 = 100

—— CO2/TPES   —— CO2/GDP   - - - - CO2/capita

Economies in Transition / Economies en transition

Key indicators

	1990	1995	2000	2003	2004	2005	2006	% change 90-06
CO$_2$ Sectoral Approach (Mt of CO$_2$)	3 970.5	2 828.0	2 559.6	2 647.8	2 616.8	2 618.1	2 697.6	-32.1%
CO$_2$ Reference Approach (Mt of CO$_2$)	4 126.3	2 888.5	2 605.0	2 704.1	2 678.0	2 679.5	2 746.1	-33.4%
TPES (PJ)	63 365	46 187	43 150	45 440	45 549	46 220	47 201	-25.5%
TPES (Mtoe)	1 513.4	1 103.2	1 030.6	1 085.3	1 087.9	1 104.0	1 127.4	-25.5%
GDP (billion 2000 US$ using exch. rates)	838.2	628.0	712.3	813.3	867.0	913.5	973.5	16.1%
GDP (billion 2000 US$ using PPPs)	3 007.1	2 110.1	2 332.2	2 694.5	2 885.5	3 041.7	3 244.9	7.9%
Population (millions)	321.1	319.5	313.9	309.3	308.0	306.8	305.6	-4.8%
CO$_2$ / TPES (t CO$_2$ per TJ)	62.7	61.2	59.3	58.3	57.4	56.6	57.2	-8.8%
CO$_2$ / GDP (kg CO$_2$ per 2000 US$)	4.74	4.50	3.59	3.26	3.02	2.87	2.77	-41.5%
CO$_2$ / GDP (kg CO$_2$ per 2000 US$ PPP)	1.32	1.34	1.10	0.98	0.91	0.86	0.83	-37.0%
CO$_2$ / population (t CO$_2$ per capita)	12.37	8.85	8.16	8.56	8.50	8.53	8.83	-28.6%

Ratios are based on the Sectoral Approach.

2006 CO$_2$ emissions by sector

million tonnes of CO$_2$	Coal/peat	Oil	Gas	Other *	Total	% change 90-06
Sectoral Approach	**995.6**	**569.3**	**1 110.1**	**22.5**	**2 697.6**	**-32.1%**
Main activity producer elec. and heat	576.0	30.0	405.8	0.4	1 012.1	-46.5%
Unallocated autoproducers	161.2	37.7	203.1	15.3	417.2	189.0%
Other energy industries	17.3	54.6	33.3	1.6	106.8	-6.0%
Manufacturing industries and construction	173.1	86.8	185.7	5.2	450.7	-39.4%
Transport	0.0	289.9	88.7	-	378.7	-13.1%
of which: road	-	*254.9*	*0.4*	-	*255.3*	*-7.2%*
Other sectors	68.0	70.3	193.6	0.1	332.1	-48.0%
of which: residential	*48.7*	*30.2*	*162.7*	-	*241.5*	*-26.9%*
Reference Approach	**997.9**	**590.5**	**1 134.3**	**23.4**	**2 746.1**	**-33.4%**
Diff. due to losses and/or transformation	- 3.0	20.4	23.5	0.9	41.8	
Statistical differences	5.3	0.8	0.7	- 0.0	6.7	
Memo: international marine bunkers	-	*3.1*	-	-	*3.1*	*-68.0%*
Memo: international aviation	-	*21.9*	-	-	*21.9*	*-40.3%*

* Other includes industrial waste and non-renewable municipal waste.

Key sources for CO$_2$ emissions from fuel combustion in 2006

IPCC source category	CO$_2$ emissions (Mt of CO$_2$)	% change 90-06	Level assessment (%) **	Cumulative total (%)
Main activity prod. elec. and heat - coal/peat	576.0	-34.2%	14.4	14.4
Main activity prod. elec. and heat - gas	405.8	-40.7%	10.1	24.6
Road - oil	254.9	-6.5%	6.4	30.9
Unallocated autoproducers - gas	203.1	436.4%	5.1	36.0
Manufacturing industries - gas	185.7	-23.3%	4.6	40.7
Manufacturing industries - coal/peat	173.1	-43.4%	4.3	45.0
Residential - gas	162.7	5.5%	4.1	49.1
Unallocated autoproducers - coal/peat	161.2	102.4%	4.0	53.1
Other transport - gas	88.3	14.5%	2.2	55.3
Manufacturing industries - oil	86.8	-55.3%	2.2	57.5
Other energy industries - oil	54.6	-12.7%	1.4	58.8
Memo: total CO$_2$ from fuel combustion	*2 697.6*	*-32.1%*	*67.5*	*67.5*

** Percent calculated using the total GHG estimate for CO$_2$, CH$_4$, N$_2$O, HFCs, PFCs and SF$_6$ excluding CO$_2$ emissions/removals from land use change and forestry.

Non-Annex I Parties / Parties ne figurant pas à l'Annexe I

Figure 1. CO$_2$ emissions by fuel

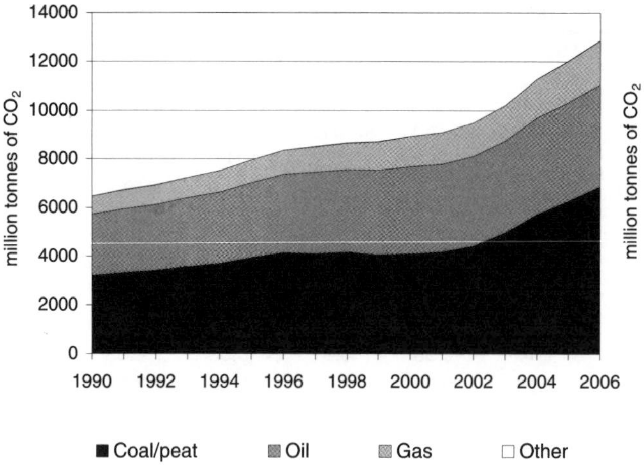

■ Coal/peat   ■ Oil   ▨ Gas   ☐ Other

Figure 2. CO$_2$ emissions by sector

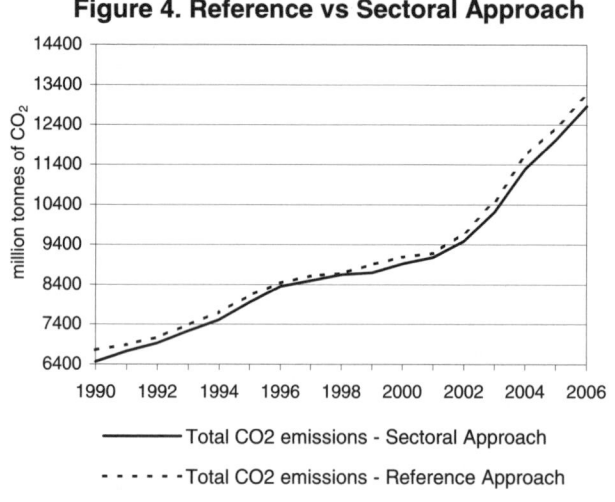

■ Electricity and heat   ☐ Other energy industries
■ Manuf. ind. and construction   ▨ Transport
▨ Residential   ■ Other

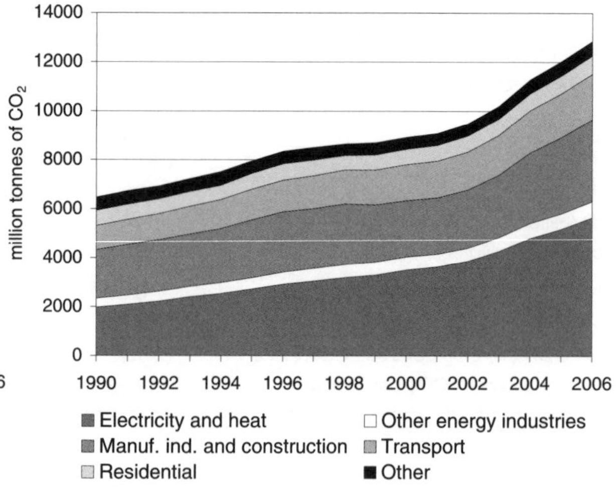

Figure 3. CO$_2$ emissions by sector

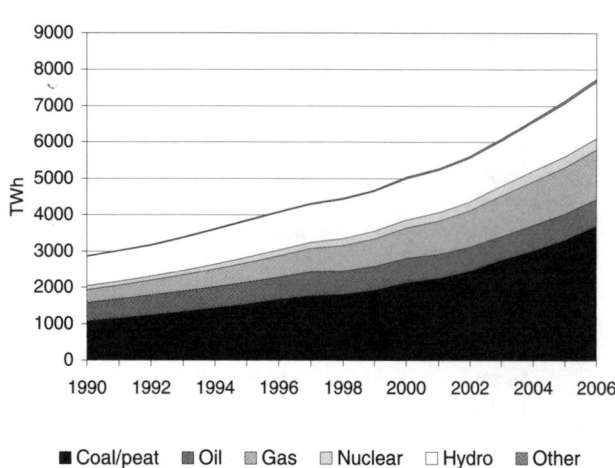

not available

■ Electricity and heat   ☐ Other energy industries
■ Manuf. ind. and construction   ▨ Transport
▨ Residential   ■ Other

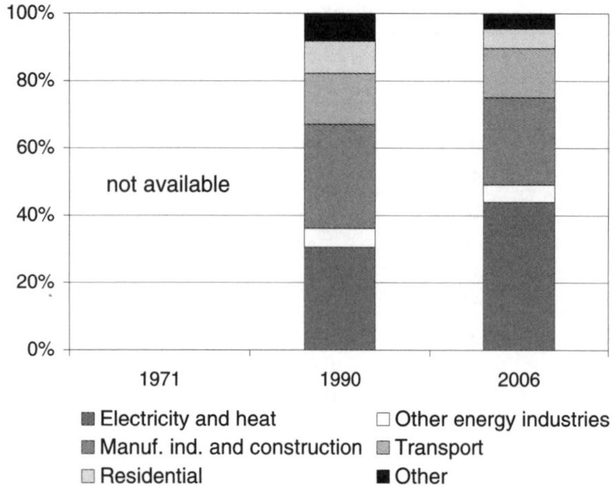

Figure 4. Reference vs Sectoral Approach

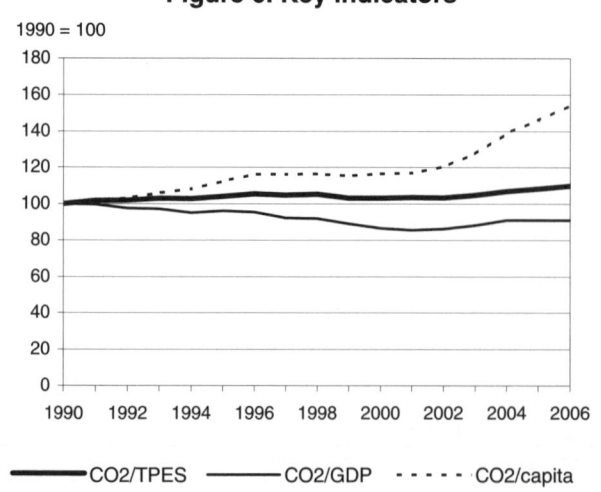

——— Total CO2 emissions - Sectoral Approach
- - - - - Total CO2 emissions - Reference Approach

Figure 5. Electricity generation by fuel

■ Coal/peat   ■ Oil   ▨ Gas   ▨ Nuclear   ☐ Hydro   ▨ Other

Figure 6. Key indicators

1990 = 100

——— CO2/TPES   ——— CO2/GDP   - - - - - CO2/capita

Non-Annex I Parties / Parties ne figurant pas à l'Annexe I

Key indicators

	1990	1995	2000	2003	2004	2005	2006	% change 90-06
CO$_2$ Sectoral Approach (Mt of CO$_2$)	6 467.2	7 946.5	8 922.0	10 211.3	11 288.5	12 026.2	12 865.0	98.9%
CO$_2$ Reference Approach (Mt of CO$_2$)	6 751.2	8 114.8	9 090.2	10 479.7	11 621.5	12 336.5	13 136.7	94.6%
TPES (PJ)	126 689	149 585	169 333	190 940	206 969	217 715	229 276	81.0%
TPES (Mtoe)	3 025.9	3 572.8	4 044.5	4 560.5	4 943.4	5 200.0	5 476.2	81.0%
GDP (billion 2000 US$ using exch. rates)	4 265.5	5 453.9	6 802.3	7 638.0	8 181.9	8 713.3	9 327.3	118.7%
GDP (billion 2000 US$ using PPPs)	10 813.1	14 149.5	18 075.9	20 997.2	22 586.7	24 242.7	26 143.0	141.8%
Population (millions)	4 085.9	4 467.1	4 838.4	5 054.9	5 126.5	5 198.4	5 269.3	29.0%
CO$_2$ / TPES (t CO$_2$ per TJ)	51.1	53.1	52.7	53.5	54.5	55.2	56.1	9.9%
CO$_2$ / GDP (kg CO$_2$ per 2000 US$)	1.52	1.46	1.31	1.34	1.38	1.38	1.38	-9.0%
CO$_2$ / GDP (kg CO$_2$ per 2000 US$ PPP)	0.60	0.56	0.49	0.49	0.50	0.50	0.49	-17.7%
CO$_2$ / population (t CO$_2$ per capita)	1.58	1.78	1.84	2.02	2.20	2.31	2.44	54.3%

Ratios are based on the Sectoral Approach.

2006 CO$_2$ emissions by sector

million tonnes of CO$_2$	Coal/peat	Oil	Gas	Other *	Total	% change 90-06
Sectoral Approach	**6 861.7**	**4 193.6**	**1 800.3**	**9.5**	**12 865.0**	**98.9%**
Main activity producer elec. and heat	4 105.7	512.5	682.5	-	5 300.7	188.2%
Unallocated autoproducers	200.5	69.0	77.8	2.7	350.0	165.9%
Other energy industries	136.4	274.9	254.1	-	665.3	83.2%
Manufacturing industries and construction	2 054.7	812.7	460.8	6.3	3 334.5	66.6%
Transport	14.3	1 827.7	32.2	-	1 874.3	92.5%
of which: road	-	*1 641.7*	*17.2*	-	*1 658.8*	*95.7%*
Other sectors	350.1	696.7	292.9	0.4	1 340.1	15.7%
of which: residential	*210.0*	*331.2*	*205.8*	-	*746.9*	*19.9%*
Reference Approach	**7 007.9**	**4 268.8**	**1 850.5**	**9.5**	**13 136.7**	**94.6%**
Diff. due to losses and/or transformation	202.4	89.0	60.5	-	351.8	
Statistical differences	- 56.1	- 13.7	- 10.3	0.0	- 80.1	
Memo: international marine bunkers	-	*295.2*	-	-	*295.2*	*137.6%*
Memo: international aviation	-	*166.7*	-	-	*166.7*	*81.2%*

* Other includes industrial waste and non-renewable municipal waste.

Key sources for CO$_2$ emissions from fuel combustion in 2006

IPCC source category	CO$_2$ emissions (Mt of CO$_2$)	% change 90-06	Level assessment (%) **	Cumulative total (%)
Main activity prod. elec. and heat - coal/peat	4 105.7	238.0%	18.1	18.1
Manufacturing industries - coal/peat	2 054.7	64.2%	9.1	27.2
Road - oil	1 641.7	93.8%	7.2	34.4
Manufacturing industries - oil	812.7	53.1%	3.6	38.0
Main activity prod. elec. and heat - gas	682.5	208.7%	3.0	41.0
Main activity prod. elec. and heat - oil	512.5	27.0%	2.3	43.3
Manufacturing industries - gas	460.8	110.8%	2.0	45.3
Non-specified other sectors - oil	365.5	41.6%	1.6	46.9
Residential - oil	331.2	59.0%	1.5	48.4
Other energy industries - oil	274.9	64.9%	1.2	49.6
Other energy industries - gas	254.1	91.5%	1.1	50.7
Memo: total CO$_2$ from fuel combustion	*12 865.0*	*98.9%*	*56.8*	*56.8*

** Percent calculated using the total GHG estimate for CO$_2$, CH$_4$, N$_2$O, HFCs, PFCs and SF$_6$ excluding CO$_2$ emissions/removals from land use change and forestry.

INTERNATIONAL ENERGY AGENCY

Annex I Kyoto Parties / Parties avec objectifs dans Kyoto

Figure 1. CO$_2$ emissions by fuel

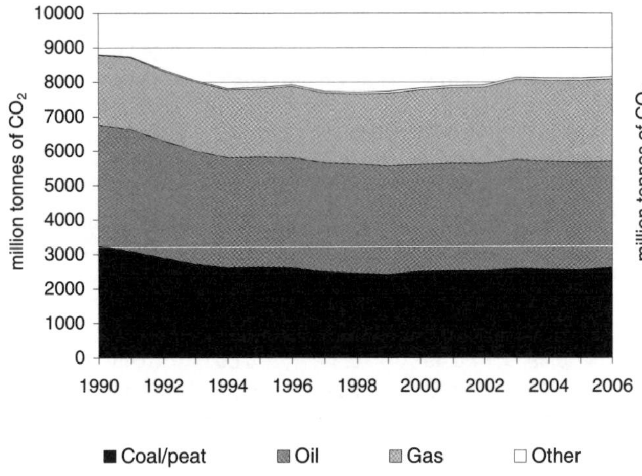

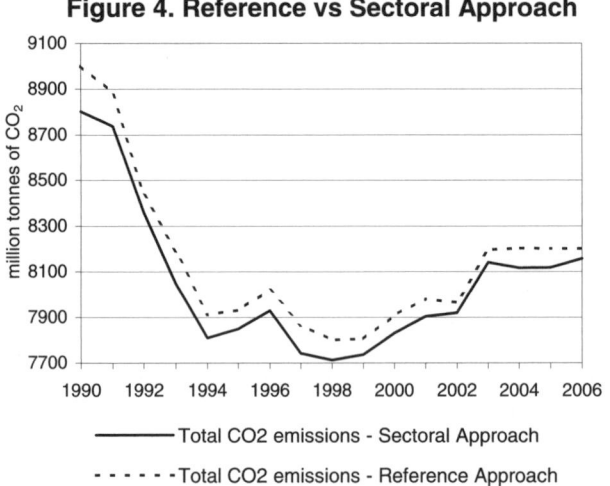

■ Coal/peat   ■ Oil   ▨ Gas   ☐ Other

Figure 2. CO$_2$ emissions by sector

■ Electricity and heat   ☐ Other energy industries
■ Manuf. ind. and construction ▨ Transport
▨ Residential   ■ Other

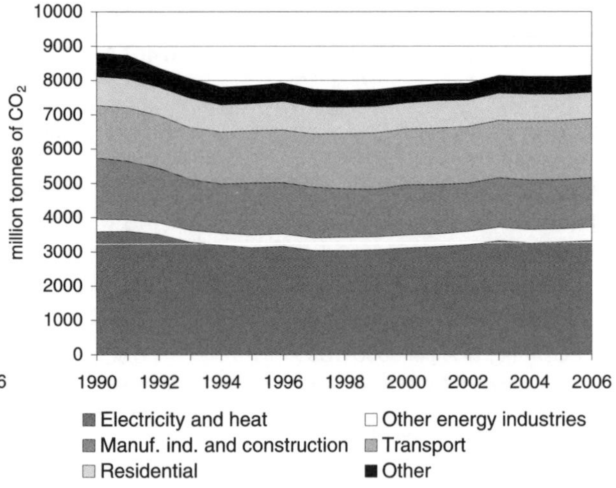

Figure 3. CO$_2$ emissions by sector

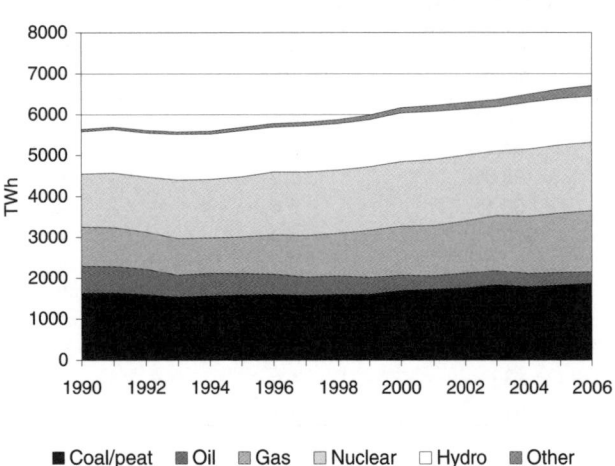

not available

■ Electricity and heat   ☐ Other energy industries
■ Manuf. ind. and construction ▨ Transport
▨ Residential   ■ Other

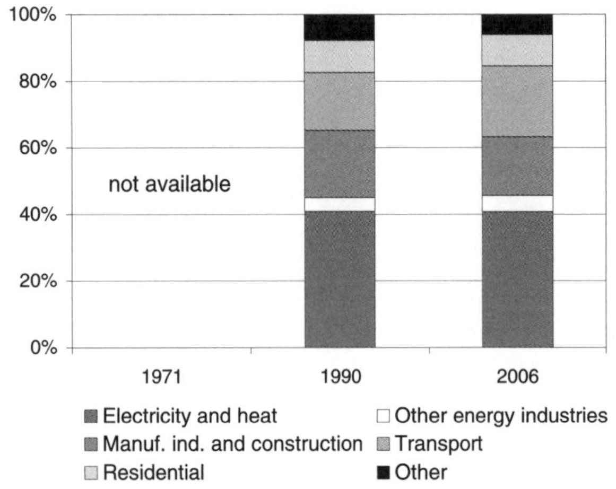

Figure 4. Reference vs Sectoral Approach

——— Total CO2 emissions - Sectoral Approach

- - - - - Total CO2 emissions - Reference Approach

Figure 5. Electricity generation by fuel

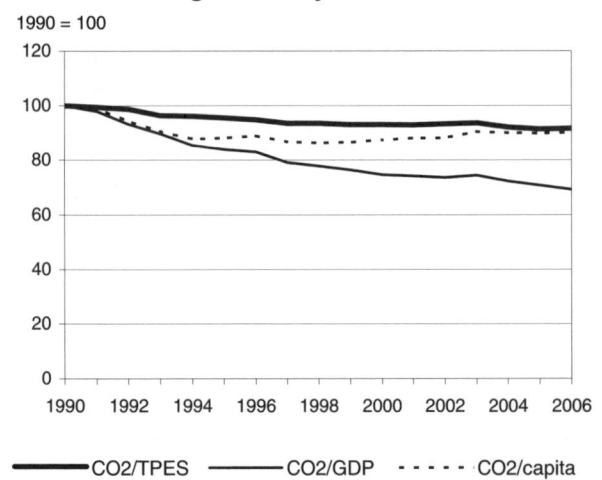

■ Coal/peat   ■ Oil   ▨ Gas   ▨ Nuclear   ☐ Hydro   ▨ Other

Figure 6. Key indicators

1990 = 100

——— CO2/TPES   ——— CO2/GDP   - - - - CO2/capita

INTERNATIONAL ENERGY AGENCY

Annex I Kyoto Parties / Parties avec objectifs dans Kyoto

Key indicators

	1990	1995	2000	2003	2004	2005	2006	% change 90-06
CO$_2$ Sectoral Approach (Mt of CO$_2$)	8 802.1	7 849.1	7 830.0	8 140.6	8 117.5	8 117.8	8 157.5	-7.3%
CO$_2$ Reference Approach (Mt of CO$_2$)	9 001.5	7 931.8	7 909.9	8 195.4	8 202.5	8 200.9	8 201.3	-8.9%
TPES (PJ)	150 666	140 561	144 017	148 725	150 712	151 980	152 296	1.1%
TPES (Mtoe)	3 598.6	3 357.3	3 439.8	3 552.2	3 599.7	3 630.0	3 637.5	1.1%
GDP (billion 2000 US$ using exch. rates)	12 605.5	13 400.9	15 023.1	15 666.7	16 094.4	16 424.0	16 885.6	34.0%
GDP (billion 2000 US$ using PPPs)	14 838.5	14 984.3	16 911.3	17 879.2	18 442.8	18 884.9	19 503.5	31.4%
Population (millions)	859.9	870.3	874.5	879.0	880.8	882.6	884.1	2.8%
CO$_2$ / TPES (t CO$_2$ per TJ)	58.4	55.8	54.4	54.7	53.9	53.4	53.6	-8.3%
CO$_2$ / GDP (kg CO$_2$ per 2000 US$)	0.70	0.59	0.52	0.52	0.50	0.49	0.48	-30.8%
CO$_2$ / GDP (kg CO$_2$ per 2000 US$ PPP)	0.59	0.52	0.46	0.46	0.44	0.43	0.42	-29.5%
CO$_2$ / population (t CO$_2$ per capita)	10.24	9.02	8.95	9.26	9.22	9.20	9.23	-9.9%

Ratios are based on the Sectoral Approach.

2006 CO$_2$ emissions by sector

million tonnes of CO$_2$	Coal/peat	Oil	Gas	Other *	Total	% change 90-06
Sectoral Approach	**2 630.6**	**3 084.7**	**2 375.7**	**66.6**	**8 157.5**	**-7.3%**
Main activity producer elec. and heat	1 769.1	142.1	743.0	16.1	2 670.3	-18.2%
Unallocated autoproducers	264.3	86.1	272.0	29.0	651.3	98.7%
Other energy industries	56.2	227.9	110.0	1.6	395.6	7.6%
Manufacturing industries and construction	457.4	479.3	479.7	17.9	1 434.3	-19.2%
Transport	0.3	1 641.1	100.1	-	1 741.5	13.4%
of which: road	*-*	*1 483.7*	*1.7*	*-*	*1 485.4*	*17.7%*
Other sectors	83.3	508.3	670.9	2.1	1 264.6	-17.5%
of which: residential	*58.0*	*238.9*	*469.0*	*0.0*	*766.0*	*-9.4%*
Reference Approach	**2 620.0**	**3 100.5**	**2 413.3**	**67.5**	**8 201.3**	**-8.9%**
Diff. due to losses and/or transformation	4.5	23.7	30.8	0.9	59.9	
Statistical differences	- 15.0	- 7.9	6.8	0.0	- 16.1	
Memo: international marine bunkers	*-*	*196.2*	*-*	*-*	*196.2*	*37.6%*
Memo: international aviation	*-*	*179.6*	*-*	*-*	*179.6*	*44.7%*

* Other includes industrial waste and non-renewable municipal waste.

Key sources for CO$_2$ emissions from fuel combustion in 2006

IPCC source category	CO$_2$ emissions (Mt of CO$_2$)	% change 90-06	Level assessment (%) **	Cumulative total (%)
Main activity prod. elec. and heat - coal/peat	1 769.1	-5.3%	16.1	16.1
Road - oil	1 483.7	17.9%	13.5	29.6
Main activity prod. elec. and heat - gas	743.0	-9.4%	6.8	36.4
Manufacturing industries - gas	479.7	-0.4%	4.4	40.7
Manufacturing industries - oil	479.3	-14.5%	4.4	45.1
Residential - gas	469.0	30.9%	4.3	49.4
Manufacturing industries - coal/peat	457.4	-36.9%	4.2	53.5
Unallocated autoproducers - gas	272.0	390.3%	2.5	56.0
Non-specified other sectors - oil	269.3	-24.2%	2.5	58.4
Unallocated autoproducers - coal/peat	264.3	31.2%	2.4	60.8
Residential - oil	238.9	-15.2%	2.2	63.0
Memo: total CO$_2$ from fuel combustion	*8 157.5*	*-7.3%*	*74.2*	*74.2*

** Percent calculated using the total GHG estimate for CO$_2$, CH$_4$, N$_2$O, HFCs, PFCs and SF$_6$ excluding CO$_2$ emissions/removals from land use change and forestry.

OECD Total / Total OCDE

Figure 1. CO$_2$ emissions by fuel

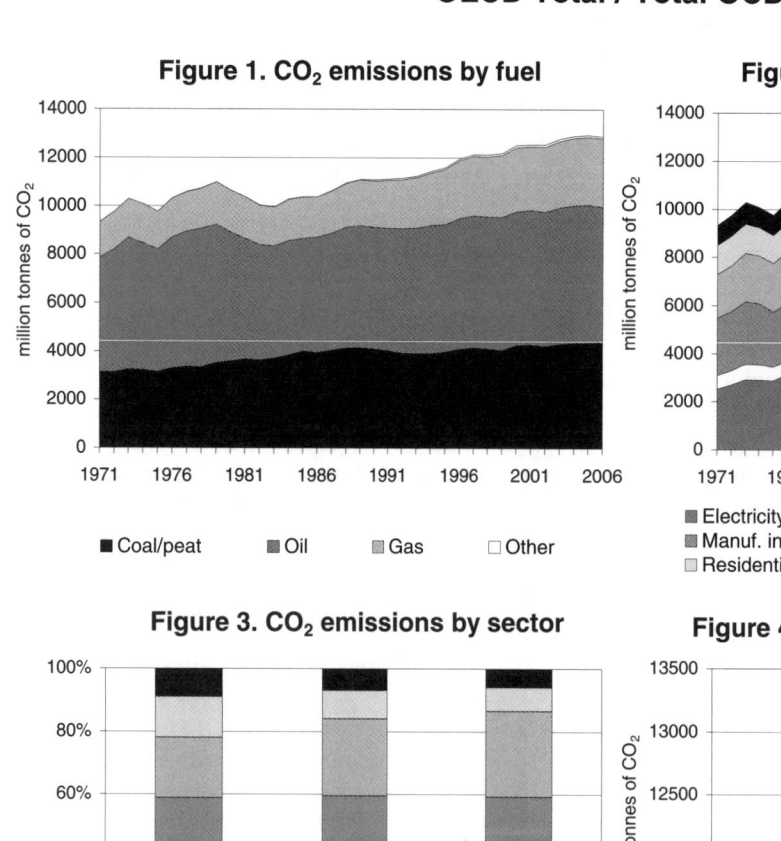

■ Coal/peat ■ Oil ▨ Gas ☐ Other

Figure 2. CO$_2$ emissions by sector

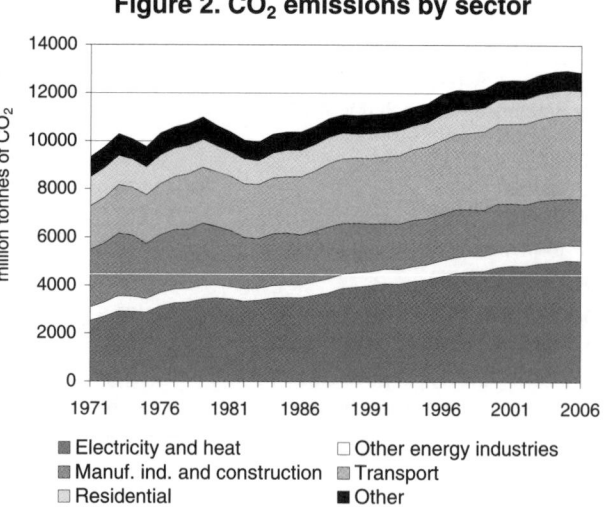

■ Electricity and heat ☐ Other energy industries
■ Manuf. ind. and construction ▨ Transport
☐ Residential ■ Other

Figure 3. CO$_2$ emissions by sector

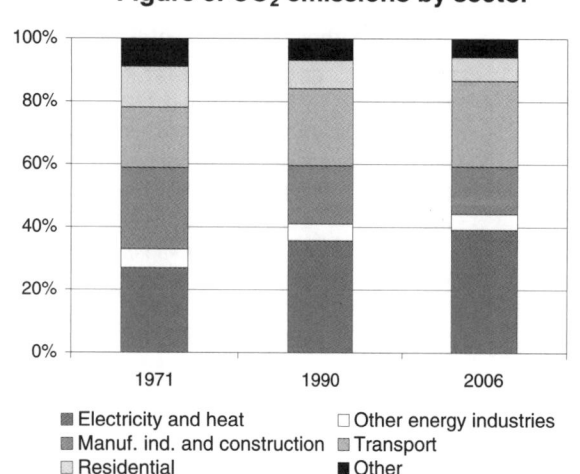

■ Electricity and heat ☐ Other energy industries
■ Manuf. ind. and construction ▨ Transport
☐ Residential ■ Other

Figure 4. Reference vs Sectoral Approach

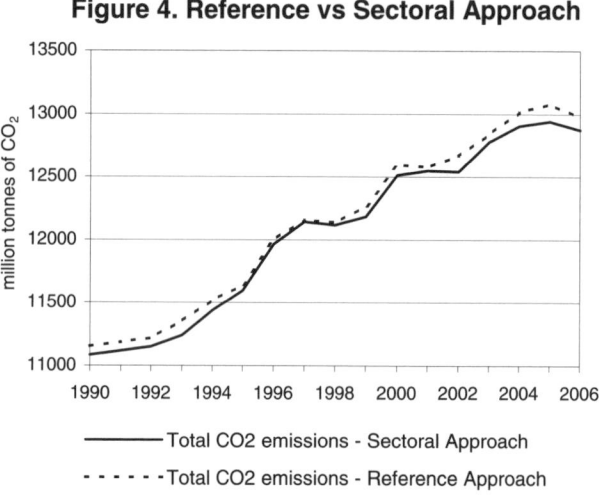

—— Total CO2 emissions - Sectoral Approach
- - - - Total CO2 emissions - Reference Approach

Figure 5. Electricity generation by fuel

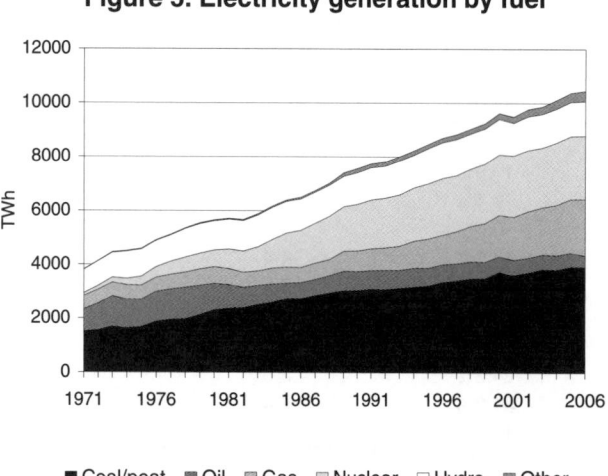

■ Coal/peat ■ Oil ▨ Gas ☐ Nuclear ☐ Hydro ■ Other

Figure 6. Key indicators

1990 = 100

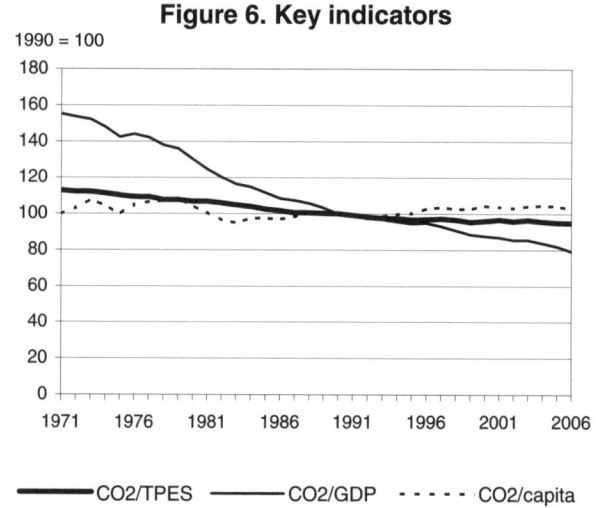

—— CO2/TPES —— CO2/GDP - - - - CO2/capita

OECD Total / Total OCDE

Key indicators

	1990	1995	2000	2003	2004	2005	2006	% change 90-06
CO$_2$ Sectoral Approach (Mt of CO$_2$)	11 083.2	11 595.5	12 513.5	12 778.6	12 904.3	12 941.7	12 873.7	16.2%
CO$_2$ Reference Approach (Mt of CO$_2$)	11 153.0	11 635.8	12 593.5	12 844.0	13 016.4	13 077.4	12 978.7	16.4%
TPES (PJ)	189 318	204 758	222 965	226 099	230 619	232 535	231 841	22.5%
TPES (Mtoe)	4 521.8	4 890.6	5 325.4	5 400.3	5 508.3	5 554.0	5 537.4	22.5%
GDP (billion 2000 US$ using exch. rates)	19 910.1	22 018.6	25 676.5	26 828.9	27 666.3	28 352.6	29 168.7	46.5%
GDP (billion 2000 US$ using PPPs)	20 916.9	23 164.5	27 246.3	28 564.4	29 480.1	30 239.5	31 157.5	49.0%
Population (millions)	1 043.6	1 089.8	1 129.9	1 155.2	1 163.2	1 170.4	1 177.9	12.9%
CO$_2$ / TPES (t CO$_2$ per TJ)	58.5	56.6	56.1	56.5	56.0	55.7	55.5	-5.1%
CO$_2$ / GDP (kg CO$_2$ per 2000 US$)	0.56	0.53	0.49	0.48	0.47	0.46	0.44	-20.7%
CO$_2$ / GDP (kg CO$_2$ per 2000 US$ PPP)	0.53	0.50	0.46	0.45	0.44	0.43	0.41	-22.0%
CO$_2$ / population (t CO$_2$ per capita)	10.62	10.64	11.07	11.06	11.09	11.06	10.93	2.9%

Ratios are based on the Sectoral Approach.

2006 CO$_2$ emissions by sector

million tonnes of CO$_2$	Coal/peat	Oil	Gas	Other *	Total	% change 90-06
Sectoral Approach	**4 392.1**	**5 591.0**	**2 807.8**	**82.8**	**12 873.7**	**16.2%**
Main activity producer elec. and heat	3 541.3	227.8	816.3	29.6	4 615.0	29.9%
Unallocated autoproducers	185.3	74.2	140.1	20.2	419.8	6.9%
Other energy industries	69.1	375.6	207.7	0.0	652.5	9.1%
Manufacturing industries and construction	524.7	738.5	633.7	29.8	1 926.7	-5.8%
Transport	0.3	3 469.5	50.9	-	3 520.7	29.1%
of which: road	-	*3 076.6*	*3.9*	-	*3 080.5*	*33.4%*
Other sectors	71.4	705.4	959.0	3.2	1 739.0	-1.7%
of which: residential	*51.8*	*322.2*	*607.4*	*0.0*	*981.4*	*-1.6%*
Reference Approach	**4 458.7**	**5 634.1**	**2 803.1**	**82.8**	**12 978.7**	**16.4%**
Diff. due to losses and/or transformation	31.2	4.6	6.5	0.0	42.3	
Statistical differences	35.5	38.5	- 11.1	0.0	62.8	
Memo: international marine bunkers	-	*321.2*	-	-	*321.2*	*38.2%*
Memo: international aviation	-	*229.0*	-	-	*229.0*	*69.7%*

* Other includes industrial waste and non-renewable municipal waste.

Key sources for CO$_2$ emissions from fuel combustion in 2006

IPCC source category	CO$_2$ emissions (Mt of CO$_2$)	% change 90-06	Level assessment (%) **	Cumulative total (%)
Main activity prod. elec. and heat - coal/peat	3 541.3	26.6%	21.8	21.8
Road - oil	3 076.6	33.2%	19.0	40.8
Main activity prod. elec. and heat - gas	816.3	149.5%	5.0	45.8
Manufacturing industries - oil	738.5	2.6%	4.6	50.4
Manufacturing industries - gas	633.7	9.4%	3.9	54.3
Residential - gas	607.4	31.0%	3.7	58.0
Manufacturing industries - coal/peat	524.7	-28.9%	3.2	61.2
Other transport - oil	392.9	5.4%	2.4	63.7
Non-specified other sectors - oil	383.2	-7.3%	2.4	66.0
Other energy industries - oil	375.6	1.9%	2.3	68.3
Non-specified other sectors - gas	351.7	36.4%	2.2	70.5
Memo: total CO$_2$ from fuel combustion	*12 873.7*	*16.2%*	*79.3*	*79.3*

** Percent calculated using the total GHG estimate for CO$_2$, CH$_4$, N$_2$O, HFCs, PFCs and SF$_6$ excluding CO$_2$ emissions/removals from land use change and forestry.

OECD North America / OCDE Amérique du Nord

Figure 1. CO$_2$ emissions by fuel

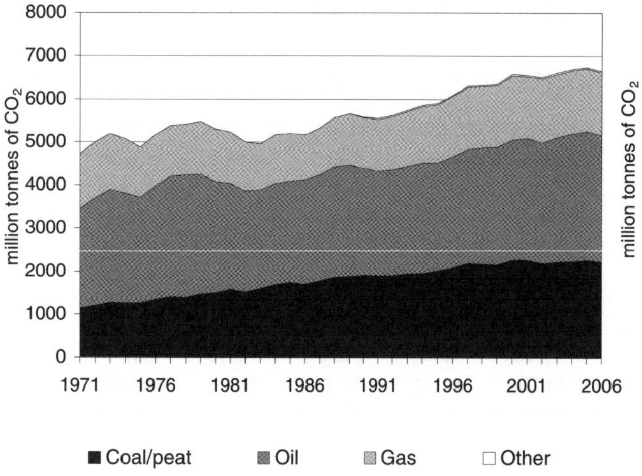

■ Coal/peat   ▨ Oil   ▨ Gas   ☐ Other

Figure 2. CO$_2$ emissions by sector

▨ Electricity and heat   ☐ Other energy industries
▨ Manuf. ind. and construction   ▨ Transport
☐ Residential   ■ Other

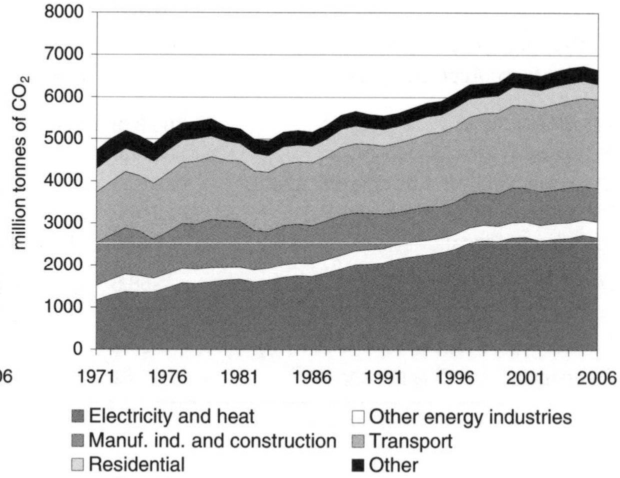

Figure 3. CO$_2$ emissions by sector

▨ Electricity and heat   ☐ Other energy industries
▨ Manuf. ind. and construction   ▨ Transport
☐ Residential   ■ Other

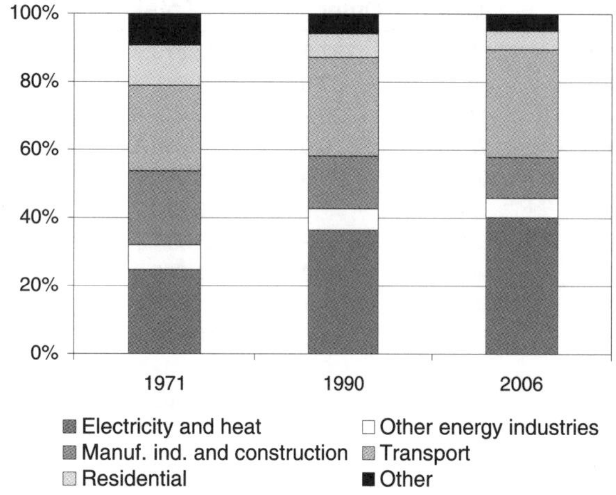

Figure 4. Reference vs Sectoral Approach

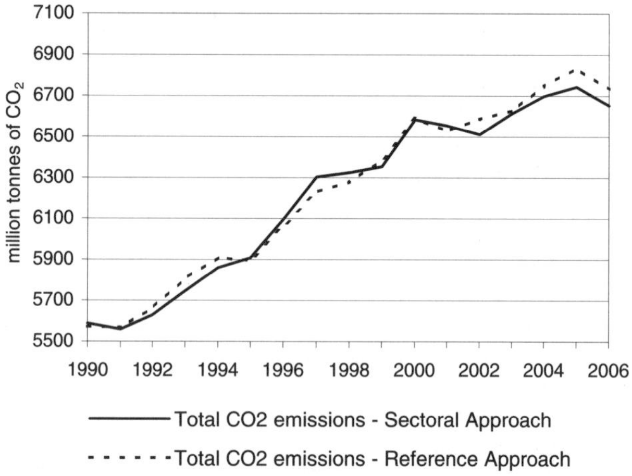

——— Total CO2 emissions - Sectoral Approach
- - - - - Total CO2 emissions - Reference Approach

Figure 5. Electricity generation by fuel

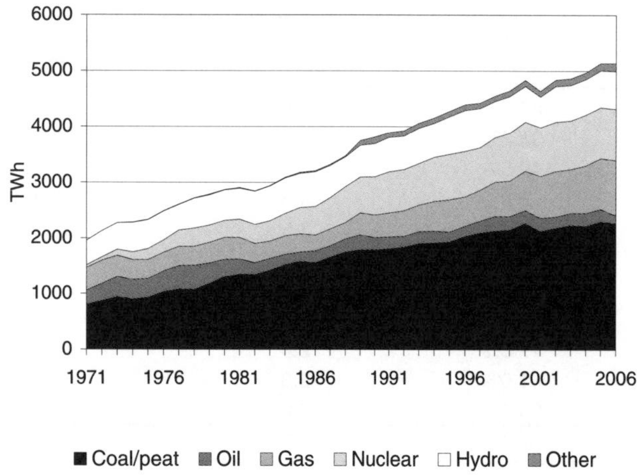

■ Coal/peat   ▨ Oil   ▨ Gas   ▨ Nuclear   ☐ Hydro   ▨ Other

Figure 6. Key indicators

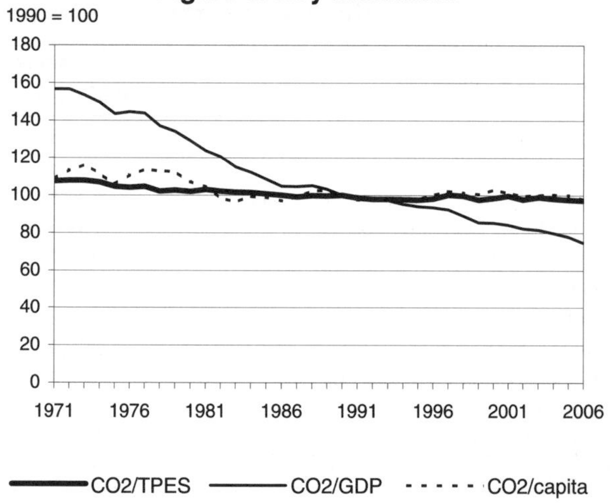

1990 = 100

——— CO2/TPES   ——— CO2/GDP   - - - - - CO2/capita

OECD North America / OCDE Amérique du Nord

Key indicators

	1990	1995	2000	2003	2004	2005	2006	% change 90-06
CO$_2$ Sectoral Approach (Mt of CO$_2$)	5 588.5	5 908.0	6 582.4	6 613.9	6 697.2	6 743.0	6 651.8	19.0%
CO$_2$ Reference Approach (Mt of CO$_2$)	5 571.5	5 894.8	6 588.7	6 628.8	6 747.9	6 834.6	6 733.1	20.8%
TPES (PJ)	94 571	102 570	113 245	113 171	115 646	116 903	115 885	22.5%
TPES (Mtoe)	2 258.8	2 449.8	2 704.8	2 703.0	2 762.2	2 792.2	2 767.9	22.5%
GDP (billion 2000 US$ using exch. rates)	8 011.4	9 010.2	11 070.5	11 616.7	12 039.3	12 407.7	12 775.3	59.5%
GDP (billion 2000 US$ using PPPs)	8 348.8	9 375.3	11 537.0	12 100.0	12 540.9	12 923.9	13 312.7	59.5%
Population (millions)	359.1	387.0	411.4	424.9	429.0	433.1	437.2	21.7%
CO$_2$ / TPES (t CO$_2$ per TJ)	59.1	57.6	58.1	58.4	57.9	57.7	57.4	-2.9%
CO$_2$ / GDP (kg CO$_2$ per 2000 US$)	0.70	0.66	0.59	0.57	0.56	0.54	0.52	-25.4%
CO$_2$ / GDP (kg CO$_2$ per 2000 US$ PPP)	0.67	0.63	0.57	0.55	0.53	0.52	0.50	-25.4%
CO$_2$ / population (t CO$_2$ per capita)	15.56	15.27	16.00	15.57	15.61	15.57	15.21	-2.2%

Ratios are based on the Sectoral Approach.

2006 CO$_2$ emissions by sector

million tonnes of CO$_2$	Coal/peat	Oil	Gas	Other *	Total	% change 90-06
Sectoral Approach	**2 232.9**	**2 932.2**	**1 459.7**	**27.0**	**6 651.8**	**19.0%**
Main activity producer elec. and heat	2 042.5	100.3	396.9	13.6	2 553.4	31.8%
Unallocated autoproducers	32.1	17.2	63.3	4.8	117.4	23.4%
Other energy industries	13.3	204.5	161.9	-	379.7	7.4%
Manufacturing industries and construction	139.5	300.3	344.6	7.9	792.3	-7.6%
Transport	-	2 063.4	45.1	-	2 108.6	29.4%
of which: road	-	*1 782.4*	*1.5*	-	*1 783.9*	*35.4%*
Other sectors	5.4	246.4	447.9	0.8	700.4	-2.2%
of which: residential	*0.2*	*98.1*	*271.0*	-	*369.2*	*-3.8%*
Reference Approach	**2 299.5**	**2 950.3**	**1 456.3**	**27.0**	**6 733.1**	**20.8%**
Diff. due to losses and/or transformation	9.2	- 24.3	1.4	-	- 13.7	
Statistical differences	57.4	42.4	- 4.8	0.0	94.9	
Memo: international marine bunkers	-	*92.6*	-	-	*92.6*	*-3.1%*
Memo: international aviation	-	*58.9*	-	-	*58.9*	*25.3%*

* Other includes industrial waste and non-renewable municipal waste.

Key sources for CO$_2$ emissions from fuel combustion in 2006

IPCC source category	CO$_2$ emissions (Mt of CO$_2$)	% change 90-06	Level assessment (%) **	Cumulative total (%)
Main activity prod. elec. and heat - coal/peat	2 042.5	25.8%	24.5	24.5
Road - oil	1 782.4	35.3%	21.4	46.0
Main activity prod. elec. and heat - gas	396.9	142.6%	4.8	50.7
Manufacturing industries - gas	344.6	-2.2%	4.1	54.9
Manufacturing industries - oil	300.3	7.2%	3.6	58.5
Other transport - oil	281.1	4.2%	3.4	61.9
Residential - gas	271.0	1.1%	3.3	65.1
Other energy industries - oil	204.5	-3.7%	2.5	67.6
Non-specified other sectors - gas	176.9	8.0%	2.1	69.7
Other energy industries - gas	161.9	17.3%	1.9	71.6
Non-specified other sectors - oil	148.4	8.2%	1.8	73.4
Memo: total CO$_2$ from fuel combustion	*6 651.8*	*19.0%*	*79.9*	*79.9*

** Percent calculated using the total GHG estimate for CO$_2$, CH$_4$, N$_2$O, HFCs, PFCs and SF$_6$ excluding CO$_2$ emissions/removals from land use change and forestry.

OECD Pacific / OCDE Pacifique

Figure 1. CO₂ emissions by fuel

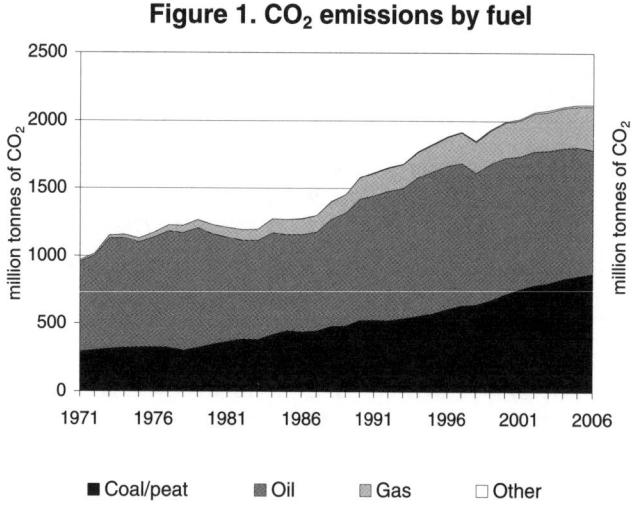

Figure 2. CO₂ emissions by sector

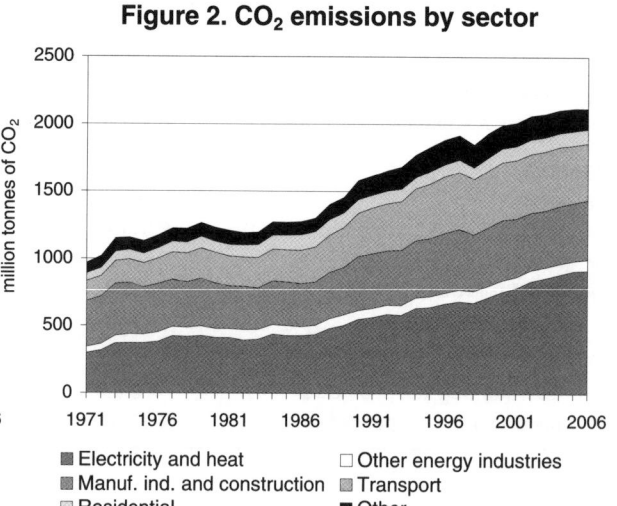

Figure 3. CO₂ emissions by sector

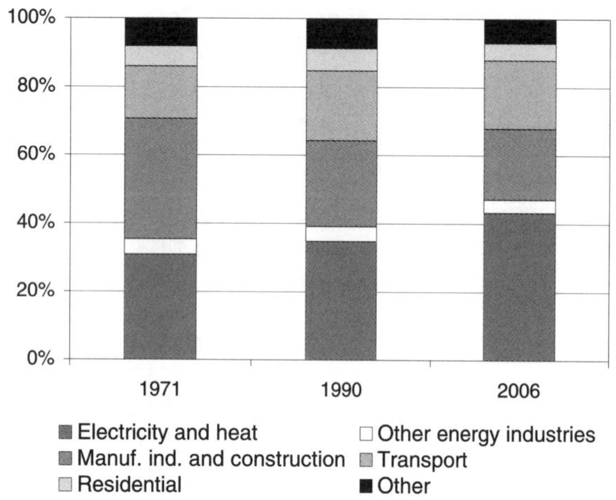

Figure 4. Reference vs Sectoral Approach

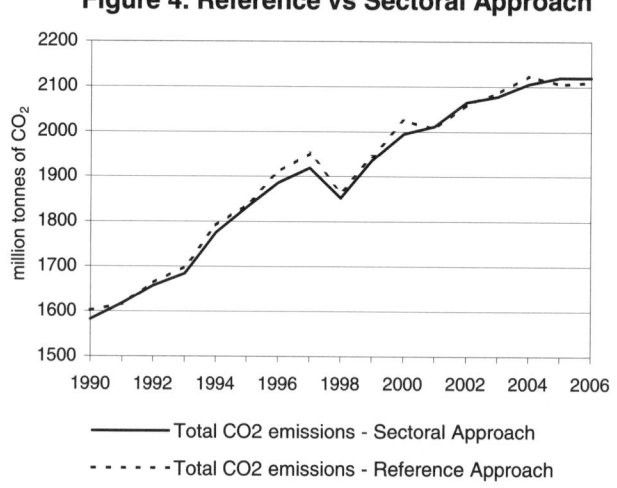

Figure 5. Electricity generation by fuel

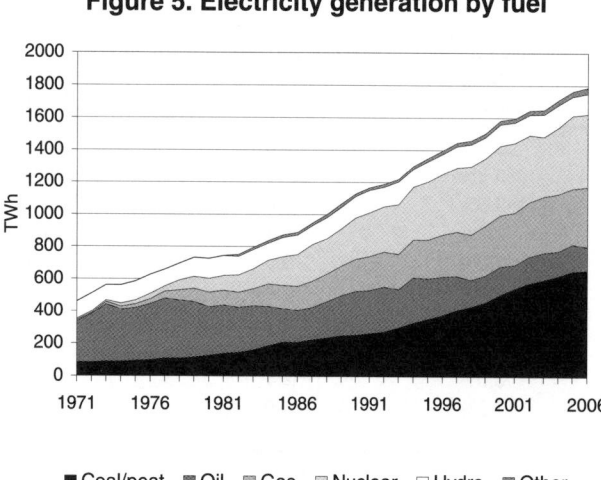

Figure 6. Key indicators

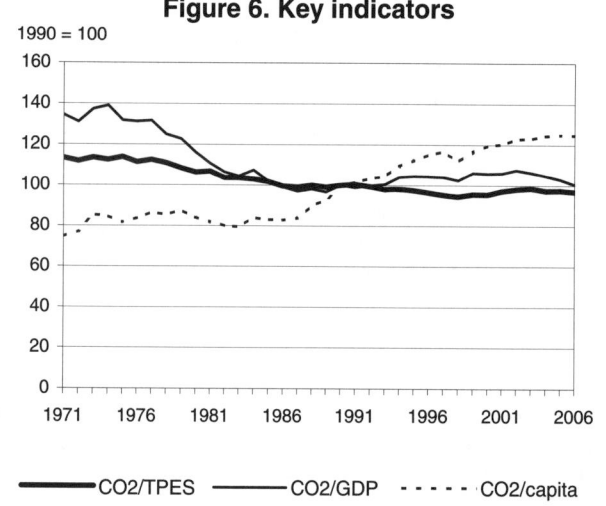

OECD Pacific / OCDE Pacifique

Key indicators

	1990	1995	2000	2003	2004	2005	2006	% change 90-06
CO_2 Sectoral Approach (Mt of CO_2)	1 581.9	1 831.1	1 994.6	2 078.2	2 106.3	2 120.0	2 120.0	34.0%
CO_2 Reference Approach (Mt of CO_2)	1 600.9	1 836.8	2 025.0	2 086.1	2 123.6	2 105.2	2 110.4	31.8%
TPES (PJ)	26 742	31 755	35 366	35 634	36 583	36 801	37 015	38.4%
TPES (Mtoe)	638.7	758.5	844.7	851.1	873.8	879.0	884.1	38.4%
GDP (billion 2000 US$ using exch. rates)	4 726.8	5 234.9	5 631.5	5 844.6	6 016.9	6 149.9	6 303.4	33.4%
GDP (billion 2000 US$ using PPPs)	3 724.9	4 219.6	4 623.8	4 865.9	5 017.4	5 139.8	5 280.7	41.8%
Population (millions)	186.9	192.4	197.0	199.6	200.1	200.5	200.9	7.5%
CO_2 / TPES (t CO_2 per TJ)	59.2	57.7	56.4	58.3	57.6	57.6	57.3	-3.2%
CO_2 / GDP (kg CO_2 per 2000 US$)	0.33	0.35	0.35	0.36	0.35	0.34	0.34	0.5%
CO_2 / GDP (kg CO_2 per 2000 US$ PPP)	0.42	0.43	0.43	0.43	0.42	0.41	0.40	-5.5%
CO_2 / population (t CO_2 per capita)	8.46	9.52	10.13	10.41	10.53	10.57	10.55	24.6%

Ratios are based on the Sectoral Approach.

2006 CO_2 emissions by sector

million tonnes of CO_2	Coal/peat	Oil	Gas	Other *	Total	% change 90-06
Sectoral Approach	**874.1**	**912.9**	**320.7**	**12.4**	**2 120.0**	**34.0%**
Main activity producer elec. and heat	570.2	63.3	154.9	1.2	789.7	69.3%
Unallocated autoproducers	80.6	28.8	13.1	2.9	125.5	52.2%
Other energy industries	23.5	50.7	8.9	-	83.1	20.7%
Manufacturing industries and construction	191.7	190.1	50.4	7.8	440.0	10.2%
Transport	0.3	421.8	2.0	-	424.0	31.3%
of which: road	-	*377.5*	*1.1*	-	*378.6*	*35.0%*
Other sectors	7.7	158.2	91.5	0.4	257.8	6.6%
of which: residential	*4.4*	*53.0*	*47.9*	-	*105.3*	*2.8%*
Reference Approach	**859.6**	**929.1**	**309.3**	**12.4**	**2 110.4**	**31.8%**
Diff. due to losses and/or transformation	7.0	8.1	- 2.6	-	12.5	
Statistical differences	- 21.5	8.1	- 8.8	0.0	- 22.2	
Memo: international marine bunkers	-	*56.1*	-	-	*56.1*	*114.8%*
Memo: international aviation	-	*38.4*	-	-	*38.4*	*93.7%*

* Other includes industrial waste and non-renewable municipal waste.

Key sources for CO_2 emissions from fuel combustion in 2006

IPCC source category	CO_2 emissions (Mt of CO_2)	% change 90-06	Level assessment (%) **	Cumulative total (%)
Main activity prod. elec. and heat - coal/peat	570.2	151.5%	22.1	22.1
Road - oil	377.5	34.6%	14.6	36.7
Manufacturing industries - coal/peat	191.7	3.8%	7.4	44.1
Manufacturing industries - oil	190.1	1.4%	7.4	51.5
Main activity prod. elec. and heat - gas	154.9	68.3%	6.0	57.5
Non-specified other sectors - oil	105.2	-14.7%	4.1	61.5
Unallocated autoproducers - coal/peat	80.6	49.8%	3.1	64.7
Main activity prod. elec. and heat - oil	63.3	-57.1%	2.5	67.1
Residential - oil	53.0	16.3%	2.1	69.2
Other energy industries - oil	50.7	20.4%	2.0	71.1
Manufacturing industries - gas	50.4	101.2%	2.0	73.1
Memo: total CO_2 from fuel combustion	*2 120.0*	*34.0%*	*82.1*	*82.1*

** Percent calculated using the total GHG estimate for CO_2, CH_4, N_2O, HFCs, PFCs and SF_6 excluding CO_2 emissions/removals from land use change and forestry.

OECD Europe / OCDE Europe

Figure 1. CO_2 emissions by fuel

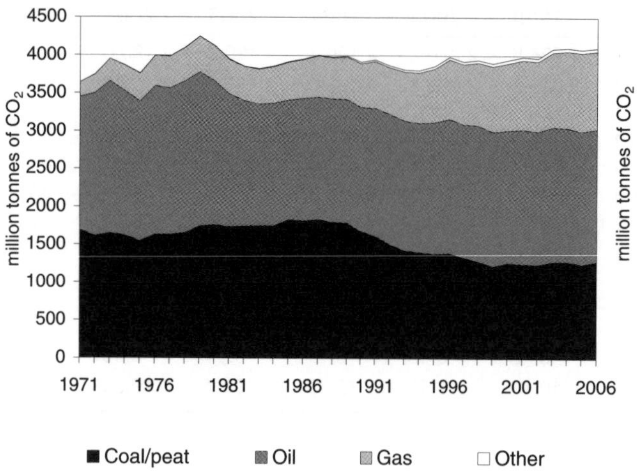

■ Coal/peat ■ Oil ▨ Gas ☐ Other

Figure 2. CO_2 emissions by sector

■ Electricity and heat ☐ Other energy industries
■ Manuf. ind. and construction ▨ Transport
▨ Residential ■ Other

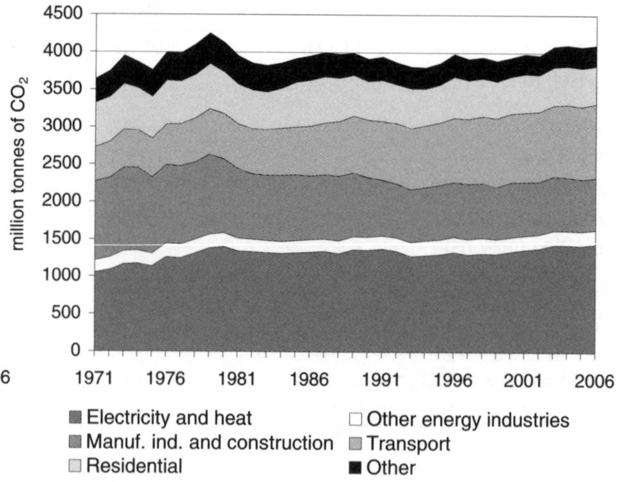

Figure 3. CO_2 emissions by sector

■ Electricity and heat ☐ Other energy industries
■ Manuf. ind. and construction ▨ Transport
▨ Residential ■ Other

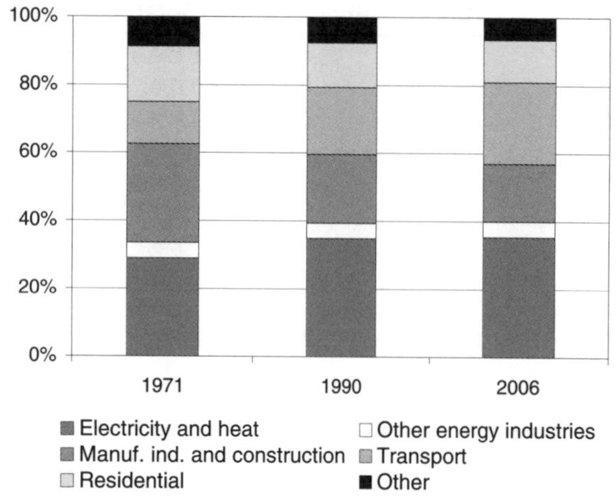

Figure 4. Reference vs Sectoral Approach

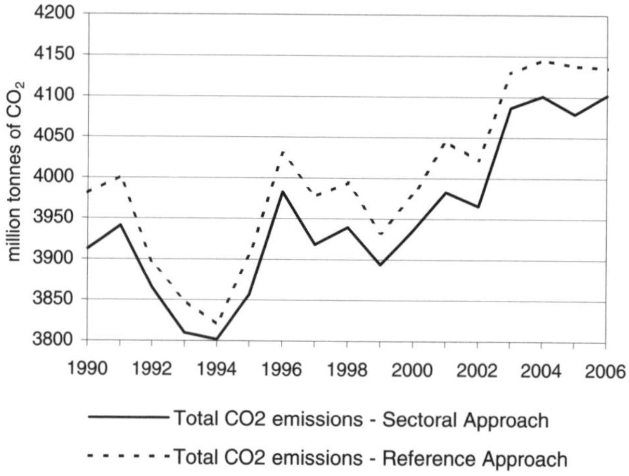

——— Total CO2 emissions - Sectoral Approach
- - - - Total CO2 emissions - Reference Approach

Figure 5. Electricity generation by fuel

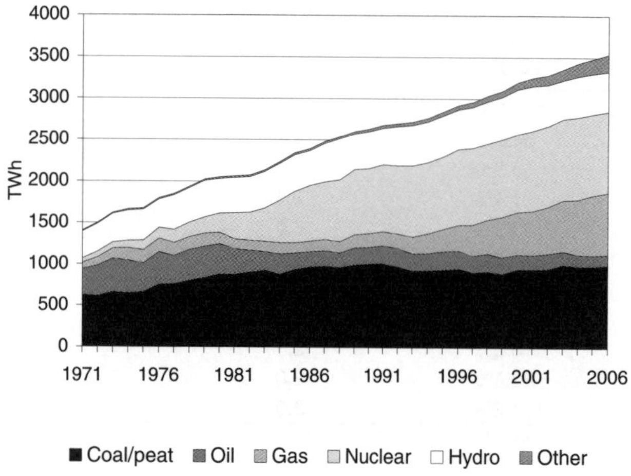

■ Coal/peat ■ Oil ▨ Gas ▨ Nuclear ☐ Hydro ▨ Other

Figure 6. Key indicators

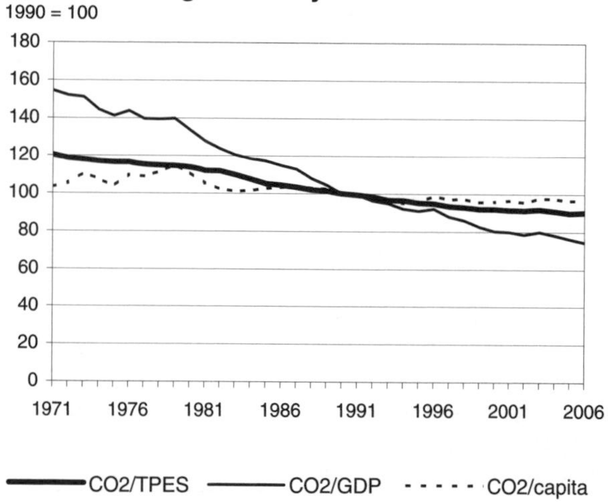

1990 = 100

——— CO2/TPES ——— CO2/GDP · · · · · CO2/capita

OECD Europe / OCDE Europe

Key indicators

	1990	1995	2000	2003	2004	2005	2006	% change 90-06
CO$_2$ Sectoral Approach (Mt of CO$_2$)	3 912.8	3 856.4	3 936.5	4 086.5	4 100.8	4 078.7	4 101.8	4.8%
CO$_2$ Reference Approach (Mt of CO$_2$)	3 980.6	3 904.1	3 979.7	4 129.1	4 144.9	4 137.6	4 135.2	3.9%
TPES (PJ)	68 005	70 433	74 355	77 295	78 390	78 831	78 941	16.1%
TPES (Mtoe)	1 624.3	1 682.3	1 775.9	1 846.2	1 872.3	1 882.9	1 885.5	16.1%
GDP (billion 2000 US$ using exch. rates)	7 171.9	7 773.5	8 974.5	9 367.6	9 610.1	9 795.0	10 090.0	40.7%
GDP (billion 2000 US$ using PPPs)	8 843.3	9 569.7	11 085.5	11 598.6	11 921.8	12 175.8	12 564.2	42.1%
Population (millions)	497.6	510.4	521.6	530.8	534.2	536.8	539.8	8.5%
CO$_2$ / TPES (t CO$_2$ per TJ)	57.5	54.8	52.9	52.9	52.3	51.7	52.0	-9.7%
CO$_2$ / GDP (kg CO$_2$ per 2000 US$)	0.55	0.50	0.44	0.44	0.43	0.42	0.41	-25.5%
CO$_2$ / GDP (kg CO$_2$ per 2000 US$ PPP)	0.44	0.40	0.36	0.35	0.34	0.34	0.33	-26.2%
CO$_2$ / population (t CO$_2$ per capita)	7.86	7.56	7.55	7.70	7.68	7.60	7.60	-3.4%

Ratios are based on the Sectoral Approach.

2006 CO$_2$ emissions by sector

million tonnes of CO$_2$	Coal/peat	Oil	Gas	Other *	Total	% change 90-06
Sectoral Approach	**1 285.1**	**1 745.9**	**1 027.3**	**43.4**	**4 101.8**	**4.8%**
Main activity producer elec. and heat	928.5	64.2	264.5	14.8	1 271.9	10.8%
Unallocated autoproducers	72.5	28.2	63.7	12.5	176.9	-17.7%
Other energy industries	32.2	120.5	37.0	0.0	189.7	7.9%
Manufacturing industries and construction	193.5	248.0	238.7	14.2	694.3	-12.0%
Transport	0.0	984.3	3.9	-	988.1	27.7%
of which: road	*-*	*916.7*	*1.3*	*-*	*918.0*	*29.0%*
Other sectors	58.3	300.7	419.7	2.0	780.8	-3.7%
of which: residential	*47.2*	*171.1*	*288.4*	*0.0*	*506.8*	*-0.9%*
Reference Approach	**1 299.6**	**1 754.7**	**1 037.5**	**43.4**	**4 135.2**	**3.9%**
Diff. due to losses and/or transformation	15.0	20.8	7.6	0.0	43.4	
Statistical differences	- 0.5	- 12.0	2.5	0.0	- 9.9	
Memo: international marine bunkers	*-*	*172.5*	*-*	*-*	*172.5*	*55.9%*
Memo: international aviation	*-*	*131.8*	*-*	*-*	*131.8*	*93.3%*

* Other includes industrial waste and non-renewable municipal waste.

Key sources for CO$_2$ emissions from fuel combustion in 2006

IPCC source category	CO$_2$ emissions (Mt of CO$_2$)	% change 90-06	Level assessment (%) **	Cumulative total (%)
Main activity prod. elec. and heat - coal/peat	928.5	-2.0%	17.4	17.4
Road - oil	916.7	28.9%	17.2	34.7
Residential - gas	288.4	66.9%	5.4	40.1
Main activity prod. elec. and heat - gas	264.5	269.4%	5.0	45.1
Manufacturing industries - oil	248.0	-1.5%	4.7	49.7
Manufacturing industries - gas	238.7	18.4%	4.5	54.2
Manufacturing industries - coal/peat	193.5	-41.2%	3.6	57.8
Residential - oil	171.1	-13.6%	3.2	61.1
Non-specified other sectors - gas	131.3	58.8%	2.5	63.5
Non-specified other sectors - oil	129.6	-15.3%	2.4	66.0
Other energy industries - oil	120.5	5.7%	2.3	68.2
Memo: total CO$_2$ from fuel combustion	*4 101.8*	*4.8%*	*77.1*	*77.1*

** Percent calculated using the total GHG estimate for CO$_2$, CH$_4$, N$_2$O, HFCs, PFCs and SF$_6$ excluding CO$_2$ emissions/removals from land use change and forestry.

European Union - 27 / Union européenne - 27

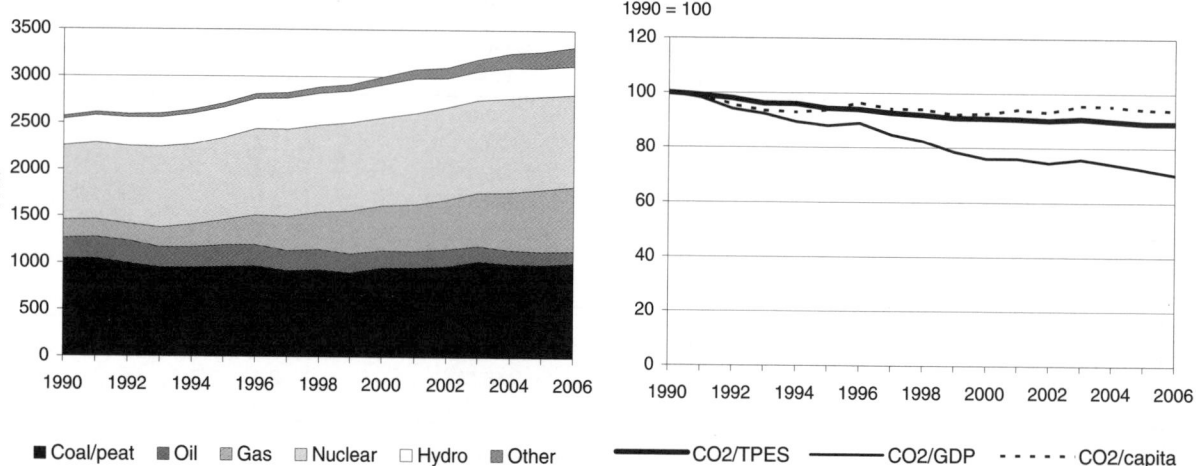

Figure 1. CO_2 emissions by fuel

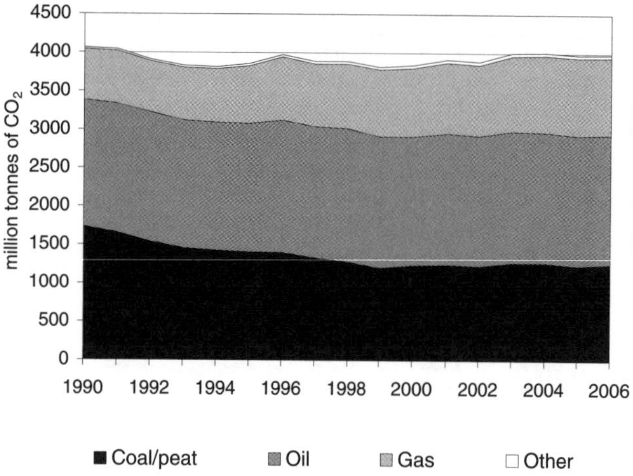

4500
4000
3500
3000
2500
2000
1500
1000
500
0
million tonnes of CO2
1990
1992
1994
1996
1998
2000
2002
2004
2006
Coal/peat
Oil
Gas
Other

Figure 2. CO_2 emissions by sector

4500
4000
3500
3000
2500
2000
1500
1000
500
0
million tonnes of CO2
1990
1992
1994
1996
1998
2000
2002
2004
2006
Electricity and heat
Other energy industries
Manuf. ind. and construction
Transport
Residential
Other

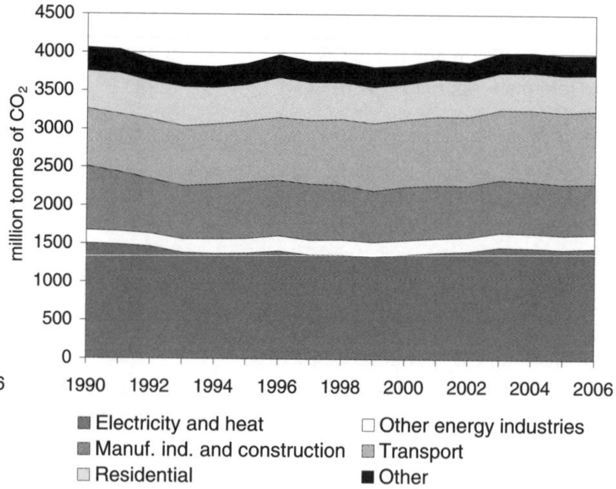

Figure 3. CO_2 emissions by sector

100%
80%
60%
40%
20%
0%
not available
1971
1990
2006
Electricity and heat
Other energy industries
Manuf. ind. and construction
Transport
Residential
Other

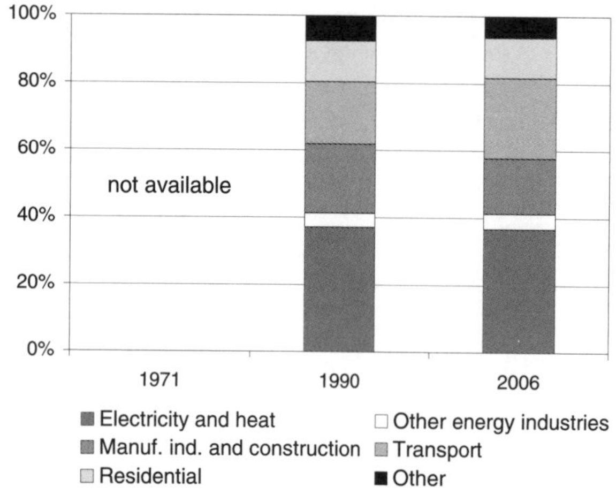

Figure 4. Reference vs Sectoral Approach

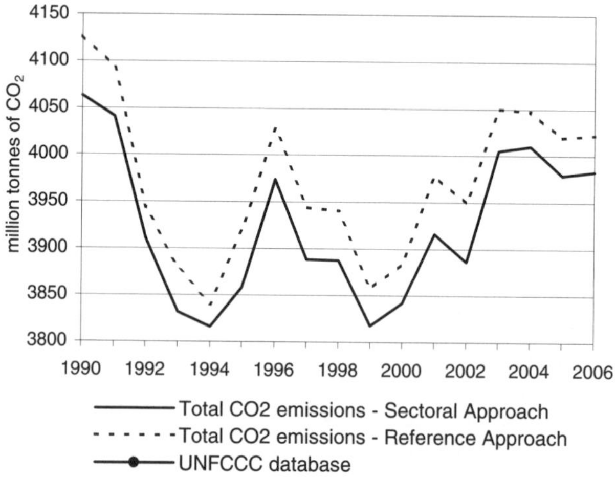

4150
4100
4050
4000
3950
3900
3850
3800
million tonnes of CO2
1990
1992
1994
1996
1998
2000
2002
2004
2006
Total CO2 emissions - Sectoral Approach
Total CO2 emissions - Reference Approach
UNFCCC database

Figure 5. Electricity generation by fuel

3500
3000
2500
2000
1500
1000
500
0
TWh
1990
1992
1994
1996
1998
2000
2002
2004
2006
Coal/peat
Oil
Gas
Nuclear
Hydro
Other

Figure 6. Key indicators

1990 = 100
120
100
80
60
40
20
0
1990
1992
1994
1996
1998
2000
2002
2004
2006
CO2/TPES
CO2/GDP
CO2/capita

European Union - 27 / Union européenne - 27
Key indicators

	1990	1995	2000	2003	2004	2005	2006	% change 90-06
CO$_2$ Sectoral Approach (Mt of CO$_2$)	4 063.1	3 857.9	3 841.6	4 004.9	4 009.9	3 978.7	3 983.0	-2.0%
CO$_2$ Reference Approach (Mt of CO$_2$)	4 126.2	3 919.9	3 884.3	4 050.0	4 047.6	4 019.4	4 022.2	-2.5%
TPES (PJ)	69 329	69 767	72 191	75 269	76 103	76 245	76 304	10.1%
TPES (Mtoe)	1 655.9	1 666.3	1 724.2	1 797.8	1 817.7	1 821.1	1 822.5	10.1%
GDP (billion 2000 US$ using exch. rates)	6 799.4	7 334.6	8 455.2	8 842.0	9 060.1	9 223.4	9 500.6	39.7%
GDP (billion 2000 US$ using PPPs)	8 548.3	9 144.3	10 544.8	11 071.0	11 364.5	11 590.4	11 962.6	39.9%
Population (millions)	472.9	478.7	482.9	487.6	489.8	492.0	493.8	4.4%
CO$_2$ / TPES (t CO$_2$ per TJ)	58.6	55.3	53.2	53.2	52.7	52.2	52.2	-10.9%
CO$_2$ / GDP (kg CO$_2$ per 2000 US$)	0.60	0.53	0.45	0.45	0.44	0.43	0.42	-29.9%
CO$_2$ / GDP (kg CO$_2$ per 2000 US$ PPP)	0.48	0.42	0.36	0.36	0.35	0.34	0.33	-29.9%
CO$_2$ / population (t CO$_2$ per capita)	8.59	8.06	7.95	8.21	8.19	8.09	8.07	-6.1%

Ratios are based on the Sectoral Approach.

2006 CO$_2$ emissions by sector

million tonnes of CO$_2$	Coal/peat	Oil	Gas	Other *	Total	% change 90-06
Sectoral Approach	**1 262.5**	**1 681.7**	**998.7**	**40.1**	**3 983,0**	**-2.0%**
Main activity producer elec. and heat	951.5	70.8	254.3	14.3	1 290.9	1.3%
Unallocated autoproducers	70.3	27.5	60.9	11.0	169.7	-26.2%
Other energy industries	32.2	119.9	29.1	0.2	181.3	5.4%
Manufacturing industries and construction	158.7	239.8	243.8	13.5	655.8	-21.3%
Transport	0.0	947.7	4.3	-	952.0	26.4%
of which: road	-	*888.1*	*1.3*	-	*889.4*	*28.0%*
Other sectors	49.9	276.0	406.3	1.1	733.3	-8.4%
of which: residential	*38.3*	*159.1*	*278.6*	*0.0*	*476.1*	*-3.9%*
Reference Approach	**1 278.0**	**1 691.8**	**1 012.3**	**40.2**	**4 022.2**	**-2.5%**
Diff. due to losses and/or transformation	16.6	20.1	9.8	0.0	46.5	
Statistical differences	- 1.1	- 10.1	3.9	0.0	- 7.4	
Memo: international marine bunkers	-	*170.9*	-	-	*170.9*	*53.2%*
Memo: international aviation	-	*126.2*	-	-	*126.2*	*90.3%*

* Other includes industrial waste and non-renewable municipal waste.

Key sources for CO$_2$ emissions from fuel combustion in 2006

IPCC source category	CO$_2$ emissions (Mt of CO$_2$)	% change 90-06	Level assessment (%) **	Cumulative total (%)
Main activity prod. elec. and heat - coal/peat	951.5	-5.3%	18.4	18.4
Road - oil	888.1	27.9%	17.1	35.5
Residential - gas	278.6	56.9%	5.4	40.9
Main activity prod. elec. and heat - gas	254.3	144.7%	4.9	45.8
Manufacturing industries - gas	243.8	-2.4%	4.7	50.5
Manufacturing industries - oil	239.8	-4.8%	4.6	55.1
Residential - oil	159.1	-11.9%	3.1	58.2
Manufacturing industries - coal/peat	158.7	-51.2%	3.1	61.2
Non-specified other sectors - gas	127.7	50.1%	2.5	63.7
Other energy industries - oil	119.9	3.3%	2.3	66.0
Non-specified other sectors - oil	116.8	-23.4%	2.3	68.2
Memo: total CO$_2$ from fuel combustion	*3 983.0*	*-2.0%*	*76.8*	*76.8*

** Percent calculated using the total GHG estimate for CO$_2$, CH$_4$, N$_2$O, HFCs, PFCs and SF$_6$ excluding CO$_2$ emissions/removals from land use change and forestry.

Africa / Afrique

Figure 1. CO$_2$ emissions by fuel

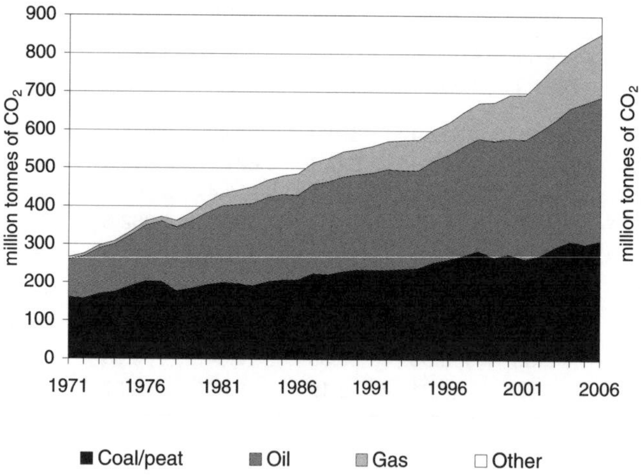

■ Coal/peat   ■ Oil   ■ Gas   □ Other

Figure 2. CO$_2$ emissions by sector

■ Electricity and heat   □ Other energy industries
■ Manuf. ind. and construction   ■ Transport
□ Residential   ■ Other

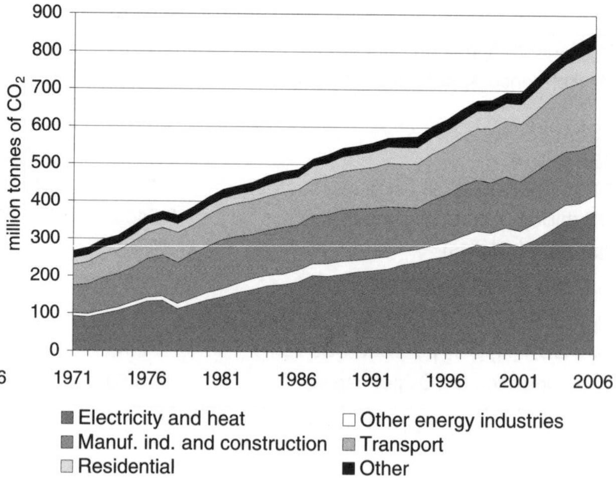

Figure 3. CO$_2$ emissions by sector

■ Electricity and heat   □ Other energy industries
■ Manuf. ind. and construction   ■ Transport
□ Residential   ■ Other

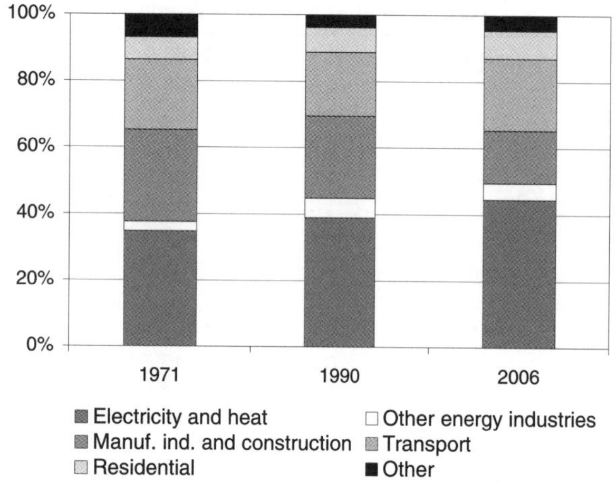

Figure 4. Reference vs Sectoral Approach

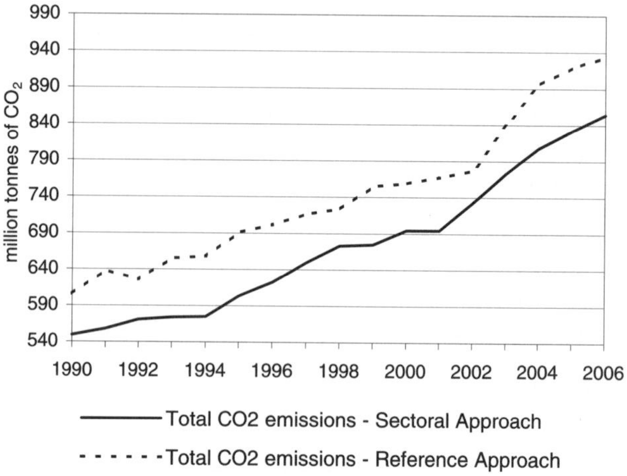

——— Total CO2 emissions - Sectoral Approach
- - - - Total CO2 emissions - Reference Approach

Figure 5. Electricity generation by fuel

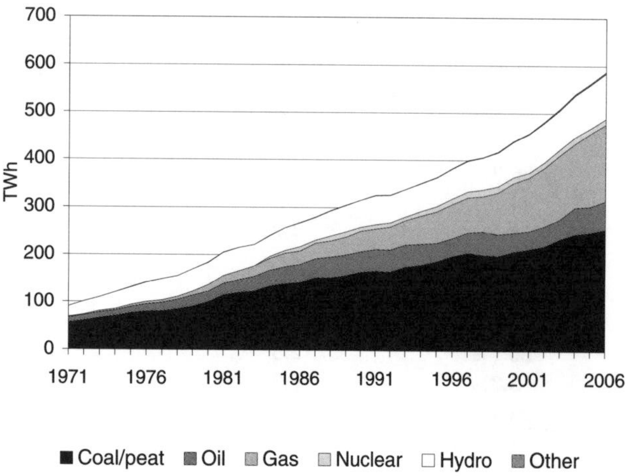

■ Coal/peat   ■ Oil   ■ Gas   ■ Nuclear   □ Hydro   ■ Other

Figure 6. Key indicators

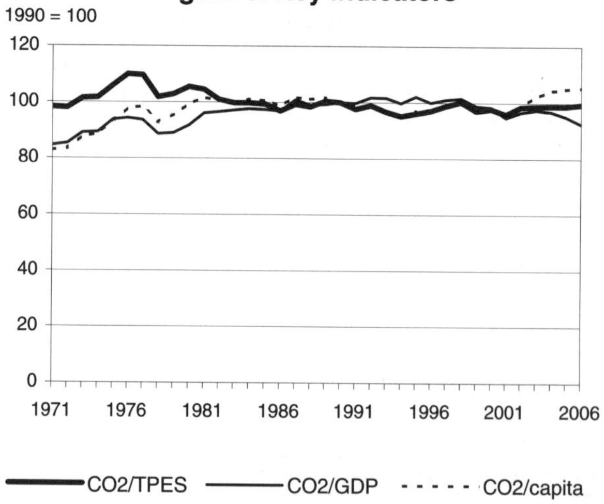

1990 = 100

——— CO2/TPES   ——— CO2/GDP   - - - - CO2/capita

Africa / Afrique
Key indicators

	1990	1995	2000	2003	2004	2005	2006	% change 90-06
CO$_2$ Sectoral Approach (Mt of CO$_2$)	549.3	603.2	694.4	773.1	807.8	831.8	854.2	55.5%
CO$_2$ Reference Approach (Mt of CO$_2$)	605.2	691.0	759.4	840.0	895.7	919.2	933.8	54.3%
TPES (PJ)	16 441	18 788	21 244	23 440	24 461	25 171	25 718	56.4%
TPES (Mtoe)	392.7	448.7	507.4	559.9	584.2	601.2	614.3	56.4%
GDP (billion 2000 US$ using exch. rates)	459.6	494.2	590.8	663.8	697.6	732.4	773.3	68.3%
GDP (billion 2000 US$ using PPPs)	1 331.5	1 417.4	1 692.4	1 892.5	1 989.8	2 089.6	2 207.4	65.8%
Population (millions)	634.9	719.3	815.2	874.8	895.2	916.2	937.5	47.6%
CO$_2$ / TPES (t CO$_2$ per TJ)	33.4	32.1	32.7	33.0	33.0	33.0	33.2	-0.6%
CO$_2$ / GDP (kg CO$_2$ per 2000 US$)	1.20	1.22	1.18	1.16	1.16	1.14	1.10	-7.6%
CO$_2$ / GDP (kg CO$_2$ per 2000 US$ PPP)	0.41	0.43	0.41	0.41	0.41	0.40	0.39	-6.2%
CO$_2$ / population (t CO$_2$ per capita)	0.87	0.84	0.85	0.88	0.90	0.91	0.91	5.3%

Ratios are based on the Sectoral Approach.

2006 CO$_2$ emissions by sector

million tonnes of CO$_2$	Coal/peat	Oil	Gas	Other *	Total	% change 90-06
Sectoral Approach	**313.3**	**375.7**	**165.2**	-	**854.2**	**55.5%**
Main activity producer elec. and heat	228.3	47.0	87.4	-	362.7	80.4%
Unallocated autoproducers	11.3	5.4	0.1	-	16.7	34.0%
Other energy industries	0.1	14.9	28.2	-	43.2	33.4%
Manufacturing industries and construction	52.9	51.4	31.2	-	135.4	-0.5%
Transport	0.0	180.5	4.2	-	184.8	75.2%
of which: road	-	*168.4*	*0.7*	-	*169.1*	*70.3%*
Other sectors	20.8	76.6	14.1	-	111.4	80.0%
of which: residential	*12.7*	*45.6*	*13.2*	-	*71.4*	*75.2%*
Reference Approach	**397.3**	**360.0**	**176.5**	-	**933.8**	**54.3%**
Diff. due to losses and/or transformation	82.4	- 15.7	11.5	-	78.2	
Statistical differences	1.6	0.1	- 0.3	-	1.4	
Memo: international marine bunkers	-	*19.1*	-	-	*19.1*	*14.0%*
Memo: international aviation	-	*15.9*	-	-	*15.9*	*50.1%*

* Other includes industrial waste and non-renewable municipal waste.

Key sources for CO$_2$ emissions from fuel combustion in 2006

IPCC source category	CO$_2$ emissions (Mt of CO$_2$)	% change 90-06	Level assessment (%) **	Cumulative total (%)
Main activity prod. elec. and heat - coal/peat	228.3	59.4%	9.9	9.9
Road - oil	168.4	69.6%	7.3	17.2
Main activity prod. elec. and heat - gas	87.4	236.6%	3.8	21.0
Manufacturing industries - coal/peat	52.9	-25.1%	2.3	23.3
Manufacturing industries - oil	51.4	1.9%	2.2	25.5
Main activity prod. elec. and heat - oil	47.0	47.6%	2.0	27.5
Residential - oil	45.6	44.0%	2.0	29.5
Manufacturing industries - gas	31.2	106.2%	1.4	30.9
Non-specified other sectors - oil	31.0	101.7%	1.3	32.2
Other energy industries - gas	28.2	37.5%	1.2	33.4
Other energy industries - oil	14.9	27.9%	0.6	34.1
Memo: total CO$_2$ from fuel combustion	*854.2*	*55.5%*	*37.0*	*37.0*

** Percent calculated using the total GHG estimate for CO$_2$, CH$_4$, N$_2$O, HFCs, PFCs and SF$_6$ excluding CO$_2$ emissions/removals from land use change and forestry.

Middle East / Moyen-Orient

Figure 1. CO$_2$ emissions by fuel

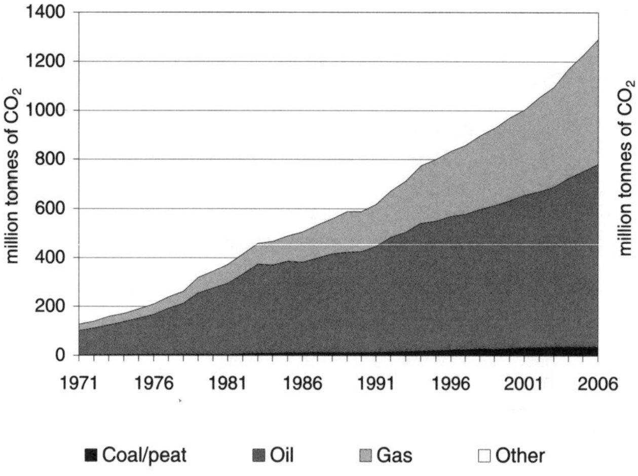

■ Coal/peat   ■ Oil   ▨ Gas   ☐ Other

Figure 2. CO$_2$ emissions by sector

■ Electricity and heat   ☐ Other energy industries
■ Manuf. ind. and construction ▨ Transport
▨ Residential   ■ Other

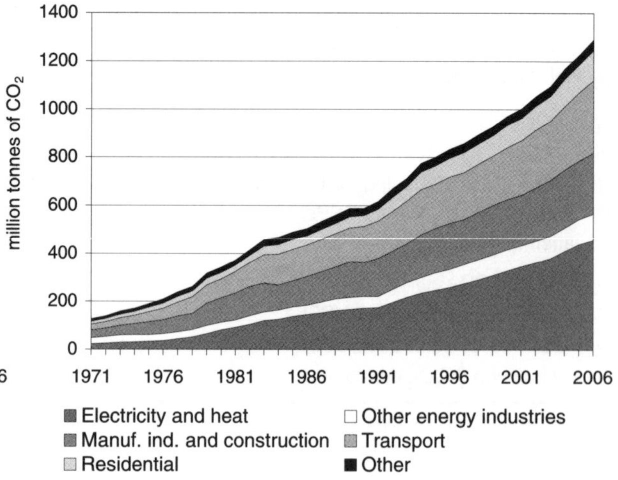

Figure 3. CO$_2$ emissions by sector

■ Electricity and heat   ☐ Other energy industries
■ Manuf. ind. and construction ▨ Transport
▨ Residential   ■ Other

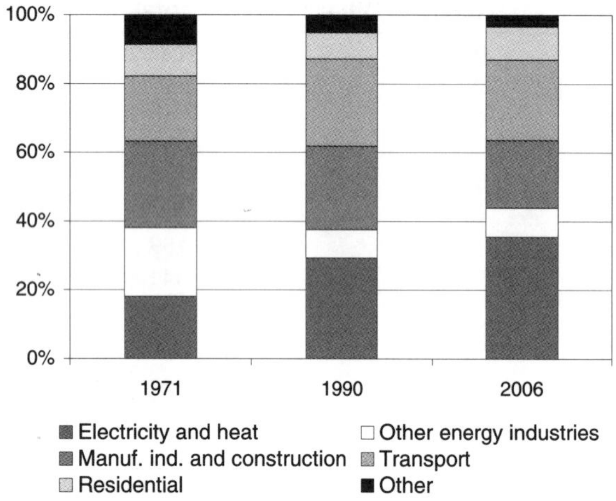

Figure 4. Reference vs Sectoral Approach

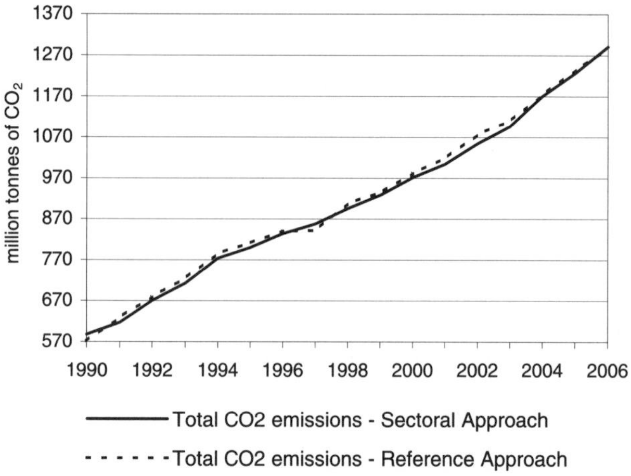

——— Total CO2 emissions - Sectoral Approach
- - - - - Total CO2 emissions - Reference Approach

Figure 5. Electricity generation by fuel

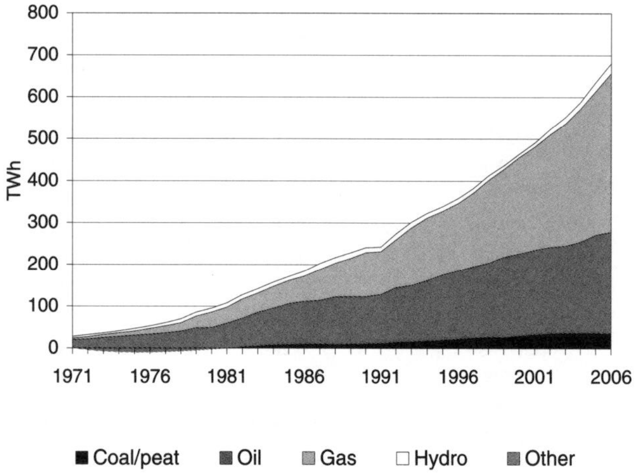

■ Coal/peat   ■ Oil   ▨ Gas   ☐ Hydro   ▨ Other

Figure 6. Key indicators

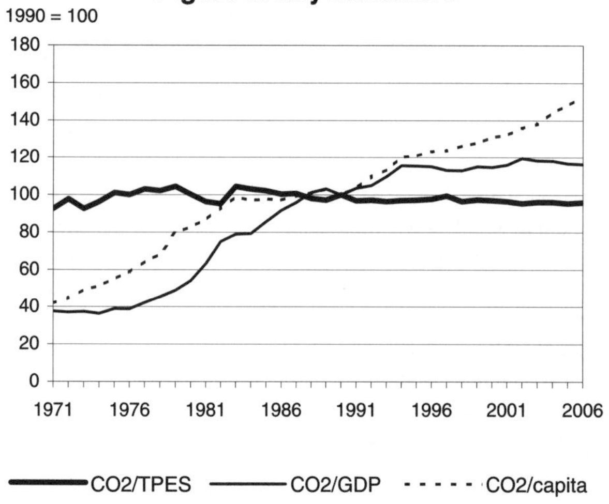

—— CO2/TPES   —— CO2/GDP   - - - - CO2/capita

Middle East / Moyen-Orient

Key indicators

	1990	1995	2000	2003	2004	2005	2006	% change 90-06
CO$_2$ Sectoral Approach (Mt of CO$_2$)	587.9	800.4	971.5	1 096.6	1 170.6	1 227.2	1 291.0	119.6%
CO$_2$ Reference Approach (Mt of CO$_2$)	571.4	811.8	982.0	1 110.7	1 174.4	1 235.1	1 286.8	125.2%
TPES (PJ)	9 566	13 403	16 285	18 577	19 826	20 917	21 885	128.8%
TPES (Mtoe)	228.5	320.1	389.0	443.7	473.5	499.6	522.7	128.8%
GDP (billion 2000 US$ using exch. rates)	443.6	523.5	639.1	699.4	747.8	793.1	837.8	88.8%
GDP (billion 2000 US$ using PPPs)	770.6	911.0	1 104.6	1 228.4	1 305.5	1 378.8	1 455.5	88.9%
Population (millions)	131.5	147.9	165.9	177.4	181.3	185.3	189.3	44.0%
CO$_2$ / TPES (t CO$_2$ per TJ)	61.5	59.7	59.7	59.0	59.0	58.7	59.0	-4.0%
CO$_2$ / GDP (kg CO$_2$ per 2000 US$)	1.33	1.53	1.52	1.57	1.57	1.55	1.54	16.3%
CO$_2$ / GDP (kg CO$_2$ per 2000 US$ PPP)	0.76	0.88	0.88	0.89	0.90	0.89	0.89	16.3%
CO$_2$ / population (t CO$_2$ per capita)	4.47	5.41	5.85	6.18	6.46	6.62	6.82	52.5%

Ratios are based on the Sectoral Approach.

2006 CO$_2$ emissions by sector

million tonnes of CO$_2$	Coal/peat	Oil	Gas	Other *	Total	% change 90-06
Sectoral Approach	**35.7**	**745.5**	**509.8**	-	**1 291.0**	**119.6%**
Main activity producer elec. and heat	30.9	184.2	201.9	-	417.0	189.4%
Unallocated autoproducers	0.1	6.3	33.2	-	39.6	41.1%
Other energy industries	-	40.5	69.1	-	109.5	125.5%
Manufacturing industries and construction	4.7	126.7	121.3	-	252.8	77.8%
Transport	-	301.9	1.0	-	303.0	102.4%
of which: road	-	*299.5*	*1.0*	-	*300.5*	*103.6%*
Other sectors	0.0	85.8	83.3	-	169.1	124.6%
of which: residential	*0.0*	*51.6*	*72.9*	-	*124.5*	*176.8%*
Reference Approach	**35.1**	**734.1**	**517.6**	-	**1 286.8**	**125.2%**
Diff. due to losses and/or transformation	0.5	- 4.9	10.4	-	6.1	
Statistical differences	- 1.2	- 6.5	- 2.6	-	- 10.3	
Memo: international marine bunkers	-	*53.9*	-	-	*53.9*	*86.3%*
Memo: international aviation	-	*32.8*	-	-	*32.8*	*21.4%*

* Other includes industrial waste and non-renewable municipal waste.

Key sources for CO$_2$ emissions from fuel combustion in 2006

IPCC source category	CO$_2$ emissions (Mt of CO$_2$)	% change 90-06	Level assessment (%) **	Cumulative total (%)
Road - oil	299.5	102.9%	17.4	17.4
Main activity prod. elec. and heat - gas	201.9	285.3%	11.7	29.1
Main activity prod. elec. and heat - oil	184.2	123.5%	10.7	39.8
Manufacturing industries - oil	126.7	57.9%	7.4	47.2
Manufacturing industries - gas	121.3	103.8%	7.0	54.2
Residential - gas	72.9	+	4.2	58.5
Other energy industries - gas	69.1	222.1%	4.0	62.5
Residential - oil	51.6	32.6%	3.0	65.5
Other energy industries - oil	40.5	49.1%	2.3	67.8
Non-specified other sectors - oil	34.3	20.6%	2.0	69.8
Unallocated autoproducers - gas	33.2	55.8%	1.9	71.7
Memo: total CO$_2$ from fuel combustion	*1 291.0*	*119.6%*	*75.0*	*75.0*

** Percent calculated using the total GHG estimate for CO$_2$, CH$_4$, N$_2$O, HFCs, PFCs and SF$_6$ excluding CO$_2$ emissions/removals from land use change and forestry.

Non-OECD Europe / Europe non-OCDE

Figure 1. CO$_2$ emissions by fuel

Figure 2. CO$_2$ emissions by sector

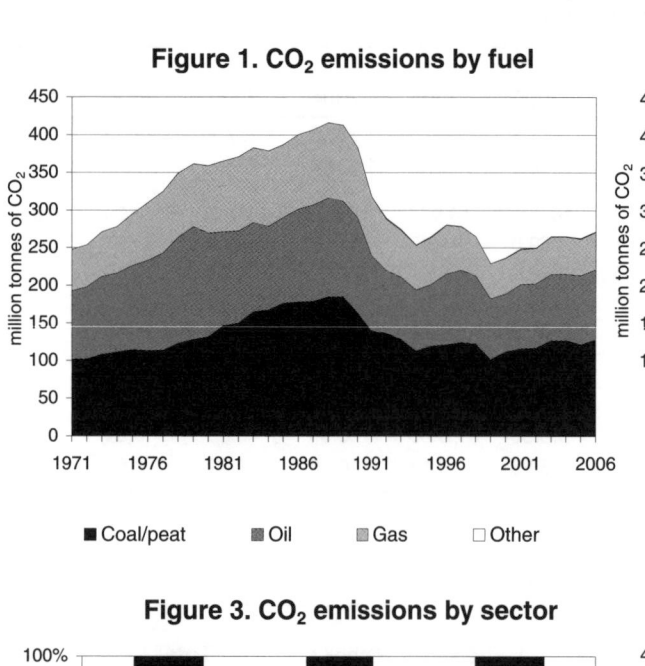

■ Coal/peat　　■ Oil　　▨ Gas　　□ Other

■ Electricity and heat　　□ Other energy industries
▨ Manuf. ind. and construction　　▨ Transport
▨ Residential　　■ Other

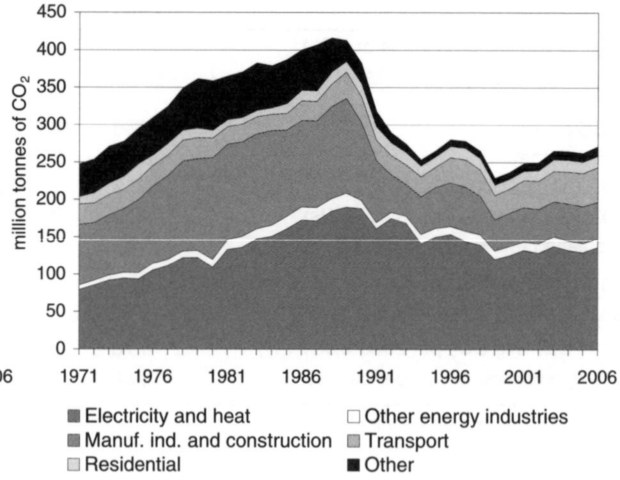

Figure 3. CO$_2$ emissions by sector

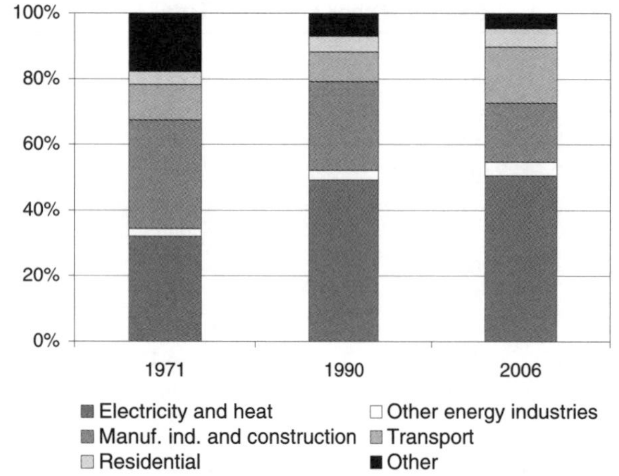

Figure 4. Reference vs Sectoral Approach

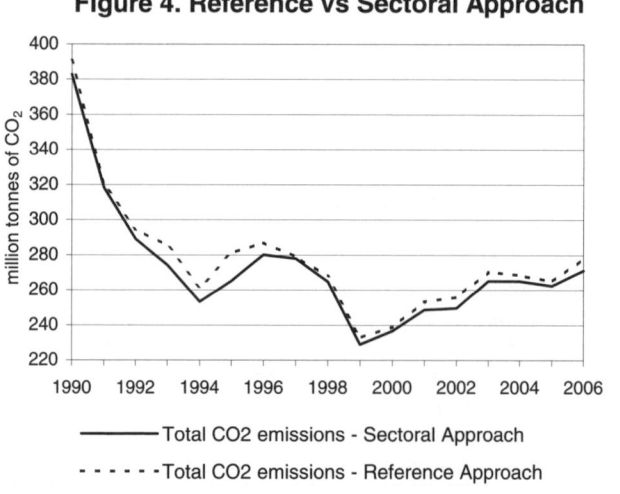

■ Electricity and heat　　□ Other energy industries
▨ Manuf. ind. and construction　　▨ Transport
▨ Residential　　■ Other

——— Total CO2 emissions - Sectoral Approach

- - - - - Total CO2 emissions - Reference Approach

Figure 5. Electricity generation by fuel

Figure 6. Key indicators

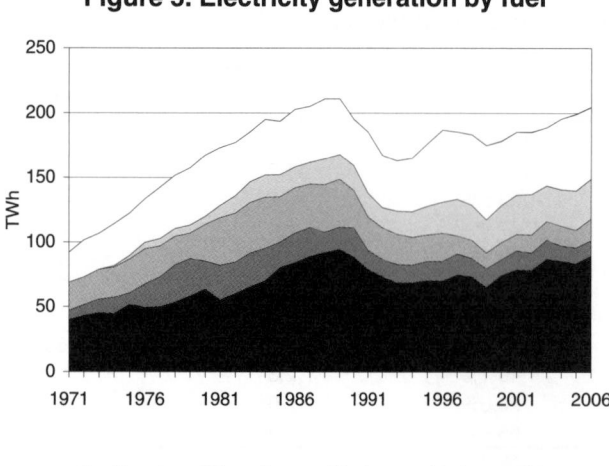

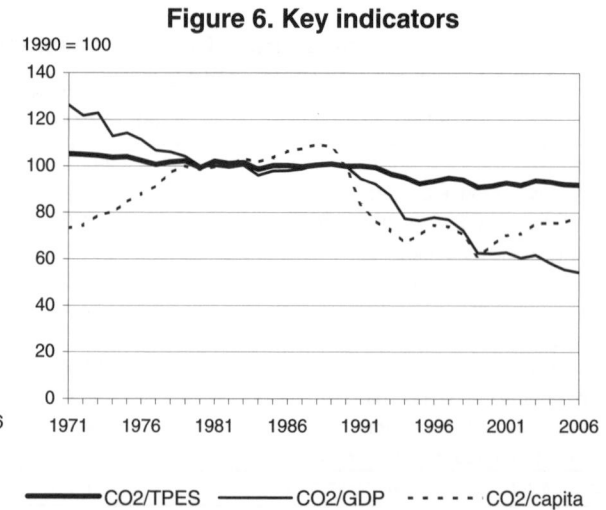

■ Coal/peat　■ Oil　▨ Gas　▨ Nuclear　□ Hydro　■ Other

——— CO2/TPES　——— CO2/GDP　- - - - CO2/capita

Non-OECD Europe / Europe non-OCDE
Key indicators

	1990	1995	2000	2003	2004	2005	2006	% change 90-06
CO$_2$ Sectoral Approach (Mt of CO$_2$)	382.8	265.1	236.6	265.2	265.1	262.4	271.2	-29.1%
CO$_2$ Reference Approach (Mt of CO$_2$)	390.7	281.0	239.1	270.5	268.6	265.0	278.1	-28.8%
TPES (PJ)	5 875	4 401	3 971	4 338	4 364	4 373	4 530	-22.9%
TPES (Mtoe)	140.3	105.1	94.8	103.6	104.2	104.5	108.2	-22.9%
GDP (billion 2000 US$ using exch. rates)	124.4	112.5	123.4	139.4	147.7	153.3	162.2	30.5%
GDP (billion 2000 US$ using PPPs)	371.1	333.0	357.2	406.2	432.8	449.1	476.8	28.5%
Population (millions)	59.1	58.2	55.2	54.3	54.2	53.6	53.5	-9.5%
CO$_2$ / TPES (t CO$_2$ per TJ)	65.2	60.2	59.6	61.1	60.7	60.0	59.9	-8.1%
CO$_2$ / GDP (kg CO$_2$ per 2000 US$)	3.08	2.36	1.92	1.90	1.79	1.71	1.67	-45.7%
CO$_2$ / GDP (kg CO$_2$ per 2000 US$ PPP)	1.03	0.80	0.66	0.65	0.61	0.58	0.57	-44.8%
CO$_2$ / population (t CO$_2$ per capita)	6.48	4.56	4.29	4.88	4.89	4.90	5.07	-21.7%

Ratios are based on the Sectoral Approach.

2006 CO$_2$ emissions by sector

million tonnes of CO$_2$	Coal/peat	Oil	Gas	Other *	Total	% change 90-06
Sectoral Approach	**128.4**	**92.6**	**49.5**	**0.7**	**271.2**	**-29.1%**
Main activity producer elec. and heat	103.8	10.4	13.9	-	128.0	-24.6%
Unallocated autoproducers	4.5	2.5	1.7	0.0	8.7	-52.8%
Other energy industries	1.7	7.2	2.3	0.2	11.4	1.3%
Manufacturing industries and construction	13.9	16.3	18.5	0.5	49.1	-52.7%
Transport	0.0	45.4	0.7	-	46.0	34.5%
of which: road	*-*	*44.1*	*0.1*	*-*	*44.1*	*39.1%*
Other sectors	4.6	10.9	12.5	0.0	27.9	-38.2%
of which: residential	*3.0*	*4.2*	*8.1*	*-*	*15.3*	*-16.4%*
Reference Approach	**130.6**	**94.2**	**52.5**	**0.7**	**278.1**	**-28.8%**
Diff. due to losses and/or transformation	3.6	0.3	2.3	-	6.2	
Statistical differences	- 1.4	1.3	0.7	- 0.0	0.7	
Memo: international marine bunkers	*-*	*5.2*	*-*	*-*	*5.2*	*163.6%*
Memo: international aviation	*-*	*2.7*	*-*	*-*	*2.7*	*-12.4%*

* Other includes industrial waste and non-renewable municipal waste.

Key sources for CO$_2$ emissions from fuel combustion in 2006

IPCC source category	CO$_2$ emissions (Mt of CO$_2$)	% change 90-06	Level assessment (%) **	Cumulative total (%)
Main activity prod. elec. and heat - coal/peat	103.8	-5.6%	26.0	26.0
Road - oil	44.1	38.9%	11.0	37.0
Manufacturing industries - gas	18.5	-63.8%	4.6	41.7
Manufacturing industries - oil	16.3	-37.0%	4.1	45.7
Manufacturing industries - coal/peat	13.9	-48.8%	3.5	49.2
Main activity prod. elec. and heat - gas	13.9	-52.4%	3.5	52.7
Main activity prod. elec. and heat - oil	10.4	-66.0%	2.6	55.3
Residential - gas	8.1	39.0%	2.0	57.3
Other energy industries - oil	7.2	-25.9%	1.8	59.1
Non-specified other sectors - oil	6.7	-43.9%	1.7	60.8
Unallocated autoproducers - coal/peat	4.5	-49.9%	1.1	61.9
Memo: total CO$_2$ from fuel combustion	*271.2*	*-29.1%*	*67.9*	*67.9*

** Percent calculated using the total GHG estimate for CO$_2$, CH$_4$, N$_2$O, HFCs, PFCs and SF$_6$ excluding CO$_2$ emissions/removals from land use change and forestry.

Former USSR / Ex-URSS *

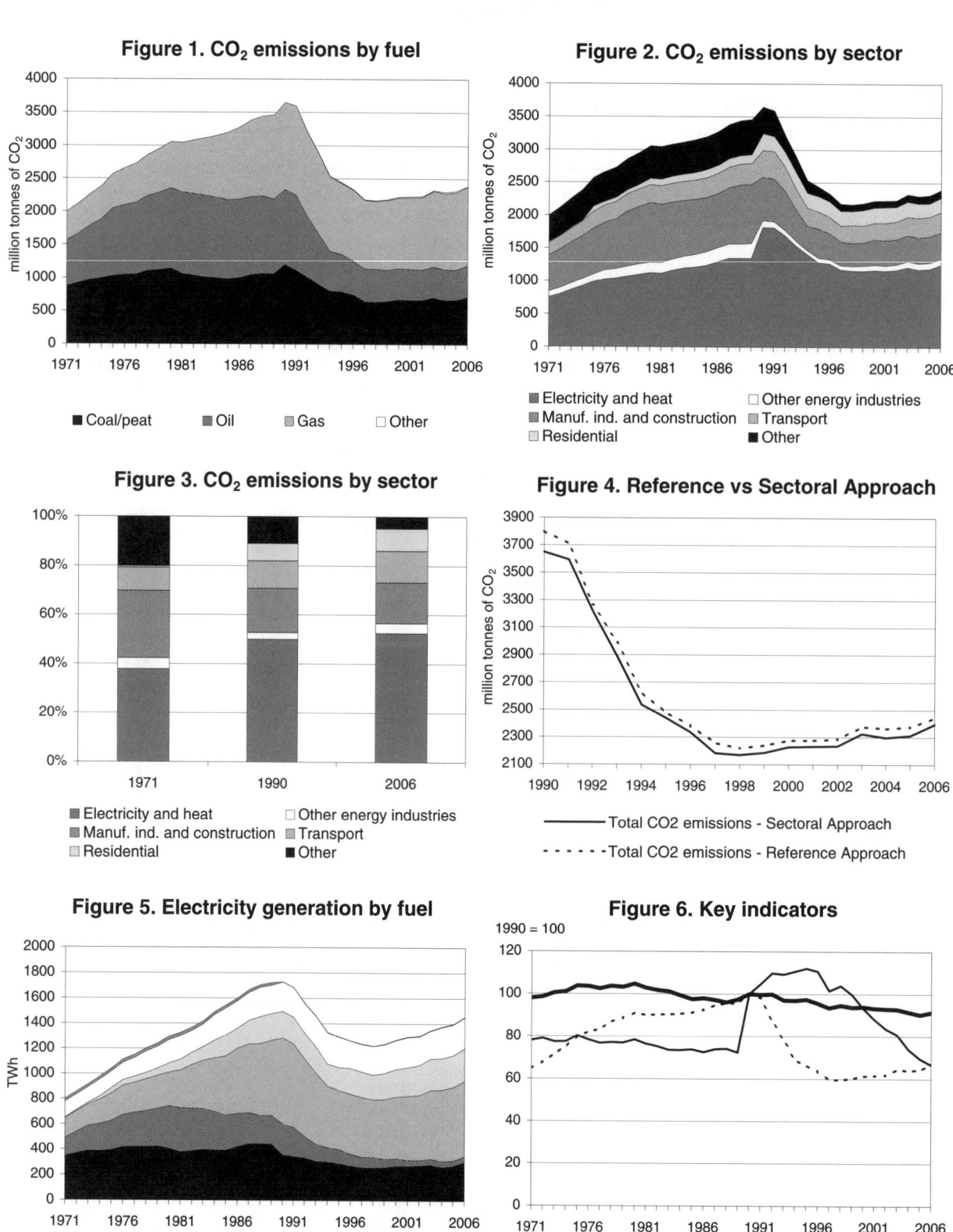

Figure 1. CO$_2$ emissions by fuel

■ Coal/peat   ■ Oil   ■ Gas   □ Other

Figure 2. CO$_2$ emissions by sector

■ Electricity and heat   □ Other energy industries
■ Manuf. ind. and construction ■ Transport
□ Residential   ■ Other

Figure 3. CO$_2$ emissions by sector

■ Electricity and heat   □ Other energy industries
■ Manuf. ind. and construction ■ Transport
□ Residential   ■ Other

Figure 4. Reference vs Sectoral Approach

—— Total CO2 emissions - Sectoral Approach
- - - - Total CO2 emissions - Reference Approach

Figure 5. Electricity generation by fuel

■ Coal/peat   ■ Oil   ■ Gas   ■ Nuclear   □ Hydro   ■ Other

Figure 6. Key indicators

1990 = 100

—— CO2/TPES   —— CO2/GDP   - - - - CO2/capita

* Data for 1990 and 1991 have been revised for the individual countries of Former USSR. This causes breaks in the regional time series.

Former USSR / Ex-URSS *

Key indicators

	1990	1995	2000	2003	2004	2005	2006	% change 90-06
CO$_2$ Sectoral Approach (Mt of CO$_2$)	3 649.5	2 439.3	2 227.5	2 325.7	2 298.3	2 312.7	2 394.6	-34.4%
CO$_2$ Reference Approach (Mt of CO$_2$)	3 799.4	2 478.9	2 276.0	2 375.8	2 362.9	2 375.3	2 442.5	-35.7%
TPES (PJ)	59 358	40 747	38 539	40 736	40 870	41 630	42 591	-28.2%
TPES (Mtoe)	1 417.7	973.2	920.5	973.0	976.2	994.3	1 017.3	-28.2%
GDP (billion 2000 US$ using exch. rates)	577.1	344.1	377.4	455.1	491.9	526.2	567.7	-1.6%
GDP (billion 2000 US$ using PPPs)	2 377.6	1 394.5	1 506.0	1 820.2	1 971.9	2 102.7	2 266.1	-4.7%
Population (millions)	289.1	290.9	287.8	285.8	285.2	284.7	284.4	-1.6%
CO$_2$ / TPES (t CO$_2$ per TJ)	61.5	59.9	57.8	57.1	56.2	55.6	56.2	-8.6%
CO$_2$ / GDP (kg CO$_2$ per 2000 US$)	6.32	7.09	5.90	5.11	4.67	4.40	4.22	-33.3%
CO$_2$ / GDP (kg CO$_2$ per 2000 US$ PPP)	1.53	1.75	1.48	1.28	1.17	1.10	1.06	-31.2%
CO$_2$ / population (t CO$_2$ per capita)	12.62	8.39	7.74	8.14	8.06	8.12	8.42	-33.3%

Ratios are based on the Sectoral Approach.
* Data for 1990 and 1991 have been estimated for the individual countries of Former USSR. This may cause breaks in the regional time series.

2006 CO$_2$ emissions by sector

million tonnes of CO$_2$	Coal/peat	Oil	Gas	Other **	Total	% change 90-06
Sectoral Approach	**716.3**	**477.7**	**1 182.8**	**17.8**	**2 394.6**	**-34.4%**
Main activity producer elec. and heat	386.4	35.5	440.8	0.1	862.7	-51.1%
Unallocated autoproducers	141.7	34.9	200.9	14.5	392.0	634.8%
Other energy industries	6.9	46.6	44.3	1.4	99.2	-2.9%
Manufacturing industries and construction	148.3	75.0	172.9	1.8	397.9	-39.5%
Transport	0.0	217.6	89.9	-	307.5	-25.2%
of which: road	-	*182.5*	*0.5*	-	*182.9*	*-27.8%*
Other sectors	33.0	68.2	233.9	0.1	335.2	-49.2%
of which: residential	*20.9*	*25.7*	*170.6*	-	*217.2*	*-15.0%*
Reference Approach	**711.6**	**504.1**	**1 208.1**	**18.7**	**2 442.5**	**-35.7%**
Diff. due to losses and/or transformation	- 3.4	26.6	25.4	0.9	49.5	
Statistical differences	- 1.3	- 0.2	- 0.1	-	- 1.6	
Memo: international marine bunkers	-	*1.7*	-	-	*1.7*	*-79.1%*
Memo: international aviation	-	*20.1*	-	-	*20.1*	*-47.2%*

** Other includes industrial waste and non-renewable municipal waste.

Key sources for CO$_2$ emissions from fuel combustion in 2006

IPCC source category	CO$_2$ emissions (Mt of CO$_2$)	% change 90-06	Level assessment (%) ***	Cumulative total (%)
Main activity prod. elec. and heat - gas	440.8	-38.4%	12.1	12.1
Main activity prod. elec. and heat - coal/peat	386.4	-44.7%	10.6	22.8
Unallocated autoproducers - gas	200.9	478.3%	5.5	28.3
Road - oil	182.5	-27.2%	5.0	33.4
Manufacturing industries - gas	172.9	-8.4%	4.8	38.1
Residential - gas	170.6	18.9%	4.7	42.8
Manufacturing industries - coal/peat	148.3	-47.0%	4.1	46.9
Unallocated autoproducers - coal/peat	141.7	+	3.9	50.8
Other transport - gas	89.4	15.4%	2.5	53.3
Manufacturing industries - oil	75.0	-60.4%	2.1	55.4
Non-specified other sectors - gas	63.3	-46.4%	1.7	57.1
Memo: total CO$_2$ from fuel combustion	*2 394.6*	*-34.4%*	*66.0*	*66.0*

*** Percent calculated using the total GHG estimate for CO$_2$, CH$_4$, N$_2$O, HFCs, PFCs and SF$_6$ excluding CO$_2$ emissions/removals from land use change and forestry.

Latin America / Amérique latine

Figure 1. CO₂ emissions by fuel

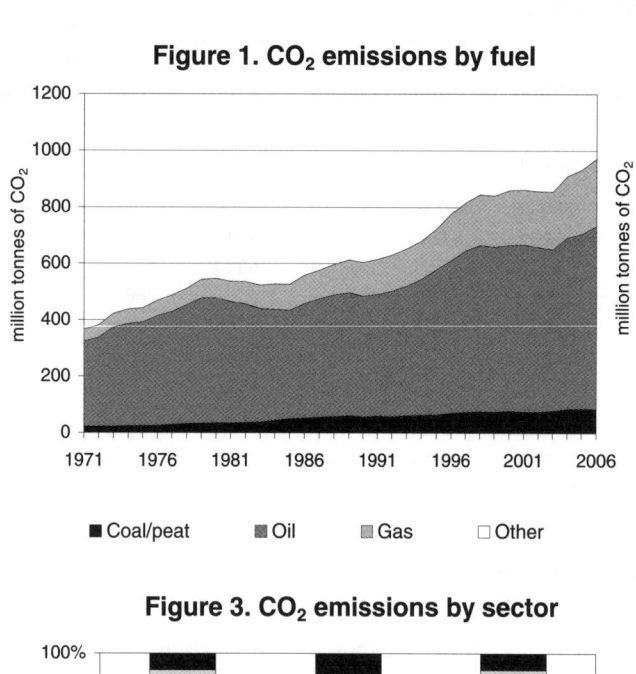

Figure 2. CO₂ emissions by sector

- Electricity and heat
- Manuf. ind. and construction
- Residential
- Other energy industries
- Transport
- Other

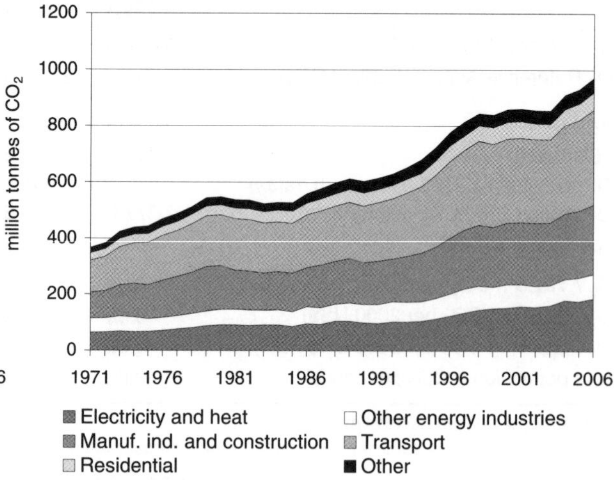

Figure 3. CO₂ emissions by sector

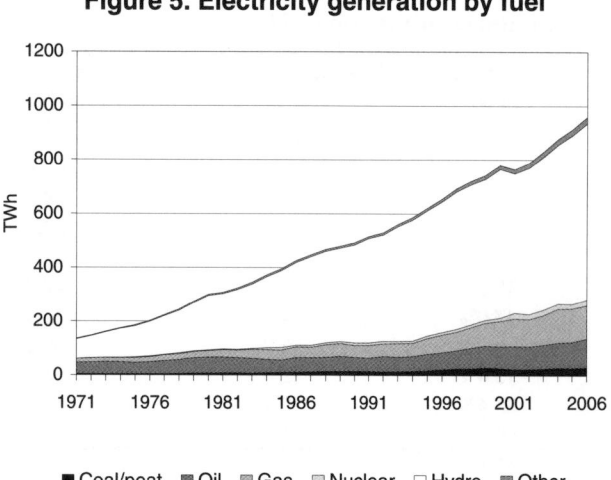

- Electricity and heat
- Manuf. ind. and construction
- Residential
- Other energy industries
- Transport
- Other

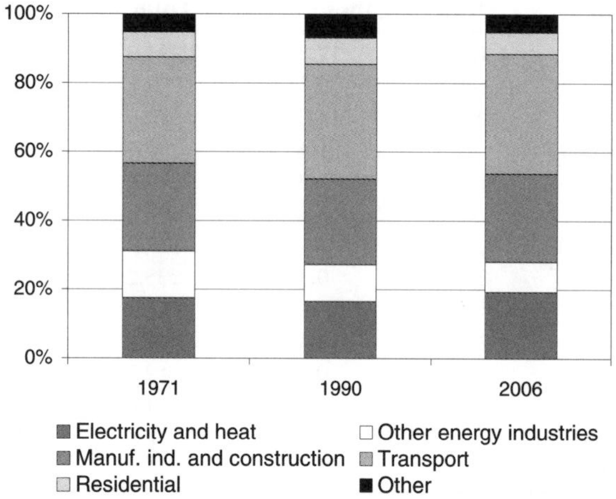

Figure 4. Reference vs Sectoral Approach

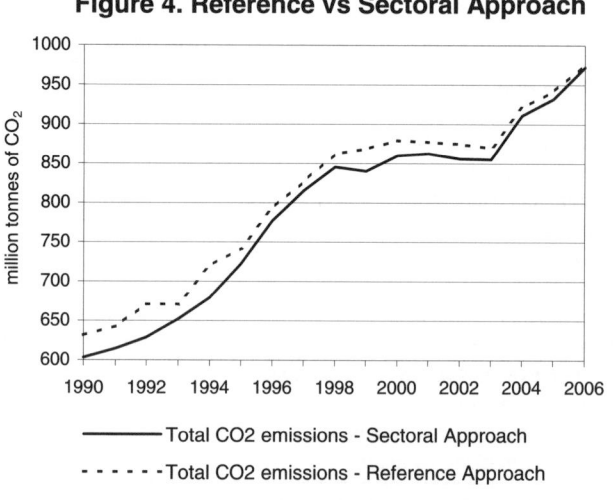

—— Total CO2 emissions - Sectoral Approach
- - - - Total CO2 emissions - Reference Approach

Figure 5. Electricity generation by fuel

- Coal/peat
- Oil
- Gas
- Nuclear
- Hydro
- Other

Figure 6. Key indicators

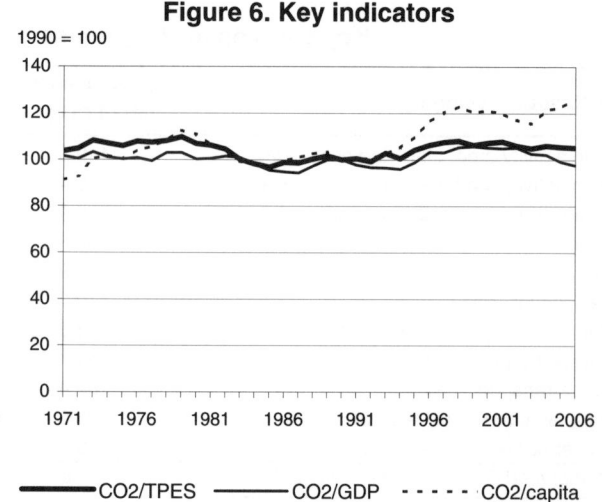

—— CO2/TPES
—— CO2/GDP
- - - - CO2/capita

Latin America / Amérique latine

Key indicators

	1990	1995	2000	2003	2004	2005	2006	% change 90-06
CO$_2$ Sectoral Approach (Mt of CO$_2$)	603.1	722.3	859.8	855.0	910.9	931.9	972.1	61.2%
CO$_2$ Reference Approach (Mt of CO$_2$)	631.4	741.9	879.1	869.2	921.2	941.9	976.3	54.6%
TPES (PJ)	14 498	16 653	19 265	19 587	20 656	21 223	22 216	53.2%
TPES (Mtoe)	346.3	397.8	460.1	467.8	493.4	506.9	530.6	53.2%
GDP (billion 2000 US$ using exch. rates)	1 087.6	1 316.3	1 474.1	1 503.5	1 607.5	1 694.9	1 796.0	65.1%
GDP (billion 2000 US$ using PPPs)	2 078.2	2 500.4	2 803.7	2 891.9	3 076.9	3 236.2	3 424.5	64.8%
Population (millions)	356.3	387.8	418.9	437.1	443.1	449.1	455.0	27.7%
CO$_2$ / TPES (t CO$_2$ per TJ)	41.6	43.4	44.6	43.6	44.1	43.9	43.8	5.2%
CO$_2$ / GDP (kg CO$_2$ per 2000 US$)	0.55	0.55	0.58	0.57	0.57	0.55	0.54	-2.4%
CO$_2$ / GDP (kg CO$_2$ per 2000 US$ PPP)	0.29	0.29	0.31	0.30	0.30	0.29	0.28	-2.2%
CO$_2$ / population (t CO$_2$ per capita)	1.69	1.86	2.05	1.96	2.06	2.08	2.14	26.2%

Ratios are based on the Sectoral Approach.

2006 CO$_2$ emissions by sector

million tonnes of CO$_2$	Coal/peat	Oil	Gas	Other *	Total	% change 90-06
Sectoral Approach	**85.1**	**648.1**	**238.9**	**-**	**972.1**	**61.2%**
Main activity producer elec. and heat	27.0	69.7	54.9	-	151.6	103.0%
Unallocated autoproducers	12.1	12.7	9.8	-	34.6	41.6%
Other energy industries	3.3	43.0	40.3	-	86.6	32.7%
Manufacturing industries and construction	42.1	112.9	93.3	-	248.3	66.1%
Transport	0.1	323.7	14.2	-	337.9	68.0%
of which: road	-	*298.6*	*11.8*	-	*310.4*	*70.6%*
Other sectors	0.6	86.1	26.4	-	113.2	28.4%
of which: residential	*0.5*	*40.9*	*20.5*	-	*62.0*	*33.5%*
Reference Approach	**84.6**	**652.5**	**239.1**	**-**	**976.3**	**54.6%**
Diff. due to losses and/or transformation	1.1	20.9	1.7	-	23.7	
Statistical differences	- 1.6	- 16.5	- 1.5	-	- 19.6	
Memo: international marine bunkers	-	*30.5*	-	-	*30.5*	*94.7%*
Memo: international aviation	-	*16.5*	-	-	*16.5*	*77.1%*

* Other includes industrial waste and non-renewable municipal waste.

Key sources for CO$_2$ emissions from fuel combustion in 2006

IPCC source category	CO$_2$ emissions (Mt of CO$_2$)	% change 90-06	Level assessment (%) **	Cumulative total (%)
Road - oil	298.6	64.5%	12.1	12.1
Manufacturing industries - oil	112.9	46.3%	4.6	16.7
Manufacturing industries - gas	93.3	125.5%	3.8	20.5
Main activity prod. elec. and heat - oil	69.7	87.5%	2.8	23.3
Main activity prod. elec. and heat - gas	54.9	112.0%	2.2	25.5
Non-specified other sectors - oil	45.2	22.8%	1.8	27.4
Other energy industries - oil	43.0	41.6%	1.7	29.1
Manufacturing industries - coal/peat	42.1	36.2%	1.7	30.8
Residential - oil	40.9	14.5%	1.7	32.5
Other energy industries - gas	40.3	27.2%	1.6	34.1
Main activity prod. elec. and heat - coal/peat	27.0	132.8%	1.1	35.2
Memo: total CO$_2$ from fuel combustion	*972.1*	*61.2%*	*39.5*	*39.5*

** Percent calculated using the total GHG estimate for CO$_2$, CH$_4$, N$_2$O, HFCs, PFCs and SF$_6$ excluding CO$_2$ emissions/removals from land use change and forestry.

Asia (excluding China) / Asie (Chine non incluse)

Figure 1. CO_2 emissions by fuel

million tonnes of CO2
3000
2500
2000
1500
1000
500
0
1971
1976
1981
1986
1991
1996
2001
2006
Coal/peat
Oil
Gas
Other

Figure 2. CO_2 emissions by sector

million tonnes of CO2
3000
2500
2000
1500
1000
500
0
1971
1976
1981
1986
1991
1996
2001
2006
Electricity and heat
Manuf. ind. and construction
Residential
Other energy industries
Transport
Other

Figure 3. CO_2 emissions by sector

100%
80%
60%
40%
20%
0%
1971
1990
2006
Electricity and heat
Manuf. ind. and construction
Residential
Other energy industries
Transport
Other

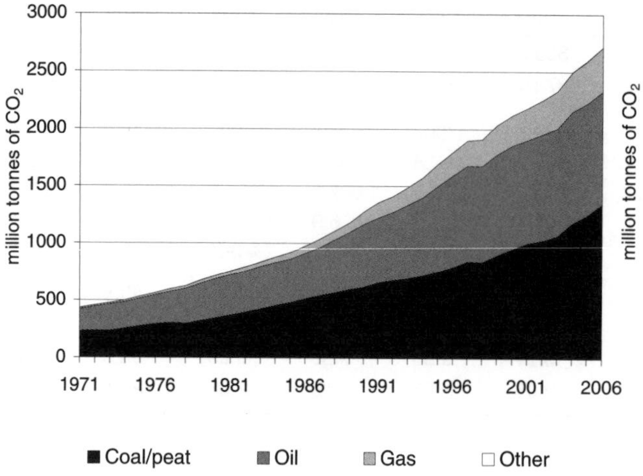

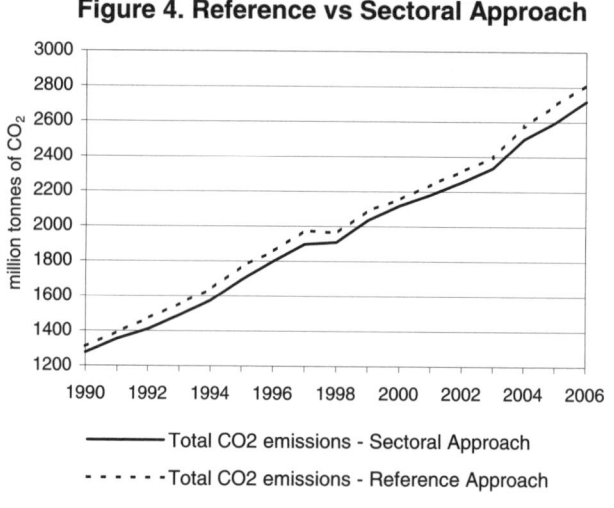

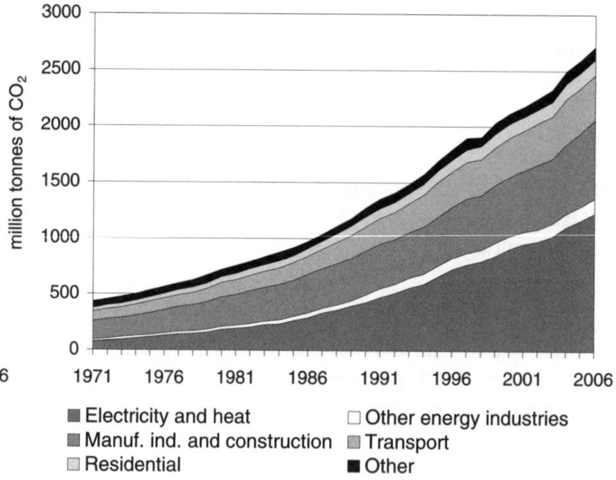

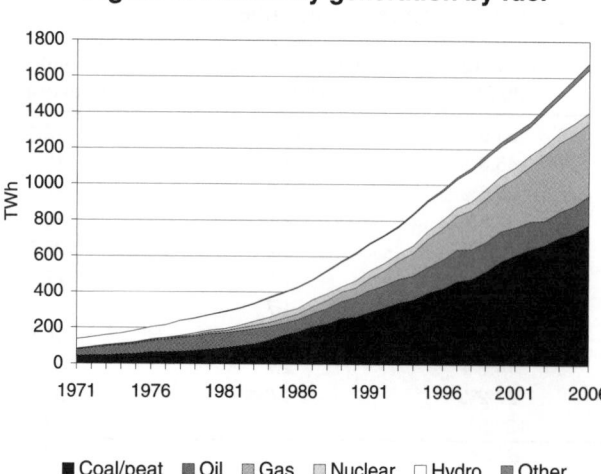

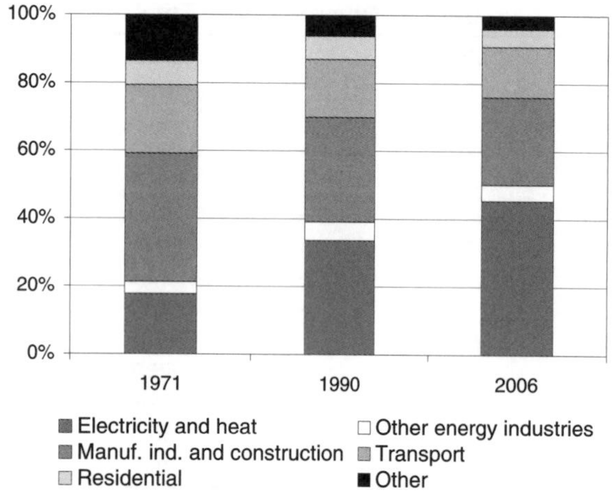

Figure 4. Reference vs Sectoral Approach

million tonnes of CO2
3000
2800
2600
2400
2200
2000
1800
1600
1400
1200
1990
1992
1994
1996
1998
2000
2002
2004
2006
Total CO2 emissions - Sectoral Approach
Total CO2 emissions - Reference Approach

Figure 5. Electricity generation by fuel

TWh
1800
1600
1400
1200
1000
800
600
400
200
0
1971
1976
1981
1986
1991
1996
2001
2006
Coal/peat
Oil
Gas
Nuclear
Hydro
Other

Figure 6. Key indicators

1990 = 100
180
160
140
120
100
80
60
40
20
0
1971
1976
1981
1986
1991
1996
2001
2006
CO2/TPES
CO2/GDP
CO2/capita

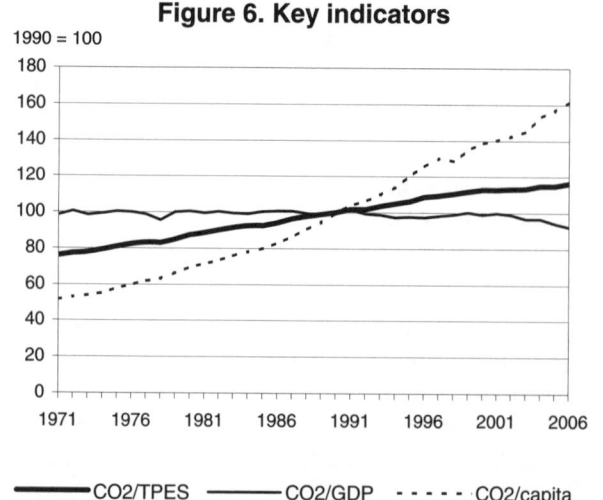

Asia (excluding China) / Asie (Chine non incluse)

Key indicators

	1990	1995	2000	2003	2004	2005	2006	% change 90-06
CO$_2$ Sectoral Approach (Mt of CO$_2$)	1 274.6	1 693.4	2 120.0	2 334.7	2 501.0	2 597.7	2 717.8	113.2%
CO$_2$ Reference Approach (Mt of CO$_2$)	1 308.5	1 768.8	2 156.5	2 398.3	2 579.1	2 700.6	2 812.9	115.0%
TPES (PJ)	30 347	37 939	44 769	49 038	51 815	53 824	55 667	83.4%
TPES (Mtoe)	724.8	906.2	1 069.3	1 171.3	1 237.6	1 285.6	1 329.6	83.4%
GDP (billion 2000 US$ using exch. rates)	925.1	1 257.0	1 553.8	1 753.8	1 878.6	2 001.7	2 138.6	131.2%
GDP (billion 2000 US$ using PPPs)	3 266.5	4 345.6	5 380.0	6 192.7	6 645.9	7 133.7	7 660.9	134.5%
Population (millions)	1 607.0	1 771.0	1 930.6	2 026.0	2 057.8	2 089.2	2 119.7	31.9%
CO$_2$ / TPES (t CO$_2$ per TJ)	42.0	44.6	47.4	47.6	48.3	48.3	48.8	16.2%
CO$_2$ / GDP (kg CO$_2$ per 2000 US$)	1.38	1.35	1.36	1.33	1.33	1.30	1.27	-7.8%
CO$_2$ / GDP (kg CO$_2$ per 2000 US$ PPP)	0.39	0.39	0.39	0.38	0.38	0.36	0.35	-9.1%
CO$_2$ / population (t CO$_2$ per capita)	0.79	0.96	1.10	1.15	1.22	1.24	1.28	61.7%

Ratios are based on the Sectoral Approach.

2006 CO$_2$ emissions by sector

million tonnes of CO$_2$	Coal/peat	Oil	Gas	Other *	Total	% change 90-06
Sectoral Approach	**1 345.8**	**985.9**	**384.0**	**2.1**	**2 717.8**	**113.2%**
Main activity producer elec. and heat	816.8	99.4	183.2	-	1 099.4	178.6%
Unallocated autoproducers	96.2	19.0	14.9	2.1	132.2	299.3%
Other energy industries	3.8	72.2	55.3	-	131.4	87.1%
Manufacturing industries and construction	368.7	228.8	103.4	-	700.9	78.2%
Transport	0.2	396.3	5.5	-	402.0	84.8%
of which: road	*-*	*368.8*	*2.3*	*-*	*371.1*	*93.4%*
Other sectors	60.1	170.1	21.6	-	251.9	51.8%
of which: residential	*14.8*	*108.5*	*17.2*	*-*	*140.5*	*62.9%*
Reference Approach	**1 370.9**	**1 022.5**	**417.5**	**2.1**	**2 812.9**	**115.0%**
Diff. due to losses and/or transformation	20.7	39.0	28.7	-	88.3	
Statistical differences	4.4	- 2.4	4.8	-	6.8	
Memo: international marine bunkers	*-*	*102.0*	*-*	*-*	*102.0*	*127.7%*
Memo: international aviation	*-*	*58.7*	*-*	*-*	*58.7*	*123.4%*

* Other includes industrial waste and non-renewable municipal waste.

Key sources for CO$_2$ emissions from fuel combustion in 2006

IPCC source category	CO$_2$ emissions (Mt of CO$_2$)	% change 90-06	Level assessment (%) **	Cumulative total (%)
Main activity prod. elec. and heat - coal/peat	816.8	201.3%	15.8	15.8
Road - oil	368.8	92.3%	7.1	22.9
Manufacturing industries - coal/peat	368.7	50.8%	7.1	30.1
Manufacturing industries - oil	228.8	103.1%	4.4	34.5
Main activity prod. elec. and heat - gas	183.2	425.6%	3.5	38.0
Residential - oil	108.5	60.2%	2.1	40.1
Manufacturing industries - gas	103.4	187.0%	2.0	42.1
Main activity prod. elec. and heat - oil	99.4	12.2%	1.9	44.1
Unallocated autoproducers - coal/peat	96.2	261.4%	1.9	45.9
Other energy industries - oil	72.2	121.4%	1.4	47.3
Non-specified other sectors - oil	61.6	101.4%	1.2	48.5
Memo: total CO$_2$ from fuel combustion	*2 717.8*	*113.2%*	*52.6*	*52.6*

** Percent calculated using the total GHG estimate for CO$_2$, CH$_4$, N$_2$O, HFCs, PFCs and SF$_6$ excluding CO$_2$ emissions/removals from land use change and forestry.

China (incl. Hong Kong) / Chine (Hong Kong incl.)

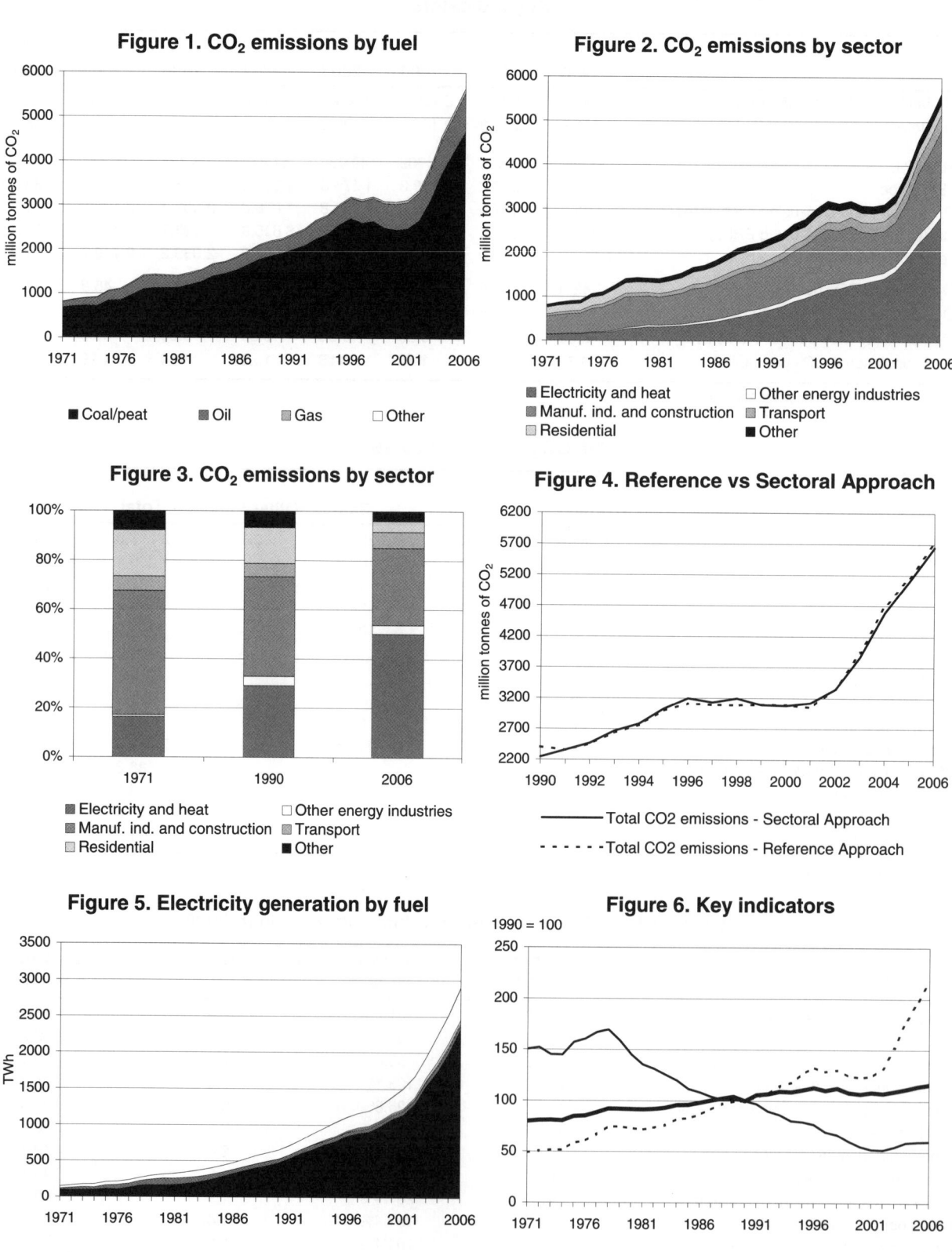

Figure 1. CO$_2$ emissions by fuel

- Coal/peat
- Oil
- Gas
- Other

Figure 2. CO$_2$ emissions by sector

- Electricity and heat
- Manuf. ind. and construction
- Residential
- Other energy industries
- Transport
- Other

Figure 3. CO$_2$ emissions by sector

- Electricity and heat
- Manuf. ind. and construction
- Residential
- Other energy industries
- Transport
- Other

Figure 4. Reference vs Sectoral Approach

Total CO2 emissions - Sectoral Approach
Total CO2 emissions - Reference Approach

Figure 5. Electricity generation by fuel

- Coal/peat
- Oil
- Gas
- Nuclear
- Hydro
- Other

Figure 6. Key indicators

1990 = 100

- CO2/TPES
- CO2/GDP
- CO2/capita

China (incl. Hong Kong) / Chine (Hong Kong incl.)

Key indicators

	1990	1995	2000	2003	2004	2005	2006	% change 90-06
CO$_2$ Sectoral Approach (Mt of CO$_2$)	2 244.0	3 021.8	3 077.6	3 871.1	4 587.3	5 100.5	5 648.5	151.7%
CO$_2$ Reference Approach (Mt of CO$_2$)	2 402.5	2 992.9	3 093.1	3 943.9	4 697.1	5 167.0	5 719.5	138.1%
TPES (PJ)	36 589	44 454	46 967	57 738	67 090	72 773	79 421	117.1%
TPES (Mtoe)	873.9	1 061.8	1 121.8	1 379.0	1 602.4	1 738.2	1 896.9	117.1%
GDP (billion 2000 US$ using exch. rates)	553.0	935.0	1 367.2	1 736.2	1 908.8	2 098.3	2 315.0	318.6%
GDP (billion 2000 US$ using PPPs)	1 957.9	3 438.3	5 149.9	6 651.0	7 320.0	8 061.2	8 915.7	355.4%
Population (millions)	1 140.9	1 211.0	1 269.3	1 295.2	1 302.9	1 311.3	1 318.7	15.6%
CO$_2$ / TPES (t CO$_2$ per TJ)	61.3	68.0	65.5	67.0	68.4	70.1	71.1	16.0%
CO$_2$ / GDP (kg CO$_2$ per 2000 US$)	4.06	3.23	2.25	2.23	2.40	2.43	2.44	-39.9%
CO$_2$ / GDP (kg CO$_2$ per 2000 US$ PPP)	1.15	0.88	0.60	0.58	0.63	0.63	0.63	-44.7%
CO$_2$ / population (t CO$_2$ per capita)	1.97	2.50	2.42	2.99	3.52	3.89	4.28	117.8%

Ratios are based on the Sectoral Approach.

2006 CO$_2$ emissions by sector

million tonnes of CO$_2$	Coal/peat	Oil	Gas	Other *	Total	% change 90-06
Sectoral Approach	**4 669.6**	**872.1**	**106.8**	-	**5 648.5**	**151.7%**
Main activity producer elec. and heat	2 707.6	37.9	17.8	-	2 763.3	331.3%
Unallocated autoproducers	50.2	15.3	-	-	65.5	459.5%
Other energy industries	122.6	65.7	16.2	-	204.5	142.4%
Manufacturing industries and construction	1 515.4	204.4	46.1	-	1 766.0	94.6%
Transport	14.1	356.9	0.1	-	371.2	206.7%
of which: road	-	*253.5*	*0.1*	-	*253.6*	*287.2%*
Other sectors	259.7	191.9	26.6	-	478.1	-0.2%
of which: residential	*175.4*	*51.8*	*20.1*	-	*247.3*	*-24.7%*
Reference Approach	**4 703.3**	**905.6**	**110.7**	-	**5 719.5**	**138.1%**
Diff. due to losses and/or transformation	82.6	29.4	2.5	-	114.6	
Statistical differences	- 48.9	4.0	1.4	-	- 43.5	
Memo: international marine bunkers	-	*48.9*	-	-	*48.9*	*436.5%*
Memo: international aviation	-	*21.3*	-	-	*21.3*	*248.3%*

* Other includes industrial waste and non-renewable municipal waste.

Key sources for CO$_2$ emissions from fuel combustion in 2006

IPCC source category	CO$_2$ emissions (Mt of CO$_2$)	% change 90-06	Level assessment (%) **	Cumulative total (%)
Main activity prod. elec. and heat - coal/peat	2 707.6	354.4%	33.4	33.4
Manufacturing industries - coal/peat	1 515.4	88.2%	18.7	52.2
Road - oil	253.5	287.0%	3.1	55.3
Manufacturing industries - oil	204.4	130.5%	2.5	57.8
Residential - coal/peat	175.4	-44.6%	2.2	60.0
Non-specified other sectors - oil	140.1	205.1%	1.7	61.7
Other energy industries - coal/peat	122.6	140.5%	1.5	63.2
Other transport - oil	103.5	506.7%	1.3	64.5
Non-specified other sectors - coal/peat	84.2	-19.1%	1.0	65.5
Other energy industries - oil	65.7	142.7%	0.8	66.4
Residential - oil	51.8	541.5%	0.6	67.0
Memo: total CO$_2$ from fuel combustion	*5 648.5*	*151.7%*	*69.8*	*69.8*

** Percent calculated using the total GHG estimate for CO$_2$, CH$_4$, N$_2$O, HFCs, PFCs and SF$_6$ excluding CO$_2$ emissions/removals from land use change and forestry.

COUNTRY TABLES

TABLEAUX PAR PAYS

Albania / Albanie

Figure 1. CO₂ emissions by fuel

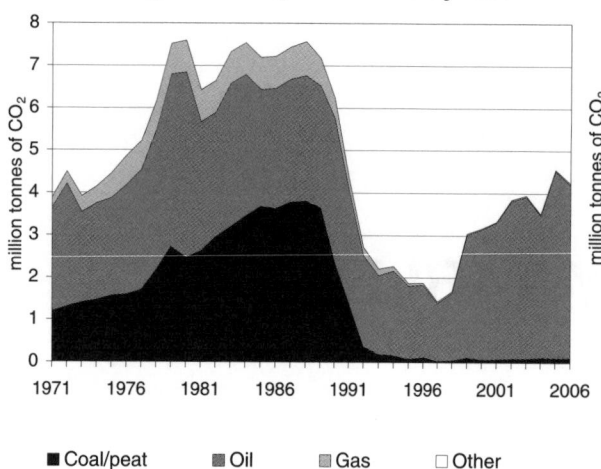

Coal/peat | Oil | Gas | Other

Figure 2. CO₂ emissions by sector

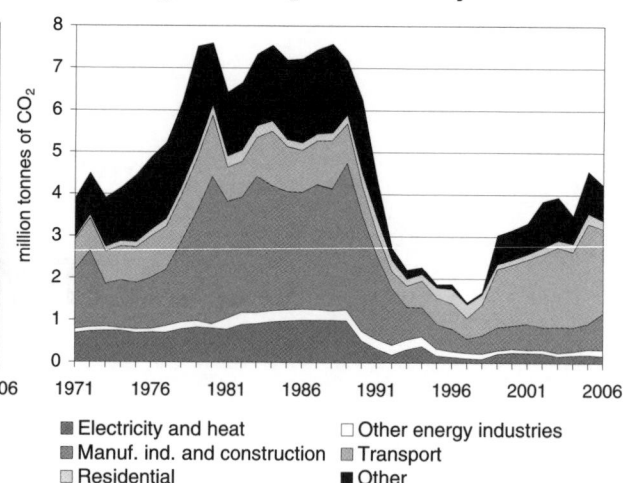

Electricity and heat | Other energy industries
Manuf. ind. and construction | Transport
Residential | Other

Figure 3. CO₂ emissions by sector

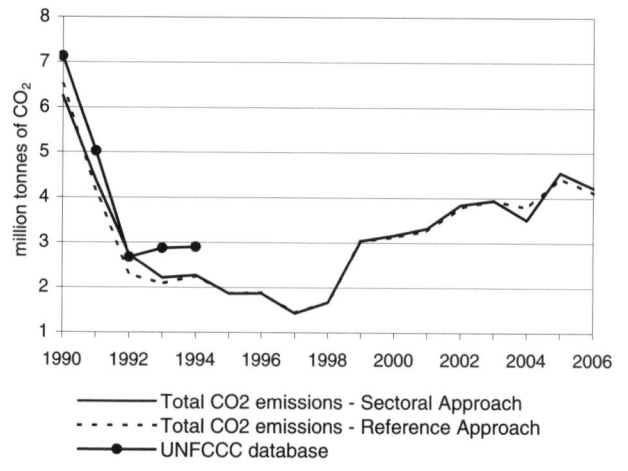

Electricity and heat | Other energy industries
Manuf. ind. and construction | Transport
Residential | Other

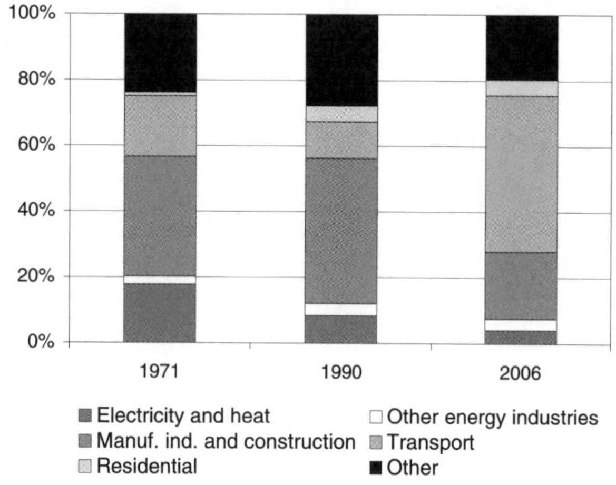

Figure 4. Reference vs Sectoral Approach

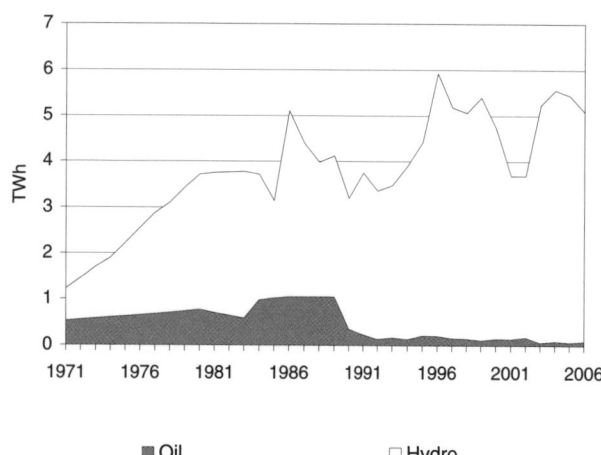

Total CO2 emissions - Sectoral Approach
Total CO2 emissions - Reference Approach
UNFCCC database

Figure 5. Electricity generation by fuel

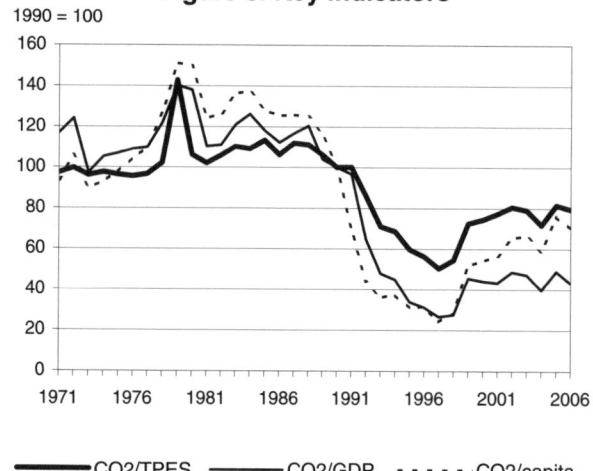

Oil | Hydro

Figure 6. Key indicators

1990 = 100

CO2/TPES | CO2/GDP | CO2/capita

Albania / Albanie

Key indicators

	1990	1995	2000	2003	2004	2005	2006	% change 90-06
CO$_2$ Sectoral Approach (Mt of CO$_2$)	6.25	1.86	3.16	3.94	3.50	4.56	4.23	-32.3%
CO$_2$ Reference Approach (Mt of CO$_2$)	6.51	1.87	3.13	3.94	3.79	4.44	4.11	-36.8%
TPES (PJ)	111	55	76	89	87	100	95	-14.8%
TPES (Mtoe)	2.66	1.32	1.81	2.13	2.08	2.38	2.27	-14.8%
GDP (billion 2000 US$ using exch. rates)	3.22	2.83	3.69	4.29	4.54	4.79	5.03	56.5%
GDP (billion 2000 US$ using PPPs)	9.93	8.73	11.39	13.25	14.03	14.81	15.55	56.5%
Population (millions)	3.29	3.15	3.08	3.12	3.13	3.15	3.17	-3.6%
CO$_2$ / TPES (t CO$_2$ per TJ)	56.0	33.5	41.7	44.3	40.2	45.7	44.5	-20.5%
CO$_2$ / GDP (kg CO$_2$ per 2000 US$)	1.94	0.66	0.86	0.92	0.77	0.95	0.84	-56.8%
CO$_2$ / GDP (kg CO$_2$ per 2000 US$ PPP)	0.63	0.21	0.28	0.30	0.25	0.31	0.27	-56.8%
CO$_2$ / population (t CO$_2$ per capita)	1.90	0.59	1.03	1.26	1.12	1.45	1.33	-29.8%

Ratios are based on the Sectoral Approach.

2006 CO$_2$ emissions by sector

million tonnes of CO$_2$	Coal/peat	Oil	Gas	Other *	Total	% change 90-06
Sectoral Approach	**0.10**	**4.09**	**0.03**	**-**	**4.23**	**-32.3%**
Main activity producer elec. and heat	0.03	-	-	-	0.03	-94.9%
Unallocated autoproducers	-	0.14	-	-	0.14	x
Other energy industries	-	0.12	0.03	-	0.15	-35.2%
Manufacturing industries and construction	0.06	0.81	-	-	0.87	-68.6%
Transport	-	2.01	-	-	2.01	187.3%
of which: road	-	*1.82*	-	-	*1.82*	*159.9%*
Other sectors	0.02	1.02	-	-	1.04	-49.3%
of which: residential	*0.02*	*0.19*	-	-	*0.20*	*-33.0%*
Reference Approach	**0.10**	**3.98**	**0.03**	**-**	**4.11**	**-36.8%**
Diff. due to losses and/or transformation	-	- 0.01	-	-	- 0.01	
Statistical differences	-	- 0.10	-	-	- 0.10	
Memo: international marine bunkers	-	..	-	-	..	..
Memo: international aviation	-	*0.25*	-	-	*0.25*	..

* Other includes industrial waste and non-renewable municipal waste.

Key sources for CO$_2$ emissions from fuel combustion in 2006

IPCC source category	CO$_2$ emissions (Mt of CO$_2$)	% change 90-06	Level assessment (%) **	Cumulative total (%)
Road - oil	1.82	159.9%	22.3	22.3
Non-specified other sectors - oil	0.83	x	10.2	32.5
Manufacturing industries - oil	0.81	-51.7%	9.9	42.4
Other transport - oil	0.19	x	2.3	44.7
Residential - oil	0.19	-33.8%	2.3	47.0
Unallocated autoproducers - oil	0.14	x	1.7	48.7
Other energy industries - oil	0.12	-49.9%	1.4	50.1
Manufacturing industries - coal/peat	0.06	-91.5%	0.7	50.9
Other energy industries - gas	0.03	x	0.4	51.3
Main activity prod. elec. and heat - coal/peat	0.03	x	0.3	51.6
Residential - coal/peat	0.02	x	0.2	51.8
Memo: total CO$_2$ from fuel combustion	*4.23*	*-32.3%*	*51.8*	*51.8*

** Percent calculated using the total GHG estimate for CO$_2$, CH$_4$, N$_2$O, HFCs, PFCs and SF$_6$ excluding CO$_2$ emissions/removals from land use change and forestry.

Algeria / Algérie

Figure 1. CO₂ emissions by fuel

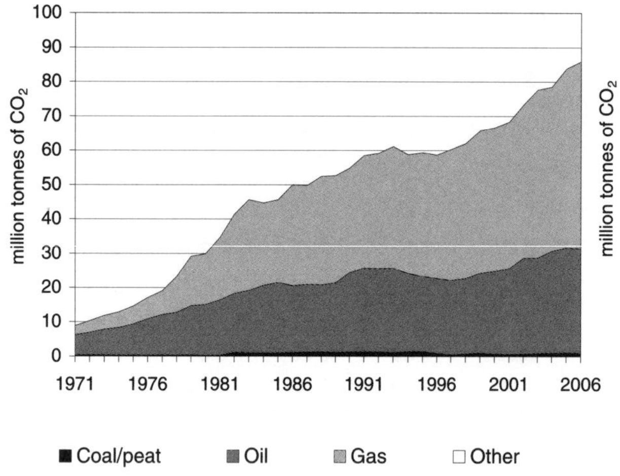

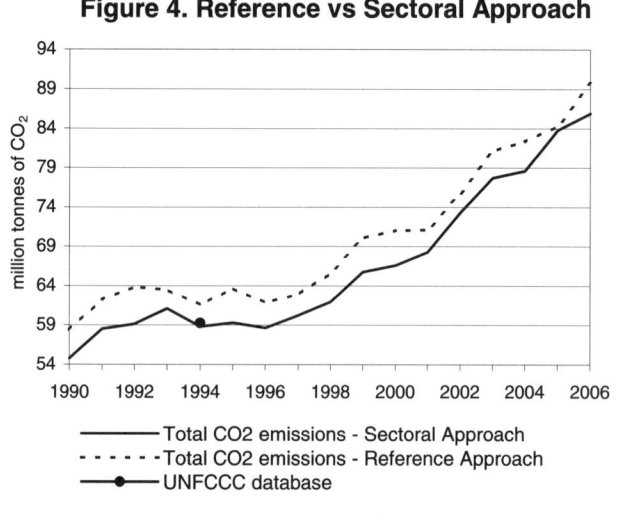

■ Coal/peat   ■ Oil   ■ Gas   □ Other

Figure 2. CO₂ emissions by sector

■ Electricity and heat   □ Other energy industries
■ Manuf. ind. and construction ■ Transport
■ Residential   ■ Other

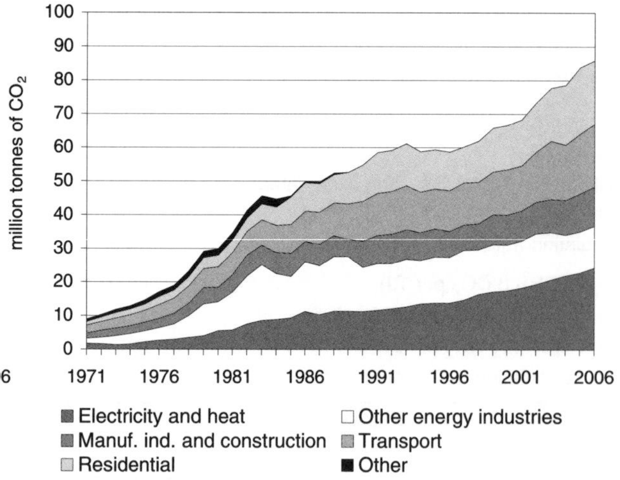

Figure 3. CO₂ emissions by sector

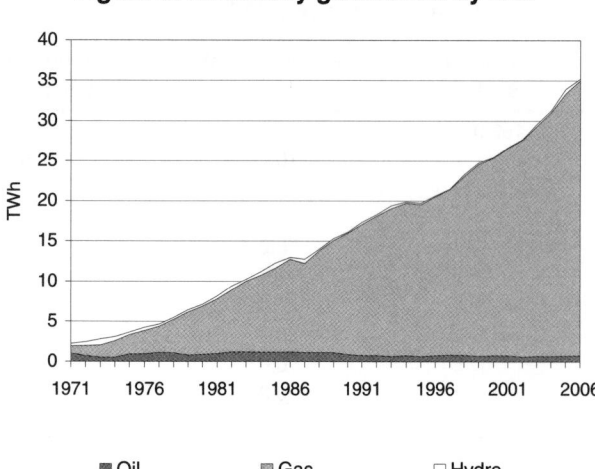

■ Electricity and heat   □ Other energy industries
■ Manuf. ind. and construction ■ Transport
■ Residential   ■ Other

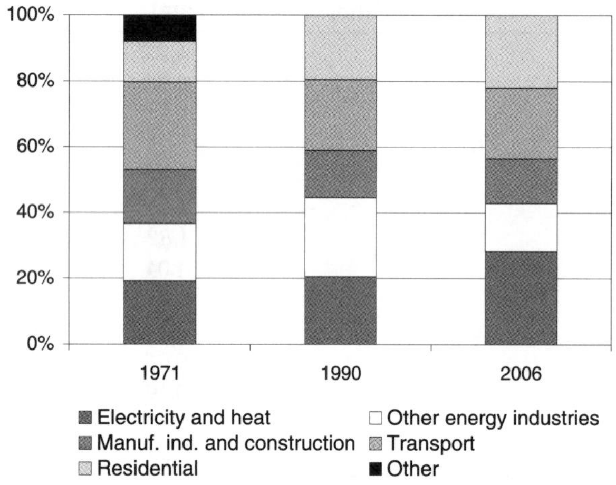

Figure 4. Reference vs Sectoral Approach

——— Total CO2 emissions - Sectoral Approach
- - - - Total CO2 emissions - Reference Approach
—●— UNFCCC database

Figure 5. Electricity generation by fuel

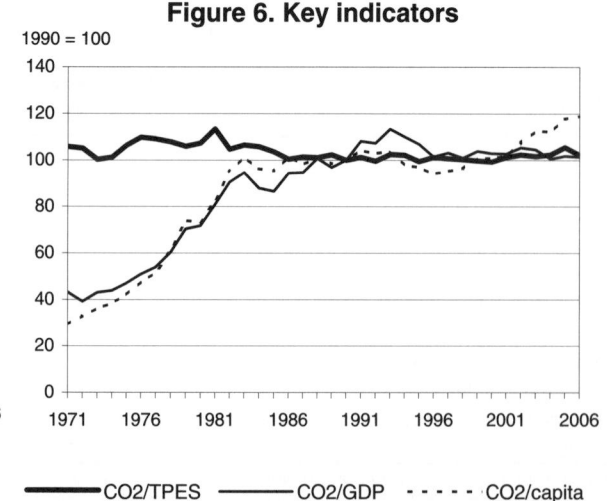

■ Oil   ■ Gas   □ Hydro

Figure 6. Key indicators

1990 = 100

━━ CO2/TPES   ─── CO2/GDP   - - - CO2/capita

Algeria / Algérie

Key indicators

	1990	1995	2000	2003	2004	2005	2006	% change 90-06
CO$_2$ Sectoral Approach (Mt of CO$_2$)	54.76	59.30	66.62	77.70	78.56	83.78	85.91	56.9%
CO$_2$ Reference Approach (Mt of CO$_2$)	58.38	63.66	71.06	81.13	82.36	84.32	89.72	53.7%
TPES (PJ)	1 001	1 091	1 227	1 397	1 404	1 452	1 537	53.4%
TPES (Mtoe)	23.92	26.05	29.30	33.37	33.54	34.69	36.70	53.4%
GDP (billion 2000 US$ using exch. rates)	46.37	46.96	54.79	62.92	66.19	69.70	71.79	54.8%
GDP (billion 2000 US$ using PPPs)	137.32	139.09	162.27	186.34	196.03	206.42	212.61	54.8%
Population (millions)	25.28	28.27	30.51	31.89	32.37	32.85	33.35	31.9%
CO$_2$ / TPES (t CO$_2$ per TJ)	54.7	54.4	54.3	55.6	55.9	57.7	55.9	2.3%
CO$_2$ / GDP (kg CO$_2$ per 2000 US$)	1.18	1.26	1.22	1.23	1.19	1.20	1.20	1.3%
CO$_2$ / GDP (kg CO$_2$ per 2000 US$ PPP)	0.40	0.43	0.41	0.42	0.40	0.41	0.40	1.3%
CO$_2$ / population (t CO$_2$ per capita)	2.17	2.10	2.18	2.44	2.43	2.55	2.58	18.9%

Ratios are based on the Sectoral Approach.

2006 CO$_2$ emissions by sector

million tonnes of CO$_2$	Coal/peat	Oil	Gas	Other *	Total	% change 90-06
Sectoral Approach	**0.99**	**30.53**	**54.39**	**-**	**85.91**	**56.9%**
Main activity producer elec. and heat	-	0.32	23.52	-	23.84	127.7%
Unallocated autoproducers	-	0.40	-	-	0.40	-44.7%
Other energy industries	-	1.43	11.12	-	12.55	-5.1%
Manufacturing industries and construction	0.99	3.37	7.23	-	11.60	48.7%
Transport	-	15.02	3.55	-	18.56	57.6%
of which: road	-	*15.02*	-	-	*15.02*	*36.3%*
Other sectors	-	10.00	8.96	-	18.96	76.3%
of which: residential	-	*10.00*	*8.96*	-	*18.96*	*76.3%*
Reference Approach	**2.70**	**32.16**	**54.86**	**-**	**89.72**	**53.7%**
Diff. due to losses and/or transformation	1.71	- 0.93	0.46	-	1.24	
Statistical differences	- 0.00	2.56	0.01	-	2.57	
Memo: international marine bunkers	-	*0.98*	-	-	*0.98*	*-27.6%*
Memo: international aviation	-	*1.14*	-	-	*1.14*	*4.3%*

* Other includes industrial waste and non-renewable municipal waste.

Key sources for CO$_2$ emissions from fuel combustion in 2006

IPCC source category	CO$_2$ emissions (Mt of CO$_2$)	% change 90-06	Level assessment (%) **	Cumulative total (%)
Main activity prod. elec. and heat - gas	23.52	128.9%	17.8	17.8
Road - oil	15.02	36.3%	11.4	29.2
Other energy industries - gas	11.12	-9.0%	8.4	37.6
Residential - oil	10.00	24.3%	7.6	45.1
Residential - gas	8.96	230.2%	6.8	51.9
Manufacturing industries - gas	7.23	60.9%	5.5	57.4
Other transport - gas	3.55	364.9%	2.7	60.1
Manufacturing industries - oil	3.37	67.5%	2.6	62.6
Other energy industries - oil	1.43	41.9%	1.1	63.7
Manufacturing industries - coal/peat	0.99	-23.0%	0.8	64.4
Unallocated autoproducers - oil	0.40	-44.7%	0.3	64.8
Memo: total CO$_2$ from fuel combustion	*85.91*	*56.9%*	*65.0*	*65.0*

** Percent calculated using the total GHG estimate for CO$_2$, CH$_4$, N$_2$O, HFCs, PFCs and SF$_6$ excluding CO$_2$ emissions/removals from land use change and forestry.

Angola

Figure 1. CO$_2$ emissions by fuel

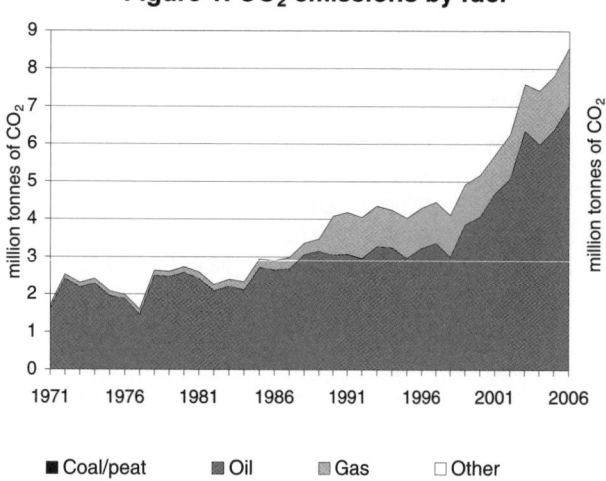

■ Coal/peat ■ Oil ■ Gas □ Other

Figure 2. CO$_2$ emissions by sector

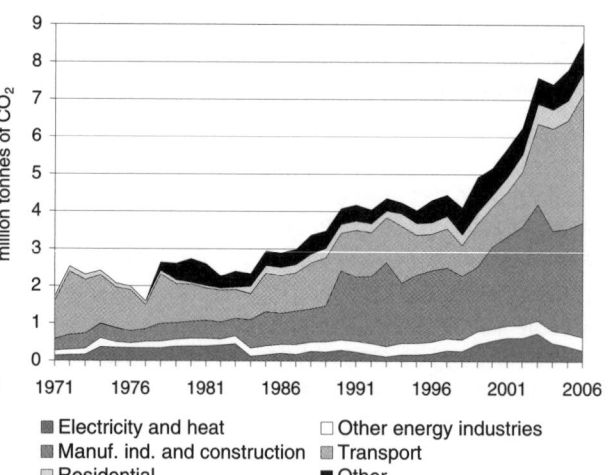

■ Electricity and heat □ Other energy industries
■ Manuf. ind. and construction ■ Transport
□ Residential ■ Other

Figure 3. CO$_2$ emissions by sector

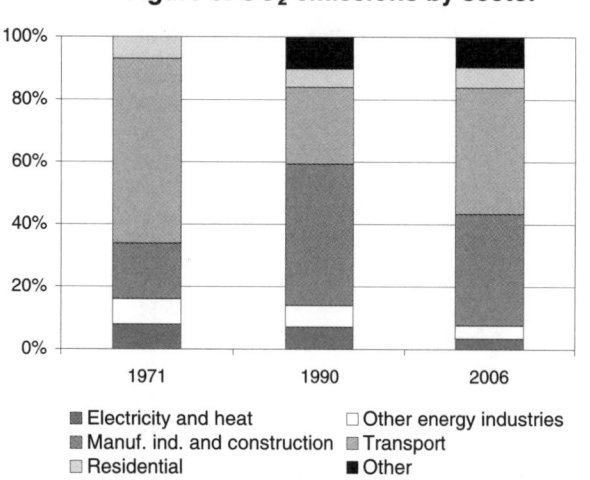

■ Electricity and heat □ Other energy industries
■ Manuf. ind. and construction ■ Transport
□ Residential ■ Other

Figure 4. Reference vs Sectoral Approach

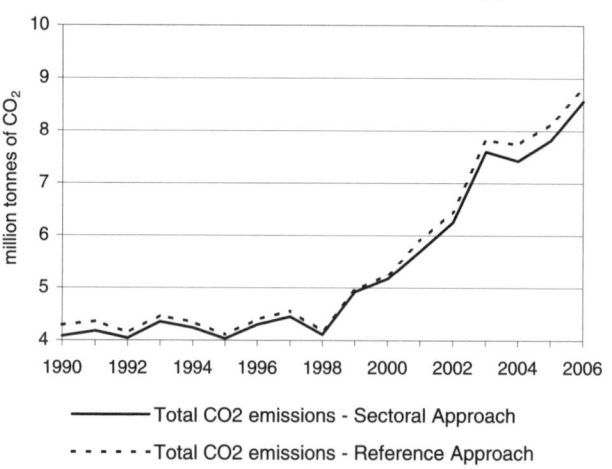

——— Total CO2 emissions - Sectoral Approach
- - - - - Total CO2 emissions - Reference Approach

Figure 5. Electricity generation by fuel

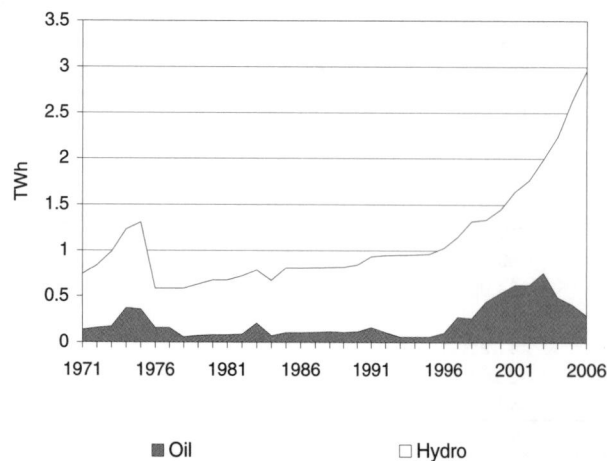

■ Oil □ Hydro

Figure 6. Key indicators

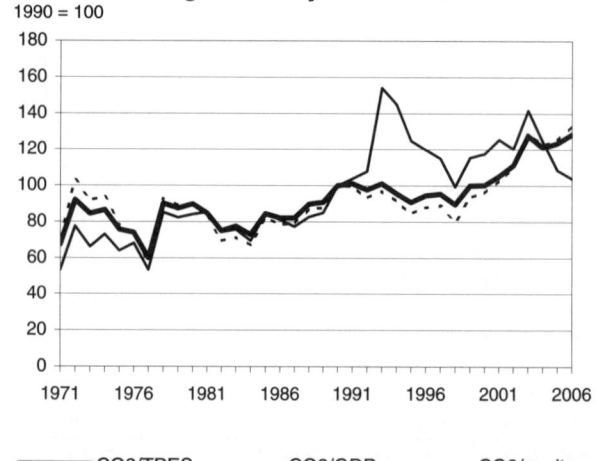

——CO2/TPES ——CO2/GDP - - - - - CO2/capita

Angola
Key indicators

	1990	1995	2000	2003	2004	2005	2006	% change 90-06
CO$_2$ Sectoral Approach (Mt of CO$_2$)	4.08	4.03	5.17	7.60	7.42	7.81	8.56	109.9%
CO$_2$ Reference Approach (Mt of CO$_2$)	4.29	4.11	5.26	7.82	7.73	8.13	8.81	105.3%
TPES (PJ)	263	287	333	384	395	408	430	63.3%
TPES (Mtoe)	6.28	6.84	7.96	9.17	9.44	9.74	10.26	63.3%
GDP (billion 2000 US$ using exch. rates)	8.46	6.70	9.13	11.14	12.38	14.94	17.11	102.2%
GDP (billion 2000 US$ using PPPs)	18.77	14.85	20.24	24.69	27.45	33.11	37.94	102.2%
Population (millions)	10.53	12.32	13.93	15.18	15.64	16.10	16.56	57.2%
CO$_2$ / TPES (t CO$_2$ per TJ)	15.5	14.1	15.5	19.8	18.8	19.2	19.9	28.5%
CO$_2$ / GDP (kg CO$_2$ per 2000 US$)	0.48	0.60	0.57	0.68	0.60	0.52	0.50	3.8%
CO$_2$ / GDP (kg CO$_2$ per 2000 US$ PPP)	0.22	0.27	0.26	0.31	0.27	0.24	0.23	3.9%
CO$_2$ / population (t CO$_2$ per capita)	0.39	0.33	0.37	0.50	0.47	0.49	0.52	33.5%

Ratios are based on the Sectoral Approach.

2006 CO$_2$ emissions by sector

million tonnes of CO$_2$	Coal/peat	Oil	Gas	Other *	Total	% change 90-06
Sectoral Approach	-	7.03	1.53	-	8.56	109.9%
Main activity producer elec. and heat	-	0.26	-	-	0.26	21.6%
Unallocated autoproducers	-	0.03	-	-	0.03	-
Other energy industries	-	0.36	-	-	0.36	29.2%
Manufacturing industries and construction	-	1.53	1.53	-	3.06	65.6%
Transport	-	3.46	-	-	3.46	244.0%
of which: road	-	3.46	-	-	3.46	244.0%
Other sectors	-	1.39	-	-	1.39	111.4%
of which: residential	-	0.55	-	-	0.55	130.5%
Reference Approach	-	7.28	1.53	-	8.81	105.3%
Diff. due to losses and/or transformation	-	0.25	-	-	0.25	
Statistical differences	-	- 0.00	-	-	- 0.00	
Memo: international marine bunkers	-	0.00	-	-	0.00	-80.0%
Memo: international aviation	-	1.04	-	-	1.04	1.2%

* Other includes industrial waste and non-renewable municipal waste.

Key sources for CO$_2$ emissions from fuel combustion in 2006

IPCC source category	CO$_2$ emissions (Mt of CO$_2$)	% change 90-06	Level assessment (%) **	Cumulative total (%)
Road - oil	3.46	244.0%	4.5	4.5
Manufacturing industries - oil	1.53	87.6%	2.0	6.5
Manufacturing industries - gas	1.53	48.1%	2.0	8.5
Non-specified other sectors - oil	0.84	100.4%	1.1	9.6
Residential - oil	0.55	130.5%	0.7	10.4
Other energy industries - oil	0.36	29.2%	0.5	10.8
Main activity prod. elec. and heat - oil	0.26	21.6%	0.3	11.2
Unallocated autoproducers - oil	0.03	-60.9%	0.0	11.2
-	-	-	-	-
-	-	-	-	-
-	-	-	-	-
Memo: total CO$_2$ from fuel combustion	8.56	109.9%	11.2	11.2

** Percent calculated using the total GHG estimate for CO$_2$, CH$_4$, N$_2$O, HFCs, PFCs and SF$_6$ excluding CO$_2$ emissions/removals from land use change and forestry.

Argentina / Argentine

Figure 1. CO₂ emissions by fuel

Figure 2. CO₂ emissions by sector

Figure 3. CO₂ emissions by sector

Figure 4. Reference vs Sectoral Approach

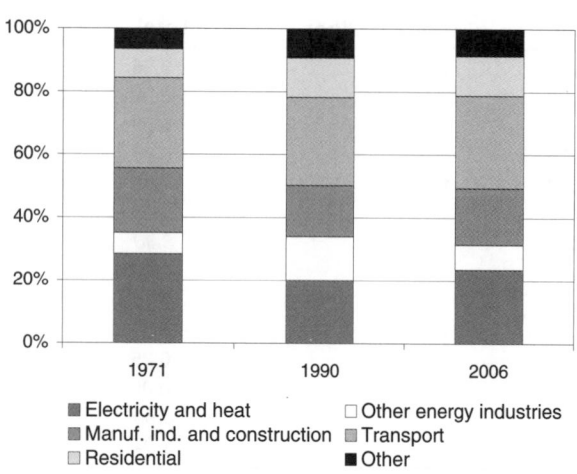

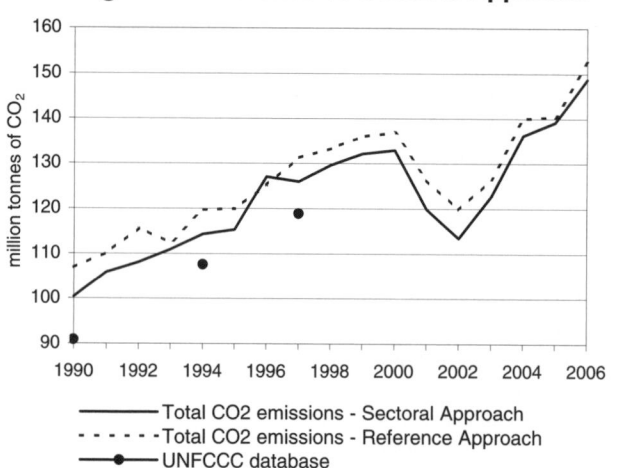

Figure 5. Electricity generation by fuel

Figure 6. Key indicators

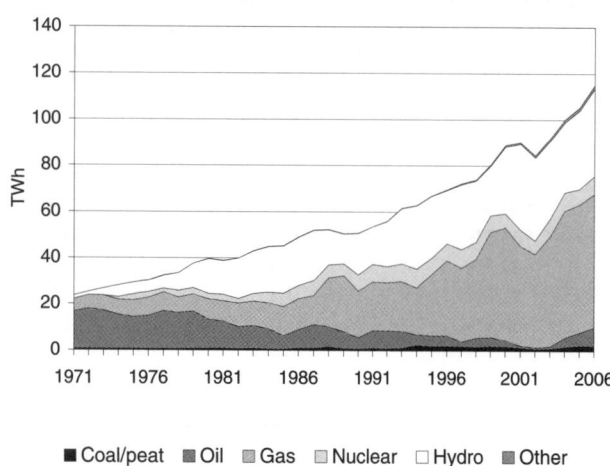

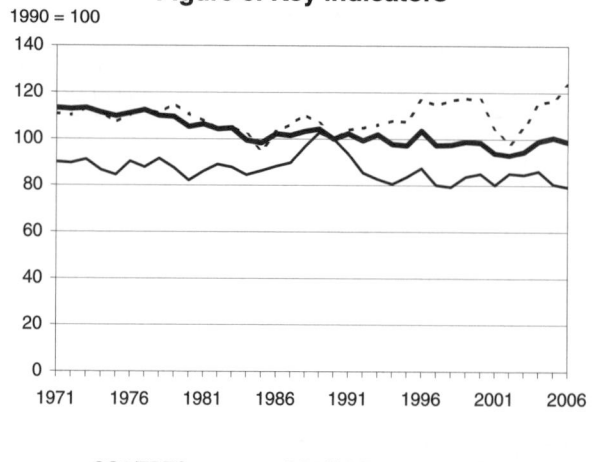

Argentina / Argentine

Key indicators

	1990	1995	2000	2003	2004	2005	2006	% change 90-06
CO$_2$ Sectoral Approach (Mt of CO$_2$)	100.38	115.32	132.94	122.77	136.23	139.14	148.73	48.2%
CO$_2$ Reference Approach (Mt of CO$_2$)	106.81	119.92	136.92	126.63	140.05	140.35	152.54	42.8%
TPES (PJ)	1 929	2 281	2 592	2 499	2 643	2 659	2 893	50.0%
TPES (Mtoe)	46.07	54.47	61.92	59.68	63.13	63.51	69.10	50.0%
GDP (billion 2000 US$ using exch. rates)	182.21	250.26	284.20	263.47	287.26	313.63	340.15	86.7%
GDP (billion 2000 US$ using PPPs)	286.10	392.95	446.25	413.69	451.05	492.45	534.09	86.7%
Population (millions)	32.58	34.84	36.90	38.01	38.37	38.75	39.13	20.1%
CO$_2$ / TPES (t CO$_2$ per TJ)	52.0	50.6	51.3	49.1	51.5	52.3	51.4	-1.2%
CO$_2$ / GDP (kg CO$_2$ per 2000 US$)	0.55	0.46	0.47	0.47	0.47	0.44	0.44	-20.6%
CO$_2$ / GDP (kg CO$_2$ per 2000 US$ PPP)	0.35	0.29	0.30	0.30	0.30	0.28	0.28	-20.6%
CO$_2$ / population (t CO$_2$ per capita)	3.08	3.31	3.60	3.23	3.55	3.59	3.80	23.4%

Ratios are based on the Sectoral Approach.

2006 CO$_2$ emissions by sector

million tonnes of CO$_2$	Coal/peat	Oil	Gas	Other *	Total	% change 90-06
Sectoral Approach	**4.79**	**64.91**	**79.03**	**-**	**148.73**	**48.2%**
Main activity producer elec. and heat	0.98	5.08	21.83	-	27.90	82.2%
Unallocated autoproducers	1.61	0.67	4.71	-	6.99	48.8%
Other energy industries	0.00	2.84	9.03	-	11.88	-15.6%
Manufacturing industries and construction	2.19	5.69	18.72	-	26.60	63.3%
Transport	-	35.73	8.12	-	43.86	55.8%
of which: road	-	*32.03*	*5.95*	-	*37.98*	*45.6%*
Other sectors	-	14.90	16.62	-	31.52	44.2%
of which: residential	-	*4.23*	*14.46*	-	*18.70*	*49.4%*
Reference Approach	**2.73**	**71.56**	**78.26**	**-**	**152.54**	**42.8%**
Diff. due to losses and/or transformation	- 2.14	6.96	0.32	-	5.15	
Statistical differences	0.08	- 0.32	- 1.10	-	- 1.34	
Memo: international marine bunkers	-	*2.34*	-	-	*2.34*	*5.3%*
Memo: international aviation	-	*..*	-	-	*..*	*..*

* Other includes industrial waste and non-renewable municipal waste.

Key sources for CO$_2$ emissions from fuel combustion in 2006

IPCC source category	CO$_2$ emissions (Mt of CO$_2$)	% change 90-06	Level assessment (%) **	Cumulative total (%)
Road - oil	32.03	24.8%	9.5	9.5
Main activity prod. elec. and heat - gas	21.83	109.7%	6.5	16.0
Manufacturing industries - gas	18.72	88.3%	5.6	21.6
Residential - gas	14.46	71.6%	4.3	25.9
Non-specified other sectors - oil	10.66	81.4%	3.2	29.0
Other energy industries - gas	9.03	1.6%	2.7	31.7
Road - gas	5.95	+	1.8	33.5
Manufacturing industries - oil	5.69	16.7%	1.7	35.2
Main activity prod. elec. and heat - oil	5.08	11.7%	1.5	36.7
Unallocated autoproducers - gas	4.71	161.3%	1.4	38.1
Residential - oil	4.23	3.7%	1.3	39.4
Memo: total CO$_2$ from fuel combustion	*148.73*	*48.2%*	*44.2*	*44.2*

** Percent calculated using the total GHG estimate for CO$_2$, CH$_4$, N$_2$O, HFCs, PFCs and SF$_6$ excluding CO$_2$ emissions/removals from land use change and forestry.

Armenia / Arménie *

Figure 1. CO$_2$ emissions by fuel

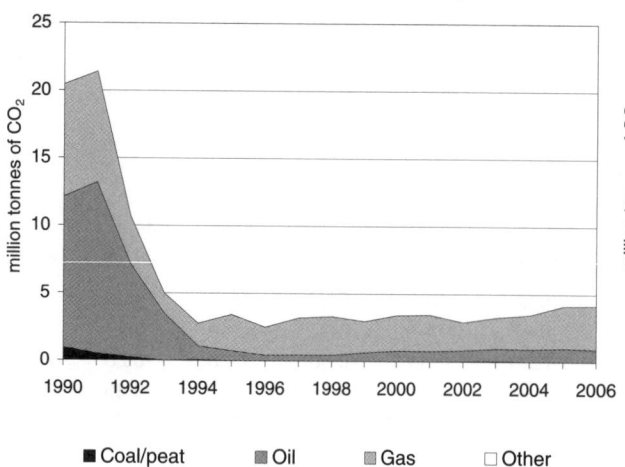

Coal/peat Oil Gas Other

Figure 2. CO$_2$ emissions by sector

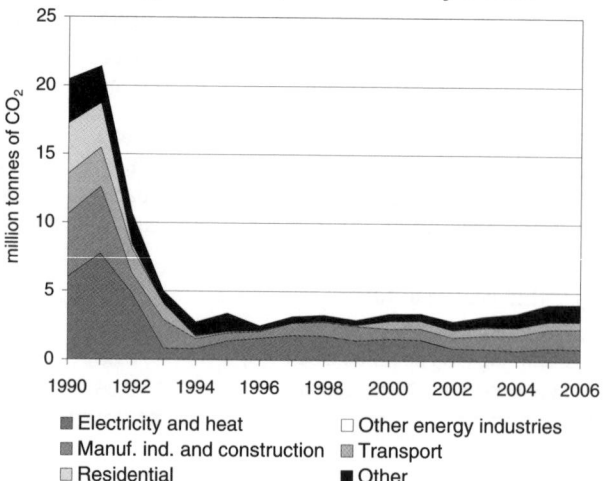

Electricity and heat Other energy industries
Manuf. ind. and construction Transport
Residential Other

Figure 3. CO$_2$ emissions by sector

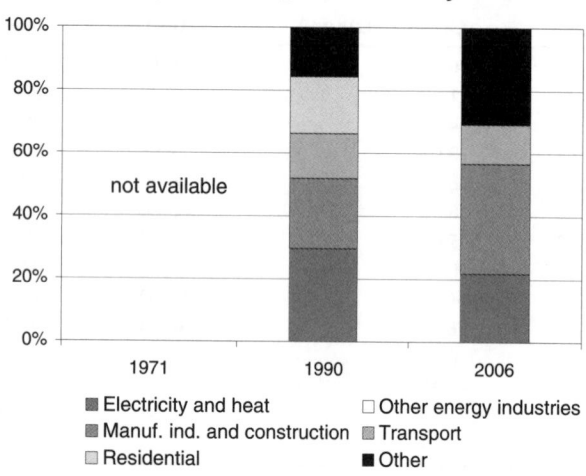

Electricity and heat Other energy industries
Manuf. ind. and construction Transport
Residential Other

Figure 4. Reference vs Sectoral Approach

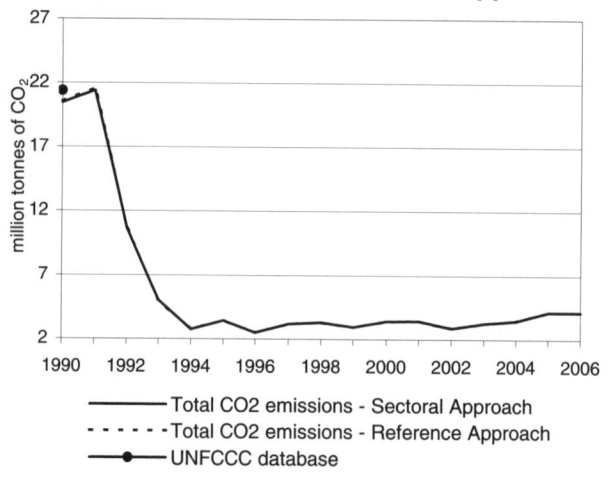

Total CO2 emissions - Sectoral Approach
Total CO2 emissions - Reference Approach
UNFCCC database

Figure 5. Electricity generation by fuel

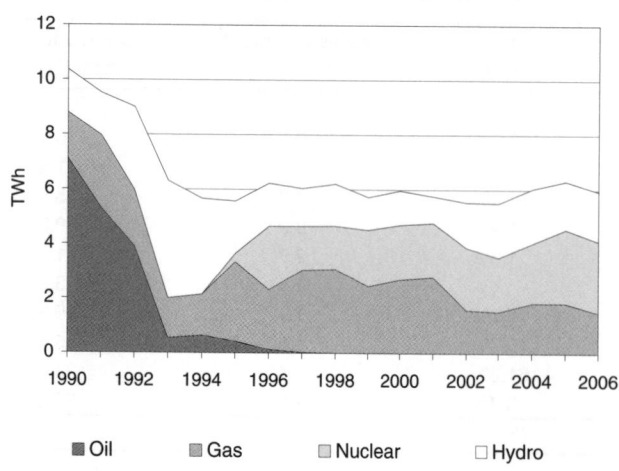

Oil Gas Nuclear Hydro

Figure 6. Key indicators

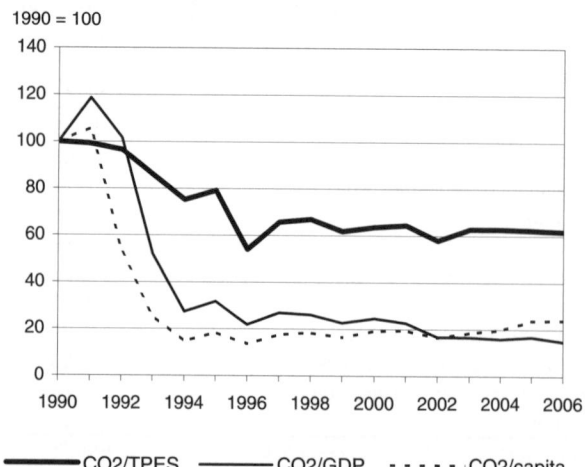

CO2/TPES CO2/GDP CO2/capita

* From 1992 to 2005, emissions for the residential sector have been included with Other sectors.

Armenia / Arménie

Key indicators

	1990	1995	2000	2003	2004	2005	2006	% change 90-06
CO$_2$ Sectoral Approach (Mt of CO$_2$)	20.46	3.42	3.40	3.25	3.46	4.12	4.14	-79.8%
CO$_2$ Reference Approach (Mt of CO$_2$)	20.52	3.42	3.40	3.25	3.46	4.12	4.14	-79.8%
TPES (PJ)	331	70	86	84	89	107	108	-67.2%
TPES (Mtoe)	7.90	1.67	2.07	2.00	2.12	2.55	2.59	-67.2%
GDP (billion 2000 US$ using exch. rates)	2.82	1.49	1.91	2.70	2.99	3.40	3.86	37.1%
GDP (billion 2000 US$ using PPPs)	10.99	5.80	7.46	10.55	11.66	13.29	15.07	37.1%
Population (millions)	3.55	3.23	3.08	3.04	3.03	3.02	3.01	-15.1%
CO$_2$ / TPES (t CO$_2$ per TJ)	61.9	49.0	39.3	38.9	38.9	38.6	38.3	-38.2%
CO$_2$ / GDP (kg CO$_2$ per 2000 US$)	7.27	2.30	1.78	1.20	1.16	1.21	1.07	-85.2%
CO$_2$ / GDP (kg CO$_2$ per 2000 US$ PPP)	1.86	0.59	0.46	0.31	0.30	0.31	0.27	-85.2%
CO$_2$ / population (t CO$_2$ per capita)	5.77	1.06	1.10	1.07	1.14	1.37	1.38	-76.2%

Ratios are based on the Sectoral Approach.

2006 CO$_2$ emissions by sector

million tonnes of CO$_2$	Coal/peat	Oil	Gas	Other *	Total	% change 90-06
Sectoral Approach	**0.00**	**0.93**	**3.21**	-	**4.14**	**-79.8%**
Main activity producer elec. and heat	-	-	0.90	-	0.90	-85.1%
Unallocated autoproducers	-	-	-	-	-	-
Other energy industries	-	-	-	-	-	-
Manufacturing industries and construction	-	0.02	1.43	-	1.45	-68.3%
Transport	-	0.52	-	-	0.52	-82.3%
of which: road	-	*0.52*	-	-	*0.52*	*-82.3%*
Other sectors	0.00	0.40	0.88	-	1.28	-81.5%
of which: residential	*0.00*	-	-	-	*0.00*	*-100.0%*
Reference Approach	**0.00**	**0.93**	**3.21**	-	**4.14**	**-79.8%**
Diff. due to losses and/or transformation	-	-	-	-	-	
Statistical differences	-	-	0.00	-	0.00	
Memo: international marine bunkers	-	-	-	-	-	-
Memo: international aviation	-	*0.12*	-	-	*0.12*	*-79.9%*

* Other includes industrial waste and non-renewable municipal waste.

Key sources for CO$_2$ emissions from fuel combustion in 2006

IPCC source category	CO$_2$ emissions (Mt of CO$_2$)	% change 90-06	Level assessment (%) **	Cumulative total (%)
Manufacturing industries - gas	1.43	-37.0%	19.7	19.7
Main activity prod. elec. and heat - gas	0.90	-53.2%	12.4	32.1
Non-specified other sectors - gas	0.88	-41.9%	12.1	44.2
Road - oil	0.52	-82.3%	7.2	51.4
Non-specified other sectors - oil	0.40	-76.8%	5.5	56.9
Manufacturing industries - oil	0.02	-99.2%	0.3	57.1
Residential - coal/peat	0.00	-99.8%	0.0	57.2
-	-	-	-	-
-	-	-	-	-
-	-	-	-	-
-	-	-	-	-
Memo: total CO$_2$ from fuel combustion	*4.14*	*-79.8%*	*57.2*	*57.2*

** Percent calculated using the total GHG estimate for CO$_2$, CH$_4$, N$_2$O, HFCs, PFCs and SF$_6$ excluding CO$_2$ emissions/removals from land use change and forestry.

Australia / Australie

Figure 1. CO$_2$ emissions by fuel

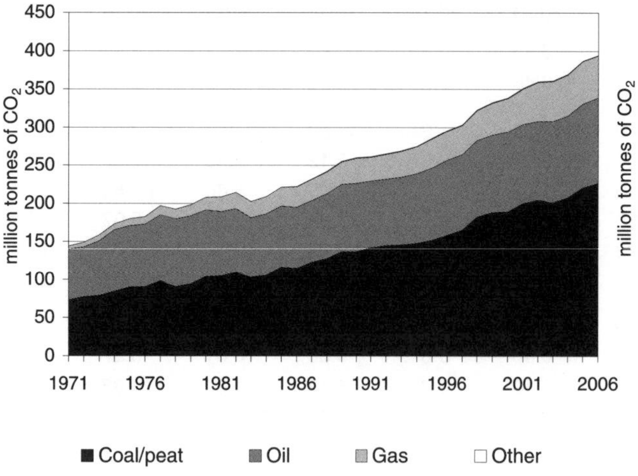

■ Coal/peat ■ Oil ▨ Gas ☐ Other

Figure 2. CO$_2$ emissions by sector

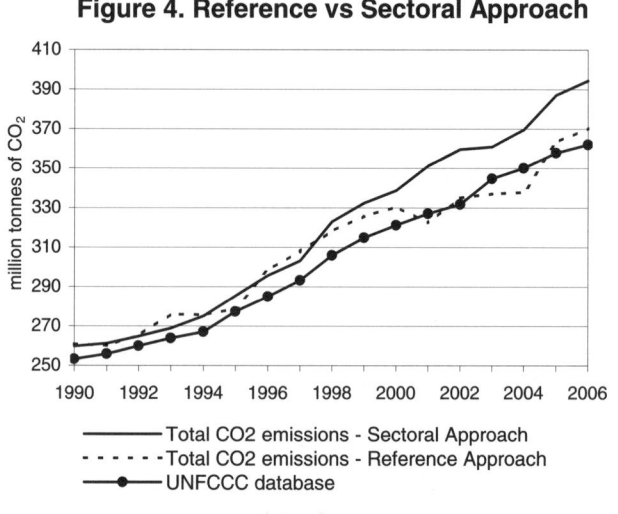

■ Electricity and heat   ☐ Other energy industries
■ Manuf. ind. and construction ▨ Transport
☐ Residential   ■ Other

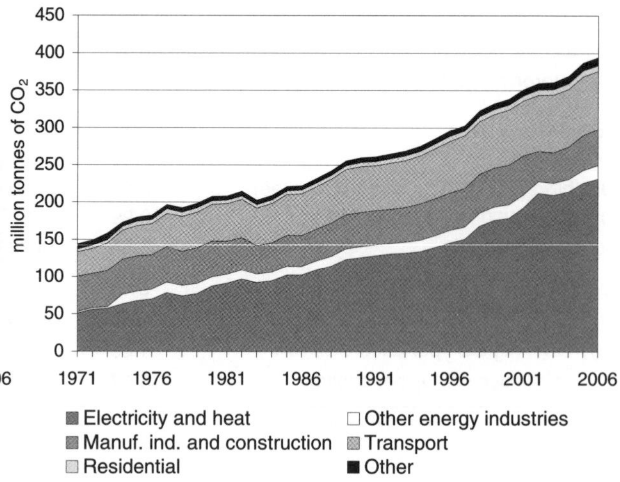

Figure 3. CO$_2$ emissions by sector

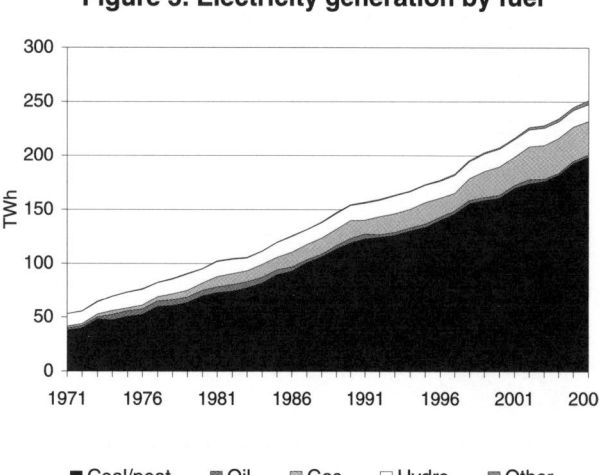

■ Electricity and heat   ☐ Other energy industries
■ Manuf. ind. and construction ▨ Transport
☐ Residential   ■ Other

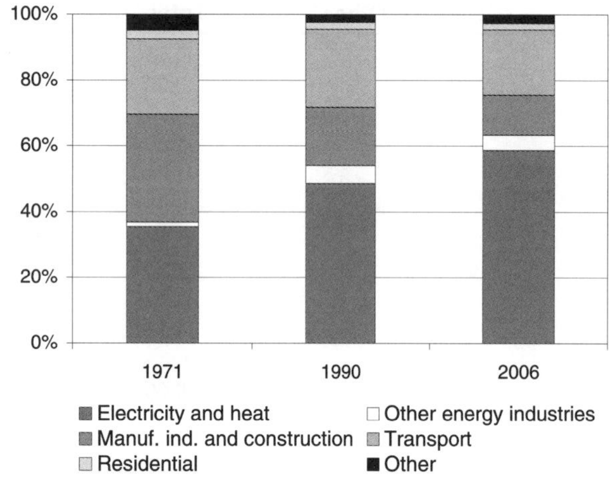

Figure 4. Reference vs Sectoral Approach

—— Total CO2 emissions - Sectoral Approach
- - - - Total CO2 emissions - Reference Approach
—●— UNFCCC database

Figure 5. Electricity generation by fuel

■ Coal/peat ■ Oil ▨ Gas ☐ Hydro ■ Other

Figure 6. Key indicators

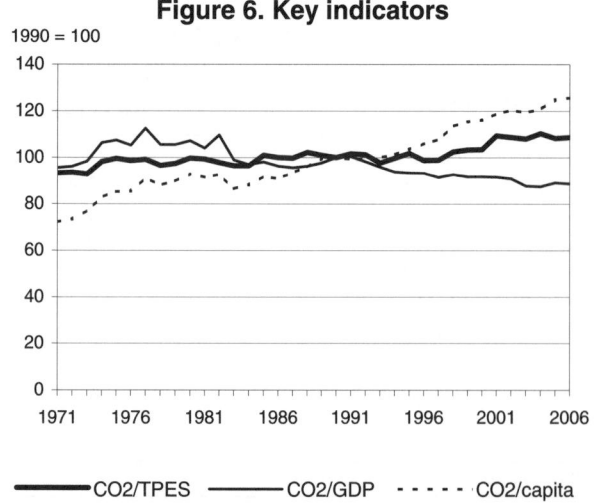

1990 = 100

━━━ CO2/TPES   —— CO2/GDP   - - - - CO2/capita

Australia / Australie

Key indicators

	1990	1995	2000	2003	2004	2005	2006	% change 90-06
CO$_2$ Sectoral Approach (Mt of CO$_2$)	259.81	285.19	338.66	360.95	369.57	387.17	394.45	51.8%
CO$_2$ Reference Approach (Mt of CO$_2$)	260.93	278.56	330.38	336.99	337.78	363.36	370.42	42.0%
TPES (PJ)	3 671	3 956	4 629	4 723	4 733	5 055	5 128	39.7%
TPES (Mtoe)	87.68	94.50	110.55	112.82	113.06	120.75	122.47	39.7%
GDP (billion 2000 US$ using exch. rates)	281.00	330.10	399.60	445.10	457.00	469.80	481.40	71.3%
GDP (billion 2000 US$ using PPPs)	368.86	433.37	524.61	584.28	599.92	616.77	631.93	71.3%
Population (millions)	17.17	18.19	19.27	19.98	20.20	20.47	20.74	20.8%
CO$_2$ / TPES (t CO$_2$ per TJ)	70.8	72.1	73.2	76.4	78.1	76.6	76.9	8.7%
CO$_2$ / GDP (kg CO$_2$ per 2000 US$)	0.92	0.86	0.85	0.81	0.81	0.82	0.82	-11.4%
CO$_2$ / GDP (kg CO$_2$ per 2000 US$ PPP)	0.70	0.66	0.65	0.62	0.62	0.63	0.62	-11.4%
CO$_2$ / population (t CO$_2$ per capita)	15.13	15.68	17.57	18.07	18.29	18.91	19.02	25.7%

Ratios are based on the Sectoral Approach.

2006 CO$_2$ emissions by sector

million tonnes of CO$_2$	Coal/peat	Oil	Gas	Other *	Total	% change 90-06
Sectoral Approach	**226.63**	**112.29**	**55.06**	**0.47**	**394.45**	**51.8%**
Main activity producer elec. and heat	210.83	1.18	11.27	-	223.29	84.7%
Unallocated autoproducers	0.15	1.54	6.38	-	8.07	55.4%
Other energy industries	2.38	8.72	7.28	-	18.38	27.8%
Manufacturing industries and construction	12.56	14.94	20.33	0.47	48.30	5.0%
Transport	0.31	76.81	0.89	-	78.00	27.1%
of which: road	-	*67.39*	*0.07*	-	*67.46*	*23.8%*
Other sectors	0.39	9.10	8.91	-	18.40	53.6%
of which: residential	*0.05*	*0.83*	*6.71*	-	*7.59*	*34.8%*
Reference Approach	**212.90**	**102.81**	**54.24**	**0.47**	**370.42**	**42.0%**
Diff. due to losses and/or transformation	- 0.54	- 6.27	0.95	-	- 5.86	
Statistical differences	- 13.19	- 3.21	- 1.77	0.00	- 18.17	
Memo: international marine bunkers	-	*3.21*	-	-	*3.21*	*50.2%*
Memo: international aviation	-	*7.29*	-	-	*7.29*	*69.7%*

* Other includes industrial waste and non-renewable municipal waste.

Key sources for CO$_2$ emissions from fuel combustion in 2006

IPCC source category	CO$_2$ emissions (Mt of CO$_2$)	% change 90-06	Level assessment (%) **	Cumulative total (%)
Main activity prod. elec. and heat - coal/peat	210.83	87.2%	37.1	37.1
Road - oil	67.39	23.6%	11.9	48.9
Manufacturing industries - gas	20.33	48.2%	3.6	52.5
Manufacturing industries - oil	14.94	15.9%	2.6	55.1
Manufacturing industries - coal/peat	12.56	-32.2%	2.2	57.4
Main activity prod. elec. and heat - gas	11.27	59.3%	2.0	59.3
Other transport - oil	9.42	43.0%	1.7	61.0
Other energy industries - oil	8.72	21.0%	1.5	62.5
Non-specified other sectors - oil	8.27	101.4%	1.5	64.0
Other energy industries - gas	7.28	51.1%	1.3	65.3
Residential - gas	6.71	51.9%	1.2	66.4
Memo: total CO$_2$ from fuel combustion	*394.45*	*51.8%*	*69.4*	*69.4*

** Percent calculated using the total GHG estimate for CO$_2$, CH$_4$, N$_2$O, HFCs, PFCs and SF$_6$ excluding CO$_2$ emissions/removals from land use change and forestry.

Austria / Autriche

Figure 1. CO$_2$ emissions by fuel

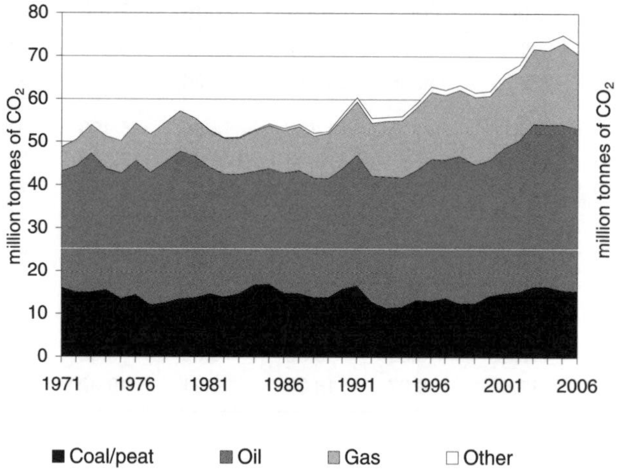

■ Coal/peat   ■ Oil   ▤ Gas   ☐ Other

Figure 2. CO$_2$ emissions by sector

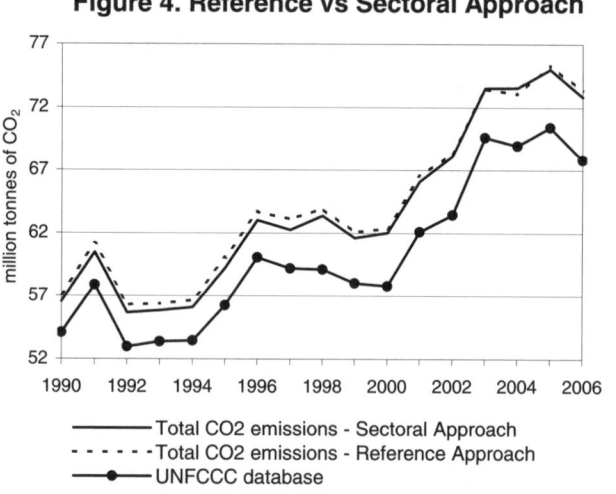

▤ Electricity and heat   ☐ Other energy industries
▤ Manuf. ind. and construction   ▤ Transport
▥ Residential   ■ Other

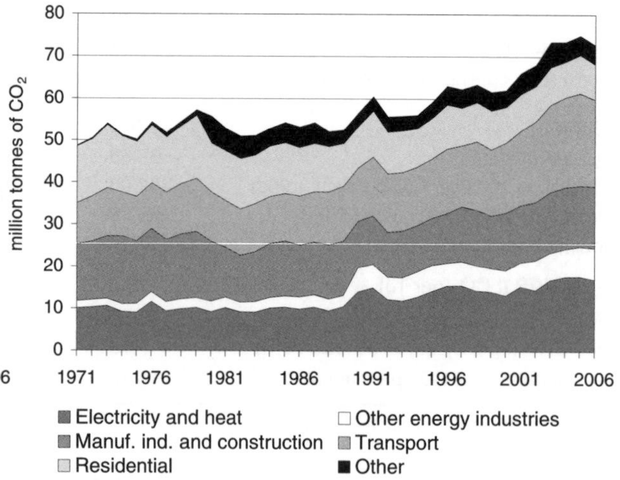

Figure 3. CO$_2$ emissions by sector

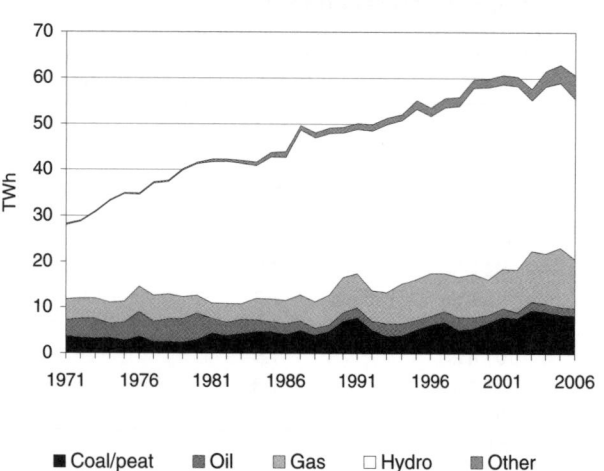

■ Electricity and heat   ☐ Other energy industries
▤ Manuf. ind. and construction   ▤ Transport
▥ Residential   ■ Other

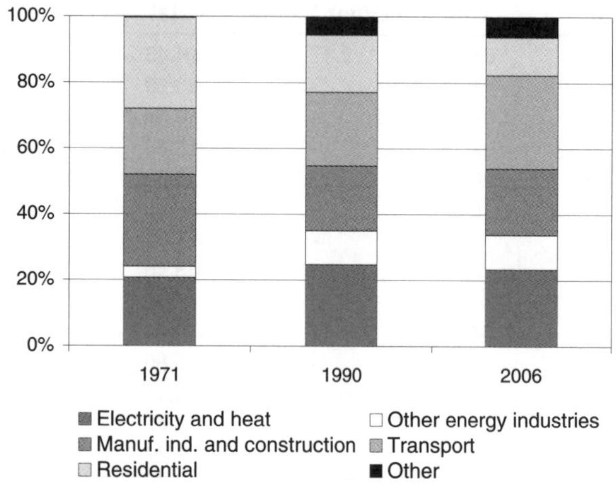

Figure 4. Reference vs Sectoral Approach

—— Total CO2 emissions - Sectoral Approach
- - - - Total CO2 emissions - Reference Approach
—●— UNFCCC database

Figure 5. Electricity generation by fuel

■ Coal/peat   ■ Oil   ▤ Gas   ☐ Hydro   ▤ Other

Figure 6. Key indicators

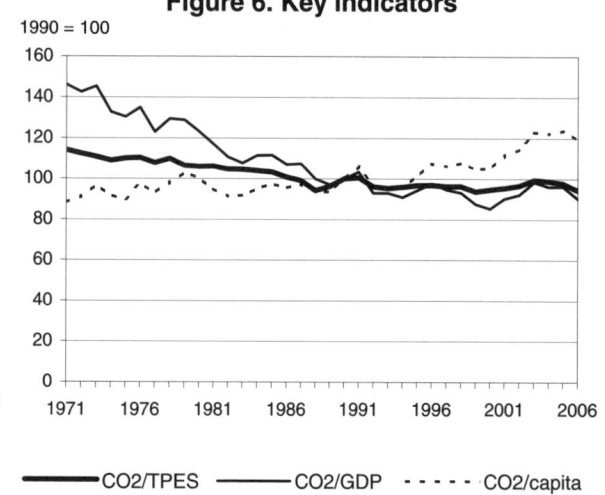

1990 = 100

—— CO2/TPES   —— CO2/GDP   - - - - CO2/capita

Austria / Autriche

Key indicators

	1990	1995	2000	2003	2004	2005	2006	% change 90-06
CO$_2$ Sectoral Approach (Mt of CO$_2$)	56.56	59.21	62.01	73.51	73.55	75.02	72.84	28.8%
CO$_2$ Reference Approach (Mt of CO$_2$)	57.12	60.06	62.38	73.45	73.06	75.36	73.35	28.4%
TPES (PJ)	1 049	1 136	1 216	1 373	1 381	1 425	1 433	36.6%
TPES (Mtoe)	25.05	27.13	29.04	32.80	33.00	34.04	34.23	36.6%
GDP (billion 2000 US$ using exch. rates)	150.70	167.70	193.80	199.50	204.10	208.30	215.20	42.8%
GDP (billion 2000 US$ using PPPs)	181.43	201.95	233.41	240.25	245.80	250.82	259.10	42.8%
Population (millions)	7.68	7.95	8.01	8.12	8.18	8.23	8.28	7.9%
CO$_2$ / TPES (t CO$_2$ per TJ)	53.9	52.1	51.0	53.5	53.2	52.6	50.8	-5.7%
CO$_2$ / GDP (kg CO$_2$ per 2000 US$)	0.38	0.35	0.32	0.37	0.36	0.36	0.34	-9.8%
CO$_2$ / GDP (kg CO$_2$ per 2000 US$ PPP)	0.31	0.29	0.27	0.31	0.30	0.30	0.28	-9.8%
CO$_2$ / population (t CO$_2$ per capita)	7.37	7.45	7.74	9.06	9.00	9.11	8.80	19.4%

Ratios are based on the Sectoral Approach.

2006 CO$_2$ emissions by sector

million tonnes of CO$_2$	Coal/peat	Oil	Gas	Other *	Total	% change 90-06
Sectoral Approach	**15.37**	**37.96**	**17.21**	**2.31**	**72.84**	**28.8%**
Main activity producer elec. and heat	5.67	1.11	4.56	0.66	12.01	14.9%
Unallocated autoproducers	2.94	0.63	1.02	0.37	4.97	40.4%
Other energy industries	4.29	2.16	1.14	-	7.60	31.1%
Manufacturing industries and construction	1.86	5.82	5.76	1.19	14.64	32.1%
Transport	-	20.21	0.45	-	20.66	63.1%
of which: road	-	*19.65*	-	-	*19.65*	*63.2%*
Other sectors	0.60	8.02	4.28	0.08	12.97	-0.4%
of which: residential	*0.52*	*4.87*	*3.03*	-	*8.41*	*-14.5%*
Reference Approach	**16.00**	**37.83**	**17.21**	**2.31**	**73.35**	**28.4%**
Diff. due to losses and/or transformation	0.62	- 0.07	-	-	0.55	
Statistical differences	0.00	- 0.05	0.00	0.00	- 0.04	
Memo: international marine bunkers	-	-	-	-	-	-
Memo: international aviation	-	*1.75*	-	-	*1.75*	*113.8%*

* Other includes industrial waste and non-renewable municipal waste.

Key sources for CO$_2$ emissions from fuel combustion in 2006

IPCC source category	CO$_2$ emissions (Mt of CO$_2$)	% change 90-06	Level assessment (%) **	Cumulative total (%)
Road - oil	19.65	63.2%	20.4	20.4
Manufacturing industries - oil	5.82	51.2%	6.1	26.5
Manufacturing industries - gas	5.76	31.9%	6.0	32.5
Main activity prod. elec. and heat - coal/peat	5.67	-2.8%	5.9	38.4
Residential - oil	4.87	-7.9%	5.1	43.5
Main activity prod. elec. and heat - gas	4.56	38.9%	4.7	48.2
Other energy industries - coal/peat	4.29	42.3%	4.5	52.7
Non-specified other sectors - oil	3.15	27.7%	3.3	56.0
Residential - gas	3.03	69.4%	3.1	59.1
Unallocated autoproducers - coal/peat	2.94	100.5%	3.1	62.2
Other energy industries - oil	2.16	13.6%	2.2	64.4
Memo: total CO$_2$ from fuel combustion	*72.84*	*28.8%*	*75.8*	*75.8*

** Percent calculated using the total GHG estimate for CO$_2$, CH$_4$, N$_2$O, HFCs, PFCs and SF$_6$ excluding CO$_2$ emissions/removals from land use change and forestry.

Azerbaijan / Azerbaïdjan

Figure 1. CO$_2$ emissions by fuel

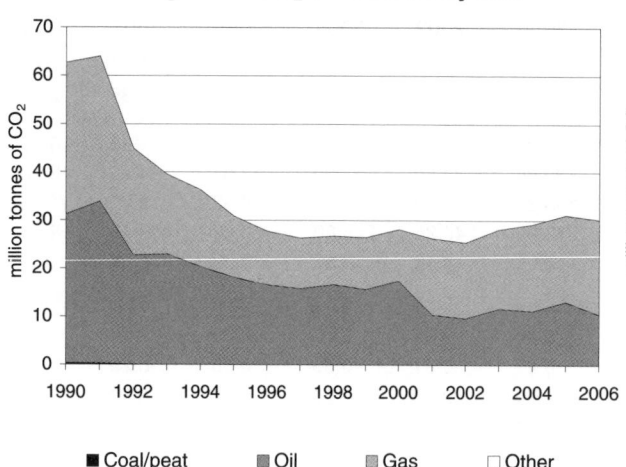

Coal/peat ■   Oil ■   Gas ▨   Other ☐

Figure 2. CO$_2$ emissions by sector

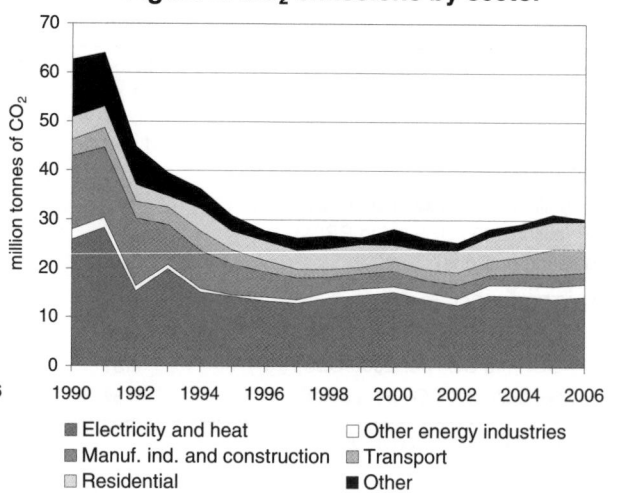

■ Electricity and heat   ☐ Other energy industries
■ Manuf. ind. and construction ▨ Transport
☐ Residential   ■ Other

Figure 3. CO$_2$ emissions by sector

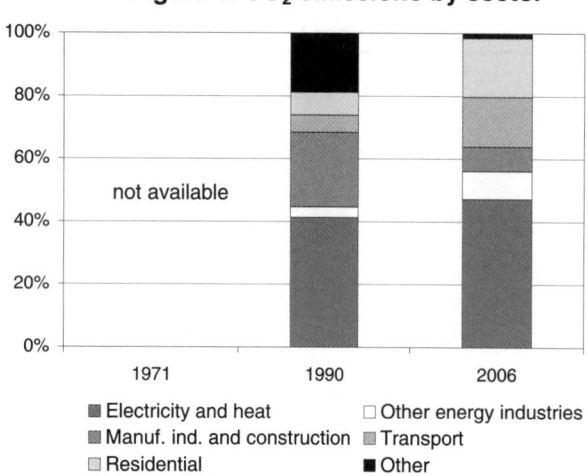

■ Electricity and heat   ☐ Other energy industries
■ Manuf. ind. and construction ▨ Transport
☐ Residential   ■ Other

Figure 4. Reference vs Sectoral Approach

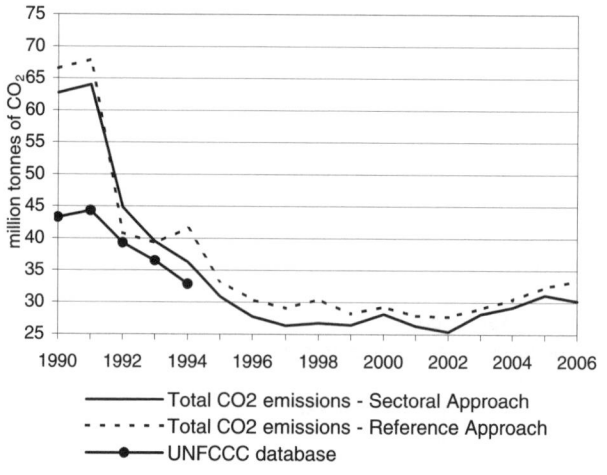

—— Total CO2 emissions - Sectoral Approach
- - - - Total CO2 emissions - Reference Approach
—●— UNFCCC database

Figure 5. Electricity generation by fuel

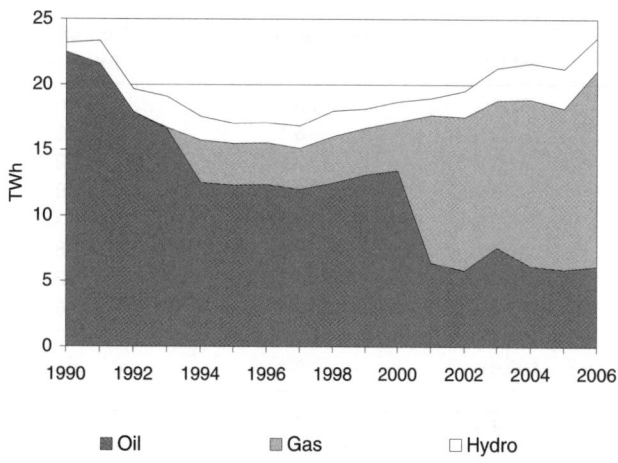

Oil ■   Gas ▨   Hydro ☐

Figure 6. Key indicators

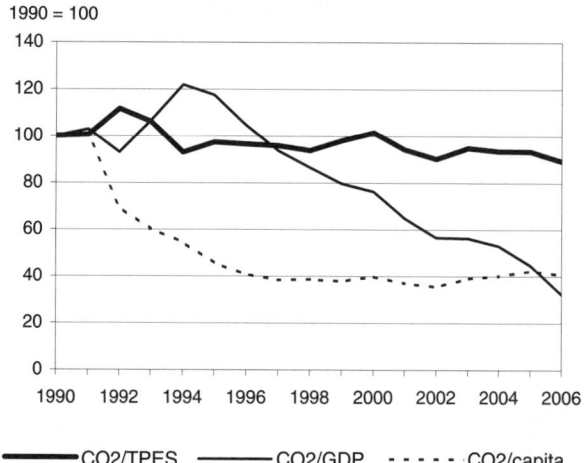

1990 = 100

━━ CO2/TPES   —— CO2/GDP   - - - - CO2/capita

Azerbaijan / Azerbaïdjan

Key indicators

	1990	1995	2000	2003	2004	2005	2006	% change 90-06
CO$_2$ Sectoral Approach (Mt of CO$_2$)	62.69	30.85	28.17	28.14	29.19	31.14	30.23	-51.8%
CO$_2$ Reference Approach (Mt of CO$_2$)	66.54	33.25	29.33	29.06	30.41	32.37	33.37	-49.9%
TPES (PJ)	1 092	552	484	516	544	581	589	-46.0%
TPES (Mtoe)	26.08	13.17	11.55	12.33	12.99	13.87	14.08	-46.0%
GDP (billion 2000 US$ using exch. rates)	8.95	3.75	5.27	7.13	7.85	9.93	13.35	49.1%
GDP (billion 2000 US$ using PPPs)	33.83	14.16	19.92	26.93	29.68	37.51	50.45	49.1%
Population (millions)	7.16	7.69	8.05	8.23	8.31	8.39	8.48	18.5%
CO$_2$ / TPES (t CO$_2$ per TJ)	57.4	55.9	58.2	54.5	53.7	53.6	51.3	-10.7%
CO$_2$ / GDP (kg CO$_2$ per 2000 US$)	7.00	8.23	5.34	3.95	3.72	3.14	2.26	-67.7%
CO$_2$ / GDP (kg CO$_2$ per 2000 US$ PPP)	1.85	2.18	1.41	1.04	0.98	0.83	0.60	-67.7%
CO$_2$ / population (t CO$_2$ per capita)	8.76	4.01	3.50	3.42	3.51	3.71	3.56	-59.3%

Ratios are based on the Sectoral Approach.

2006 CO$_2$ emissions by sector

million tonnes of CO$_2$	Coal/peat	Oil	Gas	Other *	Total	% change 90-06
Sectoral Approach	-	10.54	19.69	-	30.23	-51.8%
Main activity producer elec. and heat	-	4.03	9.98	-	14.01	-45.8%
Unallocated autoproducers	-	-	0.25	-	0.25	x
Other energy industries	-	0.48	2.18	-	2.66	24.0%
Manufacturing industries and construction	-	0.96	1.41	-	2.37	-84.1%
Transport	-	4.53	0.27	-	4.80	40.0%
of which: road	-	4.47	-	-	4.47	42.5%
Other sectors	-	0.53	5.61	-	6.14	-62.6%
of which: residential	-	0.18	5.46	-	5.64	23.2%
Reference Approach	-	12.47	20.90	-	33.37	-49.9%
Diff. due to losses and/or transformation	-	1.93	1.21	-	3.14	
Statistical differences	-	-	-	-	-	
Memo: international marine bunkers	-	..	-	-	..	..
Memo: international aviation	-	1.48	-	-	1.48	108.2%

* Other includes industrial waste and non-renewable municipal waste.

Key sources for CO$_2$ emissions from fuel combustion in 2006

IPCC source category	CO$_2$ emissions (Mt of CO$_2$)	% change 90-06	Level assessment (%) **	Cumulative total (%)
Main activity prod. elec. and heat - gas	9.98	-3.7%	16.8	16.8
Residential - gas	5.46	19.4%	9.2	26.0
Road - oil	4.47	48.2%	7.5	33.5
Main activity prod. elec. and heat - oil	4.03	-73.9%	6.8	40.3
Other energy industries - gas	2.18	x	3.7	44.0
Manufacturing industries - gas	1.41	-90.0%	2.4	46.3
Manufacturing industries - oil	0.96	21.1%	1.6	48.0
Other energy industries - oil	0.48	-77.6%	0.8	48.8
Non-specified other sectors - oil	0.36	-96.2%	0.6	49.4
Other transport - gas	0.27	-7.1%	0.4	49.8
Unallocated autoproducers - gas	0.25	x	0.4	50.2
Memo: total CO$_2$ from fuel combustion	30.23	-51.8%	50.9	50.9

** Percent calculated using the total GHG estimate for CO$_2$, CH$_4$, N$_2$O, HFCs, PFCs and SF$_6$ excluding CO$_2$ emissions/removals from land use change and forestry.

Bahrain / Bahrein

Figure 1. CO$_2$ emissions by fuel

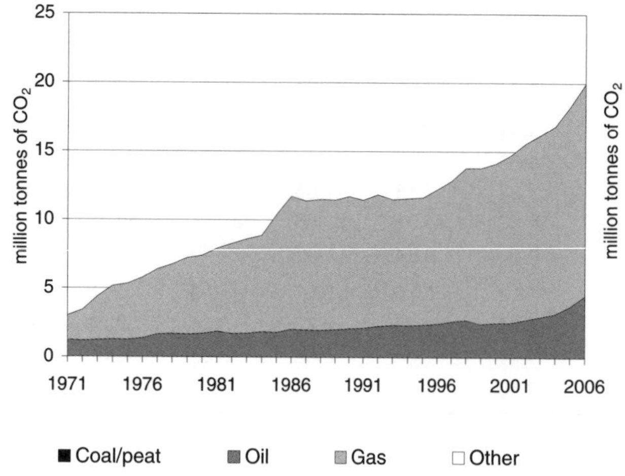

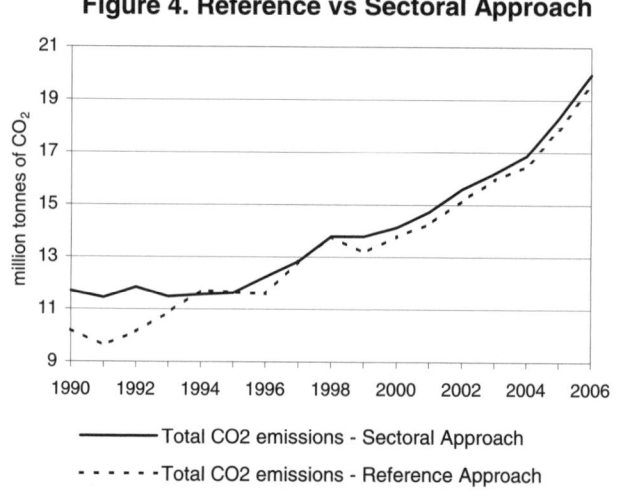

- Coal/peat
- Oil
- Gas
- Other

Figure 2. CO$_2$ emissions by sector

- Electricity and heat
- Other energy industries
- Manuf. ind. and construction
- Transport
- Residential
- Other

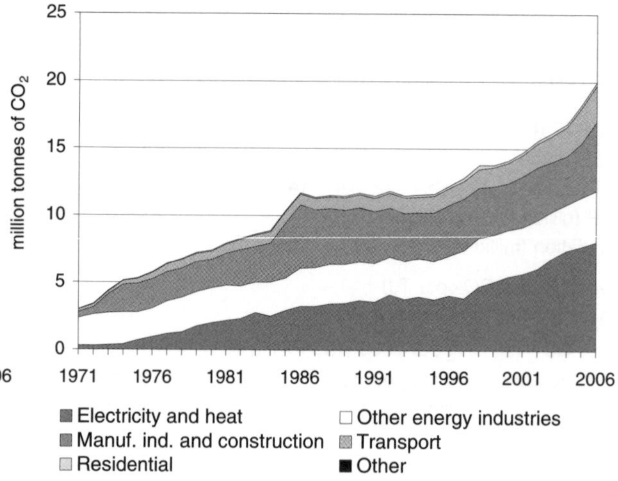

Figure 3. CO$_2$ emissions by sector

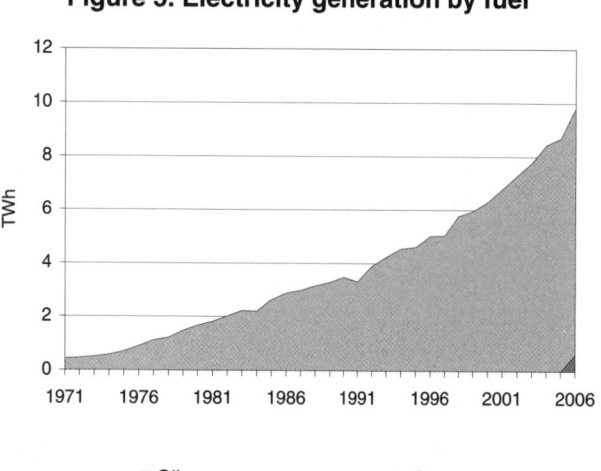

- Electricity and heat
- Other energy industries
- Manuf. ind. and construction
- Transport
- Residential
- Other

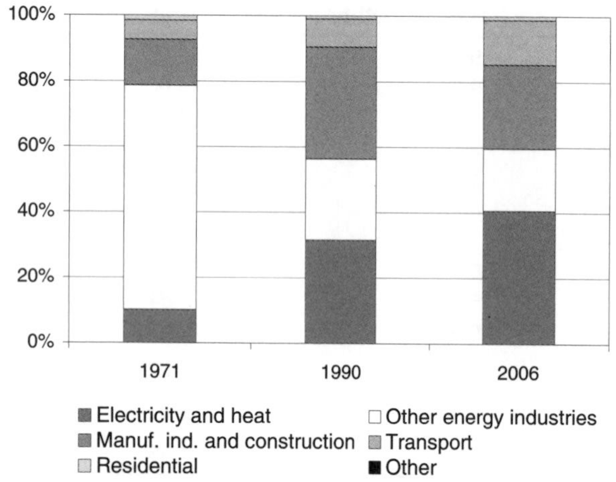

Figure 4. Reference vs Sectoral Approach

—— Total CO2 emissions - Sectoral Approach

· · · · · Total CO2 emissions - Reference Approach

Figure 5. Electricity generation by fuel

- Oil
- Gas

Figure 6. Key indicators

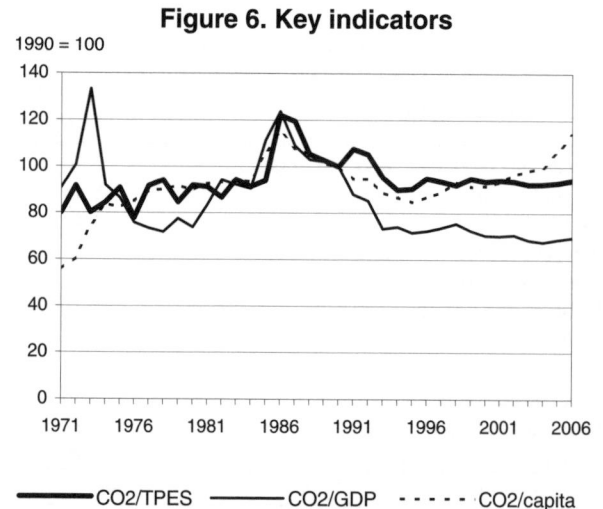

1990 = 100

—— CO2/TPES —— CO2/GDP · · · · · CO2/capita

Bahrain / Bahrein
Key indicators

	1990	1995	2000	2003	2004	2005	2006	% change 90-06
CO$_2$ Sectoral Approach (Mt of CO$_2$)	11.70	11.63	14.13	16.19	16.86	18.31	19.97	70.7%
CO$_2$ Reference Approach (Mt of CO$_2$)	10.20	11.65	13.79	15.95	16.47	17.90	19.57	91.9%
TPES (PJ)	202	223	261	303	315	341	367	81.6%
TPES (Mtoe)	4.83	5.32	6.24	7.24	7.53	8.14	8.77	81.6%
GDP (billion 2000 US$ using exch. rates)	4.65	6.45	7.97	9.41	9.92	10.60	11.42	145.7%
GDP (billion 2000 US$ using PPPs)	6.09	8.46	10.45	12.33	13.00	13.89	14.96	145.7%
Population (millions)	0.49	0.58	0.65	0.70	0.71	0.73	0.74	49.9%
CO$_2$ / TPES (t CO$_2$ per TJ)	57.8	52.2	54.1	53.4	53.5	53.7	54.4	-6.0%
CO$_2$ / GDP (kg CO$_2$ per 2000 US$)	2.52	1.80	1.77	1.72	1.70	1.73	1.75	-30.5%
CO$_2$ / GDP (kg CO$_2$ per 2000 US$ PPP)	1.92	1.37	1.35	1.31	1.30	1.32	1.33	-30.5%
CO$_2$ / population (t CO$_2$ per capita)	23.73	20.11	21.74	23.30	23.74	25.26	27.02	13.9%

Ratios are based on the Sectoral Approach.

2006 CO$_2$ emissions by sector

million tonnes of CO$_2$	Coal/peat	Oil	Gas	Other *	Total	% change 90-06
Sectoral Approach	-	4.51	15.46	-	19.97	70.7%
Main activity producer elec. and heat	-	0.61	6.03	-	6.64	79.9%
Unallocated autoproducers	-	0.13	1.32	-	1.46	x
Other energy industries	-	0.82	2.97	-	3.79	31.5%
Manufacturing industries and construction	-	-	5.13	-	5.13	28.0%
Transport	-	2.71	-	-	2.71	173.4%
of which: road	-	2.71	-	-	2.71	173.4%
Other sectors	-	0.24	-	-	0.24	90.1%
of which: residential	-	0.24	-	-	0.24	90.1%
Reference Approach	-	4.10	15.46	-	19.57	91.9%
Diff. due to losses and/or transformation	-	- 0.40	-	-	- 0.40	
Statistical differences	-	0.00	-	-	0.00	
Memo: international marine bunkers	-	..	-	-	..	..
Memo: international aviation	-	1.76	-	-	1.76	23.4%

* Other includes industrial waste and non-renewable municipal waste.

Key sources for CO$_2$ emissions from fuel combustion in 2006

IPCC source category	CO$_2$ emissions (Mt of CO$_2$)	% change 90-06	Level assessment (%) **	Cumulative total (%)
Main activity prod. elec. and heat - gas	6.03	63.4%	27.1	27.1
Manufacturing industries - gas	5.13	28.0%	23.0	50.1
Other energy industries - gas	2.97	54.9%	13.3	63.4
Road - oil	2.71	173.4%	12.1	75.6
Unallocated autoproducers - gas	1.32	x	5.9	81.5
Other energy industries - oil	0.82	-15.1%	3.7	85.2
Main activity prod. elec. and heat - oil	0.61	x	2.7	87.9
Residential - oil	0.24	90.1%	1.1	89.0
Unallocated autoproducers - oil	0.13	x	0.6	89.6
-	-	-	-	-
-	-	-	-	-
Memo: total CO$_2$ from fuel combustion	19.97	70.7%	89.6	89.6

** Percent calculated using the total GHG estimate for CO$_2$, CH$_4$, N$_2$O, HFCs, PFCs and SF$_6$ excluding CO$_2$ emissions/removals from land use change and forestry.

Bangladesh

Figure 1. CO₂ emissions by fuel

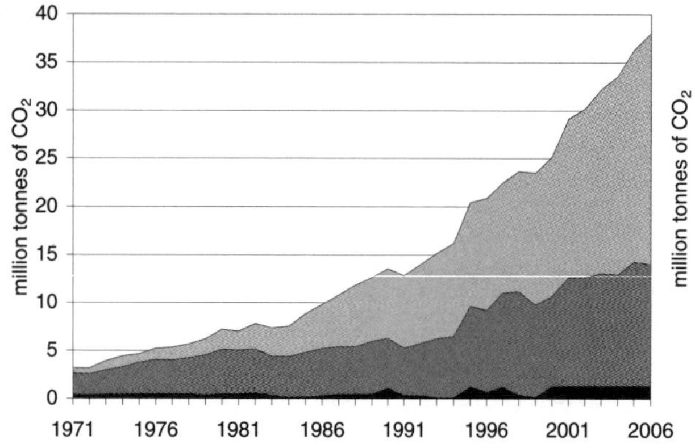

■ Coal/peat   ■ Oil   ▨ Gas   ☐ Other

Figure 2. CO₂ emissions by sector

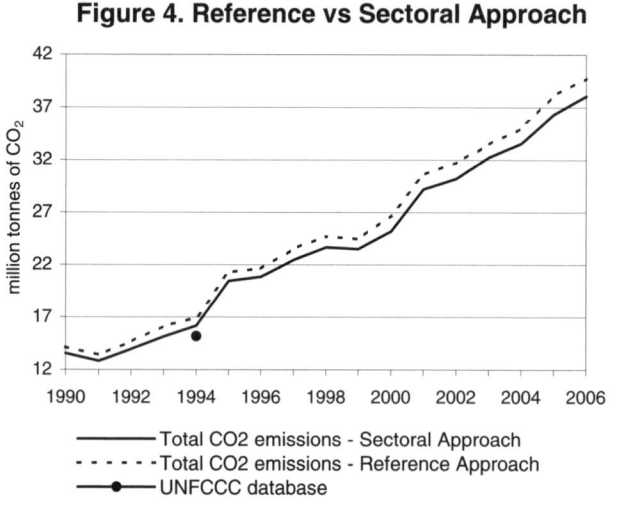

■ Electricity and heat   ☐ Other energy industries
■ Manuf. ind. and construction ▨ Transport
☐ Residential   ■ Other

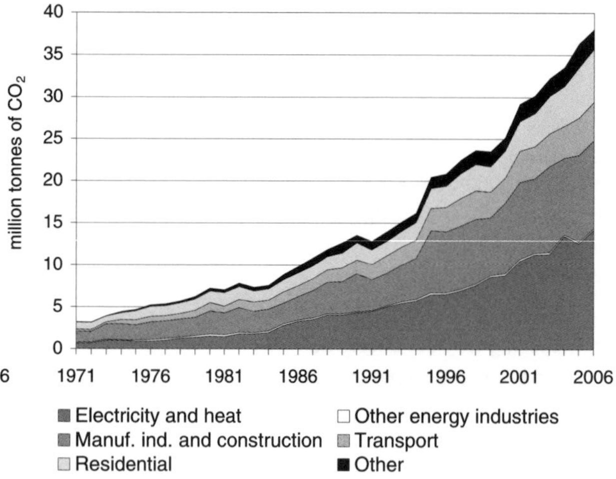

Figure 3. CO₂ emissions by sector

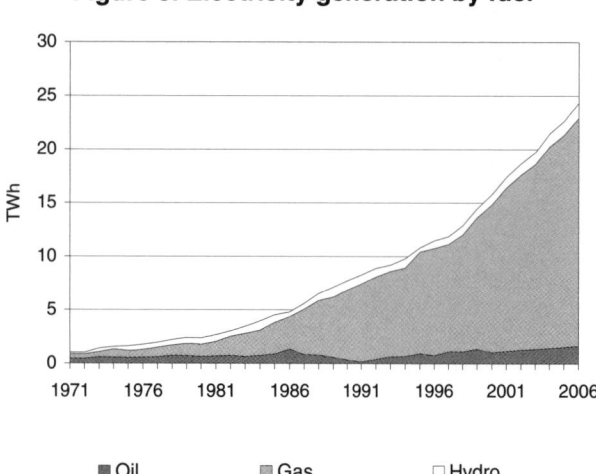

■ Electricity and heat   ☐ Other energy industries
■ Manuf. ind. and construction ▨ Transport
☐ Residential   ■ Other

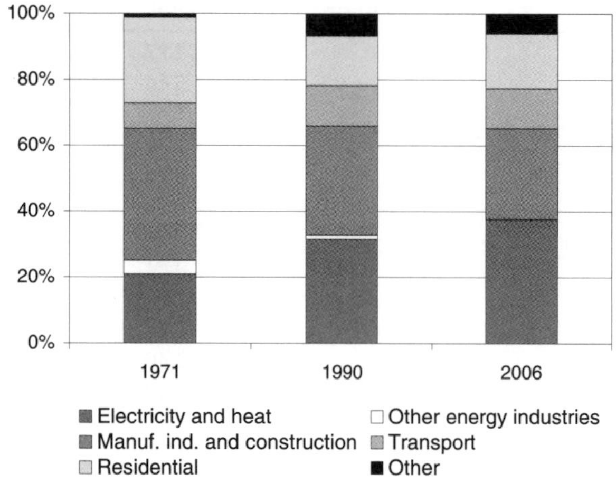

Figure 4. Reference vs Sectoral Approach

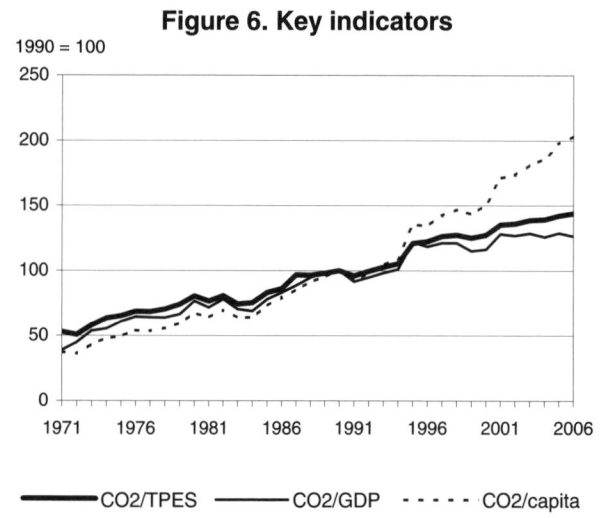

———— Total CO2 emissions - Sectoral Approach
- - - - Total CO2 emissions - Reference Approach
—●— UNFCCC database

Figure 5. Electricity generation by fuel

■ Oil   ▨ Gas   ☐ Hydro

Figure 6. Key indicators

1990 = 100

━━━ CO2/TPES   ——— CO2/GDP   - - - - CO2/capita

Bangladesh
Key indicators

	1990	1995	2000	2003	2004	2005	2006	% change 90-06
CO$_2$ Sectoral Approach (Mt of CO$_2$)	13.56	20.45	25.19	32.23	33.55	36.34	38.06	180.7%
CO$_2$ Reference Approach (Mt of CO$_2$)	14.13	21.27	26.72	33.47	35.03	38.16	39.74	181.1%
TPES (PJ)	537	670	783	920	954	1 013	1 049	95.2%
TPES (Mtoe)	12.83	16.00	18.71	21.98	22.79	24.19	25.04	95.2%
GDP (billion 2000 US$ using exch. rates)	29.47	36.54	47.10	54.49	57.91	61.36	65.48	122.2%
GDP (billion 2000 US$ using PPPs)	124.50	154.34	198.96	230.19	244.62	259.19	276.59	122.2%
Population (millions)	113.05	126.30	139.43	147.74	150.53	153.28	155.99	38.0%
CO$_2$ / TPES (t CO$_2$ per TJ)	25.3	30.5	32.2	35.0	35.2	35.9	36.3	43.8%
CO$_2$ / GDP (kg CO$_2$ per 2000 US$)	0.46	0.56	0.53	0.59	0.58	0.59	0.58	26.4%
CO$_2$ / GDP (kg CO$_2$ per 2000 US$ PPP)	0.11	0.13	0.13	0.14	0.14	0.14	0.14	26.4%
CO$_2$ / population (t CO$_2$ per capita)	0.12	0.16	0.18	0.22	0.22	0.24	0.24	103.3%

Ratios are based on the Sectoral Approach.

2006 CO$_2$ emissions by sector

million tonnes of CO$_2$	Coal/peat	Oil	Gas	Other *	Total	% change 90-06
Sectoral Approach	**1.36**	**12.69**	**24.02**	-	**38.06**	**180.7%**
Main activity producer elec. and heat	-	1.80	12.42	-	14.22	231.7%
Unallocated autoproducers	-	-	-	-	-	-
Other energy industries	-	0.18	-	-	0.18	17.8%
Manufacturing industries and construction	1.36	2.17	6.92	-	10.44	131.7%
Transport	-	4.59	-	-	4.59	178.4%
of which: road	-	3.37	-	-	3.37	183.1%
Other sectors	-	3.95	4.68	-	8.63	190.9%
of which: residential	-	2.26	4.05	-	6.31	209.7%
Reference Approach	**1.36**	**12.63**	**25.75**	-	**39.74**	**181.1%**
Diff. due to losses and/or transformation	-	0.22	1.74	-	1.96	
Statistical differences	-	- 0.28	-	-	- 0.28	
Memo: international marine bunkers	-	0.11	-	-	0.11	78.6%
Memo: international aviation	-	0.84	-	-	0.84	209.3%

* Other includes industrial waste and non-renewable municipal waste.

Key sources for CO$_2$ emissions from fuel combustion in 2006

IPCC source category	CO$_2$ emissions (Mt of CO$_2$)	% change 90-06	Level assessment (%) **	Cumulative total (%)
Main activity prod. elec. and heat - gas	12.42	216.8%	7.3	7.3
Manufacturing industries - gas	6.92	157.7%	4.0	11.3
Residential - gas	4.05	665.2%	2.4	13.7
Road - oil	3.37	183.1%	2.0	15.6
Residential - oil	2.26	49.9%	1.3	16.9
Manufacturing industries - oil	2.17	197.0%	1.3	18.2
Main activity prod. elec. and heat - oil	1.80	390.7%	1.1	19.3
Non-specified other sectors - oil	1.70	119.8%	1.0	20.2
Manufacturing industries - coal/peat	1.36	24.3%	0.8	21.0
Other transport - oil	1.23	166.2%	0.7	21.8
Non-specified other sectors - gas	0.63	294.3%	0.4	22.1
Memo: total CO$_2$ from fuel combustion	38.06	180.7%	22.2	22.2

** Percent calculated using the total GHG estimate for CO$_2$, CH$_4$, N$_2$O, HFCs, PFCs and SF$_6$ excluding CO$_2$ emissions/removals from land use change and forestry.

Belarus / Bélarus

Figure 1. CO_2 emissions by fuel

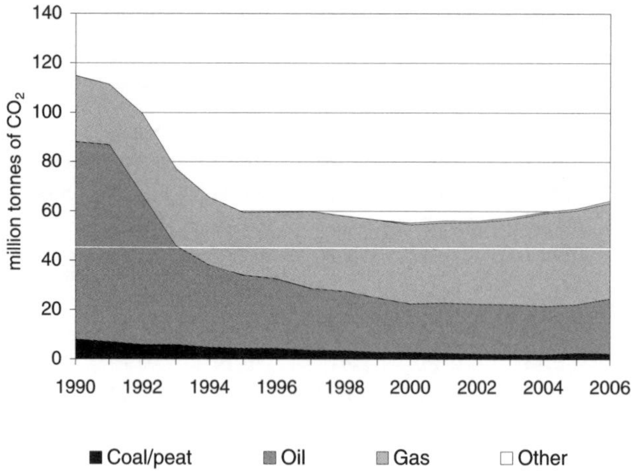

140
120
100
80
60
40
20
0
million tonnes of CO2
1990 1992 1994 1996 1998 2000 2002 2004 2006
Coal/peat Oil Gas Other

Figure 2. CO_2 emissions by sector

140
120
100
80
60
40
20
0
million tonnes of CO2
1990 1992 1994 1996 1998 2000 2002 2004 2006
Electricity and heat
Other energy industries
Manuf. ind. and construction
Transport
Residential
Other

Figure 3. CO_2 emissions by sector

100%
80%
60%
40%
20%
0%
not available
1971 1990 2006
Electricity and heat
Other energy industries
Manuf. ind. and construction
Transport
Residential
Other

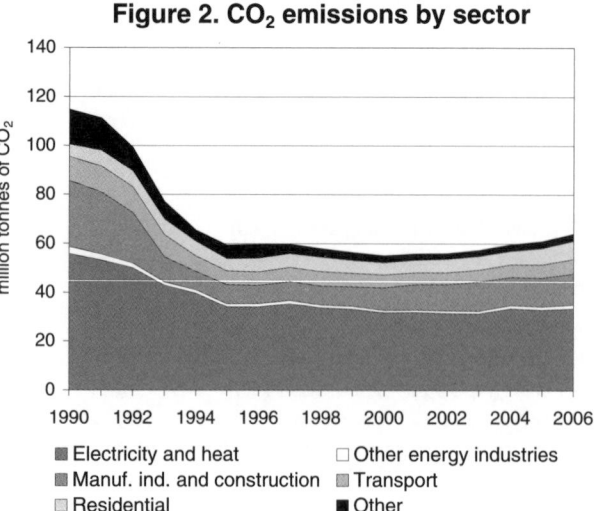

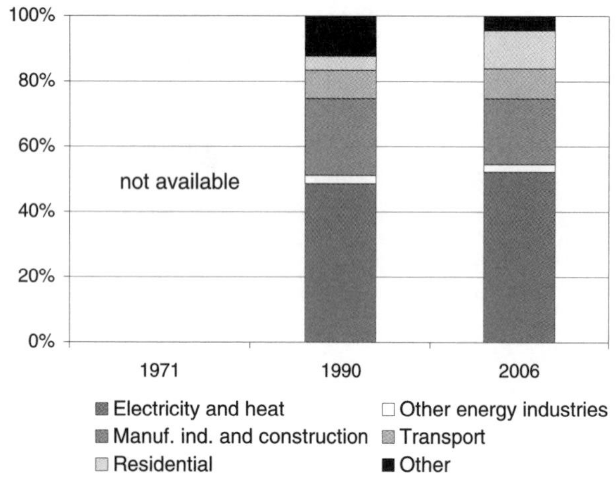

Figure 4. Reference vs Sectoral Approach

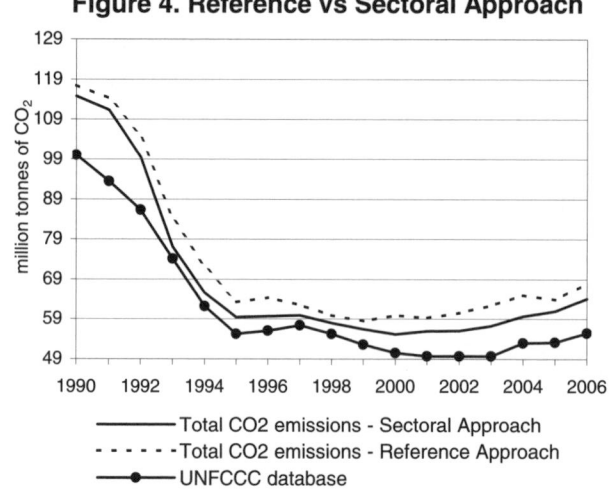

129
119
109
99
89
79
69
59
49
million tonnes of CO2
1990 1992 1994 1996 1998 2000 2002 2004 2006
Total CO2 emissions - Sectoral Approach
Total CO2 emissions - Reference Approach
UNFCCC database

Figure 5. Electricity generation by fuel

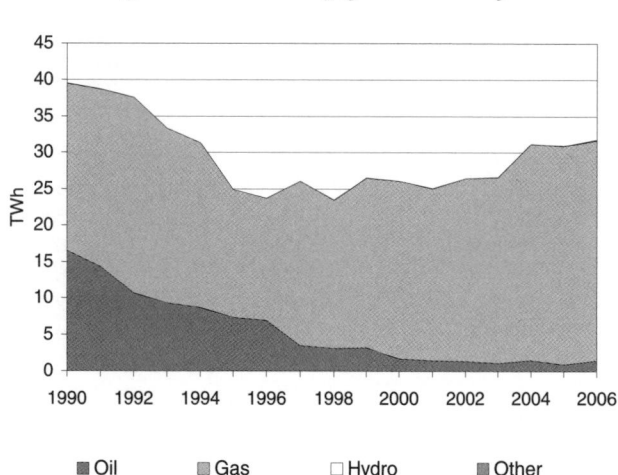

45
40
35
30
25
20
15
10
5
0
TWh
1990 1992 1994 1996 1998 2000 2002 2004 2006
Oil Gas Hydro Other

Figure 6. Key indicators

1990 = 100
120
100
80
60
40
20
0
1990 1992 1994 1996 1998 2000 2002 2004 2006
CO2/TPES CO2/GDP CO2/capita

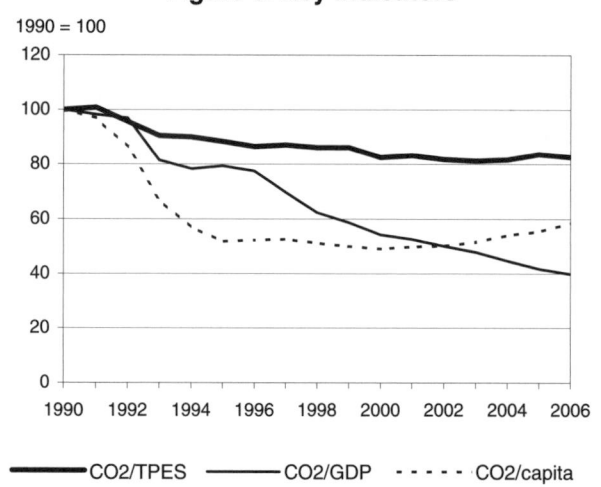

Belarus / Bélarus

Key indicators

	1990	1995	2000	2003	2004	2005	2006	% change 90-06
CO$_2$ Sectoral Approach (Mt of CO$_2$)	114.79	59.45	55.20	57.30	59.66	60.97	64.09	-44.2%
CO$_2$ Reference Approach (Mt of CO$_2$)	117.43	63.16	59.90	62.39	65.00	63.81	68.01	-42.1%
TPES (PJ)	1 772	1 038	1 033	1 089	1 127	1 124	1 198	-32.4%
TPES (Mtoe)	42.31	24.78	24.67	26.01	26.91	26.84	28.61	-32.4%
GDP (billion 2000 US$ using exch. rates)	14.36	9.38	12.74	15.00	16.72	18.26	20.11	40.0%
GDP (billion 2000 US$ using PPPs)	54.19	35.38	48.05	56.59	63.06	68.89	75.88	40.0%
Population (millions)	10.19	10.19	10.01	9.87	9.82	9.78	9.73	-4.5%
CO$_2$ / TPES (t CO$_2$ per TJ)	64.8	57.3	53.4	52.6	53.0	54.2	53.5	-17.4%
CO$_2$ / GDP (kg CO$_2$ per 2000 US$)	7.99	6.34	4.33	3.82	3.57	3.34	3.19	-60.1%
CO$_2$ / GDP (kg CO$_2$ per 2000 US$ PPP)	2.12	1.68	1.15	1.01	0.95	0.88	0.84	-60.1%
CO$_2$ / population (t CO$_2$ per capita)	11.27	5.83	5.52	5.80	6.07	6.24	6.58	-41.6%

Ratios are based on the Sectoral Approach.

2006 CO$_2$ emissions by sector

million tonnes of CO$_2$	Coal/peat	Oil	Gas	Other *	Total	% change 90-06
Sectoral Approach	**2.31**	**22.14**	**38.93**	**0.71**	**64.09**	**-44.2%**
Main activity producer elec. and heat	0.10	2.31	24.62	-	27.03	-30.5%
Unallocated autoproducers	0.47	0.75	4.96	0.20	6.38	-62.3%
Other energy industries	0.06	1.47	-	-	1.53	-47.1%
Manufacturing industries and construction	0.29	6.55	5.56	0.51	12.91	-52.2%
Transport	0.03	5.01	0.84	-	5.88	-41.0%
of which: road	-	*4.15*	*0.04*	-	*4.20*	*-48.5%*
Other sectors	1.36	6.05	2.94	-	10.35	-45.9%
of which: residential	*1.06*	*3.64*	*2.78*	-	*7.48*	*50.7%*
Reference Approach	**2.51**	**25.45**	**39.34**	**0.71**	**68.01**	**-42.1%**
Diff. due to losses and/or transformation	0.19	3.20	0.41	-	3.81	
Statistical differences	0.00	0.11	- 0.00	-	0.11	
Memo: international marine bunkers	-	-	-	-	-	-
Memo: international aviation	-	..	-	-	..	..

* Other includes industrial waste and non-renewable municipal waste.

Key sources for CO$_2$ emissions from fuel combustion in 2006

IPCC source category	CO$_2$ emissions (Mt of CO$_2$)	% change 90-06	Level assessment (%) **	Cumulative total (%)
Main activity prod. elec. and heat - gas	24.62	78.0%	27.5	27.5
Manufacturing industries - oil	6.55	-70.5%	7.3	34.8
Manufacturing industries - gas	5.56	26.1%	6.2	41.0
Unallocated autoproducers - gas	4.96	21.4%	5.5	46.5
Road - oil	4.15	-49.0%	4.6	51.2
Residential - oil	3.64	88.8%	4.1	55.2
Residential - gas	2.78	58.2%	3.1	58.3
Non-specified other sectors - oil	2.41	-67.4%	2.7	61.0
Main activity prod. elec. and heat - oil	2.31	-90.8%	2.6	63.6
Other energy industries - oil	1.47	-47.4%	1.6	65.2
Residential - coal/peat	1.06	-17.0%	1.2	66.4
Memo: total CO$_2$ from fuel combustion	*64.09*	*-44.2%*	*71.5*	*71.5*

** Percent calculated using the total GHG estimate for CO$_2$, CH$_4$, N$_2$O, HFCs, PFCs and SF$_6$ excluding CO$_2$ emissions/removals from land use change and forestry.

Belgium / Belgique

Figure 1. CO$_2$ emissions by fuel

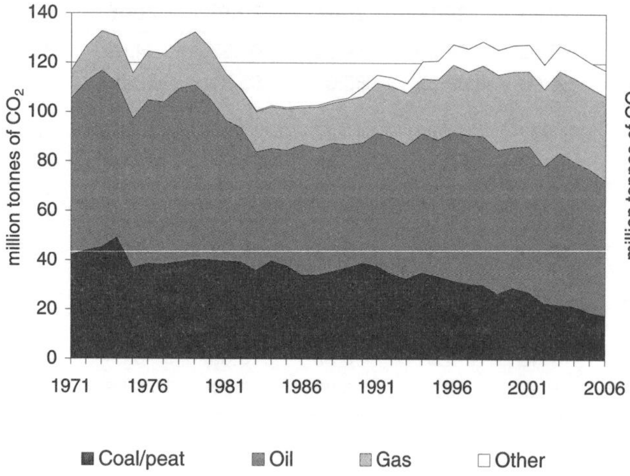

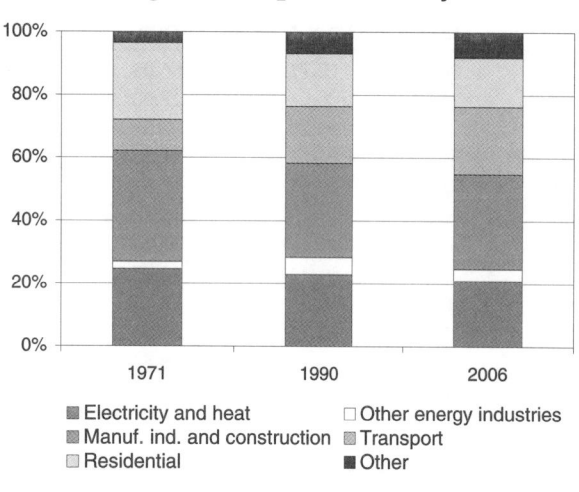

Coal/peat ■ Oil ■ Gas ■ Other □

Figure 2. CO$_2$ emissions by sector

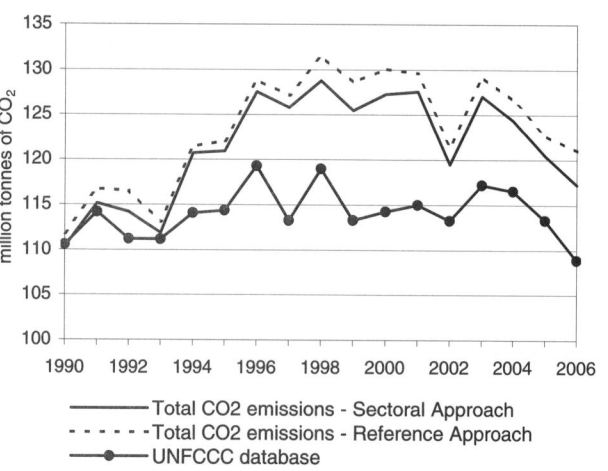

■ Electricity and heat   □ Other energy industries
■ Manuf. ind. and construction ■ Transport
□ Residential   ■ Other

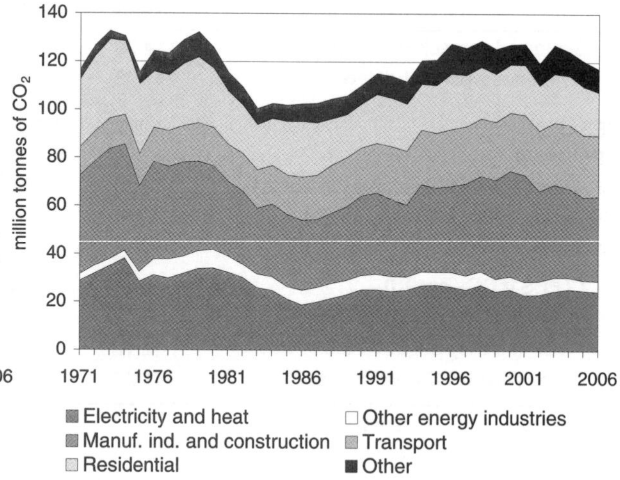

Figure 3. CO$_2$ emissions by sector

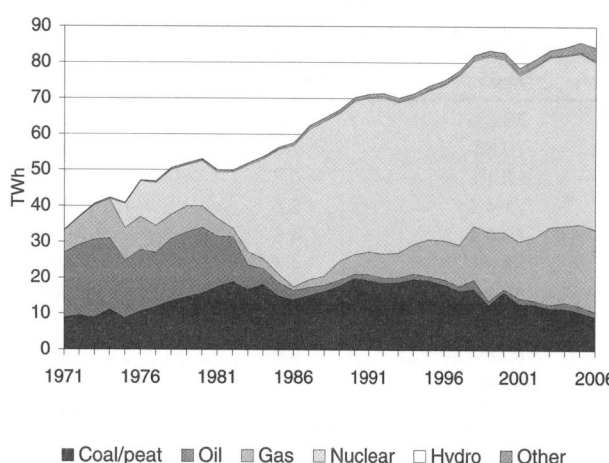

■ Electricity and heat   □ Other energy industries
■ Manuf. ind. and construction ■ Transport
□ Residential   ■ Other

Figure 4. Reference vs Sectoral Approach

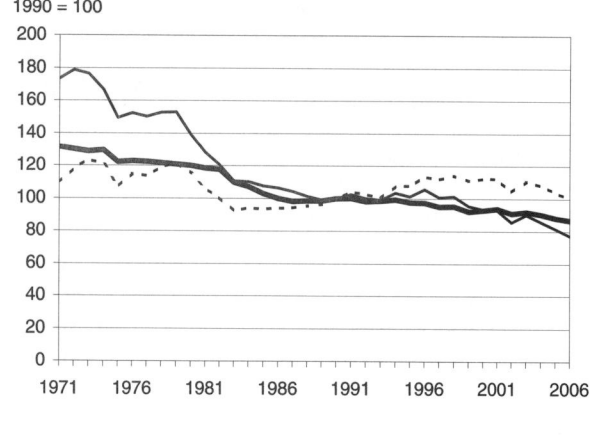

——— Total CO2 emissions - Sectoral Approach
- - - - Total CO2 emissions - Reference Approach
——●—— UNFCCC database

Figure 5. Electricity generation by fuel

■ Coal/peat ■ Oil ■ Gas ■ Nuclear □ Hydro ■ Other

Figure 6. Key indicators

1990 = 100

——— CO2/TPES ——— CO2/GDP - - - - CO2/capita

Belgium / Belgique

Key indicators

	1990	1995	2000	2003	2004	2005	2006	% change 90-06
CO$_2$ Sectoral Approach (Mt of CO$_2$)	110.29	120.94	127.30	127.02	124.38	120.45	117.24	6.3%
CO$_2$ Reference Approach (Mt of CO$_2$)	111.79	122.05	130.10	129.21	126.67	122.71	121.00	8.2%
TPES (PJ)	2 082	2 340	2 591	2 611	2 603	2 584	2 554	22.7%
TPES (Mtoe)	49.72	55.88	61.89	62.36	62.16	61.71	60.99	22.7%
GDP (billion 2000 US$ using exch. rates)	187.50	203.00	231.90	239.70	246.80	250.90	258.10	37.7%
GDP (billion 2000 US$ using PPPs)	228.18	246.94	282.19	291.58	300.25	305.28	313.97	37.6%
Population (millions)	9.97	10.14	10.25	10.37	10.42	10.47	10.54	5.8%
CO$_2$ / TPES (t CO$_2$ per TJ)	53.0	51.7	49.1	48.7	47.8	46.6	45.9	-13.3%
CO$_2$ / GDP (kg CO$_2$ per 2000 US$)	0.59	0.60	0.55	0.53	0.50	0.48	0.45	-22.8%
CO$_2$ / GDP (kg CO$_2$ per 2000 US$ PPP)	0.48	0.49	0.45	0.44	0.41	0.39	0.37	-22.8%
CO$_2$ / population (t CO$_2$ per capita)	11.06	11.93	12.42	12.25	11.94	11.50	11.12	0.5%

Ratios are based on the Sectoral Approach.

2006 CO$_2$ emissions by sector

million tonnes of CO$_2$	Coal/peat	Oil	Gas	Other *	Total	% change 90-06
Sectoral Approach	**17.71**	**54.92**	**34.09**	**10.52**	**117.24**	**6.3%**
Main activity producer elec. and heat	10.55	0.98	9.14	2.14	22.82	3.9%
Unallocated autoproducers	1.25	0.06	0.28	-	1.59	-49.9%
Other energy industries	0.37	4.01	0.16	-	4.54	-25.4%
Manufacturing industries and construction	5.03	9.71	12.15	8.35	35.24	6.7%
Transport	-	25.22	-	-	25.22	26.1%
of which: road	-	*24.36*	-	-	*24.36*	*26.5%*
Other sectors	0.51	14.93	12.37	0.02	27.84	6.8%
of which: residential	*0.51*	*9.64*	*8.08*	-	*18.23*	*-1.2%*
Reference Approach	**18.12**	**58.02**	**34.34**	**10.52**	**121.00**	**8.2%**
Diff. due to losses and/or transformation	0.90	3.96	-	-	4.87	
Statistical differences	- 0.50	- 0.86	0.25	0.00	- 1.11	
Memo: international marine bunkers	-	*26.40*	-	-	*26.40*	*103.6%*
Memo: international aviation	-	*3.49*	-	-	*3.49*	*23.9%*

* Other includes industrial waste and non-renewable municipal waste.

Key sources for CO$_2$ emissions from fuel combustion in 2006

IPCC source category	CO$_2$ emissions (Mt of CO$_2$)	% change 90-06	Level assessment (%) **	Cumulative total (%)
Road - oil	24.36	26.5%	16.8	16.8
Manufacturing industries - gas	12.15	64.4%	8.4	25.1
Main activity prod. elec. and heat - coal/peat	10.55	-41.0%	7.3	32.4
Manufacturing industries - oil	9.71	24.4%	6.7	39.1
Residential - oil	9.64	-9.2%	6.6	45.7
Main activity prod. elec. and heat - gas	9.14	238.1%	6.3	52.0
Manufacturing industries -other	8.35	215.6%	5.7	57.7
Residential - gas	8.08	39.2%	5.6	63.3
Non-specified other sectors - oil	5.29	2.2%	3.6	66.9
Manufacturing industries - coal/peat	5.03	-66.8%	3.5	70.4
Non-specified other sectors - gas	4.29	77.4%	3.0	73.3
Memo: total CO$_2$ from fuel combustion	*117.24*	*6.3%*	*80.7*	*80.7*

** Percent calculated using the total GHG estimate for CO$_2$, CH$_4$, N$_2$O, HFCs, PFCs and SF$_6$ excluding CO$_2$ emissions/removals from land use change and forestry.

Benin / Bénin

Figure 1. CO$_2$ emissions by fuel

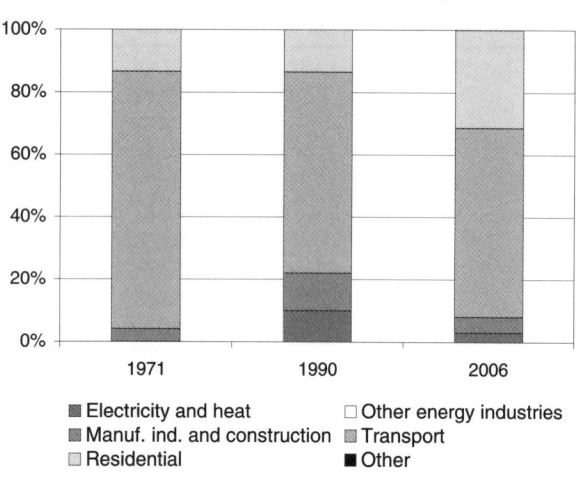

■ Coal/peat   ■ Oil   ▨ Gas   ☐ Other

Figure 2. CO$_2$ emissions by sector

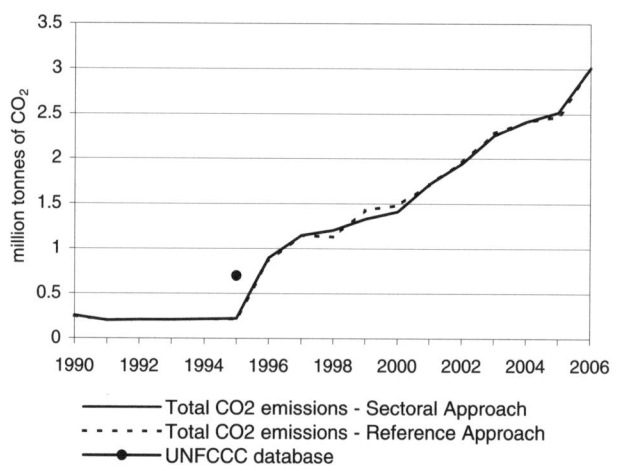

■ Electricity and heat   ☐ Other energy industries
▨ Manuf. ind. and construction   ▨ Transport
☐ Residential   ■ Other

Figure 3. CO$_2$ emissions by sector

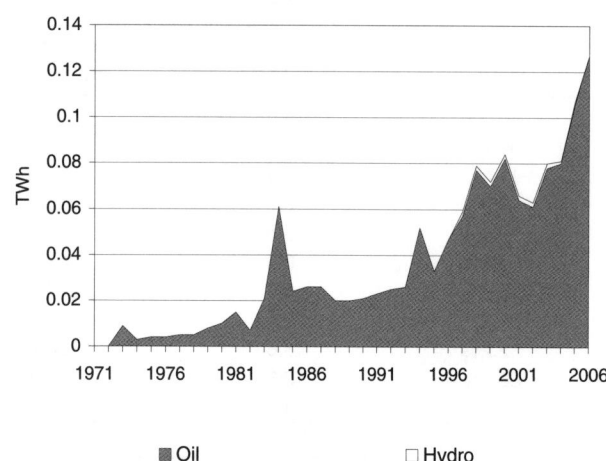

■ Electricity and heat   ☐ Other energy industries
▨ Manuf. ind. and construction   ▨ Transport
☐ Residential   ■ Other

Figure 4. Reference vs Sectoral Approach

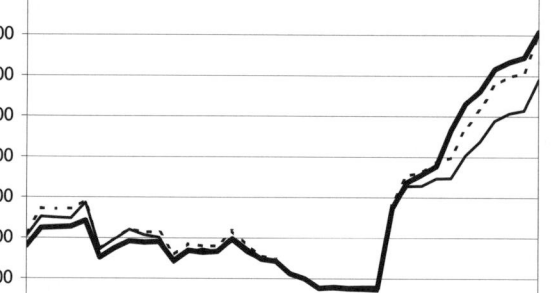

——— Total CO2 emissions - Sectoral Approach
- - - - - Total CO2 emissions - Reference Approach
——●— UNFCCC database

Figure 5. Electricity generation by fuel

■ Oil   ☐ Hydro

Figure 6. Key indicators

1990 = 100

——— CO2/TPES   ——— CO2/GDP   - - - - - CO2/capita

Benin / Bénin

Key indicators

	1990	1995	2000	2003	2004	2005	2006	% change 90-06
CO$_2$ Sectoral Approach (Mt of CO$_2$)	0.25	0.22	1.41	2.26	2.41	2.52	3.01	+
CO$_2$ Reference Approach (Mt of CO$_2$)	0.24	0.21	1.48	2.29	2.42	2.47	3.01	+
TPES (PJ)	70	78	84	101	105	108	118	67.7%
TPES (Mtoe)	1.68	1.87	2.01	2.42	2.52	2.58	2.82	67.7%
GDP (billion 2000 US$ using exch. rates)	1.41	1.74	2.26	2.57	2.65	2.73	2.84	101.1%
GDP (billion 2000 US$ using PPPs)	4.39	5.41	7.02	8.00	8.25	8.48	8.83	101.1%
Population (millions)	5.18	6.21	7.23	7.96	8.22	8.49	8.76	69.1%
CO$_2$ / TPES (t CO$_2$ per TJ)	3.6	2.8	16.8	22.2	22.9	23.3	25.5	607.4%
CO$_2$ / GDP (kg CO$_2$ per 2000 US$)	0.18	0.13	0.63	0.88	0.91	0.92	1.06	490.3%
CO$_2$ / GDP (kg CO$_2$ per 2000 US$ PPP)	0.06	0.04	0.20	0.28	0.29	0.30	0.34	489.8%
CO$_2$ / population (t CO$_2$ per capita)	0.05	0.04	0.20	0.28	0.29	0.30	0.34	601.4%

Ratios are based on the Sectoral Approach.

2006 CO$_2$ emissions by sector

million tonnes of CO$_2$	Coal/peat	Oil	Gas	Other *	Total	% change 90-06
Sectoral Approach	-	3.01	-	-	3.01	+
Main activity producer elec. and heat	-	0.07	-	-	0.07	175.2%
Unallocated autoproducers	-	0.02	-	-	0.02	x
Other energy industries	-	-	-	-	-	-
Manufacturing industries and construction	-	0.15	-	-	0.15	400.6%
Transport	-	1.82	-	-	1.82	+
of which: road	-	1.82	-	-	1.82	+
Other sectors	-	0.95	-	-	0.95	+
of which: residential	-	0.94	-	-	0.94	+
Reference Approach	-	3.01	-	-	3.01	+
Diff. due to losses and/or transformation	-	-	-	-	-	
Statistical differences	-	0.00	-	-	0.00	
Memo: international marine bunkers	-	..	-	-	..	..
Memo: international aviation	-	0.08	-	-	0.08	50.0%

* Other includes industrial waste and non-renewable municipal waste.

Key sources for CO$_2$ emissions from fuel combustion in 2006

IPCC source category	CO$_2$ emissions (Mt of CO$_2$)	% change 90-06	Level assessment (%) **	Cumulative total (%)
Road - oil	1.82	+	14.3	14.3
Residential - oil	0.94	+	7.4	21.7
Manufacturing industries - oil	0.15	400.6%	1.2	22.9
Main activity prod. elec. and heat - oil	0.07	175.2%	0.5	23.5
Unallocated autoproducers - oil	0.02	x	0.1	23.6
Non-specified other sectors - oil	0.00	x	0.0	23.7
-	-	-	-	-
-	-	-	-	-
-	-	-	-	-
-	-	-	-	-
-	-	-	-	-
Memo: total CO$_2$ from fuel combustion	3.01	+	23.7	23.7

** Percent calculated using the total GHG estimate for CO$_2$, CH$_4$, N$_2$O, HFCs, PFCs and SF$_6$ excluding CO$_2$ emissions/removals from land use change and forestry.

Bolivia / Bolivie

Figure 1. CO₂ emissions by fuel

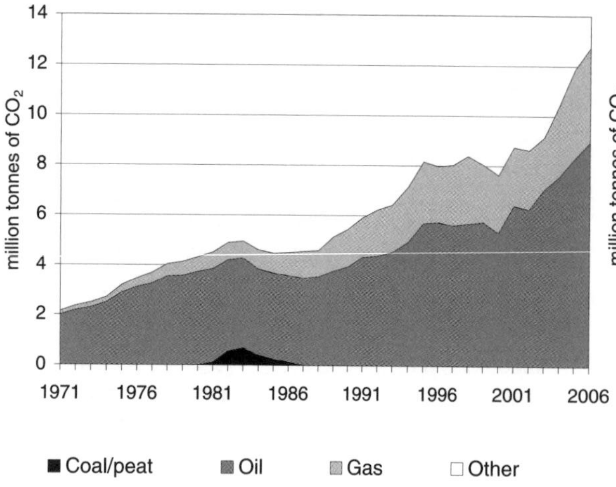

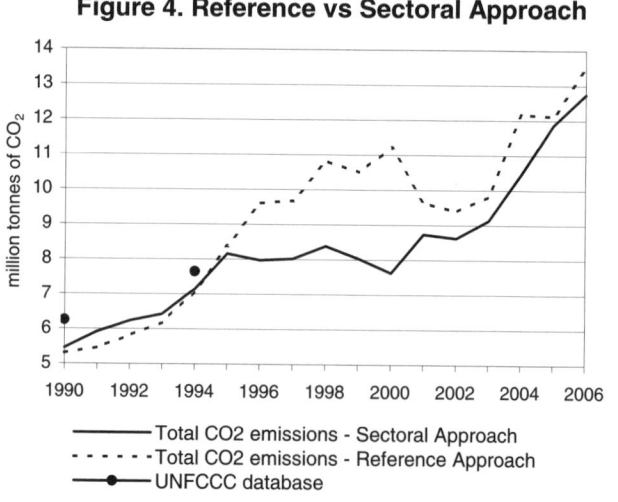

■ Coal/peat   ■ Oil   ▨ Gas   ☐ Other

Figure 2. CO₂ emissions by sector

■ Electricity and heat   ☐ Other energy industries
▨ Manuf. ind. and construction ▨ Transport
☐ Residential   ■ Other

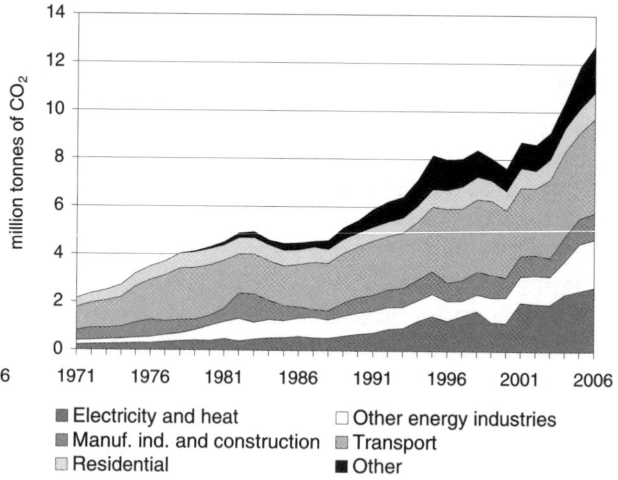

Figure 3. CO₂ emissions by sector

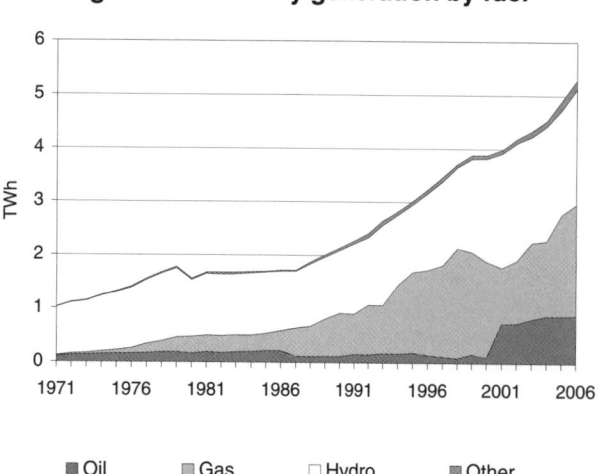

■ Electricity and heat   ☐ Other energy industries
▨ Manuf. ind. and construction ▨ Transport
☐ Residential   ■ Other

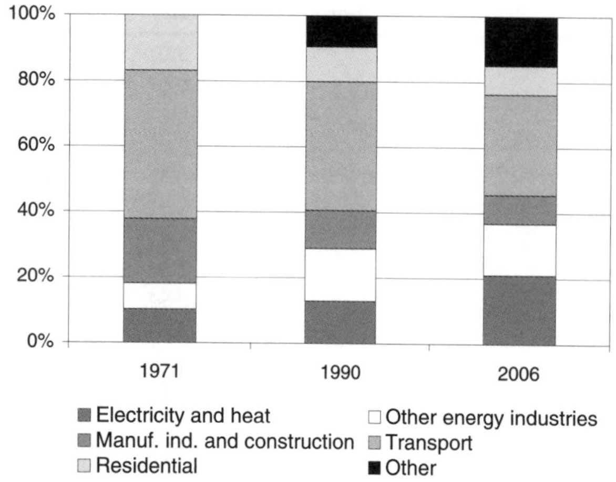

Figure 4. Reference vs Sectoral Approach

—— Total CO2 emissions - Sectoral Approach
- - - Total CO2 emissions - Reference Approach
●—— UNFCCC database

Figure 5. Electricity generation by fuel

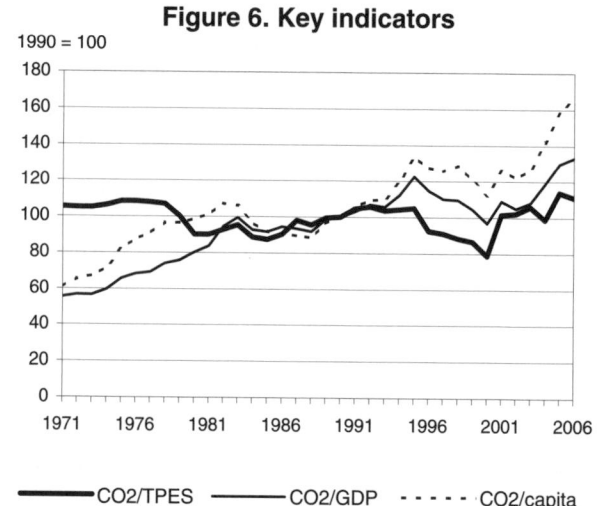

■ Oil   ▨ Gas   ☐ Hydro   ▨ Other

Figure 6. Key indicators

1990 = 100

—— CO2/TPES   —— CO2/GDP   - - - CO2/capita

Bolivia / Bolivie

Key indicators

	1990	1995	2000	2003	2004	2005	2006	% change 90-06
CO$_2$ Sectoral Approach (Mt of CO$_2$)	5.45	8.16	7.63	9.13	10.45	11.87	12.75	134.1%
CO$_2$ Reference Approach (Mt of CO$_2$)	5.30	8.37	11.22	9.82	12.16	12.12	13.49	154.7%
TPES (PJ)	116	166	207	184	225	222	245	110.9%
TPES (Mtoe)	2.77	3.96	4.94	4.39	5.38	5.31	5.85	110.9%
GDP (billion 2000 US$ using exch. rates)	5.80	7.09	8.40	8.99	9.36	9.74	10.19	75.7%
GDP (billion 2000 US$ using PPPs)	13.72	16.77	19.86	21.25	22.14	23.04	24.10	75.7%
Population (millions)	6.67	7.48	8.32	8.84	9.01	9.18	9.35	40.3%
CO$_2$ / TPES (t CO$_2$ per TJ)	46.9	49.2	36.9	49.7	46.3	53.4	52.0	11.0%
CO$_2$ / GDP (kg CO$_2$ per 2000 US$)	0.94	1.15	0.91	1.02	1.12	1.22	1.25	33.2%
CO$_2$ / GDP (kg CO$_2$ per 2000 US$ PPP)	0.40	0.49	0.38	0.43	0.47	0.52	0.53	33.2%
CO$_2$ / population (t CO$_2$ per capita)	0.82	1.09	0.92	1.03	1.16	1.29	1.36	66.9%

Ratios are based on the Sectoral Approach.

2006 CO$_2$ emissions by sector

million tonnes of CO$_2$	Coal/peat	Oil	Gas	Other *	Total	% change 90-06
Sectoral Approach	-	**8.95**	**3.79**	-	**12.75**	**134.1%**
Main activity producer elec. and heat	-	1.05	1.53	-	2.58	310.3%
Unallocated autoproducers	-	0.08	0.02	-	0.09	32.0%
Other energy industries	-	1.16	0.85	-	2.01	128.2%
Manufacturing industries and construction	-	0.17	0.94	-	1.11	76.5%
Transport	-	3.55	0.36	-	3.91	82.6%
of which: road	-	*3.06*	*0.36*	-	*3.43*	*94.3%*
Other sectors	-	2.95	0.09	-	3.04	178.0%
of which: residential	-	*1.07*	*0.05*	-	*1.12*	*95.1%*
Reference Approach	-	**9.73**	**3.77**	-	**13.49**	**154.7%**
Diff. due to losses and/or transformation	-	0.79	0.38	-	1.17	
Statistical differences	-	- 0.01	- 0.41	-	- 0.42	
Memo: international marine bunkers	-	-	-	-	-	-
Memo: international aviation	-	..	-	-	..	..

* Other includes industrial waste and non-renewable municipal waste.

Key sources for CO$_2$ emissions from fuel combustion in 2006

IPCC source category	CO$_2$ emissions (Mt of CO$_2$)	% change 90-06	Level assessment (%) **	Cumulative total (%)
Road - oil	3.06	73.7%	4.4	4.4
Non-specified other sectors - oil	1.88	262.1%	2.7	7.1
Main activity prod. elec. and heat - gas	1.53	163.1%	2.2	9.3
Other energy industries - oil	1.16	235.1%	1.7	10.9
Residential - oil	1.07	85.6%	1.5	12.5
Main activity prod. elec. and heat - oil	1.05	+	1.5	14.0
Manufacturing industries - gas	0.94	143.5%	1.3	15.3
Other energy industries - gas	0.85	59.2%	1.2	16.5
Other transport - oil	0.49	28.3%	0.7	17.2
Road - gas	0.36	x	0.5	17.7
Manufacturing industries - oil	0.17	-29.9%	0.2	18.0
Memo: total CO$_2$ from fuel combustion	*12.75*	*134.1%*	*18.3*	*18.3*

** Percent calculated using the total GHG estimate for CO$_2$, CH$_4$, N$_2$O, HFCs, PFCs and SF$_6$ excluding CO$_2$ emissions/removals from land use change and forestry.

Bosnia and Herzegovina / Bosnie-Herzégovine

Figure 1. CO$_2$ emissions by fuel

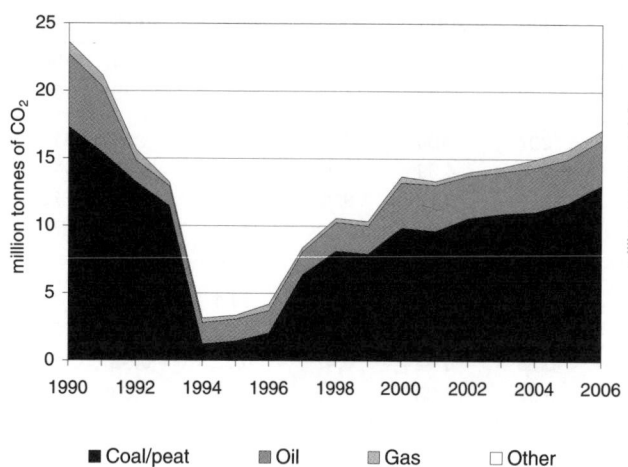

■ Coal/peat   ▨ Oil   ▨ Gas   ☐ Other

Figure 2. CO$_2$ emissions by sector

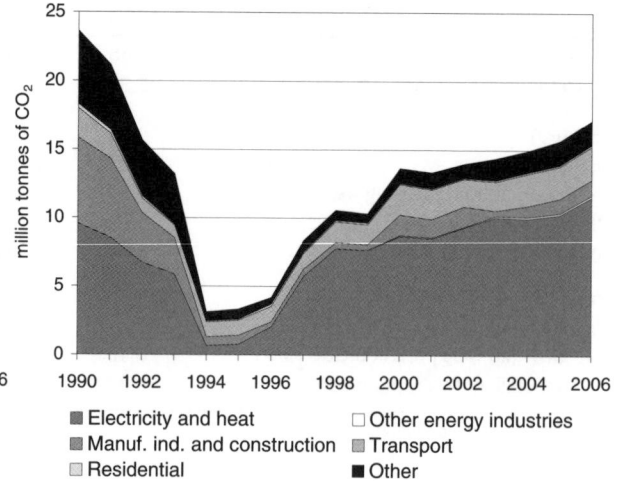

■ Electricity and heat   ☐ Other energy industries
■ Manuf. ind. and construction   ▨ Transport
☐ Residential   ■ Other

Figure 3. CO$_2$ emissions by sector

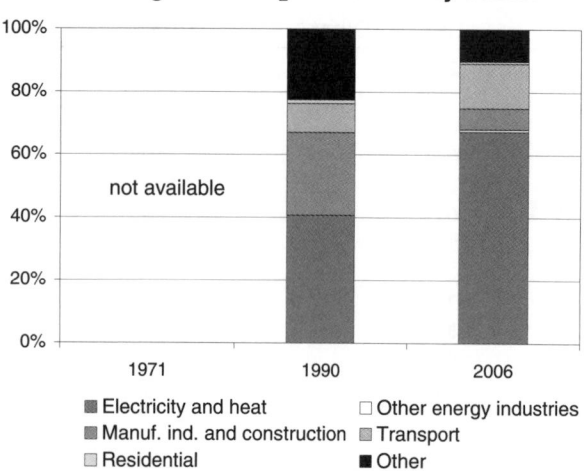

not available

■ Electricity and heat   ☐ Other energy industries
■ Manuf. ind. and construction   ▨ Transport
☐ Residential   ■ Other

Figure 4. Reference vs Sectoral Approach

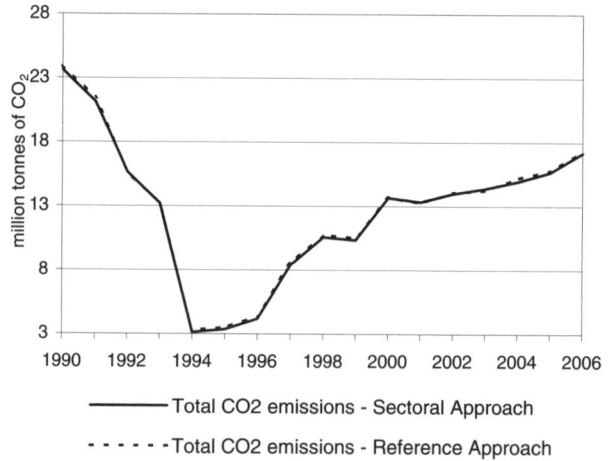

—— Total CO2 emissions - Sectoral Approach
- - - - - Total CO2 emissions - Reference Approach

Figure 5. Electricity generation by fuel

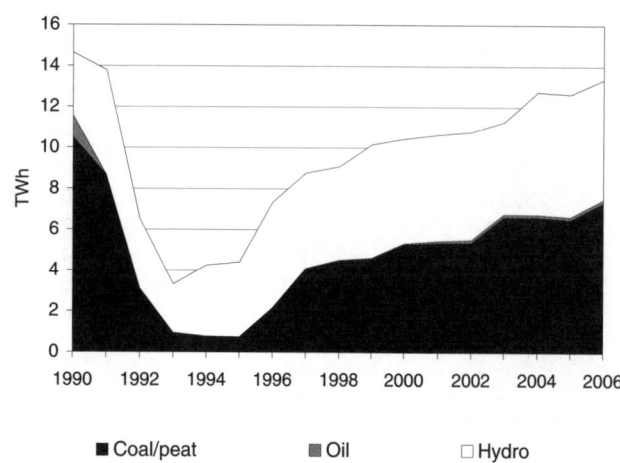

■ Coal/peat   ■ Oil   ☐ Hydro

Figure 6. Key indicators

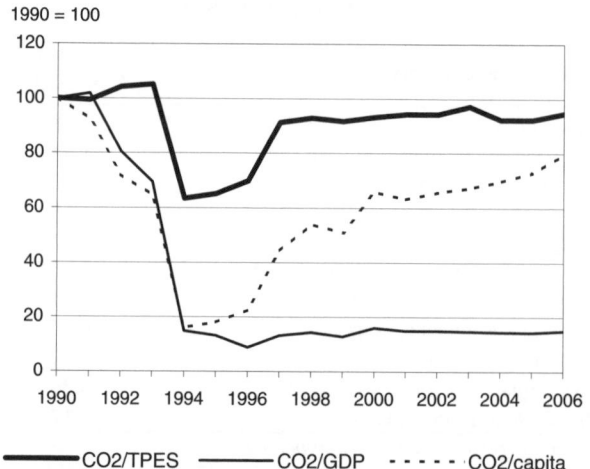

—— CO2/TPES   —— CO2/GDP   - - - - CO2/capita

Bosnia and Herzegovina / Bosnie-Herzégovine
Key indicators

	1990	1995	2000	2003	2004	2005	2006	% change 90-06
CO$_2$ Sectoral Approach (Mt of CO$_2$)	23.63	3.35	13.66	14.38	14.94	15.66	17.16	-27.4%
CO$_2$ Reference Approach (Mt of CO$_2$)	23.94	3.50	13.69	14.22	15.21	15.80	17.35	-27.5%
TPES (PJ)	295	64	182	184	202	211	226	-23.4%
TPES (Mtoe)	7.04	1.53	4.36	4.41	4.81	5.05	5.39	-23.4%
GDP (billion 2000 US$ using exch. rates)	1.40	1.51	5.05	5.77	6.13	6.44	6.83	388.3%
GDP (billion 2000 US$ using PPPs)	5.69	6.14	20.54	23.47	24.93	26.19	27.76	388.2%
Population (millions)	4.31	3.42	3.79	3.90	3.91	3.92	3.93	-8.9%
CO$_2$ / TPES (t CO$_2$ per TJ)	80.2	52.2	74.9	77.9	74.1	74.1	76.0	-5.2%
CO$_2$ / GDP (kg CO$_2$ per 2000 US$)	16.90	2.22	2.71	2.49	2.44	2.43	2.51	-85.1%
CO$_2$ / GDP (kg CO$_2$ per 2000 US$ PPP)	4.16	0.55	0.67	0.61	0.60	0.60	0.62	-85.1%
CO$_2$ / population (t CO$_2$ per capita)	5.49	0.98	3.61	3.69	3.83	4.00	4.37	-20.3%

Ratios are based on the Sectoral Approach.

2006 CO$_2$ emissions by sector

million tonnes of CO$_2$	Coal/peat	Oil	Gas	Other *	Total	% change 90-06
Sectoral Approach	**13.04**	**3.38**	**0.74**	-	**17.16**	**-27.4%**
Main activity producer elec. and heat	11.17	-	0.13	-	11.30	31.8%
Unallocated autoproducers	0.10	0.16	-	-	0.26	-74.9%
Other energy industries	0.06	0.07	-	-	0.13	x
Manufacturing industries and construction	0.64	0.03	0.48	-	1.14	-81.7%
Transport	-	2.45	-	-	2.45	12.9%
of which: road	-	*2.41*	-	-	*2.41*	*11.0%*
Other sectors	1.08	0.67	0.13	-	1.88	-66.5%
of which: residential	-	-	*0.11*	-	*0.11*	*-61.7%*
Reference Approach	**13.22**	**3.39**	**0.75**	-	**17.35**	**-27.5%**
Diff. due to losses and/or transformation	0.15	0.01	0.01	-	0.17	
Statistical differences	0.02	- 0.00	0.00	-	0.02	
Memo: international marine bunkers	-	..	-	-	..	..
Memo: international aviation	-	..	-	-	..	..

* Other includes industrial waste and non-renewable municipal waste.

Key sources for CO$_2$ emissions from fuel combustion in 2006

IPCC source category	CO$_2$ emissions (Mt of CO$_2$)	% change 90-06	Level assessment (%) **	Cumulative total (%)
Main activity prod. elec. and heat - coal/peat	11.17	32.0%	49.7	49.7
Road - oil	2.41	11.0%	10.7	60.3
Non-specified other sectors - coal/peat	1.08	-79.7%	4.8	65.2
Non-specified other sectors - oil	0.67	x	3.0	68.1
Manufacturing industries - coal/peat	0.64	-82.1%	2.8	71.0
Manufacturing industries - gas	0.48	-34.2%	2.1	73.1
Unallocated autoproducers - oil	0.16	-84.6%	0.7	73.8
Main activity prod. elec. and heat - gas	0.13	18.1%	0.6	74.4
Residential - gas	0.11	52.6%	0.5	74.9
Unallocated autoproducers - coal/peat	0.10	x	0.4	75.3
Other energy industries - oil	0.07	x	0.3	75.6
Memo: total CO$_2$ from fuel combustion	*17.16*	*-27.4%*	*76.3*	*76.3*

** Percent calculated using the total GHG estimate for CO$_2$, CH$_4$, N$_2$O, HFCs, PFCs and SF$_6$ excluding CO$_2$ emissions/removals from land use change and forestry.

Botswana

Figure 1. CO$_2$ emissions by fuel

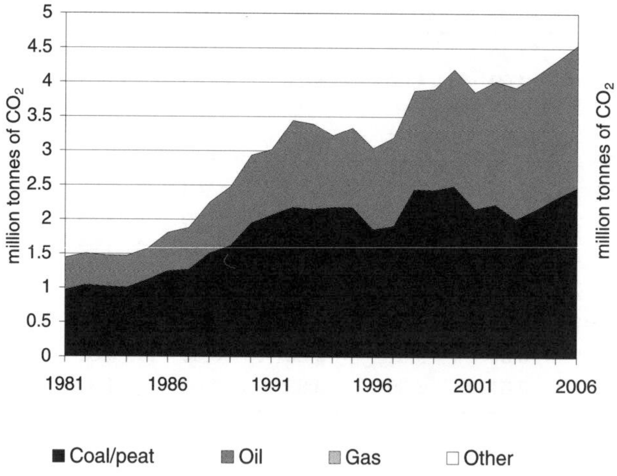

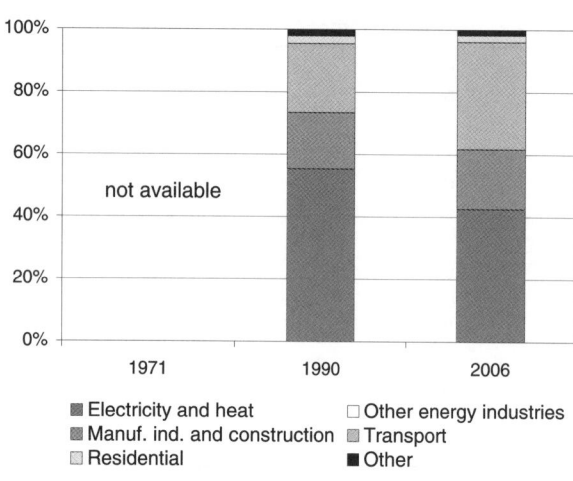

■ Coal/peat   ■ Oil   ▨ Gas   □ Other

Figure 2. CO$_2$ emissions by sector

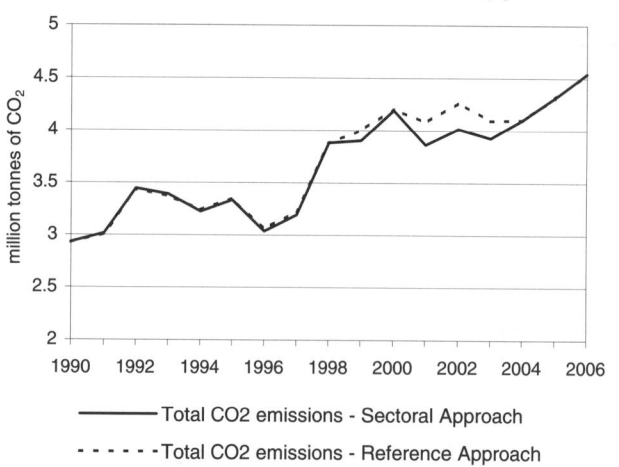

■ Electricity and heat   □ Other energy industries
■ Manuf. ind. and construction   ▨ Transport
□ Residential   ■ Other

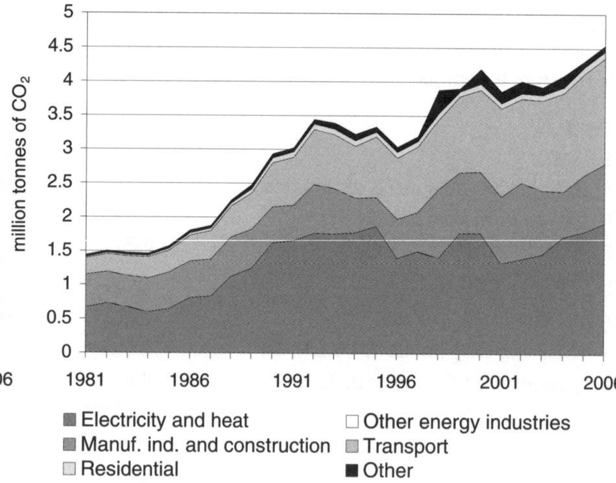

Figure 3. CO$_2$ emissions by sector

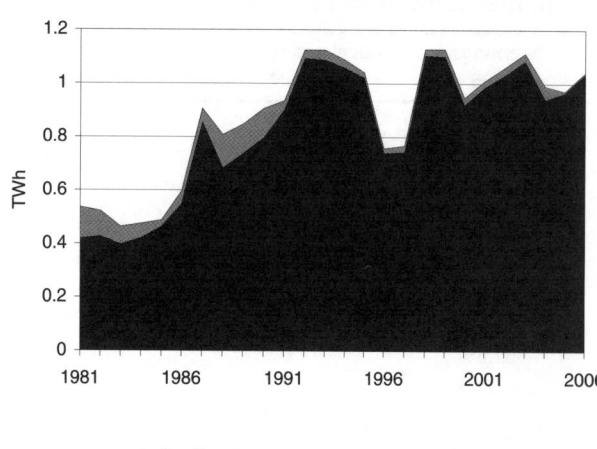

not available

■ Electricity and heat   □ Other energy industries
■ Manuf. ind. and construction   ▨ Transport
□ Residential   ■ Other

Figure 4. Reference vs Sectoral Approach

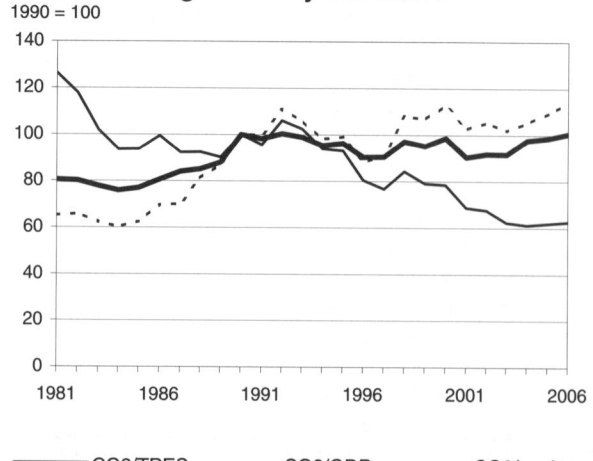

—— Total CO2 emissions - Sectoral Approach
- - - - - Total CO2 emissions - Reference Approach

Figure 5. Electricity generation by fuel

■ Coal/peat   ■ Oil

Figure 6. Key indicators

1990 = 100

—— CO2/TPES   —— CO2/GDP   - - - - CO2/capita

Botswana

Key indicators

	1990	1995	2000	2003	2004	2005	2006	% change 90-06
CO$_2$ Sectoral Approach (Mt of CO$_2$)	2.93	3.33	4.19	3.93	4.10	4.31	4.54	54.7%
CO$_2$ Reference Approach (Mt of CO$_2$)	2.93	3.35	4.20	4.09	4.10	4.31	4.54	55.1%
TPES (PJ)	53	63	77	78	76	79	82	53.9%
TPES (Mtoe)	1.27	1.50	1.84	1.86	1.82	1.90	1.96	53.9%
GDP (billion 2000 US$ using exch. rates)	3.39	4.14	6.18	7.29	7.74	8.05	8.39	147.1%
GDP (billion 2000 US$ using PPPs)	8.05	9.82	14.65	17.29	18.36	19.08	19.89	147.0%
Population (millions)	1.37	1.57	1.73	1.80	1.82	1.84	1.86	35.9%
CO$_2$ / TPES (t CO$_2$ per TJ)	55.1	53.0	54.3	50.4	53.8	54.3	55.4	0.6%
CO$_2$ / GDP (kg CO$_2$ per 2000 US$)	0.86	0.81	0.68	0.54	0.53	0.54	0.54	-37.4%
CO$_2$ / GDP (kg CO$_2$ per 2000 US$ PPP)	0.36	0.34	0.29	0.23	0.22	0.23	0.23	-37.4%
CO$_2$ / population (t CO$_2$ per capita)	2.15	2.13	2.42	2.19	2.26	2.35	2.44	13.8%

Ratios are based on the Sectoral Approach.

2006 CO$_2$ emissions by sector

million tonnes of CO$_2$	Coal/peat	Oil	Gas	Other *	Total	% change 90-06
Sectoral Approach	**2.47**	**2.07**	-	-	**4.54**	**54.7%**
Main activity producer elec. and heat	1.48	0.01	-	-	1.48	15.3%
Unallocated autoproducers	0.44	-	-	-	0.44	32.9%
Other energy industries	-	-	-	-	-	-
Manufacturing industries and construction	0.54	0.33	-	-	0.87	64.0%
Transport	-	1.56	-	-	1.56	140.9%
of which: road	-	*1.52*	-	-	*1.52*	*152.8%*
Other sectors	0.01	0.17	-	-	0.18	35.6%
of which: residential	-	*0.10*	-	-	*0.10*	*35.8%*
Reference Approach	**2.47**	**2.07**	-	-	**4.54**	**55.1%**
Diff. due to losses and/or transformation	-	-	-	-	-	
Statistical differences	0.00	0.00	-	-	0.00	
Memo: international marine bunkers	-	..	-	-	..	..
Memo: international aviation	-	*0.03*	-	-	*0.03*	*-9.1%*

* Other includes industrial waste and non-renewable municipal waste.

Key sources for CO$_2$ emissions from fuel combustion in 2006

IPCC source category	CO$_2$ emissions (Mt of CO$_2$)	% change 90-06	Level assessment (%) **	Cumulative total (%)
Road - oil	1.52	152.8%	13.1	13.1
Main activity prod. elec. and heat - coal/peat	1.48	26.4%	12.8	26.0
Manufacturing industries - coal/peat	0.54	24.4%	4.6	30.6
Unallocated autoproducers - coal/peat	0.44	32.9%	3.9	34.5
Manufacturing industries - oil	0.33	234.9%	2.9	37.3
Residential - oil	0.10	56.2%	0.9	38.2
Non-specified other sectors - oil	0.07	25.8%	0.6	38.8
Other transport - oil	0.04	-10.8%	0.4	39.2
Non-specified other sectors - coal/peat	0.01	150.1%	0.1	39.3
Main activity prod. elec. and heat - oil	0.01	-94.8%	0.1	39.4
-	-	-	-	-
Memo: total CO$_2$ from fuel combustion	*4.54*	*54.7%*	*39.4*	*39.4*

** Percent calculated using the total GHG estimate for CO$_2$, CH$_4$, N$_2$O, HFCs, PFCs and SF$_6$ excluding CO$_2$ emissions/removals from land use change and forestry.

Brazil / Brésil

Figure 1. CO_2 emissions by fuel

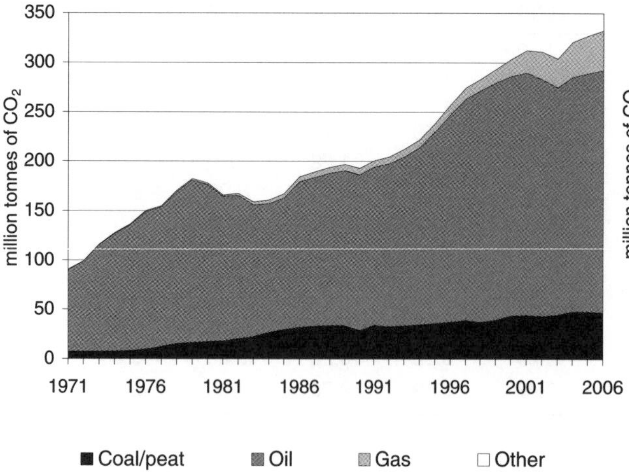

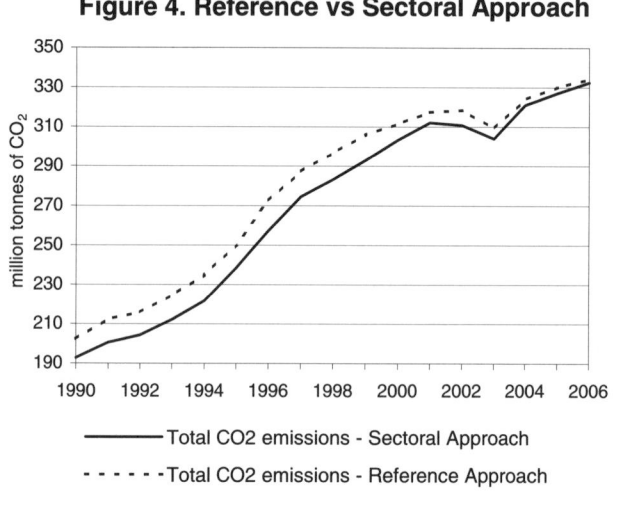

- ■ Coal/peat
- ■ Oil
- ■ Gas
- □ Other

Figure 2. CO_2 emissions by sector

- ■ Electricity and heat
- □ Other energy industries
- ■ Manuf. ind. and construction
- ▨ Transport
- ▨ Residential
- ■ Other

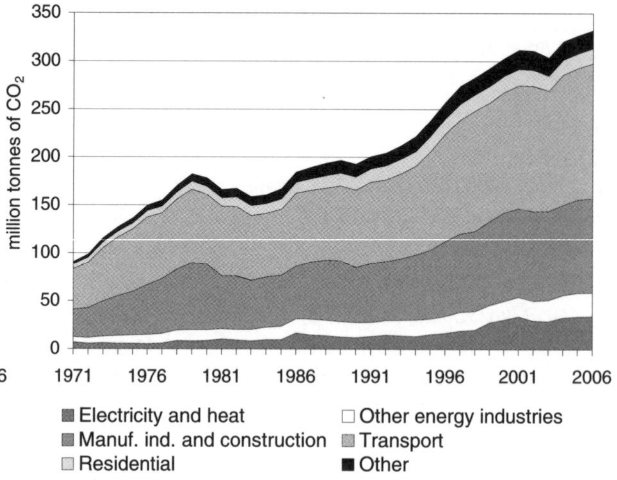

Figure 3. CO_2 emissions by sector

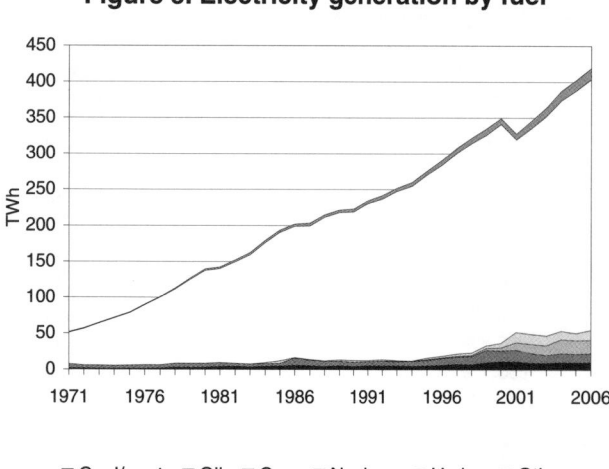

- ■ Electricity and heat
- □ Other energy industries
- ■ Manuf. ind. and construction
- ▨ Transport
- ▨ Residential
- ■ Other

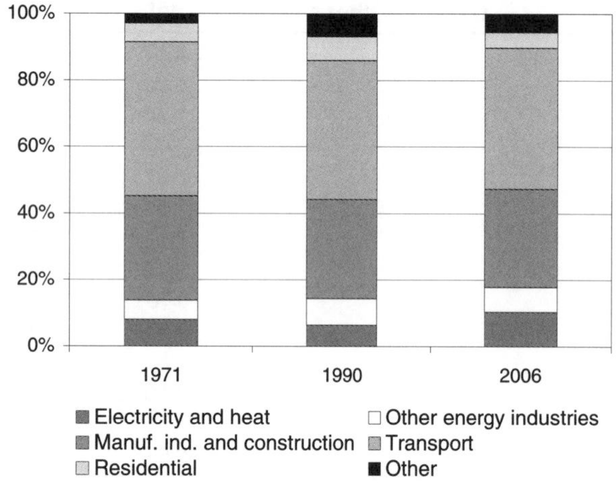

Figure 4. Reference vs Sectoral Approach

—— Total CO2 emissions - Sectoral Approach

- - - - Total CO2 emissions - Reference Approach

Figure 5. Electricity generation by fuel

- ■ Coal/peat
- ■ Oil
- ■ Gas
- ▨ Nuclear
- □ Hydro
- ▨ Other

Figure 6. Key indicators

1990 = 100

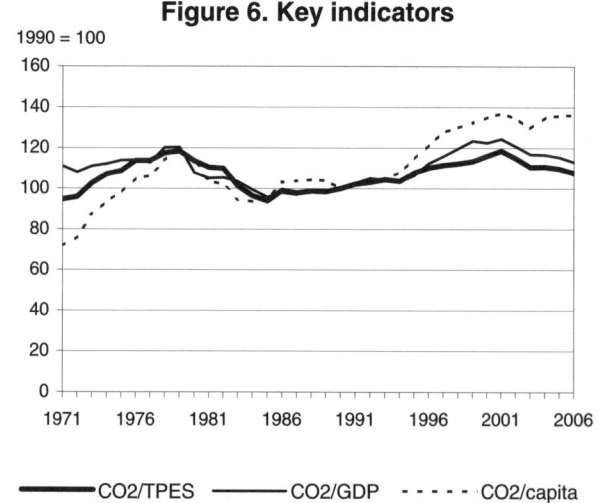

—— CO2/TPES   —— CO2/GDP   - - - - CO2/capita

Brazil / Brésil

Key indicators

	1990	1995	2000	2003	2004	2005	2006	% change 90-06
CO$_2$ Sectoral Approach (Mt of CO$_2$)	192.72	238.40	303.41	304.06	321.02	327.06	332.42	72.5%
CO$_2$ Reference Approach (Mt of CO$_2$)	202.40	250.17	311.55	309.44	324.21	330.22	334.22	65.1%
TPES (PJ)	5 861	6 735	7 948	8 370	8 829	9 065	9 384	60.1%
TPES (Mtoe)	139.99	160.87	189.83	199.92	210.87	216.52	224.13	60.1%
GDP (billion 2000 US$ using exch. rates)	501.60	583.42	644.48	677.99	716.70	737.81	765.13	52.5%
GDP (billion 2000 US$ using PPPs)	968.07	1 125.99	1 243.83	1 308.51	1 383.22	1 423.96	1 476.68	52.5%
Population (millions)	149.52	161.62	174.16	181.79	184.32	186.83	189.32	26.6%
CO$_2$ / TPES (t CO$_2$ per TJ)	32.9	35.4	38.2	36.3	36.4	36.1	35.4	7.7%
CO$_2$ / GDP (kg CO$_2$ per 2000 US$)	0.38	0.41	0.47	0.45	0.45	0.44	0.43	13.1%
CO$_2$ / GDP (kg CO$_2$ per 2000 US$ PPP)	0.20	0.21	0.24	0.23	0.23	0.23	0.23	13.1%
CO$_2$ / population (t CO$_2$ per capita)	1.29	1.48	1.74	1.67	1.74	1.75	1.76	36.2%

Ratios are based on the Sectoral Approach.

2006 CO$_2$ emissions by sector

million tonnes of CO$_2$	Coal/peat	Oil	Gas	Other *	Total	% change 90-06
Sectoral Approach	**47.00**	**245.54**	**39.88**	-	**332.42**	**72.5%**
Main activity producer elec. and heat	8.40	6.22	5.70	-	20.32	219.3%
Unallocated autoproducers	8.63	2.81	2.53	-	13.97	141.7%
Other energy industries	3.23	13.85	7.75	-	24.82	61.0%
Manufacturing industries and construction	26.68	53.31	18.24	-	98.23	70.9%
Transport	0.06	136.22	4.49	-	140.76	74.6%
of which: road	-	123.70	4.49	-	128.19	83.7%
Other sectors	-	33.14	1.17	-	34.32	26.7%
of which: residential	-	15.10	0.46	-	15.56	13.2%
Reference Approach	**49.30**	**244.76**	**40.16**	-	**334.22**	**65.1%**
Diff. due to losses and/or transformation	2.24	3.91	0.26	-	6.41	
Statistical differences	0.06	- 4.68	0.02	-	- 4.61	
Memo: international marine bunkers	-	10.63	-	-	10.63	519.6%
Memo: international aviation	-	3.87	-	-	3.87	173.9%

* Other includes industrial waste and non-renewable municipal waste.

Key sources for CO$_2$ emissions from fuel combustion in 2006

IPCC source category	CO$_2$ emissions (Mt of CO$_2$)	% change 90-06	Level assessment (%) **	Cumulative total (%)
Road - oil	123.70	77.3%	11.3	11.3
Manufacturing industries - oil	53.31	49.7%	4.9	16.1
Manufacturing industries - coal/peat	26.68	52.7%	2.4	18.6
Manufacturing industries - gas	18.24	317.3%	1.7	20.2
Non-specified other sectors - oil	18.04	36.7%	1.6	21.9
Residential - oil	15.10	12.5%	1.4	23.3
Other energy industries - oil	13.85	28.2%	1.3	24.5
Other transport - oil	12.52	15.5%	1.1	25.7
Unallocated autoproducers - coal/peat	8.63	124.5%	0.8	26.5
Main activity prod. elec. and heat - coal/peat	8.40	107.0%	0.8	27.2
Other energy industries - gas	7.75	329.6%	0.7	27.9
Memo: total CO$_2$ from fuel combustion	332.42	72.5%	30.3	30.3

** Percent calculated using the total GHG estimate for CO$_2$, CH$_4$, N$_2$O, HFCs, PFCs and SF$_6$ excluding CO$_2$ emissions/removals from land use change and forestry.

Brunei Darussalam

Figure 1. CO_2 emissions by fuel

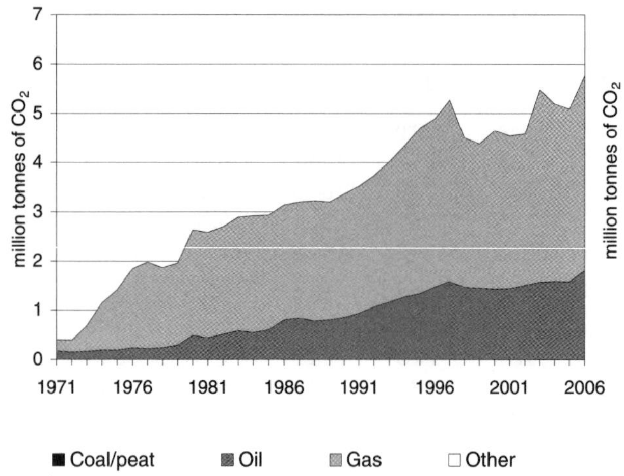

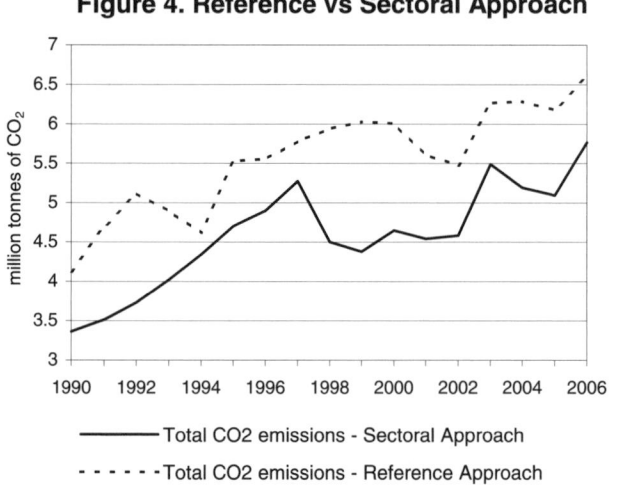

million tonnes of CO2
Coal/peat
Oil
Gas
Other

Figure 2. CO_2 emissions by sector

million tonnes of CO2
Electricity and heat
Other energy industries
Manuf. ind. and construction
Transport
Residential
Other

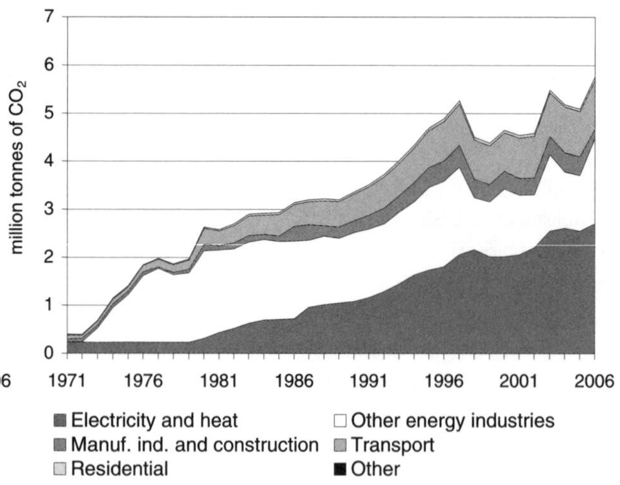

Figure 3. CO_2 emissions by sector

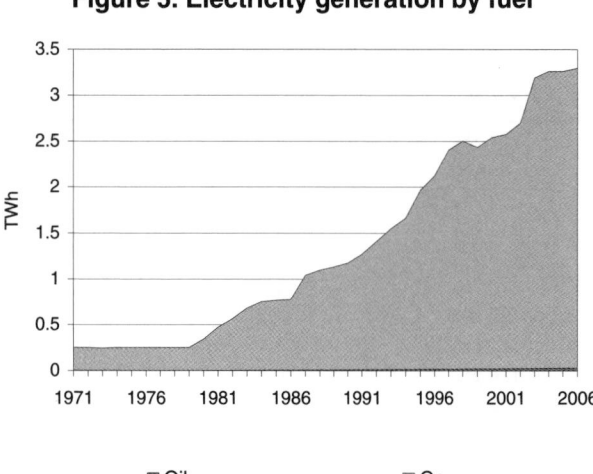

Electricity and heat
Other energy industries
Manuf. ind. and construction
Transport
Residential
Other

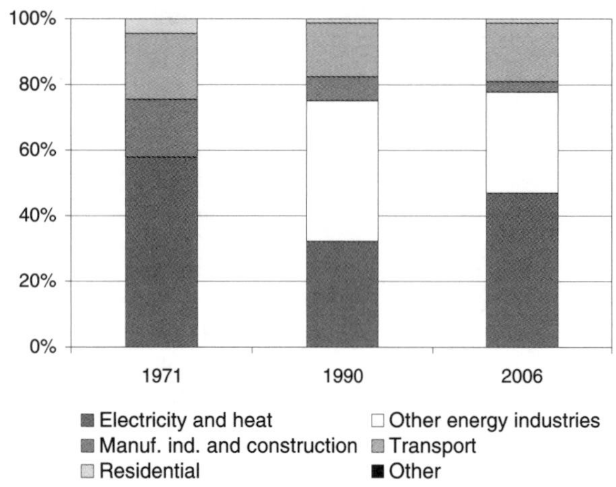

Figure 4. Reference vs Sectoral Approach

million tonnes of CO2
Total CO2 emissions - Sectoral Approach
Total CO2 emissions - Reference Approach

Figure 5. Electricity generation by fuel

TWh
Oil
Gas

Figure 6. Key indicators

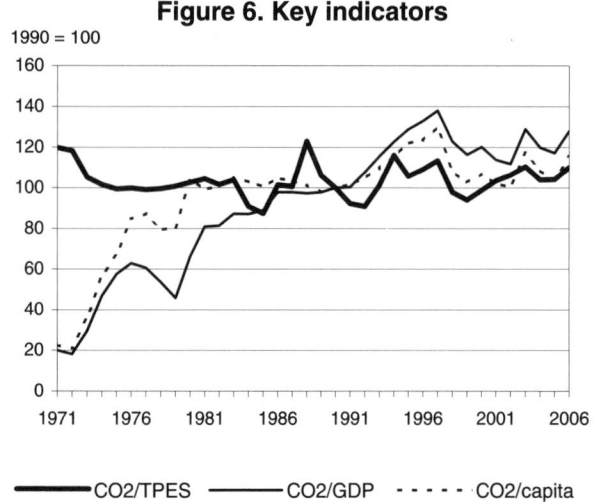

1990 = 100
CO2/TPES
CO2/GDP
CO2/capita

Brunei Darussalam
Key indicators

	1990	1995	2000	2003	2004	2005	2006	% change 90-06
CO$_2$ Sectoral Approach (Mt of CO$_2$)	3.36	4.70	4.65	5.49	5.19	5.09	5.77	71.5%
CO$_2$ Reference Approach (Mt of CO$_2$)	4.13	5.52	6.01	6.27	6.28	6.18	6.60	59.8%
TPES (PJ)	75	100	106	111	112	110	117	55.8%
TPES (Mtoe)	1.80	2.38	2.52	2.66	2.68	2.62	2.81	55.8%
GDP (billion 2000 US$ using exch. rates)	3.75	4.07	4.32	4.75	4.83	4.85	5.03	34.2%
GDP (billion 2000 US$ using PPPs)	4.48	4.86	5.16	5.67	5.77	5.79	6.01	34.2%
Population (millions)	0.26	0.30	0.33	0.36	0.37	0.37	0.38	48.6%
CO$_2$ / TPES (t CO$_2$ per TJ)	44.6	47.1	44.0	49.2	46.3	46.4	49.1	10.1%
CO$_2$ / GDP (kg CO$_2$ per 2000 US$)	0.90	1.16	1.08	1.15	1.07	1.05	1.15	27.8%
CO$_2$ / GDP (kg CO$_2$ per 2000 US$ PPP)	0.75	0.97	0.90	0.97	0.90	0.88	0.96	27.8%
CO$_2$ / population (t CO$_2$ per capita)	13.08	15.94	13.96	15.32	14.18	13.62	15.10	15.4%

Ratios are based on the Sectoral Approach.

2006 CO$_2$ emissions by sector

million tonnes of CO$_2$	Coal/peat	Oil	Gas	Other *	Total	% change 90-06
Sectoral Approach	-	1.81	3.96	-	**5.77**	**71.5%**
Main activity producer elec. and heat	-	0.03	2.43	-	2.45	126.8%
Unallocated autoproducers	-	-	0.25	-	0.25	x
Other energy industries	-	0.53	1.24	-	1.77	23.0%
Manufacturing industries and construction	-	0.19	-	-	0.19	-23.7%
Transport	-	1.02	-	-	1.02	86.4%
of which: road	-	1.02	-	-	1.02	86.4%
Other sectors	-	0.05	0.03	-	0.08	72.6%
of which: residential	-	0.05	0.03	-	0.08	72.6%
Reference Approach	-	1.81	4.79	-	**6.60**	**59.8%**
Diff. due to losses and/or transformation	-	0.10	0.83	-	0.93	
Statistical differences	-	- 0.11	0.01	-	- 0.10	
Memo: international marine bunkers	-	..	-	-	..	..
Memo: international aviation	-	0.23	-	-	0.23	105.6%

* Other includes industrial waste and non-renewable municipal waste.

Key sources for CO$_2$ emissions from fuel combustion in 2006

IPCC source category	CO$_2$ emissions (Mt of CO$_2$)	% change 90-06	Level assessment (%) **	Cumulative total (%)
Main activity prod. elec. and heat - gas	2.43	126.4%	27.0	27.0
Other energy industries - gas	1.24	-13.5%	13.8	40.8
Road - oil	1.02	86.4%	11.3	52.1
Other energy industries - oil	0.53	+	5.9	58.0
Unallocated autoproducers - gas	0.25	x	2.8	60.8
Manufacturing industries - oil	0.19	-23.7%	2.1	62.9
Residential - oil	0.05	5.1%	0.5	63.4
Residential - gas	0.03	x	0.3	63.8
Main activity prod. elec. and heat - oil	0.03	166.6%	0.3	64.1
-	-	-	-	-
-	-	-	-	-
Memo: total CO$_2$ from fuel combustion	5.77	71.5%	64.1	64.1

** Percent calculated using the total GHG estimate for CO$_2$, CH$_4$, N$_2$O, HFCs, PFCs and SF$_6$ excluding CO$_2$ emissions/removals from land use change and forestry.

Bulgaria / Bulgarie

Figure 1. CO$_2$ emissions by fuel

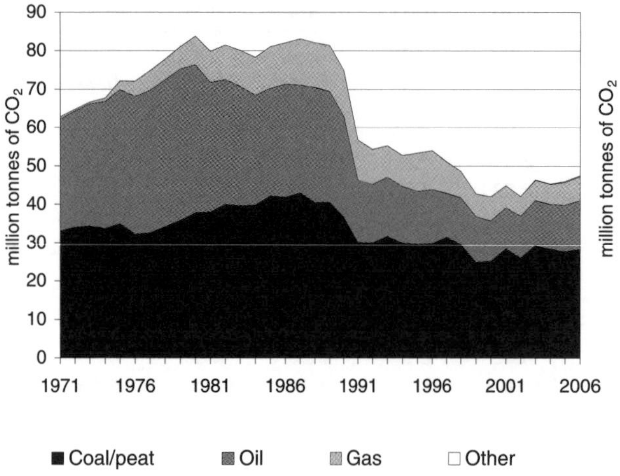

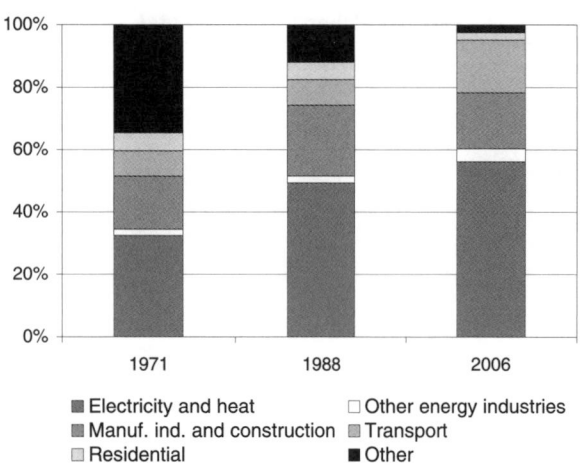

■ Coal/peat   ■ Oil   ▨ Gas   ☐ Other

Figure 2. CO$_2$ emissions by sector

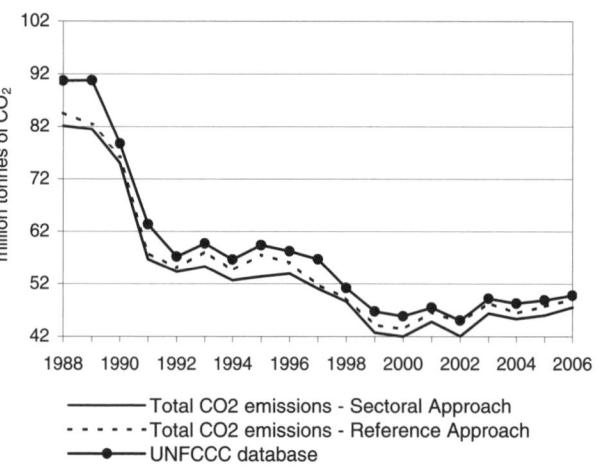

■ Electricity and heat   ☐ Other energy industries
▨ Manuf. ind. and construction ▨ Transport
▨ Residential   ■ Other

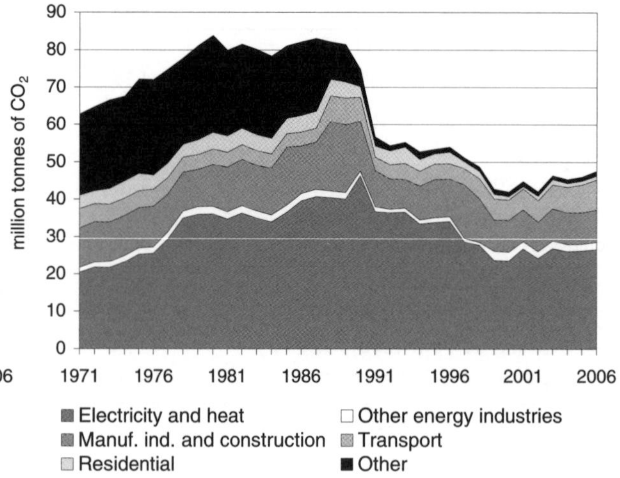

Figure 3. CO$_2$ emissions by sector

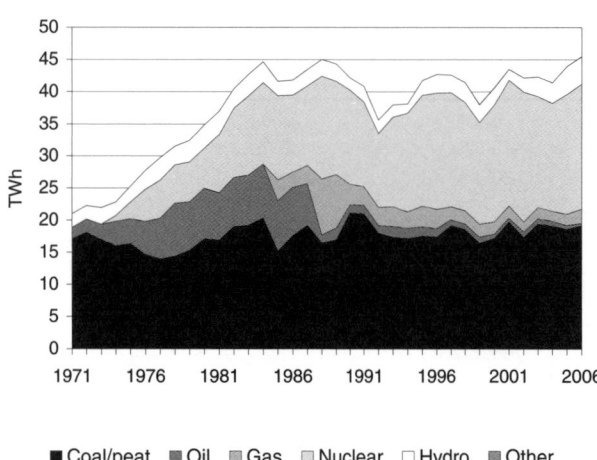

■ Electricity and heat   ☐ Other energy industries
▨ Manuf. ind. and construction ▨ Transport
▨ Residential   ■ Other

Figure 4. Reference vs Sectoral Approach

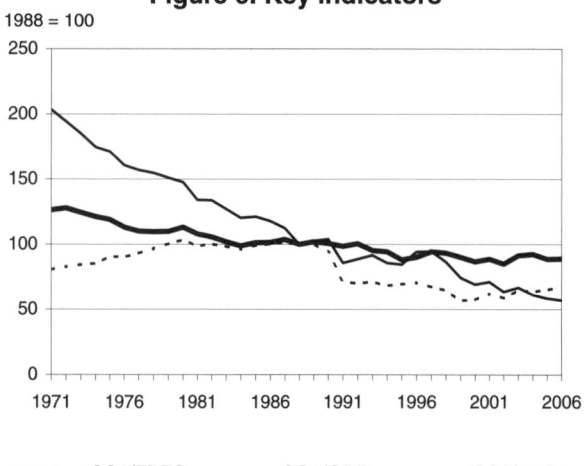

——— Total CO2 emissions - Sectoral Approach
- - - - Total CO2 emissions - Reference Approach
—●— UNFCCC database

Figure 5. Electricity generation by fuel

■ Coal/peat   ■ Oil   ▨ Gas   ▨ Nuclear   ☐ Hydro   ▨ Other

Figure 6. Key indicators

1988 = 100

━━━ CO2/TPES   ——— CO2/GDP   - - - - CO2/capita

Bulgaria / Bulgarie *

Key indicators

	1988	1990	1995	2003	2004	2005	2006	% change 88-06
CO$_2$ Sectoral Approach (Mt of CO$_2$)	82.07	74.94	53.40	46.38	45.34	46.02	47.54	-42.1%
CO$_2$ Reference Approach (Mt of CO$_2$)	84.56	76.17	57.54	48.40	46.47	47.74	49.06	-42.0%
TPES (PJ)	1 330	1 206	981	823	794	840	867	-34.8%
TPES (Mtoe)	31.76	28.81	23.43	19.67	18.97	20.07	20.70	-34.8%
GDP (billion 2000 US$ using exch. rates)	17.06	15.00	13.14	14.45	15.41	16.37	17.37	1.8%
GDP (billion 2000 US$ using PPPs)	66.22	58.20	50.98	56.07	59.79	63.53	67.40	1.8%
Population (millions)	8.98	8.72	8.40	7.82	7.78	7.74	7.69	-14.3%
CO$_2$ / TPES (t CO$_2$ per TJ)	61.7	62.1	54.4	56.3	57.1	54.8	54.9	-11.1%
CO$_2$ / GDP (kg CO$_2$ per 2000 US$)	4.81	5.00	4.06	3.21	2.94	2.81	2.74	-43.1%
CO$_2$ / GDP (kg CO$_2$ per 2000 US$ PPP)	1.24	1.29	1.05	0.83	0.76	0.72	0.71	-43.1%
CO$_2$ / population (t CO$_2$ per capita)	9.14	8.60	6.36	5.93	5.83	5.95	6.18	-32.4%

Ratios are based on the Sectoral Approach.
* According to the provisions of Article 4.6 of the Convention and Decisions 9/CP.2 and 11/CP.4, Bulgaria is allowed to use 1988 as the base year.

2006 CO$_2$ emissions by sector

million tonnes of CO$_2$	Coal/peat	Oil	Gas	Other **	Total	% change 88-06
Sectoral Approach	**28.43**	**12.64**	**6.20**	**0.27**	**47.54**	**-42.1%**
Main activity producer elec. and heat	23.23	0.15	1.91	-	25.30	-34.5%
Unallocated autoproducers	0.68	0.21	0.45	0.02	1.37	-23.1%
Other energy industries	1.08	0.73	0.16	-	1.97	7.1%
Manufacturing industries and construction	2.40	3.08	2.81	0.25	8.55	-54.1%
Transport	-	7.45	0.59	-	8.04	18.5%
of which: road	-	7.29	0.06	-	7.34	8.3%
Other sectors	1.03	1.01	0.28	-	2.32	-83.9%
of which: residential	0.98	0.07	0.06	-	1.10	-75.6%
Reference Approach	**28.69**	**13.63**	**6.47**	**0.27**	**49.06**	**-42.0%**
Diff. due to losses and/or transformation	0.93	0.50	0.14	-	1.57	
Statistical differences	- 0.67	0.49	0.12	-	- 0.05	
Memo: international marine bunkers	-	0.33	-	-	0.33	-64.7%
Memo: international aviation	-	0.53	-	-	0.53	-57.9%

** Other includes industrial waste and non-renewable municipal waste.

Key sources for CO$_2$ emissions from fuel combustion in 2006

IPCC source category	CO$_2$ emissions (Mt of CO$_2$)	% change 88-06	Level assessment (%) ***	Cumulative total (%)
Main activity prod. elec. and heat - coal/peat	23.23	-2.8%	33.6	33.6
Road - oil	7.29	7.4%	10.5	44.2
Manufacturing industries - oil	3.08	-59.4%	4.5	48.7
Manufacturing industries - gas	2.81	x	4.1	52.7
Manufacturing industries - coal/peat	2.40	-78.2%	3.5	56.2
Main activity prod. elec. and heat - gas	1.91	-71.0%	2.8	59.0
Other energy industries - coal/peat	1.08	x	1.6	60.5
Residential - coal/peat	0.98	-70.8%	1.4	62.0
Non-specified other sectors - oil	0.95	-78.6%	1.4	63.3
Other energy industries - oil	0.73	-60.4%	1.1	64.4
Unallocated autoproducers - coal/peat	0.68	-61.6%	1.0	65.4
Memo: total CO$_2$ from fuel combustion	47.54	-42.1%	68.8	68.8

*** Percent calculated using the total GHG estimate for CO$_2$, CH$_4$, N$_2$O, HFCs, PFCs and SF$_6$ excluding CO$_2$ emissions/removals from land use change and forestry.

Cambodia / Cambodge

Figure 1. CO₂ emissions by fuel

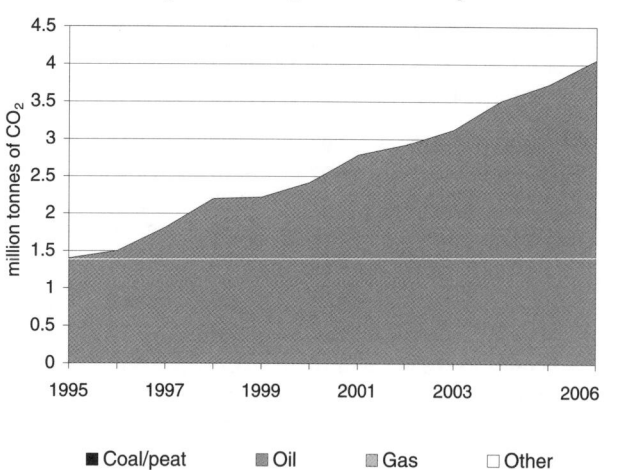

Coal/peat ■ Oil ■ Gas ■ Other □

Figure 2. CO₂ emissions by sector

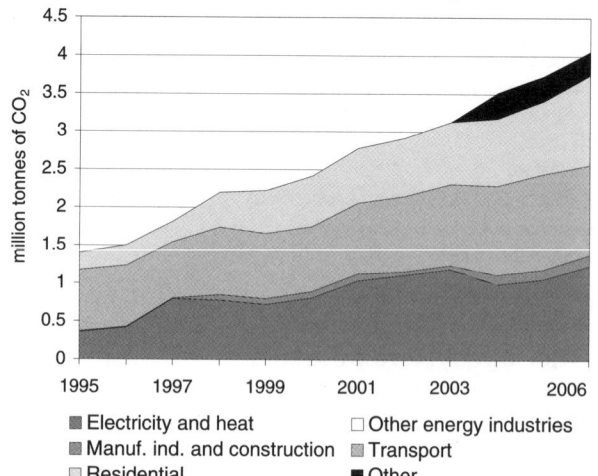

Electricity and heat ■ Other energy industries □
Manuf. ind. and construction ■ Transport ■
Residential ■ Other ■

Figure 3. CO₂ emissions by sector

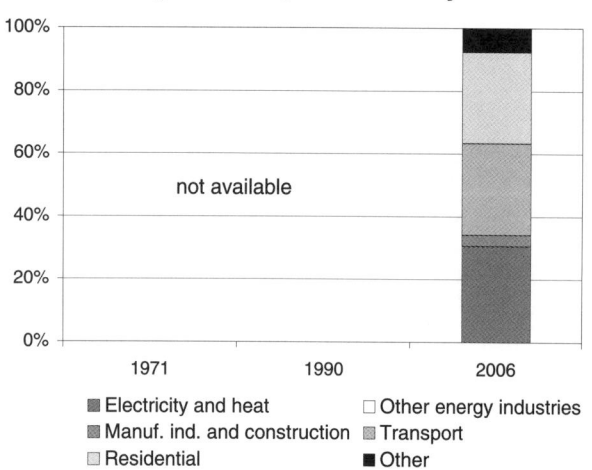

Electricity and heat ■ Other energy industries □
Manuf. ind. and construction ■ Transport ■
Residential ■ Other ■

Figure 4. Reference vs Sectoral Approach

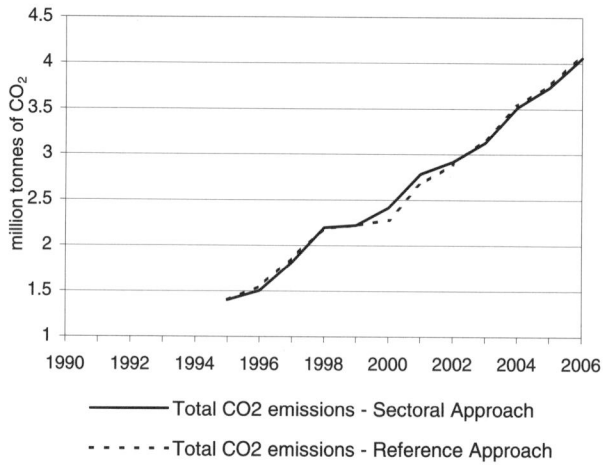

Total CO2 emissions - Sectoral Approach
Total CO2 emissions - Reference Approach

Figure 5. Electricity generation by fuel

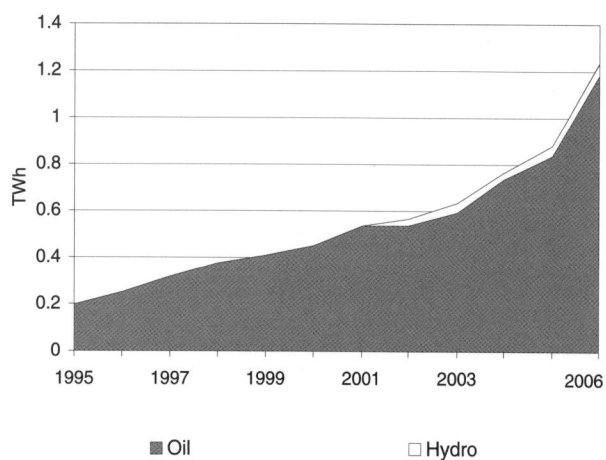

Oil ■ Hydro □

Figure 6. Key indicators

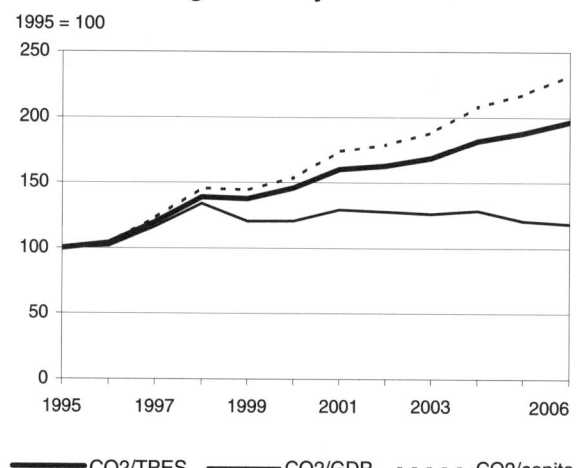

CO2/TPES CO2/GDP CO2/capita

Cambodia / Cambodge *

Key indicators

	1990	1995	2000	2003	2004	2005	2006	% change 90-06
CO$_2$ Sectoral Approach (Mt of CO$_2$)	..	1.40	2.42	3.13	3.51	3.73	4.06	..
CO$_2$ Reference Approach (Mt of CO$_2$)	..	1.40	2.28	3.16	3.54	3.76	4.11	..
TPES (PJ)	..	142	167	187	195	201	209	..
TPES (Mtoe)	..	3.38	4.00	4.48	4.66	4.80	4.99	..
GDP (billion 2000 US$ using exch. rates)	..	2.57	3.67	4.55	5.01	5.68	6.28	..
GDP (billion 2000 US$ using PPPs)	..	15.47	22.05	27.38	30.11	34.14	37.73	..
Population (millions)	..	11.40	12.78	13.49	13.72	13.96	14.20	..
CO$_2$ / TPES (t CO$_2$ per TJ)	..	9.9	14.4	16.7	18.0	18.6	19.4	..
CO$_2$ / GDP (kg CO$_2$ per 2000 US$)	..	0.55	0.66	0.69	0.70	0.66	0.65	..
CO$_2$ / GDP (kg CO$_2$ per 2000 US$ PPP)	..	0.09	0.11	0.11	0.12	0.11	0.11	..
CO$_2$ / population (t CO$_2$ per capita)	..	0.12	0.19	0.23	0.26	0.27	0.29	..

Ratios are based on the Sectoral Approach.
* Prior to 1995, data for Cambodia were included in Other Asia.

2006 CO$_2$ emissions by sector

million tonnes of CO$_2$	Coal/peat	Oil	Gas	Other **	Total	% change 90-06
Sectoral Approach	-	4.06	-	-	**4.06**	..
Main activity producer elec. and heat	-	1.24	-	-	1.24	..
Unallocated autoproducers	-	-	-	-	-	..
Other energy industries	-	-	-	-	-	..
Manufacturing industries and construction	-	0.15	-	-	0.15	..
Transport	-	1.18	-	-	1.18	..
of which: road	-	1.17	-	-	1.17	..
Other sectors	-	1.49	-	-	1.49	..
of which: residential	-	1.18	-	-	1.18	..
Reference Approach	-	4.11	-	-	**4.11**	..
Diff. due to losses and/or transformation	-	-	-	-	-	
Statistical differences	-	0.05	-	-	0.05	
Memo: international marine bunkers	-	..	-	-	..	..
Memo: international aviation	-	0.08	-	-	0.08	..

** Other includes industrial waste and non-renewable municipal waste.

Key sources for CO$_2$ emissions from fuel combustion in 2006

IPCC source category	CO$_2$ emissions (Mt of CO$_2$)	% change 90-06	Level assessment (%) ***	Cumulative total (%)
Main activity prod. elec. and heat - oil	1.24	..	5.4	5.4
Residential - oil	1.18	..	5.2	10.6
Road - oil	1.17	..	5.1	15.7
Non-specified other sectors - oil	0.31	..	1.4	17.0
Manufacturing industries - oil	0.15	..	0.6	17.7
Other transport - oil	0.01	..	0.0	17.7
-	-	..	-	-
-	-	..	-	-
-	-	..	-	-
-	-	..	-	-
-	-	..	-	-
Memo: total CO$_2$ from fuel combustion	4.06	..	17.7	17.7

*** Percent calculated using the total GHG estimate for CO$_2$, CH$_4$, N$_2$O, HFCs, PFCs and SF$_6$ excluding CO$_2$ emissions/removals from land use change and forestry.

Cameroon / Cameroun

Figure 1. CO₂ emissions by fuel

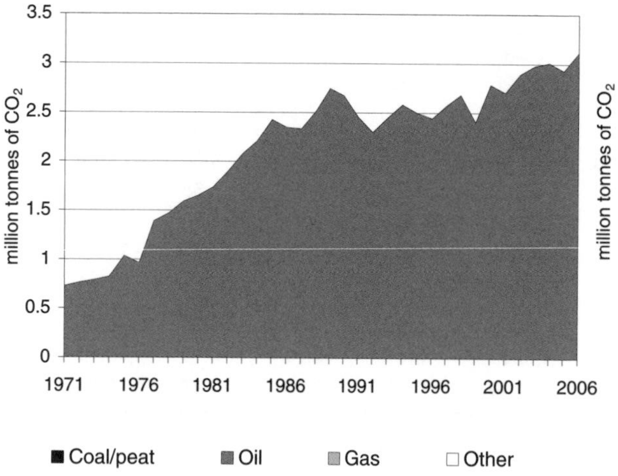

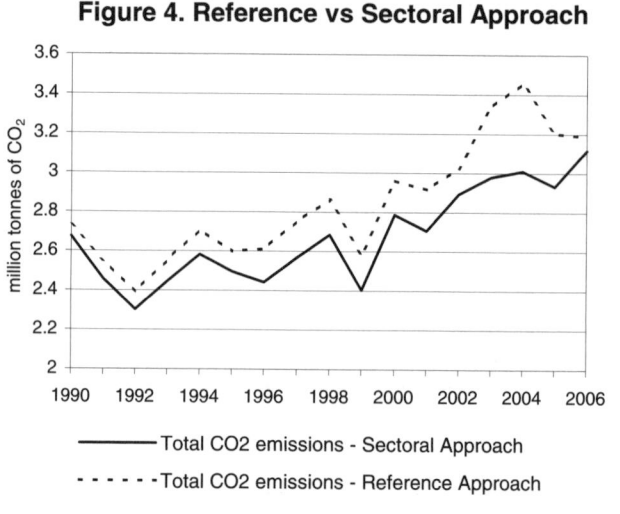

■ Coal/peat   ■ Oil   ■ Gas   □ Other

Figure 2. CO₂ emissions by sector

■ Electricity and heat   □ Other energy industries
■ Manuf. ind. and construction   ■ Transport
□ Residential   ■ Other

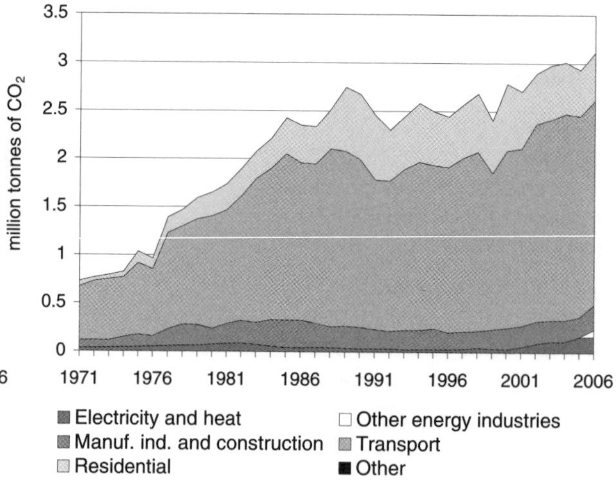

Figure 3. CO₂ emissions by sector

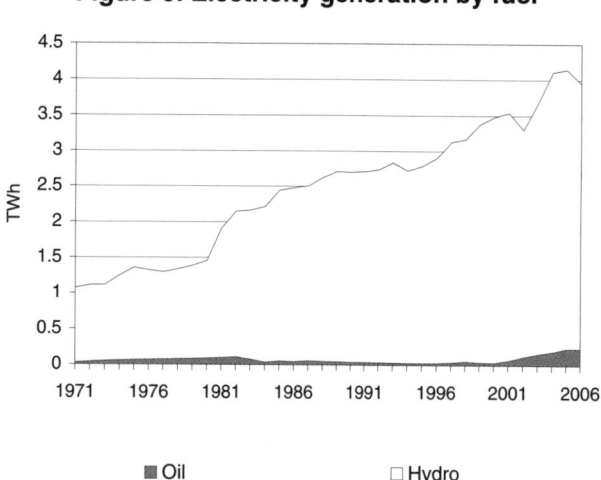

■ Electricity and heat   □ Other energy industries
■ Manuf. ind. and construction   ■ Transport
□ Residential   ■ Other

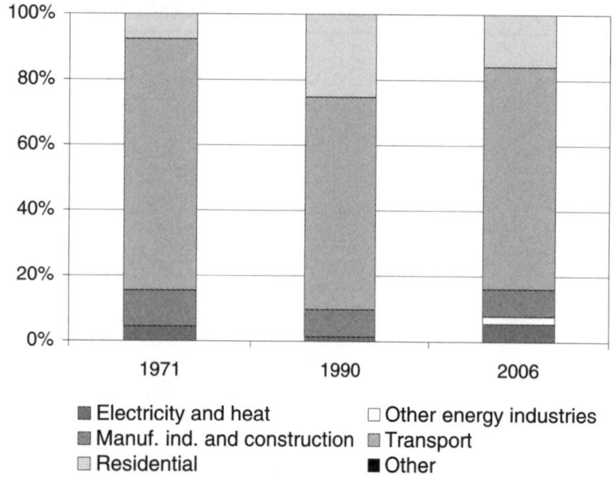

Figure 4. Reference vs Sectoral Approach

——— Total CO2 emissions - Sectoral Approach
- - - - Total CO2 emissions - Reference Approach

Figure 5. Electricity generation by fuel

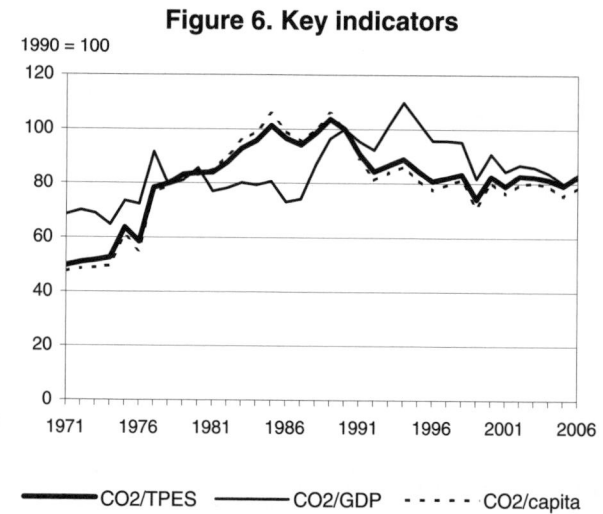

■ Oil   □ Hydro

Figure 6. Key indicators

1990 = 100

——— CO2/TPES   ——— CO2/GDP   - - - - CO2/capita

Cameroon / Cameroun

Key indicators

	1990	1995	2000	2003	2004	2005	2006	% change 90-06
CO$_2$ Sectoral Approach (Mt of CO$_2$)	2.67	2.50	2.79	2.98	3.01	2.93	3.12	16.6%
CO$_2$ Reference Approach (Mt of CO$_2$)	2.73	2.60	2.96	3.34	3.46	3.20	3.19	16.9%
TPES (PJ)	211	233	266	285	292	292	297	40.8%
TPES (Mtoe)	5.03	5.55	6.35	6.81	6.97	6.97	7.08	40.8%
GDP (billion 2000 US$ using exch. rates)	8.79	7.99	10.08	11.39	11.82	12.06	12.53	42.5%
GDP (billion 2000 US$ using PPPs)	24.35	22.13	27.90	31.56	32.72	33.39	34.69	42.5%
Population (millions)	12.24	14.06	15.86	17.02	17.41	17.80	18.18	48.5%
CO$_2$ / TPES (t CO$_2$ per TJ)	12.7	10.7	10.5	10.5	10.3	10.0	10.5	-17.2%
CO$_2$ / GDP (kg CO$_2$ per 2000 US$)	0.30	0.31	0.28	0.26	0.25	0.24	0.25	-18.2%
CO$_2$ / GDP (kg CO$_2$ per 2000 US$ PPP)	0.11	0.11	0.10	0.09	0.09	0.09	0.09	-18.2%
CO$_2$ / population (t CO$_2$ per capita)	0.22	0.18	0.18	0.18	0.17	0.16	0.17	-21.5%

Ratios are based on the Sectoral Approach.

2006 CO$_2$ emissions by sector

million tonnes of CO$_2$	Coal/peat	Oil	Gas	Other *	Total	% change 90-06
Sectoral Approach	-	**3.12**	-	-	**3.12**	**16.6%**
Main activity producer elec. and heat	-	0.17	-	-	0.17	381.6%
Unallocated autoproducers	-	-	-	-	-	-
Other energy industries	-	0.07	-	-	0.07	x
Manufacturing industries and construction	-	0.26	-	-	0.26	15.2%
Transport	-	2.12	-	-	2.12	22.1%
of which: road	-	*2.12*	-	-	*2.12*	*22.1%*
Other sectors	-	0.50	-	-	0.50	-26.6%
of which: residential	-	*0.50*	-	-	*0.50*	*-26.6%*
Reference Approach	-	**3.19**	-	-	**3.19**	**16.9%**
Diff. due to losses and/or transformation	-	0.07	-	-	0.07	
Statistical differences	-	- 0.00	-	-	- 0.00	
Memo: international marine bunkers	-	*0.13*	-	-	*0.13*	*221.2%*
Memo: international aviation	-	*0.22*	-	-	*0.22*	*45.0%*

* Other includes industrial waste and non-renewable municipal waste.

Key sources for CO$_2$ emissions from fuel combustion in 2006

IPCC source category	CO$_2$ emissions (Mt of CO$_2$)	% change 90-06	Level assessment (%) **	Cumulative total (%)
Road - oil	2.12	22.1%	5.6	5.6
Residential - oil	0.50	-26.6%	1.3	7.0
Manufacturing industries - oil	0.26	15.2%	0.7	7.7
Main activity prod. elec. and heat - oil	0.17	381.6%	0.4	8.1
Other energy industries - oil	0.07	x	0.2	8.3
-	-	-	-	-
-	-	-	-	-
-	-	-	-	-
-	-	-	-	-
-	-	-	-	-
-	-	-	-	-
Memo: total CO$_2$ from fuel combustion	*3.12*	*16.6%*	*8.3*	*8.3*

** Percent calculated using the total GHG estimate for CO$_2$, CH$_4$, N$_2$O, HFCs, PFCs and SF$_6$ excluding CO$_2$ emissions/removals from land use change and forestry.

Canada

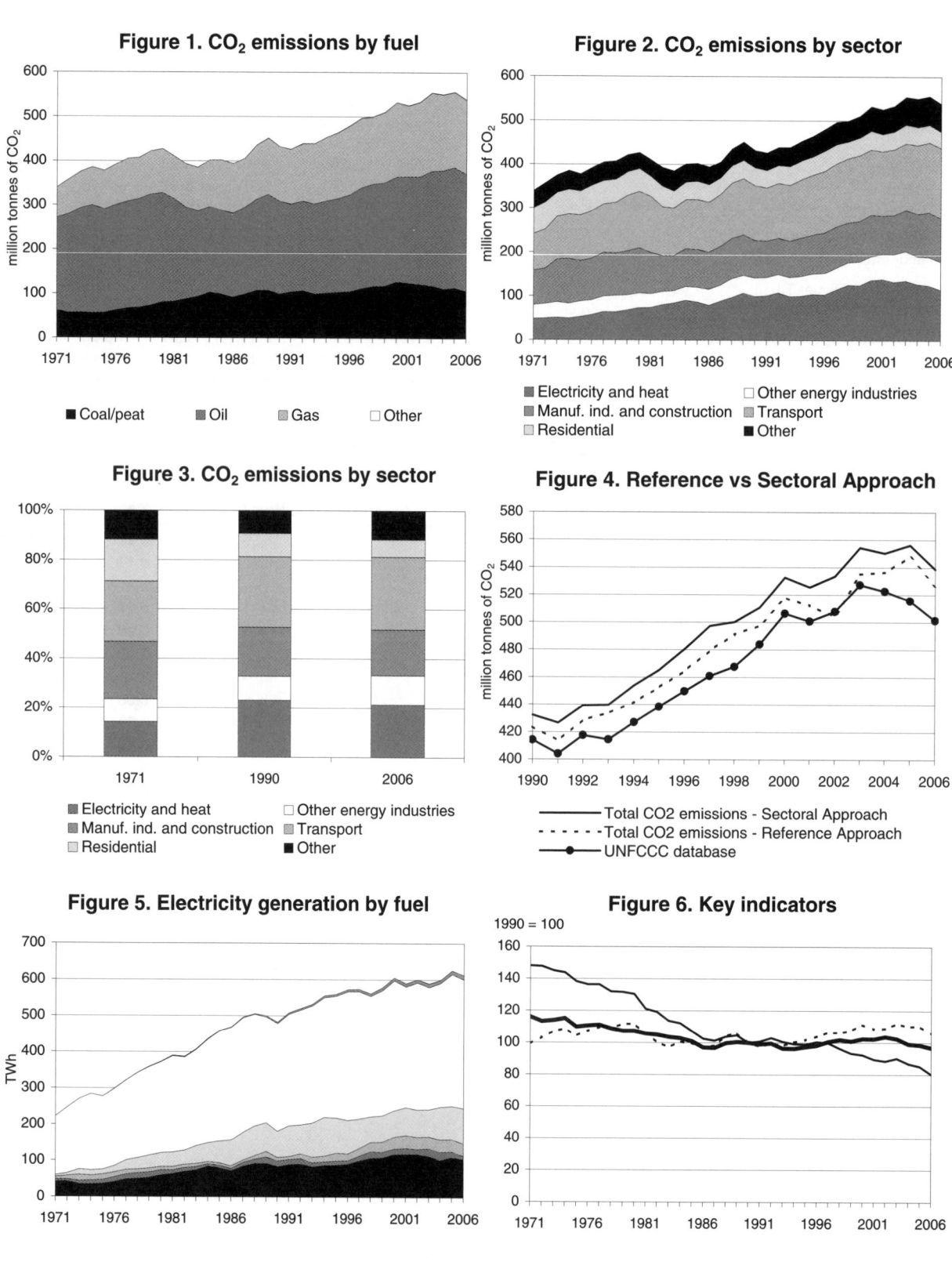

Figure 1. CO₂ emissions by fuel

■ Coal/peat ■ Oil ▨ Gas □ Other

Figure 2. CO₂ emissions by sector

■ Electricity and heat □ Other energy industries
■ Manuf. ind. and construction ▨ Transport
□ Residential ■ Other

Figure 3. CO₂ emissions by sector

■ Electricity and heat □ Other energy industries
■ Manuf. ind. and construction ▨ Transport
□ Residential ■ Other

Figure 4. Reference vs Sectoral Approach

—— Total CO2 emissions - Sectoral Approach
- - - - Total CO2 emissions - Reference Approach
—●— UNFCCC database

Figure 5. Electricity generation by fuel

■ Coal/peat ■ Oil ▨ Gas □ Nuclear □ Hydro ■ Other

Figure 6. Key indicators

1990 = 100

—— CO2/TPES —— CO2/GDP - - - - CO2/capita

Canada

Key indicators

	1990	1995	2000	2003	2004	2005	2006	% change 90-06
CO$_2$ Sectoral Approach (Mt of CO$_2$)	432.22	465.06	532.62	554.35	550.41	556.28	538.82	24.7%
CO$_2$ Reference Approach (Mt of CO$_2$)	423.43	452.53	517.78	535.29	536.44	548.02	526.86	24.4%
TPES (PJ)	8 772	9 700	10 555	10 978	11 261	11 457	11 294	28.8%
TPES (Mtoe)	209.51	231.68	252.09	262.21	268.96	273.66	269.74	28.8%
GDP (billion 2000 US$ using exch. rates)	543.60	592.10	724.90	773.70	797.50	821.90	844.60	55.4%
GDP (billion 2000 US$ using PPPs)	654.63	712.93	872.92	931.67	960.28	989.73	1 017.03	55.4%
Population (millions)	27.70	29.30	30.69	31.68	31.99	32.30	32.62	17.8%
CO$_2$ / TPES (t CO$_2$ per TJ)	49.3	47.9	50.5	50.5	48.9	48.6	47.7	-3.2%
CO$_2$ / GDP (kg CO$_2$ per 2000 US$)	0.80	0.79	0.73	0.72	0.69	0.68	0.64	-19.8%
CO$_2$ / GDP (kg CO$_2$ per 2000 US$ PPP)	0.66	0.65	0.61	0.60	0.57	0.56	0.53	-19.8%
CO$_2$ / population (t CO$_2$ per capita)	15.60	15.87	17.36	17.50	17.21	17.22	16.52	5.8%

Ratios are based on the Sectoral Approach.

2006 CO$_2$ emissions by sector

million tonnes of CO$_2$	Coal/peat	Oil	Gas	Other *	Total	% change 90-06
Sectoral Approach	**107.25**	**263.63**	**167.44**	**0.50**	**538.82**	**24.7%**
Main activity producer elec. and heat	90.16	6.78	12.71	0.02	109.66	13.6%
Unallocated autoproducers	0.36	0.43	4.13	-	4.93	63.2%
Other energy industries	0.06	29.79	34.80	-	64.64	52.6%
Manufacturing industries and construction	16.52	31.63	50.59	0.48	99.21	16.2%
Transport	-	149.98	9.58	-	159.56	28.8%
of which: road	-	*123.92*	*0.09*	-	*124.01*	*29.7%*
Other sectors	0.16	45.02	55.64	-	100.81	24.4%
of which: residential	*0.16*	*6.47*	*31.07*	-	*37.70*	*-7.6%*
Reference Approach	**108.14**	**235.12**	**183.11**	**0.50**	**526.86**	**24.4%**
Diff. due to losses and/or transformation	1.09	- 23.62	4.21	-	- 18.32	
Statistical differences	- 0.21	- 4.89	11.46	-	6.37	
Memo: international marine bunkers	-	*1.70*	-	-	*1.70*	*-40.6%*
Memo: international aviation	-	*2.53*	-	-	*2.53*	*-6.7%*

* Other includes industrial waste and non-renewable municipal waste.

Key sources for CO$_2$ emissions from fuel combustion in 2006

IPCC source category	CO$_2$ emissions (Mt of CO$_2$)	% change 90-06	Level assessment (%) **	Cumulative total (%)
Road - oil	123.92	29.7%	16.3	16.3
Main activity prod. elec. and heat - coal/peat	90.16	8.7%	11.9	28.2
Manufacturing industries - gas	50.59	13.2%	6.7	34.9
Non-specified other sectors - oil	38.55	96.2%	5.1	40.0
Other energy industries - gas	34.80	67.1%	4.6	44.6
Manufacturing industries - oil	31.63	24.7%	4.2	48.8
Residential - gas	31.07	17.1%	4.1	52.9
Other energy industries - oil	29.79	40.8%	3.9	56.8
Other transport - oil	26.06	21.2%	3.4	60.2
Non-specified other sectors - gas	24.56	19.2%	3.2	63.5
Manufacturing industries - coal/peat	16.52	8.7%	2.2	65.7
Memo: total CO$_2$ from fuel combustion	*538.82*	*24.7%*	*71.1*	*71.1*

** Percent calculated using the total GHG estimate for CO$_2$, CH$_4$, N$_2$O, HFCs, PFCs and SF$_6$ excluding CO$_2$ emissions/removals from land use change and forestry.

Chile / Chili

Figure 1. CO$_2$ emissions by fuel

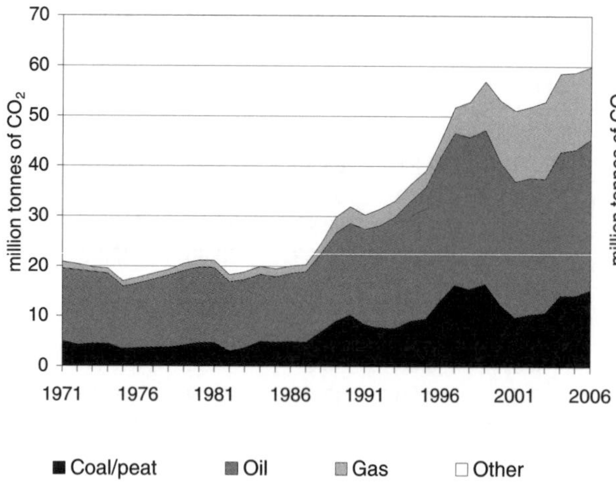

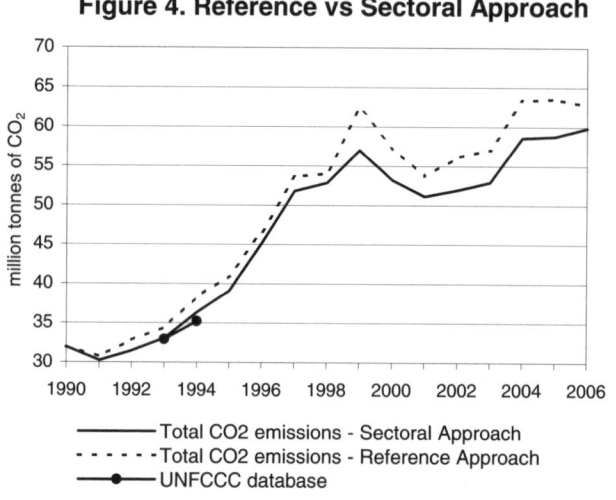

■ Coal/peat   ■ Oil   ▨ Gas   ☐ Other

Figure 2. CO$_2$ emissions by sector

▨ Electricity and heat   ☐ Other energy industries
▨ Manuf. ind. and construction   ▨ Transport
☐ Residential   ■ Other

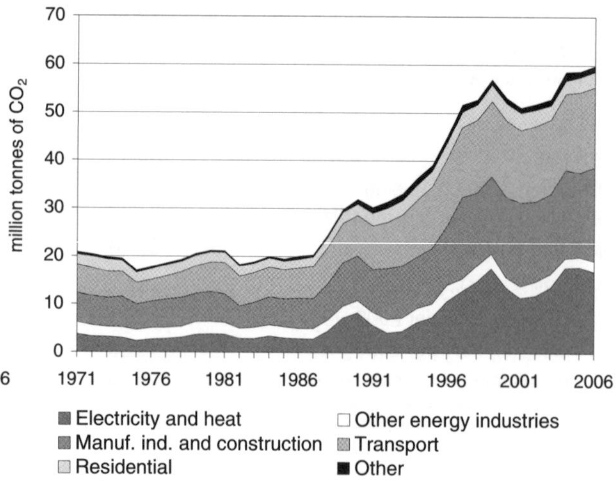

Figure 3. CO$_2$ emissions by sector

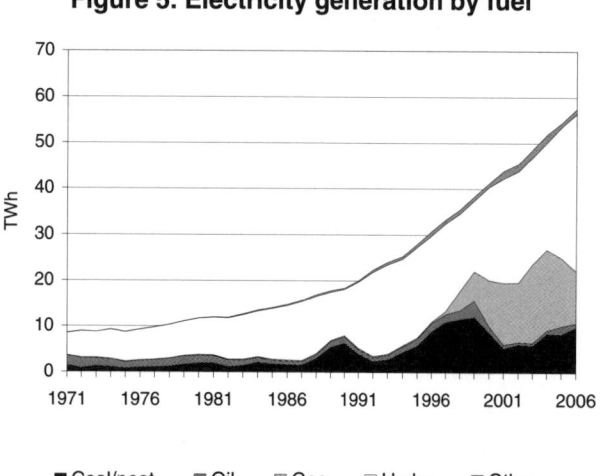

▨ Electricity and heat   ☐ Other energy industries
▨ Manuf. ind. and construction   ▨ Transport
☐ Residential   ■ Other

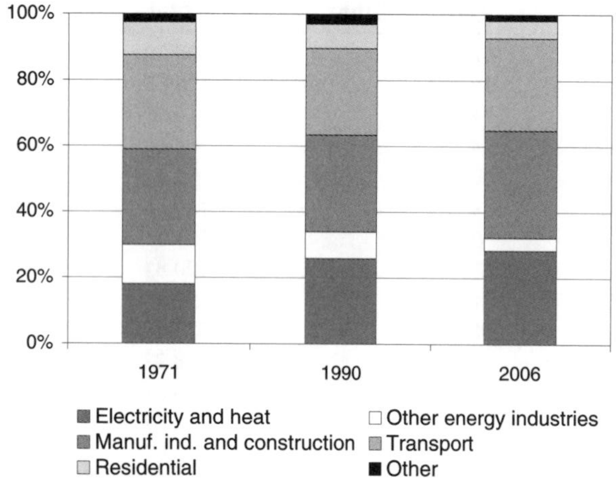

Figure 4. Reference vs Sectoral Approach

—— Total CO2 emissions - Sectoral Approach
- - - - Total CO2 emissions - Reference Approach
—●— UNFCCC database

Figure 5. Electricity generation by fuel

■ Coal/peat   ■ Oil   ▨ Gas   ☐ Hydro   ▨ Other

Figure 6. Key indicators

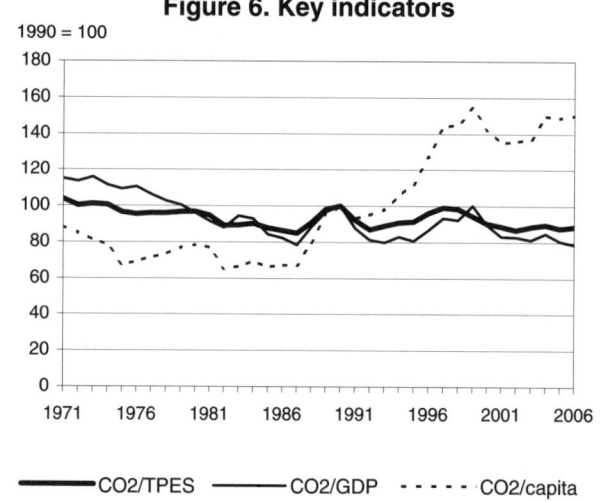

1990 = 100

—— CO2/TPES   —— CO2/GDP   - - - - CO2/capita

Chile / Chili

Key indicators

	1990	1995	2000	2003	2004	2005	2006	% change 90-06
CO$_2$ Sectoral Approach (Mt of CO$_2$)	31.94	39.08	53.20	52.92	58.57	58.76	59.84	87.3%
CO$_2$ Reference Approach (Mt of CO$_2$)	31.97	41.01	57.31	57.07	63.33	63.54	62.75	96.3%
TPES (PJ)	589	789	1 087	1 103	1 205	1 237	1 247	111.7%
TPES (Mtoe)	14.07	18.85	25.96	26.35	28.77	29.54	29.78	111.7%
GDP (billion 2000 US$ using exch. rates)	40.46	61.36	75.21	82.56	87.50	92.50	96.17	137.7%
GDP (billion 2000 US$ using PPPs)	75.70	114.82	140.74	154.49	163.74	173.09	179.96	137.7%
Population (millions)	13.18	14.40	15.41	15.95	16.12	16.30	16.43	24.7%
CO$_2$ / TPES (t CO$_2$ per TJ)	54.2	49.5	49.0	48.0	48.6	47.5	48.0	-11.5%
CO$_2$ / GDP (kg CO$_2$ per 2000 US$)	0.79	0.64	0.71	0.64	0.67	0.64	0.62	-21.2%
CO$_2$ / GDP (kg CO$_2$ per 2000 US$ PPP)	0.42	0.34	0.38	0.34	0.36	0.34	0.33	-21.2%
CO$_2$ / population (t CO$_2$ per capita)	2.42	2.71	3.45	3.32	3.63	3.61	3.64	50.2%

Ratios are based on the Sectoral Approach.

2006 CO$_2$ emissions by sector

million tonnes of CO$_2$	Coal/peat	Oil	Gas	Other *	Total	% change 90-06
Sectoral Approach	**15.32**	**30.02**	**14.50**	-	**59.84**	**87.3%**
Main activity producer elec. and heat	11.35	0.43	4.48	-	16.26	223.3%
Unallocated autoproducers	0.03	0.38	0.26	-	0.67	-79.2%
Other energy industries	0.01	1.87	0.45	-	2.33	-10.5%
Manufacturing industries and construction	3.84	7.51	8.12	-	19.47	108.8%
Transport	-	16.68	0.08	-	16.76	99.0%
of which: road	-	*15.61*	*0.08*	-	*15.69*	*108.6%*
Other sectors	0.10	3.14	1.11	-	4.35	30.6%
of which: residential	*0.03*	*2.34*	*0.81*	-	*3.18*	*35.2%*
Reference Approach	**15.44**	**32.08**	**15.24**	-	**62.75**	**96.3%**
Diff. due to losses and/or transformation	0.10	2.03	0.74	-	2.87	
Statistical differences	0.02	0.03	-	-	0.04	
Memo: international marine bunkers	-	*4.36*	-	-	*4.36*	*673.8%*
Memo: international aviation	-	*2.09*	-	-	*2.09*	*134.0%*

* Other includes industrial waste and non-renewable municipal waste.

Key sources for CO$_2$ emissions from fuel combustion in 2006

IPCC source category	CO$_2$ emissions (Mt of CO$_2$)	% change 90-06	Level assessment (%) **	Cumulative total (%)
Road - oil	15.61	108.0%	16.5	16.5
Main activity prod. elec. and heat - coal/peat	11.35	150.6%	12.0	28.5
Manufacturing industries - gas	8.12	366.2%	8.6	37.0
Manufacturing industries - oil	7.51	65.6%	7.9	45.0
Main activity prod. elec. and heat - gas	4.48	x	4.7	49.7
Manufacturing industries - coal/peat	3.84	26.0%	4.0	53.7
Residential - oil	2.34	22.4%	2.5	56.2
Other energy industries - oil	1.87	48.2%	2.0	58.2
Other transport - oil	1.07	19.0%	1.1	59.3
Residential - gas	0.81	182.7%	0.9	60.2
Non-specified other sectors - oil	0.80	10.1%	0.8	61.0
Memo: total CO$_2$ from fuel combustion	*59.84*	*87.3%*	*63.2*	*63.2*

** Percent calculated using the total GHG estimate for CO$_2$, CH$_4$, N$_2$O, HFCs, PFCs and SF$_6$ excluding CO$_2$ emissions/removals from land use change and forestry.

People's Republic of China / République populaire de Chine

Figure 1. CO$_2$ emissions by fuel

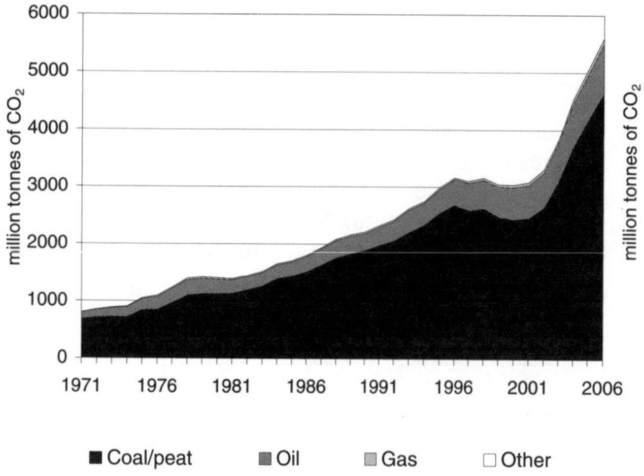

Coal/peat ■ Oil ■ Gas □ Other

Figure 2. CO$_2$ emissions by sector

■ Electricity and heat □ Other energy industries
■ Manuf. ind. and construction ■ Transport
□ Residential ■ Other

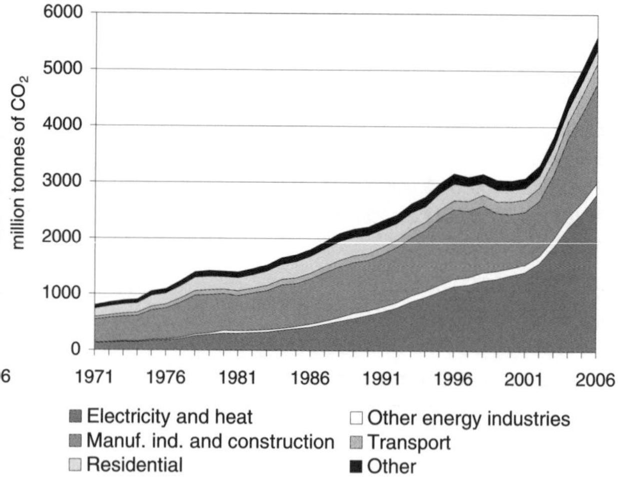

Figure 3. CO$_2$ emissions by sector

■ Electricity and heat □ Other energy industries
■ Manuf. ind. and construction ■ Transport
□ Residential ■ Other

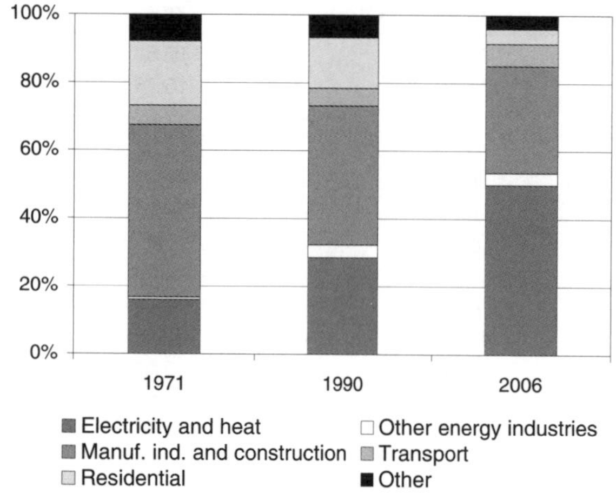

Figure 4. Reference vs Sectoral Approach

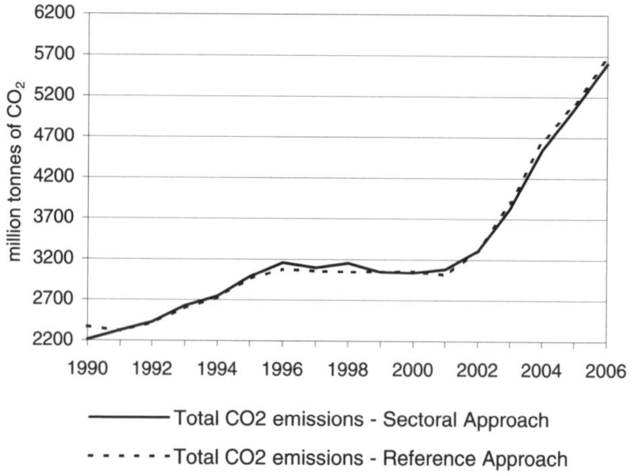

—— Total CO2 emissions - Sectoral Approach
- - - - - Total CO2 emissions - Reference Approach

Figure 5. Electricity generation by fuel

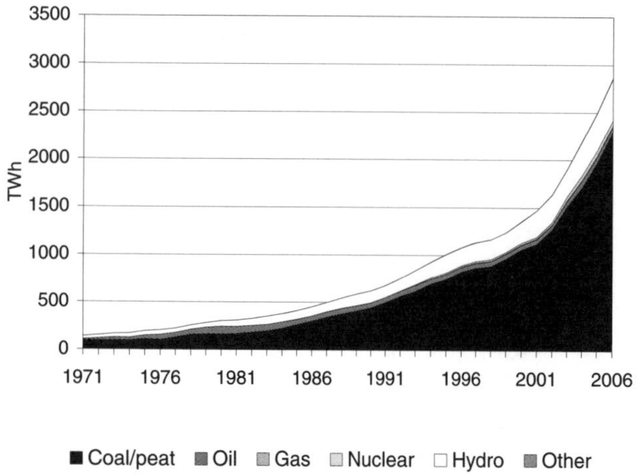

■ Coal/peat ■ Oil ■ Gas ■ Nuclear □ Hydro ■ Other

Figure 6. Key indicators

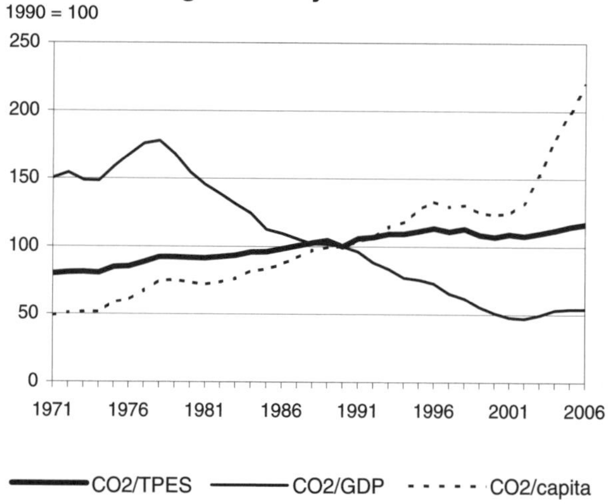

1990 = 100

—— CO2/TPES —— CO2/GDP - - - - CO2/capita

People's Republic of China / République populaire de Chine
Key indicators

	1990	1995	2000	2003	2004	2005	2006	% change 90-06
CO$_2$ Sectoral Approach (Mt of CO$_2$)	2 210.95	2 985.91	3 037.85	3 829.99	4 546.98	5 059.82	5 606.54	153.6%
CO$_2$ Reference Approach (Mt of CO$_2$)	2 371.19	2 957.90	3 054.80	3 901.10	4 656.13	5 125.61	5 676.90	139.4%
TPES (PJ)	36 142	43 877	46 301	57 034	66 355	72 016	78 659	117.6%
TPES (Mtoe)	863.24	1 047.98	1 105.89	1 362.24	1 584.87	1 720.08	1 878.74	117.6%
GDP (billion 2000 US$ using exch. rates)	444.60	792.79	1 198.48	1 557.68	1 715.00	1 889.93	2 092.15	370.6%
GDP (billion 2000 US$ using PPPs)	1 845.63	3 291.04	4 975.16	6 466.25	7 119.34	7 845.51	8 684.98	370.6%
Population (millions)	1 135.19	1 204.86	1 262.65	1 288.40	1 296.16	1 304.50	1 311.80	15.6%
CO$_2$ / TPES (t CO$_2$ per TJ)	61.2	68.1	65.6	67.2	68.5	70.3	71.3	16.5%
CO$_2$ / GDP (kg CO$_2$ per 2000 US$)	4.97	3.77	2.53	2.46	2.65	2.68	2.68	-46.1%
CO$_2$ / GDP (kg CO$_2$ per 2000 US$ PPP)	1.20	0.91	0.61	0.59	0.64	0.64	0.65	-46.1%
CO$_2$ / population (t CO$_2$ per capita)	1.95	2.48	2.41	2.97	3.51	3.88	4.27	119.4%

Ratios are based on the Sectoral Approach.

2006 CO$_2$ emissions by sector

million tonnes of CO$_2$	Coal/peat	Oil	Gas	Other *	Total	% change 90-06
Sectoral Approach	**4 640.98**	**864.40**	**101.16**	-	**5 606.54**	**153.6%**
Main activity producer elec. and heat	2 680.33	37.76	12.18	-	2 730.27	342.7%
Unallocated autoproducers	50.18	15.32	-	-	65.50	459.5%
Other energy industries	122.64	65.66	16.17	-	204.46	142.4%
Manufacturing industries and construction	1 515.39	202.46	46.10	-	1 763.95	95.1%
Transport	14.08	352.53	0.14	-	366.75	214.6%
of which: road	*-*	*249.07*	*0.12*	*-*	*249.19*	*308.2%*
Other sectors	258.36	190.67	26.57	-	475.60	-0.4%
of which: residential	*174.68*	*51.72*	*20.06*	*-*	*246.47*	*-24.8%*
Reference Approach	**4 675.99**	**895.81**	**105.10**	-	**5 676.90**	**139.4%**
Diff. due to losses and/or transformation	83.94	27.38	2.52	-	113.85	
Statistical differences	- 48.94	4.03	1.42	-	- 43.49	
Memo: international marine bunkers	*-*	*26.10*	*-*	*-*	*26.10*	*468.5%*
Memo: international aviation	*-*	*7.29*	*-*	*-*	*7.29*	*+*

* Other includes industrial waste and non-renewable municipal waste.

Key sources for CO$_2$ emissions from fuel combustion in 2006

IPCC source category	CO$_2$ emissions (Mt of CO$_2$)	% change 90-06	Level assessment (%) **	Cumulative total (%)
Main activity prod. elec. and heat - coal/peat	2680.33	368.4%	33.3	33.3
Manufacturing industries - coal/peat	1515.39	88.2%	18.8	52.1
Road - oil	249.07	308.0%	3.1	55.2
Manufacturing industries - oil	202.46	136.5%	2.5	57.7
Residential - coal/peat	174.68	-44.8%	2.2	59.9
Non-specified other sectors - oil	138.95	206.2%	1.7	61.6
Other energy industries - coal/peat	122.64	140.5%	1.5	63.1
Other transport - oil	103.46	506.9%	1.3	64.4
Non-specified other sectors - coal/peat	83.68	-19.4%	1.0	65.5
Other energy industries - oil	65.66	142.7%	0.8	66.3
Residential - oil	51.72	559.3%	0.6	66.9
Memo: total CO$_2$ from fuel combustion	*5606.54*	*153.6%*	*69.6*	*69.6*

** Percent calculated using the total GHG estimate for CO$_2$, CH$_4$, N$_2$O, HFCs, PFCs and SF$_6$ excluding CO$_2$ emissions/removals from land use change and forestry.

Chinese Taipei / Taipei chinois

Figure 1. CO_2 emissions by fuel

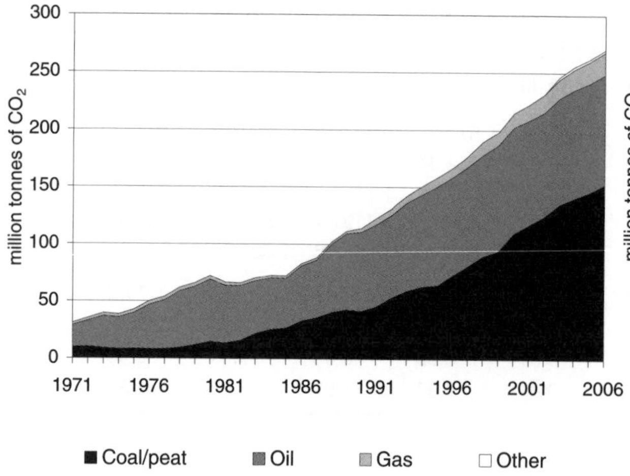
million tonnes of CO2
300
250
200
150
100
50
0
1971
1976
1981
1986
1991
1996
2001
2006
Coal/peat
Oil
Gas
Other

Figure 2. CO_2 emissions by sector

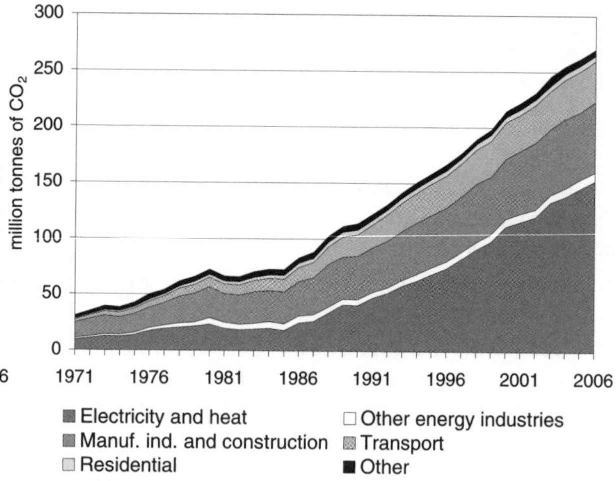
million tonnes of CO2
300
250
200
150
100
50
0
1971
1976
1981
1986
1991
1996
2001
2006
Electricity and heat
Other energy industries
Manuf. ind. and construction
Transport
Residential
Other

Figure 3. CO_2 emissions by sector

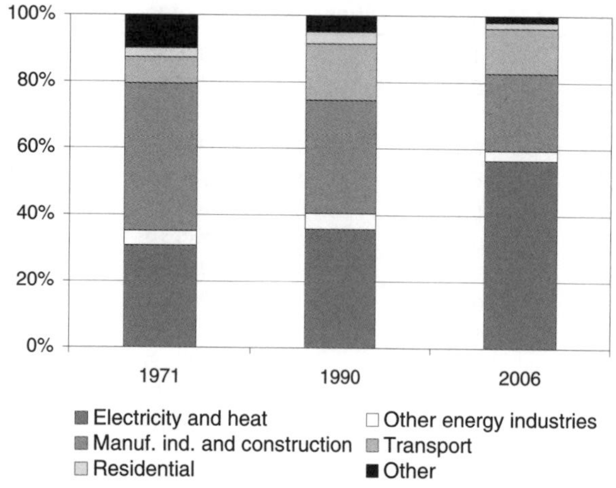
100%
80%
60%
40%
20%
0%
1971
1990
2006
Electricity and heat
Other energy industries
Manuf. ind. and construction
Transport
Residential
Other

Figure 4. Reference vs Sectoral Approach

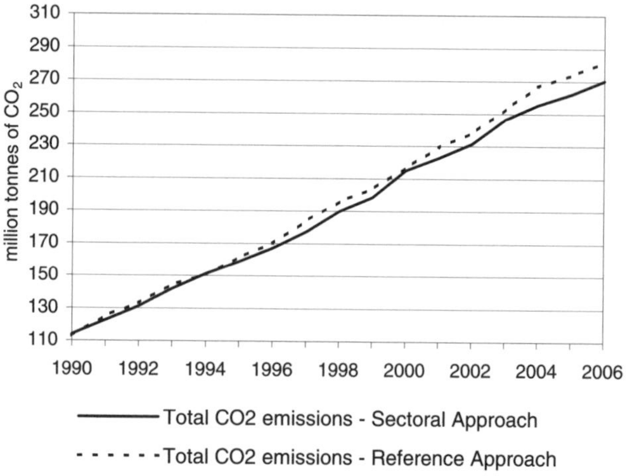
million tonnes of CO2
310
290
270
250
230
210
190
170
150
130
110
1990
1992
1994
1996
1998
2000
2002
2004
2006
Total CO2 emissions - Sectoral Approach
Total CO2 emissions - Reference Approach

Figure 5. Electricity generation by fuel

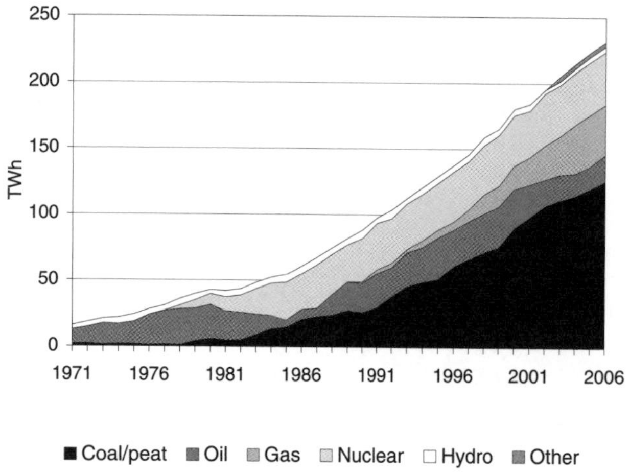
TWh
250
200
150
100
50
0
1971
1976
1981
1986
1991
1996
2001
2006
Coal/peat
Oil
Gas
Nuclear
Hydro
Other

Figure 6. Key indicators

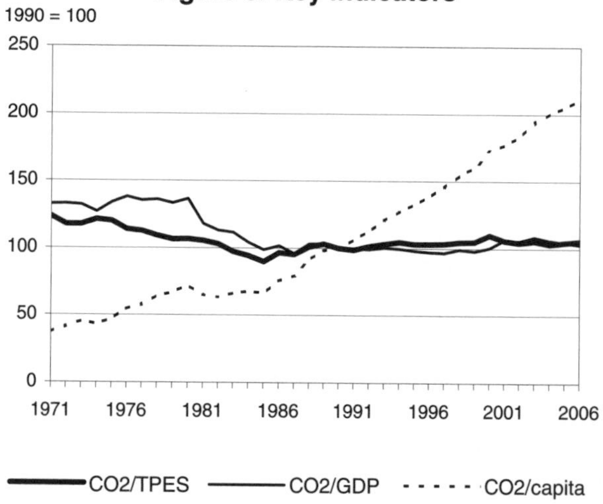
1990 = 100
250
200
150
100
50
0
1971
1976
1981
1986
1991
1996
2001
2006
CO2/TPES
CO2/GDP
CO2/capita

Chinese Taipei / Taipei chinois

Key indicators

	1990	1995	2000	2003	2004	2005	2006	% change 90-06
CO$_2$ Sectoral Approach (Mt of CO$_2$)	113.88	158.72	215.02	246.37	255.43	262.13	270.33	137.4%
CO$_2$ Reference Approach (Mt of CO$_2$)	112.77	161.29	216.79	252.88	267.00	273.88	281.70	149.8%
TPES (PJ)	2 008	2 711	3 455	4 116	4 352	4 418	4 517	124.9%
TPES (Mtoe)	47.97	64.75	82.52	98.31	103.94	105.53	107.88	124.9%
GDP (billion 2000 US$ using exch. rates)	170.92	242.44	321.23	340.35	361.28	375.99	393.58	130.3%
GDP (billion 2000 US$ using PPPs)	261.44	370.83	491.35	520.60	552.62	575.11	602.02	130.3%
Population (millions)	20.28	21.29	22.18	22.54	22.62	22.70	22.78	12.3%
CO$_2$ / TPES (t CO$_2$ per TJ)	56.7	58.5	62.2	59.9	58.7	59.3	59.9	5.6%
CO$_2$ / GDP (kg CO$_2$ per 2000 US$)	0.67	0.65	0.67	0.72	0.71	0.70	0.69	3.1%
CO$_2$ / GDP (kg CO$_2$ per 2000 US$ PPP)	0.44	0.43	0.44	0.47	0.46	0.46	0.45	3.1%
CO$_2$ / population (t CO$_2$ per capita)	5.62	7.45	9.69	10.93	11.29	11.55	11.87	111.3%

Ratios are based on the Sectoral Approach.

2006 CO$_2$ emissions by sector

million tonnes of CO$_2$	Coal/peat	Oil	Gas	Other *	Total	% change 90-06
Sectoral Approach	**152.60**	**96.15**	**19.51**	**2.06**	**270.33**	**137.4%**
Main activity producer elec. and heat	88.65	10.07	14.34	-	113.06	215.8%
Unallocated autoproducers	32.29	4.78	0.31	2.06	39.44	724.7%
Other energy industries	-	7.53	0.56	-	8.08	46.5%
Manufacturing industries and construction	31.66	29.54	1.81	-	63.01	62.7%
Transport	-	36.36	-	-	36.36	89.0%
of which: road	-	35.33	-	-	35.33	91.2%
Other sectors	-	7.88	2.49	-	10.37	5.7%
of which: residential	-	3.11	1.88	-	4.99	20.9%
Reference Approach	**157.13**	**99.84**	**22.67**	**2.06**	**281.70**	**149.8%**
Diff. due to losses and/or transformation	1.23	3.78	3.16	-	8.16	
Statistical differences	3.30	- 0.09	0.00	-	3.22	
Memo: international marine bunkers	-	7.38	-	-	7.38	52.0%
Memo: international aviation	-	7.76	-	-	7.76	172.7%

* Other includes industrial waste and non-renewable municipal waste.

Key sources for CO$_2$ emissions from fuel combustion in 2006

IPCC source category	CO$_2$ emissions (Mt of CO$_2$)	% change 90-06	Level assessment (%) **	Cumulative total (%)
Main activity prod. elec. and heat - coal/peat	88.65	348.1%	30.4	30.4
Road - oil	35.33	91.2%	12.1	42.6
Unallocated autoproducers - coal/peat	32.29	707.5%	11.1	53.7
Manufacturing industries - coal/peat	31.66	81.0%	10.9	64.5
Manufacturing industries - oil	29.54	44.4%	10.1	74.7
Main activity prod. elec. and heat - gas	14.34	+	4.9	79.6
Main activity prod. elec. and heat - oil	10.07	-34.8%	3.5	83.1
Other energy industries - oil	7.53	57.3%	2.6	85.7
Unallocated autoproducers - oil	4.78	560.0%	1.6	87.3
Non-specified other sectors - oil	4.77	-12.4%	1.6	88.9
Residential - oil	3.11	1.1%	1.1	90.0
Memo: total CO$_2$ from fuel combustion	270.33	137.4%	92.8	92.8

** Percent calculated using the total GHG estimate for CO$_2$, CH$_4$, N$_2$O, HFCs, PFCs and SF$_6$ excluding CO$_2$ emissions/removals from land use change and forestry.

Colombia / Colombie

Figure 1. CO₂ emissions by fuel

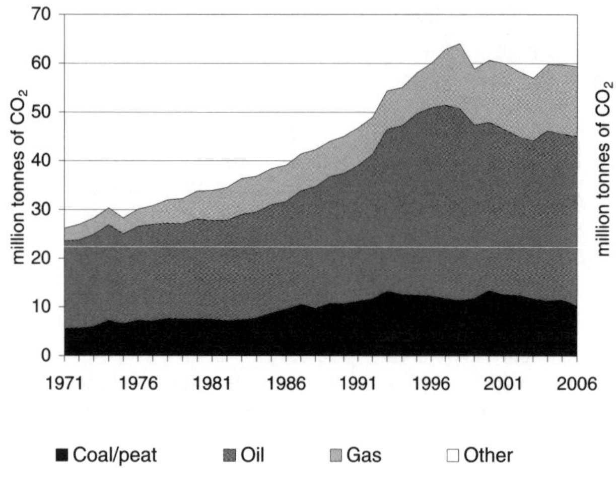

■ Coal/peat ■ Oil ■ Gas □ Other

Figure 2. CO₂ emissions by sector

■ Electricity and heat   □ Other energy industries
■ Manuf. ind. and construction   ■ Transport
□ Residential   ■ Other

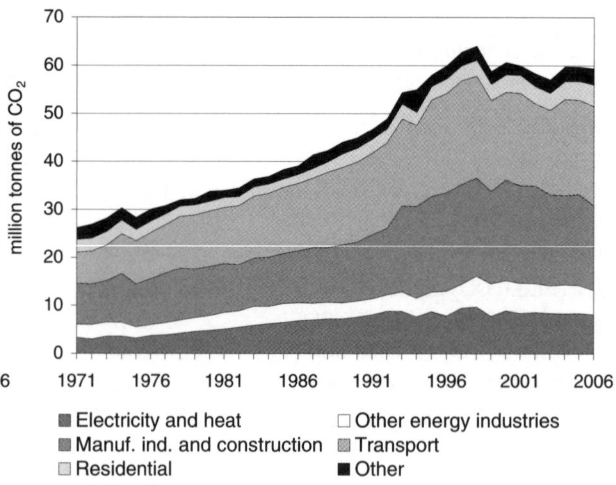

Figure 3. CO₂ emissions by sector

■ Electricity and heat   □ Other energy industries
■ Manuf. ind. and construction   ■ Transport
□ Residential   ■ Other

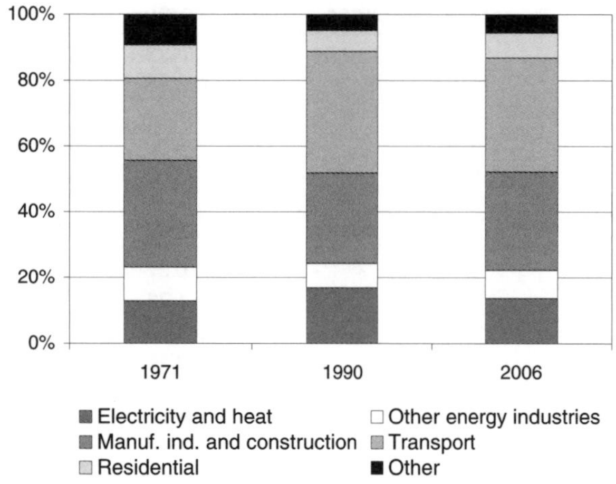

Figure 4. Reference vs Sectoral Approach

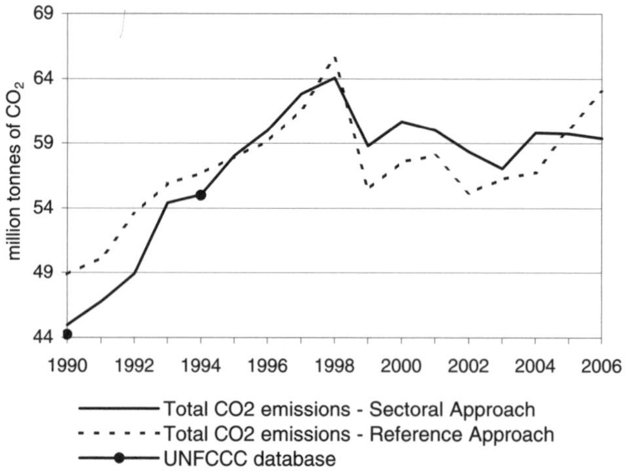

—— Total CO2 emissions - Sectoral Approach
- - - - Total CO2 emissions - Reference Approach
—●— UNFCCC database

Figure 5. Electricity generation by fuel

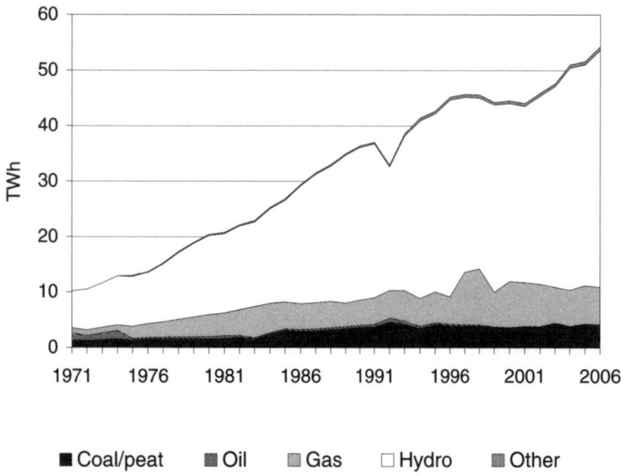

■ Coal/peat ■ Oil ■ Gas □ Hydro ■ Other

Figure 6. Key indicators

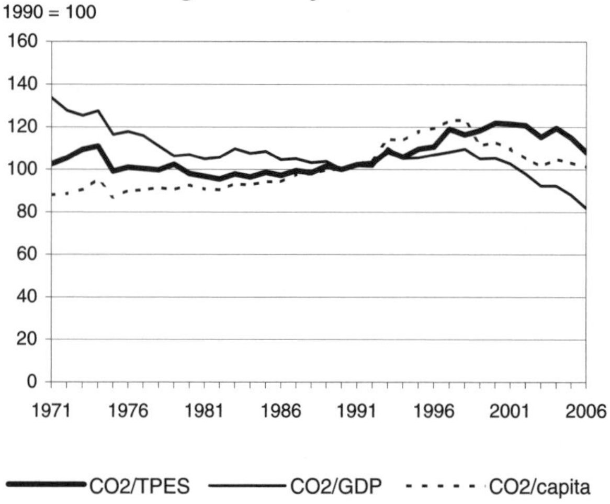

1990 = 100

——CO2/TPES ——CO2/GDP - - - - CO2/capita

Colombia / Colombie

Key indicators

	1990	1995	2000	2003	2004	2005	2006	% change 90-06
CO$_2$ Sectoral Approach (Mt of CO$_2$)	44.96	58.05	60.68	57.05	59.82	59.73	59.39	32.1%
CO$_2$ Reference Approach (Mt of CO$_2$)	48.87	57.93	57.59	56.23	56.77	60.17	62.98	28.9%
TPES (PJ)	1 036	1 222	1 148	1 141	1 154	1 198	1 265	22.1%
TPES (Mtoe)	24.75	29.18	27.42	27.26	27.56	28.60	30.21	22.1%
GDP (billion 2000 US$ using exch. rates)	65.37	80.04	83.78	90.00	94.38	98.84	105.55	61.5%
GDP (billion 2000 US$ using PPPs)	194.29	237.89	249.00	267.48	280.50	293.75	313.70	61.5%
Population (millions)	34.88	38.26	41.68	43.68	44.32	44.95	45.56	30.6%
CO$_2$ / TPES (t CO$_2$ per TJ)	43.4	47.5	52.9	50.0	51.9	49.9	47.0	8.2%
CO$_2$ / GDP (kg CO$_2$ per 2000 US$)	0.69	0.73	0.72	0.63	0.63	0.60	0.56	-18.2%
CO$_2$ / GDP (kg CO$_2$ per 2000 US$ PPP)	0.23	0.24	0.24	0.21	0.21	0.20	0.19	-18.2%
CO$_2$ / population (t CO$_2$ per capita)	1.29	1.52	1.46	1.31	1.35	1.33	1.30	1.1%

Ratios are based on the Sectoral Approach.

2006 CO$_2$ emissions by sector

million tonnes of CO$_2$	Coal/peat	Oil	Gas	Other *	Total	% change 90-06
Sectoral Approach	**10.25**	**34.81**	**14.33**	-	**59.39**	**32.1%**
Main activity producer elec. and heat	2.62	0.06	3.34	-	6.02	3.4%
Unallocated autoproducers	1.82	0.04	0.25	-	2.10	19.6%
Other energy industries	0.06	1.78	3.24	-	5.08	51.0%
Manufacturing industries and construction	5.51	8.40	3.77	-	17.68	43.3%
Transport	-	19.73	0.90	-	20.63	24.1%
of which: road	-	*18.85*	*0.90*	-	*19.75*	*26.2%*
Other sectors	0.24	4.79	2.84	-	7.87	55.5%
of which: residential	*0.24*	*1.84*	*2.41*	-	*4.49*	*57.2%*
Reference Approach	**9.51**	**39.14**	**14.33**	-	**62.98**	**28.9%**
Diff. due to losses and/or transformation	1.03	2.00	-	-	3.04	
Statistical differences	- 1.77	2.33	- 0.00	-	0.56	
Memo: international marine bunkers	-	*1.21*	-	-	*1.21*	*267.3%*
Memo: international aviation	-	*1.75*	-	-	*1.75*	*12.0%*

* Other includes industrial waste and non-renewable municipal waste.

Key sources for CO$_2$ emissions from fuel combustion in 2006

IPCC source category	CO$_2$ emissions (Mt of CO$_2$)	% change 90-06	Level assessment (%) **	Cumulative total (%)
Road - oil	18.85	20.4%	12.3	12.3
Manufacturing industries - oil	8.40	78.8%	5.5	17.8
Manufacturing industries - coal/peat	5.51	-4.7%	3.6	21.4
Manufacturing industries - gas	3.77	103.3%	2.5	23.8
Main activity prod. elec. and heat - gas	3.34	15.0%	2.2	26.0
Other energy industries - gas	3.24	30.6%	2.1	28.1
Non-specified other sectors - oil	2.95	36.3%	1.9	30.1
Main activity prod. elec. and heat - coal/peat	2.62	0.5%	1.7	31.8
Residential - gas	2.41	+	1.6	33.3
Residential - oil	1.84	-15.2%	1.2	34.5
Unallocated autoproducers - coal/peat	1.82	4.8%	1.2	35.7
Memo: total CO$_2$ from fuel combustion	*59.39*	*32.1%*	*38.8*	*38.8*

** Percent calculated using the total GHG estimate for CO$_2$, CH$_4$, N$_2$O, HFCs, PFCs and SF$_6$ excluding CO$_2$ emissions/removals from land use change and forestry.

Congo

Figure 1. CO₂ emissions by fuel

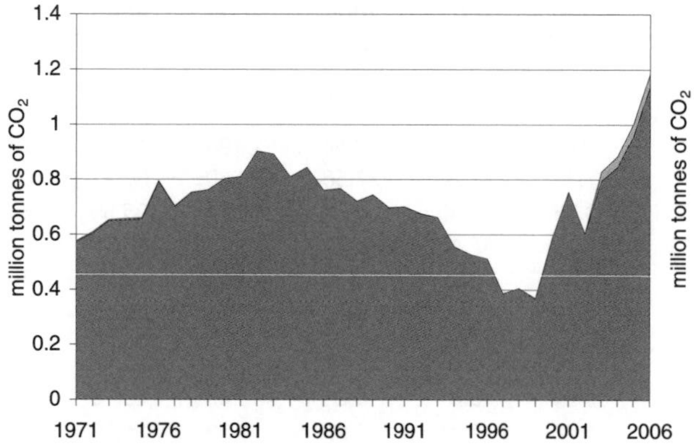

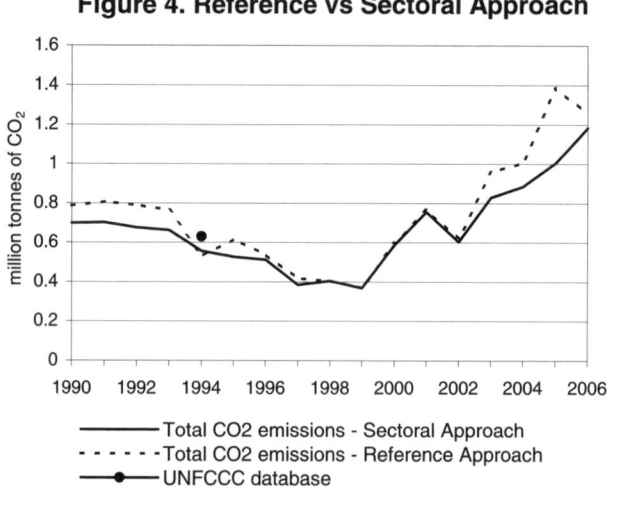

Figure 2. CO₂ emissions by sector

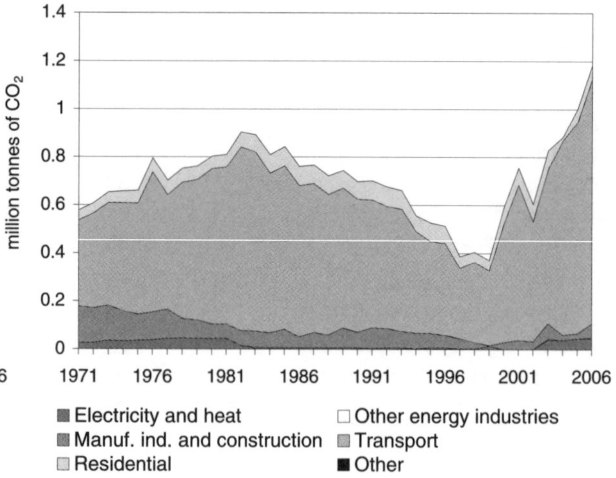

Figure 3. CO₂ emissions by sector

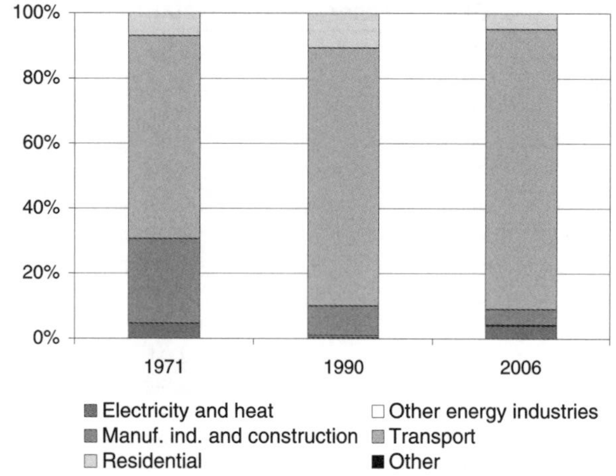

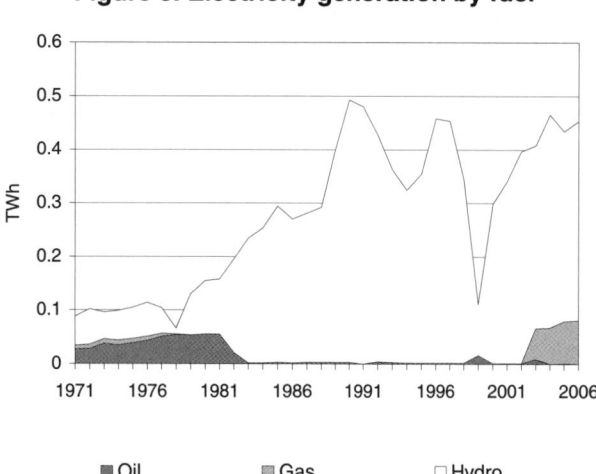

Figure 4. Reference vs Sectoral Approach

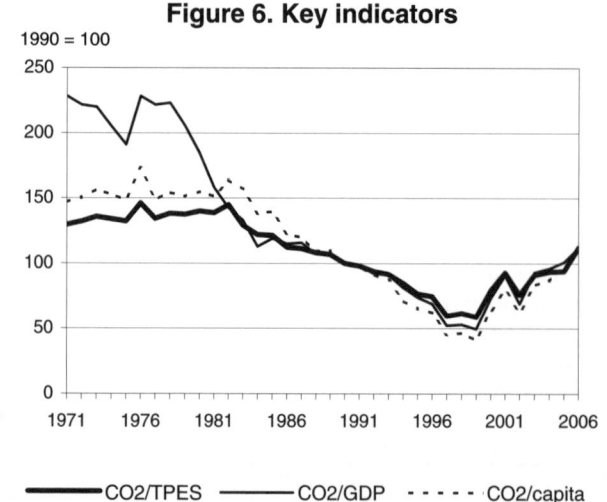

Figure 5. Electricity generation by fuel

Figure 6. Key indicators

Congo
Key indicators

	1990	1995	2000	2003	2004	2005	2006	% change 90-06
CO$_2$ Sectoral Approach (Mt of CO$_2$)	0.70	0.53	0.59	0.83	0.88	1.00	1.18	69.6%
CO$_2$ Reference Approach (Mt of CO$_2$)	0.79	0.62	0.60	0.96	1.00	1.38	1.26	59.9%
TPES (PJ)	33	33	36	43	45	51	50	51.2%
TPES (Mtoe)	0.80	0.79	0.85	1.04	1.08	1.22	1.21	51.2%
GDP (billion 2000 US$ using exch. rates)	2.80	2.86	3.22	3.56	3.69	3.98	4.23	51.3%
GDP (billion 2000 US$ using PPPs)	3.15	3.22	3.62	4.01	4.15	4.47	4.76	51.3%
Population (millions)	2.42	2.79	3.20	3.45	3.53	3.61	3.69	52.3%
CO$_2$ / TPES (t CO$_2$ per TJ)	20.9	16.0	16.6	19.1	19.6	19.7	23.5	12.2%
CO$_2$ / GDP (kg CO$_2$ per 2000 US$)	0.25	0.18	0.18	0.23	0.24	0.25	0.28	12.1%
CO$_2$ / GDP (kg CO$_2$ per 2000 US$ PPP)	0.22	0.16	0.16	0.21	0.21	0.22	0.25	12.1%
CO$_2$ / population (t CO$_2$ per capita)	0.29	0.19	0.18	0.24	0.25	0.28	0.32	11.4%

Ratios are based on the Sectoral Approach.

2006 CO$_2$ emissions by sector

million tonnes of CO$_2$	Coal/peat	Oil	Gas	Other *	Total	% change 90-06
Sectoral Approach	-	**1.14**	**0.05**	-	**1.18**	**69.6%**
Main activity producer elec. and heat	-	-	0.05	-	0.05	+
Unallocated autoproducers	-	-	-	-	-	-
Other energy industries	-	0.00	-	-	0.00	x
Manufacturing industries and construction	-	0.06	-	-	0.06	-10.5%
Transport	-	1.02	-	-	1.02	84.1%
of which: road	-	*0.80*	-	-	*0.80*	*77.0%*
Other sectors	-	0.06	-	-	0.06	-21.7%
of which: residential	-	*0.06*	-	-	*0.06*	*-21.7%*
Reference Approach	-	**1.21**	**0.05**	-	**1.26**	**59.9%**
Diff. due to losses and/or transformation	-	0.07	-	-	0.07	
Statistical differences	-	0.00	-	-	0.00	
Memo: international marine bunkers	-	..	-	-	..	..
Memo: international aviation	-	..	-	-	..	..

* Other includes industrial waste and non-renewable municipal waste.

Key sources for CO$_2$ emissions from fuel combustion in 2006

IPCC source category	CO$_2$ emissions (Mt of CO$_2$)	% change 90-06	Level assessment (%) **	Cumulative total (%)
Road - oil	0.80	77.0%	8.7	8.7
Other transport - oil	0.22	115.8%	2.4	11.0
Residential - oil	0.06	-21.7%	0.6	11.6
Manufacturing industries - oil	0.06	-10.5%	0.6	12.3
Main activity prod. elec. and heat - gas	0.05	x	0.5	12.8
Other energy industries - oil	0.00	-	0.0	12.8
-	-	-	-	-
-	-	-	-	-
-	-	-	-	-
-	-	-	-	-
-	-	-	-	-
Memo: total CO$_2$ from fuel combustion	*1.18*	*69.6%*	*12.8*	*12.8*

** Percent calculated using the total GHG estimate for CO$_2$, CH$_4$, N$_2$O, HFCs, PFCs and SF$_6$ excluding CO$_2$ emissions/removals from land use change and forestry.

Democratic Republic of Congo / République démocratique du Congo

Figure 1. CO_2 emissions by fuel

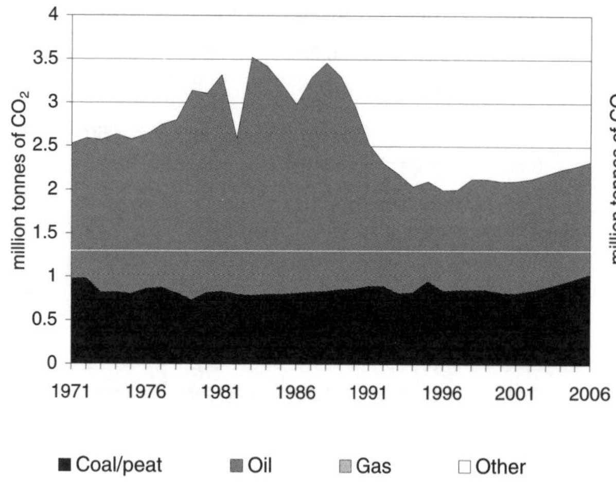
million tonnes of CO2
Coal/peat
Oil
Gas
Other

Figure 2. CO_2 emissions by sector

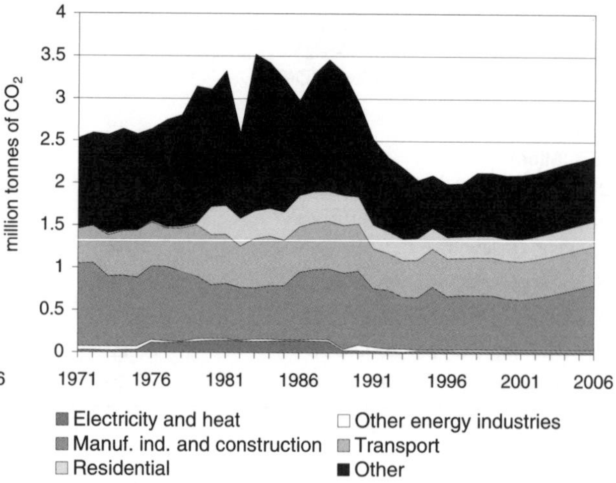
million tonnes of CO2
Electricity and heat
Other energy industries
Manuf. ind. and construction
Transport
Residential
Other

Figure 3. CO_2 emissions by sector

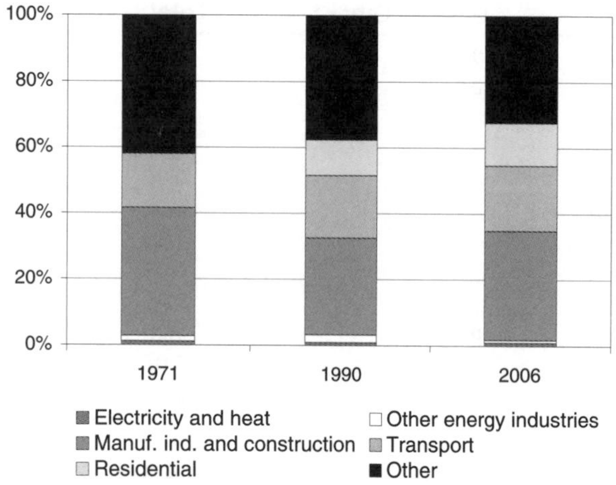
Electricity and heat
Other energy industries
Manuf. ind. and construction
Transport
Residential
Other

Figure 4. Reference vs Sectoral Approach

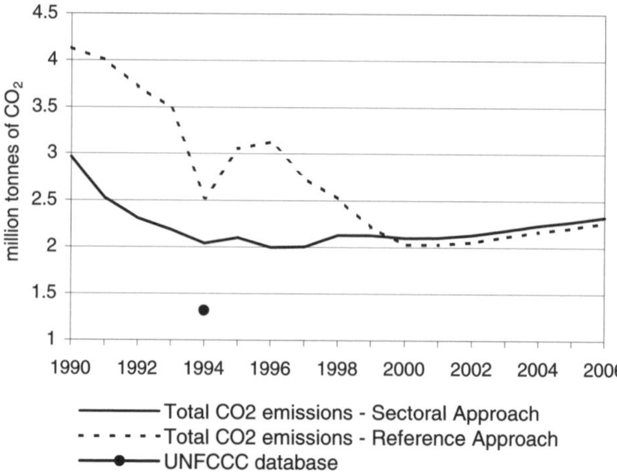
million tonnes of CO2
Total CO2 emissions - Sectoral Approach
Total CO2 emissions - Reference Approach
UNFCCC database

Figure 5. Electricity generation by fuel

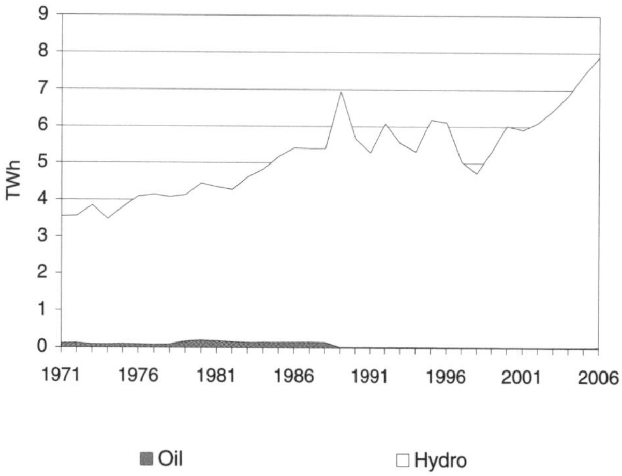
TWh
Oil
Hydro

Figure 6. Key indicators

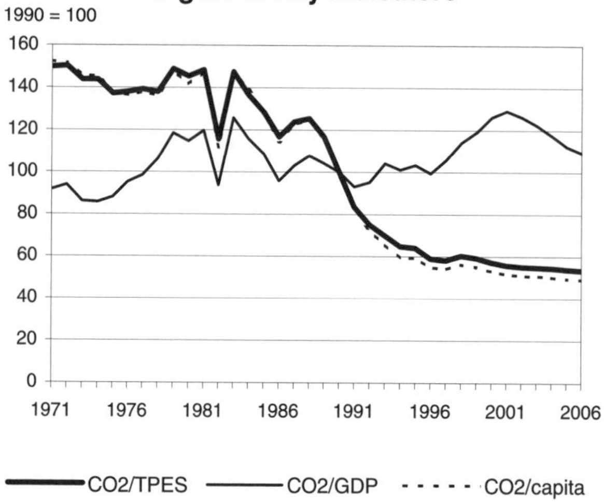
1990 = 100
CO2/TPES
CO2/GDP
CO2/capita

Democratic Republic of Congo / République démocratique du Congo
Key indicators

	1990	1995	2000	2003	2004	2005	2006	% change 90-06
CO$_2$ Sectoral Approach (Mt of CO$_2$)	2.96	2.10	2.10	2.18	2.24	2.28	2.33	-21.5%
CO$_2$ Reference Approach (Mt of CO$_2$)	4.13	3.05	2.03	2.11	2.17	2.21	2.27	-45.1%
TPES (PJ)	499	553	618	670	690	711	733	47.1%
TPES (Mtoe)	11.91	13.20	14.76	16.00	16.48	16.97	17.51	47.1%
GDP (billion 2000 US$ using exch. rates)	7.66	5.26	4.31	4.61	4.92	5.24	5.51	-28.1%
GDP (billion 2000 US$ using PPPs)	53.57	36.76	30.11	32.27	34.41	36.64	38.50	-28.1%
Population (millions)	37.94	45.34	50.69	55.18	56.92	58.74	60.64	59.8%
CO$_2$ / TPES (t CO$_2$ per TJ)	5.9	3.8	3.4	3.3	3.2	3.2	3.2	-46.6%
CO$_2$ / GDP (kg CO$_2$ per 2000 US$)	0.39	0.40	0.49	0.47	0.45	0.43	0.42	9.3%
CO$_2$ / GDP (kg CO$_2$ per 2000 US$ PPP)	0.06	0.06	0.07	0.07	0.07	0.06	0.06	9.2%
CO$_2$ / population (t CO$_2$ per capita)	0.08	0.05	0.04	0.04	0.04	0.04	0.04	-50.8%

Ratios are based on the Sectoral Approach.

2006 CO$_2$ emissions by sector

million tonnes of CO$_2$	Coal/peat	Oil	Gas	Other *	Total	% change 90-06
Sectoral Approach	**1.04**	**1.29**	-	-	**2.33**	**-21.5%**
Main activity producer elec. and heat	-	0.02	-	-	0.02	-13.3%
Unallocated autoproducers	-	-	-	-	-	-
Other energy industries	-	0.02	-	-	0.02	-73.9%
Manufacturing industries and construction	0.76	0.01	-	-	0.77	-11.3%
Transport	-	0.46	-	-	0.46	-18.2%
of which: road	-	*0.46*	-	-	*0.46*	*-18.2%*
Other sectors	0.28	0.78	-	-	1.06	-26.5%
of which: residential	*0.28*	*0.02*	-	-	*0.30*	*-5.2%*
Reference Approach	**1.08**	**1.19**	-	-	**2.27**	**-45.1%**
Diff. due to losses and/or transformation	0.05	-	-	-	0.05	
Statistical differences	0.00	- 0.10	-	-	- 0.10	
Memo: international marine bunkers	-	*0.01*	-	-	*0.01*	*-94.1%*
Memo: international aviation	-	*0.36*	-	-	*0.36*	*13.6%*

* Other includes industrial waste and non-renewable municipal waste.

Key sources for CO$_2$ emissions from fuel combustion in 2006

IPCC source category	CO$_2$ emissions (Mt of CO$_2$)	% change 90-06	Level assessment (%) **	Cumulative total (%)
Manufacturing industries - coal/peat	0.76	15.2%	0.8	0.8
Non-specified other sectors - oil	0.76	-32.5%	0.8	1.6
Road - oil	0.46	-18.2%	0.5	2.1
Residential - coal/peat	0.28	33.3%	0.3	2.4
Main activity prod. elec. and heat - oil	0.02	-13.3%	0.0	2.4
Residential - oil	0.02	-79.8%	0.0	2.5
Other energy industries - oil	0.02	-73.9%	0.0	2.5
Manufacturing industries - oil	0.01	-93.6%	0.0	2.5
-	-	-	-	-
-	-	-	-	-
-	-	-	-	-
Memo: total CO$_2$ from fuel combustion	*2.33*	*-21.5%*	*2.5*	*2.5*

** Percent calculated using the total GHG estimate for CO$_2$, CH$_4$, N$_2$O, HFCs, PFCs and SF$_6$ excluding CO$_2$ emissions/removals from land use change and forestry.

Costa Rica

Figure 1. CO₂ emissions by fuel

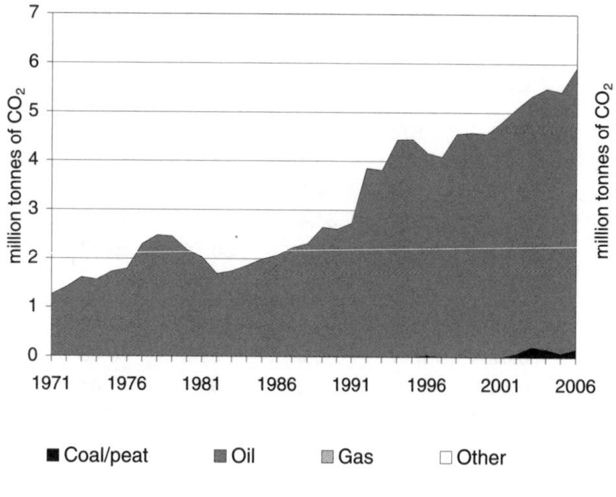

Legend: ■ Coal/peat ■ Oil ▨ Gas ☐ Other

Figure 2. CO₂ emissions by sector

Legend: ■ Electricity and heat ☐ Other energy industries ■ Manuf. ind. and construction ▨ Transport ☐ Residential ■ Other

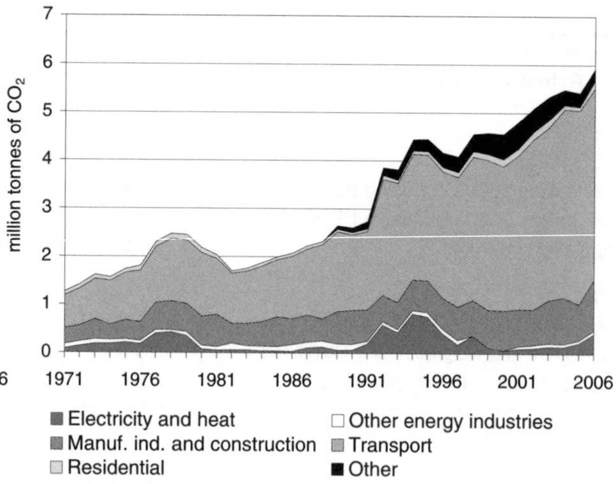

Figure 3. CO₂ emissions by sector

Legend: ■ Electricity and heat ☐ Other energy industries ■ Manuf. ind. and construction ▨ Transport ☐ Residential ■ Other

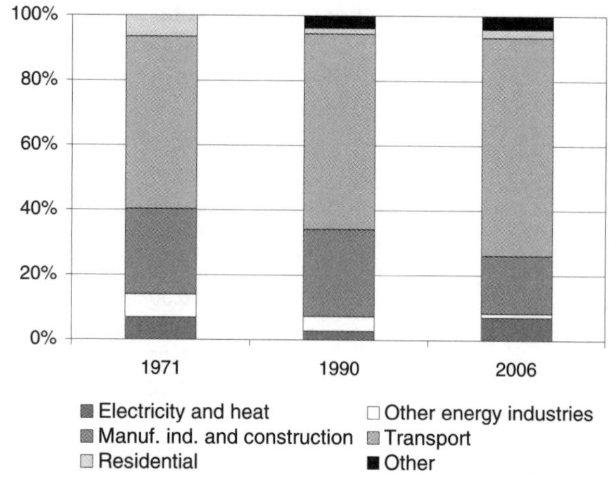

Figure 4. Reference vs Sectoral Approach

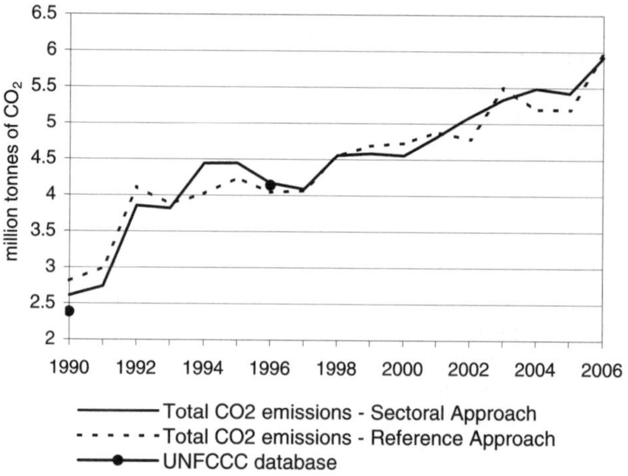

Legend: —— Total CO2 emissions - Sectoral Approach - - - - Total CO2 emissions - Reference Approach —●— UNFCCC database

Figure 5. Electricity generation by fuel

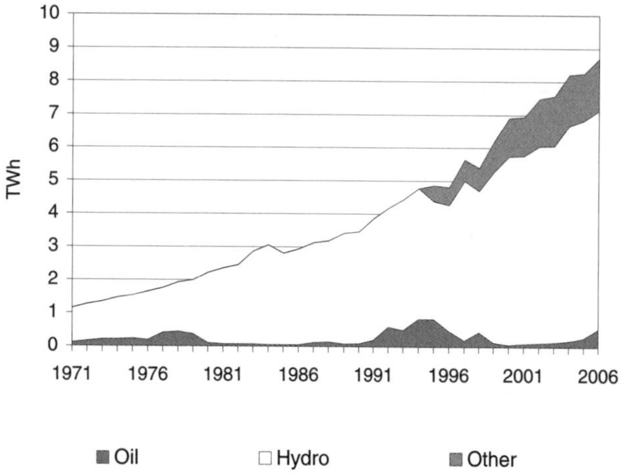

Legend: ■ Oil ☐ Hydro ■ Other

Figure 6. Key indicators

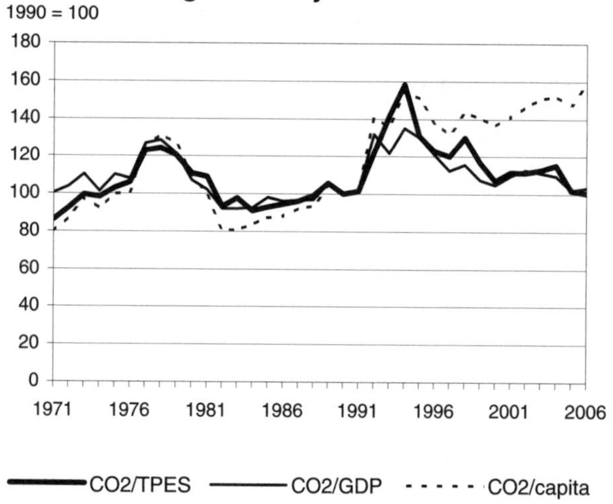

1990 = 100

Legend: —— CO2/TPES —— CO2/GDP - - - - CO2/capita

Costa Rica
Key indicators

	1990	1995	2000	2003	2004	2005	2006	% change 90-06
CO$_2$ Sectoral Approach (Mt of CO$_2$)	2.61	4.45	4.55	5.34	5.49	5.42	5.92	127.1%
CO$_2$ Reference Approach (Mt of CO$_2$)	2.80	4.24	4.72	5.49	5.20	5.20	5.96	112.6%
TPES (PJ)	85	110	138	154	155	173	191	125.9%
TPES (Mtoe)	2.03	2.64	3.31	3.67	3.70	4.13	4.57	125.8%
GDP (billion 2000 US$ using exch. rates)	9.58	12.54	15.95	17.65	18.40	19.49	21.03	119.6%
GDP (billion 2000 US$ using PPPs)	19.28	25.23	32.10	35.52	37.05	39.24	42.33	119.5%
Population (millions)	3.08	3.48	3.93	4.18	4.25	4.33	4.40	43.0%
CO$_2$ / TPES (t CO$_2$ per TJ)	30.8	40.2	32.9	34.7	35.4	31.4	30.9	0.6%
CO$_2$ / GDP (kg CO$_2$ per 2000 US$)	0.27	0.35	0.29	0.30	0.30	0.28	0.28	3.5%
CO$_2$ / GDP (kg CO$_2$ per 2000 US$ PPP)	0.14	0.18	0.14	0.15	0.15	0.14	0.14	3.4%
CO$_2$ / population (t CO$_2$ per capita)	0.85	1.28	1.16	1.28	1.29	1.25	1.35	58.8%

Ratios are based on the Sectoral Approach.

2006 CO$_2$ emissions by sector

million tonnes of CO$_2$	Coal/peat	Oil	Gas	Other *	Total	% change 90-06
Sectoral Approach	**0.17**	**5.76**	-	-	**5.92**	**127.1%**
Main activity producer elec. and heat	-	0.27	-	-	0.27	568.1%
Unallocated autoproducers	-	0.14	-	-	0.14	388.9%
Other energy industries	-	0.08	-	-	0.08	-34.3%
Manufacturing industries and construction	0.17	0.89	-	-	1.05	49.8%
Transport	-	3.98	-	-	3.98	153.2%
of which: road	-	3.97	-	-	3.97	569.6%
Other sectors	-	0.40	-	-	0.40	172.8%
of which: residential	-	0.15	-	-	0.15	244.5%
Reference Approach	**0.19**	**5.77**	-	-	**5.96**	**112.6%**
Diff. due to losses and/or transformation	0.02	- 0.03	-	-	- 0.01	
Statistical differences	-	0.05	-	-	0.05	
Memo: international marine bunkers	-	..	-	-	..	..
Memo: international aviation	-	0.58	-	-	0.58	340.3%

* Other includes industrial waste and non-renewable municipal waste.

Key sources for CO$_2$ emissions from fuel combustion in 2006

IPCC source category	CO$_2$ emissions (Mt of CO$_2$)	% change 90-06	Level assessment (%) **	Cumulative total (%)
Road - oil	3.97	569.6%	32.4	32.4
Manufacturing industries - oil	0.89	27.4%	7.2	39.6
Main activity prod. elec. and heat - oil	0.27	568.1%	2.2	41.8
Non-specified other sectors - oil	0.25	141.7%	2.0	43.8
Manufacturing industries - coal/peat	0.17	+	1.4	45.2
Residential - oil	0.15	244.5%	1.3	46.4
Unallocated autoproducers - oil	0.14	388.9%	1.1	47.6
Other energy industries - oil	0.08	-34.3%	0.6	48.2
Other transport - oil	0.01	-99.4%	0.1	48.2
-	-	-	-	-
-	-	-	-	-
Memo: total CO$_2$ from fuel combustion	5.92	127.1%	48.2	48.2

** Percent calculated using the total GHG estimate for CO$_2$, CH$_4$, N$_2$O, HFCs, PFCs and SF$_6$ excluding CO$_2$ emissions/removals from land use change and forestry.

Côte d'Ivoire

Figure 1. CO$_2$ emissions by fuel

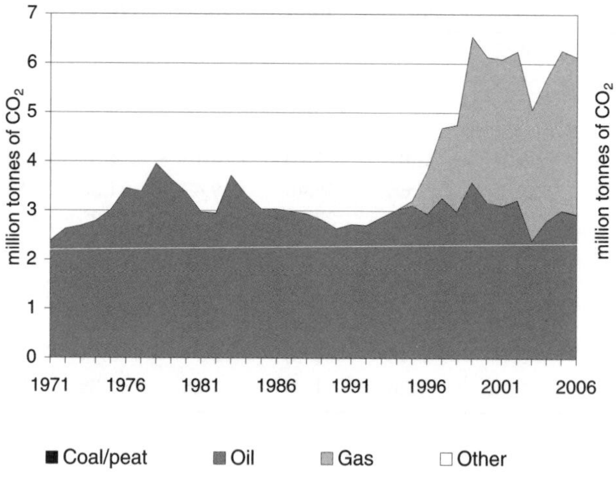

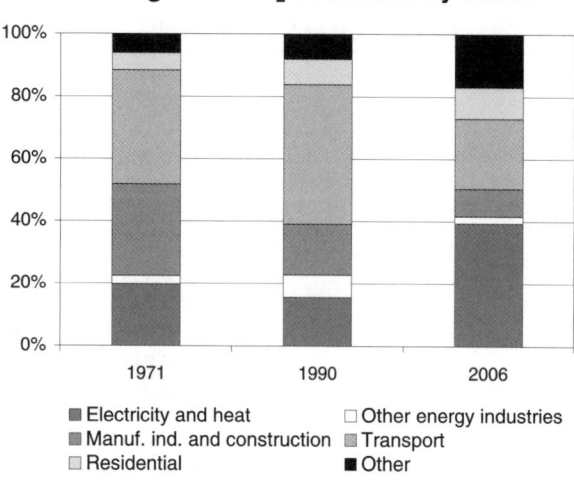

■ Coal/peat   ■ Oil   ▨ Gas   □ Other

Figure 2. CO$_2$ emissions by sector

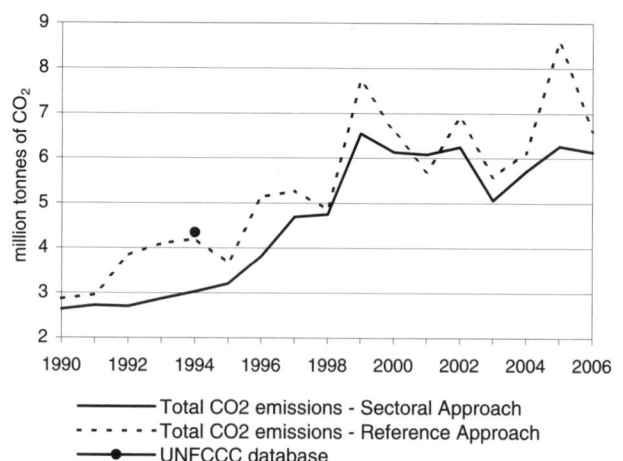

■ Electricity and heat   □ Other energy industries
▨ Manuf. ind. and construction ▨ Transport
▢ Residential   ■ Other

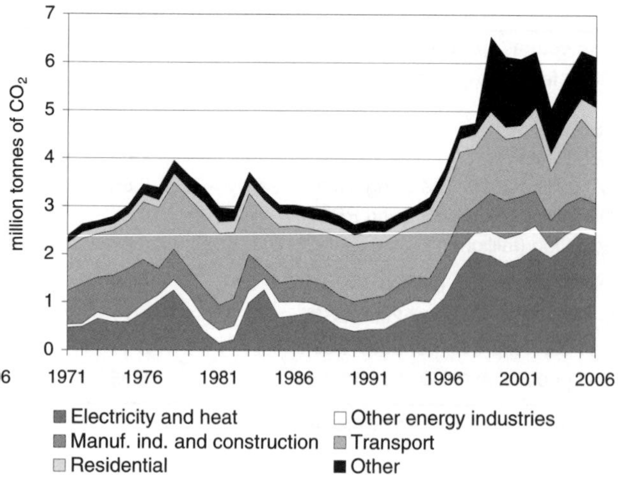

Figure 3. CO$_2$ emissions by sector

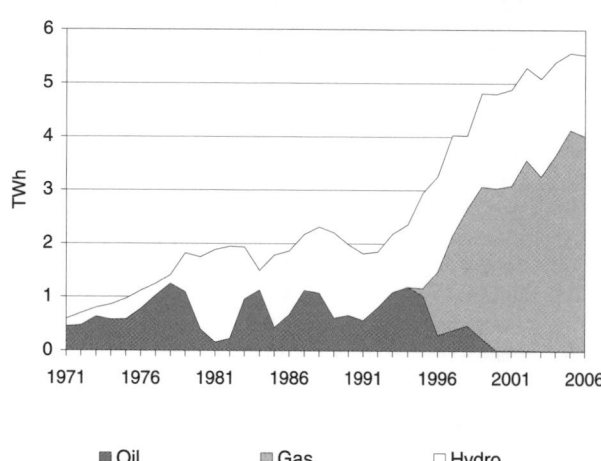

■ Electricity and heat   □ Other energy industries
■ Manuf. ind. and construction ▨ Transport
▢ Residential   ■ Other

Figure 4. Reference vs Sectoral Approach

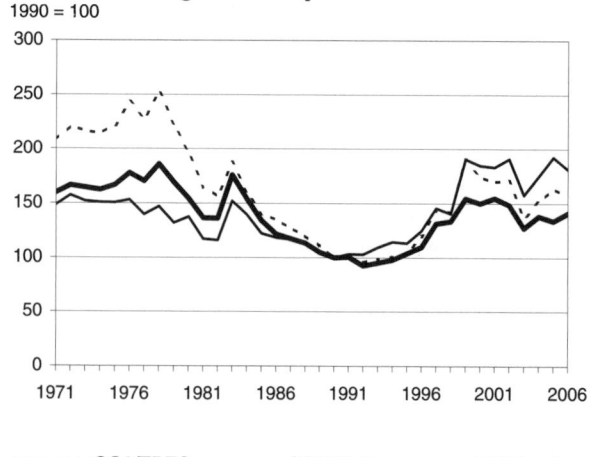

——— Total CO2 emissions - Sectoral Approach
- - - - Total CO2 emissions - Reference Approach
——●— UNFCCC database

Figure 5. Electricity generation by fuel

■ Oil   ▨ Gas   □ Hydro

Figure 6. Key indicators

1990 = 100

■■■CO2/TPES   ———CO2/GDP   - - - - CO2/capita

Côte d'Ivoire

Key indicators

	1990	1995	2000	2003	2004	2005	2006	% change 90-06
CO$_2$ Sectoral Approach (Mt of CO$_2$)	2.63	3.21	6.13	5.06	5.71	6.26	6.13	132.9%
CO$_2$ Reference Approach (Mt of CO$_2$)	2.86	3.67	6.58	5.59	6.13	8.59	6.61	130.9%
TPES (PJ)	185	217	287	279	290	329	305	65.1%
TPES (Mtoe)	4.41	5.17	6.86	6.67	6.93	7.85	7.29	65.1%
GDP (billion 2000 US$ using exch. rates)	8.27	8.90	10.43	10.10	10.26	10.23	10.65	28.7%
GDP (billion 2000 US$ using PPPs)	21.11	22.71	26.60	25.76	26.18	26.10	27.16	28.7%
Population (millions)	12.78	14.99	17.05	17.98	18.28	18.59	18.91	48.0%
CO$_2$ / TPES (t CO$_2$ per TJ)	14.3	14.8	21.3	18.1	19.7	19.1	20.1	41.1%
CO$_2$ / GDP (kg CO$_2$ per 2000 US$)	0.32	0.36	0.59	0.50	0.56	0.61	0.58	81.1%
CO$_2$ / GDP (kg CO$_2$ per 2000 US$ PPP)	0.12	0.14	0.23	0.20	0.22	0.24	0.23	81.0%
CO$_2$ / population (t CO$_2$ per capita)	0.21	0.21	0.36	0.28	0.31	0.34	0.32	57.4%

Ratios are based on the Sectoral Approach.

2006 CO$_2$ emissions by sector

million tonnes of CO$_2$	Coal/peat	Oil	Gas	Other *	Total	% change 90-06
Sectoral Approach	-	**2.94**	**3.20**	-	**6.13**	**132.9%**
Main activity producer elec. and heat	-	0.00	2.41	-	2.41	501.5%
Unallocated autoproducers	..	..	..	..	..	..
Other energy industries	-	0.14	0.00	-	0.14	-26.1%
Manufacturing industries and construction	-	0.54	-	-	0.54	25.9%
Transport	-	1.38	-	-	1.38	17.0%
of which: road	-	1.18	-	-	1.18	15.2%
Other sectors	-	0.87	0.79	-	1.66	288.7%
of which: residential	-	0.62	-	-	0.62	187.7%
Reference Approach	-	**3.41**	**3.20**	-	**6.61**	**130.9%**
Diff. due to losses and/or transformation	-	0.45	-	-	0.45	
Statistical differences	-	0.02	0.00	-	0.02	
Memo: international marine bunkers	-	0.20	-	-	0.20	67.3%
Memo: international aviation	-	0.28	-	-	0.28	4.7%

* Other includes industrial waste and non-renewable municipal waste.

Key sources for CO$_2$ emissions from fuel combustion in 2006

IPCC source category	CO$_2$ emissions (Mt of CO$_2$)	% change 90-06	Level assessment (%) **	Cumulative total (%)
Main activity prod. elec. and heat - gas	2.41	x	7.0	7.0
Road - oil	1.18	15.2%	3.4	10.4
Non-specified other sectors - gas	0.79	x	2.3	12.7
Residential - oil	0.62	187.7%	1.8	14.5
Manufacturing industries - oil	0.54	25.9%	1.6	16.1
Non-specified other sectors - oil	0.26	20.0%	0.7	16.8
Other transport - oil	0.20	28.7%	0.6	17.4
Other energy industries - oil	0.14	-26.2%	0.4	17.8
Main activity prod. elec. and heat - oil	0.00	-99.2%	0.0	17.8
Other energy industries - gas	0.00	x	0.0	17.8
-	-	-	-	-
Memo: total CO$_2$ from fuel combustion	6.13	132.9%	17.8	17.8

** Percent calculated using the total GHG estimate for CO$_2$, CH$_4$, N$_2$O, HFCs, PFCs and SF$_6$ excluding CO$_2$ emissions/removals from land use change and forestry.

Croatia / Croatie

Figure 1. CO$_2$ emissions by fuel

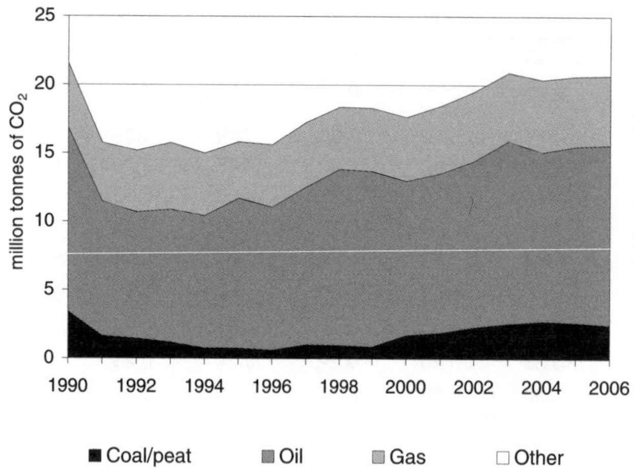

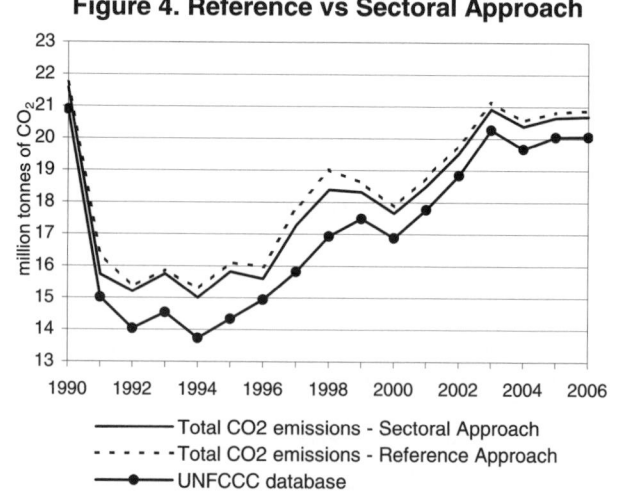

Figure 2. CO$_2$ emissions by sector

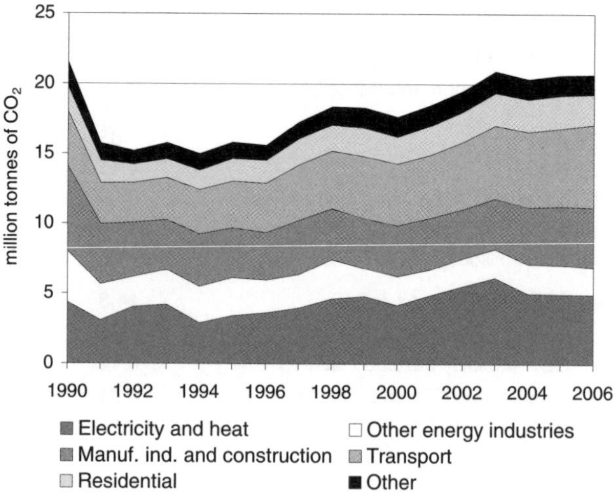

Figure 3. CO$_2$ emissions by sector

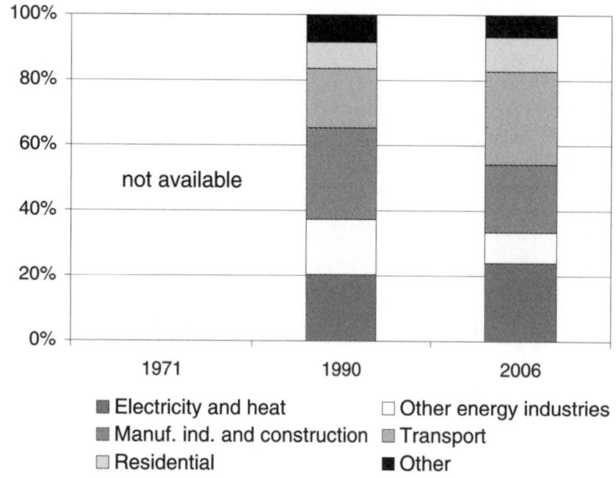

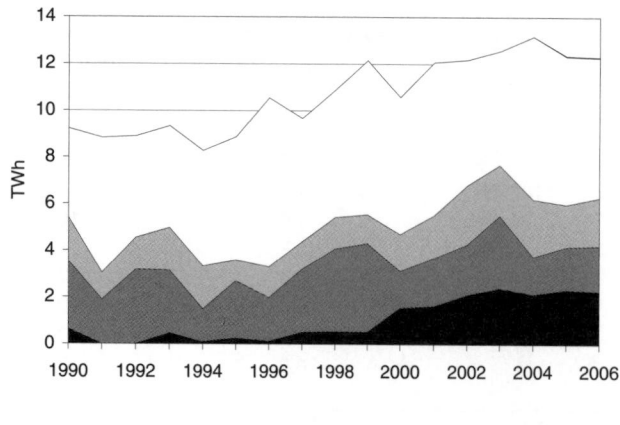

Figure 4. Reference vs Sectoral Approach

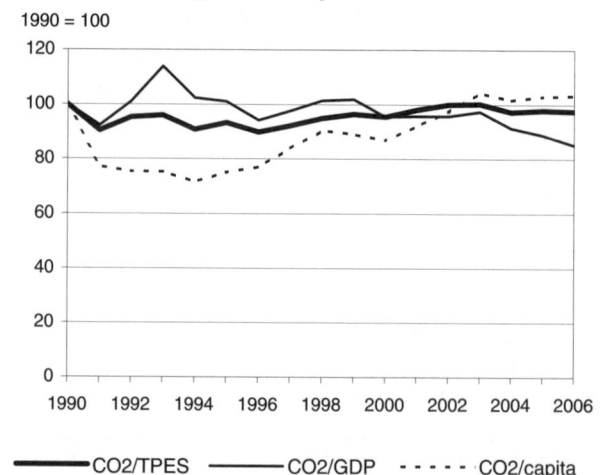

Total CO2 emissions - Sectoral Approach
Total CO2 emissions - Reference Approach
UNFCCC database

Figure 5. Electricity generation by fuel

Figure 6. Key indicators

Croatia / Croatie

Key indicators

	1990	1995	2000	2003	2004	2005	2006	% change 90-06
CO$_2$ Sectoral Approach (Mt of CO$_2$)	21.57	15.82	17.66	20.92	20.38	20.65	20.70	-4.1%
CO$_2$ Reference Approach (Mt of CO$_2$)	21.73	16.10	17.86	21.13	20.56	20.82	20.88	-3.9%
TPES (PJ)	381	300	327	369	370	373	375	-1.6%
TPES (Mtoe)	9.11	7.15	7.80	8.80	8.84	8.91	8.96	-1.6%
GDP (billion 2000 US$ using exch. rates)	21.50	15.59	18.43	21.41	22.22	23.17	24.24	12.7%
GDP (billion 2000 US$ using PPPs)	47.89	34.72	41.04	47.68	49.49	51.61	53.98	12.7%
Population (millions)	4.78	4.67	4.50	4.44	4.44	4.44	4.44	-7.1%
CO$_2$ / TPES (t CO$_2$ per TJ)	56.6	52.8	54.0	56.7	55.0	55.4	55.2	-2.5%
CO$_2$ / GDP (kg CO$_2$ per 2000 US$)	1.00	1.01	0.96	0.98	0.92	0.89	0.85	-14.9%
CO$_2$ / GDP (kg CO$_2$ per 2000 US$ PPP)	0.45	0.46	0.43	0.44	0.41	0.40	0.38	-14.9%
CO$_2$ / population (t CO$_2$ per capita)	4.51	3.39	3.92	4.71	4.59	4.65	4.66	3.3%

Ratios are based on the Sectoral Approach.

2006 CO$_2$ emissions by sector

million tonnes of CO$_2$	Coal/peat	Oil	Gas	Other *	Total	% change 90-06
Sectoral Approach	**2.47**	**13.15**	**5.08**	-	**20.70**	**-4.1%**
Main activity producer elec. and heat	1.90	1.55	1.22	-	4.67	18.2%
Unallocated autoproducers	0.02	0.12	0.15	-	0.29	-29.4%
Other energy industries	-	1.61	0.33	-	1.93	-47.3%
Manufacturing industries and construction	0.49	1.99	1.82	-	4.30	-29.1%
Transport	-	5.90	-	-	5.90	50.8%
of which: road	-	*5.48*	-	-	*5.48*	*74.2%*
Other sectors	0.05	1.98	1.56	-	3.59	0.9%
of which: residential	*0.04*	*0.90*	*1.24*	-	*2.19*	*25.8%*
Reference Approach	**2.44**	**13.24**	**5.20**	-	**20.88**	**-3.9%**
Diff. due to losses and/or transformation	- 0.03	0.09	0.12	-	0.18	
Statistical differences	0.00	0.00	0.00	-	0.00	
Memo: international marine bunkers	-	*0.06*	-	-	*0.06*	*-57.5%*
Memo: international aviation	-	*0.12*	-	-	*0.12*	*-18.8%*

* Other includes industrial waste and non-renewable municipal waste.

Key sources for CO$_2$ emissions from fuel combustion in 2006

IPCC source category	CO$_2$ emissions (Mt of CO$_2$)	% change 90-06	Level assessment (%) **	Cumulative total (%)
Road - oil	5.48	74.2%	17.4	17.4
Manufacturing industries - oil	1.99	-9.3%	6.3	23.7
Main activity prod. elec. and heat - coal/peat	1.90	196.2%	6.0	29.8
Manufacturing industries - gas	1.82	-10.7%	5.8	35.6
Other energy industries - oil	1.61	-35.2%	5.1	40.7
Main activity prod. elec. and heat - oil	1.55	-30.7%	4.9	45.6
Residential - gas	1.24	225.9%	4.0	49.6
Main activity prod. elec. and heat - gas	1.22	13.9%	3.9	53.4
Non-specified other sectors - oil	1.08	-29.7%	3.4	56.9
Residential - oil	0.90	3.4%	2.9	59.7
Manufacturing industries - coal/peat	0.49	-73.2%	1.6	61.3
Memo: total CO$_2$ from fuel combustion	*20.70*	*-4.1%*	*65.8*	*65.8*

** Percent calculated using the total GHG estimate for CO$_2$, CH$_4$, N$_2$O, HFCs, PFCs and SF$_6$ excluding CO$_2$ emissions/removals from land use change and forestry.

Cuba

Figure 1. CO₂ emissions by fuel

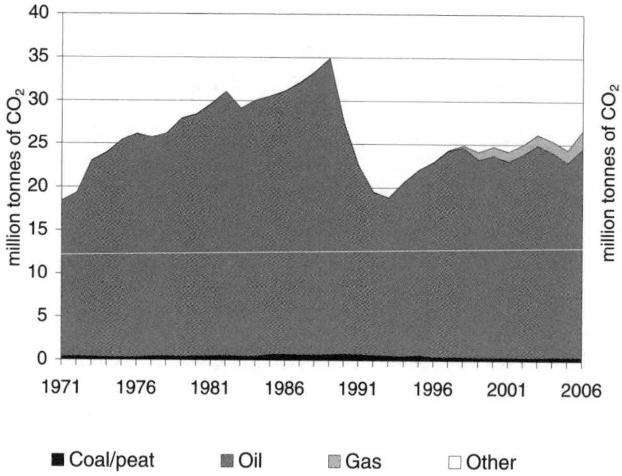

■ Coal/peat   ■ Oil   ■ Gas   □ Other

Figure 2. CO₂ emissions by sector

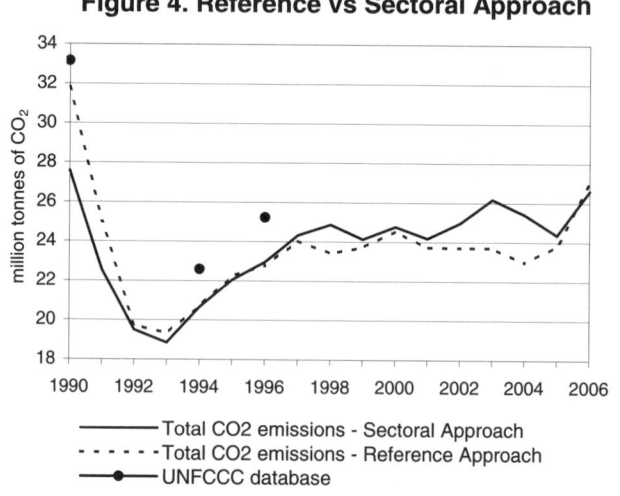

■ Electricity and heat   □ Other energy industries
■ Manuf. ind. and construction   ■ Transport
□ Residential   ■ Other

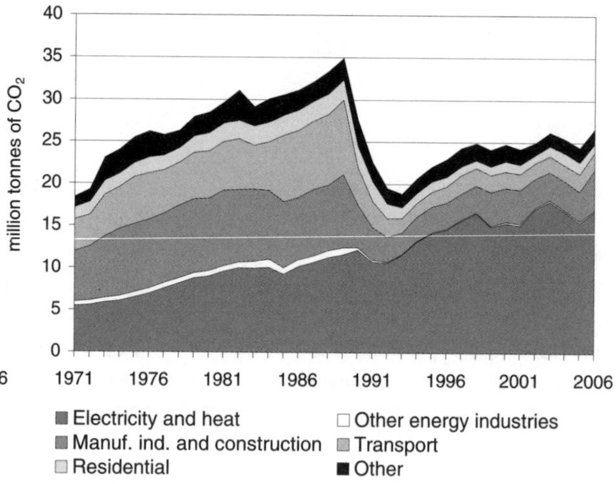

Figure 3. CO₂ emissions by sector

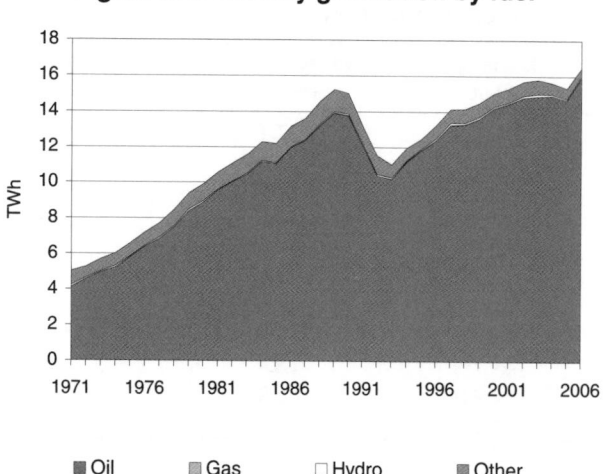

■ Electricity and heat   □ Other energy industries
■ Manuf. ind. and construction   ■ Transport
□ Residential   ■ Other

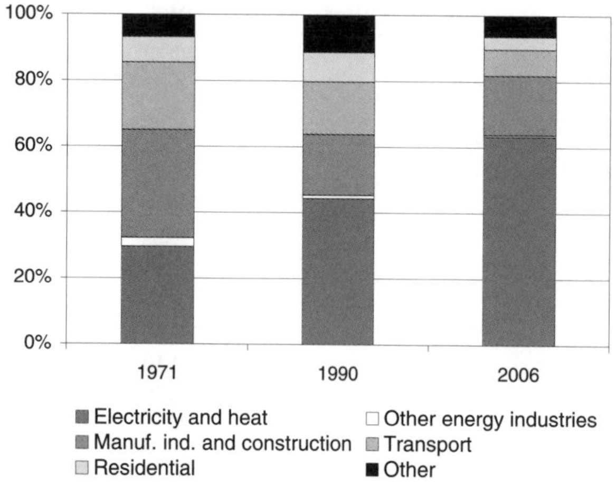

Figure 4. Reference vs Sectoral Approach

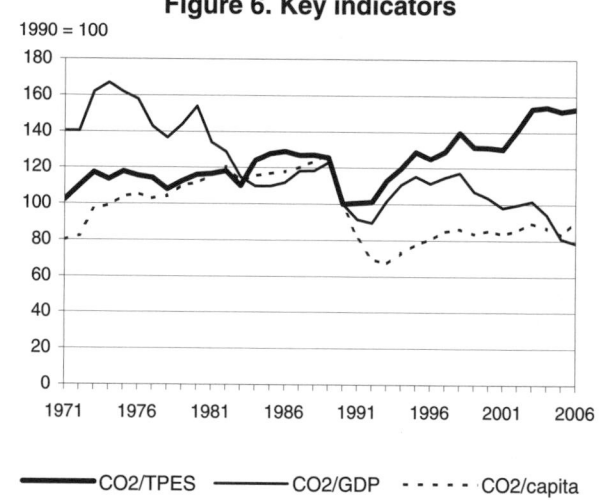

—— Total CO2 emissions - Sectoral Approach
---- Total CO2 emissions - Reference Approach
—●— UNFCCC database

Figure 5. Electricity generation by fuel

■ Oil   ■ Gas   □ Hydro   ■ Other

Figure 6. Key indicators

1990 = 100

—— CO2/TPES   —— CO2/GDP   ---- CO2/capita

Cuba

Key indicators

	1990	1995	2000	2003	2004	2005	2006	% change 90-06
CO$_2$ Sectoral Approach (Mt of CO$_2$)	27.57	22.05	24.77	26.17	25.40	24.37	26.61	-3.5%
CO$_2$ Reference Approach (Mt of CO$_2$)	31.80	22.25	24.54	23.71	22.97	23.82	26.97	-15.2%
TPES (PJ)	705	437	482	438	422	411	445	-36.8%
TPES (Mtoe)	16.83	10.44	11.50	10.45	10.09	9.82	10.64	-36.8%
GDP (billion 2000 US$ using exch. rates)	32.49	22.54	28.21	30.36	31.72	35.46	39.90	22.8%
GDP (billion 2000 US$ using PPPs)	74.98	52.01	65.09	70.06	73.20	81.84	92.07	22.8%
Population (millions)	10.61	10.93	11.14	11.23	11.25	11.26	11.27	6.2%
CO$_2$ / TPES (t CO$_2$ per TJ)	39.1	50.5	51.4	59.8	60.1	59.3	59.7	52.7%
CO$_2$ / GDP (kg CO$_2$ per 2000 US$)	0.85	0.98	0.88	0.86	0.80	0.69	0.67	-21.4%
CO$_2$ / GDP (kg CO$_2$ per 2000 US$ PPP)	0.37	0.42	0.38	0.37	0.35	0.30	0.29	-21.4%
CO$_2$ / population (t CO$_2$ per capita)	2.60	2.02	2.22	2.33	2.26	2.16	2.36	-9.2%

Ratios are based on the Sectoral Approach.

2006 CO$_2$ emissions by sector

million tonnes of CO$_2$	Coal/peat	Oil	Gas	Other *	Total	% change 90-06
Sectoral Approach	**0.43**	**24.10**	**2.07**	**-**	**26.61**	**-3.5%**
Main activity producer elec. and heat	-	16.24	-	-	16.24	44.5%
Unallocated autoproducers	-	0.55	-	-	0.55	-42.3%
Other energy industries	-	0.15	-	-	0.15	-47.3%
Manufacturing industries and construction	0.16	2.58	2.07	-	4.80	-5.4%
Transport	-	2.10	-	-	2.10	-52.5%
of which: road	-	2.09	-	-	2.09	-52.4%
Other sectors	0.28	2.49	0.00	-	2.76	-50.7%
of which: residential	0.28	0.77	-	-	1.05	-57.6%
Reference Approach	**0.09**	**24.80**	**2.07**	**-**	**26.97**	**-15.2%**
Diff. due to losses and/or transformation	- 0.33	1.52	-	-	1.19	
Statistical differences	- 0.00	- 0.82	0.00	-	- 0.83	
Memo: international marine bunkers	-	0.20	-	-	0.20	-73.6%
Memo: international aviation	-	0.57	-	-	0.57	-43.6%

* Other includes industrial waste and non-renewable municipal waste.

Key sources for CO$_2$ emissions from fuel combustion in 2006

IPCC source category	CO$_2$ emissions (Mt of CO$_2$)	% change 90-06	Level assessment (%) **	Cumulative total (%)
Main activity prod. elec. and heat - oil	16.24	44.5%	35.6	35.6
Manufacturing industries - oil	2.58	-42.8%	5.6	41.2
Road - oil	2.09	-52.4%	4.6	45.8
Manufacturing industries - gas	2.07	+	4.5	50.4
Non-specified other sectors - oil	1.71	-45.2%	3.8	54.1
Residential - oil	0.77	-65.4%	1.7	55.8
Unallocated autoproducers - oil	0.55	-41.7%	1.2	57.0
Residential - coal/peat	0.28	15.0%	0.6	57.6
Manufacturing industries - coal/peat	0.16	-69.1%	0.3	58.0
Other energy industries - oil	0.15	-47.3%	0.3	58.3
Other transport - oil	0.01	-68.4%	0.0	58.3
Memo: total CO$_2$ from fuel combustion	26.61	-3.5%	58.3	58.3

** Percent calculated using the total GHG estimate for CO$_2$, CH$_4$, N$_2$O, HFCs, PFCs and SF$_6$ excluding CO$_2$ emissions/removals from land use change and forestry.

Cyprus / Chypre

Figure 1. CO$_2$ emissions by fuel

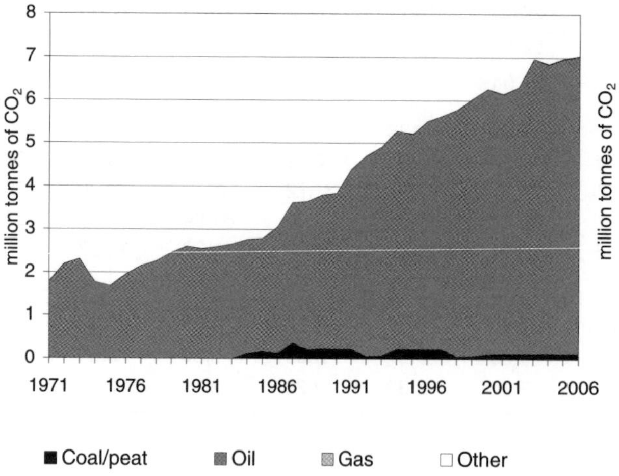

■ Coal/peat   ■ Oil   ▨ Gas   ☐ Other

Figure 2. CO$_2$ emissions by sector

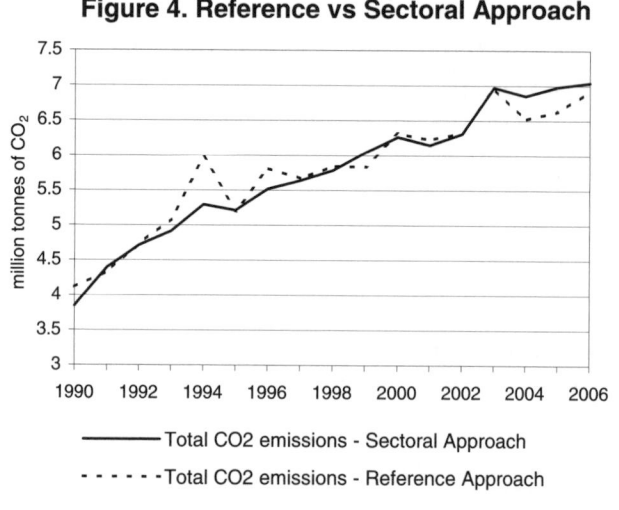

■ Electricity and heat   ☐ Other energy industries
■ Manuf. ind. and construction   ▨ Transport
▨ Residential   ■ Other

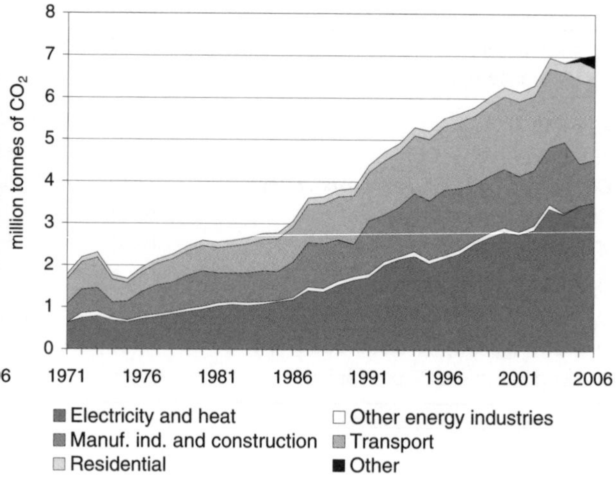

Figure 3. CO$_2$ emissions by sector

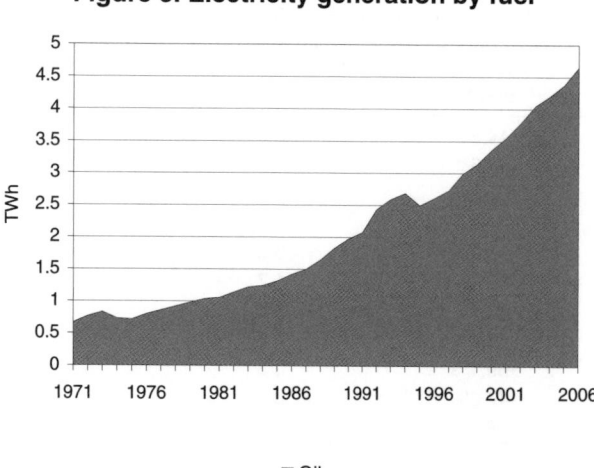

■ Electricity and heat   ☐ Other energy industries
■ Manuf. ind. and construction   ▨ Transport
▨ Residential   ■ Other

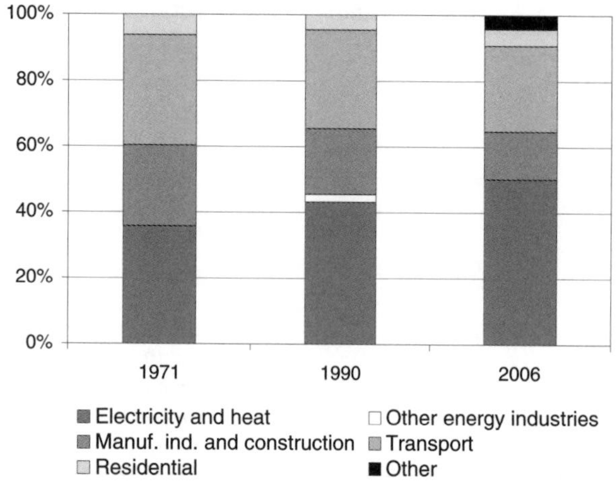

Figure 4. Reference vs Sectoral Approach

——— Total CO2 emissions - Sectoral Approach
- - - - - Total CO2 emissions - Reference Approach

Figure 5. Electricity generation by fuel

■ Oil

Figure 6. Key indicators

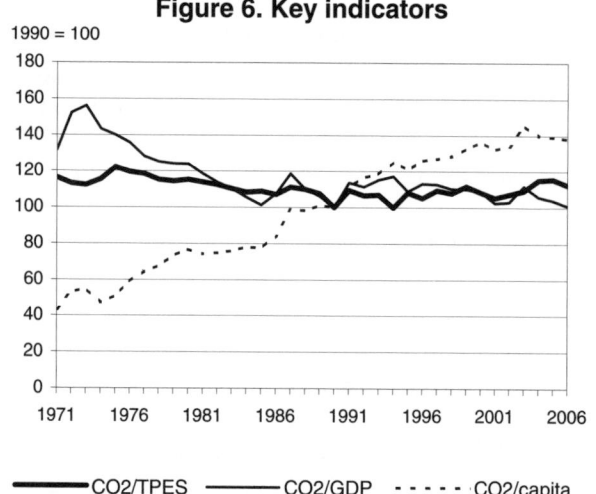

1990 = 100

■■■CO2/TPES   ———CO2/GDP   - - - - -CO2/capita

Cyprus / Chypre
Key indicators

	1990	1995	2000	2003	2004	2005	2006	% change 90-06
CO$_2$ Sectoral Approach (Mt of CO$_2$)	3.84	5.21	6.26	6.97	6.85	6.98	7.04	83.3%
CO$_2$ Reference Approach (Mt of CO$_2$)	4.11	5.20	6.31	6.96	6.52	6.63	6.93	68.5%
TPES (PJ)	67	84	101	112	104	105	110	63.1%
TPES (Mtoe)	1.60	2.01	2.41	2.66	2.49	2.52	2.62	63.1%
GDP (billion 2000 US$ using exch. rates)	6.10	7.60	9.15	9.91	10.27	10.67	11.08	81.7%
GDP (billion 2000 US$ using PPPs)	8.87	11.06	13.31	14.41	14.95	15.53	16.12	81.7%
Population (millions)	0.58	0.65	0.69	0.72	0.74	0.76	0.77	32.9%
CO$_2$ / TPES (t CO$_2$ per TJ)	57.2	61.9	62.0	62.5	65.9	66.2	64.3	12.4%
CO$_2$ / GDP (kg CO$_2$ per 2000 US$)	0.63	0.69	0.68	0.70	0.67	0.65	0.64	0.9%
CO$_2$ / GDP (kg CO$_2$ per 2000 US$ PPP)	0.43	0.47	0.47	0.48	0.46	0.45	0.44	0.9%
CO$_2$ / population (t CO$_2$ per capita)	6.62	8.01	9.03	9.64	9.26	9.21	9.13	37.9%

Ratios are based on the Sectoral Approach.

2006 CO$_2$ emissions by sector

million tonnes of CO$_2$	Coal/peat	Oil	Gas	Other *	Total	% change 90-06
Sectoral Approach	**0.13**	**6.90**	**-**	**0.01**	**7.04**	**83.3%**
Main activity producer elec. and heat	-	3.51	-	-	3.51	111.9%
Unallocated autoproducers	-	0.02	-	-	0.02	x
Other energy industries	-	-	-	-	-	-100.0%
Manufacturing industries and construction	0.13	0.88	-	0.01	1.02	32.7%
Transport	-	1.83	-	-	1.83	59.8%
of which: road	-	*1.83*	-	-	*1.83*	*59.5%*
Other sectors	0.00	0.66	-	-	0.66	272.6%
of which: residential	-	*0.36*	-	-	*0.36*	*100.1%*
Reference Approach	**0.15**	**6.77**	**-**	**0.01**	**6.93**	**68.5%**
Diff. due to losses and/or transformation	-	-	-	-	-	
Statistical differences	0.02	- 0.13	-	-	- 0.11	
Memo: international marine bunkers	-	*0.91*	-	-	*0.91*	*410.6%*
Memo: international aviation	-	*0.91*	-	-	*0.91*	*27.1%*

* Other includes industrial waste and non-renewable municipal waste.

Key sources for CO$_2$ emissions from fuel combustion in 2006

IPCC source category	CO$_2$ emissions (Mt of CO$_2$)	% change 90-06	Level assessment (%) **	Cumulative total (%)
Main activity prod. elec. and heat - oil	3.51	111.9%	39.3	39.3
Road - oil	1.83	59.5%	20.5	59.8
Manufacturing industries - oil	0.88	64.6%	9.9	69.7
Residential - oil	0.36	100.1%	4.0	73.7
Non-specified other sectors - oil	0.30	x	3.4	77.1
Manufacturing industries - coal/peat	0.13	-44.3%	1.4	78.5
Unallocated autoproducers - oil	0.02	x	0.2	78.8
Manufacturing industries -other	0.01	x	0.1	78.9
Other transport - oil	0.00	x	0.0	78.9
Non-specified other sectors - coal/peat	0.00	x	0.0	78.9
-	-	-	-	-
Memo: total CO$_2$ from fuel combustion	*7.04*	*83.3%*	*78.9*	*78.9*

** Percent calculated using the total GHG estimate for CO$_2$, CH$_4$, N$_2$O, HFCs, PFCs and SF$_6$ excluding CO$_2$ emissions/removals from land use change and forestry.

Czech Republic / République tchèque

Figure 1. CO₂ emissions by fuel

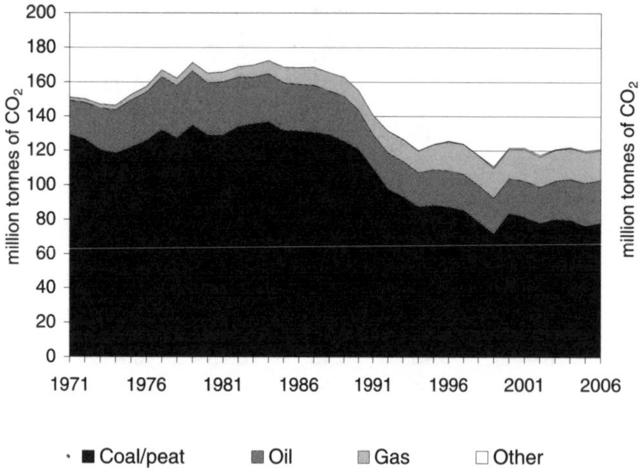

y-axis: million tonnes of CO₂ (0–200)
x-axis: 1971, 1976, 1981, 1986, 1991, 1996, 2001, 2006

Legend: ■ Coal/peat ■ Oil ■ Gas □ Other

Figure 2. CO₂ emissions by sector

y-axis: million tonnes of CO₂ (0–200)
x-axis: 1971, 1976, 1981, 1986, 1991, 1996, 2001, 2006

Legend:
■ Electricity and heat □ Other energy industries
■ Manuf. ind. and construction ■ Transport
□ Residential ■ Other

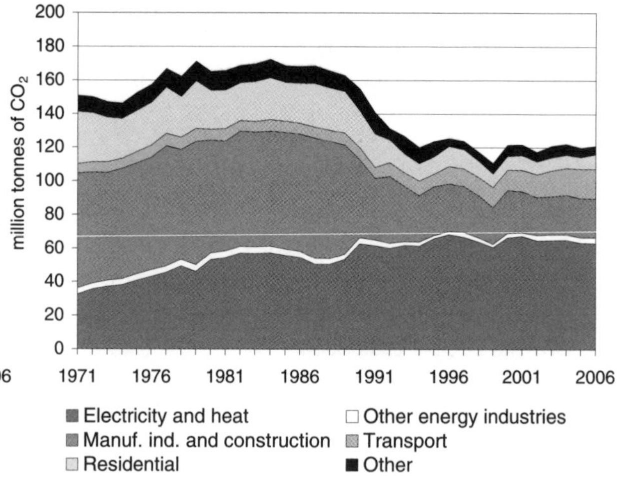

Figure 3. CO₂ emissions by sector

y-axis: 0%–100%
x-axis: 1971, 1990, 2006

Legend:
■ Electricity and heat □ Other energy industries
■ Manuf. ind. and construction ■ Transport
□ Residential ■ Other

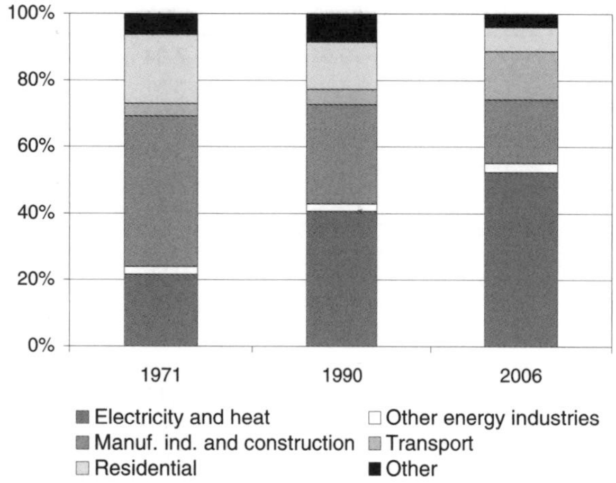

Figure 4. Reference vs Sectoral Approach

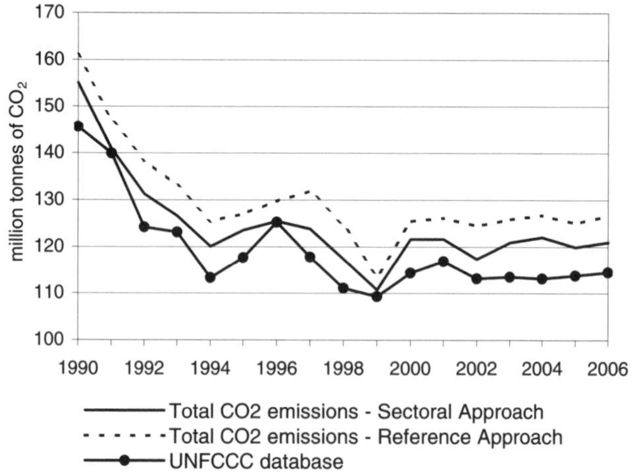

y-axis: million tonnes of CO₂ (100–170)
x-axis: 1990, 1992, 1994, 1996, 1998, 2000, 2002, 2004, 2006

Legend:
—— Total CO2 emissions - Sectoral Approach
- - - - Total CO2 emissions - Reference Approach
—●— UNFCCC database

Figure 5. Electricity generation by fuel

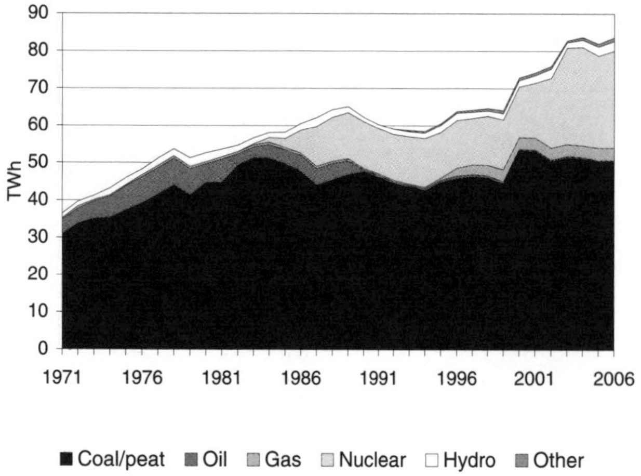

y-axis: TWh (0–90)
x-axis: 1971, 1976, 1981, 1986, 1991, 1996, 2001, 2006

Legend: ■ Coal/peat ■ Oil ■ Gas □ Nuclear □ Hydro ■ Other

Figure 6. Key indicators

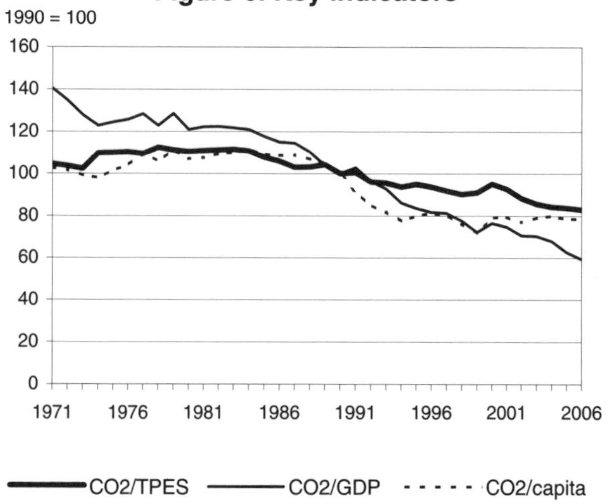

1990 = 100
y-axis: 0–160
x-axis: 1971, 1976, 1981, 1986, 1991, 1996, 2001, 2006

Legend: —— CO2/TPES —— CO2/GDP - - - - CO2/capita

Czech Republic / République tchèque

Key indicators

	1990	1995	2000	2003	2004	2005	2006	% change 90-06
CO$_2$ Sectoral Approach (Mt of CO$_2$)	155.09	123.54	121.61	120.88	122.01	119.89	120.97	-22.0%
CO$_2$ Reference Approach (Mt of CO$_2$)	161.01	127.02	125.42	125.84	126.73	125.05	126.63	-21.4%
TPES (PJ)	2 051	1 720	1 692	1 867	1 917	1 893	1 928	-6.0%
TPES (Mtoe)	48.98	41.09	40.41	44.59	45.78	45.22	46.05	-6.0%
GDP (billion 2000 US$ using exch. rates)	55.30	52.70	56.70	61.30	64.10	68.20	72.50	31.1%
GDP (billion 2000 US$ using PPPs)	149.98	142.91	153.84	166.39	173.85	184.93	196.69	31.1%
Population (millions)	10.36	10.33	10.27	10.20	10.21	10.23	10.27	-0.9%
CO$_2$ / TPES (t CO$_2$ per TJ)	75.6	71.8	71.9	64.7	63.7	63.3	62.7	-17.0%
CO$_2$ / GDP (kg CO$_2$ per 2000 US$)	2.80	2.34	2.14	1.97	1.90	1.76	1.67	-40.5%
CO$_2$ / GDP (kg CO$_2$ per 2000 US$ PPP)	1.03	0.86	0.79	0.73	0.70	0.65	0.62	-40.5%
CO$_2$ / population (t CO$_2$ per capita)	14.97	11.96	11.84	11.85	11.95	11.71	11.78	-21.3%

Ratios are based on the Sectoral Approach.

2006 CO$_2$ emissions by sector

million tonnes of CO$_2$	Coal/peat	Oil	Gas	Other *	Total	% change 90-06
Sectoral Approach	**78.09**	**24.73**	**17.44**	**0.70**	**120.97**	**-22.0%**
Main activity producer elec. and heat	52.92	0.35	2.22	0.04	55.53	5.0%
Unallocated autoproducers	6.83	0.20	0.58	0.13	7.73	-22.8%
Other energy industries	2.27	0.84	0.28	-	3.39	-2.8%
Manufacturing industries and construction	12.22	4.67	5.75	0.48	23.12	-50.0%
Transport	0.00	17.44	0.10	-	17.55	144.4%
of which: road	*-*	*16.87*	*0.03*	*-*	*16.90*	*145.6%*
Other sectors	3.85	1.24	8.51	0.06	13.66	-61.2%
of which: residential	*3.38*	*0.09*	*5.32*	*-*	*8.78*	*-60.0%*
Reference Approach	**83.84**	**24.40**	**17.68**	**0.70**	**126.63**	**-21.4%**
Diff. due to losses and/or transformation	3.16	- 0.28	0.24	-	3.12	
Statistical differences	2.59	- 0.05	0.00	- 0.00	2.54	
Memo: international marine bunkers	*-*	*-*	*-*	*-*	*-*	*-*
Memo: international aviation	*-*	*0.99*	*-*	*-*	*0.99*	*52.1%*

* Other includes industrial waste and non-renewable municipal waste.

Key sources for CO$_2$ emissions from fuel combustion in 2006

IPCC source category	CO$_2$ emissions (Mt of CO$_2$)	% change 90-06	Level assessment (%) **	Cumulative total (%)
Main activity prod. elec. and heat - coal/peat	52.92	4.5%	34.2	34.2
Road - oil	16.87	145.2%	10.9	45.1
Manufacturing industries - coal/peat	12.22	-60.3%	7.9	53.0
Unallocated autoproducers - coal/peat	6.83	-24.9%	4.4	57.4
Manufacturing industries - gas	5.75	1.8%	3.7	61.2
Residential - gas	5.32	147.8%	3.4	64.6
Manufacturing industries - oil	4.67	-52.6%	3.0	67.6
Residential - coal/peat	3.38	-82.8%	2.2	69.8
Non-specified other sectors - gas	3.19	50.5%	2.1	71.9
Other energy industries - coal/peat	2.27	-27.1%	1.5	73.3
Main activity prod. elec. and heat - gas	2.22	112.9%	1.4	74.8
Memo: total CO$_2$ from fuel combustion	*120.97*	*-22.0%*	*78.2*	*78.2*

** Percent calculated using the total GHG estimate for CO$_2$, CH$_4$, N$_2$O, HFCs, PFCs and SF$_6$ excluding CO$_2$ emissions/removals from land use change and forestry.

Denmark / Danemark

Figure 1. CO$_2$ emissions by fuel

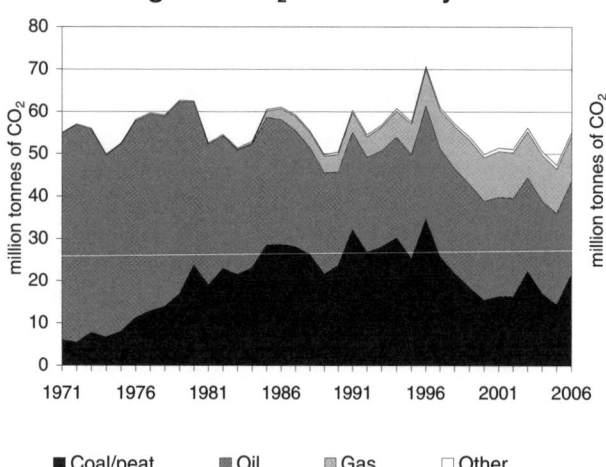

■ Coal/peat   ■ Oil   ■ Gas   □ Other

Figure 2. CO$_2$ emissions by sector

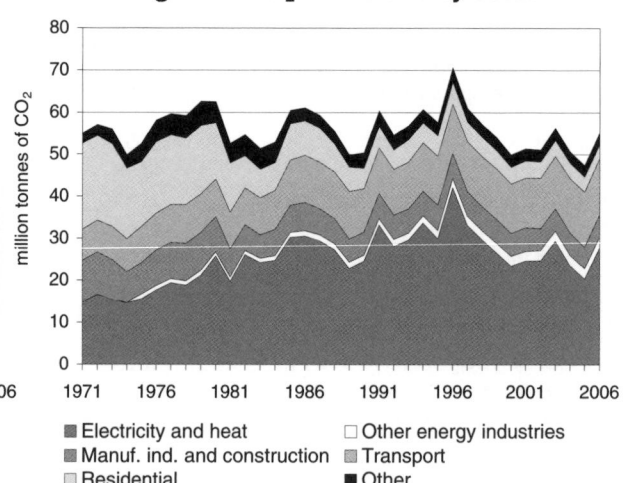

■ Electricity and heat   □ Other energy industries
■ Manuf. ind. and construction   ■ Transport
□ Residential   ■ Other

Figure 3. CO$_2$ emissions by sector

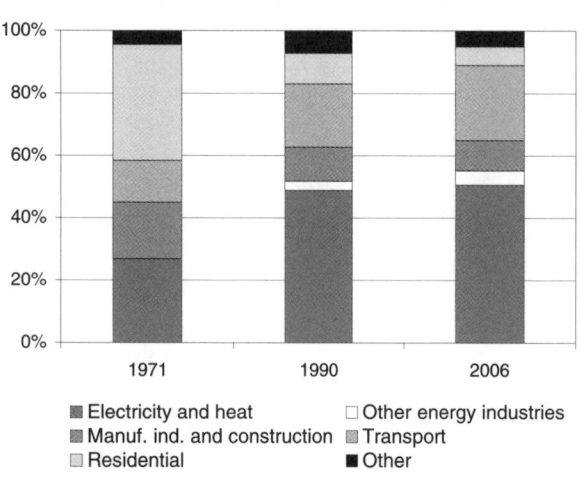

■ Electricity and heat   □ Other energy industries
■ Manuf. ind. and construction   ■ Transport
□ Residential   ■ Other

Figure 4. Reference vs Sectoral Approach

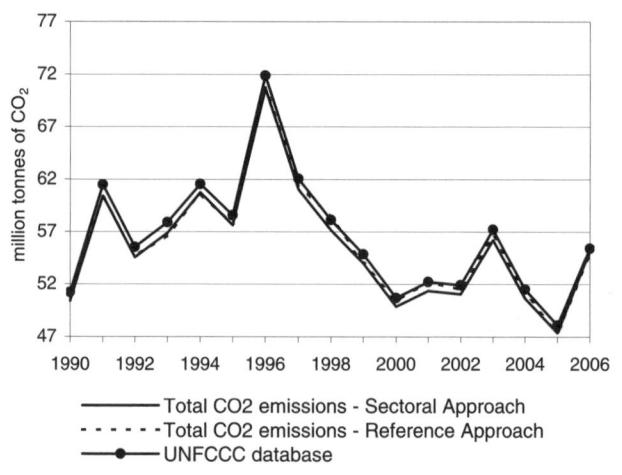

——— Total CO2 emissions - Sectoral Approach
- - - - Total CO2 emissions - Reference Approach
—●— UNFCCC database

Figure 5. Electricity generation by fuel

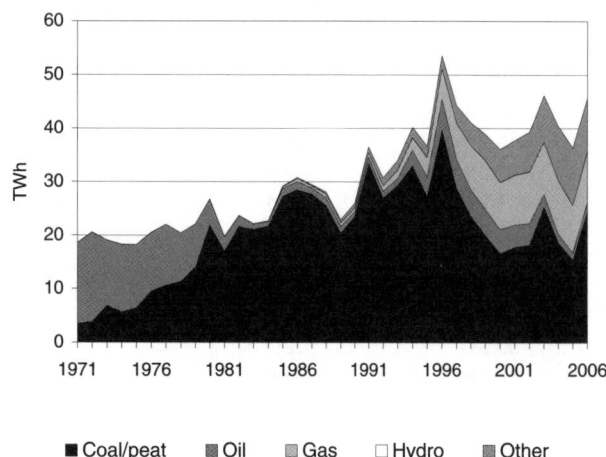

■ Coal/peat   ■ Oil   ■ Gas   □ Hydro   ■ Other

Figure 6. Key indicators

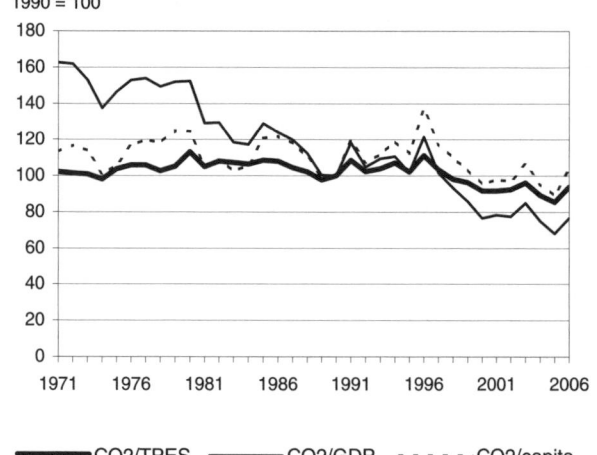

—— CO2/TPES   —— CO2/GDP   - - - - CO2/capita

Denmark / Danemark

Key indicators

	1990	1995	2000	2003	2004	2005	2006	% change 90-06
CO$_2$ Sectoral Approach (Mt of CO$_2$)	50.38	57.62	49.88	56.21	50.65	47.37	55.18	9.5%
CO$_2$ Reference Approach (Mt of CO$_2$)	50.65	57.71	50.41	56.62	51.12	47.39	54.75	8.1%
TPES (PJ)	750	839	811	870	846	825	876	16.8%
TPES (Mtoe)	17.92	20.05	19.36	20.79	20.20	19.69	20.93	16.8%
GDP (billion 2000 US$ using exch. rates)	123.90	139.10	160.10	162.60	166.00	171.10	177.20	43.0%
GDP (billion 2000 US$ using PPPs)	118.93	133.50	153.68	156.08	159.41	164.29	170.07	43.0%
Population (millions)	5.14	5.23	5.34	5.39	5.40	5.42	5.44	5.8%
CO$_2$ / TPES (t CO$_2$ per TJ)	67.2	68.6	61.5	64.6	59.9	57.4	63.0	-6.2%
CO$_2$ / GDP (kg CO$_2$ per 2000 US$)	0.41	0.41	0.31	0.35	0.31	0.28	0.31	-23.4%
CO$_2$ / GDP (kg CO$_2$ per 2000 US$ PPP)	0.42	0.43	0.32	0.36	0.32	0.29	0.32	-23.4%
CO$_2$ / population (t CO$_2$ per capita)	9.80	11.02	9.34	10.43	9.38	8.74	10.15	3.6%

Ratios are based on the Sectoral Approach.

2006 CO$_2$ emissions by sector

million tonnes of CO$_2$	Coal/peat	Oil	Gas	Other *	Total	% change 90-06
Sectoral Approach	**21.63**	**21.96**	**10.63**	**0.97**	**55.18**	**9.5%**
Main activity producer elec. and heat	20.56	1.15	4.57	0.33	26.61	11.5%
Unallocated autoproducers	0.01	0.17	0.53	0.56	1.26	76.7%
Other energy industries	-	0.95	1.59	-	2.54	74.1%
Manufacturing industries and construction	0.87	2.77	1.67	0.04	5.35	-2.9%
Transport	-	13.29	-	-	13.29	29.7%
of which: road	-	12.44	-	-	12.44	36.6%
Other sectors	0.20	3.62	2.27	0.04	6.14	-28.5%
of which: residential	0.02	1.70	1.57	-	3.29	-33.0%
Reference Approach	**21.27**	**21.91**	**10.60**	**0.97**	**54.75**	**8.1%**
Diff. due to losses and/or transformation	- 0.03	0.55	0.03	-	0.55	
Statistical differences	- 0.33	- 0.60	- 0.07	0.00	- 0.99	
Memo: international marine bunkers	-	3.34	-	-	3.34	10.7%
Memo: international aviation	-	2.56	-	-	2.56	50.4%

* Other includes industrial waste and non-renewable municipal waste.

Key sources for CO$_2$ emissions from fuel combustion in 2006

IPCC source category	CO$_2$ emissions (Mt of CO$_2$)	% change 90-06	Level assessment (%) **	Cumulative total (%)
Main activity prod. elec. and heat - coal/peat	20.56	-6.2%	29.3	29.3
Road - oil	12.44	36.6%	17.7	47.0
Main activity prod. elec. and heat - gas	4.57	366.3%	6.5	53.5
Manufacturing industries - oil	2.77	-7.1%	3.9	57.4
Non-specified other sectors - oil	1.92	-34.0%	2.7	60.2
Residential - oil	1.70	-56.3%	2.4	62.6
Manufacturing industries - gas	1.67	33.6%	2.4	65.0
Other energy industries - gas	1.59	212.0%	2.3	67.2
Residential - gas	1.57	74.9%	2.2	69.5
Main activity prod. elec. and heat - oil	1.15	25.4%	1.6	71.1
Other energy industries - oil	0.95	0.0%	1.4	72.5
Memo: total CO$_2$ from fuel combustion	55.18	9.5%	78.6	78.6

** Percent calculated using the total GHG estimate for CO$_2$, CH$_4$, N$_2$O, HFCs, PFCs and SF$_6$ excluding CO$_2$ emissions/removals from land use change and forestry.

Dominican Republic / République dominicaine

Figure 1. CO₂ emissions by fuel

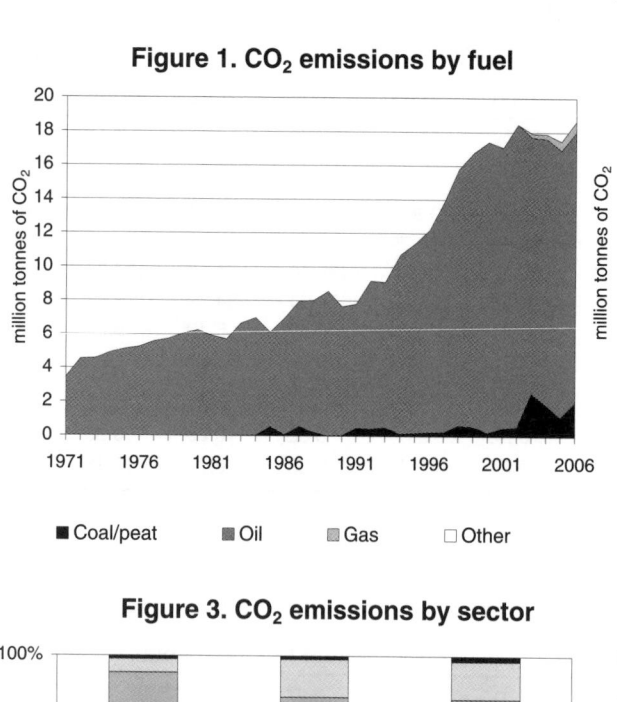

■ Coal/peat   ■ Oil   ■ Gas   □ Other

Figure 2. CO₂ emissions by sector

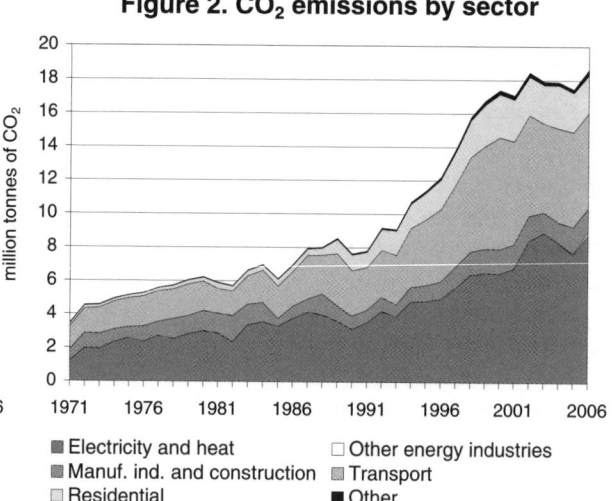

■ Electricity and heat   □ Other energy industries
■ Manuf. ind. and construction   ■ Transport
□ Residential   ■ Other

Figure 3. CO₂ emissions by sector

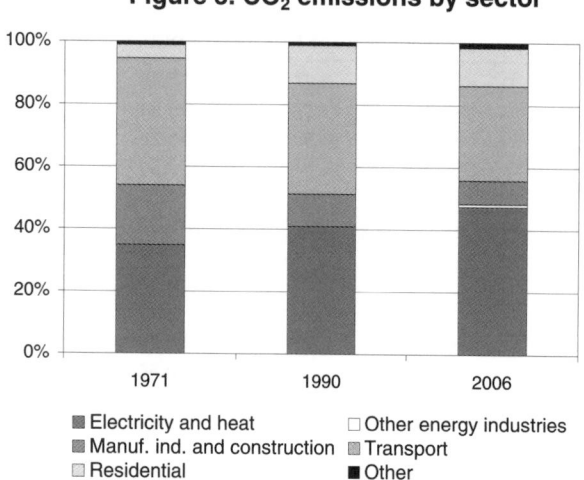

■ Electricity and heat   □ Other energy industries
■ Manuf. ind. and construction   ■ Transport
□ Residential   ■ Other

Figure 4. Reference vs Sectoral Approach

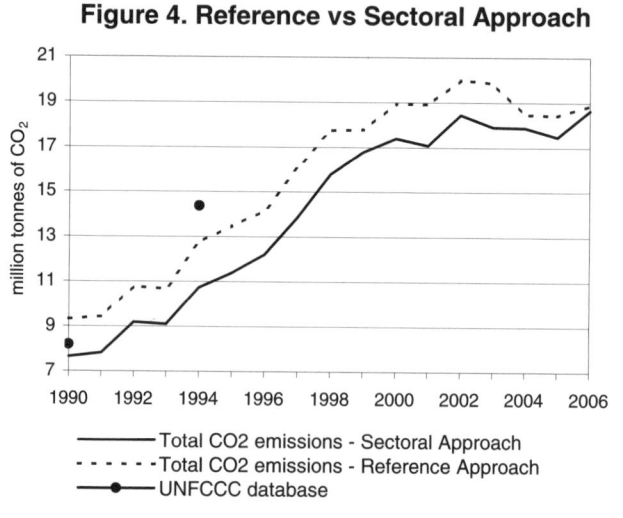

—— Total CO2 emissions - Sectoral Approach
----- Total CO2 emissions - Reference Approach
—●— UNFCCC database

Figure 5. Electricity generation by fuel

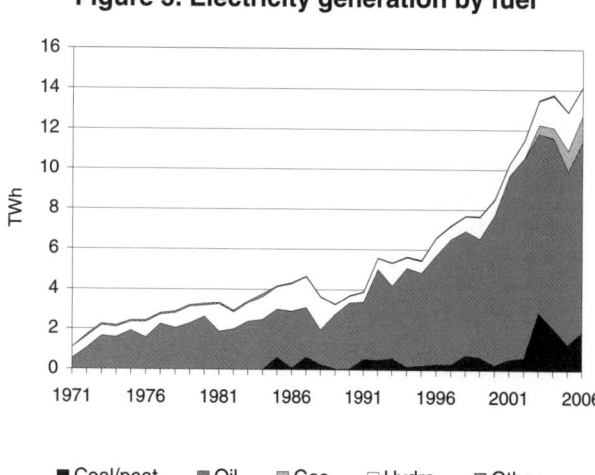

■ Coal/peat   ■ Oil   ■ Gas   □ Hydro   ■ Other

Figure 6. Key indicators

1990 = 100

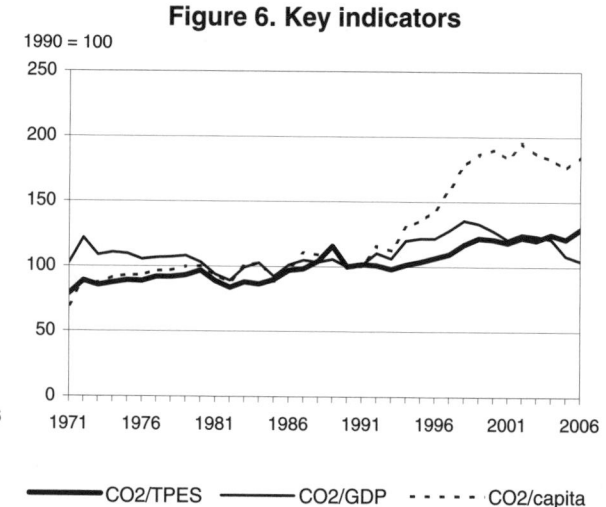

—— CO2/TPES   —— CO2/GDP   ----- CO2/capita

Dominican Republic / République dominicaine

Key indicators

	1990	1995	2000	2003	2004	2005	2006	% change 90-06
CO$_2$ Sectoral Approach (Mt of CO$_2$)	7.64	11.39	17.40	17.91	17.88	17.47	18.65	144.0%
CO$_2$ Reference Approach (Mt of CO$_2$)	9.31	13.46	18.94	19.86	18.48	18.42	18.88	102.7%
TPES (PJ)	173	249	327	337	325	327	328	89.5%
TPES (Mtoe)	4.14	5.95	7.80	8.06	7.76	7.81	7.84	89.5%
GDP (billion 2000 US$ using exch. rates)	11.08	13.58	19.77	21.00	21.41	23.40	25.90	133.7%
GDP (billion 2000 US$ using PPPs)	31.34	38.40	55.92	59.38	60.54	66.16	73.24	133.7%
Population (millions)	7.30	8.01	8.74	9.18	9.33	9.47	9.62	31.8%
CO$_2$ / TPES (t CO$_2$ per TJ)	44.1	45.7	53.3	53.1	55.0	53.4	56.8	28.8%
CO$_2$ / GDP (kg CO$_2$ per 2000 US$)	0.69	0.84	0.88	0.85	0.84	0.75	0.72	4.4%
CO$_2$ / GDP (kg CO$_2$ per 2000 US$ PPP)	0.24	0.30	0.31	0.30	0.30	0.26	0.25	4.4%
CO$_2$ / population (t CO$_2$ per capita)	1.05	1.42	1.99	1.95	1.92	1.84	1.94	85.2%

Ratios are based on the Sectoral Approach.

2006 CO$_2$ emissions by sector

million tonnes of CO$_2$	Coal/peat	Oil	Gas	Other *	Total	% change 90-06
Sectoral Approach	**2.00**	**16.00**	**0.65**	-	**18.65**	**144.0%**
Main activity producer elec. and heat	1.68	4.55	0.65	-	6.88	287.4%
Unallocated autoproducers	-	1.95	-	-	1.95	44.4%
Other energy industries	-	0.16	-	-	0.16	x
Manufacturing industries and construction	0.32	1.08	-	-	1.40	77.3%
Transport	-	5.68	-	-	5.68	108.8%
of which: road	-	*4.62*	-	-	*4.62*	*75.2%*
Other sectors	-	2.58	-	-	2.58	155.7%
of which: residential	-	*2.26*	-	-	*2.26*	*143.5%*
Reference Approach	**2.00**	**16.22**	**0.65**	-	**18.88**	**102.7%**
Diff. due to losses and/or transformation	-	0.18	-	-	0.18	
Statistical differences	-	0.05	-	-	0.05	
Memo: international marine bunkers	-	..	-	-	..	..
Memo: international aviation	-	*0.30*	-	-	*0.30*	*166.7%*

* Other includes industrial waste and non-renewable municipal waste.

Key sources for CO$_2$ emissions from fuel combustion in 2006

IPCC source category	CO$_2$ emissions (Mt of CO$_2$)	% change 90-06	Level assessment (%) **	Cumulative total (%)
Road - oil	4.62	75.2%	16.0	16.0
Main activity prod. elec. and heat - oil	4.55	162.0%	15.8	31.8
Residential - oil	2.26	143.5%	7.8	39.6
Unallocated autoproducers - oil	1.95	44.4%	6.7	46.4
Main activity prod. elec. and heat - coal/peat	1.68	+	5.8	52.2
Manufacturing industries - oil	1.08	37.1%	3.7	55.9
Other transport - oil	1.06	+	3.7	59.6
Main activity prod. elec. and heat - gas	0.65	x	2.3	61.9
Non-specified other sectors - oil	0.32	293.4%	1.1	63.0
Manufacturing industries - coal/peat	0.32	x	1.1	64.1
Other energy industries - oil	0.16	x	0.6	64.7
Memo: total CO$_2$ from fuel combustion	*18.65*	*144.0%*	*64.7*	*64.7*

** Percent calculated using the total GHG estimate for CO$_2$, CH$_4$, N$_2$O, HFCs, PFCs and SF$_6$ excluding CO$_2$ emissions/removals from land use change and forestry.

Ecuador / Equateur

Figure 1. CO₂ emissions by fuel

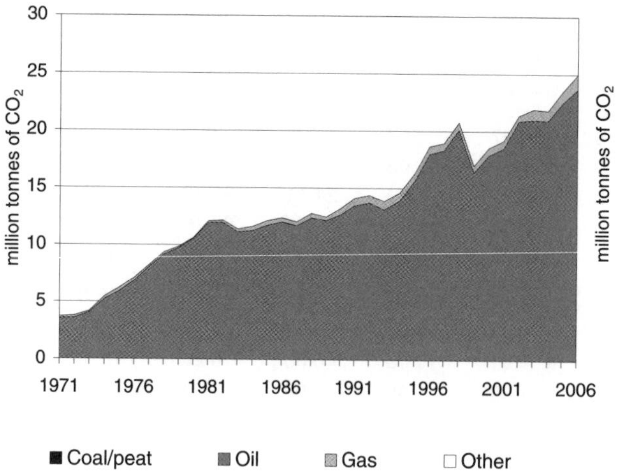

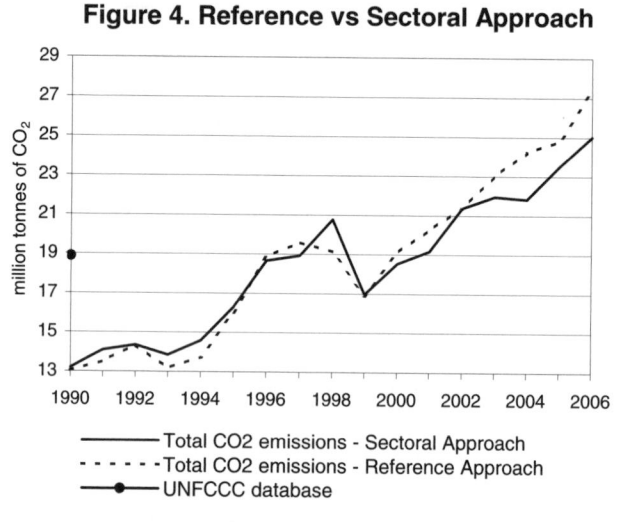

■ Coal/peat   ▨ Oil   ▨ Gas   □ Other

Figure 2. CO₂ emissions by sector

■ Electricity and heat   □ Other energy industries
▨ Manuf. ind. and construction   ▨ Transport
▨ Residential   ■ Other

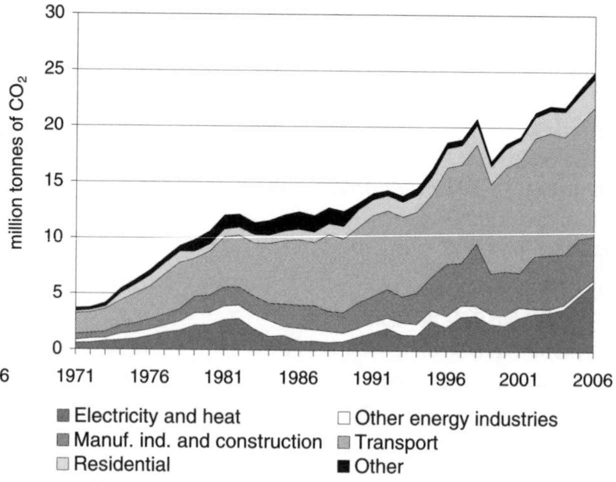

Figure 3. CO₂ emissions by sector

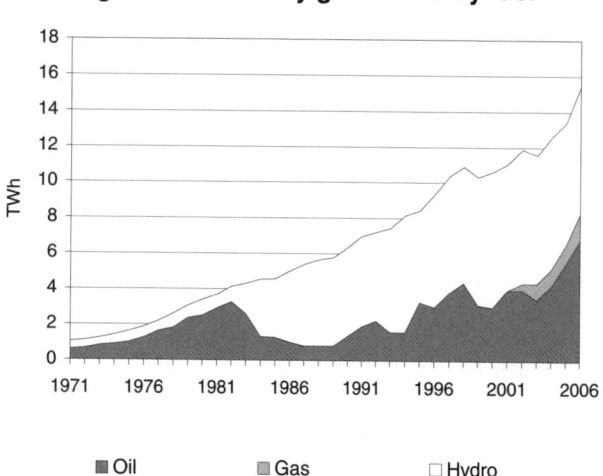

■ Electricity and heat   □ Other energy industries
▨ Manuf. ind. and construction   ▨ Transport
▨ Residential   ■ Other

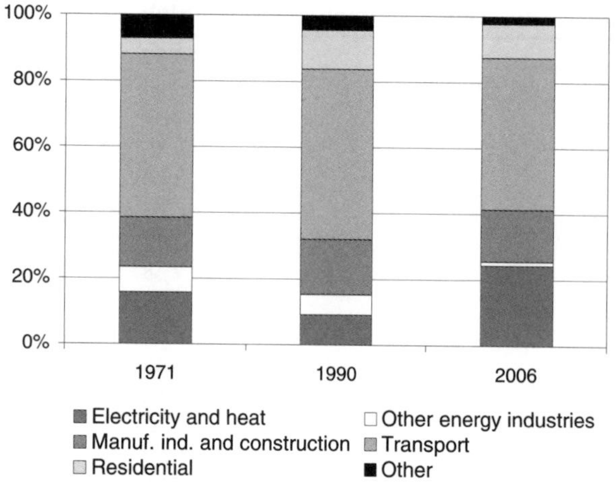

Figure 4. Reference vs Sectoral Approach

—— Total CO2 emissions - Sectoral Approach
- - - - Total CO2 emissions - Reference Approach
——●—— UNFCCC database

Figure 5. Electricity generation by fuel

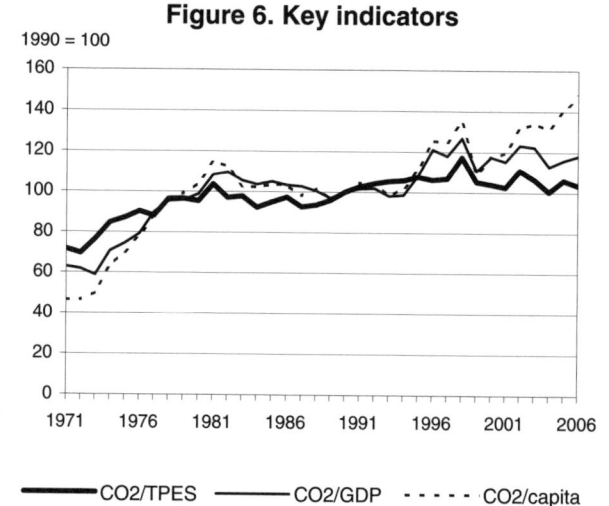

▨ Oil   ▨ Gas   □ Hydro

Figure 6. Key indicators

1990 = 100

—— CO2/TPES   —— CO2/GDP   - - - - CO2/capita

Ecuador / Equateur

Key indicators

	1990	1995	2000	2003	2004	2005	2006	% change 90-06
CO$_2$ Sectoral Approach (Mt of CO$_2$)	13.19	16.29	18.54	21.95	21.82	23.50	25.02	89.6%
CO$_2$ Reference Approach (Mt of CO$_2$)	13.03	16.00	19.12	23.03	24.24	24.79	27.40	110.4%
TPES (PJ)	257	295	347	401	423	431	471	83.4%
TPES (Mtoe)	6.13	7.04	8.29	9.58	10.10	10.30	11.24	83.4%
GDP (billion 2000 US$ using exch. rates)	13.33	15.21	15.94	18.13	19.57	20.50	21.42	60.7%
GDP (billion 2000 US$ using PPPs)	33.24	37.93	39.75	45.21	48.79	51.11	53.41	60.7%
Population (millions)	10.27	11.40	12.31	12.77	12.92	13.06	13.20	28.5%
CO$_2$ / TPES (t CO$_2$ per TJ)	51.4	55.3	53.4	54.7	51.6	54.5	53.2	3.4%
CO$_2$ / GDP (kg CO$_2$ per 2000 US$)	0.99	1.07	1.16	1.21	1.12	1.15	1.17	18.0%
CO$_2$ / GDP (kg CO$_2$ per 2000 US$ PPP)	0.40	0.43	0.47	0.49	0.45	0.46	0.47	18.0%
CO$_2$ / population (t CO$_2$ per capita)	1.28	1.43	1.51	1.72	1.69	1.80	1.89	47.5%

Ratios are based on the Sectoral Approach.

2006 CO$_2$ emissions by sector

million tonnes of CO$_2$	Coal/peat	Oil	Gas	Other *	Total	% change 90-06
Sectoral Approach	-	**23.71**	**1.31**	-	**25.02**	**89.6%**
Main activity producer elec. and heat	-	3.77	0.49	-	4.26	258.0%
Unallocated autoproducers	-	1.02	0.82	-	1.84	x
Other energy industries	-	0.29	0.00	-	0.30	-63.6%
Manufacturing industries and construction	-	3.92	-	-	3.92	76.2%
Transport	-	11.54	-	-	11.54	69.3%
of which: road	-	*10.33*	-	-	*10.33*	*76.5%*
Other sectors	-	3.16	-	-	3.16	47.0%
of which: residential	-	*2.58*	-	-	*2.58*	*65.4%*
Reference Approach	-	**26.10**	**1.31**	-	**27.40**	**110.4%**
Diff. due to losses and/or transformation	-	1.44	-	-	1.44	
Statistical differences	-	0.95	-	-	0.95	
Memo: international marine bunkers	-	*0.77*	-	-	*0.77*	*34.7%*
Memo: international aviation	-	*1.00*	-	-	*1.00*	*158.5%*

* Other includes industrial waste and non-renewable municipal waste.

Key sources for CO$_2$ emissions from fuel combustion in 2006

IPCC source category	CO$_2$ emissions (Mt of CO$_2$)	% change 90-06	Level assessment (%) **	Cumulative total (%)
Road - oil	10.33	76.5%	20.7	20.7
Manufacturing industries - oil	3.92	76.2%	7.8	28.5
Main activity prod. elec. and heat - oil	3.77	216.9%	7.5	36.1
Residential - oil	2.58	65.4%	5.2	41.2
Other transport - oil	1.20	25.4%	2.4	43.7
Unallocated autoproducers - oil	1.02	x	2.0	45.7
Unallocated autoproducers - gas	0.82	x	1.6	47.3
Non-specified other sectors - oil	0.58	-1.5%	1.2	48.5
Main activity prod. elec. and heat - gas	0.49	x	1.0	49.5
Other energy industries - oil	0.29	2.8%	0.6	50.1
Other energy industries - gas	0.00	-99.9%	0.0	50.1
Memo: total CO$_2$ from fuel combustion	*25.02*	*89.6%*	*50.1*	*50.1*

** Percent calculated using the total GHG estimate for CO$_2$, CH$_4$, N$_2$O, HFCs, PFCs and SF$_6$ excluding CO$_2$ emissions/removals from land use change and forestry.

Egypt / Egypte

Figure 1. CO$_2$ emissions by fuel

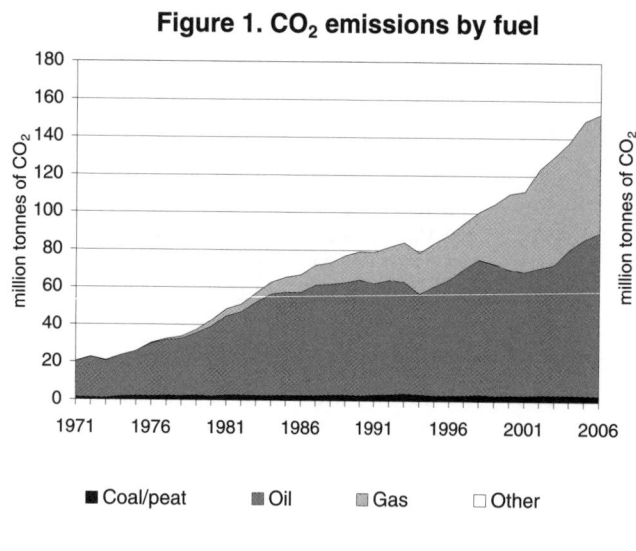

■ Coal/peat   ■ Oil   ▨ Gas   ☐ Other

Figure 2. CO$_2$ emissions by sector

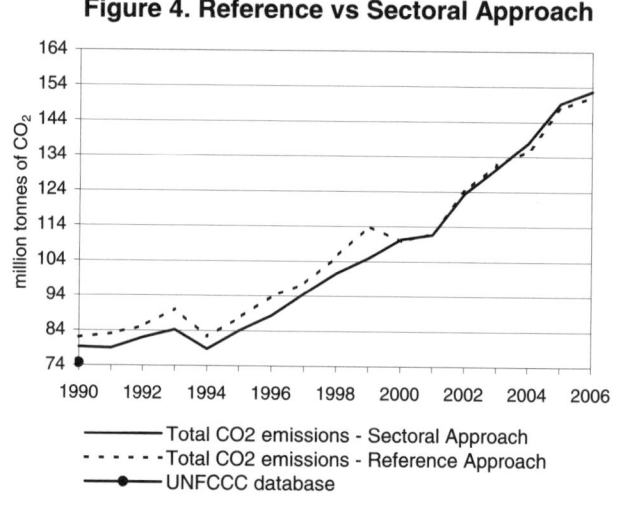

■ Electricity and heat   ☐ Other energy industries
■ Manuf. ind. and construction ▨ Transport
▨ Residential   ■ Other

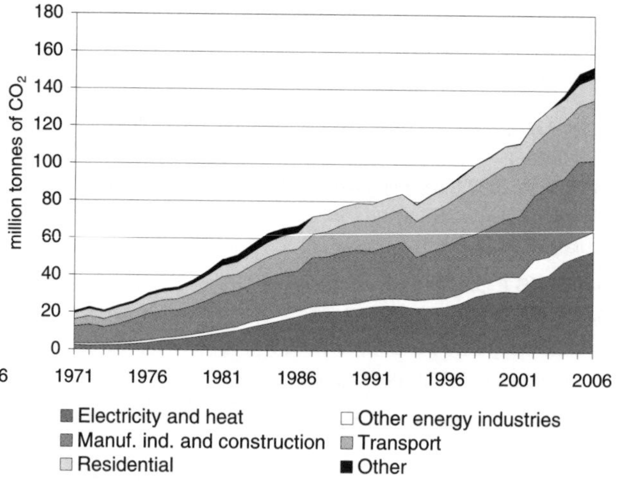

Figure 3. CO$_2$ emissions by sector

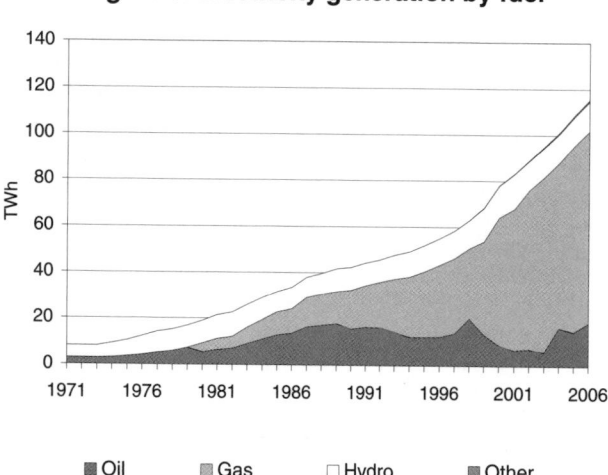

■ Electricity and heat   ☐ Other energy industries
■ Manuf. ind. and construction ▨ Transport
▨ Residential   ■ Other

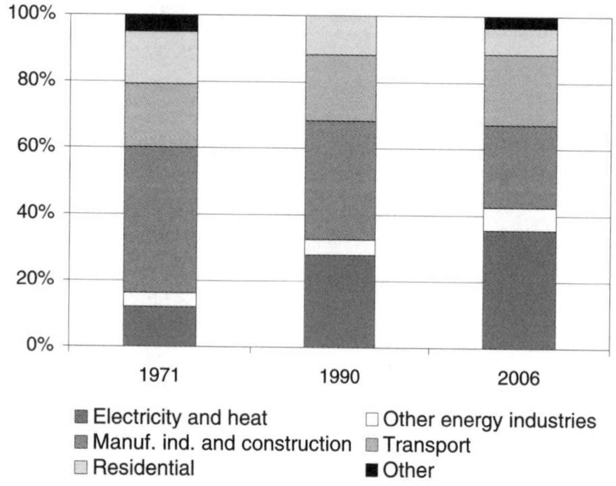

Figure 4. Reference vs Sectoral Approach

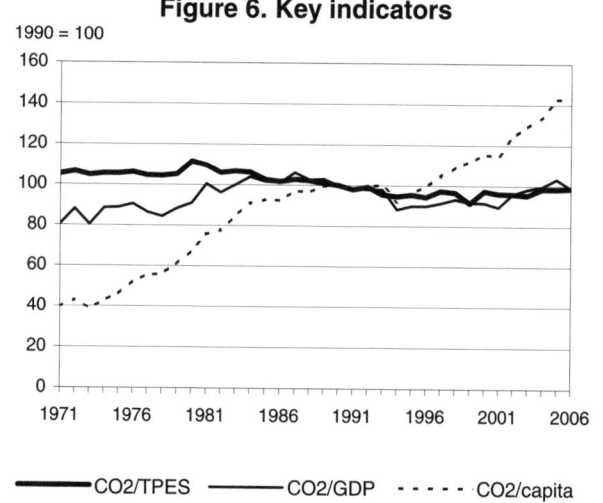

──── Total CO2 emissions - Sectoral Approach
- - - - Total CO2 emissions - Reference Approach
──●── UNFCCC database

Figure 5. Electricity generation by fuel

■ Oil   ▨ Gas   ☐ Hydro   ■ Other

Figure 6. Key indicators

1990 = 100

━━━ CO2/TPES   ──── CO2/GDP   - - - - CO2/capita

Egypt / Egypte

Key indicators

	1990	1995	2000	2003	2004	2005	2006	% change 90-06
CO$_2$ Sectoral Approach (Mt of CO$_2$)	79.21	83.99	110.24	130.52	137.95	149.28	152.74	92.8%
CO$_2$ Reference Approach (Mt of CO$_2$)	81.97	87.57	109.83	131.80	135.59	147.90	151.32	84.6%
TPES (PJ)	1 339	1 489	1 916	2 316	2 371	2 565	2 617	95.5%
TPES (Mtoe)	31.97	35.57	45.75	55.32	56.64	61.27	62.50	95.5%
GDP (billion 2000 US$ using exch. rates)	65.57	77.38	99.84	109.96	114.56	119.71	127.85	95.0%
GDP (billion 2000 US$ using PPPs)	155.88	183.94	237.33	261.40	272.32	284.58	303.93	95.0%
Population (millions)	55.14	60.65	66.53	70.27	71.55	72.85	74.17	34.5%
CO$_2$ / TPES (t CO$_2$ per TJ)	59.2	56.4	57.5	56.4	58.2	58.2	58.4	-1.4%
CO$_2$ / GDP (kg CO$_2$ per 2000 US$)	1.21	1.09	1.10	1.19	1.20	1.25	1.19	-1.1%
CO$_2$ / GDP (kg CO$_2$ per 2000 US$ PPP)	0.51	0.46	0.46	0.50	0.51	0.52	0.50	-1.1%
CO$_2$ / population (t CO$_2$ per capita)	1.44	1.38	1.66	1.86	1.93	2.05	2.06	43.4%

Ratios are based on the Sectoral Approach.

2006 CO$_2$ emissions by sector

million tonnes of CO$_2$	Coal/peat	Oil	Gas	Other *	Total	% change 90-06
Sectoral Approach	**3.08**	**86.67**	**62.99**	-	**152.74**	**92.8%**
Main activity producer elec. and heat	-	13.40	40.81	-	54.22	146.1%
Unallocated autoproducers	-	-	-	-	-	-
Other energy industries	-	3.39	7.20	-	10.60	182.6%
Manufacturing industries and construction	3.06	21.81	13.03	-	37.90	33.8%
Transport	-	31.71	0.66	-	32.37	106.0%
of which: road	-	*28.79*	*0.66*	-	*29.45*	*95.4%*
Other sectors	0.02	16.35	1.28	-	17.65	87.9%
of which: residential	*0.02*	*10.87*	*1.28*	-	*12.17*	*29.6%*
Reference Approach	**3.02**	**85.31**	**62.99**	-	**151.32**	**84.6%**
Diff. due to losses and/or transformation	0.15	- 1.47	-	-	- 1.32	
Statistical differences	- 0.21	0.11	0.00	-	- 0.10	
Memo: international marine bunkers	-	*3.36*	-	-	*3.36*	*-35.9%*
Memo: international aviation	-	*2.45*	-	-	*2.45*	*454.3%*

* Other includes industrial waste and non-renewable municipal waste.

Key sources for CO$_2$ emissions from fuel combustion in 2006

IPCC source category	CO$_2$ emissions (Mt of CO$_2$)	% change 90-06	Level assessment (%) **	Cumulative total (%)
Main activity prod. elec. and heat - gas	40.81	339.8%	17.6	17.6
Road - oil	28.79	91.0%	12.4	30.0
Manufacturing industries - oil	21.81	4.2%	9.4	39.4
Main activity prod. elec. and heat - oil	13.40	5.1%	5.8	45.1
Manufacturing industries - gas	13.03	177.2%	5.6	50.7
Residential - oil	10.87	17.8%	4.7	55.4
Other energy industries - gas	7.20	796.4%	3.1	58.5
Non-specified other sectors - oil	5.48	x	2.4	60.9
Other energy industries - oil	3.39	15.2%	1.5	62.3
Manufacturing industries - coal/peat	3.06	13.5%	1.3	63.7
Other transport - oil	2.91	358.9%	1.3	64.9
Memo: total CO$_2$ from fuel combustion	*152.74*	*92.8%*	*65.8*	*65.8*

** Percent calculated using the total GHG estimate for CO$_2$, CH$_4$, N$_2$O, HFCs, PFCs and SF$_6$ excluding CO$_2$ emissions/removals from land use change and forestry.

El Salvador

Figure 1. CO₂ emissions by fuel

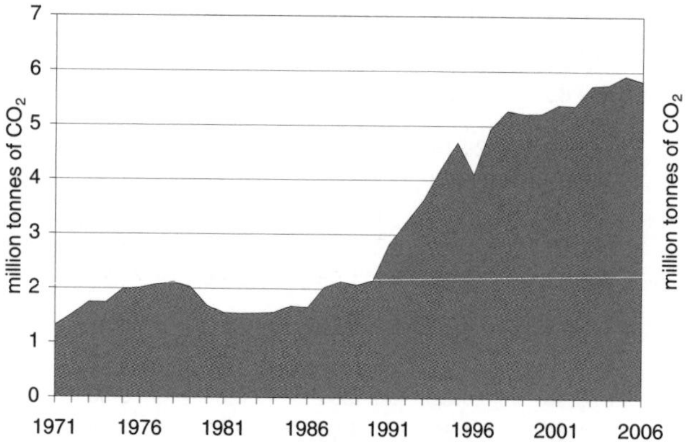

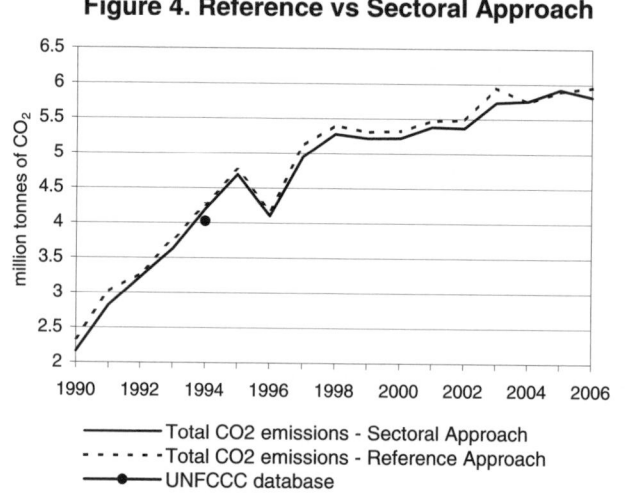

■ Coal/peat   ■ Oil   ■ Gas   □ Other

Figure 2. CO₂ emissions by sector

■ Electricity and heat   □ Other energy industries
■ Manuf. ind. and construction   ■ Transport
□ Residential   ■ Other

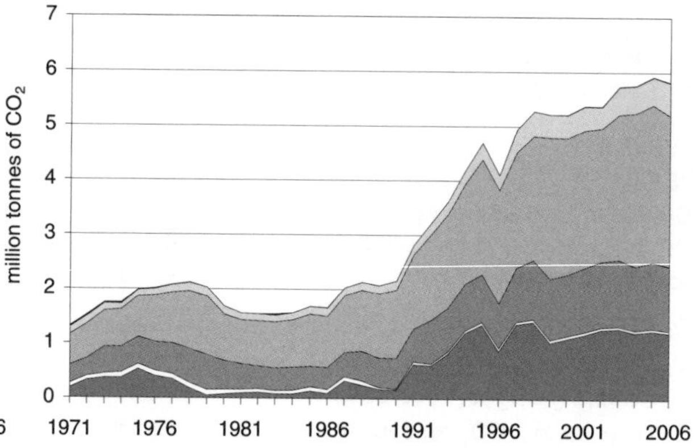

Figure 3. CO₂ emissions by sector

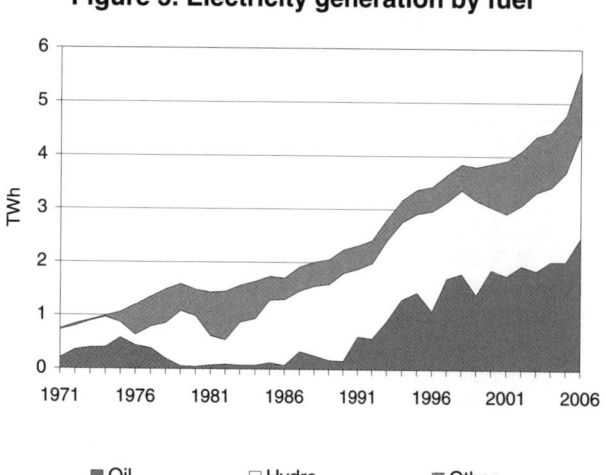

■ Electricity and heat   □ Other energy industries
■ Manuf. ind. and construction   ■ Transport
□ Residential   ■ Other

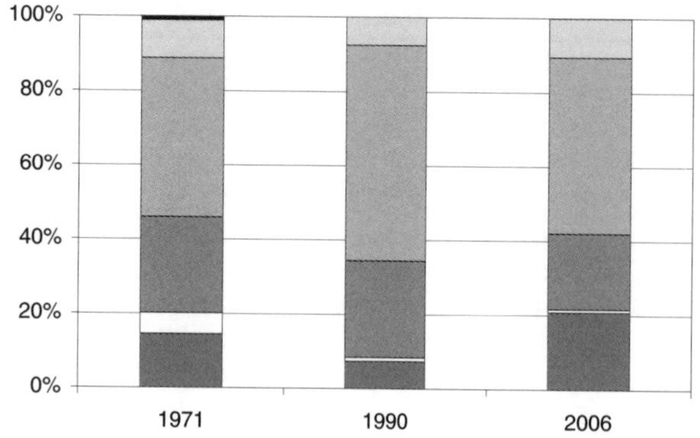

Figure 4. Reference vs Sectoral Approach

—— Total CO2 emissions - Sectoral Approach
- - - - Total CO2 emissions - Reference Approach
—●— UNFCCC database

Figure 5. Electricity generation by fuel

■ Oil   □ Hydro   ■ Other

Figure 6. Key indicators

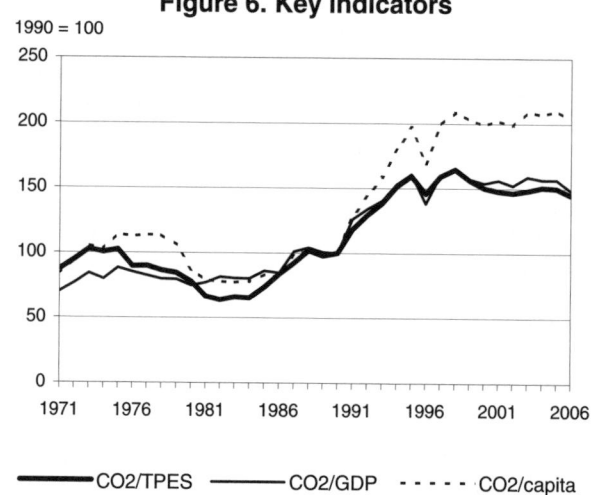

1990 = 100

—— CO2/TPES   —— CO2/GDP   - - - - CO2/capita

El Salvador

Key indicators

	1990	1995	2000	2003	2004	2005	2006	% change 90-06
CO$_2$ Sectoral Approach (Mt of CO$_2$)	2.16	4.69	5.22	5.74	5.76	5.92	5.82	169.2%
CO$_2$ Reference Approach (Mt of CO$_2$)	2.34	4.76	5.32	5.95	5.74	5.89	5.95	154.8%
TPES (PJ)	106	145	171	190	188	194	197	85.9%
TPES (Mtoe)	2.53	3.45	4.08	4.54	4.48	4.63	4.71	85.9%
GDP (billion 2000 US$ using exch. rates)	8.37	11.30	13.13	13.99	14.24	14.63	15.19	81.4%
GDP (billion 2000 US$ using PPPs)	18.40	24.84	28.87	30.74	31.31	32.17	33.39	81.4%
Population (millions)	5.11	5.63	6.20	6.49	6.58	6.67	6.76	32.3%
CO$_2$ / TPES (t CO$_2$ per TJ)	20.4	32.5	30.6	30.2	30.7	30.6	29.5	44.8%
CO$_2$ / GDP (kg CO$_2$ per 2000 US$)	0.26	0.42	0.40	0.41	0.40	0.40	0.38	48.4%
CO$_2$ / GDP (kg CO$_2$ per 2000 US$ PPP)	0.12	0.19	0.18	0.19	0.18	0.18	0.17	48.5%
CO$_2$ / population (t CO$_2$ per capita)	0.42	0.83	0.84	0.88	0.88	0.89	0.86	103.4%

Ratios are based on the Sectoral Approach.

2006 CO$_2$ emissions by sector

million tonnes of CO$_2$	Coal/peat	Oil	Gas	Other *	Total	% change 90-06
Sectoral Approach	**0.00**	**5.82**	-	-	**5.82**	**169.2%**
Main activity producer elec. and heat	-	1.17	-	-	1.17	688.7%
Unallocated autoproducers	-	0.04	-	-	0.04	333.3%
Other energy industries	-	0.05	-	-	0.05	114.3%
Manufacturing industries and construction	0.00	1.18	-	-	1.18	110.2%
Transport	-	2.76	-	-	2.76	120.2%
of which: road	-	*2.76*	-	-	*2.76*	*120.2%*
Other sectors	-	0.61	-	-	0.61	272.5%
of which: residential	-	*0.61*	-	-	*0.61*	*268.8%*
Reference Approach	**0.00**	**5.95**	-	-	**5.95**	**154.8%**
Diff. due to losses and/or transformation	0.00	0.11	-	-	0.11	
Statistical differences	-	0.03	-	-	0.03	
Memo: international marine bunkers	-	..	-	-	..	..
Memo: international aviation	-	*0.23*	-	-	*0.23*	*114.7%*

* Other includes industrial waste and non-renewable municipal waste.

Key sources for CO$_2$ emissions from fuel combustion in 2006

IPCC source category	CO$_2$ emissions (Mt of CO$_2$)	% change 90-06	Level assessment (%) **	Cumulative total (%)
Road - oil	2.76	120.2%	23.0	23.0
Manufacturing industries - oil	1.18	109.7%	9.8	32.8
Main activity prod. elec. and heat - oil	1.17	688.7%	9.8	42.6
Residential - oil	0.61	268.8%	5.1	47.6
Other energy industries - oil	0.05	114.3%	0.4	48.0
Unallocated autoproducers - oil	0.04	333.3%	0.3	48.4
Non-specified other sectors - oil	0.01	x	0.1	48.4
Manufacturing industries - coal/peat	0.00	x	0.0	48.5
-	-	-	-	-
-	-	-	-	-
-	-	-	-	-
Memo: total CO$_2$ from fuel combustion	*5.82*	*169.2%*	*48.5*	*48.5*

** Percent calculated using the total GHG estimate for CO$_2$, CH$_4$, N$_2$O, HFCs, PFCs and SF$_6$ excluding CO$_2$ emissions/removals from land use change and forestry.

Eritrea / Erythrée

Figure 1. CO$_2$ emissions by fuel

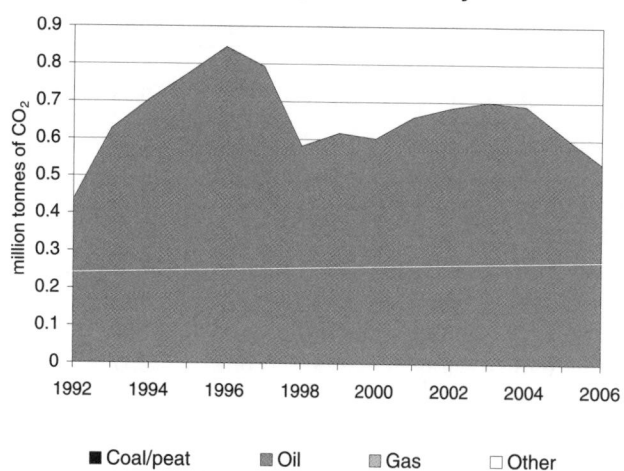

Figure 2. CO$_2$ emissions by sector

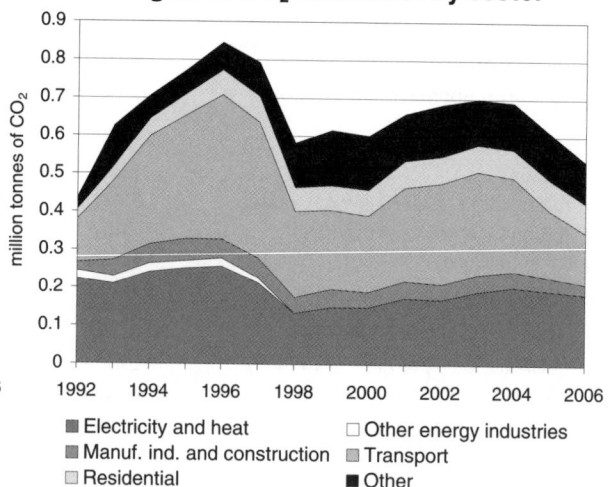

Figure 3. CO$_2$ emissions by sector

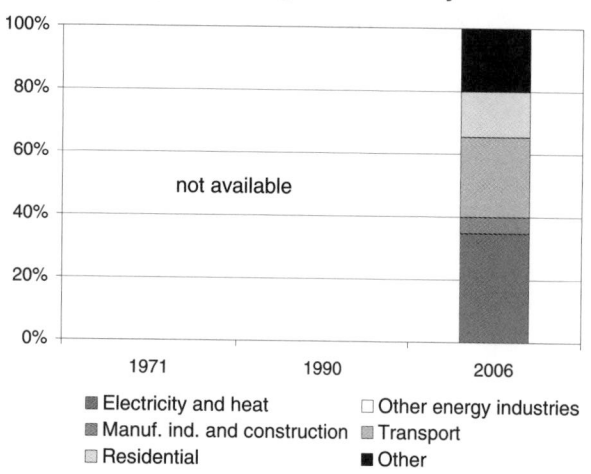

Figure 4. Reference vs Sectoral Approach

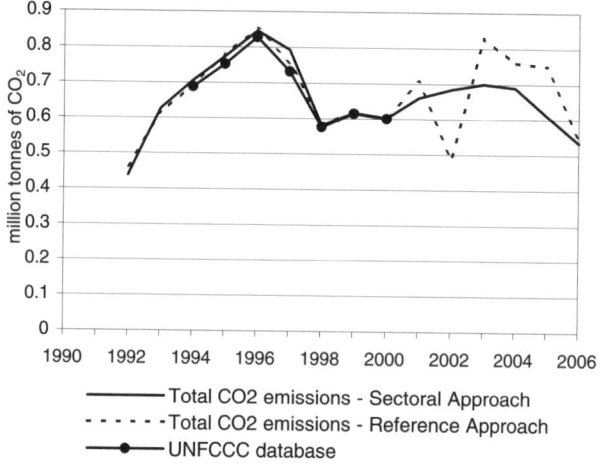

Figure 5. Electricity generation by fuel

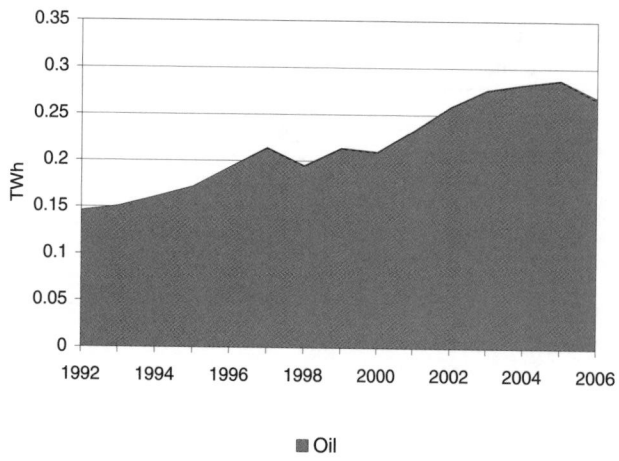

Figure 6. Key indicators

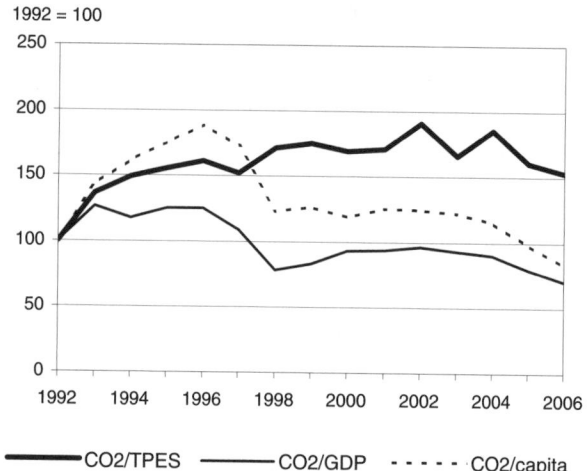

Eritrea / Erythrée *

Key indicators

	1990	1995	2000	2003	2004	2005	2006	% change 90-06
CO$_2$ Sectoral Approach (Mt of CO$_2$)	..	0.77	0.60	0.70	0.69	0.61	0.53	..
CO$_2$ Reference Approach (Mt of CO$_2$)	..	0.78	0.60	0.83	0.76	0.75	0.55	..
TPES (PJ)	..	42	30	36	31	32	29	..
TPES (Mtoe)	..	1.00	0.72	0.85	0.75	0.77	0.70	..
GDP (billion 2000 US$ using exch. rates)	..	0.61	0.63	0.74	0.75	0.76	0.75	..
GDP (billion 2000 US$ using PPPs)	..	3.49	3.64	4.24	4.32	4.34	4.30	..
Population (millions)	..	3.21	3.68	4.18	4.35	4.53	4.69	..
CO$_2$ / TPES (t CO$_2$ per TJ)	..	18.4	20.0	19.6	22.0	19.0	18.1	..
CO$_2$ / GDP (kg CO$_2$ per 2000 US$)	..	1.27	0.95	0.95	0.92	0.81	0.71	..
CO$_2$ / GDP (kg CO$_2$ per 2000 US$ PPP)	..	0.22	0.17	0.17	0.16	0.14	0.12	..
CO$_2$ / population (t CO$_2$ per capita)	..	0.24	0.16	0.17	0.16	0.14	0.11	..

Ratios are based on the Sectoral Approach.
* Prior to 1992, data for Eritrea were included in Ethiopia.

2006 CO$_2$ emissions by sector

million tonnes of CO$_2$	Coal/peat	Oil	Gas	Other **	Total	% change 90-06
Sectoral Approach	-	**0.53**	-	-	**0.53**	..
Main activity producer elec. and heat	-	0.18	-	-	0.18	..
Unallocated autoproducers	-	0.01	-	-	0.01	..
Other energy industries	-	-	-	-	-	..
Manufacturing industries and construction	-	0.03	-	-	0.03	..
Transport	-	0.14	-	-	0.14	..
of which: road	-	*0.14*	-	-	*0.14*	..
Other sectors	-	0.19	-	-	0.19	..
of which: residential	-	*0.08*	-	-	*0.08*	..
Reference Approach	-	**0.55**	-	-	**0.55**	..
Diff. due to losses and/or transformation	-	-	-	-	-	
Statistical differences	-	0.01	-	-	0.01	
Memo: international marine bunkers	-	*..*	-	-	*..*	..
Memo: international aviation	-	*0.02*	-	-	*0.02*	..

** Other includes industrial waste and non-renewable municipal waste.

Key sources for CO$_2$ emissions from fuel combustion in 2006

IPCC source category	CO$_2$ emissions (Mt of CO$_2$)	% change 90-06	Level assessment (%) ***	Cumulative total (%)
Main activity prod. elec. and heat - oil	0.18	..	3.3	3.3
Road - oil	0.14	..	2.5	5.8
Non-specified other sectors - oil	0.11	..	2.0	7.8
Residential - oil	0.08	..	1.4	9.3
Manufacturing industries - oil	0.03	..	0.5	9.8
Unallocated autoproducers - oil	0.01	..	0.2	10.0
-	-	..	-	-
-	-	..	-	-
-	-	..	-	-
-	-	..	-	-
-	-	..	-	-
Memo: total CO$_2$ from fuel combustion	*0.53*	..	*10.0*	*10.0*

*** Percent calculated using the total GHG estimate for CO$_2$, CH$_4$, N$_2$O, HFCs, PFCs and SF$_6$ excluding CO$_2$ emissions/removals from land use change and forestry.

Estonia / Estonie

Figure 1. CO$_2$ emissions by fuel

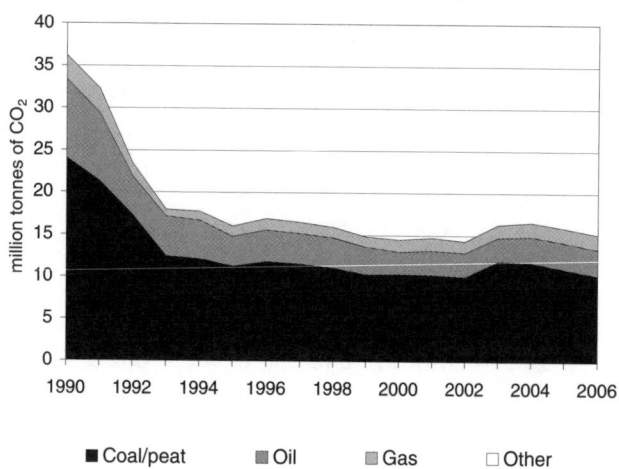

■ Coal/peat   ■ Oil   ■ Gas   □ Other

Figure 2. CO$_2$ emissions by sector

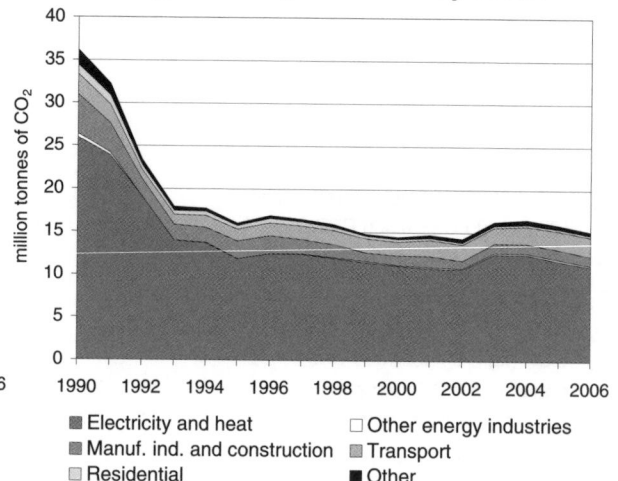

■ Electricity and heat   □ Other energy industries
■ Manuf. ind. and construction   ■ Transport
□ Residential   ■ Other

Figure 3. CO$_2$ emissions by sector

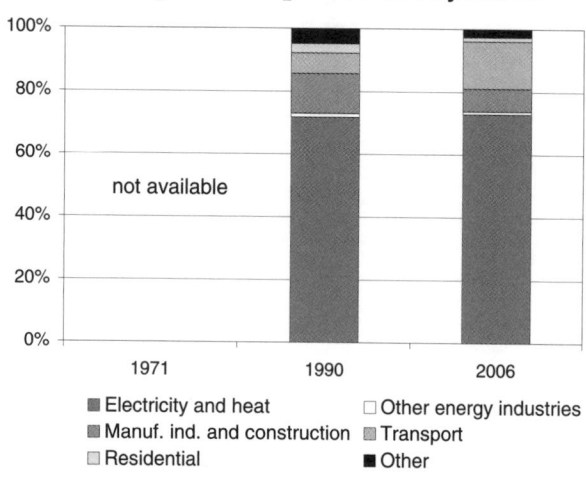

not available

■ Electricity and heat   □ Other energy industries
■ Manuf. ind. and construction   ■ Transport
□ Residential   ■ Other

Figure 4. Reference vs Sectoral Approach

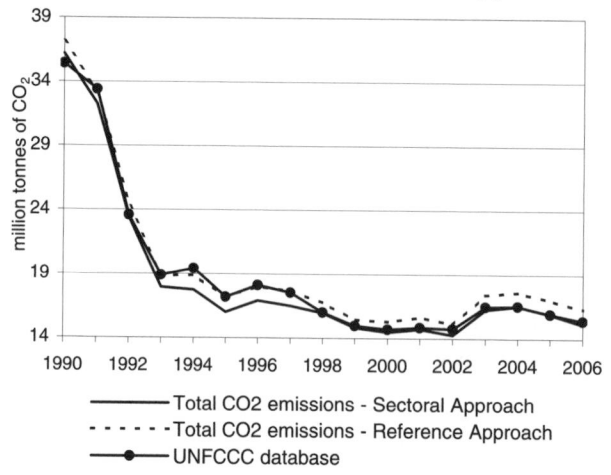

——— Total CO2 emissions - Sectoral Approach
- - - - Total CO2 emissions - Reference Approach
—●— UNFCCC database

Figure 5. Electricity generation by fuel

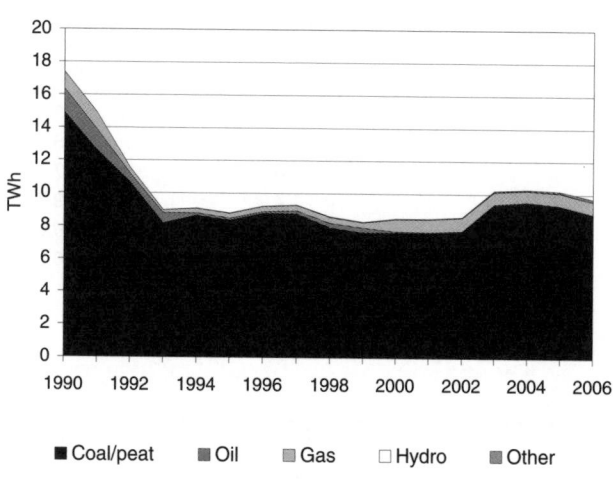

■ Coal/peat   ■ Oil   ■ Gas   □ Hydro   ■ Other

Figure 6. Key indicators

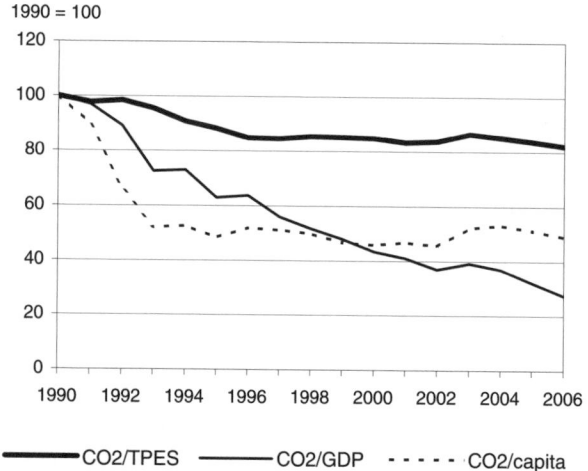

1990 = 100

——— CO2/TPES   ——— CO2/GDP   - - - - CO2/capita

Estonia / Estonie

Key indicators

	1990	1995	2000	2003	2004	2005	2006	% change 90-06
CO_2 Sectoral Approach (Mt of CO_2)	36.19	16.00	14.47	16.26	16.53	15.91	15.14	-58.2%
CO_2 Reference Approach (Mt of CO_2)	37.12	17.22	15.31	17.41	17.60	17.00	16.30	-56.1%
TPES (PJ)	402	202	190	209	216	211	205	-49.1%
TPES (Mtoe)	9.61	4.81	4.53	4.99	5.15	5.04	4.89	-49.1%
GDP (billion 2000 US$ using exch. rates)	6.11	4.29	5.62	7.00	7.57	8.36	9.31	52.5%
GDP (billion 2000 US$ using PPPs)	13.97	9.82	12.86	16.02	17.31	19.12	21.30	52.5%
Population (millions)	1.57	1.44	1.37	1.35	1.35	1.35	1.34	-14.5%
CO_2 / TPES (t CO_2 per TJ)	90.0	79.4	76.4	77.8	76.7	75.4	74.0	-17.8%
CO_2 / GDP (kg CO_2 per 2000 US$)	5.93	3.73	2.57	2.32	2.18	1.90	1.63	-72.6%
CO_2 / GDP (kg CO_2 per 2000 US$ PPP)	2.59	1.63	1.13	1.02	0.96	0.83	0.71	-72.6%
CO_2 / population (t CO_2 per capita)	23.06	11.14	10.57	12.01	12.26	11.82	11.28	-51.1%

Ratios are based on the Sectoral Approach.

2006 CO_2 emissions by sector

million tonnes of CO_2	Coal/peat	Oil	Gas	Other *	Total	% change 90-06
Sectoral Approach	**10.28**	**3.10**	**1.76**	-	**15.14**	**-58.2%**
Main activity producer elec. and heat	9.76	0.21	0.84	-	10.80	-57.6%
Unallocated autoproducers	0.05	0.04	0.13	-	0.23	-56.7%
Other energy industries	0.10	0.04	0.01	-	0.15	-66.0%
Manufacturing industries and construction	0.29	0.26	0.54	-	1.08	-76.4%
Transport	-	2.28	-	-	2.28	-3.3%
of which: road	-	*2.11*	-	-	*2.11*	*-1.7%*
Other sectors	0.08	0.28	0.24	-	0.60	-78.7%
of which: residential	*0.07*	*0.03*	*0.11*	-	*0.20*	*-81.0%*
Reference Approach	**12.58**	**1.96**	**1.76**	-	**16.30**	**-56.1%**
Diff. due to losses and/or transformation	2.40	- 1.12	-	-	1.28	
Statistical differences	- 0.10	- 0.02	- 0.00	-	- 0.12	
Memo: international marine bunkers	-	*0.67*	-	-	*0.67*	*17.4%*
Memo: international aviation	-	*0.09*	-	-	*0.09*	*-20.0%*

* Other includes industrial waste and non-renewable municipal waste.

Key sources for CO_2 emissions from fuel combustion in 2006

IPCC source category	CO_2 emissions (Mt of CO_2)	% change 90-06	Level assessment (%) **	Cumulative total (%)
Main activity prod. elec. and heat - coal/peat	9.76	-52.8%	52.4	52.4
Road - oil	2.11	-1.7%	11.3	63.7
Main activity prod. elec. and heat - gas	0.84	-52.9%	4.5	68.2
Manufacturing industries - gas	0.54	-37.8%	2.9	71.1
Manufacturing industries - coal/peat	0.29	-80.8%	1.5	72.7
Manufacturing industries - oil	0.26	-88.5%	1.4	74.0
Non-specified other sectors - oil	0.25	-77.0%	1.4	75.4
Main activity prod. elec. and heat - oil	0.21	-93.2%	1.1	76.5
Other transport - oil	0.17	-10.8%	0.9	77.4
Non-specified other sectors - gas	0.13	484.0%	0.7	78.1
Unallocated autoproducers - gas	0.13	160.8%	0.7	78.8
Memo: total CO_2 from fuel combustion	*15.14*	*-58.2%*	*81.3*	*81.3*

** Percent calculated using the total GHG estimate for CO_2, CH_4, N_2O, HFCs, PFCs and SF_6 excluding CO_2 emissions/removals from land use change and forestry.

Ethiopia / Ethiopie

Figure 1. CO_2 emissions by fuel

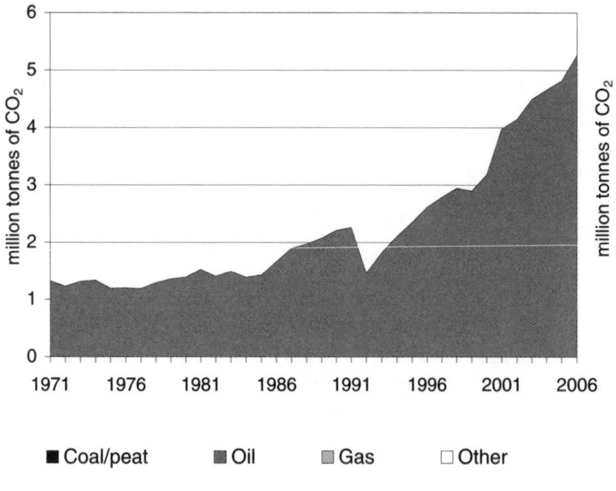

million tonnes of CO2
0
1
2
3
4
5
6
1971
1976
1981
1986
1991
1996
2001
2006
Coal/peat
Oil
Gas
Other

Figure 2. CO_2 emissions by sector

million tonnes of CO2
0
1
2
3
4
5
6
1971
1976
1981
1986
1991
1996
2001
2006
Electricity and heat
Other energy industries
Manuf. ind. and construction
Transport
Residential
Other

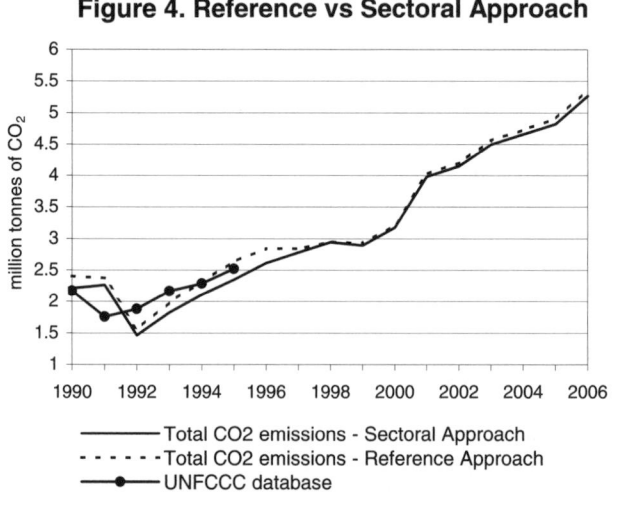

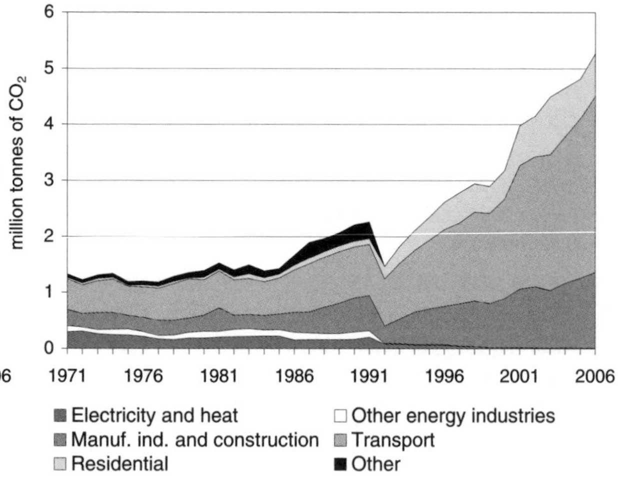

Figure 3. CO_2 emissions by sector

0%
20%
40%
60%
80%
100%
1971
1990
2006
Electricity and heat
Other energy industries
Manuf. ind. and construction
Transport
Residential
Other

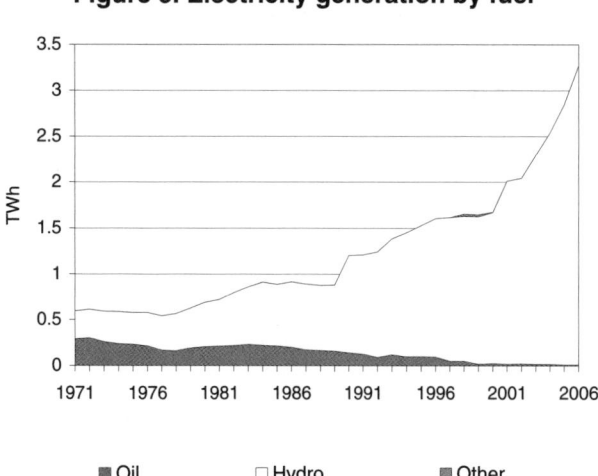

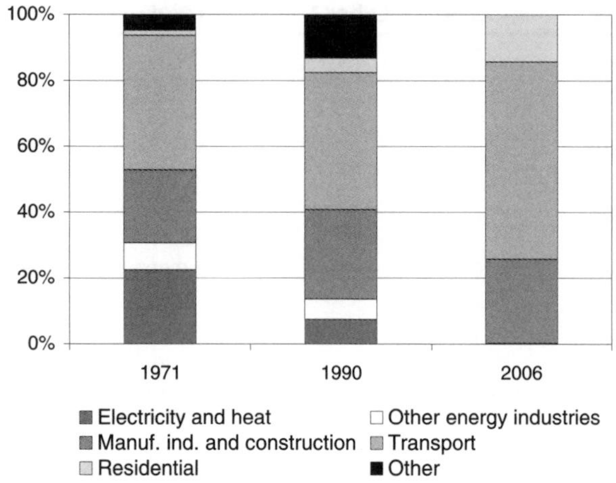

Figure 4. Reference vs Sectoral Approach

million tonnes of CO2
1
1.5
2
2.5
3
3.5
4
4.5
5
5.5
6
1990
1992
1994
1996
1998
2000
2002
2004
2006
Total CO2 emissions - Sectoral Approach
Total CO2 emissions - Reference Approach
UNFCCC database

Figure 5. Electricity generation by fuel

TWh
0
0.5
1
1.5
2
2.5
3
3.5
1971
1976
1981
1986
1991
1996
2001
2006
Oil
Hydro
Other

Figure 6. Key indicators

1990 = 100
0
20
40
60
80
100
120
140
160
180
1971
1976
1981
1986
1991
1996
2001
2006
CO2/TPES
CO2/GDP
CO2/capita

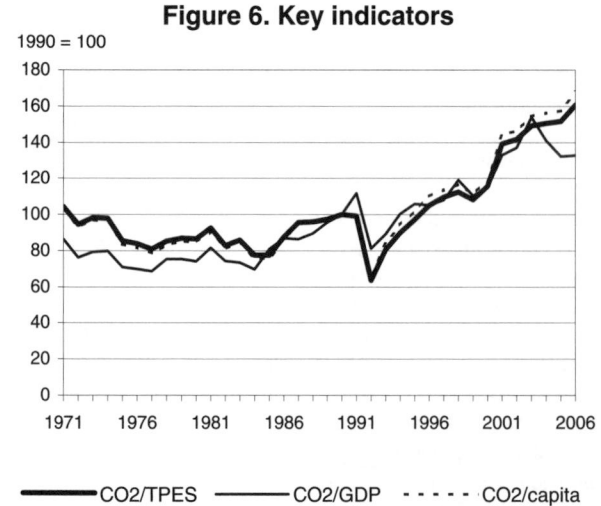

Ethiopia / Ethiopie

Key indicators

	1990	1995	2000	2003	2004	2005	2006	% change 90-06
CO₂ Sectoral Approach (Mt of CO₂)	2.21	2.35	3.18	4.50	4.66	4.82	5.27	138.4%
CO₂ Reference Approach (Mt of CO₂)	2.40	2.64	3.21	4.56	4.73	4.91	5.37	123.4%
TPES (PJ)	630	690	784	859	882	906	934	48.3%
TPES (Mtoe)	15.05	16.47	18.72	20.51	21.06	21.63	22.32	48.3%
GDP (billion 2000 US$ using exch. rates)	6.29	6.32	7.90	8.32	9.41	10.37	11.30	79.6%
GDP (billion 2000 US$ using PPPs)	41.71	41.89	52.40	55.13	62.37	68.73	74.91	79.6%
Population (millions)	54.34	56.60	65.80	71.43	73.21	75.17	77.15	42.0%
CO₂ / TPES (t CO₂ per TJ)	3.5	3.4	4.1	5.2	5.3	5.3	5.6	60.7%
CO₂ / GDP (kg CO₂ per 2000 US$)	0.35	0.37	0.40	0.54	0.50	0.46	0.47	32.8%
CO₂ / GDP (kg CO₂ per 2000 US$ PPP)	0.05	0.06	0.06	0.08	0.07	0.07	0.07	32.6%
CO₂ / population (t CO₂ per capita)	0.04	0.04	0.05	0.06	0.06	0.06	0.07	67.8%

Ratios are based on the Sectoral Approach.

2006 CO₂ emissions by sector

million tonnes of CO₂	Coal/peat	Oil	Gas	Other *	Total	% change 90-06
Sectoral Approach	-	**5.27**	-	-	**5.27**	**138.4%**
Main activity producer elec. and heat	-	0.01	-	-	0.01	-89.4%
Unallocated autoproducers	..	..	..	..	..	..
Other energy industries	-	-	-	-	-	-100.0%
Manufacturing industries and construction	-	1.35	-	-	1.35	124.2%
Transport	-	3.15	-	-	3.15	243.2%
of which: road	-	*3.15*	-	-	*3.15*	*243.2%*
Other sectors	-	0.76	-	-	0.76	94.0%
of which: residential	-	*0.76*	-	-	*0.76*	*670.6%*
Reference Approach	-	**5.37**	-	-	**5.37**	**123.4%**
Diff. due to losses and/or transformation	-	-	-	-	-	
Statistical differences	-	0.10	-	-	0.10	
Memo: international marine bunkers	-	..	-	-	..	..
Memo: international aviation	-	*0.56*	-	-	*0.56*	*5.4%*

* Other includes industrial waste and non-renewable municipal waste.

Key sources for CO₂ emissions from fuel combustion in 2006

IPCC source category	CO₂ emissions (Mt of CO₂)	% change 90-06	Level assessment (%) **	Cumulative total (%)
Road - oil	3.15	243.2%	2.7	2.7
Manufacturing industries - oil	1.35	124.2%	1.1	3.8
Residential - oil	0.76	670.6%	0.6	4.5
Main activity prod. elec. and heat - oil	0.01	-89.4%	0.0	4.5
-	-	-	-	-
-	-	-	-	-
-	-	-	-	-
-	-	-	-	-
-	-	-	-	-
-	-	-	-	-
-	-	-	-	-
Memo: total CO₂ from fuel combustion	5.27	138.4%	4.5	4.5

** Percent calculated using the total GHG estimate for CO₂, CH₄, N₂O, HFCs, PFCs and SF₆ excluding CO₂ emissions/removals from land use change and forestry.

Finland / Finlande

Figure 1. CO$_2$ emissions by fuel

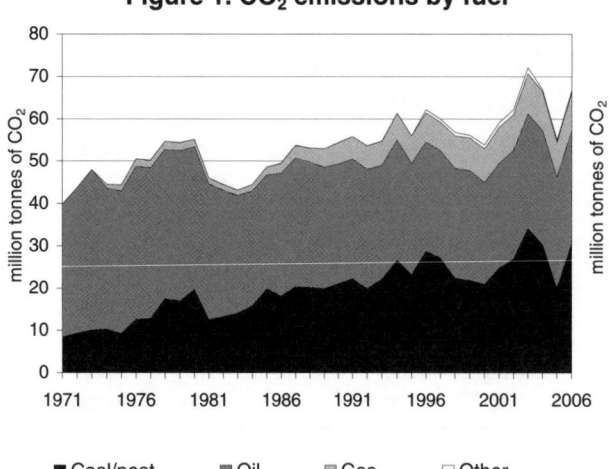

Coal/peat ■ Oil ■ Gas □ Other

Figure 2. CO$_2$ emissions by sector

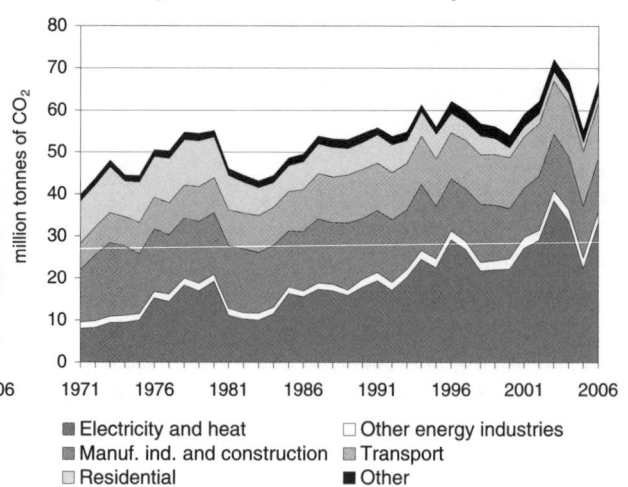

■ Electricity and heat ☐ Other energy industries
■ Manuf. ind. and construction ■ Transport
☐ Residential ■ Other

Figure 3. CO$_2$ emissions by sector

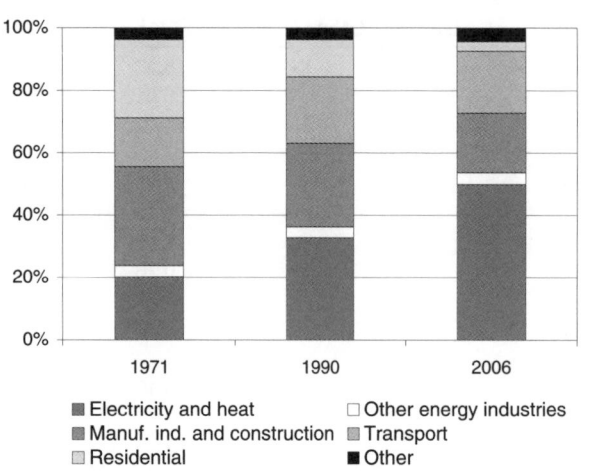

■ Electricity and heat ☐ Other energy industries
■ Manuf. ind. and construction ■ Transport
☐ Residential ■ Other

Figure 4. Reference vs Sectoral Approach

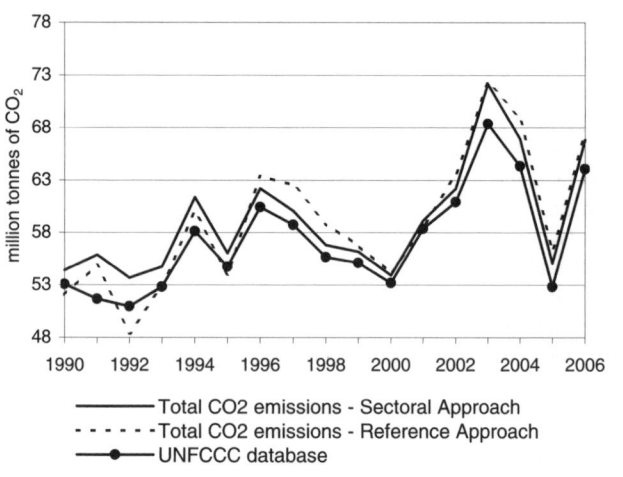

—— Total CO2 emissions - Sectoral Approach
----- Total CO2 emissions - Reference Approach
—●— UNFCCC database

Figure 5. Electricity generation by fuel

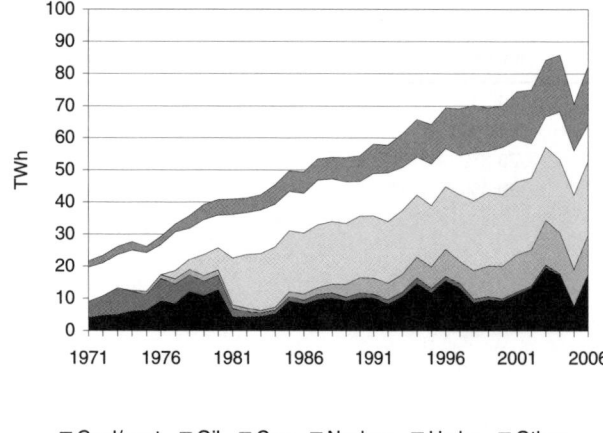

■ Coal/peat ■ Oil ☐ Gas ☐ Nuclear □ Hydro ■ Other

Figure 6. Key indicators

1990 = 100

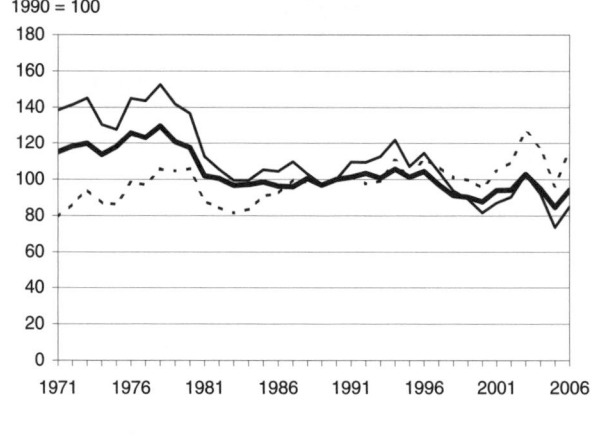

—— CO2/TPES —— CO2/GDP ----- CO2/capita

Finland / Finlande

Key indicators

	1990	1995	2000	2003	2004	2005	2006	% change 90-06
CO$_2$ Sectoral Approach (Mt of CO$_2$)	54.40	56.02	53.91	72.16	66.93	55.06	66.84	22.9%
CO$_2$ Reference Approach (Mt of CO$_2$)	52.06	53.98	54.17	72.33	68.97	56.27	67.47	29.6%
TPES (PJ)	1 202	1 223	1 359	1 549	1 559	1 439	1 567	30.4%
TPES (Mtoe)	28.71	29.21	32.45	37.00	37.23	34.38	37.44	30.4%
GDP (billion 2000 US$ using exch. rates)	100.30	96.50	121.90	129.40	134.20	138.10	145.00	44.6%
GDP (billion 2000 US$ using PPPs)	109.28	105.19	132.78	140.98	146.24	150.50	158.04	44.6%
Population (millions)	4.99	5.11	5.18	5.21	5.23	5.25	5.27	5.6%
CO$_2$ / TPES (t CO$_2$ per TJ)	45.3	45.8	39.7	46.6	42.9	38.2	42.6	-5.8%
CO$_2$ / GDP (kg CO$_2$ per 2000 US$)	0.54	0.58	0.44	0.56	0.50	0.40	0.46	-15.0%
CO$_2$ / GDP (kg CO$_2$ per 2000 US$ PPP)	0.50	0.53	0.41	0.51	0.46	0.37	0.42	-15.0%
CO$_2$ / population (t CO$_2$ per capita)	10.91	10.97	10.42	13.84	12.81	10.50	12.69	16.3%

Ratios are based on the Sectoral Approach.

2006 CO$_2$ emissions by sector

million tonnes of CO$_2$	Coal/peat	Oil	Gas	Other *	Total	% change 90-06
Sectoral Approach	**30.69**	**26.72**	**8.99**	**0.44**	**66.84**	**22.9%**
Main activity producer elec. and heat	22.83	1.21	5.32	0.13	29.49	88.1%
Unallocated autoproducers	2.37	0.42	0.82	0.17	3.78	75.7%
Other energy industries	-	1.93	0.61	-	2.55	35.2%
Manufacturing industries and construction	5.35	5.28	2.01	0.14	12.78	-12.1%
Transport	-	13.20	0.05	-	13.25	14.2%
of which: road	*-*	*11.95*	*0.01*	*-*	*11.96*	*12.2%*
Other sectors	0.13	4.68	0.18	0.01	4.99	-41.6%
of which: residential	*0.06*	*1.92*	*0.08*	*-*	*2.06*	*-68.1%*
Reference Approach	**29.80**	**28.23**	**9.00**	**0.44**	**67.47**	**29.6%**
Diff. due to losses and/or transformation	- 0.58	0.30	-	-	- 0.28	
Statistical differences	- 0.31	1.22	0.01	-	0.91	
Memo: international marine bunkers	*-*	*1.75*	*-*	*-*	*1.75*	*-1.8%*
Memo: international aviation	*-*	*1.38*	*-*	*-*	*1.38*	*41.6%*

* Other includes industrial waste and non-renewable municipal waste.

Key sources for CO$_2$ emissions from fuel combustion in 2006

IPCC source category	CO$_2$ emissions (Mt of CO$_2$)	% change 90-06	Level assessment (%) **	Cumulative total (%)
Main activity prod. elec. and heat - coal/peat	22.83	83.7%	27.5	27.5
Road - oil	11.95	12.2%	14.4	41.9
Manufacturing industries - coal/peat	5.35	-26.3%	6.4	48.3
Main activity prod. elec. and heat - gas	5.32	173.2%	6.4	54.7
Manufacturing industries - oil	5.28	3.6%	6.4	61.1
Non-specified other sectors - oil	2.76	34.0%	3.3	64.4
Unallocated autoproducers - coal/peat	2.37	76.8%	2.9	67.2
Manufacturing industries - gas	2.01	-7.8%	2.4	69.7
Other energy industries - oil	1.93	42.5%	2.3	72.0
Residential - oil	1.92	-69.6%	2.3	74.3
Other transport - oil	1.25	32.4%	1.5	75.8
Memo: total CO$_2$ from fuel combustion	*66.84*	*22.9%*	*80.5*	*80.5*

** Percent calculated using the total GHG estimate for CO$_2$, CH$_4$, N$_2$O, HFCs, PFCs and SF$_6$ excluding CO$_2$ emissions/removals from land use change and forestry.

France

Figure 1. CO₂ emissions by fuel

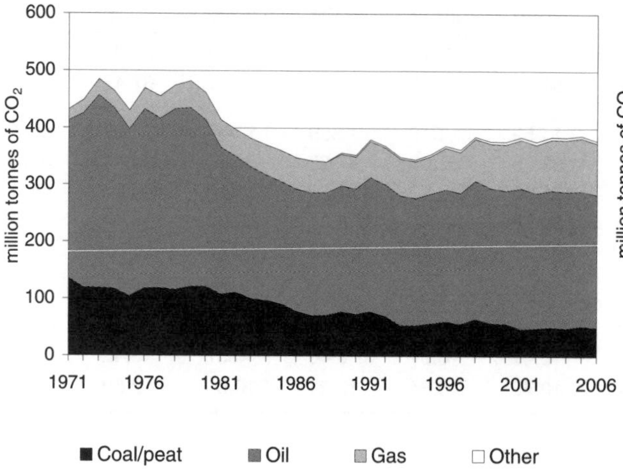

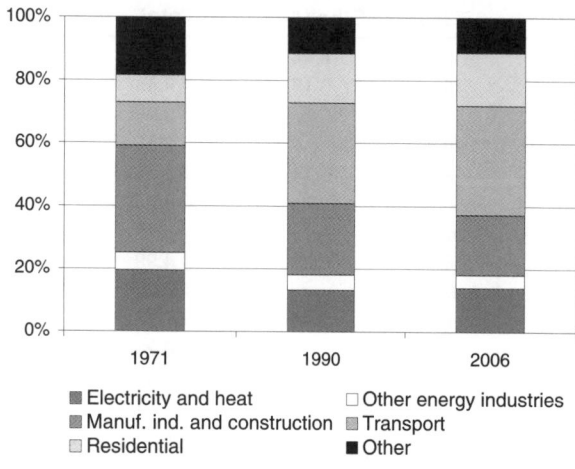

Coal/peat   Oil   Gas   Other

Figure 2. CO₂ emissions by sector

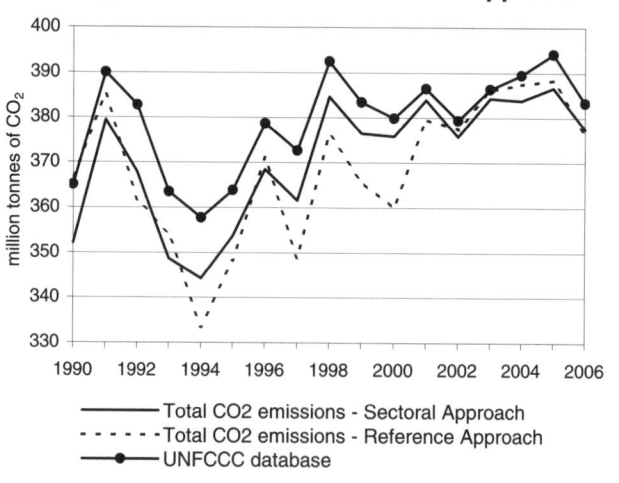

Electricity and heat   Other energy industries
Manuf. ind. and construction   Transport
Residential   Other

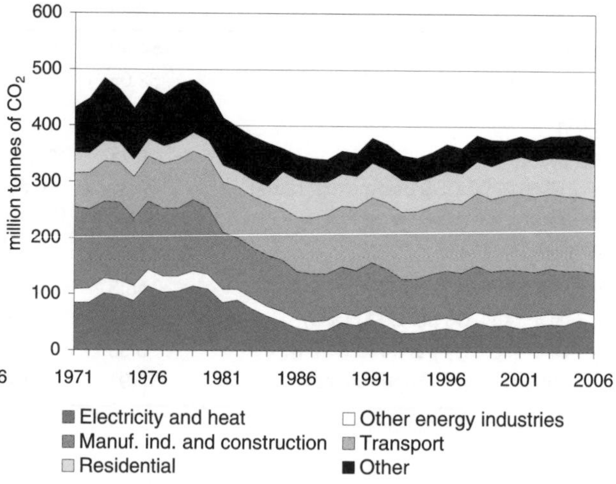

Figure 3. CO₂ emissions by sector

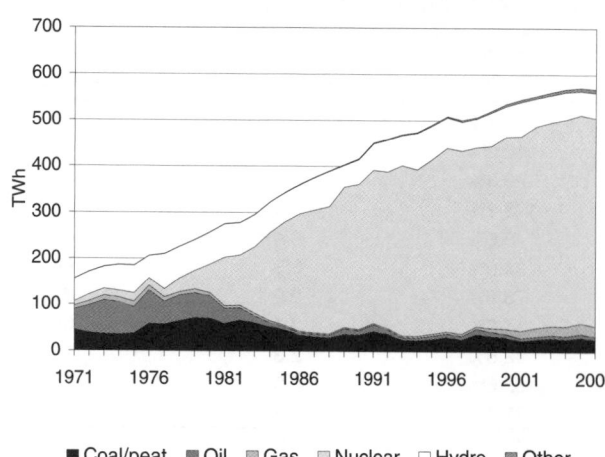

Electricity and heat   Other energy industries
Manuf. ind. and construction   Transport
Residential   Other

Figure 4. Reference vs Sectoral Approach

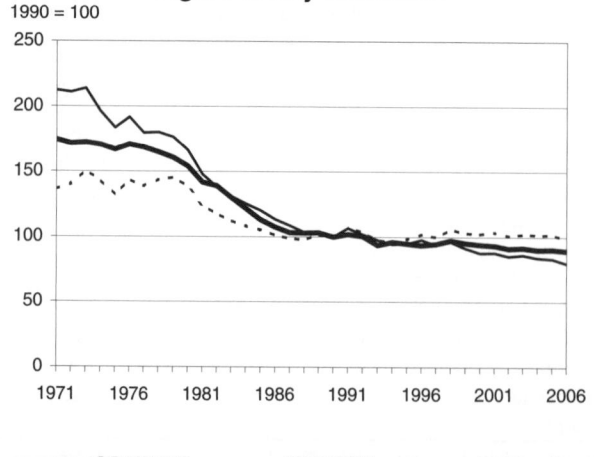

—— Total CO2 emissions - Sectoral Approach
----- Total CO2 emissions - Reference Approach
—●— UNFCCC database

Figure 5. Electricity generation by fuel

Coal/peat   Oil   Gas   Nuclear   Hydro   Other

Figure 6. Key indicators

1990 = 100

—— CO2/TPES   —— CO2/GDP   ----- CO2/capita

France
Key indicators

	1990	1995	2000	2003	2004	2005	2006	% change 90-06
CO$_2$ Sectoral Approach (Mt of CO$_2$)	352.11	353.69	375.80	384.28	383.82	386.64	377.49	7.2%
CO$_2$ Reference Approach (Mt of CO$_2$)	366.74	348.16	360.00	386.10	387.43	388.38	376.48	2.7%
TPES (PJ)	9 529	10 099	10 811	11 364	11 532	11 564	11 416	19.8%
TPES (Mtoe)	227.60	241.20	258.21	271.43	275.44	276.20	272.67	19.8%
GDP (billion 2000 US$ using exch. rates)	1 091.80	1 156.30	1 328.00	1 381.30	1 415.50	1 439.70	1 468.30	34.5%
GDP (billion 2000 US$ using PPPs)	1 260.37	1 334.77	1 532.95	1 594.56	1 633.95	1 661.91	1 694.97	34.5%
Population (millions)	58.17	59.42	60.75	62.04	62.45	62.82	63.20	8.6%
CO$_2$ / TPES (t CO$_2$ per TJ)	37.0	35.0	34.8	33.8	33.3	33.4	33.1	-10.5%
CO$_2$ / GDP (kg CO$_2$ per 2000 US$)	0.32	0.31	0.28	0.28	0.27	0.27	0.26	-20.3%
CO$_2$ / GDP (kg CO$_2$ per 2000 US$ PPP)	0.28	0.27	0.25	0.24	0.23	0.23	0.22	-20.3%
CO$_2$ / population (t CO$_2$ per capita)	6.05	5.95	6.19	6.19	6.15	6.15	5.97	-1.3%

Ratios are based on the Sectoral Approach.

2006 CO$_2$ emissions by sector

million tonnes of CO$_2$	Coal/peat	Oil	Gas	Other *	Total	% change 90-06
Sectoral Approach	**50.43**	**232.98**	**90.10**	**3.98**	**377.49**	**7.2%**
Main activity producer elec. and heat	22.64	3.85	5.11	0.35	31.96	29.7%
Unallocated autoproducers	5.38	4.32	7.81	2.80	20.30	-5.6%
Other energy industries	3.50	12.09	0.40	-	16.00	-8.3%
Manufacturing industries and construction	17.53	30.34	24.20	-	72.08	-10.0%
Transport	-	131.31	0.14	-	131.45	16.8%
of which: road	-	125.09	0.14	-	125.24	16.3%
Other sectors	1.38	51.06	52.43	0.84	105.71	10.2%
of which: residential	1.38	28.01	34.14	-	63.54	14.9%
Reference Approach	**50.80**	**230.37**	**91.32**	**3.98**	**376.48**	**2.7%**
Diff. due to losses and/or transformation	1.50	- 2.21	1.37	-	0.66	
Statistical differences	- 1.12	- 0.41	- 0.14	- 0.00	- 1.67	
Memo: international marine bunkers	-	8.97	-	-	8.97	12.7%
Memo: international aviation	-	16.86	-	-	16.86	80.8%

* Other includes industrial waste and non-renewable municipal waste.

Key sources for CO$_2$ emissions from fuel combustion in 2006

IPCC source category	CO$_2$ emissions (Mt of CO$_2$)	% change 90-06	Level assessment (%) **	Cumulative total (%)
Road - oil	125.09	16.1%	23.1	23.1
Residential - gas ***	34.14	121.8%	6.3	29.5
Manufacturing industries - oil	30.34	9.3%	5.6	35.1
Residential - oil	28.01	-16.1%	5.2	40.2
Manufacturing industries - gas	24.20	-1.1%	4.5	44.7
Non-specified other sectors - oil	23.05	-11.4%	4.3	49.0
Main activity prod. elec. and heat - coal/peat	22.64	8.3%	4.2	53.2
Non-specified other sectors - gas	18.29	25.4%	3.4	56.5
Manufacturing industries - coal/peat	17.53	-37.1%	3.2	59.8
Other energy industries - oil	12.09	-20.4%	2.2	62.0
Unallocated autoproducers - gas ***	7.81	752.4%	1.4	63.5
Memo: total CO$_2$ from fuel combustion	377.49	7.2%	69.8	69.8

** Percent calculated using the total GHG estimate for CO$_2$, CH$_4$, N$_2$O, HFCs, PFCs and SF$_6$ excluding CO$_2$ emissions/removals from land use change and forestry.

*** The high growth in gas is due to changes in methodology in 2000.

Gabon

Figure 1. CO_2 emissions by fuel

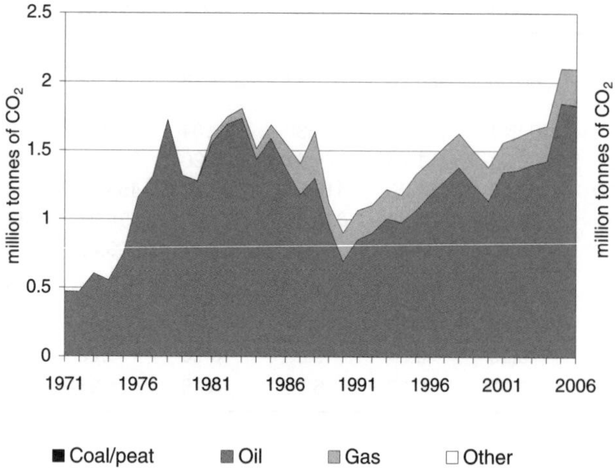

million tonnes of CO2
2.5
2
1.5
1
0.5
0
1971
1976
1981
1986
1991
1996
2001
2006
Coal/peat
Oil
Gas
Other

Figure 2. CO_2 emissions by sector

million tonnes of CO2
Electricity and heat
Other energy industries
Manuf. ind. and construction
Transport
Residential
Other

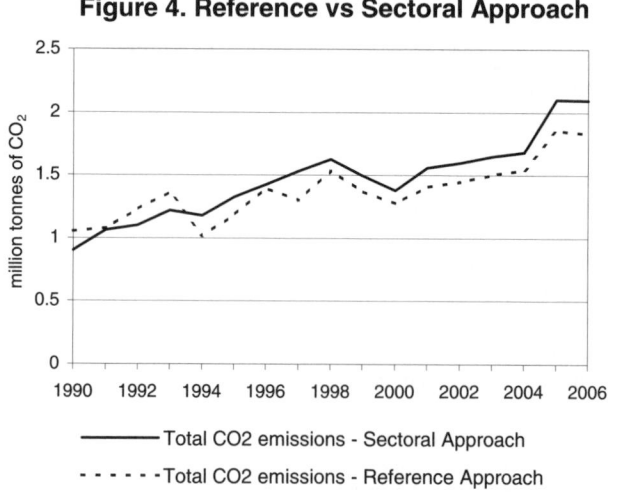

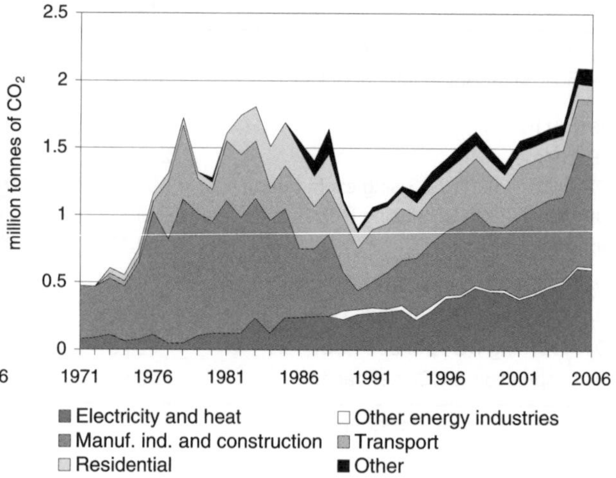

Figure 3. CO_2 emissions by sector

100%
80%
60%
40%
20%
0%
1971
1990
2006
Electricity and heat
Other energy industries
Manuf. ind. and construction
Transport
Residential
Other

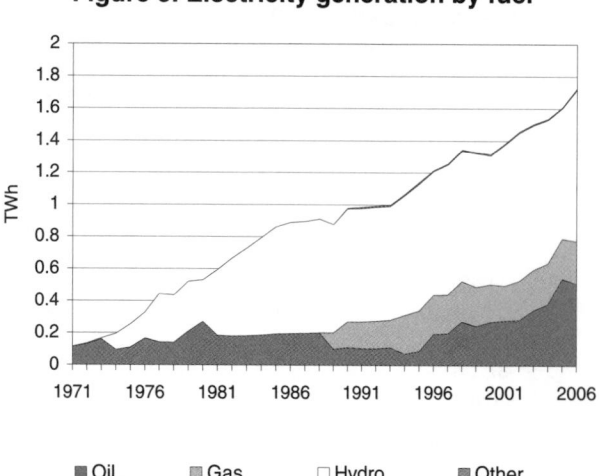

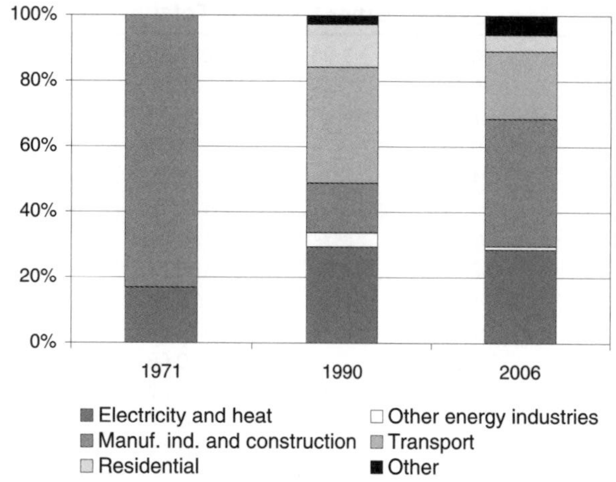

Figure 4. Reference vs Sectoral Approach

million tonnes of CO2
Total CO2 emissions - Sectoral Approach
Total CO2 emissions - Reference Approach

Figure 5. Electricity generation by fuel

TWh
Oil
Gas
Hydro
Other

Figure 6. Key indicators

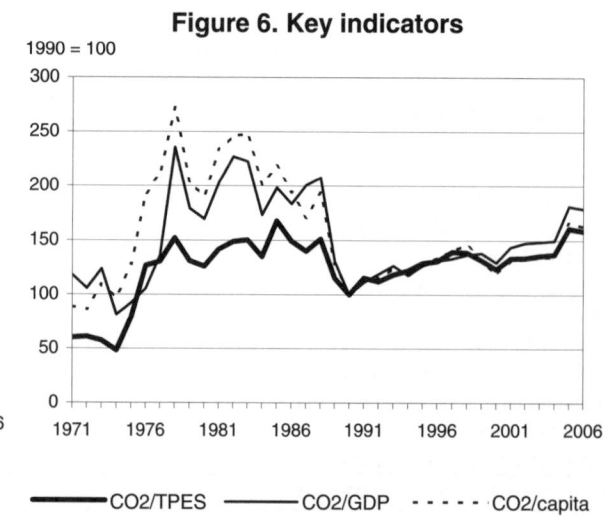

1990 = 100
CO2/TPES
CO2/GDP
CO2/capita

Gabon

Key indicators

	1990	1995	2000	2003	2004	2005	2006	% change 90-06
CO$_2$ Sectoral Approach (Mt of CO$_2$)	0.90	1.33	1.38	1.65	1.68	2.10	2.09	132.3%
CO$_2$ Reference Approach (Mt of CO$_2$)	1.05	1.18	1.28	1.50	1.54	1.86	1.83	74.1%
TPES (PJ)	52	59	65	70	71	75	76	46.6%
TPES (Mtoe)	1.24	1.42	1.54	1.68	1.69	1.80	1.82	46.6%
GDP (billion 2000 US$ using exch. rates)	4.30	5.00	5.07	5.29	5.36	5.52	5.59	30.0%
GDP (billion 2000 US$ using PPPs)	6.31	7.34	7.44	7.77	7.87	8.11	8.20	30.0%
Population (millions)	0.92	1.06	1.18	1.25	1.27	1.29	1.31	42.8%
CO$_2$ / TPES (t CO$_2$ per TJ)	17.3	22.3	21.3	23.5	23.7	27.8	27.4	58.5%
CO$_2$ / GDP (kg CO$_2$ per 2000 US$)	0.21	0.27	0.27	0.31	0.31	0.38	0.37	78.7%
CO$_2$ / GDP (kg CO$_2$ per 2000 US$ PPP)	0.14	0.18	0.19	0.21	0.21	0.26	0.26	78.7%
CO$_2$ / population (t CO$_2$ per capita)	0.98	1.26	1.17	1.32	1.32	1.63	1.60	62.7%

Ratios are based on the Sectoral Approach.

2006 CO$_2$ emissions by sector

million tonnes of CO$_2$	Coal/peat	Oil	Gas	Other *	Total	% change 90-06
Sectoral Approach	-	**1.83**	**0.27**	-	**2.09**	**132.3%**
Main activity producer elec. and heat	-	0.24	0.14	-	0.38	83.9%
Unallocated autoproducers	-	0.12	0.10	-	0.22	276.8%
Other energy industries	-	-	0.02	-	0.02	-44.1%
Manufacturing industries and construction	-	0.81	0.00	-	0.81	497.5%
Transport	-	0.43	-	-	0.43	34.9%
of which: road	-	*0.43*	-	-	*0.43*	*34.9%*
Other sectors	-	0.23	-	-	0.23	61.3%
of which: residential	-	*0.11*	-	-	*0.11*	*-9.7%*
Reference Approach	-	**1.58**	**0.25**	-	**1.83**	**74.1%**
Diff. due to losses and/or transformation	-	0.07	-	-	0.07	
Statistical differences	-	- 0.31	- 0.02	-	- 0.33	
Memo: international marine bunkers	-	*0.48*	-	-	*0.48*	*506.9%*
Memo: international aviation	-	*0.20*	-	-	*0.20*	*1.4%*

* Other includes industrial waste and non-renewable municipal waste.

Key sources for CO$_2$ emissions from fuel combustion in 2006

IPCC source category	CO$_2$ emissions (Mt of CO$_2$)	% change 90-06	Level assessment (%) **	Cumulative total (%)
Manufacturing industries - oil	0.81	508.3%	10.1	10.1
Road - oil	0.43	34.9%	5.4	15.5
Main activity prod. elec. and heat - oil	0.24	187.5%	3.0	18.4
Main activity prod. elec. and heat - gas	0.14	14.8%	1.8	20.2
Non-specified other sectors - oil	0.12	387.5%	1.5	21.7
Unallocated autoproducers - oil	0.12	660.0%	1.5	23.2
Residential - oil	0.11	-9.7%	1.3	24.6
Unallocated autoproducers - gas	0.10	132.6%	1.2	25.8
Other energy industries - gas	0.02	-44.1%	0.3	26.0
Manufacturing industries - gas	0.00	1.8%	0.0	26.1
-	-	-	-	-
Memo: total CO$_2$ from fuel combustion	*2.09*	*132.3%*	*26.1*	*26.1*

** Percent calculated using the total GHG estimate for CO$_2$, CH$_4$, N$_2$O, HFCs, PFCs and SF$_6$ excluding CO$_2$ emissions/removals from land use change and forestry.

Georgia / Géorgie

Figure 1. CO$_2$ emissions by fuel

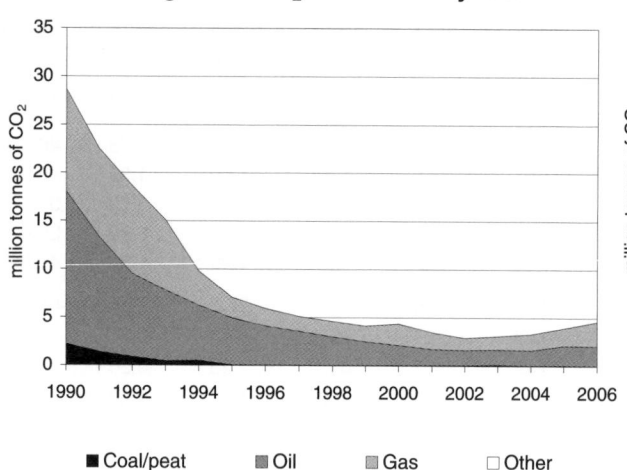

■ Coal/peat   ■ Oil   ■ Gas   □ Other

Figure 2. CO$_2$ emissions by sector

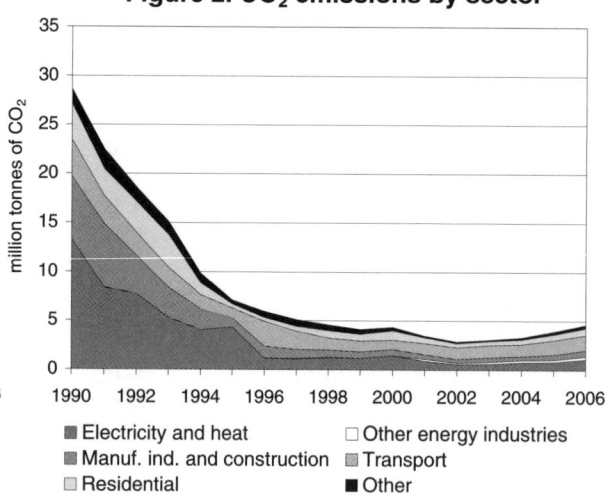

■ Electricity and heat   □ Other energy industries
■ Manuf. ind. and construction ■ Transport
□ Residential   ■ Other

Figure 3. CO$_2$ emissions by sector

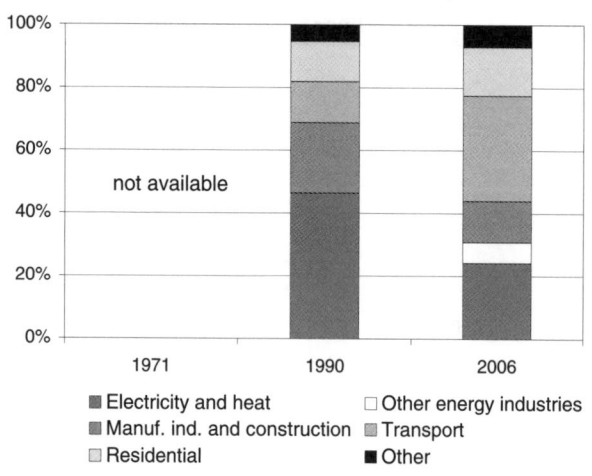

■ Electricity and heat   □ Other energy industries
■ Manuf. ind. and construction ■ Transport
□ Residential   ■ Other

Figure 4. Reference vs Sectoral Approach

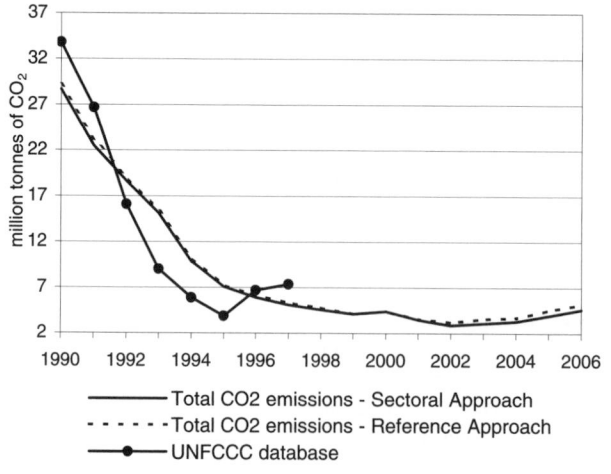

—— Total CO2 emissions - Sectoral Approach
----- Total CO2 emissions - Reference Approach
—●— UNFCCC database

Figure 5. Electricity generation by fuel

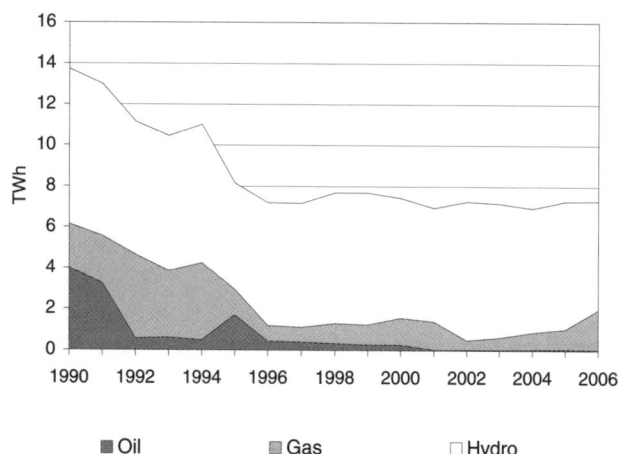

■ Oil   ■ Gas   □ Hydro

Figure 6. Key indicators

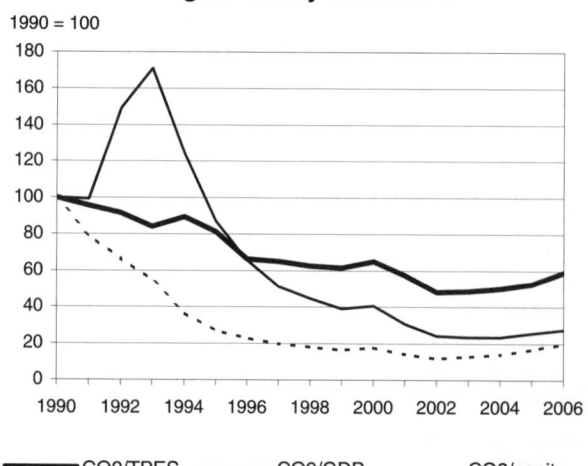

—— CO2/TPES   —— CO2/GDP   ----- CO2/capita

Georgia / Géorgie

Key indicators

	1990	1995	2000	2003	2004	2005	2006	% change 90-06
CO$_2$ Sectoral Approach (Mt of CO$_2$)	28.69	7.06	4.37	3.09	3.29	3.92	4.61	-83.9%
CO$_2$ Reference Approach (Mt of CO$_2$)	29.17	7.18	4.39	3.56	3.67	4.53	5.17	-82.3%
TPES (PJ)	515	156	121	114	118	134	140	-72.8%
TPES (Mtoe)	12.31	3.73	2.88	2.73	2.82	3.20	3.34	-72.8%
GDP (billion 2000 US$ using exch. rates)	8.15	2.30	3.06	3.76	3.98	4.34	4.75	-41.7%
GDP (billion 2000 US$ using PPPs)	25.15	7.11	9.43	11.59	12.26	13.40	14.66	-41.7%
Population (millions)	5.46	5.03	4.72	4.56	4.52	4.47	4.43	-18.8%
CO$_2$ / TPES (t CO$_2$ per TJ)	55.7	45.3	36.2	27.0	27.9	29.3	32.9	-40.9%
CO$_2$ / GDP (kg CO$_2$ per 2000 US$)	3.52	3.07	1.43	0.82	0.83	0.90	0.97	-72.5%
CO$_2$ / GDP (kg CO$_2$ per 2000 US$ PPP)	1.14	0.99	0.46	0.27	0.27	0.29	0.31	-72.5%
CO$_2$ / population (t CO$_2$ per capita)	5.25	1.40	0.93	0.68	0.73	0.88	1.04	-80.2%

Ratios are based on the Sectoral Approach.

2006 CO$_2$ emissions by sector

million tonnes of CO$_2$	Coal/peat	Oil	Gas	Other *	Total	% change 90-06
Sectoral Approach	**0.05**	**2.00**	**2.55**	**-**	**4.61**	**-83.9%**
Main activity producer elec. and heat	-	0.06	1.05	-	1.11	-91.6%
Unallocated autoproducers	-	-	-	-	-	-
Other energy industries	-	0.02	0.29	-	0.31	x
Manufacturing industries and construction	0.03	0.07	0.50	-	0.60	-90.7%
Transport	-	1.51	0.04	-	1.55	-58.7%
of which: road	-	*1.51*	*0.03*	-	*1.53*	*-55.7%*
Other sectors	0.01	0.34	0.68	-	1.04	-80.1%
of which: residential	*0.01*	*0.17*	*0.53*	-	*0.71*	*-80.7%*
Reference Approach	**0.05**	**2.01**	**3.12**	**-**	**5.17**	**-82.3%**
Diff. due to losses and/or transformation		0.00	0.56	-	0.57	
Statistical differences	0.00	- 0.00	0.00	-	0.00	
Memo: international marine bunkers	-	..	-	-	..	..
Memo: international aviation	-	*0.11*	-	-	*0.11*	*-81.2%*

* Other includes industrial waste and non-renewable municipal waste.

Key sources for CO$_2$ emissions from fuel combustion in 2006

IPCC source category	CO$_2$ emissions (Mt of CO$_2$)	% change 90-06	Level assessment (%) **	Cumulative total (%)
Road - oil	1.51	-56.5%	11.9	11.9
Main activity prod. elec. and heat - gas	1.05	-77.1%	8.3	20.2
Residential - gas	0.53	-79.8%	4.2	24.3
Manufacturing industries - gas	0.50	-83.8%	3.9	28.3
Other energy industries - gas	0.29	x	2.3	30.5
Non-specified other sectors - oil	0.18	-84.1%	1.4	31.9
Residential - oil	0.17	-83.0%	1.3	33.3
Non-specified other sectors - gas	0.15	-49.3%	1.2	34.4
Manufacturing industries - oil	0.07	-96.4%	0.6	35.0
Main activity prod. elec. and heat - oil	0.06	-99.2%	0.5	35.5
Manufacturing industries - coal/peat	0.03	-97.5%	0.3	35.8
Memo: total CO$_2$ from fuel combustion	*4.61*	*-83.9%*	*36.4*	*36.4*

** Percent calculated using the total GHG estimate for CO$_2$, CH$_4$, N$_2$O, HFCs, PFCs and SF$_6$ excluding CO$_2$ emissions/removals from land use change and forestry.

Germany / Allemagne

Figure 1. CO$_2$ emissions by fuel

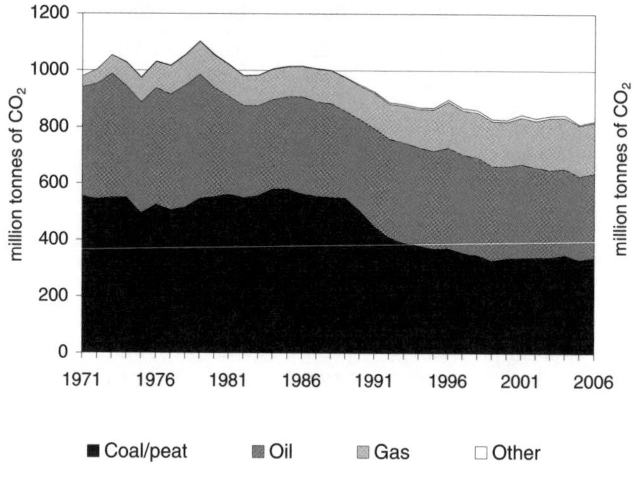

■ Coal/peat   ■ Oil   ■ Gas   □ Other

Figure 2. CO$_2$ emissions by sector

■ Electricity and heat   □ Other energy industries
■ Manuf. ind. and construction ■ Transport
□ Residential   ■ Other

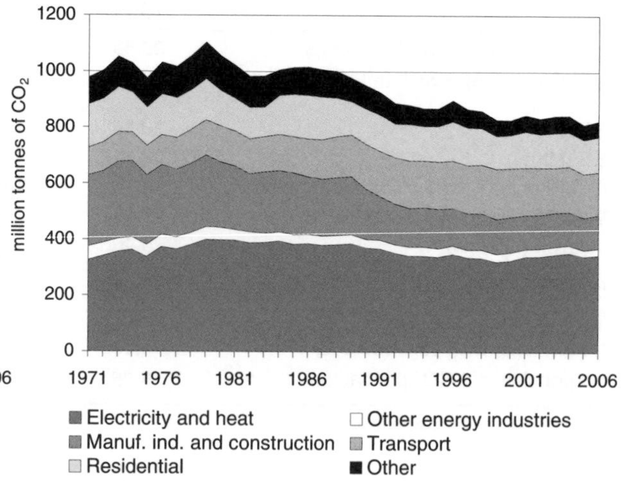

Figure 3. CO$_2$ emissions by sector

■ Electricity and heat   □ Other energy industries
■ Manuf. ind. and construction ■ Transport
□ Residential   ■ Other

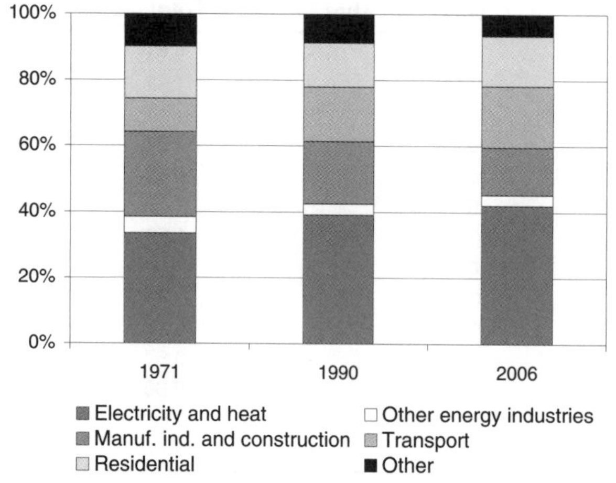

Figure 4. Reference vs Sectoral Approach

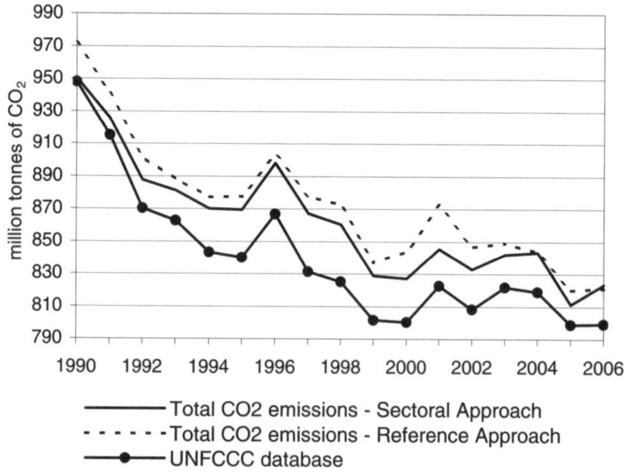

——— Total CO2 emissions - Sectoral Approach
- - - - Total CO2 emissions - Reference Approach
—●— UNFCCC database

Figure 5. Electricity generation by fuel

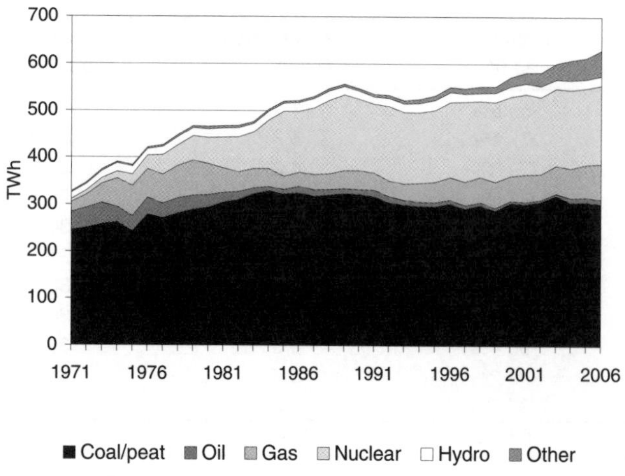

■ Coal/peat   ■ Oil   ■ Gas   □ Nuclear   □ Hydro   ■ Other

Figure 6. Key indicators

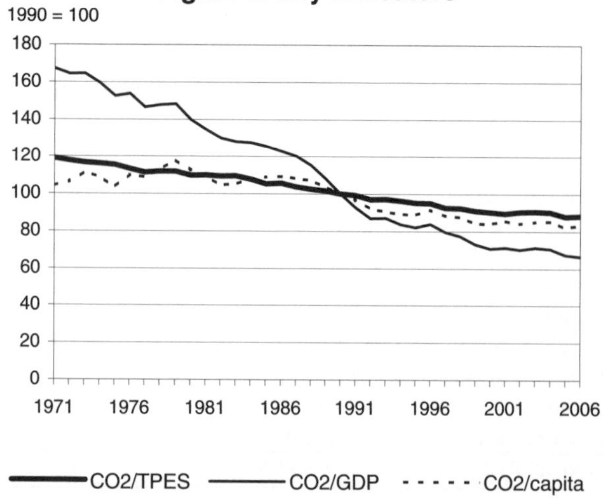

——CO2/TPES   ——CO2/GDP   - - - - CO2/capita

Germany / Allemagne
Key indicators

	1990	1995	2000	2003	2004	2005	2006	% change 90-06
CO$_2$ Sectoral Approach (Mt of CO$_2$)	950.42	869.33	827.14	842.05	843.38	811.27	823.46	-13.4%
CO$_2$ Reference Approach (Mt of CO$_2$)	971.70	877.47	843.88	849.01	843.55	820.05	821.34	-15.5%
TPES (PJ)	14 890	14 311	14 367	14 545	14 627	14 456	14 593	-2.0%
TPES (Mtoe)	355.65	341.82	343.16	347.41	349.36	345.27	348.56	-2.0%
GDP (billion 2000 US$ using exch. rates)	1 543.20	1 720.50	1 900.20	1 919.60	1 939.90	1 955.10	2 011.20	30.3%
GDP (billion 2000 US$ using PPPs)	1 730.06	1 928.79	2 130.32	2 152.05	2 174.84	2 191.89	2 254.73	30.3%
Population (millions)	79.36	81.66	82.19	82.52	82.50	82.46	82.37	3.8%
CO$_2$ / TPES (t CO$_2$ per TJ)	63.8	60.7	57.6	57.9	57.7	56.1	56.4	-11.6%
CO$_2$ / GDP (kg CO$_2$ per 2000 US$)	0.62	0.51	0.44	0.44	0.43	0.42	0.41	-33.5%
CO$_2$ / GDP (kg CO$_2$ per 2000 US$ PPP)	0.55	0.45	0.39	0.39	0.39	0.37	0.37	-33.5%
CO$_2$ / population (t CO$_2$ per capita)	11.98	10.65	10.06	10.20	10.22	9.84	10.00	-16.5%

Ratios are based on the Sectoral Approach.

2006 CO$_2$ emissions by sector

million tonnes of CO$_2$	Coal/peat	Oil	Gas	Other *	Total	% change 90-06
Sectoral Approach	**339.27**	**297.71**	**182.23**	**4.26**	**823.46**	**-13.4%**
Main activity producer elec. and heat	265.14	3.69	28.26	4.18	301.26	-2.6%
Unallocated autoproducers	23.54	4.96	14.88	0.08	43.46	-30.2%
Other energy industries	6.17	19.94	0.95	-	27.07	-13.1%
Manufacturing industries and construction	40.54	33.80	43.68	-	118.01	-34.2%
Transport	-	153.77	-	-	153.77	-2.9%
of which: road	-	*145.61*	-	-	*145.61*	*-2.1%*
Other sectors	3.87	81.55	94.47	-	179.89	-14.4%
of which: residential	*2.38*	*55.46*	*67.30*	-	*125.13*	*-1.6%*
Reference Approach	**328.53**	**304.48**	**184.07**	**4.26**	**821.34**	**-15.5%**
Diff. due to losses and/or transformation	- 3.48	10.22	0.61	-	7.34	
Statistical differences	- 7.25	- 3.45	1.24	-	- 9.46	
Memo: international marine bunkers	-	*8.11*	-	-	*8.11*	*4.1%*
Memo: international aviation	-	*20.69*	-	-	*20.69*	*64.5%*

* Other includes industrial waste and non-renewable municipal waste.

Key sources for CO$_2$ emissions from fuel combustion in 2006

IPCC source category	CO$_2$ emissions (Mt of CO$_2$)	% change 90-06	Level assessment (%) **	Cumulative total (%)
Main activity prod. elec. and heat - coal/peat	265.14	-5.4%	25.8	25.8
Road - oil	145.61	-2.1%	14.2	39.9
Residential - gas	67.30	114.8%	6.5	46.5
Residential - oil	55.46	0.3%	5.4	51.9
Manufacturing industries - gas	43.68	0.7%	4.2	56.1
Manufacturing industries - coal/peat	40.54	-56.8%	3.9	60.0
Manufacturing industries - oil	33.80	-19.6%	3.3	63.3
Main activity prod. elec. and heat - gas	28.26	53.1%	2.7	66.1
Non-specified other sectors - gas	27.17	83.1%	2.6	68.7
Non-specified other sectors - oil	26.09	-34.1%	2.5	71.2
Unallocated autoproducers - coal/peat	23.54	-54.2%	2.3	73.5
Memo: total CO$_2$ from fuel combustion	*823.46*	*-13.4%*	*80.0*	*80.0*

** Percent calculated using the total GHG estimate for CO$_2$, CH$_4$, N$_2$O, HFCs, PFCs and SF$_6$ excluding CO$_2$ emissions/removals from land use change and forestry.

Ghana

Figure 1. CO_2 emissions by fuel

million tonnes of CO2
10
9
8
7
6
5
4
3
2
1
0
1971
1976
1981
1986
1991
1996
2001
2006
Coal/peat
Oil
Gas
Other

Figure 2. CO_2 emissions by sector

million tonnes of CO2
10
9
8
7
6
5
4
3
2
1
0
1971
1976
1981
1986
1991
1996
2001
2006
Electricity and heat
Other energy industries
Manuf. ind. and construction
Transport
Residential
Other

Figure 3. CO_2 emissions by sector

100%
80%
60%
40%
20%
0%
1971
1990
2006
Electricity and heat
Other energy industries
Manuf. ind. and construction
Transport
Residential
Other

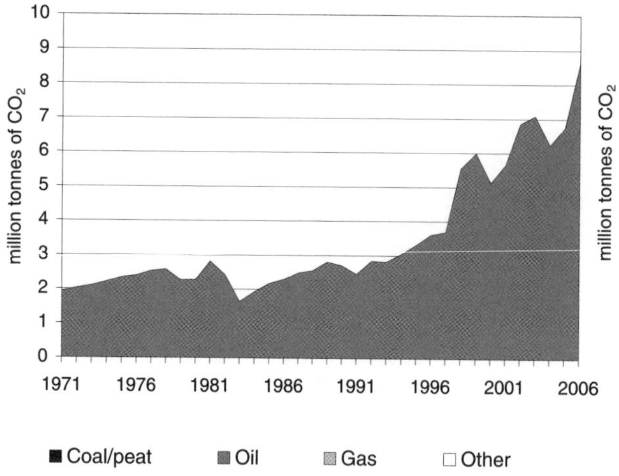

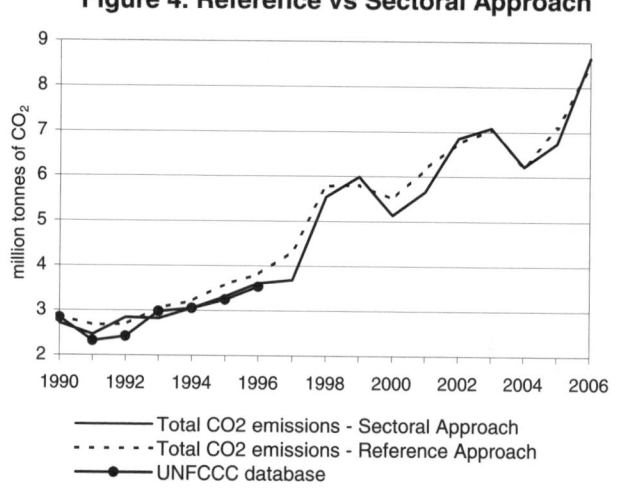

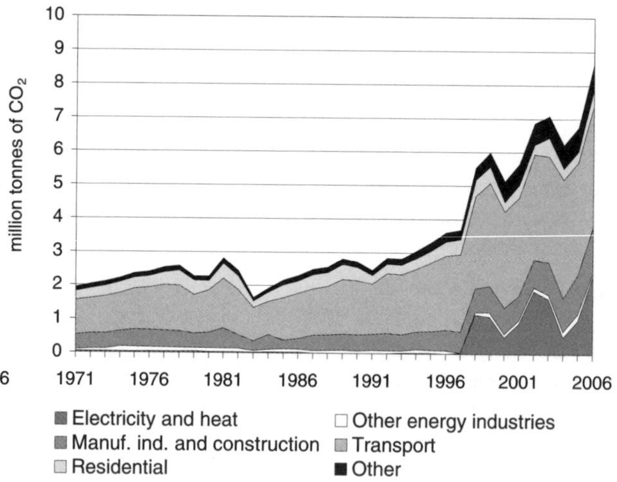

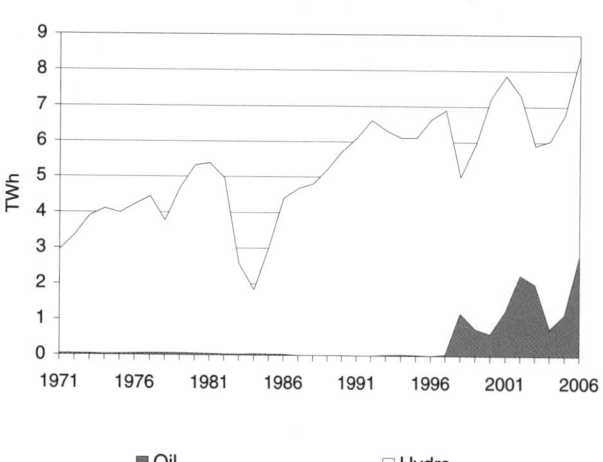

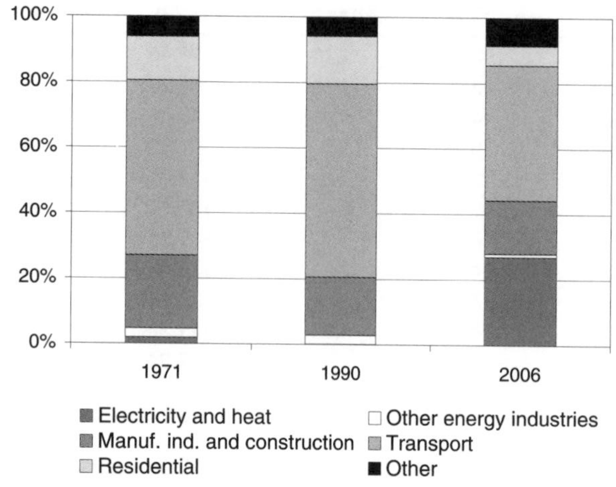

Figure 4. Reference vs Sectoral Approach

million tonnes of CO2
9
8
7
6
5
4
3
2
1990
1992
1994
1996
1998
2000
2002
2004
2006
Total CO2 emissions - Sectoral Approach
Total CO2 emissions - Reference Approach
UNFCCC database

Figure 5. Electricity generation by fuel

TWh
9
8
7
6
5
4
3
2
1
0
1971
1976
1981
1986
1991
1996
2001
2006
Oil
Hydro

Figure 6. Key indicators

1990 = 100
250
200
150
100
50
0
1971
1976
1981
1986
1991
1996
2001
2006
CO2/TPES
CO2/GDP
CO2/capita

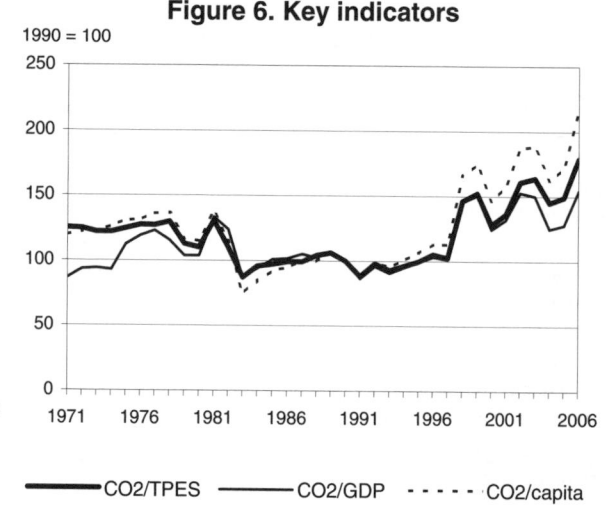

Ghana

Key indicators

	1990	1995	2000	2003	2004	2005	2006	% change 90-06
CO$_2$ Sectoral Approach (Mt of CO$_2$)	2.71	3.31	5.13	7.08	6.22	6.74	8.64	218.9%
CO$_2$ Reference Approach (Mt of CO$_2$)	2.85	3.59	5.50	7.04	6.22	7.10	8.49	198.0%
TPES (PJ)	223	273	330	357	354	372	398	78.0%
TPES (Mtoe)	5.34	6.53	7.89	8.52	8.45	8.89	9.50	78.0%
GDP (billion 2000 US$ using exch. rates)	3.26	4.03	4.97	5.69	6.00	6.36	6.75	106.9%
GDP (billion 2000 US$ using PPPs)	25.04	30.88	38.15	43.62	46.06	48.78	51.81	106.9%
Population (millions)	15.58	17.89	20.15	21.58	22.06	22.54	23.01	47.7%
CO$_2$ / TPES (t CO$_2$ per TJ)	12.1	12.1	15.5	19.9	17.6	18.1	21.7	79.2%
CO$_2$ / GDP (kg CO$_2$ per 2000 US$)	0.83	0.82	1.03	1.25	1.04	1.06	1.28	54.1%
CO$_2$ / GDP (kg CO$_2$ per 2000 US$ PPP)	0.11	0.11	0.13	0.16	0.14	0.14	0.17	54.2%
CO$_2$ / population (t CO$_2$ per capita)	0.17	0.19	0.25	0.33	0.28	0.30	0.38	116.0%

Ratios are based on the Sectoral Approach.

2006 CO$_2$ emissions by sector

million tonnes of CO$_2$	Coal/peat	Oil	Gas	Other *	Total	% change 90-06
Sectoral Approach	-	**8.64**	-	-	**8.64**	218.9%
Main activity producer elec. and heat	-	2.32	-	-	2.32	x
Unallocated autoproducers	-	-	-	-	-	-
Other energy industries	-	0.09	-	-	0.09	20.8%
Manufacturing industries and construction	-	1.40	-	-	1.40	191.1%
Transport	-	3.57	-	-	3.57	123.1%
of which: road	-	3.34	-	-	3.34	119.9%
Other sectors	-	1.26	-	-	1.26	127.6%
of which: residential	-	0.51	-	-	0.51	30.7%
Reference Approach	-	**8.49**	-	-	**8.49**	198.0%
Diff. due to losses and/or transformation	-	0.11	-	-	0.11	
Statistical differences	-	- 0.27	-	-	- 0.27	
Memo: international marine bunkers	-	..	-	-	..	..
Memo: international aviation	-	0.50	-	-	0.50	257.4%

* Other includes industrial waste and non-renewable municipal waste.

Key sources for CO$_2$ emissions from fuel combustion in 2006

IPCC source category	CO$_2$ emissions (Mt of CO$_2$)	% change 90-06	Level assessment (%) **	Cumulative total (%)
Road - oil	3.34	119.9%	11.5	11.5
Main activity prod. elec. and heat - oil	2.32	x	8.0	19.4
Manufacturing industries - oil	1.40	191.1%	4.8	24.2
Non-specified other sectors - oil	0.75	362.5%	2.6	26.8
Residential - oil	0.51	30.7%	1.8	28.6
Other transport - oil	0.23	180.8%	0.8	29.4
Other energy industries - oil	0.09	20.8%	0.3	29.7
-	-	-	-	-
-	-	-	-	-
-	-	-	-	-
-	-	-	-	-
Memo: total CO$_2$ from fuel combustion	8.64	218.9%	29.7	29.7

** Percent calculated using the total GHG estimate for CO$_2$, CH$_4$, N$_2$O, HFCs, PFCs and SF$_6$ excluding CO$_2$ emissions/removals from land use change and forestry.

Gibraltar

Figure 1. CO$_2$ emissions by fuel

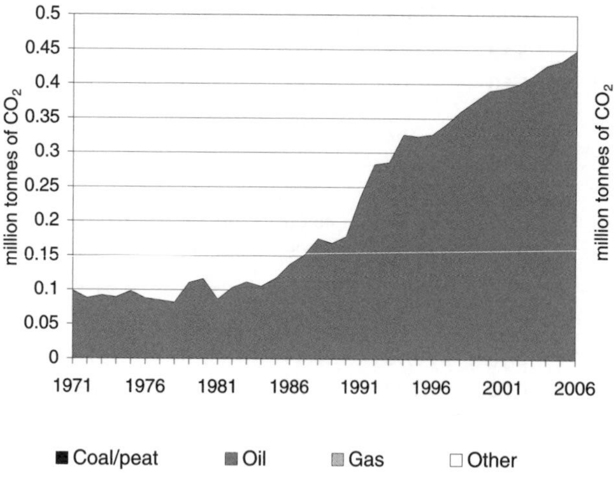

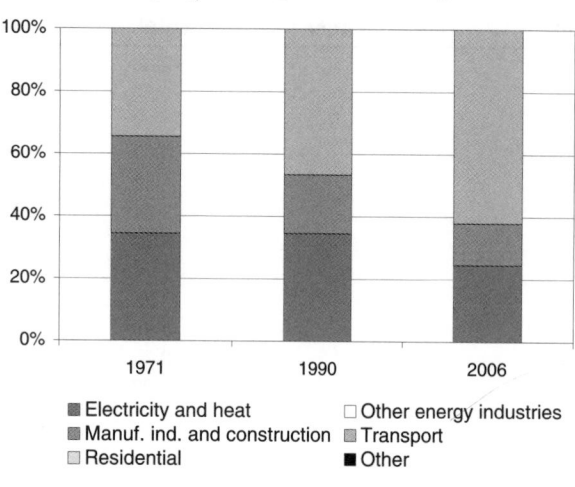

■ Coal/peat   ■ Oil   ▨ Gas   ☐ Other

Figure 2. CO$_2$ emissions by sector

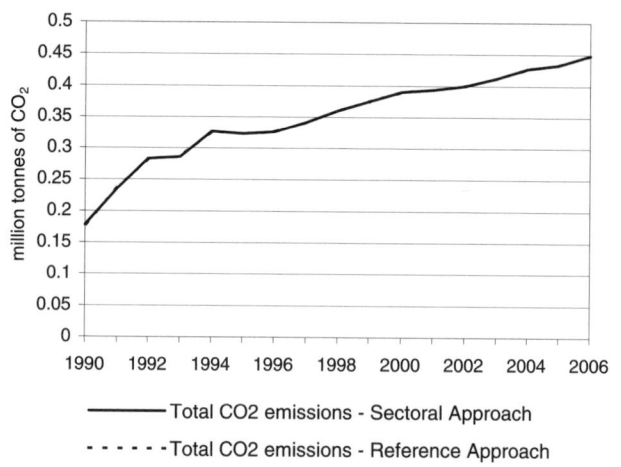

■ Electricity and heat	☐ Other energy industries
■ Manuf. ind. and construction	▨ Transport
☐ Residential	■ Other

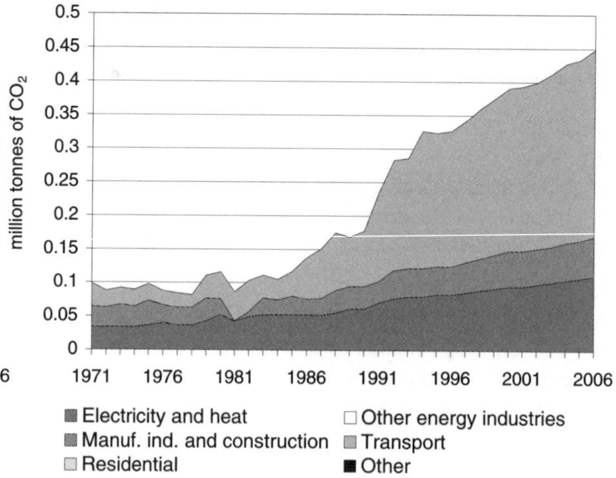

Figure 3. CO$_2$ emissions by sector

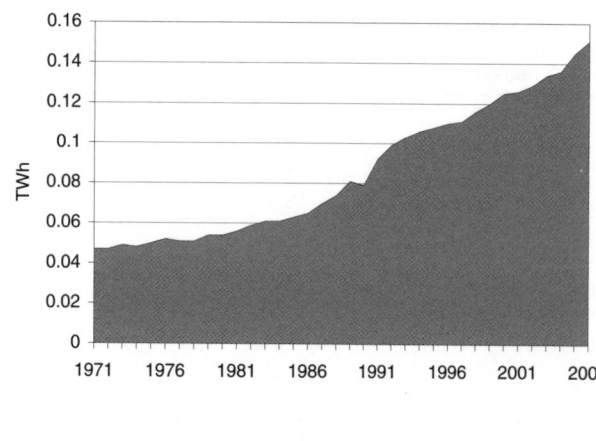

■ Electricity and heat	☐ Other energy industries
■ Manuf. ind. and construction	▨ Transport
☐ Residential	■ Other

Figure 4. Reference vs Sectoral Approach

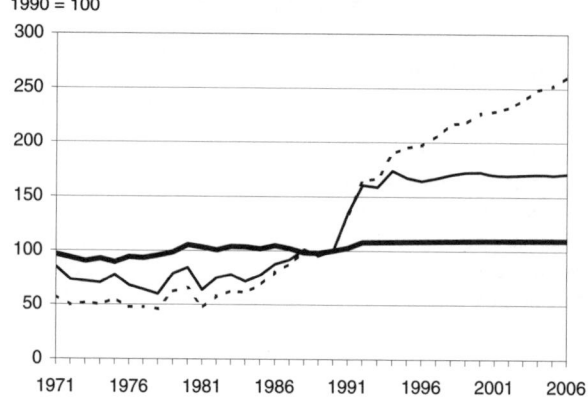

——— Total CO2 emissions - Sectoral Approach

- - - - - Total CO2 emissions - Reference Approach

Figure 5. Electricity generation by fuel

■ Oil

Figure 6. Key indicators

1990 = 100

——— CO2/TPES   ——— CO2/GDP   - - - - - CO2/capita

Gibraltar
Key indicators

	1990	1995	2000	2003	2004	2005	2006	% change 90-06
CO$_2$ Sectoral Approach (Mt of CO$_2$)	0.18	0.32	0.39	0.41	0.43	0.43	0.45	152.3%
CO$_2$ Reference Approach (Mt of CO$_2$)	0.18	0.32	0.39	0.41	0.43	0.43	0.45	152.3%
TPES (PJ)	3	5	6	6	6	6	6	129.8%
TPES (Mtoe)	0.07	0.11	0.13	0.14	0.14	0.15	0.15	129.8%
GDP (billion 2000 US$ using exch. rates)	0.58	0.63	0.74	0.79	0.82	0.83	0.85	47.5%
GDP (billion 2000 US$ using PPPs)	0.61	0.66	0.77	0.83	0.85	0.87	0.89	47.4%
Population (millions)	0.03	0.03	0.03	0.03	0.03	0.03	0.03	-3.4%
CO$_2$ / TPES (t CO$_2$ per TJ)	64.7	70.2	70.7	70.8	70.9	70.9	71.0	9.8%
CO$_2$ / GDP (kg CO$_2$ per 2000 US$)	0.31	0.51	0.53	0.52	0.52	0.52	0.53	71.1%
CO$_2$ / GDP (kg CO$_2$ per 2000 US$ PPP)	0.29	0.49	0.51	0.50	0.50	0.50	0.50	71.1%
CO$_2$ / population (t CO$_2$ per capita)	6.13	11.97	13.94	14.71	15.26	15.48	16.02	161.3%

Ratios are based on the Sectoral Approach.

2006 CO$_2$ emissions by sector

million tonnes of CO$_2$	Coal/peat	Oil	Gas	Other *	Total	% change 90-06
Sectoral Approach	-	**0.45**	-	-	**0.45**	**152.3%**
Main activity producer elec. and heat	-	0.11	-	-	0.11	80.0%
Unallocated autoproducers	-	-	-	-	-	-
Other energy industries	-	-	-	-	-	-
Manufacturing industries and construction	-	0.06	-	-	0.06	78.1%
Transport	-	0.28	-	-	0.28	235.5%
of which: road	-	*0.28*	-	-	*0.28*	*235.5%*
Other sectors	-	-	-	-	-	-
of which: residential	-	-	-	-	-	-
Reference Approach	-	**0.45**	-	-	**0.45**	**152.3%**
Diff. due to losses and/or transformation	-	-	-	-	-	
Statistical differences	-	-	-	-	-	
Memo: international marine bunkers	-	*3.73*	-	-	*3.73*	*171.4%*
Memo: international aviation	-	*0.01*	-	-	*0.01*	*-42.9%*

* Other includes industrial waste and non-renewable municipal waste.

Key sources for CO$_2$ emissions from fuel combustion in 2006

IPCC source category	CO$_2$ emissions (Mt of CO$_2$)	% change 90-06	Level assessment (%) **	Cumulative total (%)
Road - oil	0.28	235.5%	59.4	59.4
Main activity prod. elec. and heat - oil	0.11	80.0%	23.5	83.0
Manufacturing industries - oil	0.06	78.1%	12.7	95.7
-	-	-	-	-
-	-	-	-	-
-	-	-	-	-
-	-	-	-	-
-	-	-	-	-
-	-	-	-	-
-	-	-	-	-
-	-	-	-	-
Memo: total CO$_2$ from fuel combustion	*0.45*	*152.3%*	*95.7*	*95.7*

** Percent calculated using the total GHG estimate for CO$_2$, CH$_4$, N$_2$O, HFCs, PFCs and SF$_6$ excluding CO$_2$ emissions/removals from land use change and forestry.

Greece / Grèce

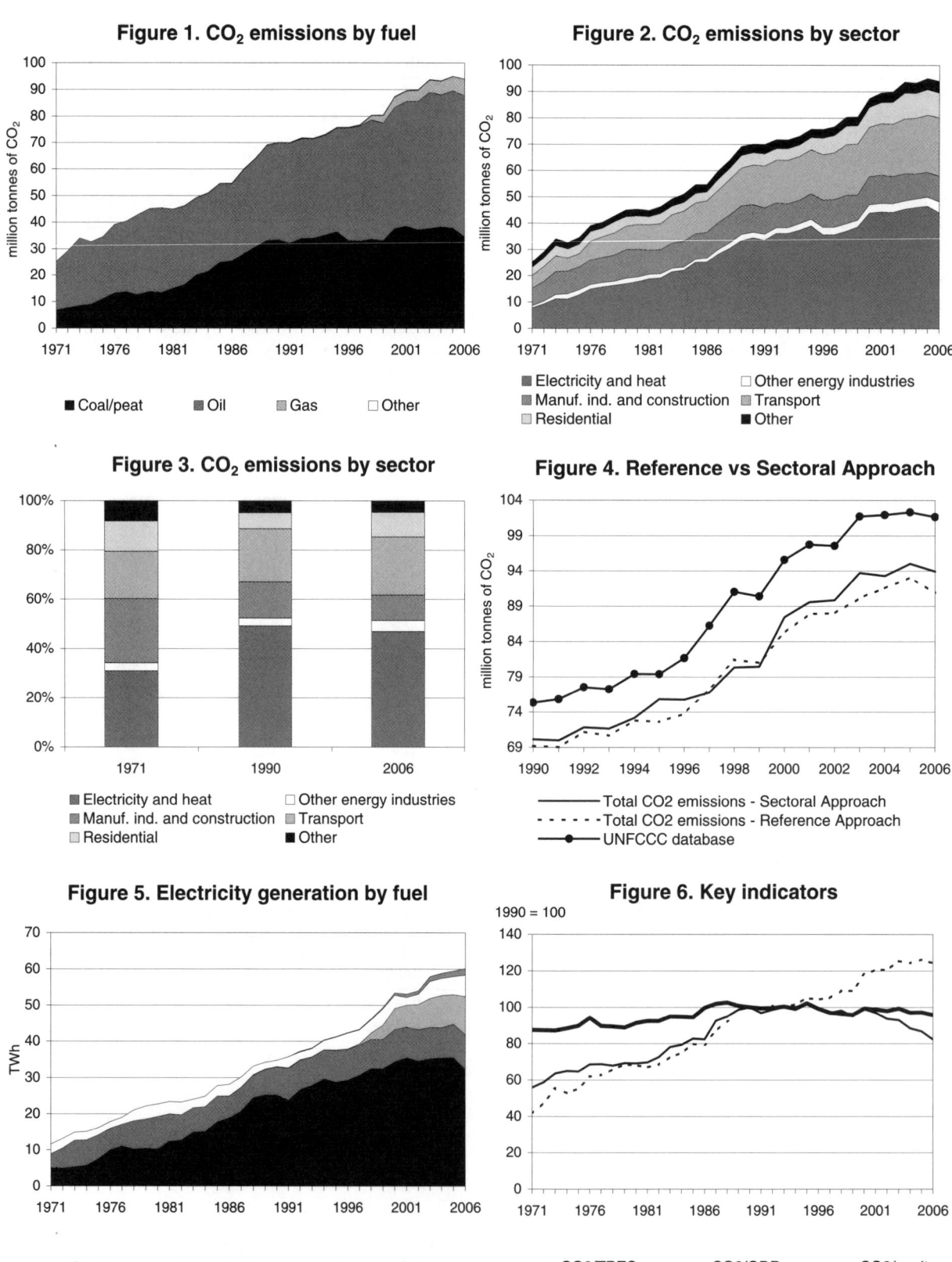

Figure 1. CO$_2$ emissions by fuel

- Coal/peat
- Oil
- Gas
- Other

Figure 2. CO$_2$ emissions by sector

- Electricity and heat
- Other energy industries
- Manuf. ind. and construction
- Transport
- Residential
- Other

Figure 3. CO$_2$ emissions by sector

- Electricity and heat
- Other energy industries
- Manuf. ind. and construction
- Transport
- Residential
- Other

Figure 4. Reference vs Sectoral Approach

- Total CO2 emissions - Sectoral Approach
- Total CO2 emissions - Reference Approach
- UNFCCC database

Figure 5. Electricity generation by fuel

- Coal/peat
- Oil
- Gas
- Hydro
- Other

Figure 6. Key indicators

1990 = 100

- CO2/TPES
- CO2/GDP
- CO2/capita

Greece / Grèce

Key indicators

	1990	1995	2000	2003	2004	2005	2006	% change 90-06
CO$_2$ Sectoral Approach (Mt of CO$_2$)	70.13	75.82	87.43	93.72	93.29	95.04	93.96	34.0%
CO$_2$ Reference Approach (Mt of CO$_2$)	69.23	72.62	85.28	90.17	91.57	93.10	90.93	31.3%
TPES (PJ)	931	985	1 168	1 253	1 277	1 299	1 303	40.0%
TPES (Mtoe)	22.23	23.53	27.90	29.92	30.51	31.03	31.12	40.0%
GDP (billion 2000 US$ using exch. rates)	100.80	107.30	127.10	144.90	151.60	157.40	164.00	62.7%
GDP (billion 2000 US$ using PPPs)	159.28	169.46	200.77	228.95	239.43	248.61	259.04	62.6%
Population (millions)	10.34	10.63	10.92	11.02	11.06	11.10	11.15	7.9%
CO$_2$ / TPES (t CO$_2$ per TJ)	75.3	77.0	74.8	74.8	73.0	73.2	72.1	-4.3%
CO$_2$ / GDP (kg CO$_2$ per 2000 US$)	0.70	0.71	0.69	0.65	0.62	0.60	0.57	-17.7%
CO$_2$ / GDP (kg CO$_2$ per 2000 US$ PPP)	0.44	0.45	0.44	0.41	0.39	0.38	0.36	-17.6%
CO$_2$ / population (t CO$_2$ per capita)	6.78	7.13	8.01	8.50	8.43	8.56	8.43	24.2%

Ratios are based on the Sectoral Approach.

2006 CO$_2$ emissions by sector

million tonnes of CO$_2$	Coal/peat	Oil	Gas	Other *	Total	% change 90-06
Sectoral Approach	**34.56**	**53.07**	**6.29**	**0.03**	**93.96**	**34.0%**
Main activity producer elec. and heat	32.98	6.42	4.36	-	43.77	28.9%
Unallocated autoproducers	-	0.25	0.05	0.03	0.33	-32.2%
Other energy industries	-	4.07	0.07	-	4.14	85.9%
Manufacturing industries and construction	1.56	6.88	1.24	-	9.68	-6.8%
Transport	-	22.20	0.03	-	22.23	47.3%
of which: road	-	18.61	0.03	-	18.64	62.0%
Other sectors	0.02	13.25	0.53	-	13.80	72.7%
of which: residential	0.01	9.06	0.33	-	9.39	104.4%
Reference Approach	**34.78**	**49.80**	**6.32**	**0.03**	**90.93**	**31.3%**
Diff. due to losses and/or transformation	0.09	- 1.41	0.02	-	- 1.30	
Statistical differences	0.12	- 1.86	0.00	-	- 1.73	
Memo: international marine bunkers	-	9.74	-	-	9.74	22.2%
Memo: international aviation	-	2.76	-	-	2.76	18.1%

* Other includes industrial waste and non-renewable municipal waste.

Key sources for CO$_2$ emissions from fuel combustion in 2006

IPCC source category	CO$_2$ emissions (Mt of CO$_2$)	% change 90-06	Level assessment (%) **	Cumulative total (%)
Main activity prod. elec. and heat - coal/peat	32.98	15.3%	26.3	26.3
Road - oil	18.61	61.8%	14.8	41.1
Residential - oil	9.06	101.0%	7.2	48.4
Manufacturing industries - oil	6.88	23.4%	5.5	53.8
Main activity prod. elec. and heat - oil	6.42	20.4%	5.1	59.0
Main activity prod. elec. and heat - gas	4.36	x	3.5	62.4
Non-specified other sectors - oil	4.19	24.4%	3.3	65.8
Other energy industries - oil	4.07	87.3%	3.2	69.0
Other transport - oil	3.59	0.2%	2.9	71.9
Manufacturing industries - coal/peat	1.56	-66.5%	1.2	73.1
Manufacturing industries - gas	1.24	721.0%	1.0	74.1
Memo: total CO$_2$ from fuel combustion	93.96	34.0%	74.9	74.9

** Percent calculated using the total GHG estimate for CO$_2$, CH$_4$, N$_2$O, HFCs, PFCs and SF$_6$ excluding CO$_2$ emissions/removals from land use change and forestry.

Guatemala

Figure 1. CO$_2$ emissions by fuel

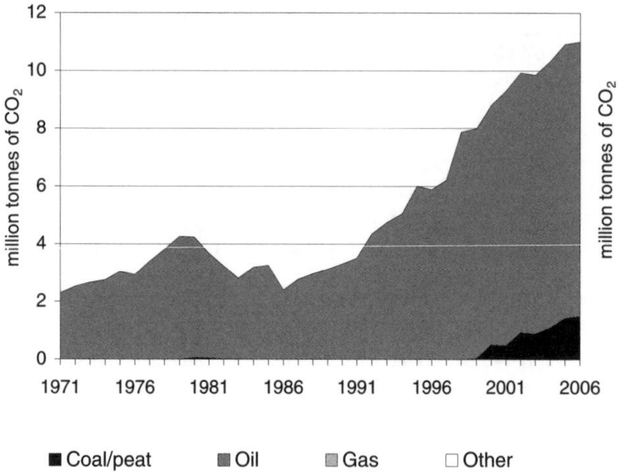

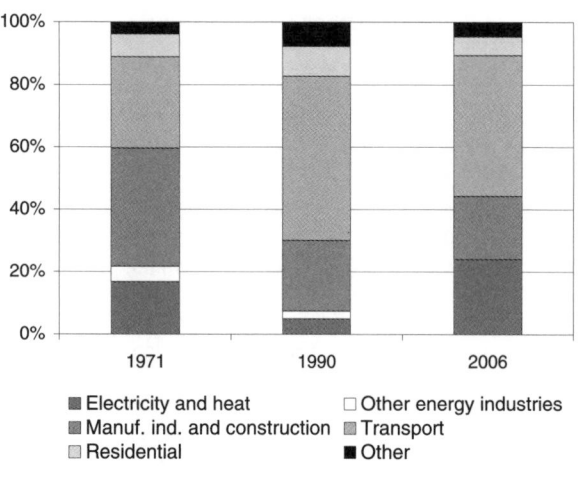

■ Coal/peat   ■ Oil   ▨ Gas   ☐ Other

Figure 2. CO$_2$ emissions by sector

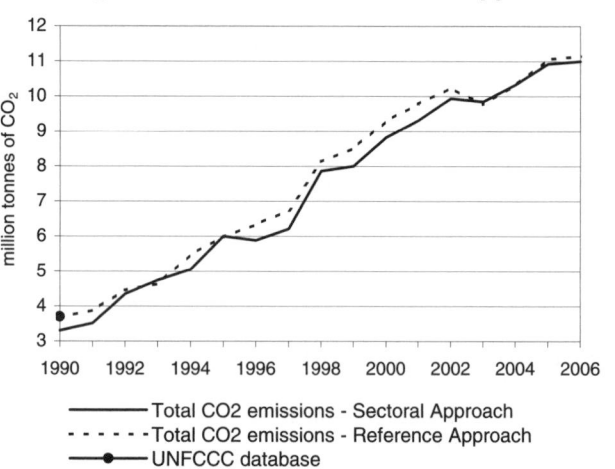

■ Electricity and heat   ☐ Other energy industries
▨ Manuf. ind. and construction   ▨ Transport
▨ Residential   ■ Other

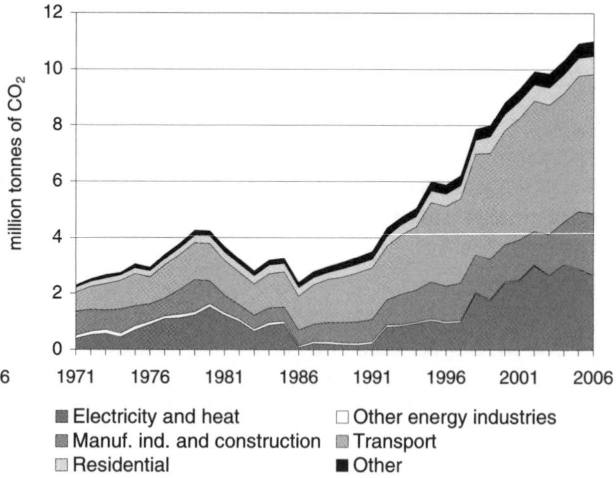

Figure 3. CO$_2$ emissions by sector

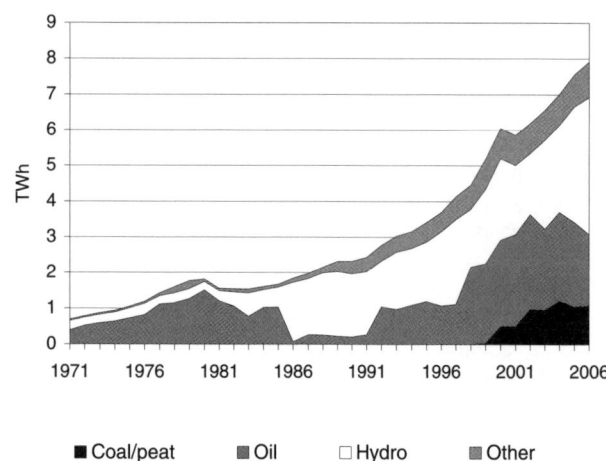

■ Electricity and heat   ☐ Other energy industries
■ Manuf. ind. and construction   ▨ Transport
▨ Residential   ■ Other

Figure 4. Reference vs Sectoral Approach

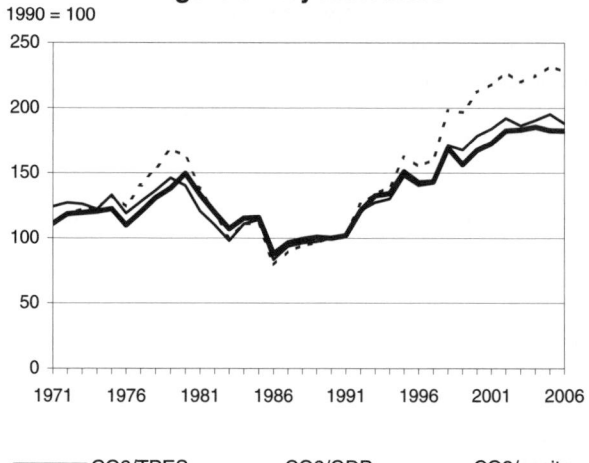

——— Total CO2 emissions - Sectoral Approach
- - - - Total CO2 emissions - Reference Approach
——●— UNFCCC database

Figure 5. Electricity generation by fuel

■ Coal/peat   ▨ Oil   ☐ Hydro   ▨ Other

Figure 6. Key indicators

1990 = 100

——CO2/TPES   ——CO2/GDP   - - - - CO2/capita

Guatemala
Key indicators

	1990	1995	2000	2003	2004	2005	2006	% change 90-06
CO$_2$ Sectoral Approach (Mt of CO$_2$)	3.30	6.01	8.83	9.85	10.33	10.92	11.01	233.5%
CO$_2$ Reference Approach (Mt of CO$_2$)	3.67	5.99	9.30	9.77	10.33	11.06	11.15	203.7%
TPES (PJ)	188	226	299	305	317	339	343	82.7%
TPES (Mtoe)	4.48	5.40	7.15	7.29	7.56	8.11	8.18	82.7%
GDP (billion 2000 US$ using exch. rates)	12.89	15.89	19.29	20.62	21.16	21.85	22.85	77.3%
GDP (billion 2000 US$ using PPPs)	30.20	37.24	45.21	48.31	49.60	51.21	53.55	77.3%
Population (millions)	8.91	10.00	11.23	12.09	12.40	12.71	13.03	46.3%
CO$_2$ / TPES (t CO$_2$ per TJ)	17.6	26.6	29.5	32.3	32.6	32.2	32.1	82.5%
CO$_2$ / GDP (kg CO$_2$ per 2000 US$)	0.26	0.38	0.46	0.48	0.49	0.50	0.48	88.1%
CO$_2$ / GDP (kg CO$_2$ per 2000 US$ PPP)	0.11	0.16	0.20	0.20	0.21	0.21	0.21	88.0%
CO$_2$ / population (t CO$_2$ per capita)	0.37	0.60	0.79	0.81	0.83	0.86	0.84	128.0%

Ratios are based on the Sectoral Approach.

2006 CO$_2$ emissions by sector

million tonnes of CO$_2$	Coal/peat	Oil	Gas	Other *	Total	% change 90-06
Sectoral Approach	**1.49**	**9.51**	-	-	**11.01**	233.5%
Main activity producer elec. and heat	1.02	1.35	-	-	2.38	+
Unallocated autoproducers	-	0.27	-	-	0.27	x
Other energy industries	-	-	-	-	-	-100.0%
Manufacturing industries and construction	0.47	1.76	-	-	2.23	197.0%
Transport	-	4.95	-	-	4.95	185.7%
of which: road	-	4.90	-	-	4.90	182.8%
Other sectors	-	1.18	-	-	1.18	105.5%
of which: residential	-	0.66	-	-	0.66	107.8%
Reference Approach	**1.49**	**9.65**	-	-	**11.15**	203.7%
Diff. due to losses and/or transformation	-	0.02	-	-	0.02	
Statistical differences	0.00	0.12	-	-	0.12	
Memo: international marine bunkers	-	0.38	-	-	0.38	-
Memo: international aviation	-	0.12	-	-	0.12	-9.5%

* Other includes industrial waste and non-renewable municipal waste.

Key sources for CO$_2$ emissions from fuel combustion in 2006

IPCC source category	CO$_2$ emissions (Mt of CO$_2$)	% change 90-06	Level assessment (%) **	Cumulative total (%)
Road - oil	4.90	182.8%	16.7	16.7
Manufacturing industries - oil	1.76	134.4%	6.0	22.7
Main activity prod. elec. and heat - oil	1.35	734.0%	4.6	27.3
Main activity prod. elec. and heat - coal/peat	1.02	x	3.5	30.8
Residential - oil	0.66	107.8%	2.2	33.1
Non-specified other sectors - oil	0.52	102.8%	1.8	34.8
Manufacturing industries - coal/peat	0.47	x	1.6	36.5
Unallocated autoproducers - oil	0.27	x	0.9	37.4
Other transport - oil	0.05	x	0.2	37.5
-	-	-	-	-
-	-	-	-	-
Memo: total CO$_2$ from fuel combustion	11.01	233.5%	37.5	37.5

** Percent calculated using the total GHG estimate for CO$_2$, CH$_4$, N$_2$O, HFCs, PFCs and SF$_6$ excluding CO$_2$ emissions/removals from land use change and forestry.

Haiti

Figure 1. CO$_2$ emissions by fuel

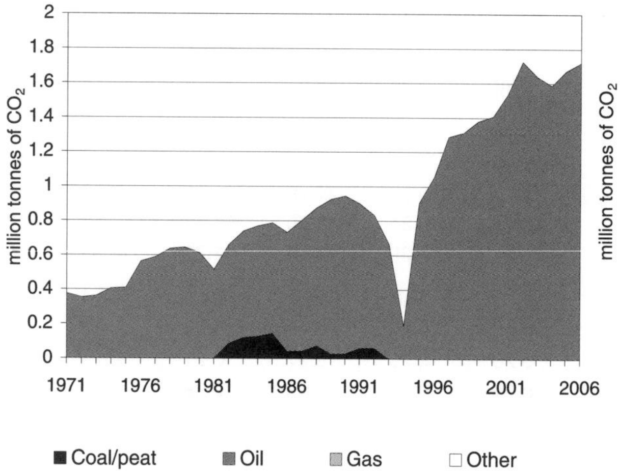

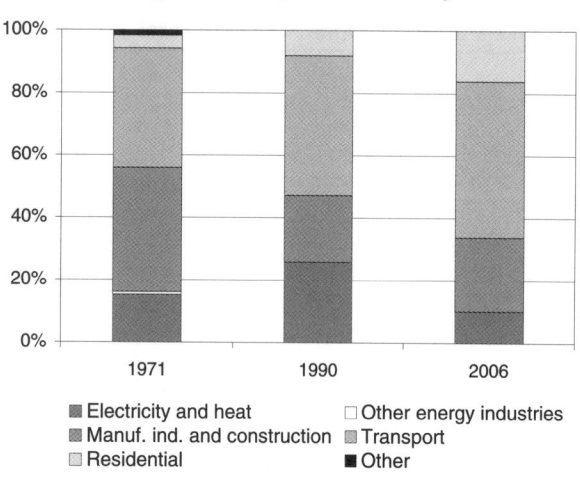

- Coal/peat
- Oil
- Gas
- Other

Figure 2. CO$_2$ emissions by sector

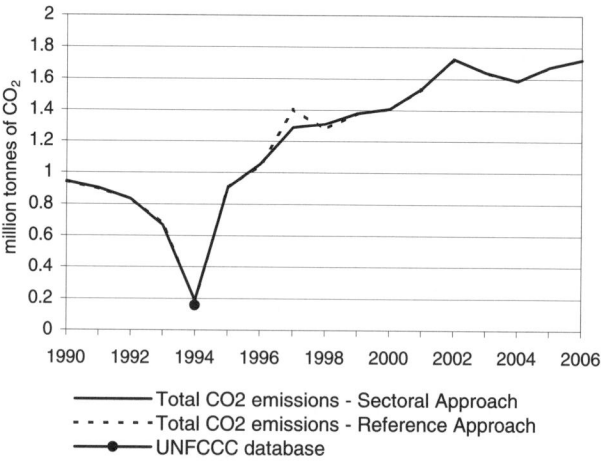

- Electricity and heat
- Manuf. ind. and construction
- Residential
- Other energy industries
- Transport
- Other

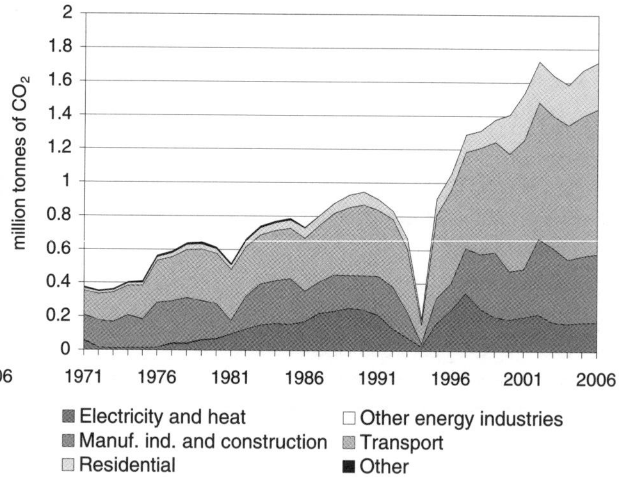

Figure 3. CO$_2$ emissions by sector

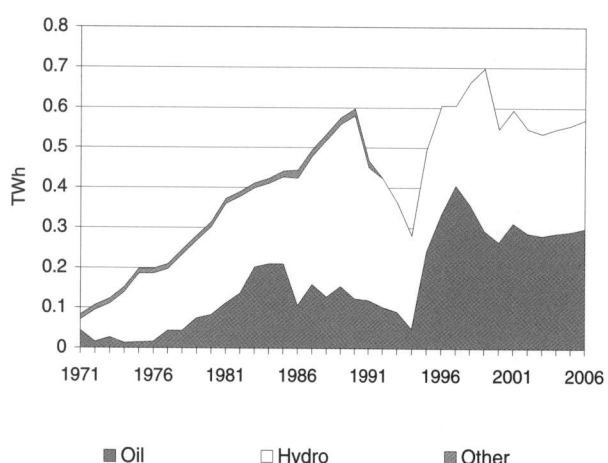

- Electricity and heat
- Manuf. ind. and construction
- Residential
- Other energy industries
- Transport
- Other

Figure 4. Reference vs Sectoral Approach

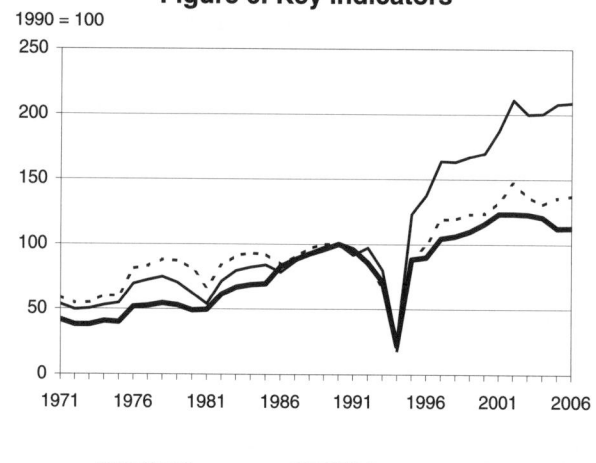

———— Total CO2 emissions - Sectoral Approach
- - - - - Total CO2 emissions - Reference Approach
——●—— UNFCCC database

Figure 5. Electricity generation by fuel

- Oil
- Hydro
- Other

Figure 6. Key indicators

1990 = 100

———— CO2/TPES ———— CO2/GDP - - - - CO2/capita

Haiti

Key indicators

	1990	1995	2000	2003	2004	2005	2006	% change 90-06
CO$_2$ Sectoral Approach (Mt of CO$_2$)	0.94	0.90	1.41	1.64	1.59	1.67	1.72	82.1%
CO$_2$ Reference Approach (Mt of CO$_2$)	0.94	0.90	1.41	1.64	1.59	1.67	1.72	82.7%
TPES (PJ)	66	72	85	94	92	105	107	61.9%
TPES (Mtoe)	1.59	1.72	2.04	2.24	2.21	2.50	2.57	61.9%
GDP (billion 2000 US$ using exch. rates)	4.39	3.42	3.85	3.81	3.68	3.74	3.83	-12.8%
GDP (billion 2000 US$ using PPPs)	14.67	11.41	12.85	12.73	12.28	12.50	12.79	-12.8%
Population (millions)	7.11	7.84	8.57	9.01	9.15	9.30	9.45	32.9%
CO$_2$ / TPES (t CO$_2$ per TJ)	14.2	12.6	16.5	17.5	17.2	16.0	16.0	12.5%
CO$_2$ / GDP (kg CO$_2$ per 2000 US$)	0.22	0.26	0.37	0.43	0.43	0.45	0.45	108.8%
CO$_2$ / GDP (kg CO$_2$ per 2000 US$ PPP)	0.06	0.08	0.11	0.13	0.13	0.13	0.13	108.9%
CO$_2$ / population (t CO$_2$ per capita)	0.13	0.12	0.16	0.18	0.17	0.18	0.18	37.1%

Ratios are based on the Sectoral Approach.

2006 CO$_2$ emissions by sector

million tonnes of CO$_2$	Coal/peat	Oil	Gas	Other *	Total	% change 90-06
Sectoral Approach	-	**1.72**	-	-	**1.72**	**82.1%**
Main activity producer elec. and heat	-	0.17	-	-	0.17	-21.5%
Unallocated autoproducers	..	..	..	..	..	..
Other energy industries	-	-	-	-	-	-
Manufacturing industries and construction	-	0.41	-	-	0.41	101.6%
Transport	-	0.86	-	-	0.86	103.8%
of which: road	-	0.37	-	-	0.37	98.3%
Other sectors	-	0.28	-	-	0.28	263.4%
of which: residential	-	0.28	-	-	0.28	263.4%
Reference Approach	-	**1.72**	-	-	**1.72**	**82.7%**
Diff. due to losses and/or transformation	-	-	-	-	-	
Statistical differences	-	- 0.00	-	-	- 0.00	
Memo: international marine bunkers	-	..	-	-	..	..
Memo: international aviation	-	0.08	-	-	0.08	4.3%

* Other includes industrial waste and non-renewable municipal waste.

Key sources for CO$_2$ emissions from fuel combustion in 2006

IPCC source category	CO$_2$ emissions (Mt of CO$_2$)	% change 90-06	Level assessment (%) **	Cumulative total (%)
Other transport - oil	0.50	108.0%	4.9	4.9
Manufacturing industries - oil	0.41	135.0%	4.0	8.9
Road - oil	0.37	98.3%	3.6	12.6
Residential - oil	0.28	263.4%	2.8	15.3
Main activity prod. elec. and heat - oil	0.17	-21.5%	1.7	17.0
-	-	-	-	-
-	-	-	-	-
-	-	-	-	-
-	-	-	-	-
-	-	-	-	-
-	-	-	-	-
Memo: total CO$_2$ from fuel combustion	1.72	82.1%	17.0	17.0

** Percent calculated using the total GHG estimate for CO$_2$, CH$_4$, N$_2$O, HFCs, PFCs and SF$_6$ excluding CO$_2$ emissions/removals from land use change and forestry.

Honduras

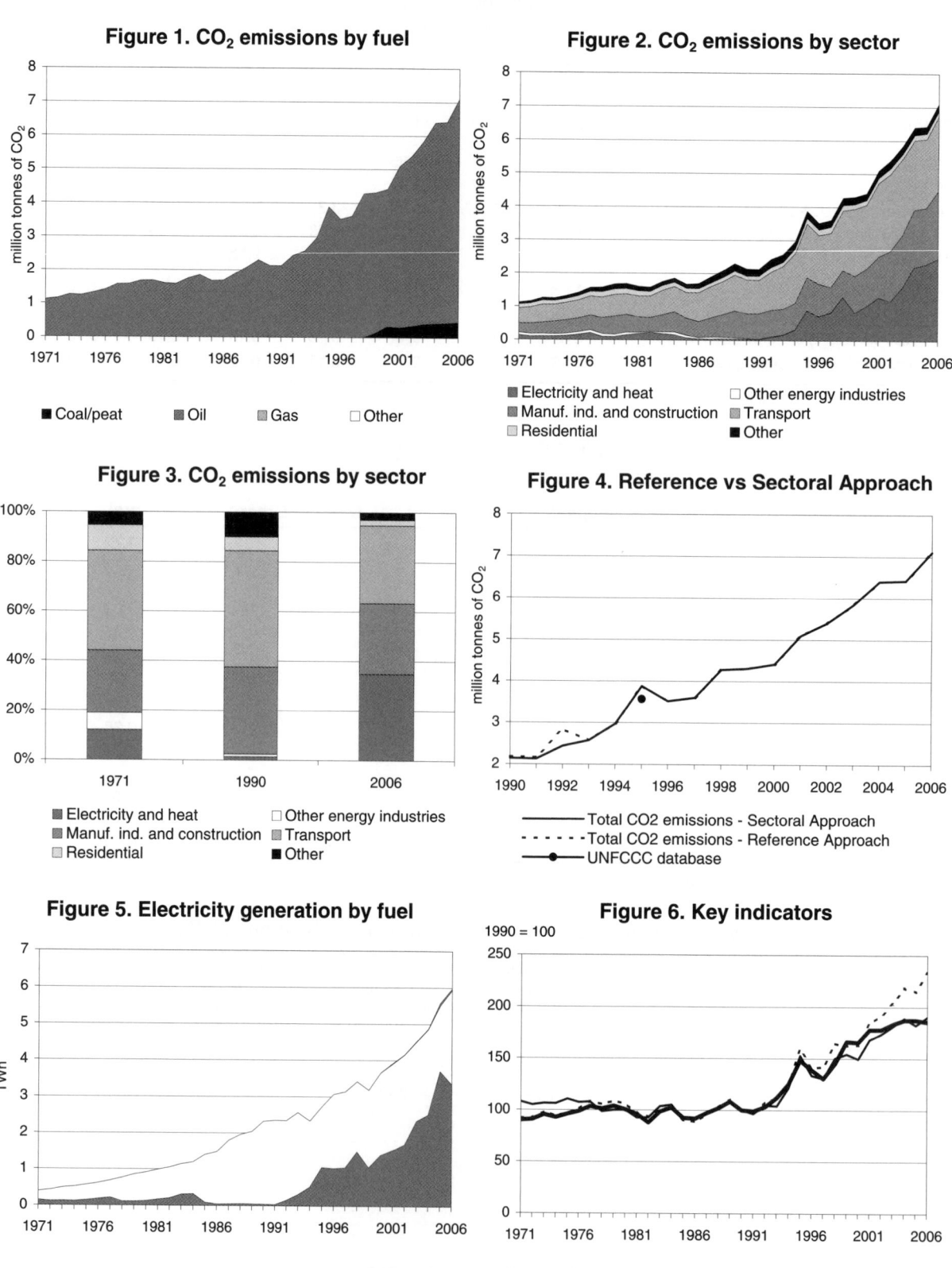

Figure 1. CO$_2$ emissions by fuel

Figure 2. CO$_2$ emissions by sector

Figure 3. CO$_2$ emissions by sector

Figure 4. Reference vs Sectoral Approach

Figure 5. Electricity generation by fuel

Figure 6. Key indicators

Honduras

Key indicators

	1990	1995	2000	2003	2004	2005	2006	% change 90-06
CO$_2$ Sectoral Approach (Mt of CO$_2$)	2.14	3.88	4.41	5.84	6.40	6.42	7.11	232.6%
CO$_2$ Reference Approach (Mt of CO$_2$)	2.18	3.88	4.41	5.84	6.40	6.42	7.11	226.7%
TPES (PJ)	101	124	126	151	162	162	181	79.2%
TPES (Mtoe)	2.42	2.96	3.01	3.60	3.86	3.87	4.33	79.1%
GDP (billion 2000 US$ using exch. rates)	4.31	5.13	5.96	6.50	6.82	7.10	7.53	74.6%
GDP (billion 2000 US$ using PPPs)	13.35	15.89	18.45	20.12	21.13	21.99	23.32	74.6%
Population (millions)	4.89	5.57	6.20	6.57	6.70	6.83	6.97	42.5%
CO$_2$ / TPES (t CO$_2$ per TJ)	21.1	31.3	35.0	38.8	39.6	39.6	39.2	85.7%
CO$_2$ / GDP (kg CO$_2$ per 2000 US$)	0.50	0.76	0.74	0.90	0.94	0.90	0.94	90.5%
CO$_2$ / GDP (kg CO$_2$ per 2000 US$ PPP)	0.16	0.24	0.24	0.29	0.30	0.29	0.30	90.4%
CO$_2$ / population (t CO$_2$ per capita)	0.44	0.70	0.71	0.89	0.95	0.94	1.02	133.4%

Ratios are based on the Sectoral Approach.

2006 CO$_2$ emissions by sector

million tonnes of CO$_2$	Coal/peat	Oil	Gas	Other *	Total	% change 90-06
Sectoral Approach	**0.45**	**6.65**	-	-	**7.11**	**232.6%**
Main activity producer elec. and heat	-	2.47	-	-	2.47	+
Unallocated autoproducers	..	..	..	..	..	..
Other energy industries	-	-	-	-	-	-100.0%
Manufacturing industries and construction	0.45	1.57	-	-	2.02	169.3%
Transport	-	2.24	-	-	2.24	123.0%
of which: road	-	*2.24*	-	-	*2.24*	*123.0%*
Other sectors	-	0.38	-	-	0.38	13.7%
of which: residential	-	*0.16*	-	-	*0.16*	*35.3%*
Reference Approach	**0.45**	**6.65**	-	-	**7.11**	**226.7%**
Diff. due to losses and/or transformation	-	-	-	-	-	
Statistical differences	0.00	-	-	-	0.00	
Memo: international marine bunkers	-	..	-	-	..	..
Memo: international aviation	-	*0.09*	-	-	*0.09*	x

* Other includes industrial waste and non-renewable municipal waste.

Key sources for CO$_2$ emissions from fuel combustion in 2006

IPCC source category	CO$_2$ emissions (Mt of CO$_2$)	% change 90-06	Level assessment (%) **	Cumulative total (%)
Main activity prod. elec. and heat - oil	2.47	+	14.2	14.2
Road - oil	2.24	123.0%	12.8	27.0
Manufacturing industries - oil	1.57	109.5%	9.0	36.0
Manufacturing industries - coal/peat	0.45	+	2.6	38.6
Non-specified other sectors - oil	0.22	2.0%	1.3	39.9
Residential - oil	0.16	35.3%	0.9	40.8
-	-	-	-	-
-	-	-	-	-
-	-	-	-	-
-	-	-	-	-
-	-	-	-	-
Memo: total CO$_2$ from fuel combustion	7.11	232.6%	40.8	40.8

** Percent calculated using the total GHG estimate for CO$_2$, CH$_4$, N$_2$O, HFCs, PFCs and SF$_6$ excluding CO$_2$ emissions/removals from land use change and forestry.

Hong Kong, China / Hong Kong, Chine

Figure 1. CO$_2$ emissions by fuel

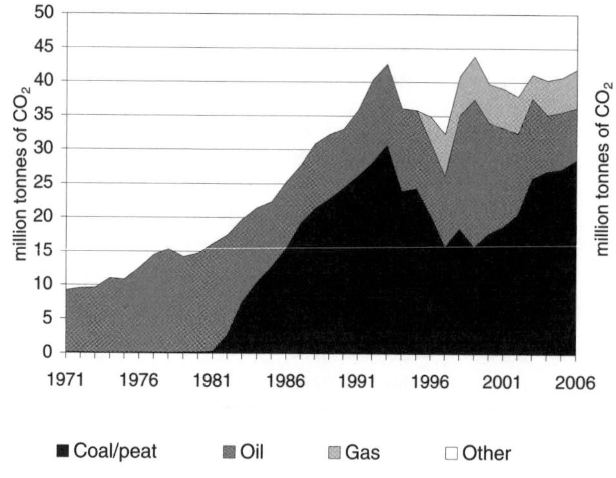

Coal/peat ■   Oil ■   Gas ■   Other □

Figure 2. CO$_2$ emissions by sector

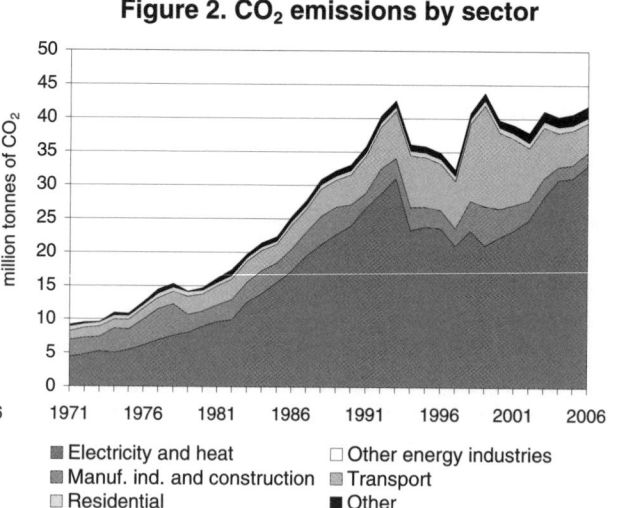

Electricity and heat ■   Other energy industries □
Manuf. ind. and construction ■   Transport ■
Residential □   Other ■

Figure 3. CO$_2$ emissions by sector

Electricity and heat ■   Other energy industries □
Manuf. ind. and construction ■   Transport ■
Residential □   Other ■

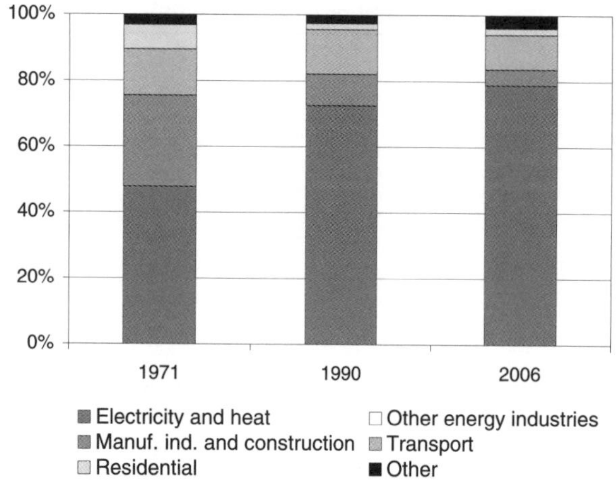

Figure 4. Reference vs Sectoral Approach

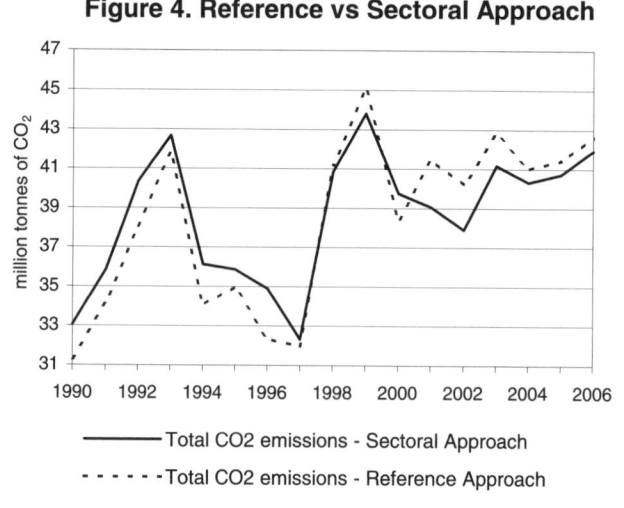

Total CO2 emissions - Sectoral Approach
Total CO2 emissions - Reference Approach

Figure 5. Electricity generation by fuel

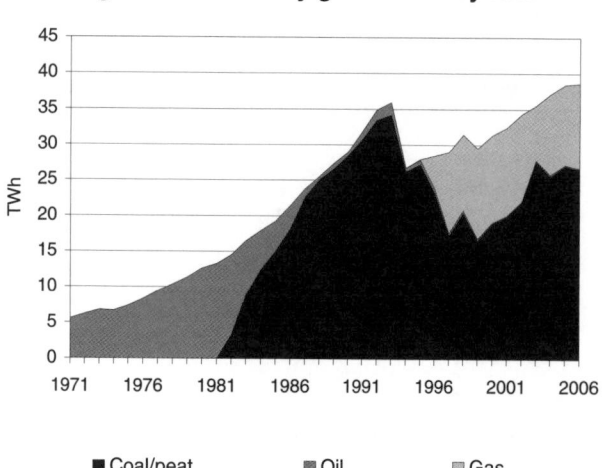

Coal/peat ■   Oil ■   Gas ■

Figure 6. Key indicators

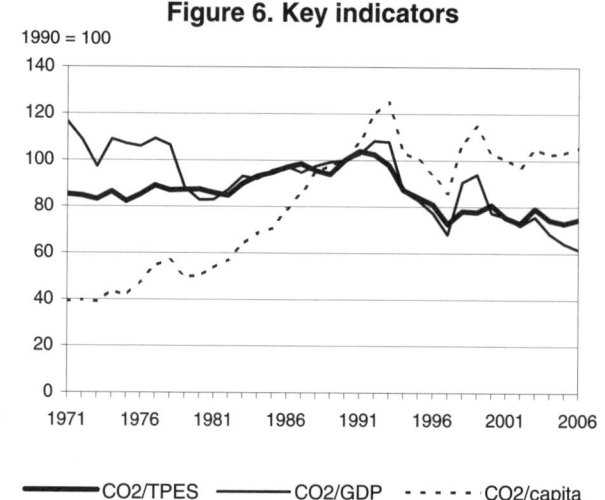

1990 = 100

CO2/TPES   CO2/GDP   CO2/capita

Hong Kong, China / Hong Kong, Chine
Key indicators

	1990	1995	2000	2003	2004	2005	2006	% change 90-06
CO$_2$ Sectoral Approach (Mt of CO$_2$)	33.05	35.87	39.74	41.15	40.31	40.72	41.92	26.8%
CO$_2$ Reference Approach (Mt of CO$_2$)	31.31	34.98	38.35	42.81	41.00	41.42	42.63	36.2%
TPES (PJ)	447	577	666	703	734	757	762	70.4%
TPES (Mtoe)	10.68	13.79	15.90	16.80	17.53	18.07	18.19	70.4%
GDP (billion 2000 US$ using exch. rates)	108.42	142.21	168.75	178.49	193.80	208.37	222.80	105.5%
GDP (billion 2000 US$ using PPPs)	112.25	147.24	174.71	184.79	200.64	215.73	230.67	105.5%
Population (millions)	5.71	6.16	6.67	6.76	6.79	6.81	6.86	20.2%
CO$_2$ / TPES (t CO$_2$ per TJ)	73.9	62.1	59.7	58.5	54.9	53.8	55.0	-25.6%
CO$_2$ / GDP (kg CO$_2$ per 2000 US$)	0.30	0.25	0.24	0.23	0.21	0.20	0.19	-38.3%
CO$_2$ / GDP (kg CO$_2$ per 2000 US$ PPP)	0.29	0.24	0.23	0.22	0.20	0.19	0.18	-38.3%
CO$_2$ / population (t CO$_2$ per capita)	5.79	5.83	5.96	6.08	5.94	5.98	6.11	5.5%

Ratios are based on the Sectoral Approach.

2006 CO$_2$ emissions by sector

million tonnes of CO$_2$	Coal/peat	Oil	Gas	Other *	Total	% change 90-06
Sectoral Approach	**28.61**	**7.69**	**5.61**	-	**41.92**	**26.8%**
Main activity producer elec. and heat	27.27	0.12	5.61	-	33.00	37.7%
Unallocated autoproducers	-	-	-	-	-	-
Other energy industries	-	-	-	-	-	-
Manufacturing industries and construction	0.04	1.97	-	-	2.01	-36.0%
Transport	-	4.41	-	-	4.41	-1.2%
of which: road	-	4.41	-	-	4.41	-1.1%
Other sectors	1.29	1.20	-	-	2.49	67.7%
of which: residential	0.75	0.06	-	-	0.81	34.0%
Reference Approach	**27.27**	**9.75**	**5.61**	-	**42.63**	**36.2%**
Diff. due to losses and/or transformation	- 1.34	2.05	-	-	0.72	
Statistical differences	-	- 0.00	-	-	- 0.00	
Memo: international marine bunkers	-	22.76	-	-	22.76	404.0%
Memo: international aviation	-	14.02	-	-	14.02	149.4%

* Other includes industrial waste and non-renewable municipal waste.

Key sources for CO$_2$ emissions from fuel combustion in 2006

IPCC source category	CO$_2$ emissions (Mt of CO$_2$)	% change 90-06	Level assessment (%) **	Cumulative total (%)
Main activity prod. elec. and heat - coal/peat	27.27	15.4%	61.9	61.9
Main activity prod. elec. and heat - gas	5.61	x	12.7	74.7
Road - oil	4.41	-1.1%	10.0	84.7
Manufacturing industries - oil	1.97	-36.7%	4.5	89.1
Non-specified other sectors - oil	1.13	109.8%	2.6	91.7
Residential - coal/peat	0.75	98.6%	1.7	93.4
Non-specified other sectors - coal/peat	0.55	60.7%	1.2	94.7
Main activity prod. elec. and heat - oil	0.12	-63.5%	0.3	94.9
Residential - oil	0.06	-72.6%	0.1	95.1
Manufacturing industries - coal/peat	0.04	31.2%	0.1	95.2
-	-	-	-	-
Memo: total CO$_2$ from fuel combustion	41.92	26.8%	95.2	95.2

** Percent calculated using the total GHG estimate for CO$_2$, CH$_4$, N$_2$O, HFCs, PFCs and SF$_6$ excluding CO$_2$ emissions/removals from land use change and forestry.

Hungary / Hongrie

Figure 1. CO₂ emissions by fuel

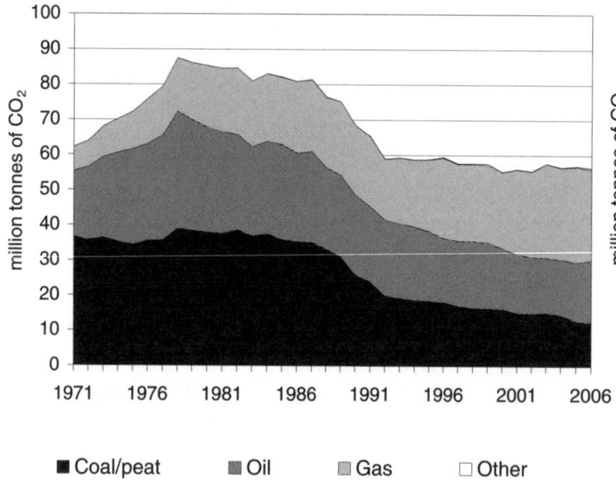

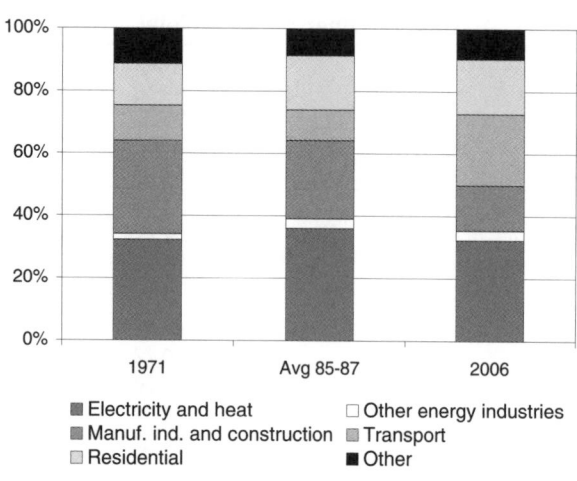

■ Coal/peat   ■ Oil   ■ Gas   □ Other

Figure 2. CO₂ emissions by sector

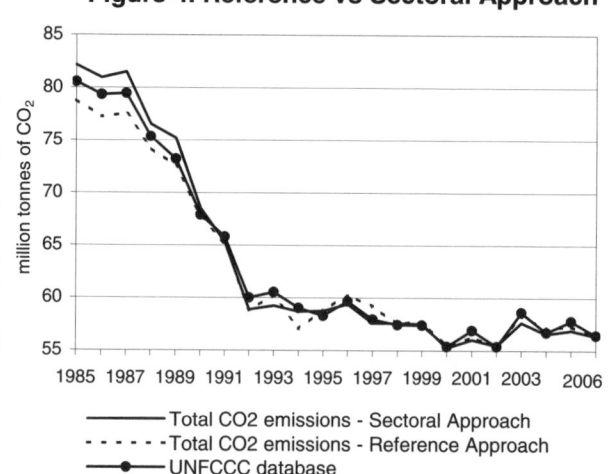

■ Electricity and heat   □ Other energy industries
■ Manuf. ind. and construction   ■ Transport
□ Residential   ■ Other

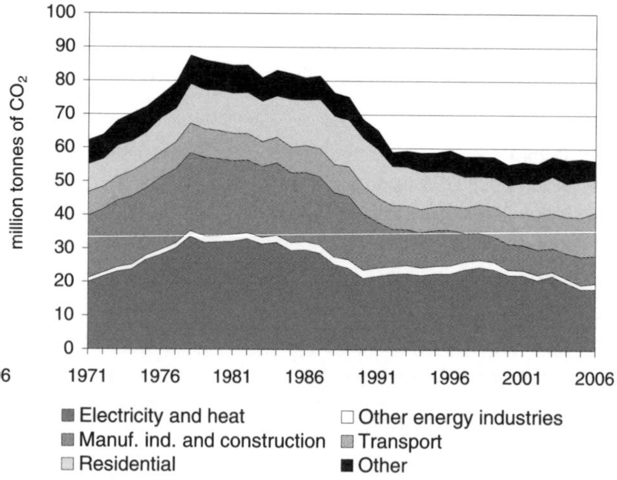

Figure 3. CO₂ emissions by sector

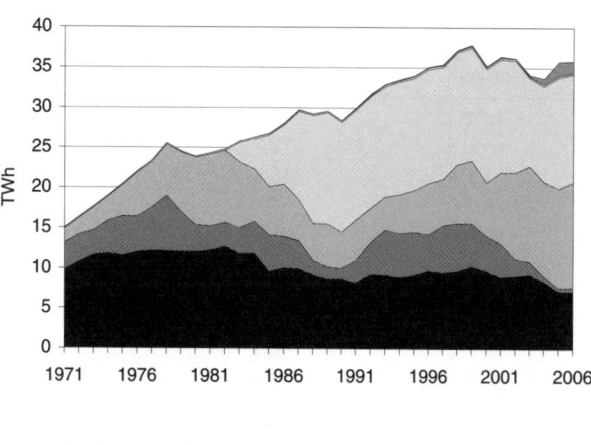

■ Electricity and heat   □ Other energy industries
■ Manuf. ind. and construction   ■ Transport
□ Residential   ■ Other

Figure 4. Reference vs Sectoral Approach

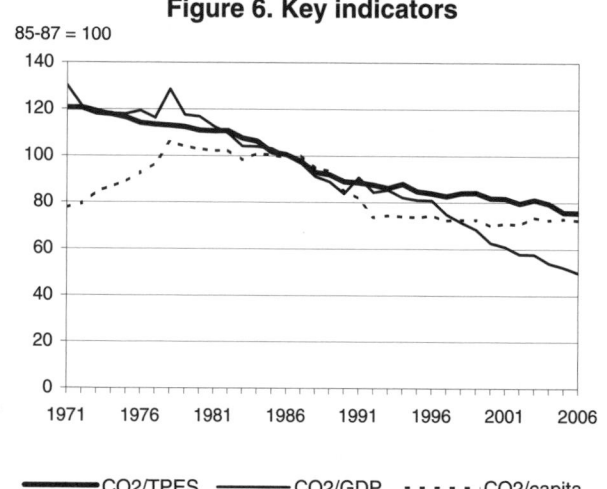

—— Total CO2 emissions - Sectoral Approach
- - - - Total CO2 emissions - Reference Approach
——●—— UNFCCC database

Figure 5. Electricity generation by fuel

■ Coal/peat   ■ Oil   ■ Gas   □ Nuclear   □ Hydro   ■ Other

Figure 6. Key indicators

85-87 = 100

━━ CO2/TPES   —— CO2/GDP   - - - - CO2/capita

Hungary / Hongrie *

Key indicators

	Avg 85-87	1990	1995	2003	2004	2005	2006	% change base-06
CO$_2$ Sectoral Approach (Mt of CO$_2$)	81.52	68.51	58.75	57.66	56.60	56.91	56.37	-30.8%
CO$_2$ Reference Approach (Mt of CO$_2$)	77.85	67.70	58.85	58.33	57.15	57.33	56.53	-27.4%
TPES (PJ)	1 264	1 196	1 075	1 103	1 105	1 165	1 155	-8.6%
TPES (Mtoe)	30.19	28.56	25.68	26.34	26.39	27.81	27.59	-8.6%
GDP (billion 2000 US$ using exch. rates)	44.27	44.38	39.40	54.30	56.90	59.20	61.50	38.9%
GDP (billion 2000 US$ using PPPs)	115.68	115.96	102.88	141.72	148.54	154.68	160.68	38.9%
Population (millions)	10.53	10.37	10.33	10.13	10.11	10.09	10.07	-4.4%
CO$_2$ / TPES (t CO$_2$ per TJ)	64.5	57.3	54.6	52.3	51.2	48.9	48.8	-24.3%
CO$_2$ / GDP (kg CO$_2$ per 2000 US$)	1.84	1.54	1.49	1.06	0.99	0.96	0.92	-50.2%
CO$_2$ / GDP (kg CO$_2$ per 2000 US$ PPP)	0.70	0.59	0.57	0.41	0.38	0.37	0.35	-50.2%
CO$_2$ / population (t CO$_2$ per capita)	7.74	6.61	5.69	5.69	5.60	5.64	5.60	-27.7%

Ratios are based on the Sectoral Approach.
* According to the provisions of Article 4.6 of the Convention and Decisions 9/CP.2 and 11/CP.4, Hungary is allowed to use average 85-87 as the base year.

2006 CO$_2$ emissions by sector

million tonnes of CO$_2$	Coal/peat	Oil	Gas	Other **	Total	% change base-06
Sectoral Approach	**12.37**	**17.83**	**25.84**	**0.34**	**56.37**	**-30.8%**
Main activity producer elec. and heat	8.99	0.62	8.10	0.26	17.97	-29.6%
Unallocated autoproducers	-	0.02	0.21	-	0.23	-94.0%
Other energy industries	0.01	1.21	0.48	-	1.70	-31.8%
Manufacturing industries and construction	2.43	2.20	3.48	0.08	8.18	-59.9%
Transport	-	12.92	0.01	-	12.92	60.8%
of which: road	-	*12.67*	*0.01*	-	*12.67*	*82.4%*
Other sectors	0.94	0.87	13.56	-	15.37	-27.8%
of which: residential	*0.91*	*0.42*	*8.51*	-	*9.85*	*-30.6%*
Reference Approach	**12.19**	**17.50**	**26.51**	**0.34**	**56.53**	**-27.4%**
Diff. due to losses and/or transformation	- 0.19	- 0.31	0.73	-	0.23	
Statistical differences	0.02	- 0.02	- 0.06	0.00	- 0.07	
Memo: international marine bunkers	-	-	-	-	-	-
Memo: international aviation	-	*0.80*	-	-	*0.80*	*82.5%*

** Other includes industrial waste and non-renewable municipal waste.

Key sources for CO$_2$ emissions from fuel combustion in 2006

IPCC source category	CO$_2$ emissions (Mt of CO$_2$)	% change base-06	Level assessment (%) ***	Cumulative total (%)
Road - oil	12.67	82.3%	16.1	16.1
Main activity prod. elec. and heat - coal/peat	8.99	-46.2%	11.5	27.6
Residential - gas	8.51	242.5%	10.8	38.4
Main activity prod. elec. and heat - gas	8.10	70.7%	10.3	48.7
Non-specified other sectors - gas	5.04	192.0%	6.4	55.2
Manufacturing industries - gas	3.48	-60.9%	4.4	59.6
Manufacturing industries - coal/peat	2.43	-66.4%	3.1	62.7
Manufacturing industries - oil	2.20	-48.7%	2.8	65.5
Other energy industries - oil	1.21	-36.0%	1.5	67.0
Residential - coal/peat	0.91	-89.9%	1.2	68.2
Main activity prod. elec. and heat - oil	0.62	-84.5%	0.8	69.0
Memo: total CO$_2$ from fuel combustion	*56.37*	*-30.8%*	*71.8*	*71.8*

*** Percent calculated using the total GHG estimate for CO$_2$, CH$_4$, N$_2$O, HFCs, PFCs and SF$_6$ excluding CO$_2$ emissions/removals from land use change and forestry.

Iceland / Islande

Figure 1. CO₂ emissions by fuel

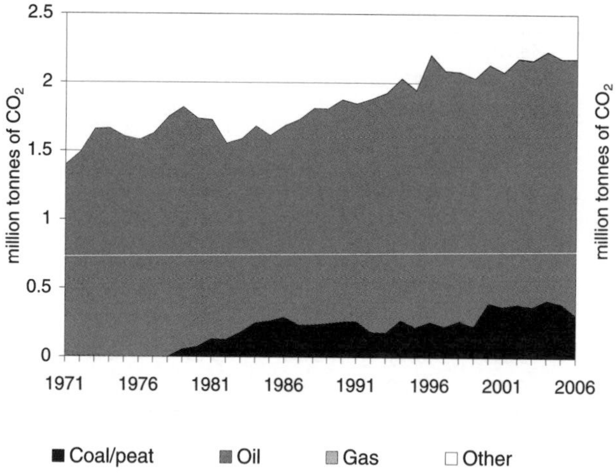

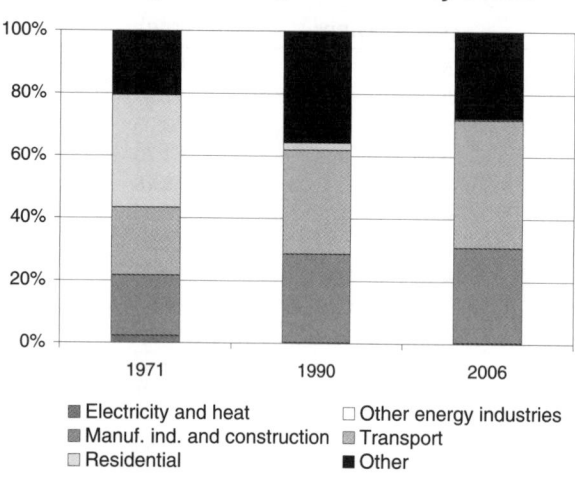

■ Coal/peat   ■ Oil   ■ Gas   ☐ Other

Figure 2. CO₂ emissions by sector

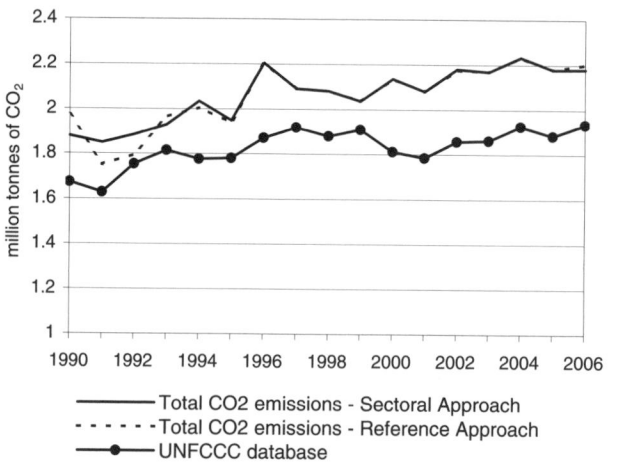

■ Electricity and heat   ☐ Other energy industries
■ Manuf. ind. and construction   ▨ Transport
☐ Residential   ■ Other

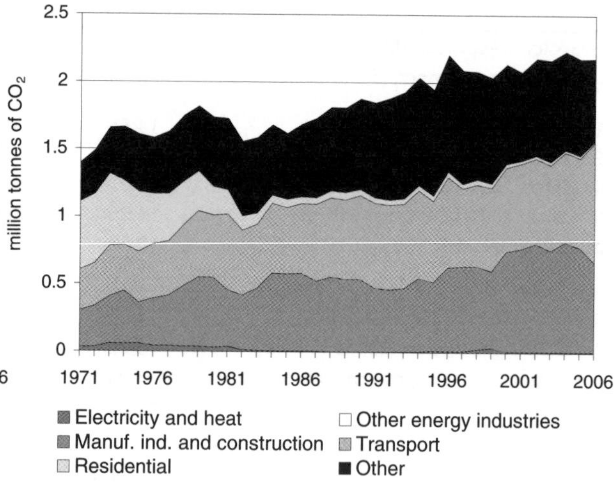

Figure 3. CO₂ emissions by sector

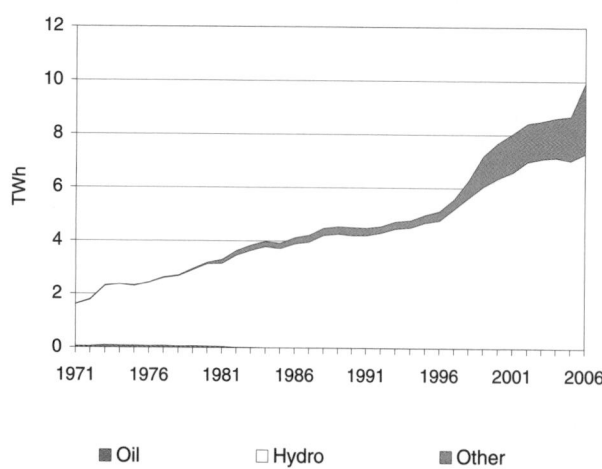

■ Electricity and heat   ☐ Other energy industries
■ Manuf. ind. and construction   ▨ Transport
☐ Residential   ■ Other

Figure 4. Reference vs Sectoral Approach

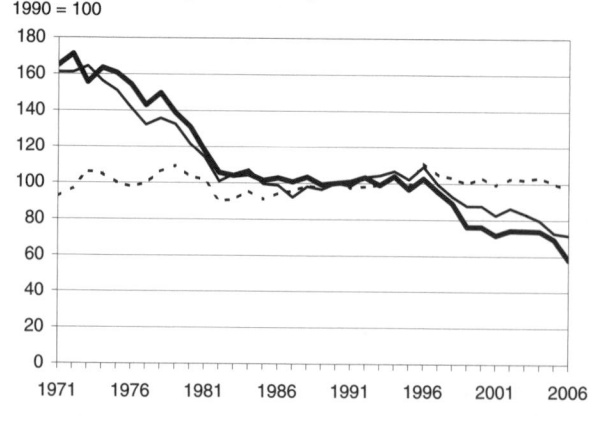

—— Total CO2 emissions - Sectoral Approach
- - - - Total CO2 emissions - Reference Approach
—●— UNFCCC database

Figure 5. Electricity generation by fuel

■ Oil   ☐ Hydro   ▨ Other

Figure 6. Key indicators

—— CO2/TPES   —— CO2/GDP   - - - - CO2/capita

Iceland / Islande

Key indicators

	1990	1995	2000	2003	2004	2005	2006	% change 90-06
CO$_2$ Sectoral Approach (Mt of CO$_2$)	1.88	1.95	2.14	2.17	2.23	2.18	2.18	16.1%
CO$_2$ Reference Approach (Mt of CO$_2$)	1.97	1.94	2.14	2.17	2.23	2.18	2.20	11.7%
TPES (PJ)	90	97	135	141	146	151	181	100.1%
TPES (Mtoe)	2.16	2.32	3.23	3.38	3.49	3.61	4.33	100.1%
GDP (billion 2000 US$ using exch. rates)	6.70	6.80	8.70	9.30	10.00	10.70	10.90	62.7%
GDP (billion 2000 US$ using PPPs)	6.28	6.36	8.08	8.62	9.28	9.94	10.20	62.4%
Population (millions)	0.26	0.27	0.28	0.29	0.29	0.30	0.30	19.2%
CO$_2$ / TPES (t CO$_2$ per TJ)	20.8	20.1	15.8	15.3	15.3	14.4	12.0	-42.0%
CO$_2$ / GDP (kg CO$_2$ per 2000 US$)	0.28	0.29	0.25	0.23	0.22	0.20	0.20	-28.6%
CO$_2$ / GDP (kg CO$_2$ per 2000 US$ PPP)	0.30	0.31	0.26	0.25	0.24	0.22	0.21	-28.5%
CO$_2$ / population (t CO$_2$ per capita)	7.37	7.30	7.60	7.51	7.62	7.36	7.18	-2.6%

Ratios are based on the Sectoral Approach.

2006 CO$_2$ emissions by sector

million tonnes of CO$_2$	Coal/peat	Oil	Gas	Other *	Total	% change 90-06
Sectoral Approach	**0.31**	**1.87**	**-**	**0.00**	**2.18**	**16.1%**
Main activity producer elec. and heat	-	0.00	-	0.00	0.01	121.7%
Unallocated autoproducers	-	-	-	-	-	-
Other energy industries	-	-	-	-	-	-
Manufacturing industries and construction	0.31	0.35	-	-	0.66	24.0%
Transport	-	0.89	-	-	0.89	43.3%
of which: road	-	*0.81*	-	-	*0.81*	*53.7%*
Other sectors	-	0.62	-	-	0.62	-13.7%
of which: residential	-	*0.01*	-	-	*0.01*	*-80.4%*
Reference Approach	**0.31**	**1.89**	**-**	**0.00**	**2.20**	**11.7%**
Diff. due to losses and/or transformation	-	-	-	-	-	
Statistical differences	-	0.02	-	-	0.02	
Memo: international marine bunkers	-	*0.11*	-	-	*0.11*	*12.7%*
Memo: international aviation	-	*0.53*	-	-	*0.53*	*143.7%*

* Other includes industrial waste and non-renewable municipal waste.

Key sources for CO$_2$ emissions from fuel combustion in 2006

IPCC source category	CO$_2$ emissions (Mt of CO$_2$)	% change 90-06	Level assessment (%) **	Cumulative total (%)
Road - oil	0.81	53.7%	18.2	18.2
Non-specified other sectors - oil	0.61	-9.1%	13.6	31.8
Manufacturing industries - oil	0.35	27.6%	7.9	39.7
Manufacturing industries - coal/peat	0.31	20.2%	6.9	46.6
Other transport - oil	0.08	-16.6%	1.7	48.3
Residential - oil	0.01	-80.4%	0.2	48.5
Main activity prod. elec. and heat - other	0.00	x	0.1	48.6
Main activity prod. elec. and heat - oil	0.00	-	0.1	48.7
-	-	-	-	-
-	-	-	-	-
-	-	-	-	-
Memo: total CO$_2$ from fuel combustion	*2.18*	*16.1%*	*48.7*	*48.7*

** Percent calculated using the total GHG estimate for CO$_2$, CH$_4$, N$_2$O, HFCs, PFCs and SF$_6$ excluding CO$_2$ emissions/removals from land use change and forestry.

India / Inde

Figure 1. CO₂ emissions by fuel

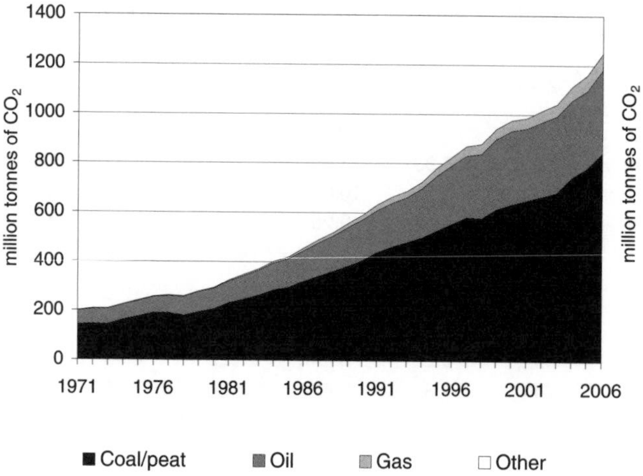

■ Coal/peat   ■ Oil   ■ Gas   □ Other

Figure 2. CO₂ emissions by sector

■ Electricity and heat   □ Other energy industries
■ Manuf. ind. and construction   ■ Transport
□ Residential   ■ Other

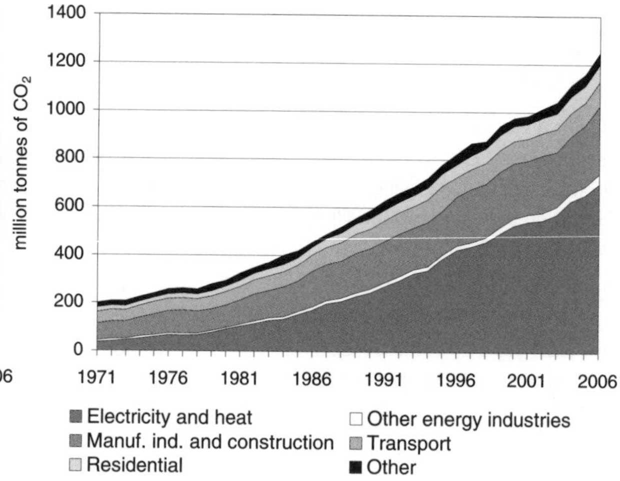

Figure 3. CO₂ emissions by sector

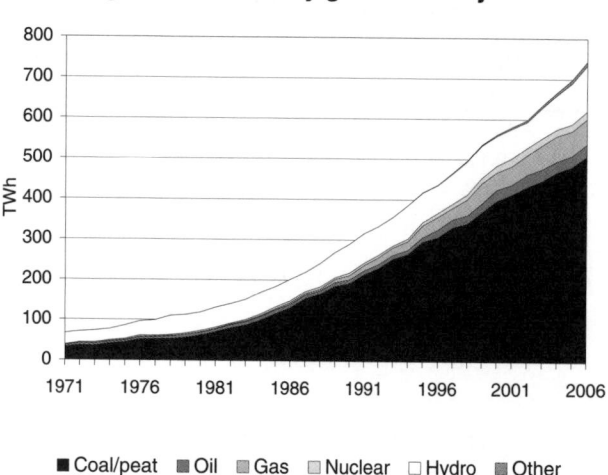

■ Electricity and heat   □ Other energy industries
■ Manuf. ind. and construction   ■ Transport
□ Residential   ■ Other

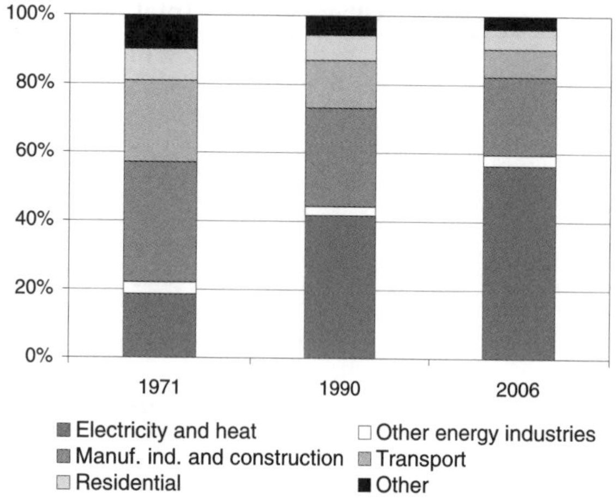

Figure 4. Reference vs Sectoral Approach

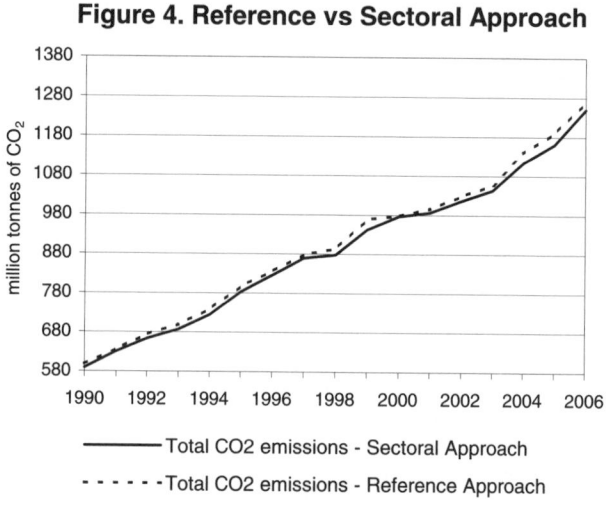

—— Total CO2 emissions - Sectoral Approach
- - - - Total CO2 emissions - Reference Approach

Figure 5. Electricity generation by fuel

■ Coal/peat   ■ Oil   ■ Gas   ■ Nuclear   □ Hydro   ■ Other

Figure 6. Key indicators

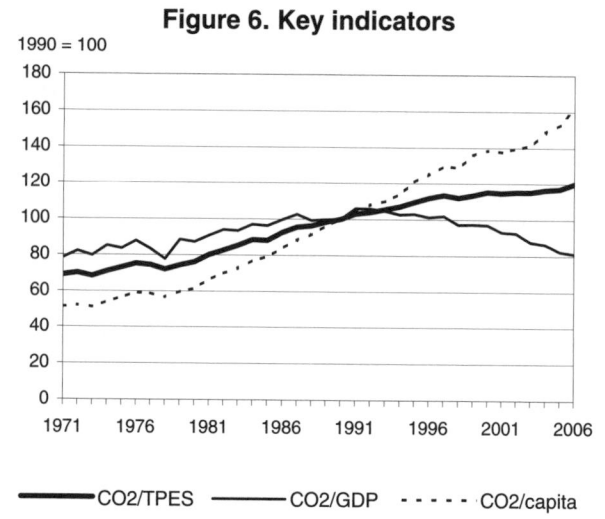

—— CO2/TPES   —— CO2/GDP   - - - - CO2/capita

India / Inde

Key indicators

	1990	1995	2000	2003	2004	2005	2006	% change 90-06
CO$_2$ Sectoral Approach (Mt of CO$_2$)	589.30	782.57	976.52	1 042.90	1 114.07	1 160.68	1 249.74	112.1%
CO$_2$ Reference Approach (Mt of CO$_2$)	597.79	797.14	978.11	1 056.86	1 140.14	1 190.23	1 269.73	112.4%
TPES (PJ)	13 394	16 224	19 250	20 569	21 745	22 529	23 690	76.9%
TPES (Mtoe)	319.92	387.49	459.78	491.28	519.38	538.10	565.82	76.9%
GDP (billion 2000 US$ using exch. rates)	269.43	347.20	460.20	544.35	589.67	644.11	703.33	161.0%
GDP (billion 2000 US$ using PPPs)	1 406.32	1 812.29	2 402.09	2 841.35	3 077.89	3 362.05	3 671.20	161.0%
Population (millions)	849.52	932.18	1 015.92	1 064.40	1 079.72	1 094.58	1 109.81	30.6%
CO$_2$ / TPES (t CO$_2$ per TJ)	44.0	48.2	50.7	50.7	51.2	51.5	52.8	19.9%
CO$_2$ / GDP (kg CO$_2$ per 2000 US$)	2.19	2.25	2.12	1.92	1.89	1.80	1.78	-18.8%
CO$_2$ / GDP (kg CO$_2$ per 2000 US$ PPP)	0.42	0.43	0.41	0.37	0.36	0.35	0.34	-18.8%
CO$_2$ / population (t CO$_2$ per capita)	0.69	0.84	0.96	0.98	1.03	1.06	1.13	62.3%

Ratios are based on the Sectoral Approach.

2006 CO$_2$ emissions by sector

million tonnes of CO$_2$	Coal/peat	Oil	Gas	Other *	Total	% change 90-06
Sectoral Approach	**844.41**	**338.67**	**66.66**	-	**1 249.74**	**112.1%**
Main activity producer elec. and heat	585.50	16.51	23.14	-	625.15	185.7%
Unallocated autoproducers	59.92	10.71	6.66	-	77.29	191.5%
Other energy industries	2.69	33.98	4.87	-	41.53	161.2%
Manufacturing industries and construction	157.19	98.58	28.00	-	283.76	67.8%
Transport	-	99.10	2.10	-	101.20	23.8%
of which: road	-	*90.80*	*2.10*	-	*92.89*	*41.2%*
Other sectors	39.12	79.79	1.89	-	120.81	56.5%
of which: residential	*10.54*	*60.20*	*1.57*	-	*72.31*	*66.1%*
Reference Approach	**863.95**	**339.12**	**66.66**	-	**1 269.73**	**112.4%**
Diff. due to losses and/or transformation	19.39	1.54	-	-	20.93	
Statistical differences	0.15	- 1.09	-	-	- 0.94	
Memo: international marine bunkers	-	*0.09*	-	-	*0.09*	*-81.5%*
Memo: international aviation	-	*12.55*	-	-	*12.55*	*137.0%*

* Other includes industrial waste and non-renewable municipal waste.

Key sources for CO$_2$ emissions from fuel combustion in 2006

IPCC source category	CO$_2$ emissions (Mt of CO$_2$)	% change 90-06	Level assessment (%) **	Cumulative total (%)
Main activity prod. elec. and heat - coal/peat	585.50	188.0%	24.9	24.9
Manufacturing industries - coal/peat	157.19	26.9%	6.7	31.5
Manufacturing industries - oil	98.58	170.7%	4.2	35.7
Road - oil	90.80	38.0%	3.9	39.6
Residential - oil	60.20	89.1%	2.6	42.1
Unallocated autoproducers - coal/peat	59.92	164.8%	2.5	44.7
Other energy industries - oil	33.98	303.0%	1.4	46.1
Non-specified other sectors - coal/peat	28.58	-3.9%	1.2	47.3
Manufacturing industries - gas	28.00	217.3%	1.2	48.5
Main activity prod. elec. and heat - gas	23.14	229.2%	1.0	49.5
Non-specified other sectors - oil	19.59	426.4%	0.8	50.3
Memo: total CO$_2$ from fuel combustion	*1249.74*	*112.1%*	*53.1*	*53.1*

** Percent calculated using the total GHG estimate for CO$_2$, CH$_4$, N$_2$O, HFCs, PFCs and SF$_6$ excluding CO$_2$ emissions/removals from land use change and forestry.

Indonesia / Indonésie

Figure 1. CO₂ emissions by fuel

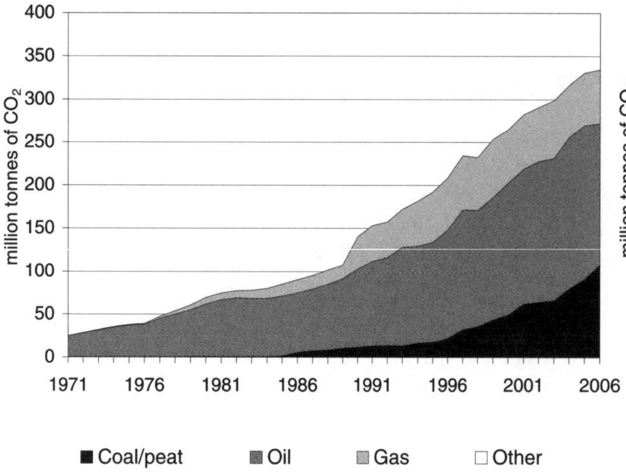

■ Coal/peat   ■ Oil   ▨ Gas   ☐ Other

Figure 2. CO₂ emissions by sector

■ Electricity and heat   ☐ Other energy industries
■ Manuf. ind. and construction ▨ Transport
▨ Residential   ■ Other

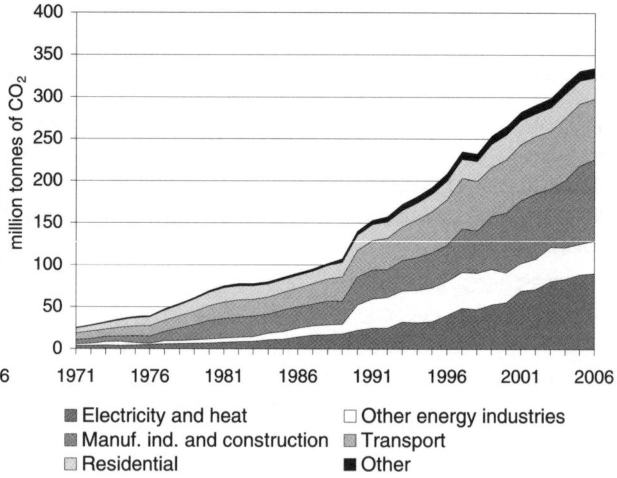

Figure 3. CO₂ emissions by sector

■ Electricity and heat   ☐ Other energy industries
■ Manuf. ind. and construction ▨ Transport
▨ Residential   ■ Other

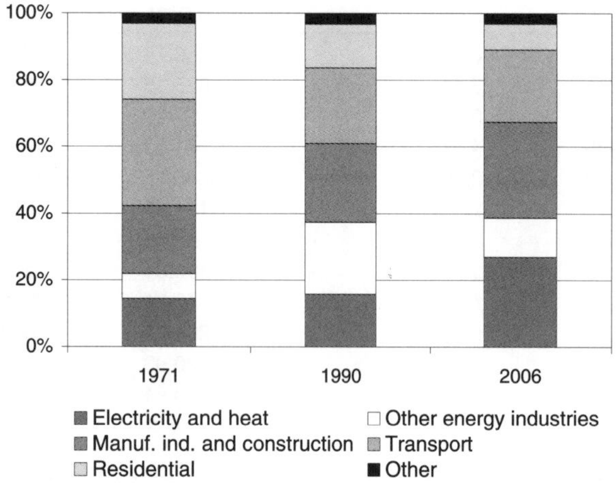

Figure 4. Reference vs Sectoral Approach

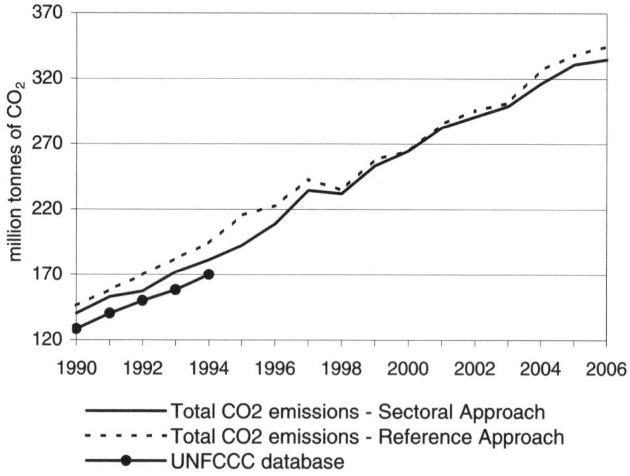

——— Total CO2 emissions - Sectoral Approach
- - - - Total CO2 emissions - Reference Approach
—●— UNFCCC database

Figure 5. Electricity generation by fuel

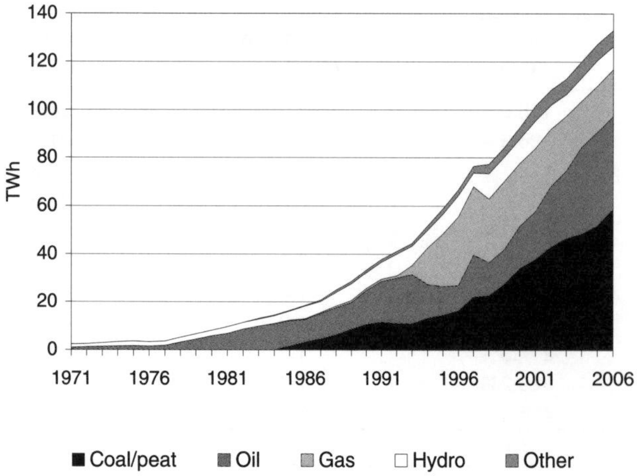

■ Coal/peat   ■ Oil   ▨ Gas   ☐ Hydro   ■ Other

Figure 6. Key indicators

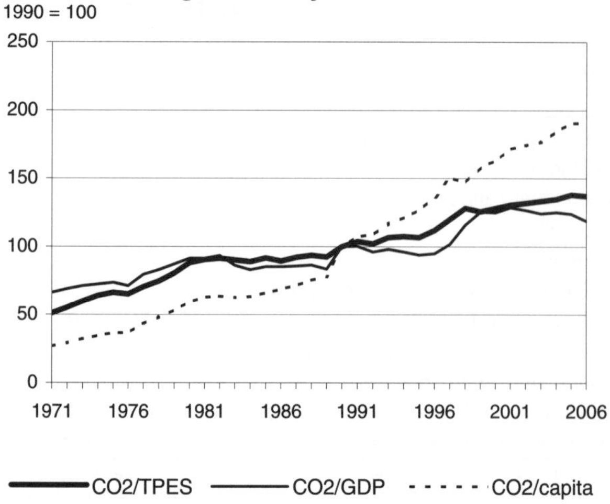

1990 = 100

——— CO2/TPES   ——— CO2/GDP   - - - - CO2/capita

Indonesia / Indonésie

Key indicators

	1990	1995	2000	2003	2004	2005	2006	% change 90-06
CO$_2$ Sectoral Approach (Mt of CO$_2$)	140.22	192.22	264.62	298.83	316.28	330.95	334.64	138.6%
CO$_2$ Reference Approach (Mt of CO$_2$)	146.10	215.43	264.36	301.47	326.77	337.91	344.75	136.0%
TPES (PJ)	4 304	5 529	6 340	6 879	7 203	7 368	7 497	74.2%
TPES (Mtoe)	102.80	132.06	151.44	164.30	172.04	175.99	179.07	74.2%
GDP (billion 2000 US$ using exch. rates)	109.15	159.38	165.02	187.27	196.69	207.87	219.27	100.9%
GDP (billion 2000 US$ using PPPs)	396.37	578.79	599.26	680.07	714.29	754.88	796.27	100.9%
Population (millions)	178.23	192.75	206.27	214.67	217.59	220.56	223.04	25.1%
CO$_2$ / TPES (t CO$_2$ per TJ)	32.6	34.8	41.7	43.4	43.9	44.9	44.6	37.0%
CO$_2$ / GDP (kg CO$_2$ per 2000 US$)	1.28	1.21	1.60	1.60	1.61	1.59	1.53	18.8%
CO$_2$ / GDP (kg CO$_2$ per 2000 US$ PPP)	0.35	0.33	0.44	0.44	0.44	0.44	0.42	18.8%
CO$_2$ / population (t CO$_2$ per capita)	0.79	1.00	1.28	1.39	1.45	1.50	1.50	90.7%

Ratios are based on the Sectoral Approach.

2006 CO$_2$ emissions by sector

million tonnes of CO$_2$	Coal/peat	Oil	Gas	Other *	Total	% change 90-06
Sectoral Approach	**108.29**	**163.61**	**62.74**	-	**334.64**	**138.6%**
Main activity producer elec. and heat	57.49	23.22	9.12	-	89.82	309.1%
Unallocated autoproducers	-	0.24	0.01	-	0.25	x
Other energy industries	-	7.99	31.18	-	39.18	28.8%
Manufacturing industries and construction	50.73	23.08	22.32	-	96.13	192.0%
Transport	-	72.35	0.01	-	72.36	127.1%
of which: road	-	65.51	0.01	-	65.52	129.1%
Other sectors	0.06	36.72	0.10	-	36.89	60.0%
of which: residential	0.06	25.76	0.04	-	25.86	41.3%
Reference Approach	**108.28**	**164.02**	**72.46**	-	**344.75**	**136.0%**
Diff. due to losses and/or transformation	- 0.01	1.67	9.71	-	11.37	
Statistical differences	- 0.00	- 1.25	0.00	-	- 1.25	
Memo: international marine bunkers	-	1.12	-	-	1.12	-33.3%
Memo: international aviation	-	2.19	-	-	2.19	127.9%

* Other includes industrial waste and non-renewable municipal waste.

Key sources for CO$_2$ emissions from fuel combustion in 2006

IPCC source category	CO$_2$ emissions (Mt of CO$_2$)	% change 90-06	Level assessment (%) **	Cumulative total (%)
Road - oil	65.51	129.1%	10.0	10.0
Main activity prod. elec. and heat - coal/peat	57.49	527.7%	8.8	18.7
Manufacturing industries - coal/peat	50.73	+	7.7	26.4
Other energy industries - gas	31.18	28.7%	4.7	31.2
Residential - oil	25.76	40.7%	3.9	35.1
Main activity prod. elec. and heat - oil	23.22	92.7%	3.5	38.6
Manufacturing industries - oil	23.08	28.3%	3.5	42.2
Manufacturing industries - gas	22.32	80.3%	3.4	45.6
Non-specified other sectors - oil	10.96	130.3%	1.7	47.2
Main activity prod. elec. and heat - gas	9.12	+	1.4	48.6
Other energy industries - oil	7.99	29.0%	1.2	49.8
Memo: total CO$_2$ from fuel combustion	334.64	138.6%	50.9	50.9

** Percent calculated using the total GHG estimate for CO$_2$, CH$_4$, N$_2$O, HFCs, PFCs and SF$_6$ excluding CO$_2$ emissions/removals from land use change and forestry.

INTERNATIONAL ENERGY AGENCY

Islamic Republic of Iran / République islamique d'Iran

Figure 1. CO_2 emissions by fuel

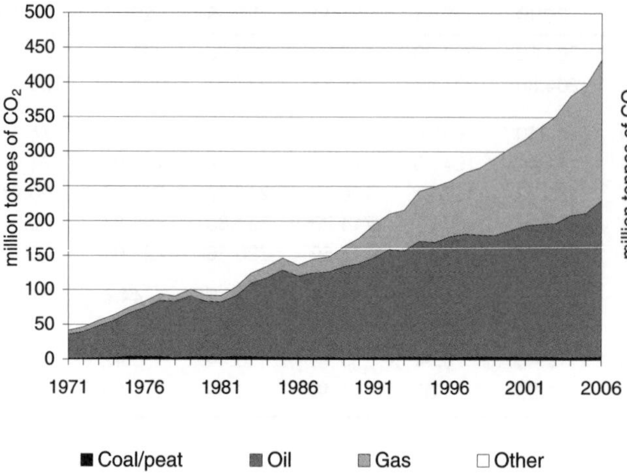
million tonnes of CO2
Coal/peat
Oil
Gas
Other

Figure 2. CO_2 emissions by sector

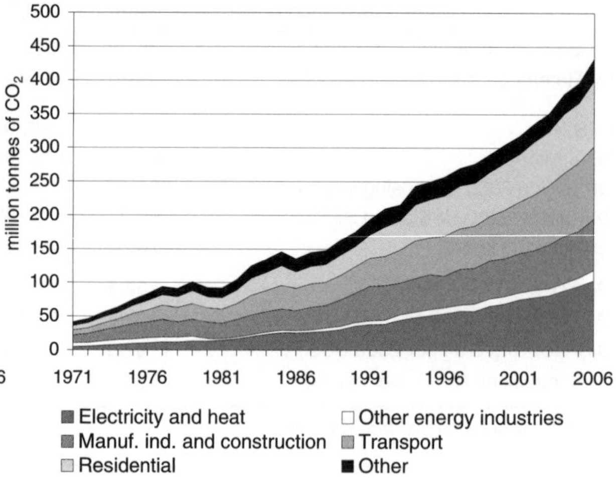
million tonnes of CO2
Electricity and heat
Other energy industries
Manuf. ind. and construction
Transport
Residential
Other

Figure 3. CO_2 emissions by sector

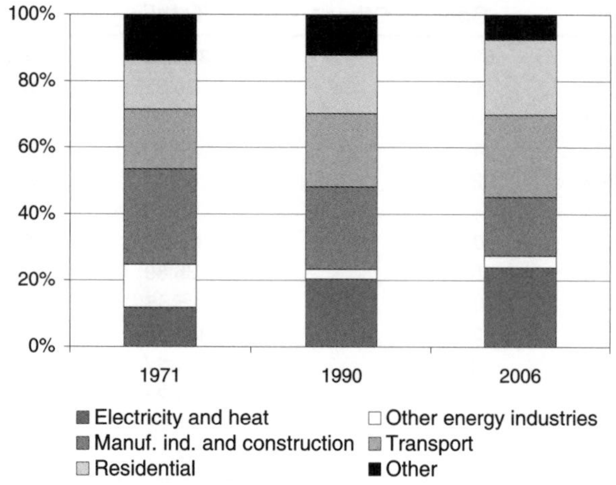
Electricity and heat
Other energy industries
Manuf. ind. and construction
Transport
Residential
Other

Figure 4. Reference vs Sectoral Approach

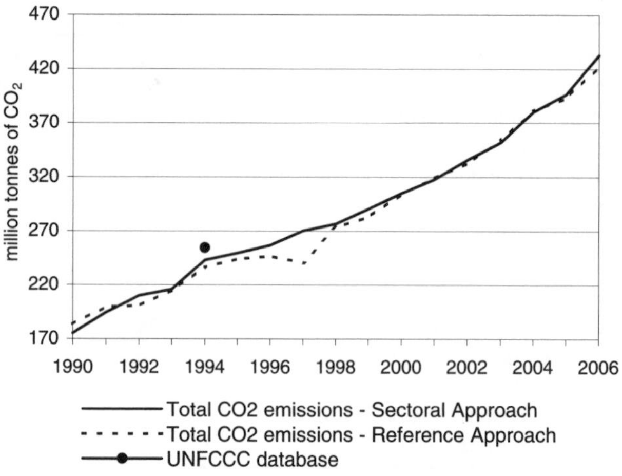
million tonnes of CO2
Total CO2 emissions - Sectoral Approach
Total CO2 emissions - Reference Approach
UNFCCC database

Figure 5. Electricity generation by fuel

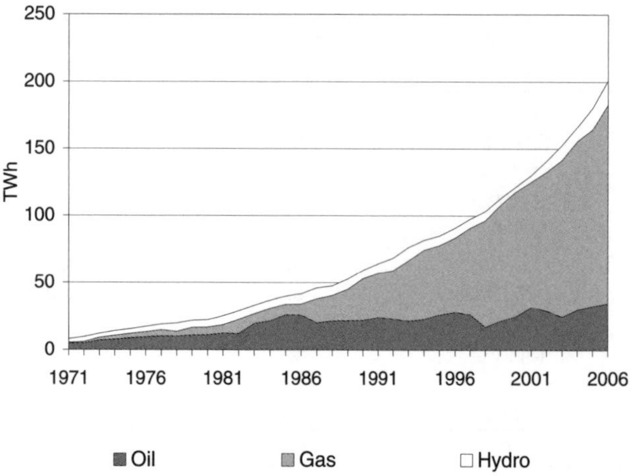
TWh
Oil
Gas
Hydro

Figure 6. Key indicators

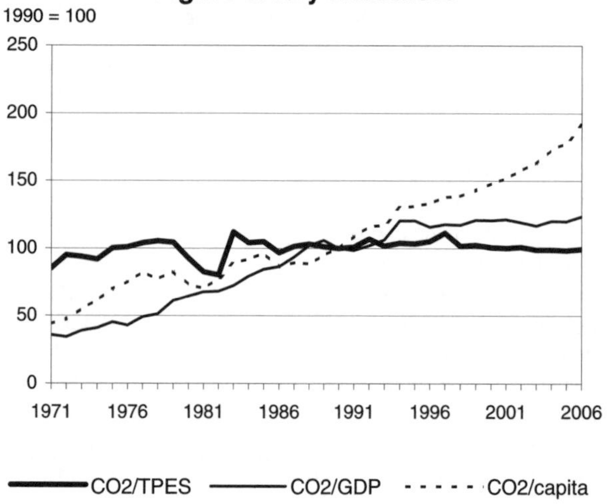
1990 = 100
CO2/TPES
CO2/GDP
CO2/capita

Islamic Republic of Iran / République islamique d'Iran
Key indicators

	1990	1995	2000	2003	2004	2005	2006	% change 90-06
CO₂ Sectoral Approach (Mt of CO₂)	175.31	249.35	304.85	351.87	380.57	396.66	432.83	146.9%
CO₂ Reference Approach (Mt of CO₂)	183.33	243.87	304.34	353.95	381.58	393.36	422.88	130.7%
TPES (PJ)	2 882	3 964	4 974	5 840	6 324	6 618	7 155	148.3%
TPES (Mtoe)	68.83	94.68	118.80	139.47	151.04	158.08	170.89	148.3%
GDP (billion 2000 US$ using exch. rates)	70.29	83.07	101.29	120.93	127.08	132.62	140.31	99.6%
GDP (billion 2000 US$ using PPPs)	256.54	303.18	369.66	441.34	463.77	484.01	512.09	99.6%
Population (millions)	54.40	58.95	63.94	67.04	68.07	69.09	70.10	28.9%
CO₂ / TPES (t CO₂ per TJ)	60.8	62.9	61.3	60.3	60.2	59.9	60.5	-0.6%
CO₂ / GDP (kg CO₂ per 2000 US$)	2.49	3.00	3.01	2.91	2.99	2.99	3.08	23.7%
CO₂ / GDP (kg CO₂ per 2000 US$ PPP)	0.68	0.82	0.82	0.80	0.82	0.82	0.85	23.7%
CO₂ / population (t CO₂ per capita)	3.22	4.23	4.77	5.25	5.59	5.74	6.17	91.6%

Ratios are based on the Sectoral Approach.

2006 CO₂ emissions by sector

million tonnes of CO₂	Coal/peat	Oil	Gas	Other *	Total	% change 90-06
Sectoral Approach	**4.23**	**225.73**	**202.87**	**-**	**432.83**	**146.9%**
Main activity producer elec. and heat	-	34.52	63.58	-	98.10	199.9%
Unallocated autoproducers	-	2.07	3.23	-	5.30	84.6%
Other energy industries	-	2.54	12.92	-	15.46	188.3%
Manufacturing industries and construction	4.21	32.64	39.42	-	76.26	75.4%
Transport	-	106.28	1.03	-	107.31	176.9%
of which: road	-	*106.28*	*1.03*	-	*107.31*	*176.9%*
Other sectors	0.02	47.68	82.69	-	130.40	150.1%
of which: residential	*0.02*	*24.75*	*72.93*	-	*97.70*	*219.1%*
Reference Approach	**4.77**	**215.24**	**202.87**	**-**	**422.88**	**130.7%**
Diff. due to losses and/or transformation	0.54	- 2.67	2.77	-	0.65	
Statistical differences	-	- 7.82	- 2.77	-	- 10.60	
Memo: international marine bunkers	-	*1.43*	-	-	*1.43*	*-8.7%*
Memo: international aviation	-	*3.14*	-	-	*3.14*	*111.7%*

* Other includes industrial waste and non-renewable municipal waste.

Key sources for CO₂ emissions from fuel combustion in 2006

IPCC source category	CO₂ emissions (Mt of CO₂)	% change 90-06	Level assessment (%) **	Cumulative total (%)
Road - oil	106.28	174.3%	16.9	16.9
Residential - gas	72.93	+	11.6	28.5
Main activity prod. elec. and heat - gas	63.58	305.8%	10.1	38.6
Manufacturing industries - gas	39.42	179.8%	6.3	44.9
Main activity prod. elec. and heat - oil	34.52	102.5%	5.5	50.4
Manufacturing industries - oil	32.64	20.4%	5.2	55.5
Residential - oil	24.75	0.9%	3.9	59.5
Non-specified other sectors - oil	22.93	6.6%	3.6	63.1
Other energy industries - gas	12.92	+	2.1	65.2
Non-specified other sectors - gas	9.77	x	1.6	66.7
Manufacturing industries - coal/peat	4.21	84.4%	0.7	67.4
Memo: total CO₂ from fuel combustion	*432.83*	*146.9%*	*68.8*	*68.8*

** Percent calculated using the total GHG estimate for CO₂, CH₄, N₂O, HFCs, PFCs and SF₆ excluding CO₂ emissions/removals from land use change and forestry.

Iraq / Irak

Figure 1. CO$_2$ emissions by fuel

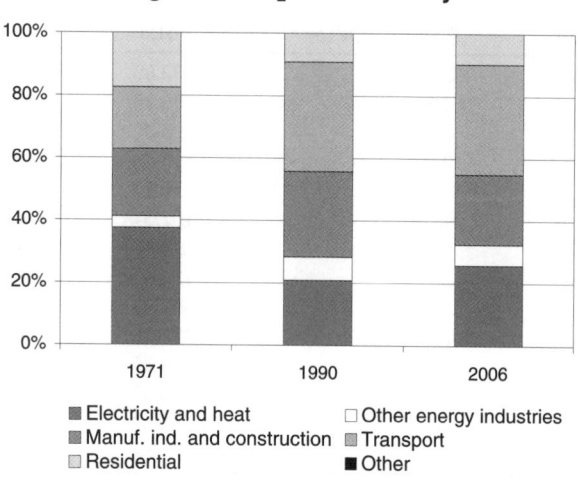

■ Coal/peat ■ Oil ■ Gas □ Other

Figure 2. CO$_2$ emissions by sector

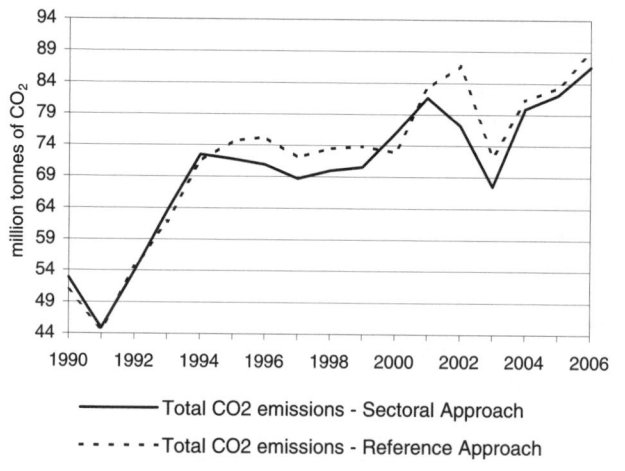

■ Electricity and heat □ Other energy industries
■ Manuf. ind. and construction ■ Transport
□ Residential ■ Other

Figure 3. CO$_2$ emissions by sector

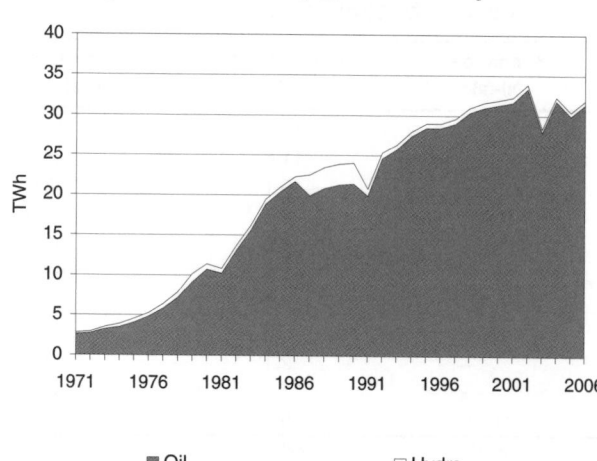

■ Electricity and heat □ Other energy industries
■ Manuf. ind. and construction ■ Transport
□ Residential ■ Other

Figure 4. Reference vs Sectoral Approach

—— Total CO2 emissions - Sectoral Approach
- - - - Total CO2 emissions - Reference Approach

Figure 5. Electricity generation by fuel

■ Oil □ Hydro

Figure 6. Key indicators

1990 = 100

—— CO2/TPES —— CO2/GDP - - - - CO2/capita

Iraq / Irak

Key indicators

	1990	1995	2000	2003	2004	2005	2006	% change 90-06
CO$_2$ Sectoral Approach (Mt of CO$_2$)	52.85	71.77	75.87	67.49	79.93	82.08	86.55	63.8%
CO$_2$ Reference Approach (Mt of CO$_2$)	50.76	74.61	72.91	72.31	81.25	83.36	89.01	75.4%
TPES (PJ)	798	1 106	1 089	1 059	1 212	1 253	1 341	68.0%
TPES (Mtoe)	19.06	26.41	26.00	25.29	28.96	29.92	32.02	68.0%
GDP (billion 2000 US$ using exch. rates)	32.96	12.62	25.90	13.10	19.10	19.81	19.87	-39.7%
GDP (billion 2000 US$ using PPPs)	45.06	17.25	35.41	17.91	26.11	27.08	27.16	-39.7%
Population (millions)	18.14	19.56	22.68	24.68	25.38	26.08	26.78	47.7%
CO$_2$ / TPES (t CO$_2$ per TJ)	66.2	64.9	69.7	63.7	65.9	65.5	64.6	-2.5%
CO$_2$ / GDP (kg CO$_2$ per 2000 US$)	1.60	5.69	2.93	5.15	4.19	4.14	4.36	171.7%
CO$_2$ / GDP (kg CO$_2$ per 2000 US$ PPP)	1.17	4.16	2.14	3.77	3.06	3.03	3.19	171.7%
CO$_2$ / population (t CO$_2$ per capita)	2.91	3.67	3.35	2.73	3.15	3.15	3.23	10.9%

Ratios are based on the Sectoral Approach.

2006 CO$_2$ emissions by sector

million tonnes of CO$_2$	Coal/peat	Oil	Gas	Other *	Total	% change 90-06
Sectoral Approach	-	**79.87**	**6.68**	-	**86.55**	**63.8%**
Main activity producer elec. and heat	-	22.34	-	-	22.34	102.6%
Unallocated autoproducers	-	-	-	-	-	-
Other energy industries	-	5.75	-	-	5.75	45.7%
Manufacturing industries and construction	-	12.72	6.68	-	19.40	34.3%
Transport	-	30.58	-	-	30.58	64.8%
of which: road	-	30.58	-	-	30.58	64.8%
Other sectors	-	8.49	-	-	8.49	74.0%
of which: residential	-	8.49	-	-	8.49	74.0%
Reference Approach	-	**82.33**	**6.68**	-	**89.01**	**75.4%**
Diff. due to losses and/or transformation	-	2.46	-	-	2.46	
Statistical differences	-	0.00	-	-	0.00	
Memo: international marine bunkers	-	..	-	-	..	..
Memo: international aviation	-	2.48	-	-	2.48	-14.1%

* Other includes industrial waste and non-renewable municipal waste.

Key sources for CO$_2$ emissions from fuel combustion in 2006

IPCC source category	CO$_2$ emissions (Mt of CO$_2$)	% change 90-06	Level assessment (%) **	Cumulative total (%)
Road - oil	30.58	64.8%	29.2	29.2
Main activity prod. elec. and heat - oil	22.34	102.6%	21.3	50.5
Manufacturing industries - oil	12.72	19.3%	12.1	62.6
Residential - oil	8.49	74.0%	8.1	70.7
Manufacturing industries - gas	6.68	76.8%	6.4	77.1
Other energy industries - oil	5.75	45.7%	5.5	82.5
-	-	-	-	-
-	-	-	-	-
-	-	-	-	-
-	-	-	-	-
-	-	-	-	-
Memo: total CO$_2$ from fuel combustion	86.55	63.8%	82.5	82.5

** Percent calculated using the total GHG estimate for CO$_2$, CH$_4$, N$_2$O, HFCs, PFCs and SF$_6$ excluding CO$_2$ emissions/removals from land use change and forestry.

Ireland / Irlande

Figure 1. CO$_2$ emissions by fuel

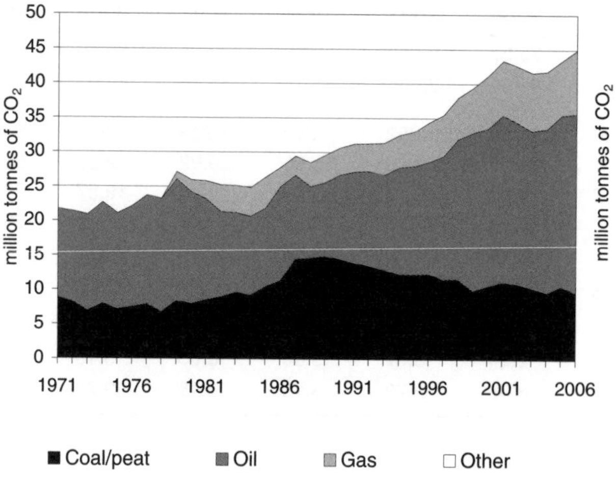

■ Coal/peat   ■ Oil   ▨ Gas   ☐ Other

Figure 2. CO$_2$ emissions by sector

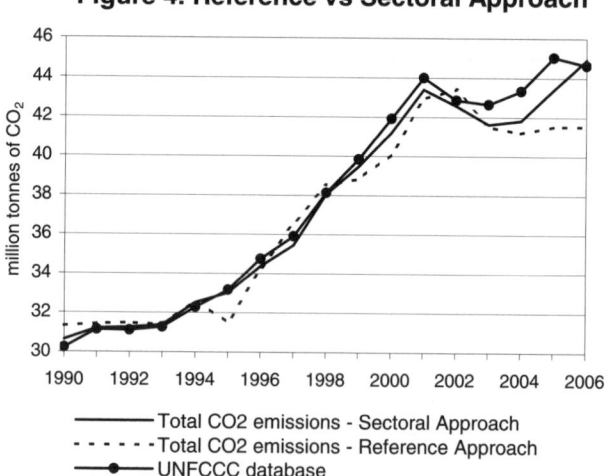

■ Electricity and heat   ☐ Other energy industries
▨ Manuf. ind. and construction   ▨ Transport
☐ Residential   ■ Other

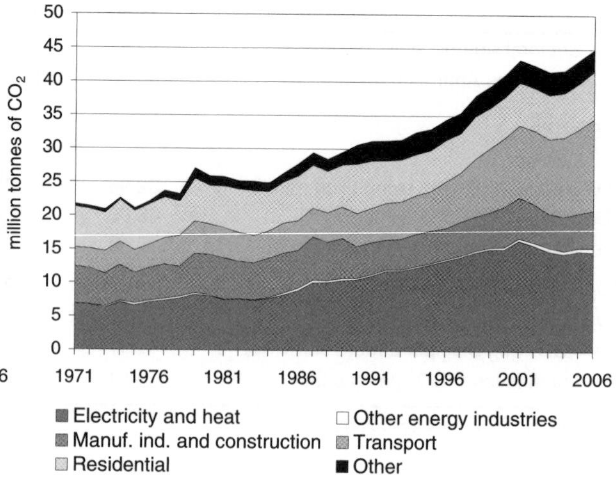

Figure 3. CO$_2$ emissions by sector

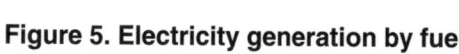

■ Electricity and heat   ☐ Other energy industries
▨ Manuf. ind. and construction   ▨ Transport
☐ Residential   ■ Other

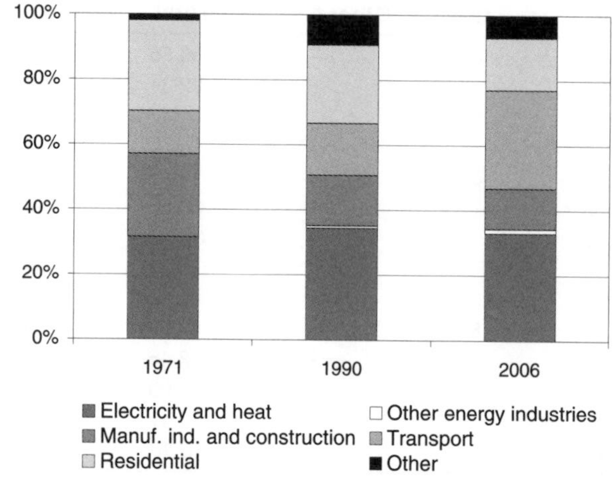

Figure 4. Reference vs Sectoral Approach

—— Total CO2 emissions - Sectoral Approach
- - - Total CO2 emissions - Reference Approach
—●— UNFCCC database

Figure 5. Electricity generation by fuel

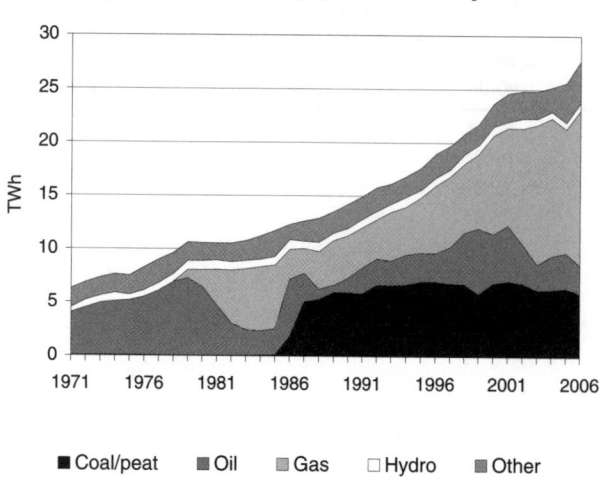

■ Coal/peat   ■ Oil   ▨ Gas   ☐ Hydro   ▨ Other

Figure 6. Key indicators

1990 = 100

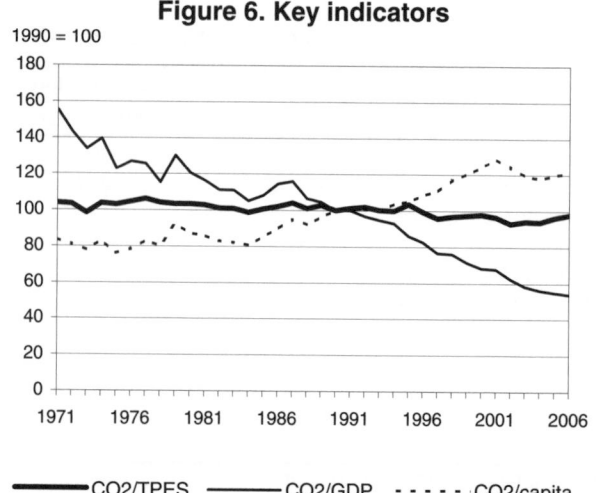

—— CO2/TPES   —— CO2/GDP   - - - - CO2/capita

Ireland / Irlande

Key indicators

	1990	1995	2000	2003	2004	2005	2006	% change 90-06
CO$_2$ Sectoral Approach (Mt of CO$_2$)	30.63	33.00	41.19	41.62	41.82	43.39	44.93	46.7%
CO$_2$ Reference Approach (Mt of CO$_2$)	31.32	31.50	40.09	41.51	41.19	41.52	41.52	32.6%
TPES (PJ)	432	450	594	623	629	635	647	49.8%
TPES (Mtoe)	10.32	10.74	14.18	14.88	15.02	15.17	15.46	49.8%
GDP (billion 2000 US$ using exch. rates)	48.90	61.30	96.40	113.80	118.80	126.00	133.20	172.4%
GDP (billion 2000 US$ using PPPs)	55.11	69.12	108.63	128.28	133.90	141.96	150.10	172.4%
Population (millions)	3.51	3.60	3.80	3.99	4.06	4.15	4.25	21.3%
CO$_2$ / TPES (t CO$_2$ per TJ)	70.9	73.4	69.4	66.8	66.5	68.3	69.4	-2.1%
CO$_2$ / GDP (kg CO$_2$ per 2000 US$)	0.63	0.54	0.43	0.37	0.35	0.34	0.34	-46.2%
CO$_2$ / GDP (kg CO$_2$ per 2000 US$ PPP)	0.56	0.48	0.38	0.32	0.31	0.31	0.30	-46.1%
CO$_2$ / population (t CO$_2$ per capita)	8.74	9.17	10.84	10.43	10.30	10.46	10.56	20.9%

Ratios are based on the Sectoral Approach.

2006 CO$_2$ emissions by sector

million tonnes of CO$_2$	Coal/peat	Oil	Gas	Other *	Total	% change 90-06
Sectoral Approach	**9.68**	**26.03**	**9.21**	**-**	**44.93**	**46.7%**
Main activity producer elec. and heat	6.89	2.21	5.21	-	14.31	37.7%
Unallocated autoproducers	0.06	0.03	0.43	-	0.51	263.4%
Other energy industries	0.08	0.52	-	-	0.60	151.1%
Manufacturing industries and construction	0.52	3.67	1.39	-	5.58	17.7%
Transport	-	13.59	-	-	13.59	176.9%
of which: road	-	*13.19*	-	-	*13.19*	*188.4%*
Other sectors	2.14	6.01	2.19	-	10.34	1.3%
of which: residential	*2.04*	*3.68*	*1.47*	-	*7.19*	*-2.1%*
Reference Approach	**9.69**	**22.45**	**9.38**	**-**	**41.52**	**32.6%**
Diff. due to losses and/or transformation	0.38	- 0.18	0.15	-	0.35	
Statistical differences	- 0.38	- 3.40	0.01	-	- 3.77	
Memo: international marine bunkers	-	*0.38*	-	-	*0.38*	*590.3%*
Memo: international aviation	-	*2.40*	-	-	*2.40*	*132.7%*

* Other includes industrial waste and non-renewable municipal waste.

Key sources for CO$_2$ emissions from fuel combustion in 2006

IPCC source category	CO$_2$ emissions (Mt of CO$_2$)	% change 90-06	Level assessment (%) **	Cumulative total (%)
Road - oil	13.19	188.4%	18.8	18.8
Main activity prod. elec. and heat - coal/peat	6.89	-7.1%	9.8	28.7
Main activity prod. elec. and heat - gas	5.21	172.8%	7.4	36.1
Residential - oil	3.68	218.5%	5.2	41.3
Manufacturing industries - oil	3.67	64.8%	5.2	46.6
Non-specified other sectors - oil	2.34	-9.8%	3.3	49.9
Main activity prod. elec. and heat - oil	2.21	108.2%	3.2	53.1
Residential - coal/peat	2.04	-65.6%	2.9	56.0
Residential - gas	1.47	439.0%	2.1	58.1
Manufacturing industries - gas	1.39	-7.7%	2.0	60.1
Non-specified other sectors - gas	0.71	225.5%	1.0	61.1
Memo: total CO$_2$ from fuel combustion	*44.93*	*46.7%*	*64.1*	*64.1*

** Percent calculated using the total GHG estimate for CO$_2$, CH$_4$, N$_2$O, HFCs, PFCs and SF$_6$ excluding CO$_2$ emissions/removals from land use change and forestry.

Israel / Israël

Figure 1. CO$_2$ emissions by fuel

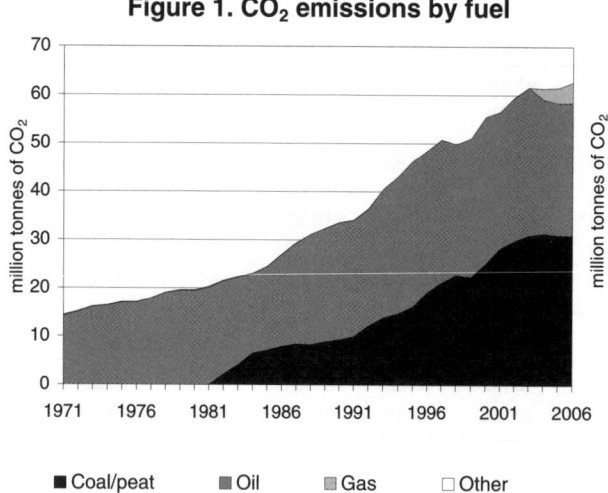

Coal/peat ■ Oil ■ Gas ■ Other □

Figure 2. CO$_2$ emissions by sector

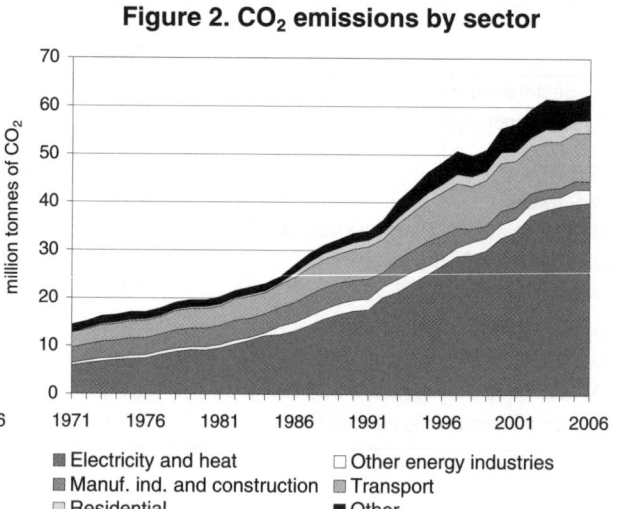

■ Electricity and heat   □ Other energy industries
■ Manuf. ind. and construction   ■ Transport
□ Residential   ■ Other

Figure 3. CO$_2$ emissions by sector

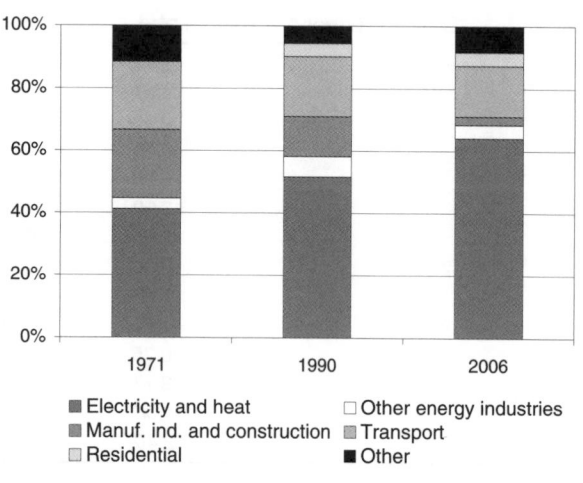

■ Electricity and heat   □ Other energy industries
■ Manuf. ind. and construction   ■ Transport
□ Residential   ■ Other

Figure 4. Reference vs Sectoral Approach

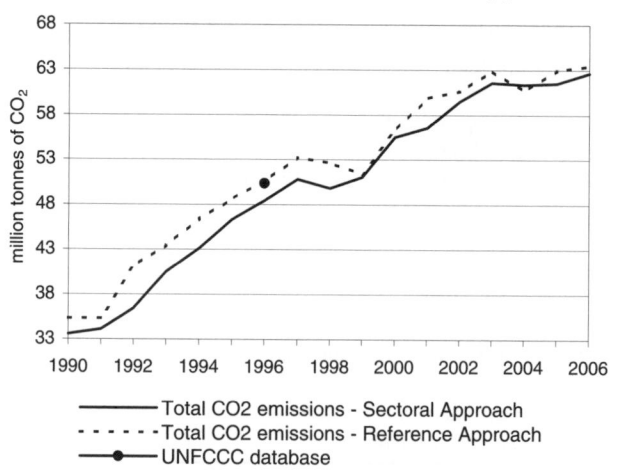

——— Total CO2 emissions - Sectoral Approach
- - - - Total CO2 emissions - Reference Approach
——●— UNFCCC database

Figure 5. Electricity generation by fuel

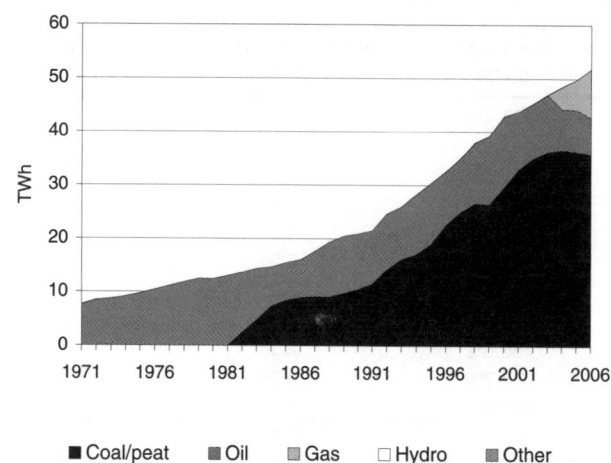

■ Coal/peat   ■ Oil   ■ Gas   □ Hydro   ■ Other

Figure 6. Key indicators

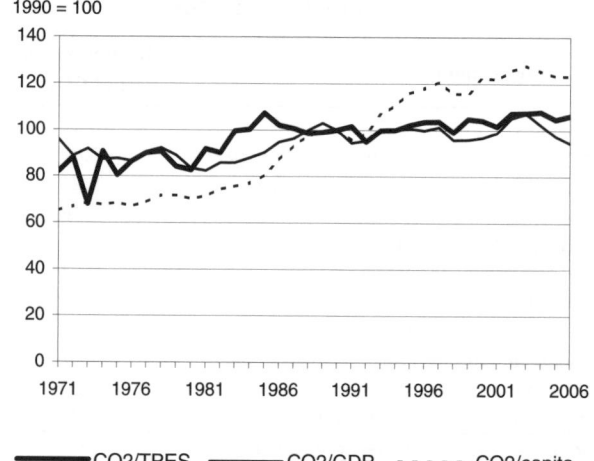

——— CO2/TPES   ——— CO2/GDP   - - - - CO2/capita

Israel / Israël
Key indicators

	1990	1995	2000	2003	2004	2005	2006	% change 90-06
CO$_2$ Sectoral Approach (Mt of CO$_2$)	33.57	46.32	55.51	61.60	61.39	61.52	62.64	86.6%
CO$_2$ Reference Approach (Mt of CO$_2$)	35.32	48.59	56.30	62.92	60.74	63.00	63.47	79.7%
TPES (PJ)	507	685	805	866	860	888	891	75.7%
TPES (Mtoe)	12.11	16.35	19.23	20.68	20.53	21.20	21.28	75.7%
GDP (billion 2000 US$ using exch. rates)	67.59	92.59	115.49	115.78	120.92	127.17	133.65	97.7%
GDP (billion 2000 US$ using PPPs)	84.72	116.04	144.74	145.11	151.55	159.38	167.51	97.7%
Population (millions)	4.66	5.55	6.29	6.69	6.80	6.92	7.05	51.3%
CO$_2$ / TPES (t CO$_2$ per TJ)	66.2	67.7	68.9	71.1	71.4	69.3	70.3	6.2%
CO$_2$ / GDP (kg CO$_2$ per 2000 US$)	0.50	0.50	0.48	0.53	0.51	0.48	0.47	-5.6%
CO$_2$ / GDP (kg CO$_2$ per 2000 US$ PPP)	0.40	0.40	0.38	0.42	0.41	0.39	0.37	-5.6%
CO$_2$ / population (t CO$_2$ per capita)	7.20	8.35	8.83	9.21	9.02	8.88	8.89	23.4%

Ratios are based on the Sectoral Approach.

2006 CO$_2$ emissions by sector

million tonnes of CO$_2$	Coal/peat	Oil	Gas	Other *	Total	% change 90-06
Sectoral Approach	**30.97**	**27.42**	**4.25**	-	**62.64**	**86.6%**
Main activity producer elec. and heat	30.90	4.43	4.25	-	39.57	134.7%
Unallocated autoproducers	0.08	0.43	-	-	0.51	11.9%
Other energy industries	-	2.74	-	-	2.74	24.9%
Manufacturing industries and construction	-	1.71	-	-	1.71	-60.3%
Transport	-	10.11	-	-	10.11	56.1%
of which: road	-	*10.11*	-	-	*10.11*	*57.4%*
Other sectors	-	8.01	-	-	8.01	143.0%
of which: residential	-	*2.71*	-	-	*2.71*	*93.3%*
Reference Approach	**29.78**	**29.30**	**4.40**	-	**63.47**	**79.7%**
Diff. due to losses and/or transformation	-	0.87	-	-	0.87	
Statistical differences	- 1.19	1.00	0.15	-	- 0.04	
Memo: international marine bunkers	-	*0.81*	-	-	*0.81*	*114.2%*
Memo: international aviation	-	*1.91*	-	-	*1.91*	*21.9%*

* Other includes industrial waste and non-renewable municipal waste.

Key sources for CO$_2$ emissions from fuel combustion in 2006

IPCC source category	CO$_2$ emissions (Mt of CO$_2$)	% change 90-06	Level assessment (%) **	Cumulative total (%)
Main activity prod. elec. and heat - coal/peat	30.90	233.5%	44.6	44.6
Road - oil	10.11	57.4%	14.6	59.2
Non-specified other sectors - oil	5.30	179.6%	7.7	66.9
Main activity prod. elec. and heat - oil	4.43	-41.7%	6.4	73.3
Main activity prod. elec. and heat - gas	4.25	x	6.1	79.4
Other energy industries - oil	2.74	24.9%	4.0	83.3
Residential - oil	2.71	93.4%	3.9	87.3
Manufacturing industries - oil	1.71	-59.4%	2.5	89.7
Unallocated autoproducers - oil	0.43	-4.7%	0.6	90.3
Unallocated autoproducers - coal/peat	0.08	x	0.1	90.5
-	-	-	-	-
Memo: total CO$_2$ from fuel combustion	*62.64*	*86.6%*	*90.5*	*90.5*

** Percent calculated using the total GHG estimate for CO$_2$, CH$_4$, N$_2$O, HFCs, PFCs and SF$_6$ excluding CO$_2$ emissions/removals from land use change and forestry.

Italy / Italie

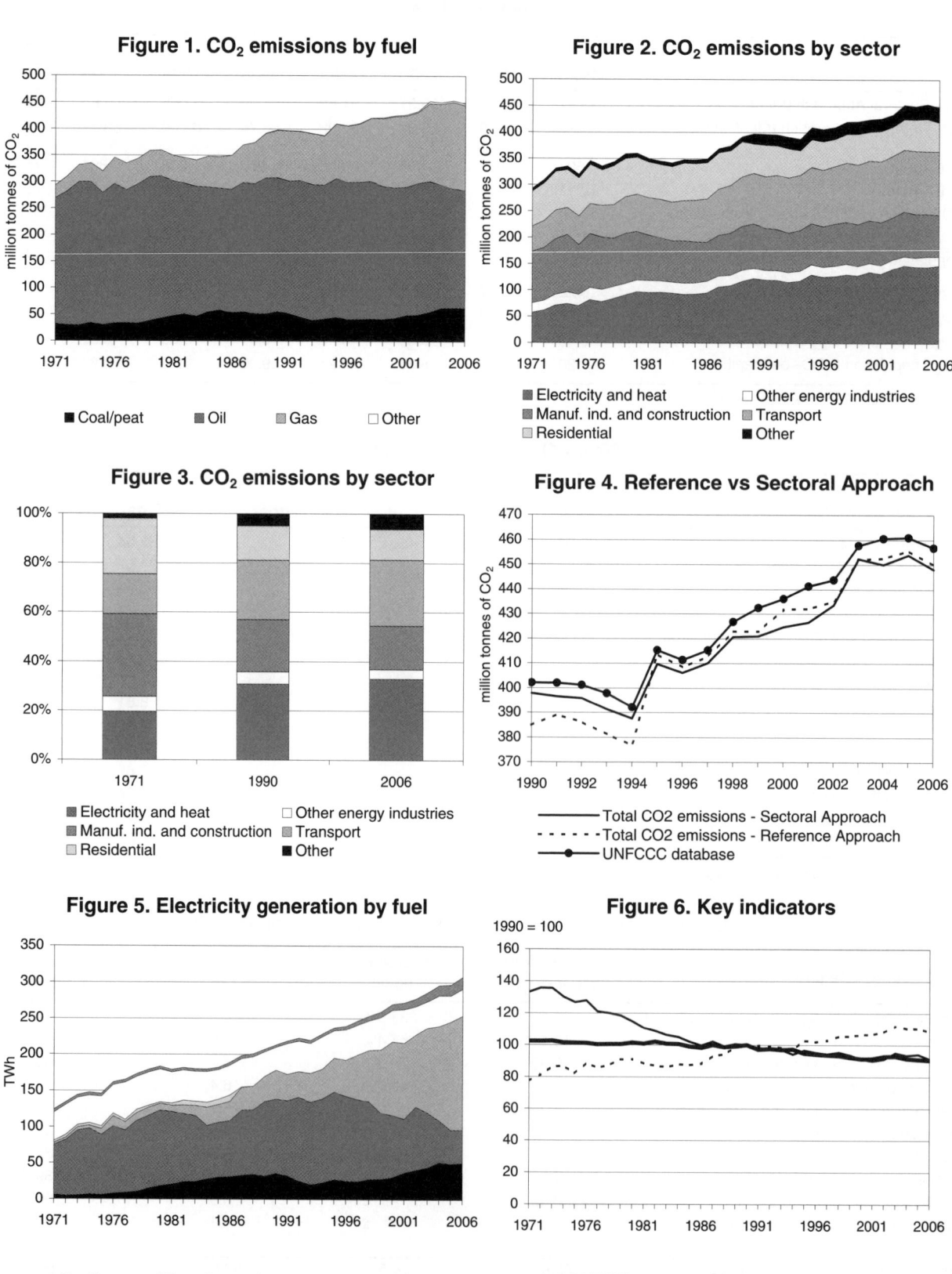

Figure 1. CO$_2$ emissions by fuel

Coal/peat   Oil   Gas   Other

Figure 2. CO$_2$ emissions by sector

Electricity and heat   Other energy industries
Manuf. ind. and construction   Transport
Residential   Other

Figure 3. CO$_2$ emissions by sector

Electricity and heat   Other energy industries
Manuf. ind. and construction   Transport
Residential   Other

Figure 4. Reference vs Sectoral Approach

—— Total CO2 emissions - Sectoral Approach
- - - Total CO2 emissions - Reference Approach
—●— UNFCCC database

Figure 5. Electricity generation by fuel

Coal/peat   Oil   Gas   Nuclear   Hydro   Other

Figure 6. Key indicators

1990 = 100

——CO2/TPES   ——CO2/GDP   - - - - CO2/capita

Italy / Italie

Key indicators

	1990	1995	2000	2003	2004	2005	2006	% change 90-06
CO$_2$ Sectoral Approach (Mt of CO$_2$)	397.79	409.66	424.68	452.38	450.01	453.82	448.03	12.6%
CO$_2$ Reference Approach (Mt of CO$_2$)	384.79	413.52	431.88	452.08	452.58	455.69	449.92	16.9%
TPES (PJ)	6 200	6 744	7 255	7 586	7 675	7 776	7 711	24.4%
TPES (Mtoe)	148.07	161.09	173.28	181.20	183.32	185.73	184.17	24.4%
GDP (billion 2000 US$ using exch. rates)	937.40	998.50	1 097.30	1 121.30	1 134.80	1 135.80	1 157.00	23.4%
GDP (billion 2000 US$ using PPPs)	1 243.55	1 324.64	1 455.77	1 487.53	1 505.43	1 506.76	1 534.96	23.4%
Population (millions)	56.72	56.84	56.94	57.61	58.18	58.61	58.86	3.8%
CO$_2$ / TPES (t CO$_2$ per TJ)	64.2	60.7	58.5	59.6	58.6	58.4	58.1	-9.4%
CO$_2$ / GDP (kg CO$_2$ per 2000 US$)	0.42	0.41	0.39	0.40	0.40	0.40	0.39	-8.8%
CO$_2$ / GDP (kg CO$_2$ per 2000 US$ PPP)	0.32	0.31	0.29	0.30	0.30	0.30	0.29	-8.8%
CO$_2$ / population (t CO$_2$ per capita)	7.01	7.21	7.46	7.85	7.74	7.74	7.61	8.5%

Ratios are based on the Sectoral Approach.

2006 CO$_2$ emissions by sector

million tonnes of CO$_2$	Coal/peat	Oil	Gas	Other *	Total	% change 90-06
Sectoral Approach	**62.44**	**222.27**	**159.84**	**3.48**	**448.03**	**12.6%**
Main activity producer elec. and heat	49.32	22.41	56.78	2.97	131.49	22.9%
Unallocated autoproducers	1.12	7.26	7.47	0.22	16.08	3.9%
Other energy industries	0.22	16.31	0.77	-	17.30	-13.7%
Manufacturing industries and construction	11.13	31.67	35.91	0.28	78.99	-5.9%
Transport	-	119.36	0.97	-	120.32	25.5%
of which: road	-	*114.92*	*0.97*	-	*115.88*	*26.7%*
Other sectors	0.65	25.25	57.95	-	83.85	11.2%
of which: residential	*0.03*	*15.49*	*39.83*	-	*55.35*	*-0.7%*
Reference Approach	**64.09**	**221.42**	**160.93**	**3.48**	**449.92**	**16.9%**
Diff. due to losses and/or transformation	1.65	- 1.15	1.09	-	1.58	
Statistical differences	- 0.00	0.30	0.00	- 0.00	0.30	
Memo: international marine bunkers	-	*10.95*	-	-	*10.95*	*30.8%*
Memo: international aviation	-	*9.00*	-	-	*9.00*	*121.2%*

* Other includes industrial waste and non-renewable municipal waste.

Key sources for CO$_2$ emissions from fuel combustion in 2006

IPCC source category	CO$_2$ emissions (Mt of CO$_2$)	% change 90-06	Level assessment (%) **	Cumulative total (%)
Road - oil	114.92	26.3%	20.6	20.6
Main activity prod. elec. and heat - gas	56.78	253.3%	10.2	30.7
Main activity prod. elec. and heat - coal/peat	49.32	78.2%	8.8	39.5
Residential - gas	39.83	50.7%	7.1	46.7
Manufacturing industries - gas	35.91	9.1%	6.4	53.1
Manufacturing industries - oil	31.67	-10.4%	5.7	58.7
Main activity prod. elec. and heat - oil	22.41	-64.5%	4.0	62.7
Non-specified other sectors - gas	18.12	83.2%	3.2	66.0
Other energy industries - oil	16.31	11.3%	2.9	68.9
Residential - oil	15.49	-45.6%	2.8	71.7
Manufacturing industries - coal/peat	11.13	-26.0%	2.0	73.7
Memo: total CO$_2$ from fuel combustion	*448.03*	*12.6%*	*80.1*	*80.1*

** Percent calculated using the total GHG estimate for CO$_2$, CH$_4$, N$_2$O, HFCs, PFCs and SF$_6$ excluding CO$_2$ emissions/removals from land use change and forestry.

Jamaica / Jamaïque

Figure 1. CO$_2$ emissions by fuel

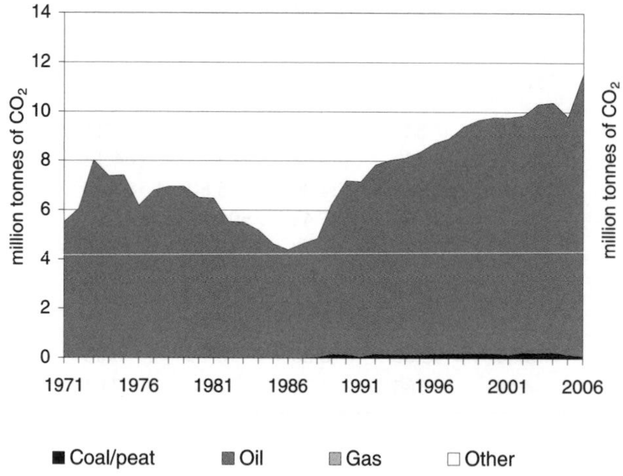

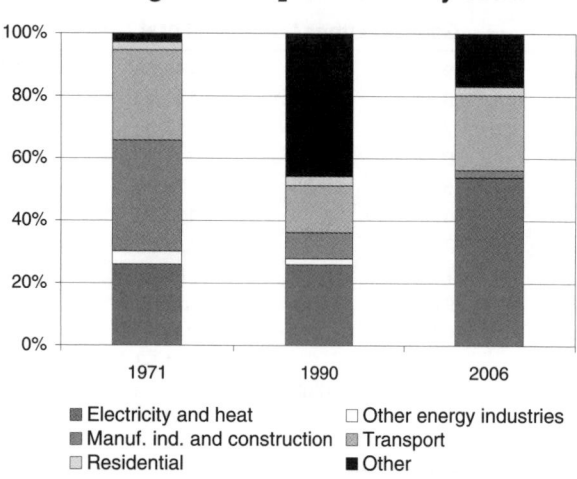

■ Coal/peat   ■ Oil   ■ Gas   □ Other

Figure 2. CO$_2$ emissions by sector

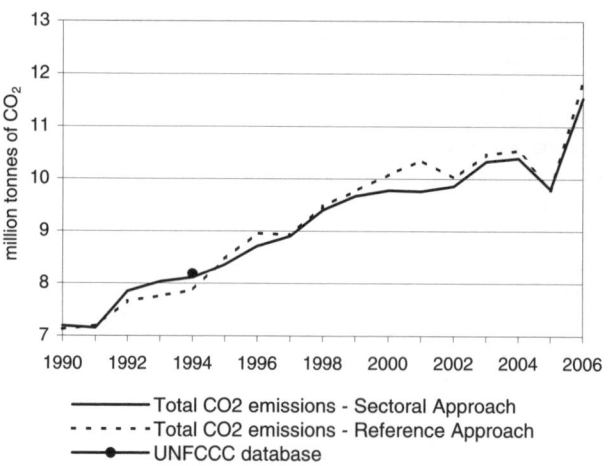

■ Electricity and heat   □ Other energy industries
■ Manuf. ind. and construction   ■ Transport
□ Residential   ■ Other

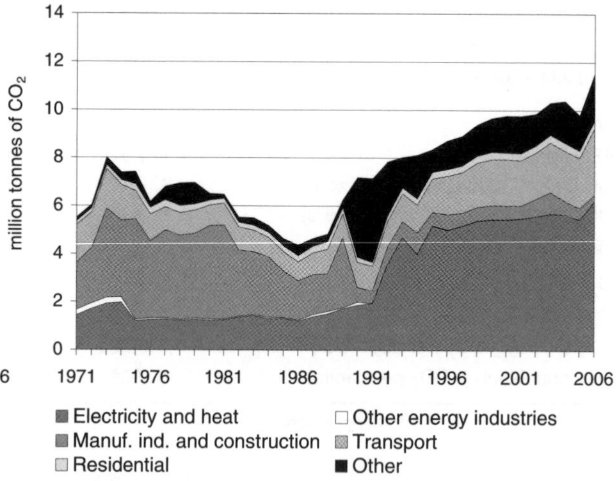

Figure 3. CO$_2$ emissions by sector

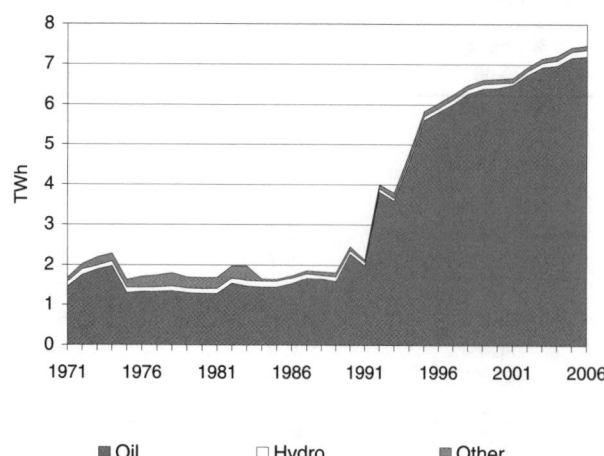

■ Electricity and heat   □ Other energy industries
■ Manuf. ind. and construction   ■ Transport
□ Residential   ■ Other

Figure 4. Reference vs Sectoral Approach

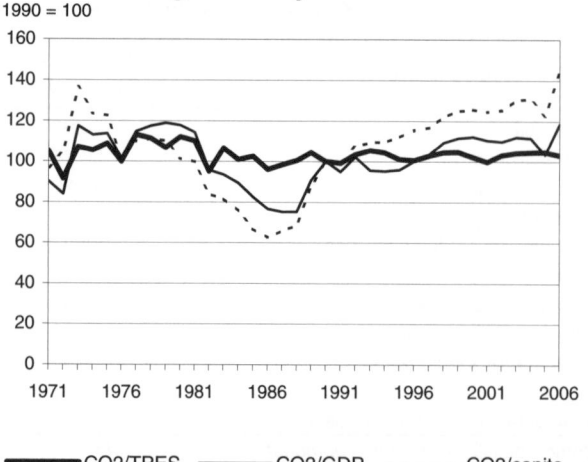

—— Total CO2 emissions - Sectoral Approach
- - - - Total CO2 emissions - Reference Approach
——●—— UNFCCC database

Figure 5. Electricity generation by fuel

■ Oil   □ Hydro   ■ Other

Figure 6. Key indicators

1990 = 100

—— CO2/TPES   —— CO2/GDP   - - - - CO2/capita

Jamaica / Jamaïque

Key indicators

	1990	1995	2000	2003	2004	2005	2006	% change 90-06
CO$_2$ Sectoral Approach (Mt of CO$_2$)	7.19	8.36	9.78	10.32	10.39	9.80	11.54	60.5%
CO$_2$ Reference Approach (Mt of CO$_2$)	7.12	8.47	10.07	10.46	10.54	9.79	11.84	66.2%
TPES (PJ)	123	142	164	170	171	161	192	55.8%
TPES (Mtoe)	2.95	3.39	3.93	4.06	4.08	3.84	4.59	55.8%
GDP (billion 2000 US$ using exch. rates)	6.62	8.04	8.03	8.49	8.58	8.74	8.97	35.5%
GDP (billion 2000 US$ using PPPs)	7.69	9.33	9.32	9.85	9.96	10.14	10.41	35.4%
Population (millions)	2.39	2.48	2.59	2.63	2.64	2.66	2.67	11.6%
CO$_2$ / TPES (t CO$_2$ per TJ)	58.3	58.9	59.5	60.7	60.9	61.0	60.0	3.0%
CO$_2$ / GDP (kg CO$_2$ per 2000 US$)	1.09	1.04	1.22	1.22	1.21	1.12	1.29	18.5%
CO$_2$ / GDP (kg CO$_2$ per 2000 US$ PPP)	0.94	0.90	1.05	1.05	1.04	0.97	1.11	18.5%
CO$_2$ / population (t CO$_2$ per capita)	3.01	3.37	3.78	3.93	3.93	3.69	4.33	43.9%

Ratios are based on the Sectoral Approach.

2006 CO$_2$ emissions by sector

million tonnes of CO$_2$	Coal/peat	Oil	Gas	Other *	Total	% change 90-06
Sectoral Approach	0.08	11.46	-	-	11.54	60.5%
Main activity producer elec. and heat	-	3.11	-	-	3.11	67.0%
Unallocated autoproducers	-	3.09	-	-	3.09	x
Other energy industries	-	0.01	-	-	0.01	-95.6%
Manufacturing industries and construction	0.08	0.19	-	-	0.27	-54.0%
Transport	-	2.77	-	-	2.77	157.3%
of which: road	-	*1.60*	-	-	*1.60*	*120.3%*
Other sectors	-	2.29	-	-	2.29	-34.9%
of which: residential	-	*0.32*	-	-	*0.32*	*50.0%*
Reference Approach	0.08	11.76	-	-	11.84	66.2%
Diff. due to losses and/or transformation	-	- 0.04	-	-	- 0.04	
Statistical differences	-	0.35	-	-	0.35	
Memo: international marine bunkers	-	*0.09*	-	-	*0.09*	-
Memo: international aviation	-	*0.72*	-	-	*0.72*	*68.4%*

* Other includes industrial waste and non-renewable municipal waste.

Key sources for CO$_2$ emissions from fuel combustion in 2006

IPCC source category	CO$_2$ emissions (Mt of CO$_2$)	% change 90-06	Level assessment (%) **	Cumulative total (%)
Main activity prod. elec. and heat - oil	3.11	67.0%	21.6	21.6
Unallocated autoproducers - oil	3.09	x	21.5	43.2
Non-specified other sectors - oil	1.96	-40.5%	13.7	56.9
Road - oil	1.60	120.3%	11.1	68.0
Other transport - oil	1.17	233.7%	8.2	76.2
Residential - oil	0.32	50.0%	2.2	78.4
Manufacturing industries - oil	0.19	-58.3%	1.4	79.8
Manufacturing industries - coal/peat	0.08	-38.5%	0.6	80.3
Other energy industries - oil	0.01	-95.6%	0.0	80.4
-	-	-	-	-
-	-	-	-	-
Memo: total CO$_2$ from fuel combustion	*11.54*	*60.5%*	*80.4*	*80.4*

** Percent calculated using the total GHG estimate for CO$_2$, CH$_4$, N$_2$O, HFCs, PFCs and SF$_6$ excluding CO$_2$ emissions/removals from land use change and forestry.

Japan / Japon

Figure 1. CO$_2$ emissions by fuel

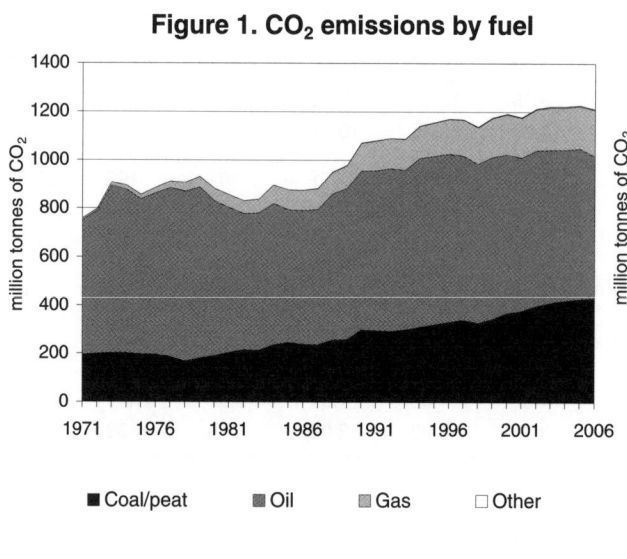

Figure 2. CO$_2$ emissions by sector

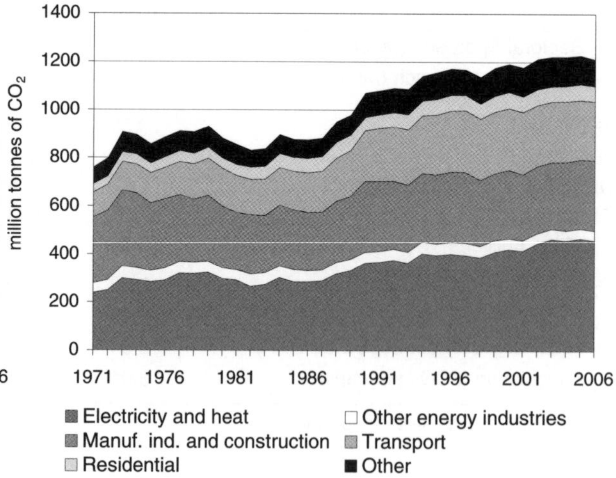

Figure 3. CO$_2$ emissions by sector

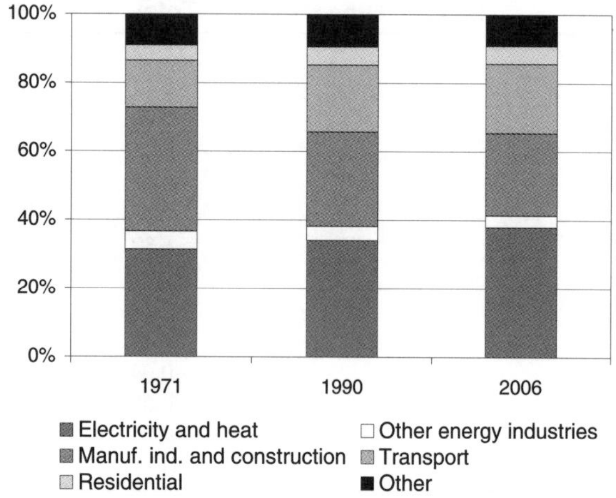

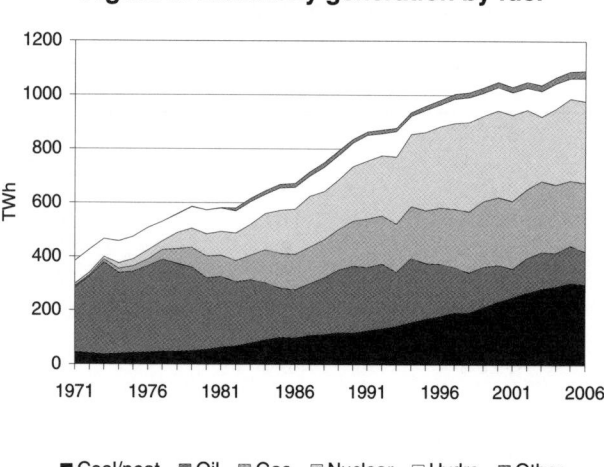

Figure 4. Reference vs Sectoral Approach

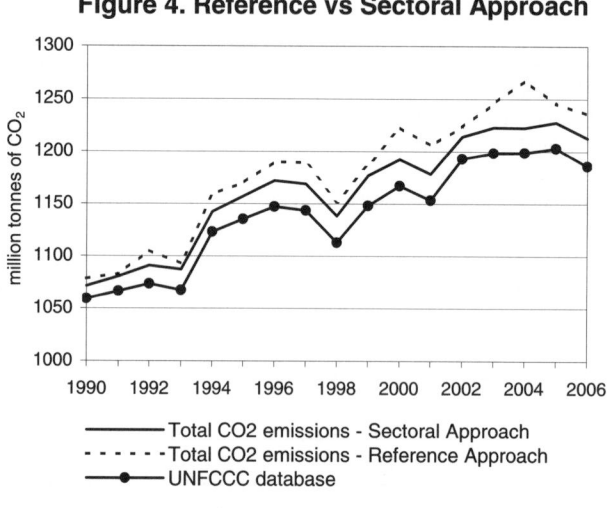

Figure 5. Electricity generation by fuel

Figure 6. Key indicators

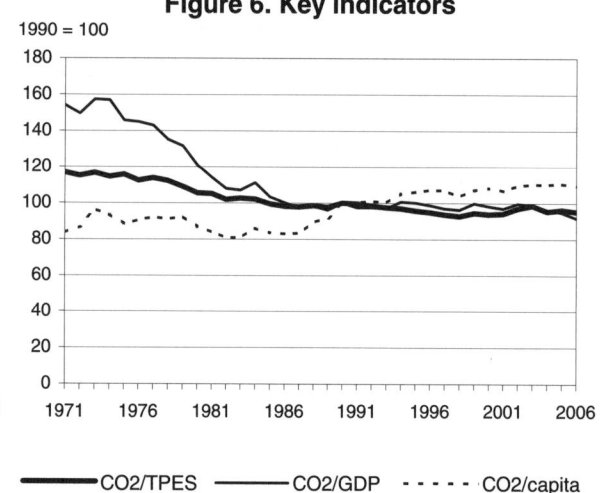

Japan / Japon *

Key indicators

	1990	1995	2000	2003	2004	2005	2006	% change 90-06
CO$_2$ Sectoral Approach (Mt of CO$_2$)	1 071.43	1 156.73	1 192.39	1 222.77	1 222.36	1 227.68	1 212.70	13.2%
CO$_2$ Reference Approach (Mt of CO$_2$)	1 078.38	1 169.77	1 222.93	1 246.03	1 267.76	1 245.59	1 235.52	14.6%
TPES (PJ)	18 586	20 966	22 049	21 528	22 225	22 122	22 088	18.8%
TPES (Mtoe)	443.92	500.77	526.62	514.20	530.83	528.38	527.56	18.8%
GDP (billion 2000 US$ using exch. rates)	4 122.40	4 445.40	4 667.50	4 754.60	4 885.10	4 978.30	5 087.10	23.4%
GDP (billion 2000 US$ using PPPs)	2 867.16	3 091.83	3 246.29	3 306.90	3 397.65	3 462.45	3 538.13	23.4%
Population (millions)	123.48	125.47	126.84	127.72	127.76	127.77	127.76	3.5%
CO$_2$ / TPES (t CO$_2$ per TJ)	57.7	55.2	54.1	56.8	55.0	55.5	54.9	-4.8%
CO$_2$ / GDP (kg CO$_2$ per 2000 US$)	0.26	0.26	0.26	0.26	0.25	0.25	0.24	-8.3%
CO$_2$ / GDP (kg CO$_2$ per 2000 US$ PPP)	0.37	0.37	0.37	0.37	0.36	0.35	0.34	-8.3%
CO$_2$ / population (t CO$_2$ per capita)	8.68	9.22	9.40	9.57	9.57	9.61	9.49	9.4%

Ratios are based on the Sectoral Approach.

* Please see the note in Chapter 1 on the revisions provided by the Japanese Administration.

2006 CO$_2$ emissions by sector

million tonnes of CO$_2$	Coal/peat	Oil	Gas	Other **	Total	% change 90-06
Sectoral Approach	**431.38**	**586.81**	**189.98**	**4.54**	**1 212.70**	**13.2%**
Main activity producer elec. and heat	223.12	45.77	111.77	1.23	381.90	24.1%
Unallocated autoproducers	47.94	22.31	4.66	2.33	77.23	37.7%
Other energy industries	14.75	26.11	0.84	-	41.70	-8.3%
Manufacturing industries and construction	143.10	130.32	17.68	0.97	292.07	-0.8%
Transport	-	245.41	-	-	245.41	17.1%
of which: road	-	219.73	-	-	219.73	17.6%
Other sectors	2.47	116.90	55.03	-	174.39	10.4%
of which: residential	-	41.90	21.54	-	63.45	13.7%
Reference Approach	**435.95**	**614.31**	**180.71**	**4.54**	**1 235.52**	**14.6%**
Diff. due to losses and/or transformation	3.54	15.40	- 3.41	-	15.52	
Statistical differences	1.03	12.10	- 5.85	0.00	7.29	
Memo: international marine bunkers	-	18.64	-	-	18.64	5.5%
Memo: international aviation	-	19.84	-	-	19.84	49.0%

** Other includes industrial waste and non-renewable municipal waste.

Key sources for CO$_2$ emissions from fuel combustion in 2006

IPCC source category	CO$_2$ emissions (Mt of CO$_2$)	% change 90-06	Level assessment (%) ***	Cumulative total (%)
Main activity prod. elec. and heat - coal/peat	223.12	126.9%	16.3	16.3
Road - oil	219.73	17.6%	16.1	32.4
Manufacturing industries - coal/peat	143.10	-4.4%	10.5	42.9
Manufacturing industries - oil	130.32	-3.9%	9.5	52.4
Main activity prod. elec. and heat - gas	111.77	44.6%	8.2	60.6
Non-specified other sectors - oil	74.99	-16.0%	5.5	66.1
Unallocated autoproducers - coal/peat	47.94	59.3%	3.5	69.6
Main activity prod. elec. and heat - oil	45.77	-65.3%	3.3	72.9
Residential - oil	41.90	9.2%	3.1	76.0
Non-specified other sectors - gas	33.48	268.4%	2.4	78.4
Other energy industries - oil	26.11	-9.9%	1.9	80.3
Memo: total CO$_2$ from fuel combustion	1212.70	13.2%	88.7	88.7

*** Percent calculated using the total GHG estimate for CO$_2$, CH$_4$, N$_2$O, HFCs, PFCs and SF$_6$ excluding CO$_2$ emissions/removals from land use change and forestry.

Jordan / Jordanie

Figure 1. CO$_2$ emissions by fuel

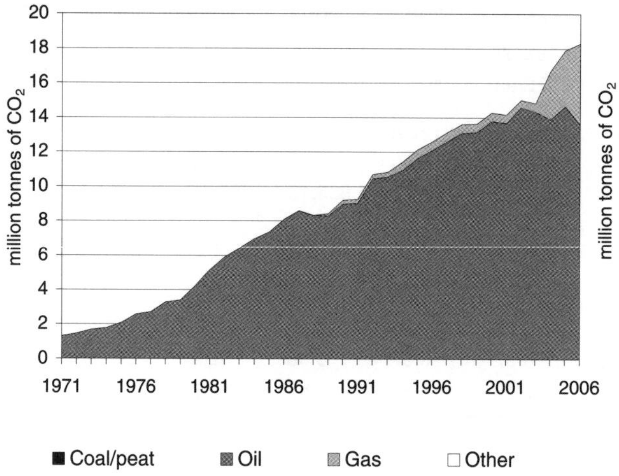

■ Coal/peat   ■ Oil   ■ Gas   □ Other

Figure 2. CO$_2$ emissions by sector

■ Electricity and heat   □ Other energy industries
■ Manuf. ind. and construction ■ Transport
□ Residential   ■ Other

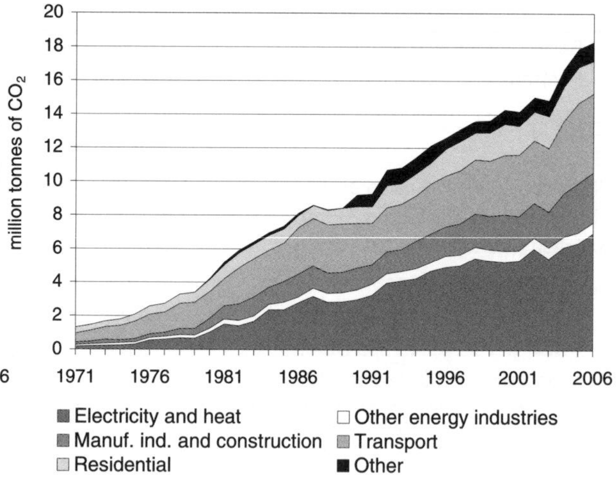

Figure 3. CO$_2$ emissions by sector

■ Electricity and heat   □ Other energy industries
■ Manuf. ind. and construction ■ Transport
□ Residential   ■ Other

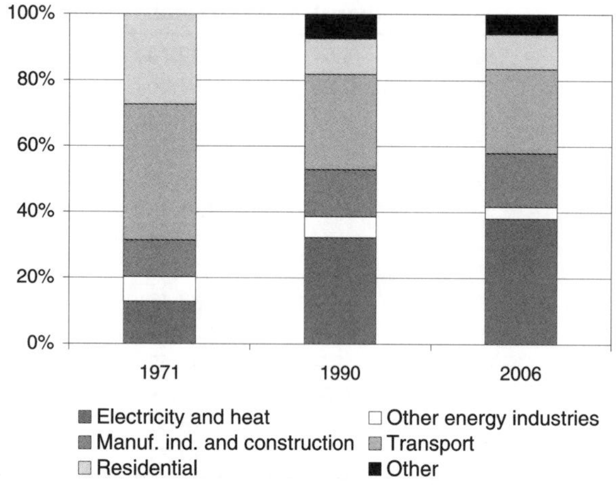

Figure 4. Reference vs Sectoral Approach

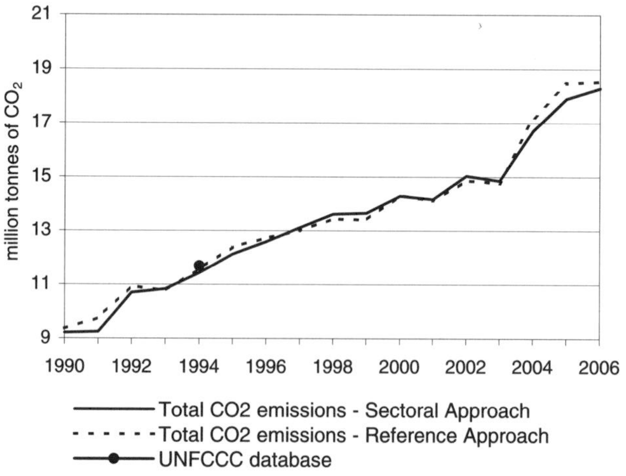

——— Total CO2 emissions - Sectoral Approach
- - - - Total CO2 emissions - Reference Approach
—●— UNFCCC database

Figure 5. Electricity generation by fuel

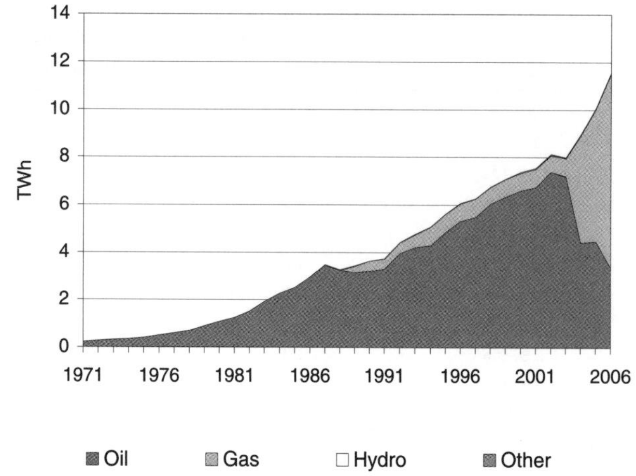

■ Oil   ■ Gas   □ Hydro   ■ Other

Figure 6. Key indicators

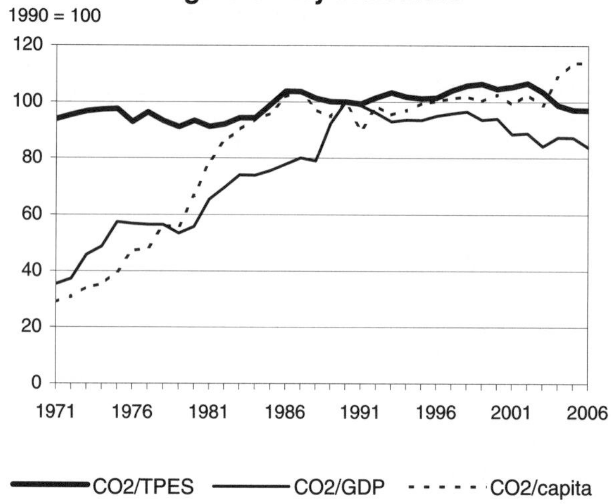

1990 = 100

━━ CO2/TPES   ━━ CO2/GDP   - - - - CO2/capita

Jordan / Jordanie

Key indicators

	1990	1995	2000	2003	2004	2005	2006	% change 90-06
CO$_2$ Sectoral Approach (Mt of CO$_2$)	9.20	12.13	14.29	14.84	16.70	17.90	18.30	98.8%
CO$_2$ Reference Approach (Mt of CO$_2$)	9.36	12.40	14.31	14.76	17.17	18.47	18.54	98.1%
TPES (PJ)	146	191	217	228	269	293	300	104.8%
TPES (Mtoe)	3.50	4.55	5.19	5.45	6.42	7.00	7.16	104.8%
GDP (billion 2000 US$ using exch. rates)	5.13	7.23	8.46	9.82	10.64	11.41	12.15	136.9%
GDP (billion 2000 US$ using PPPs)	12.10	17.05	19.97	23.16	25.12	26.93	28.91	139.0%
Population (millions)	3.17	4.20	4.80	5.16	5.29	5.41	5.54	74.7%
CO$_2$ / TPES (t CO$_2$ per TJ)	62.8	63.6	65.8	65.0	62.1	61.1	61.0	-2.9%
CO$_2$ / GDP (kg CO$_2$ per 2000 US$)	1.80	1.68	1.69	1.51	1.57	1.57	1.51	-16.1%
CO$_2$ / GDP (kg CO$_2$ per 2000 US$ PPP)	0.76	0.71	0.72	0.64	0.67	0.66	0.63	-16.8%
CO$_2$ / population (t CO$_2$ per capita)	2.90	2.89	2.98	2.87	3.16	3.31	3.30	13.8%

Ratios are based on the Sectoral Approach.

2006 CO$_2$ emissions by sector

million tonnes of CO$_2$	Coal/peat	Oil	Gas	Other *	Total	% change 90-06
Sectoral Approach	-	**13.61**	**4.68**	-	**18.30**	**98.8%**
Main activity producer elec. and heat	-	1.86	4.68	-	6.55	145.9%
Unallocated autoproducers	-	0.41	-	-	0.41	35.6%
Other energy industries	-	0.65	-	-	0.65	10.1%
Manufacturing industries and construction	-	2.96	-	-	2.96	126.6%
Transport	-	4.69	-	-	4.69	76.7%
of which: road	-	*4.65*	-	-	*4.65*	*75.1%*
Other sectors	-	3.04	-	-	3.04	80.0%
of which: residential	-	*1.93*	-	-	*1.93*	*94.4%*
Reference Approach	-	**13.85**	**4.68**	-	**18.54**	**98.1%**
Diff. due to losses and/or transformation	-	0.24	-	-	0.24	
Statistical differences	-	- 0.00	-	-	- 0.00	
Memo: international marine bunkers	-	*0.13*	-	-	*0.13*	*..*
Memo: international aviation	-	*0.94*	-	-	*0.94*	*32.9%*

* Other includes industrial waste and non-renewable municipal waste.

Key sources for CO$_2$ emissions from fuel combustion in 2006

IPCC source category	CO$_2$ emissions (Mt of CO$_2$)	% change 90-06	Level assessment (%) **	Cumulative total (%)
Main activity prod. elec. and heat - gas	4.68	+	20.2	20.2
Road - oil	4.65	75.1%	20.1	40.3
Manufacturing industries - oil	2.96	126.6%	12.8	53.1
Residential - oil	1.93	94.4%	8.3	61.4
Main activity prod. elec. and heat - oil	1.86	-23.2%	8.0	69.4
Non-specified other sectors - oil	1.10	59.3%	4.7	74.2
Other energy industries - oil	0.65	10.1%	2.8	77.0
Unallocated autoproducers - oil	0.41	35.6%	1.8	78.7
Other transport - oil	0.04	x	0.2	78.9
-	-	-	-	-
-	-	-	-	-
Memo: total CO$_2$ from fuel combustion	*18.30*	*98.8%*	*78.9*	*78.9*

** Percent calculated using the total GHG estimate for CO$_2$, CH$_4$, N$_2$O, HFCs, PFCs and SF$_6$ excluding CO$_2$ emissions/removals from land use change and forestry.

Kazakhstan

Figure 1. CO_2 emissions by fuel

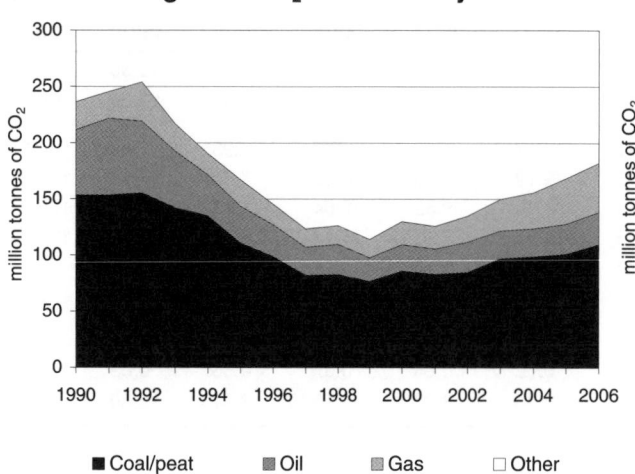

■ Coal/peat   ■ Oil   ■ Gas   □ Other

Figure 2. CO_2 emissions by sector

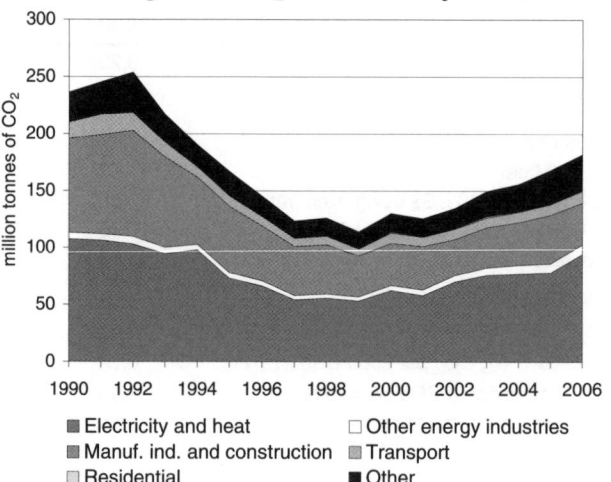

■ Electricity and heat   □ Other energy industries
■ Manuf. ind. and construction ■ Transport
▨ Residential   ■ Other

Figure 3. CO_2 emissions by sector

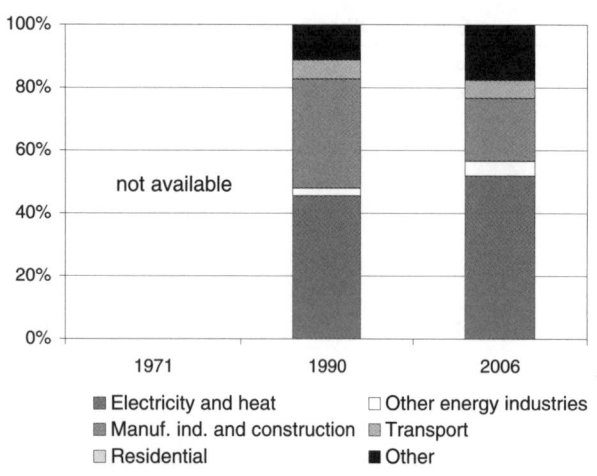

■ Electricity and heat   □ Other energy industries
■ Manuf. ind. and construction ■ Transport
▨ Residential   ■ Other

Figure 4. Reference vs Sectoral Approach

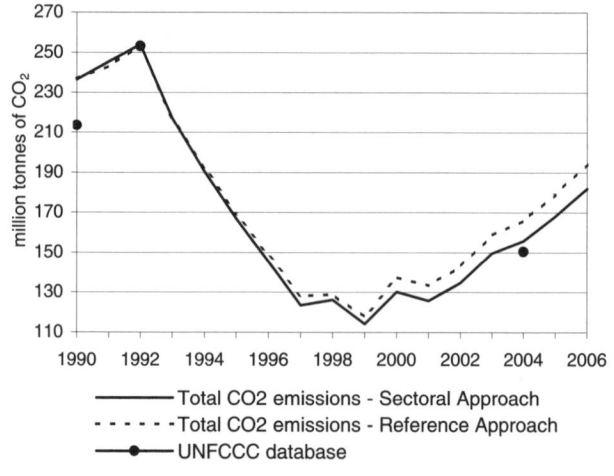

—— Total CO2 emissions - Sectoral Approach
- - - Total CO2 emissions - Reference Approach
—●— UNFCCC database

Figure 5. Electricity generation by fuel

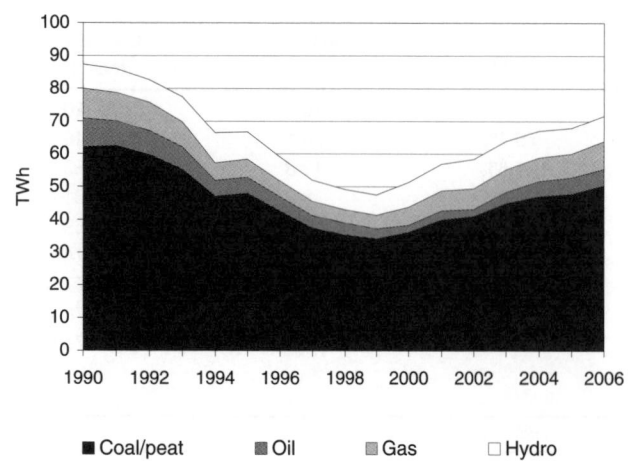

■ Coal/peat   ■ Oil   ■ Gas   □ Hydro

Figure 6. Key indicators

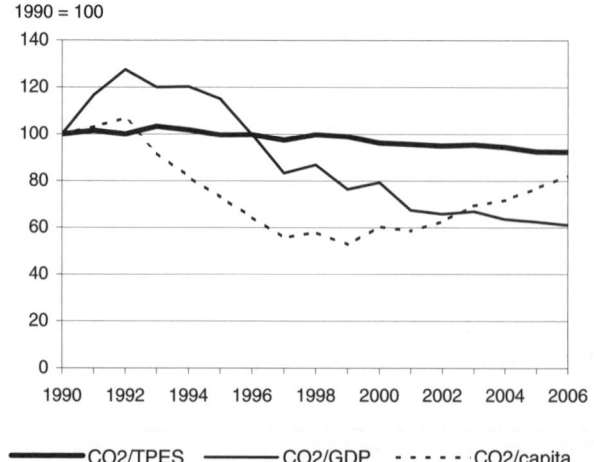

——CO2/TPES   ——CO2/GDP   - - - - CO2/capita

Kazakhstan

Key indicators

	1990	1995	2000	2003	2004	2005	2006	% change 90-06
CO$_2$ Sectoral Approach (Mt of CO$_2$)	236.41	167.02	130.18	149.57	155.81	168.15	181.96	-23.0%
CO$_2$ Reference Approach (Mt of CO$_2$)	236.96	169.27	137.40	158.76	165.94	179.16	194.29	-18.0%
TPES (PJ)	3 084	2 187	1 767	2 048	2 156	2 374	2 572	-16.6%
TPES (Mtoe)	73.65	52.24	42.20	48.92	51.49	56.69	61.42	-16.6%
GDP (billion 2000 US$ using exch. rates)	26.35	16.18	18.29	24.92	27.31	29.96	33.13	25.7%
GDP (billion 2000 US$ using PPPs)	93.16	57.20	64.67	88.09	96.55	105.91	117.14	25.7%
Population (millions)	16.35	15.82	14.88	14.91	15.01	15.15	15.31	-6.4%
CO$_2$ / TPES (t CO$_2$ per TJ)	76.7	76.4	73.7	73.0	72.3	70.8	70.8	-7.7%
CO$_2$ / GDP (kg CO$_2$ per 2000 US$)	8.97	10.32	7.12	6.00	5.71	5.61	5.49	-38.8%
CO$_2$ / GDP (kg CO$_2$ per 2000 US$ PPP)	2.54	2.92	2.01	1.70	1.61	1.59	1.55	-38.8%
CO$_2$ / population (t CO$_2$ per capita)	14.46	10.56	8.75	10.03	10.38	11.10	11.89	-17.8%

Ratios are based on the Sectoral Approach.

2006 CO$_2$ emissions by sector

million tonnes of CO$_2$	Coal/peat	Oil	Gas	Other *	Total	% change 90-06
Sectoral Approach	**109.67**	**28.67**	**43.62**	-	**181.96**	**-23.0%**
Main activity producer elec. and heat	85.66	2.46	6.25	-	94.38	-12.3%
Unallocated autoproducers	-	-	-	-	-	-
Other energy industries	-	0.97	7.51	-	8.47	50.4%
Manufacturing industries and construction	23.83	10.69	2.08	-	36.60	-55.6%
Transport	-	10.33	-	-	10.33	-27.6%
of which: road	-	9.07	-	-	9.07	-24.1%
Other sectors	0.18	4.22	27.79	-	32.18	21.7%
of which: residential	-	0.56	-	-	0.56	x
Reference Approach	**117.51**	**32.92**	**43.86**	-	**194.29**	**-18.0%**
Diff. due to losses and/or transformation	7.65	4.14	0.24	-	12.03	
Statistical differences	0.19	0.11	- 0.00	-	0.30	
Memo: international marine bunkers	-	..	-	-	..	..
Memo: international aviation	-	0.75	-	-	0.75	-71.8%

* Other includes industrial waste and non-renewable municipal waste.

Key sources for CO$_2$ emissions from fuel combustion in 2006

IPCC source category	CO$_2$ emissions (Mt of CO$_2$)	% change 90-06	Level assessment (%) **	Cumulative total (%)
Main activity prod. elec. and heat - coal/peat	85.66	-8.4%	38.9	38.9
Non-specified other sectors - gas	27.79	53.0%	12.6	51.6
Manufacturing industries - coal/peat	23.83	-60.1%	10.8	62.4
Manufacturing industries - oil	10.69	-52.8%	4.9	67.3
Road - oil	9.07	-24.1%	4.1	71.4
Other energy industries - gas	7.51	137.0%	3.4	74.8
Main activity prod. elec. and heat - gas	6.25	79.4%	2.8	77.6
Non-specified other sectors - oil	3.66	-55.9%	1.7	79.3
Main activity prod. elec. and heat - oil	2.46	-76.8%	1.1	80.4
Manufacturing industries - gas	2.08	x	0.9	81.4
Other transport - oil	1.26	-45.8%	0.6	81.9
Memo: total CO$_2$ from fuel combustion	181.96	-23.0%	82.7	82.7

** Percent calculated using the total GHG estimate for CO$_2$, CH$_4$, N$_2$O, HFCs, PFCs and SF$_6$ excluding CO$_2$ emissions/removals from land use change and forestry.

Kenya

Figure 1. CO$_2$ emissions by fuel

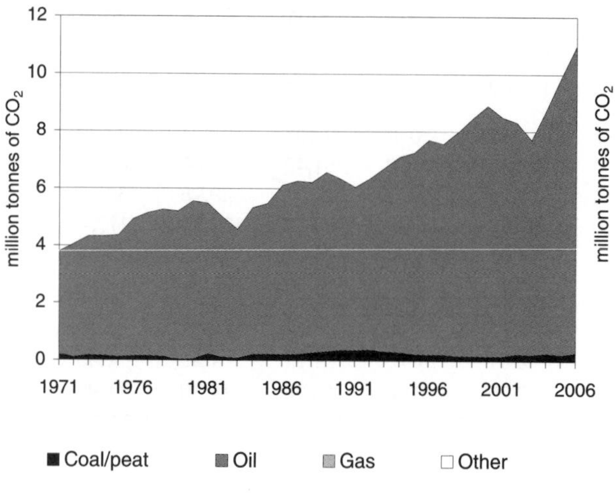

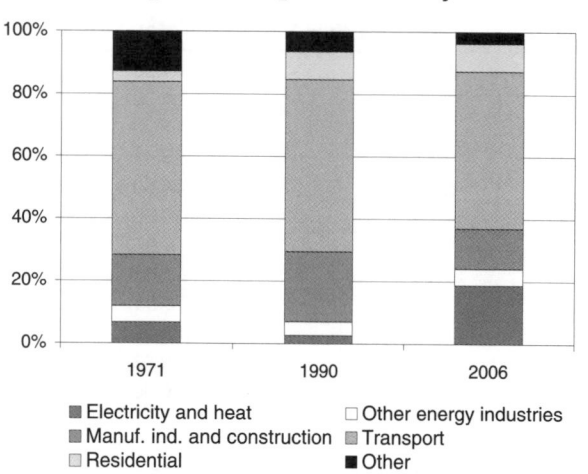

■ Coal/peat   ■ Oil   ▨ Gas   □ Other

Figure 2. CO$_2$ emissions by sector

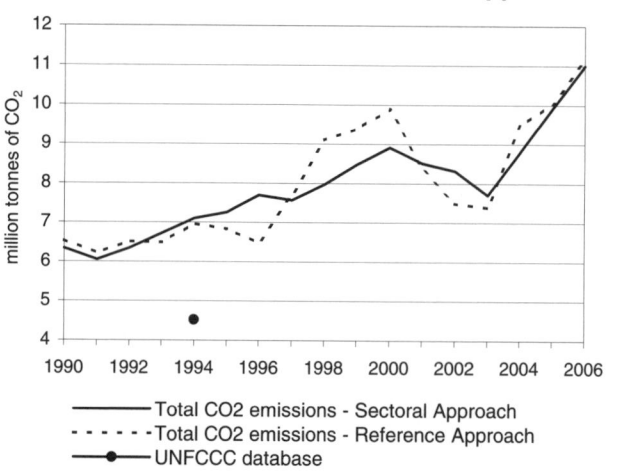

■ Electricity and heat   □ Other energy industries
■ Manuf. ind. and construction ▨ Transport
▨ Residential   ■ Other

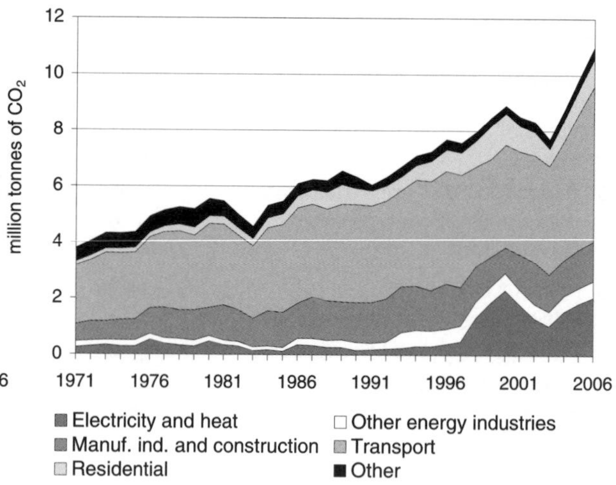

Figure 3. CO$_2$ emissions by sector

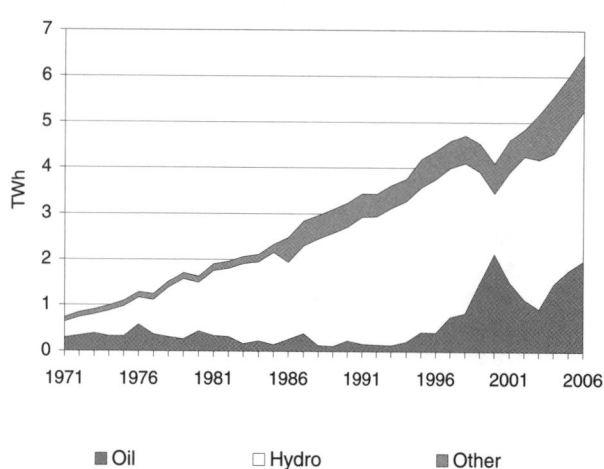

■ Electricity and heat   □ Other energy industries
■ Manuf. ind. and construction ▨ Transport
▨ Residential   ■ Other

Figure 4. Reference vs Sectoral Approach

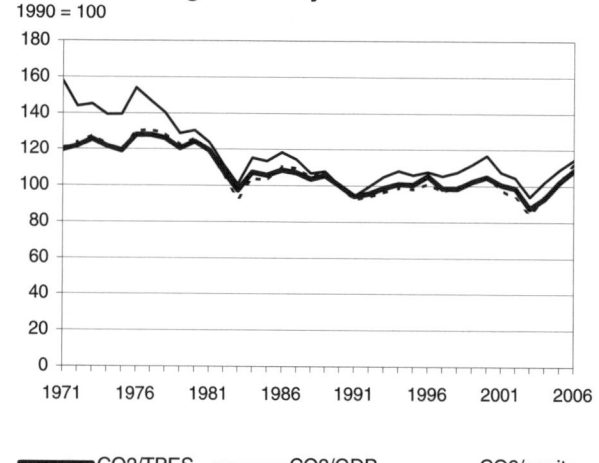

—— Total CO2 emissions - Sectoral Approach
- - - - Total CO2 emissions - Reference Approach
——●—— UNFCCC database

Figure 5. Electricity generation by fuel

■ Oil   □ Hydro   ▨ Other

Figure 6. Key indicators

1990 = 100

—— CO2/TPES   —— CO2/GDP   - - - - CO2/capita

Kenya
Key indicators

	1990	1995	2000	2003	2004	2005	2006	% change 90-06
CO$_2$ Sectoral Approach (Mt of CO$_2$)	6.34	7.26	8.91	7.71	8.79	9.91	11.00	73.6%
CO$_2$ Reference Approach (Mt of CO$_2$)	6.53	6.83	9.88	7.39	9.48	10.05	11.16	70.8%
TPES (PJ)	470	535	630	651	700	721	751	60.0%
TPES (Mtoe)	11.22	12.79	15.04	15.56	16.72	17.21	17.95	60.0%
GDP (billion 2000 US$ using exch. rates)	10.56	11.42	12.71	13.66	14.32	15.15	16.02	51.7%
GDP (billion 2000 US$ using PPPs)	26.34	28.50	31.70	34.08	35.73	37.81	39.97	51.7%
Population (millions)	23.45	27.38	31.25	33.78	34.68	35.60	36.55	55.9%
CO$_2$ / TPES (t CO$_2$ per TJ)	13.5	13.6	14.1	11.8	12.6	13.7	14.6	8.5%
CO$_2$ / GDP (kg CO$_2$ per 2000 US$)	0.60	0.64	0.70	0.56	0.61	0.65	0.69	14.4%
CO$_2$ / GDP (kg CO$_2$ per 2000 US$ PPP)	0.24	0.25	0.28	0.23	0.25	0.26	0.28	14.4%
CO$_2$ / population (t CO$_2$ per capita)	0.27	0.27	0.29	0.23	0.25	0.28	0.30	11.3%

Ratios are based on the Sectoral Approach.

2006 CO$_2$ emissions by sector

million tonnes of CO$_2$	Coal/peat	Oil	Gas	Other *	Total	% change 90-06
Sectoral Approach	**0.29**	**10.71**	**-**	**-**	**11.00**	**73.6%**
Main activity producer elec. and heat **	-	2.06	-	-	2.06	+
Unallocated autoproducers **	..	..	..	..	..	..
Other energy industries	-	0.60	-	-	0.60	113.2%
Manufacturing industries and construction	0.29	1.13	-	-	1.42	-0.4%
Transport	-	5.53	-	-	5.53	58.1%
of which: road	-	3.16	-	-	3.16	25.0%
Other sectors	-	1.40	-	-	1.40	43.7%
of which: residential	-	0.98	-	-	0.98	73.1%
Reference Approach	**0.29**	**10.87**	**-**	**-**	**11.16**	**70.8%**
Diff. due to losses and/or transformation	-	0.02	-	-	0.02	
Statistical differences	-	0.14	-	-	0.14	
Memo: international marine bunkers	-	0.15	-	-	0.15	-73.4%
Memo: international aviation	-	..	-	-	..	..

* Other includes industrial waste and non-renewable municipal waste.
** Emissions from autoproducers in 2006 have been included with main activity producer electricity and heat.

Key sources for CO$_2$ emissions from fuel combustion in 2006

IPCC source category	CO$_2$ emissions (Mt of CO$_2$)	% change 90-06	Level assessment (%) ***	Cumulative total (%)
Road - oil	3.16	25.0%	6.1	6.1
Other transport - oil	2.36	144.9%	4.6	10.7
Main activity prod. elec. and heat - oil	2.06	+	4.0	14.6
Manufacturing industries - oil	1.13	6.5%	2.2	16.8
Residential - oil	0.98	73.1%	1.9	18.7
Other energy industries - oil	0.60	113.2%	1.1	19.9
Non-specified other sectors - oil	0.42	2.8%	0.8	20.7
Manufacturing industries - coal/peat	0.29	-20.5%	0.6	21.2
-	-	-	-	-
-	-	-	-	-
-	-	-	-	-
Memo: total CO$_2$ from fuel combustion	11.00	73.6%	21.2	21.2

*** Percent calculated using the total GHG estimate for CO$_2$, CH$_4$, N$_2$O, HFCs, PFCs and SF$_6$ excluding CO$_2$ emissions/removals from land use change and forestry.

Dem. People's Rep. of Korea / Rép. pop. dém. de Corée

Figure 1. CO₂ emissions by fuel

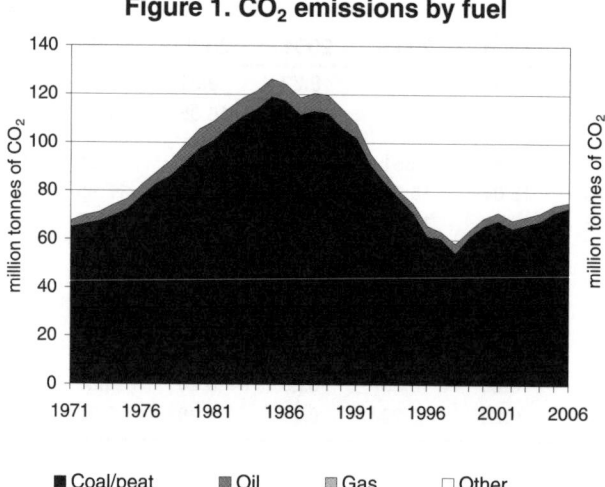

■ Coal/peat   ■ Oil   ▨ Gas   ☐ Other

Figure 2. CO₂ emissions by sector

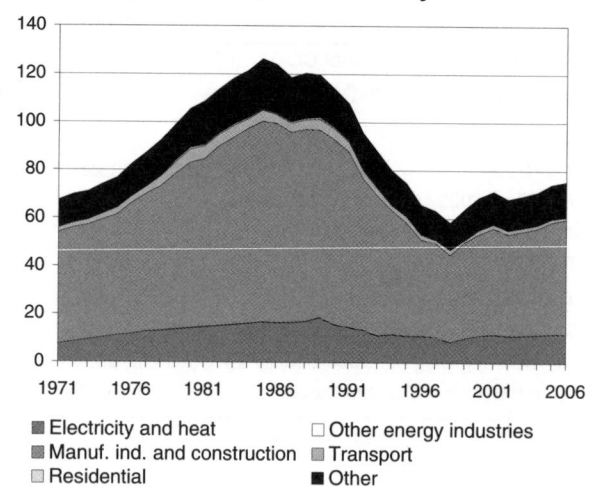

■ Electricity and heat   ☐ Other energy industries
▨ Manuf. ind. and construction ▨ Transport
▨ Residential   ■ Other

Figure 3. CO₂ emissions by sector

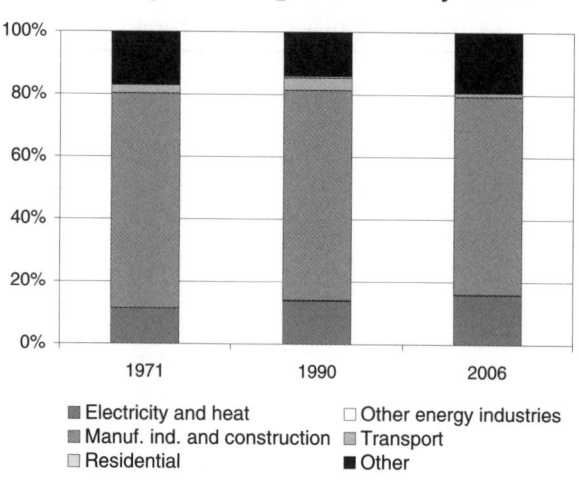

■ Electricity and heat   ☐ Other energy industries
▨ Manuf. ind. and construction ▨ Transport
☐ Residential   ■ Other

Figure 4. Reference vs Sectoral Approach

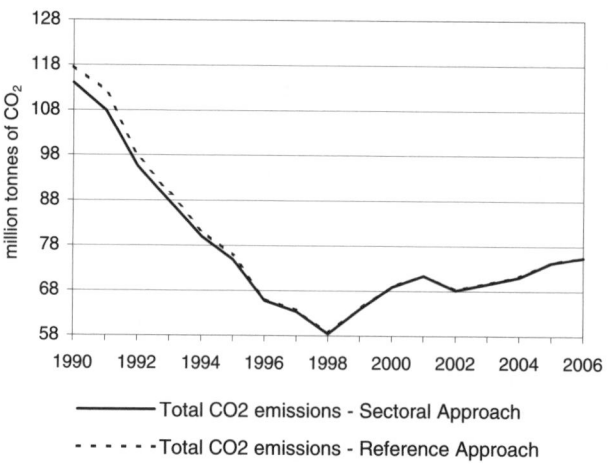

——— Total CO2 emissions - Sectoral Approach

- - - - - Total CO2 emissions - Reference Approach

Figure 5. Electricity generation by fuel

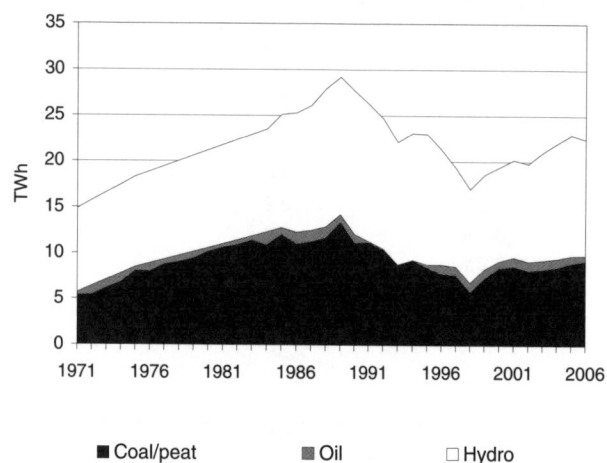

■ Coal/peat   ▨ Oil   ☐ Hydro

Figure 6. Key indicators

1990 = 100

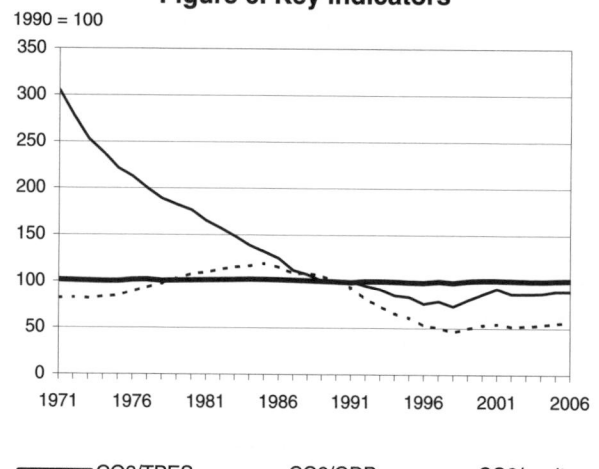

——— CO2/TPES   ——— CO2/GDP   - - - - CO2/capita

Dem. People's Rep. of Korea / Rép. pop. dém. de Corée
Key indicators

	1990	1995	2000	2003	2004	2005	2006	% change 90-06
CO$_2$ Sectoral Approach (Mt of CO$_2$)	114.01	74.86	68.82	69.52	71.06	74.26	75.43	-33.8%
CO$_2$ Reference Approach (Mt of CO$_2$)	117.57	75.77	68.92	69.65	71.19	74.38	75.54	-35.8%
TPES (PJ)	1 391	920	828	843	862	898	907	-34.8%
TPES (Mtoe)	33.22	21.99	19.78	20.13	20.60	21.44	21.66	-34.8%
GDP (billion 2000 US$ using exch. rates)	15.57	12.23	10.85	10.91	11.11	11.31	11.51	-26.1%
GDP (billion 2000 US$ using PPPs)	54.75	43.00	38.17	38.37	39.06	39.76	40.48	-26.1%
Population (millions)	20.14	21.72	22.95	23.40	23.51	23.62	23.71	17.7%
CO$_2$ / TPES (t CO$_2$ per TJ)	82.0	81.3	83.1	82.5	82.4	82.7	83.2	1.5%
CO$_2$ / GDP (kg CO$_2$ per 2000 US$)	7.32	6.12	6.34	6.37	6.40	6.57	6.55	-10.5%
CO$_2$ / GDP (kg CO$_2$ per 2000 US$ PPP)	2.08	1.74	1.80	1.81	1.82	1.87	1.86	-10.5%
CO$_2$ / population (t CO$_2$ per capita)	5.66	3.45	3.00	2.97	3.02	3.14	3.18	-43.8%

Ratios are based on the Sectoral Approach.

2006 CO$_2$ emissions by sector

million tonnes of CO$_2$	Coal/peat	Oil	Gas	Other *	Total	% change 90-06
Sectoral Approach	**73.26**	**2.18**	-	-	**75.43**	**-33.8%**
Main activity producer elec. and heat	11.08	0.88	-	-	11.96	-23.7%
Unallocated autoproducers	-	-	-	-	-	-
Other energy industries	-	0.03	-	-	0.03	-83.1%
Manufacturing industries and construction	47.65	0.20	-	-	47.84	-37.7%
Transport	-	0.99	-	-	0.99	-78.7%
of which: road	-	0.99	-	-	0.99	-78.7%
Other sectors	14.53	0.08	-	-	14.61	-12.4%
of which: residential	-	0.08	-	-	0.08	-85.3%
Reference Approach	**73.34**	**2.20**	-	-	**75.54**	**-35.8%**
Diff. due to losses and/or transformation	0.08	0.03	-	-	0.11	
Statistical differences	- 0.00	-	-	-	- 0.00	
Memo: international marine bunkers	-	..	-	-	..	..
Memo: international aviation	-	..	-	-	..	..

* Other includes industrial waste and non-renewable municipal waste.

Key sources for CO$_2$ emissions from fuel combustion in 2006

IPCC source category	CO$_2$ emissions (Mt of CO$_2$)	% change 90-06	Level assessment (%) **	Cumulative total (%)
Manufacturing industries - coal/peat	47.65	-37.0%	42.0	42.0
Non-specified other sectors - coal/peat	14.53	-10.0%	12.8	54.9
Main activity prod. elec. and heat - coal/peat	11.08	-22.8%	9.8	64.6
Road - oil	0.99	-78.7%	0.9	65.5
Main activity prod. elec. and heat - oil	0.88	-33.1%	0.8	66.3
Manufacturing industries - oil	0.20	-83.5%	0.2	66.5
Residential - oil	0.08	-85.3%	0.1	66.5
Other energy industries - oil	0.03	-83.1%	0.0	66.6
-	-	-	-	-
-	-	-	-	-
-	-	-	-	-
Memo: total CO$_2$ from fuel combustion	75.43	-33.8%	66.6	66.6

** Percent calculated using the total GHG estimate for CO$_2$, CH$_4$, N$_2$O, HFCs, PFCs and SF$_6$ excluding CO$_2$ emissions/removals from land use change and forestry.

Korea / Corée

Figure 1. CO₂ emissions by fuel

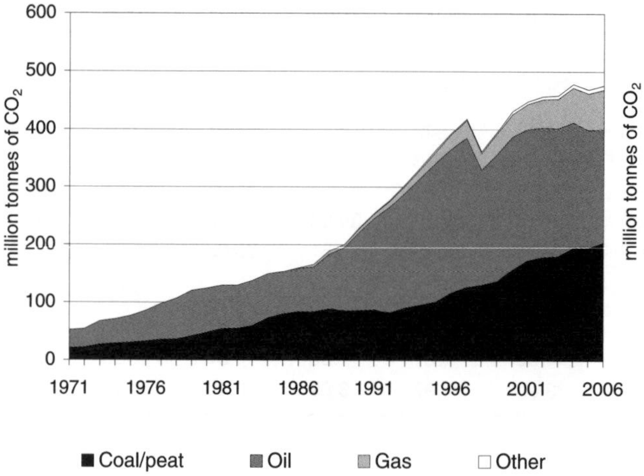

Figure 2. CO₂ emissions by sector

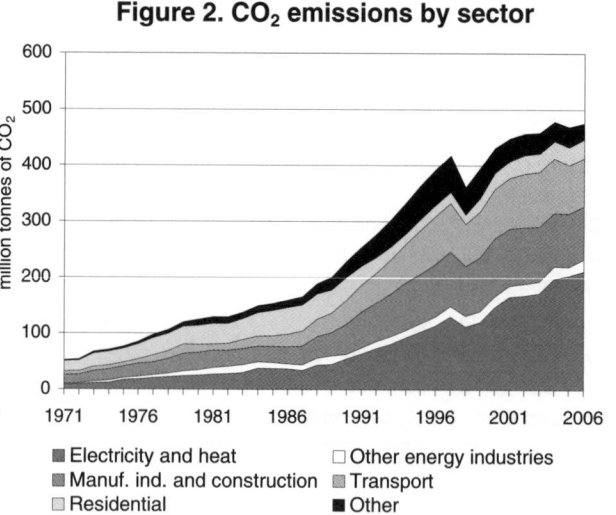

Figure 3. CO₂ emissions by sector

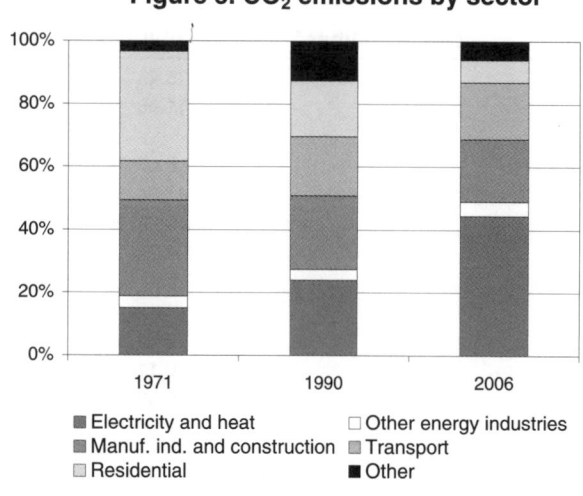

Figure 4. Reference vs Sectoral Approach

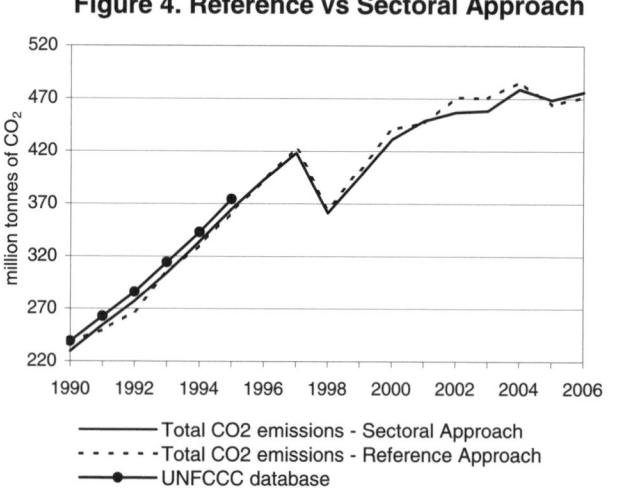

Figure 5. Electricity generation by fuel

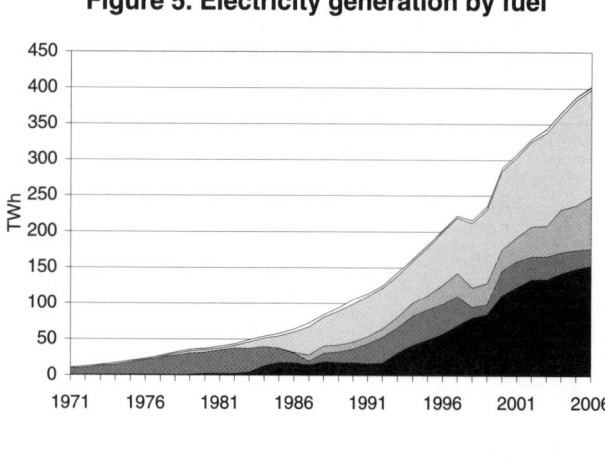

Figure 6. Key indicators

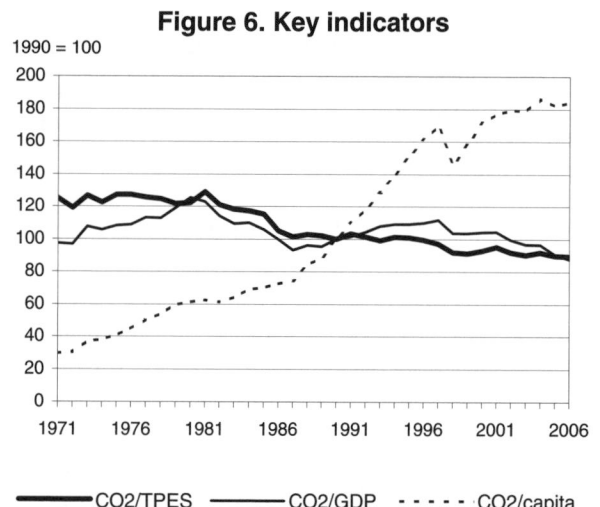

Korea / Corée

Key indicators

	1990	1995	2000	2003	2004	2005	2006	% change 90-06
CO$_2$ Sectoral Approach (Mt of CO$_2$)	229.30	364.80	431.29	458.60	478.86	468.92	476.10	107.6%
CO$_2$ Reference Approach (Mt of CO$_2$)	238.60	361.43	441.14	470.58	485.92	464.11	471.44	97.6%
TPES (PJ)	3 909	6 170	7 931	8 658	8 888	8 899	9 064	131.9%
TPES (Mtoe)	93.37	147.37	189.43	206.79	212.29	212.55	216.50	131.9%
GDP (billion 2000 US$ using exch. rates)	283.60	413.00	511.70	585.90	613.60	639.40	671.30	136.7%
GDP (billion 2000 US$ using PPPs)	428.27	623.78	772.77	884.93	926.78	965.69	1 013.90	136.7%
Population (millions)	42.87	45.09	47.01	47.86	48.04	48.14	48.30	12.7%
CO$_2$ / TPES (t CO$_2$ per TJ)	58.7	59.1	54.4	53.0	53.9	52.7	52.5	-10.5%
CO$_2$ / GDP (kg CO$_2$ per 2000 US$)	0.81	0.88	0.84	0.78	0.78	0.73	0.71	-12.3%
CO$_2$ / GDP (kg CO$_2$ per 2000 US$ PPP)	0.54	0.58	0.56	0.52	0.52	0.49	0.47	-12.3%
CO$_2$ / population (t CO$_2$ per capita)	5.35	8.09	9.17	9.58	9.97	9.74	9.86	84.3%

Ratios are based on the Sectoral Approach.

2006 CO$_2$ emissions by sector

million tonnes of CO$_2$	Coal/peat	Oil	Gas	Other *	Total	% change 90-06
Sectoral Approach	**204.81**	**195.75**	**68.20**	**7.34**	**476.10**	**107.6%**
Main activity producer elec. and heat	131.45	16.37	27.88	-	175.70	410.0%
Unallocated autoproducers	28.19	4.91	1.75	0.61	35.46	74.1%
Other energy industries	6.37	14.86	0.49	-	21.72	171.7%
Manufacturing industries and construction	34.51	43.55	10.20	6.31	94.58	76.5%
Transport	-	85.06	1.06	-	86.12	99.0%
of which: road	-	*77.36*	*1.06*	-	*78.42*	*148.5%*
Other sectors	4.28	30.99	26.82	0.43	62.53	-10.2%
of which: residential	*4.28*	*10.12*	*19.33*	-	*33.74*	*-17.2%*
Reference Approach	**202.52**	**194.51**	**67.07**	**7.34**	**471.44**	**97.6%**
Diff. due to losses and/or transformation	6.69	- 1.08	- 0.17	-	5.44	
Statistical differences	- 8.99	- 0.15	- 0.96	0.00	- 10.10	
Memo: international marine bunkers	-	*33.30*	-	-	*33.30*	*532.0%*
Memo: international aviation	-	*8.83*	-	-	*8.83*	*949.4%*

* Other includes industrial waste and non-renewable municipal waste.

Key sources for CO$_2$ emissions from fuel combustion in 2006

IPCC source category	CO$_2$ emissions (Mt of CO$_2$)	% change 90-06	Level assessment (%) **	Cumulative total (%)
Main activity prod. elec. and heat - coal/peat	131.45	761.6%	23.3	23.3
Road - oil	77.36	145.1%	13.7	37.0
Manufacturing industries - oil	43.55	14.7%	7.7	44.7
Manufacturing industries - coal/peat	34.51	142.9%	6.1	50.8
Unallocated autoproducers - coal/peat	28.19	38.4%	5.0	55.8
Main activity prod. elec. and heat - gas	27.88	485.8%	4.9	60.7
Non-specified other sectors - oil	20.87	-26.6%	3.7	64.4
Residential - gas	19.33	+	3.4	67.9
Main activity prod. elec. and heat - oil	16.37	13.4%	2.9	70.8
Other energy industries - oil	14.86	191.4%	2.6	73.4
Manufacturing industries - gas	10.20	+	1.8	75.2
Memo: total CO$_2$ from fuel combustion	*476.10*	*107.6%*	*84.3*	*84.3*

** Percent calculated using the total GHG estimate for CO$_2$, CH$_4$, N$_2$O, HFCs, PFCs and SF$_6$ excluding CO$_2$ emissions/removals from land use change and forestry.

Kuwait / Koweit

Figure 1. CO$_2$ emissions by fuel

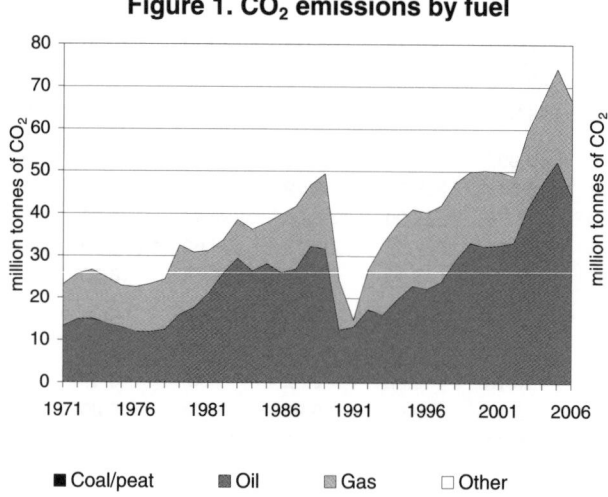

■ Coal/peat   ■ Oil   ■ Gas   ☐ Other

Figure 2. CO$_2$ emissions by sector

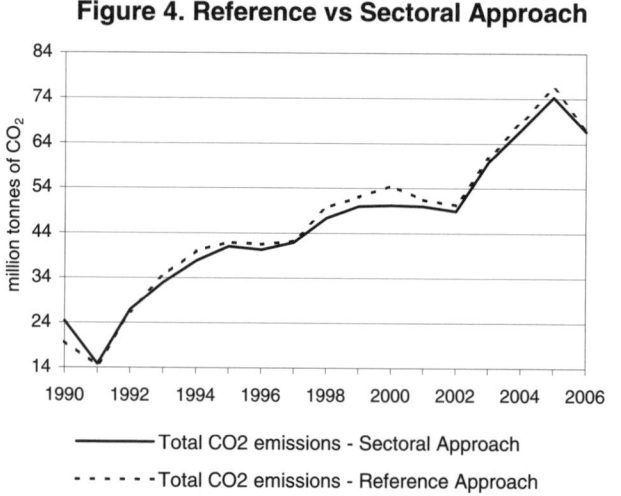

■ Electricity and heat   ☐ Other energy industries
■ Manuf. ind. and construction   ■ Transport
☐ Residential   ■ Other

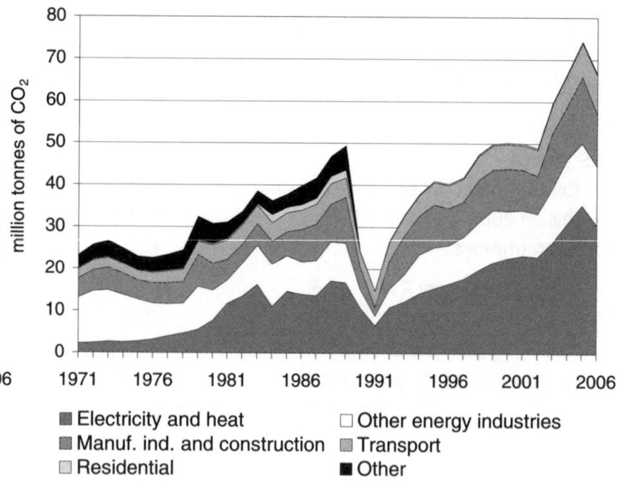

Figure 3. CO$_2$ emissions by sector

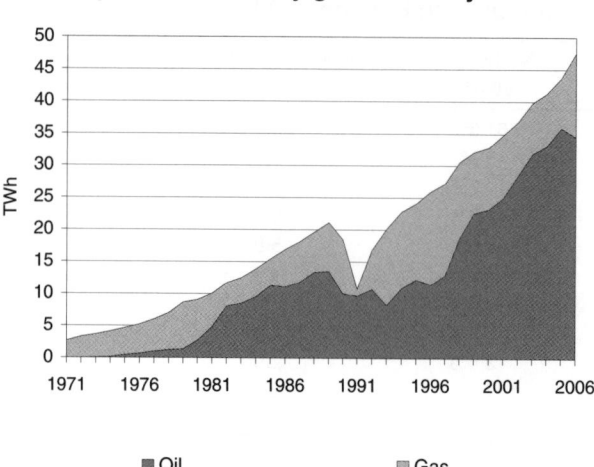

■ Electricity and heat   ☐ Other energy industries
■ Manuf. ind. and construction   ■ Transport
☐ Residential   ■ Other

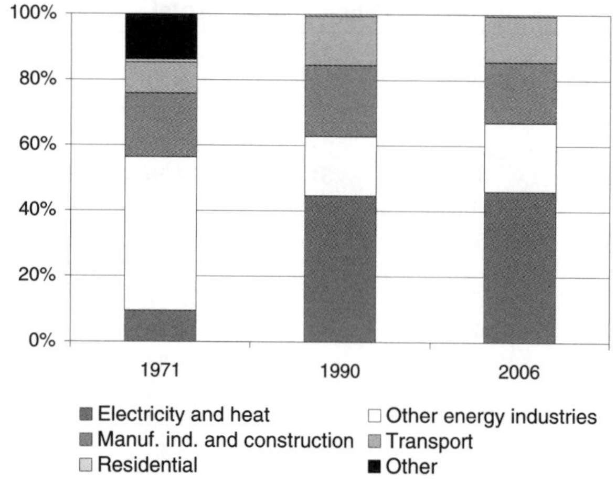

Figure 4. Reference vs Sectoral Approach

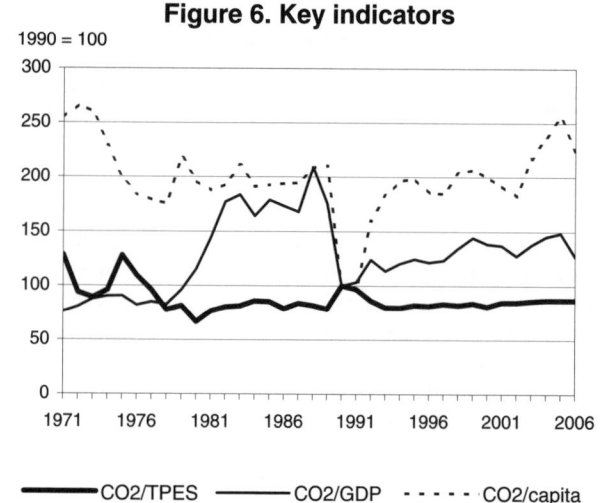

—— Total CO2 emissions - Sectoral Approach
- - - - Total CO2 emissions - Reference Approach

Figure 5. Electricity generation by fuel

■ Oil   ■ Gas

Figure 6. Key indicators

—— CO2/TPES   —— CO2/GDP   - - - - CO2/capita

Kuwait / Koweit

Key indicators

	1990	1995	2000	2003	2004	2005	2006	% change 90-06
CO$_2$ Sectoral Approach (Mt of CO$_2$)	24.35	41.01	50.15	59.76	67.02	74.34	66.69	173.9%
CO$_2$ Reference Approach (Mt of CO$_2$)	19.67	41.94	54.49	60.72	68.75	76.46	67.22	241.7%
TPES (PJ)	335	688	855	960	1 063	1 179	1 059	216.3%
TPES (Mtoe)	8.00	16.42	20.42	22.92	25.39	28.15	25.29	216.3%
GDP (billion 2000 US$ using exch. rates)	25.34	34.33	37.72	45.28	48.09	52.17	54.78	116.2%
GDP (billion 2000 US$ using PPPs)	28.84	39.06	42.92	51.53	54.72	59.37	62.34	116.2%
Population (millions)	2.13	1.80	2.19	2.40	2.46	2.54	2.60	22.3%
CO$_2$ / TPES (t CO$_2$ per TJ)	72.7	59.6	58.7	62.3	63.0	63.1	63.0	-13.4%
CO$_2$ / GDP (kg CO$_2$ per 2000 US$)	0.96	1.19	1.33	1.32	1.39	1.42	1.22	26.7%
CO$_2$ / GDP (kg CO$_2$ per 2000 US$ PPP)	0.84	1.05	1.17	1.16	1.22	1.25	1.07	26.7%
CO$_2$ / population (t CO$_2$ per capita)	11.46	22.76	22.90	24.94	27.24	29.33	25.66	123.9%

Ratios are based on the Sectoral Approach.

2006 CO$_2$ emissions by sector

million tonnes of CO$_2$	Coal/peat	Oil	Gas	Other *	Total	% change 90-06
Sectoral Approach	-	44.05	22.64	-	66.69	173.9%
Main activity producer elec. and heat	-	23.93	6.68	-	30.61	182.1%
Unallocated autoproducers	-	-	-	-	-	-
Other energy industries	-	6.02	8.05	-	14.06	219.2%
Manufacturing industries and construction	-	4.37	7.92	-	12.29	132.6%
Transport	-	9.30	-	-	9.30	155.0%
of which: road	-	*9.30*	-	-	*9.30*	*155.0%*
Other sectors	-	0.43	-	-	0.43	165.6%
of which: residential	-	*0.43*	-	-	*0.43*	*165.6%*
Reference Approach	-	44.58	22.64	-	67.22	241.7%
Diff. due to losses and/or transformation	-	0.54	-	-	0.54	
Statistical differences	-	- 0.01	-	-	- 0.01	
Memo: international marine bunkers	-	*1.97*	-	-	*1.97*	*256.2%*
Memo: international aviation	-	*1.75*	-	-	*1.75*	*242.0%*

* Other includes industrial waste and non-renewable municipal waste.

Key sources for CO$_2$ emissions from fuel combustion in 2006

IPCC source category	CO$_2$ emissions (Mt of CO$_2$)	% change 90-06	Level assessment (%) **	Cumulative total (%)
Main activity prod. elec. and heat - oil	23.93	256.5%	29.1	29.1
Road - oil	9.30	155.0%	11.3	40.4
Other energy industries - gas	8.05	123.7%	9.8	50.2
Manufacturing industries - gas	7.92	93.1%	9.6	59.8
Main activity prod. elec. and heat - gas	6.68	61.4%	8.1	67.9
Other energy industries - oil	6.02	643.8%	7.3	75.2
Manufacturing industries - oil	4.37	269.7%	5.3	80.5
Residential - oil	0.43	165.6%	0.5	81.0
-	-	-	-	-
-	-	-	-	-
-	-	-	-	-
Memo: total CO$_2$ from fuel combustion	*66.69*	*173.9%*	*81.0*	*81.0*

** Percent calculated using the total GHG estimate for CO$_2$, CH$_4$, N$_2$O, HFCs, PFCs and SF$_6$ excluding CO$_2$ emissions/removals from land use change and forestry.

Kyrgyzstan / Kirghizistan

Figure 1. CO₂ emissions by fuel

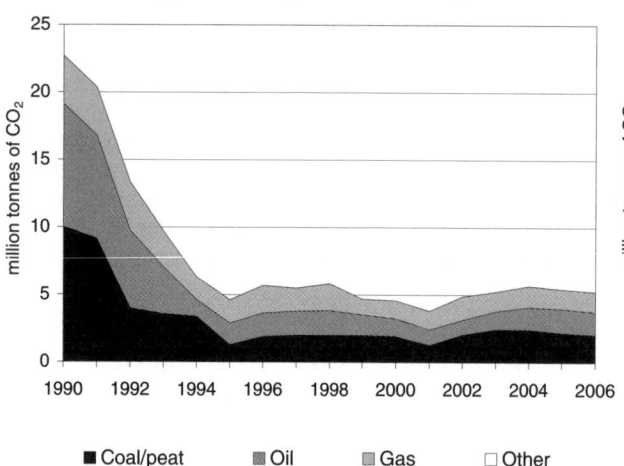

Figure 2. CO₂ emissions by sector

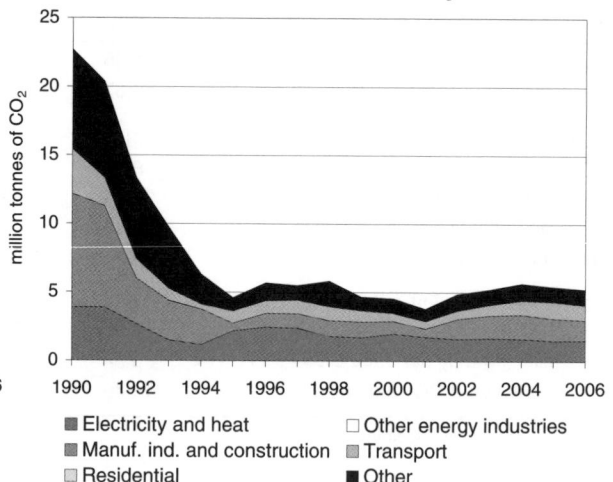

Figure 3. CO₂ emissions by sector

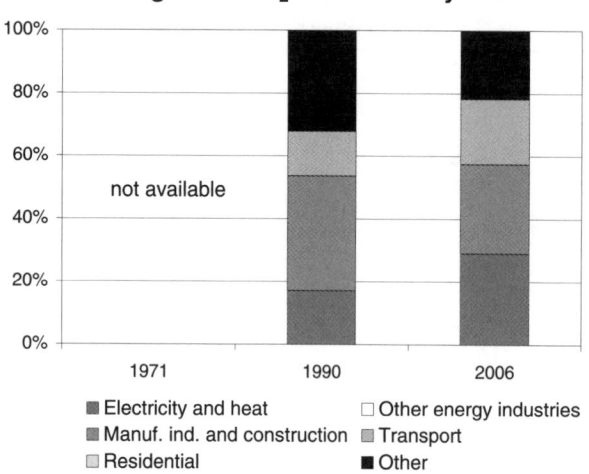

Figure 4. Reference vs Sectoral Approach

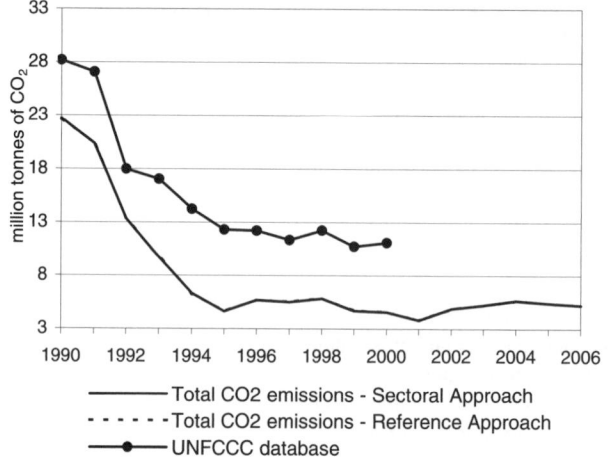

Figure 5. Electricity generation by fuel

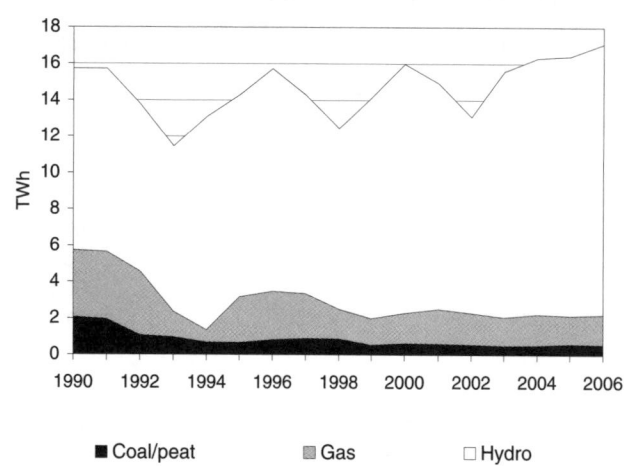

Figure 6. Key indicators

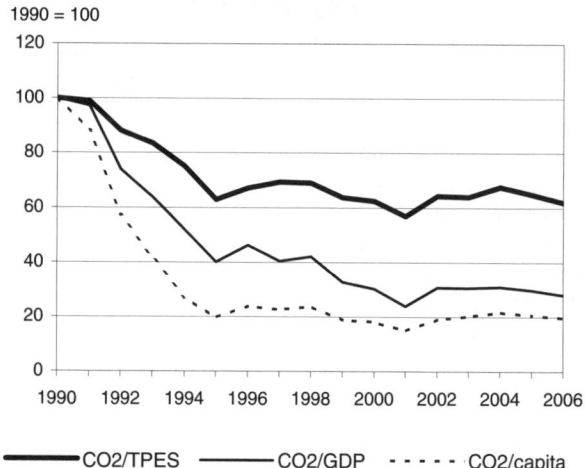

Kyrgyzstan / Kirghizistan

Key indicators

	1990	1995	2000	2003	2004	2005	2006	% change 90-06
CO$_2$ Sectoral Approach (Mt of CO$_2$)	22.72	4.61	4.57	5.22	5.65	5.42	5.23	-77.0%
CO$_2$ Reference Approach (Mt of CO$_2$)	22.72	4.61	4.59	5.24	5.66	5.40	5.23	-77.0%
TPES (PJ)	317	102	102	114	117	117	118	-62.9%
TPES (Mtoe)	7.57	2.45	2.44	2.72	2.79	2.79	2.81	-62.9%
GDP (billion 2000 US$ using exch. rates)	2.06	1.04	1.37	1.54	1.65	1.65	1.69	-17.7%
GDP (billion 2000 US$ using PPPs)	11.04	5.60	7.36	8.29	8.88	8.86	9.10	-17.6%
Population (millions)	4.42	4.59	4.92	5.04	5.09	5.14	5.19	17.4%
CO$_2$ / TPES (t CO$_2$ per TJ)	71.6	45.0	44.7	45.8	48.4	46.4	44.4	-38.0%
CO$_2$ / GDP (kg CO$_2$ per 2000 US$)	11.05	4.42	3.34	3.38	3.42	3.29	3.09	-72.1%
CO$_2$ / GDP (kg CO$_2$ per 2000 US$ PPP)	2.06	0.82	0.62	0.63	0.64	0.61	0.57	-72.1%
CO$_2$ / population (t CO$_2$ per capita)	5.14	1.01	0.93	1.04	1.11	1.05	1.01	-80.4%

Ratios are based on the Sectoral Approach.

2006 CO$_2$ emissions by sector

million tonnes of CO$_2$	Coal/peat	Oil	Gas	Other *	Total	% change 90-06
Sectoral Approach	**2.04**	**1.68**	**1.51**	**-**	**5.23**	**-77.0%**
Main activity producer elec. and heat	0.57	-	0.94	-	1.52	-60.9%
Unallocated autoproducers	-	-	-	-	-	-
Other energy industries	-	-	-	-	-	-
Manufacturing industries and construction	1.47	0.01	-	-	1.48	-82.1%
Transport	-	1.09	-	-	1.09	-66.6%
of which: road	-	*0.69*	-	-	*0.69*	*-76.8%*
Other sectors	-	0.58	0.56	-	1.14	-84.4%
of which: residential	-	-	-	-	-	-
Reference Approach	**2.04**	**1.69**	**1.51**	**-**	**5.23**	**-77.0%**
Diff. due to losses and/or transformation	-	0.01	-	-	0.01	
Statistical differences	-	-	-	-	-	
Memo: international marine bunkers	-	-	-	-	-	
Memo: international aviation	-	..	-	-	..	..

* Other includes industrial waste and non-renewable municipal waste.

Key sources for CO$_2$ emissions from fuel combustion in 2006

IPCC source category	CO$_2$ emissions (Mt of CO$_2$)	% change 90-06	Level assessment (%) **	Cumulative total (%)
Manufacturing industries - coal/peat	1.47	-82.3%	11.7	11.7
Main activity prod. elec. and heat - gas	0.94	-55.8%	7.5	19.2
Road - oil	0.69	-76.8%	5.5	24.7
Non-specified other sectors - oil	0.58	-90.2%	4.6	29.3
Main activity prod. elec. and heat - coal/peat	0.57	-67.2%	4.5	33.8
Non-specified other sectors - gas	0.56	-60.2%	4.5	38.3
Other transport - oil	0.39	50.0%	3.1	41.4
Manufacturing industries - oil	0.01	x	0.1	41.5
-	-	-	-	-
-	-	-	-	-
-	-	-	-	-
Memo: total CO$_2$ from fuel combustion	*5.23*	*-77.0%*	*41.5*	*41.5*

** Percent calculated using the total GHG estimate for CO$_2$, CH$_4$, N$_2$O, HFCs, PFCs and SF$_6$ excluding CO$_2$ emissions/removals from land use change and forestry.

Latvia / Lettonie

Figure 1. CO₂ emissions by fuel

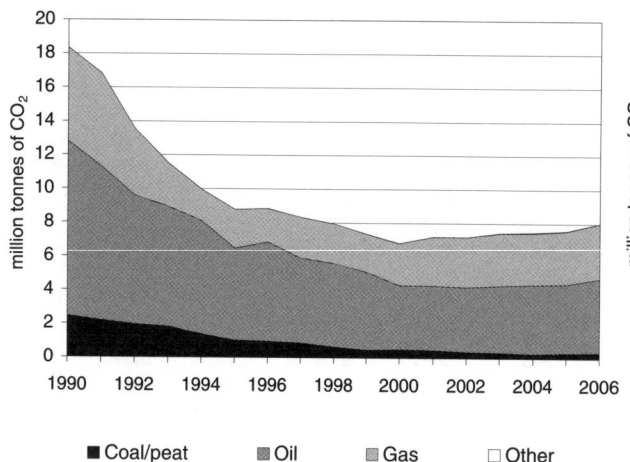

Figure 2. CO₂ emissions by sector

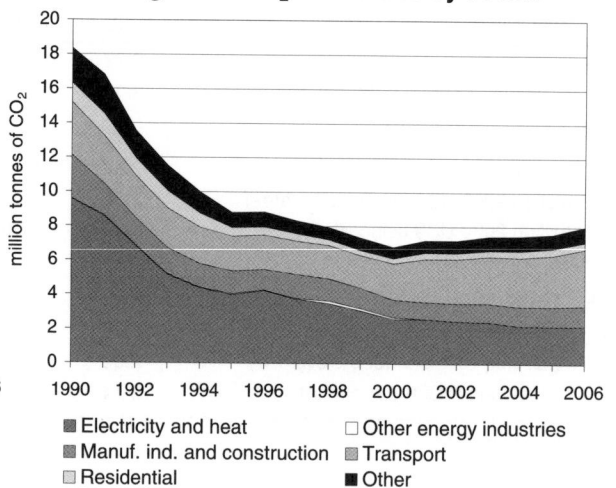

Figure 3. CO₂ emissions by sector

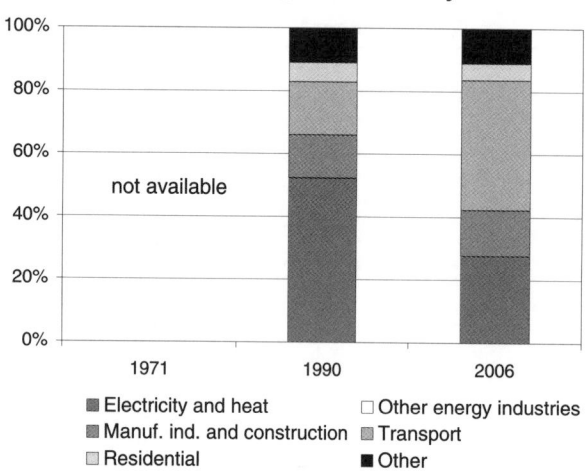

Figure 4. Reference vs Sectoral Approach

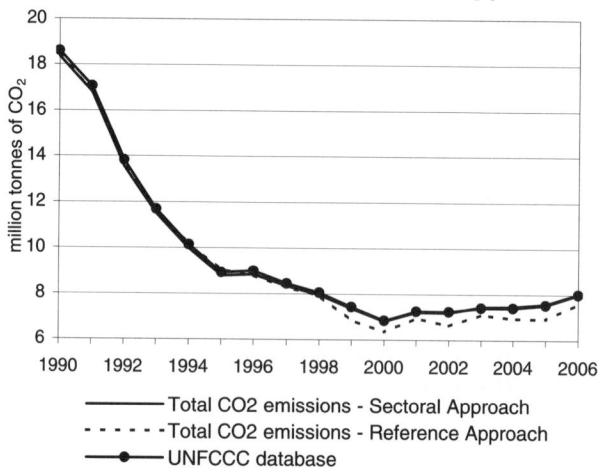

Figure 5. Electricity generation by fuel

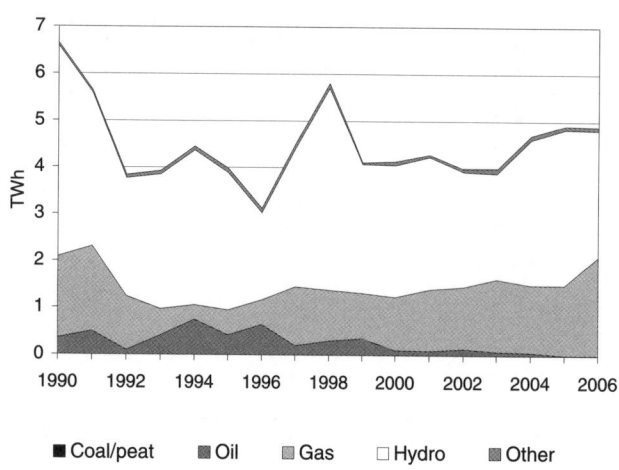

Figure 6. Key indicators

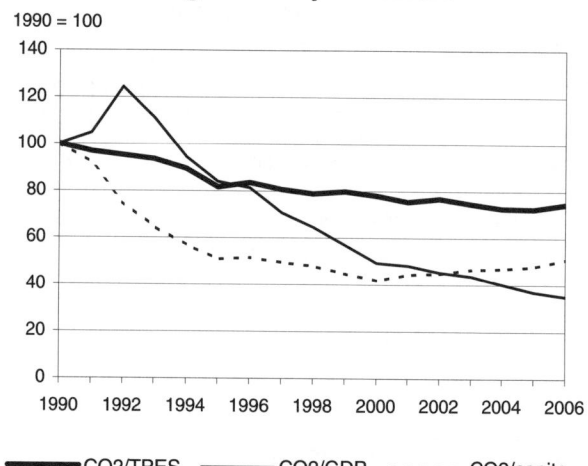

Latvia / Lettonie

Key indicators

	1990	1995	2000	2003	2004	2005	2006	% change 90-06
CO$_2$ Sectoral Approach (Mt of CO$_2$)	18.35	8.78	6.81	7.44	7.46	7.58	8.03	-56.3%
CO$_2$ Reference Approach (Mt of CO$_2$)	18.41	9.04	6.35	7.11	6.94	6.92	7.61	-58.7%
TPES (PJ)	329	193	156	179	184	187	193	-41.3%
TPES (Mtoe)	7.85	4.61	3.74	4.27	4.40	4.48	4.61	-41.3%
GDP (billion 2000 US$ using exch. rates)	10.42	5.95	7.83	9.66	10.50	11.61	13.00	24.7%
GDP (billion 2000 US$ using PPPs)	25.16	14.36	18.92	23.33	25.35	28.04	31.38	24.7%
Population (millions)	2.67	2.52	2.37	2.33	2.31	2.30	2.29	-14.3%
CO$_2$ / TPES (t CO$_2$ per TJ)	55.8	45.6	43.5	41.6	40.6	40.4	41.6	-25.5%
CO$_2$ / GDP (kg CO$_2$ per 2000 US$)	1.76	1.48	0.87	0.77	0.71	0.65	0.62	-64.9%
CO$_2$ / GDP (kg CO$_2$ per 2000 US$ PPP)	0.73	0.61	0.36	0.32	0.29	0.27	0.26	-64.9%
CO$_2$ / population (t CO$_2$ per capita)	6.87	3.49	2.87	3.20	3.23	3.29	3.51	-48.9%

Ratios are based on the Sectoral Approach.

2006 CO$_2$ emissions by sector

million tonnes of CO$_2$	Coal/peat	Oil	Gas	Other *	Total	% change 90-06
Sectoral Approach	**0.34**	**4.40**	**3.27**	**0.01**	**8.03**	**-56.3%**
Main activity producer elec. and heat	0.01	0.11	1.96	-	2.09	-65.6%
Unallocated autoproducers	0.01	0.00	0.11	-	0.13	-96.4%
Other energy industries	-	-	-	-	-	-100.0%
Manufacturing industries and construction	0.14	0.34	0.68	0.01	1.18	-53.5%
Transport	-	3.32	0.00	-	3.32	7.5%
of which: road	*-*	*3.05*	*0.00*	*-*	*3.05*	*31.2%*
Other sectors	0.17	0.62	0.52	-	1.32	-58.2%
of which: residential	*0.08*	*0.11*	*0.24*	*-*	*0.42*	*-62.3%*
Reference Approach	**0.34**	**3.97**	**3.29**	**0.01**	**7.61**	**-58.7%**
Diff. due to losses and/or transformation	-	- 0.02	0.01	-	- 0.01	
Statistical differences	- 0.00	- 0.42	- 0.00	-	- 0.42	
Memo: international marine bunkers	*-*	*0.62*	*-*	*-*	*0.62*	*-58.4%*
Memo: international aviation	*-*	*0.19*	*-*	*-*	*0.19*	*-9.9%*

* Other includes industrial waste and non-renewable municipal waste.

Key sources for CO$_2$ emissions from fuel combustion in 2006

IPCC source category	CO$_2$ emissions (Mt of CO$_2$)	% change 90-06	Level assessment (%) **	Cumulative total (%)
Road - oil	3.05	32.0%	26.2	26.2
Main activity prod. elec. and heat - gas	1.96	-28.2%	16.8	43.0
Manufacturing industries - gas	0.68	-34.0%	5.8	48.8
Non-specified other sectors - oil	0.52	-60.5%	4.5	53.3
Manufacturing industries - oil	0.34	-75.2%	3.0	56.2
Non-specified other sectors - gas	0.28	-8.6%	2.4	58.6
Other transport - oil	0.27	-61.8%	2.3	60.9
Residential - gas	0.24	8.0%	2.1	63.0
Manufacturing industries - coal/peat	0.14	19.1%	1.2	64.2
Main activity prod. elec. and heat - oil	0.11	-96.2%	1.0	65.2
Unallocated autoproducers - gas	0.11	-90.9%	0.9	66.1
Memo: total CO$_2$ from fuel combustion	*8.03*	*-56.3%*	*68.9*	*68.9*

** Percent calculated using the total GHG estimate for CO$_2$, CH$_4$, N$_2$O, HFCs, PFCs and SF$_6$ excluding CO$_2$ emissions/removals from land use change and forestry.

Lebanon / Liban

Figure 1. CO₂ emissions by fuel

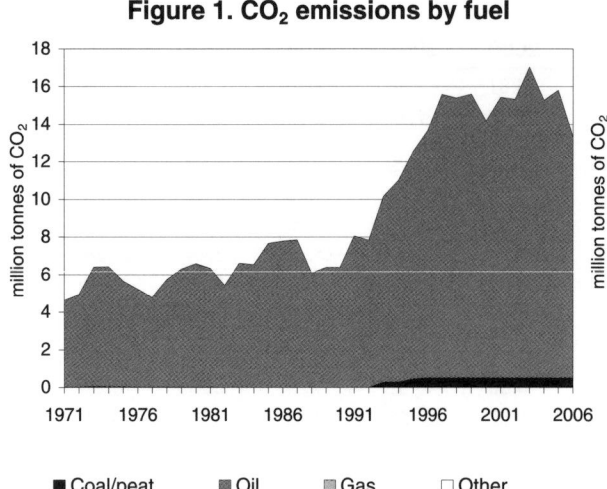

■ Coal/peat   ■ Oil   ▨ Gas   ☐ Other

Figure 2. CO₂ emissions by sector

■ Electricity and heat   ☐ Other energy industries
■ Manuf. ind. and construction   ▨ Transport
▨ Residential   ■ Other

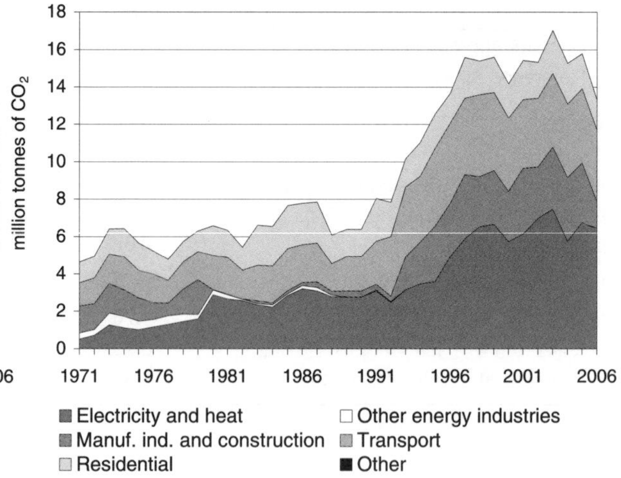

Figure 3. CO₂ emissions by sector

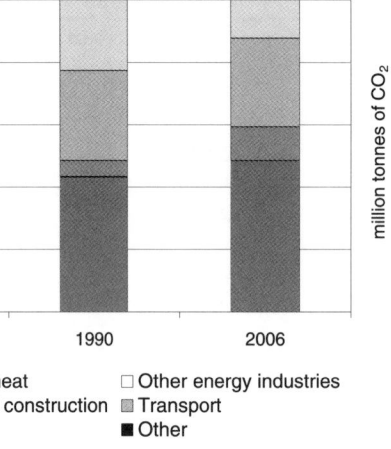

■ Electricity and heat   ☐ Other energy industries
■ Manuf. ind. and construction   ▨ Transport
▨ Residential   ■ Other

Figure 4. Reference vs Sectoral Approach

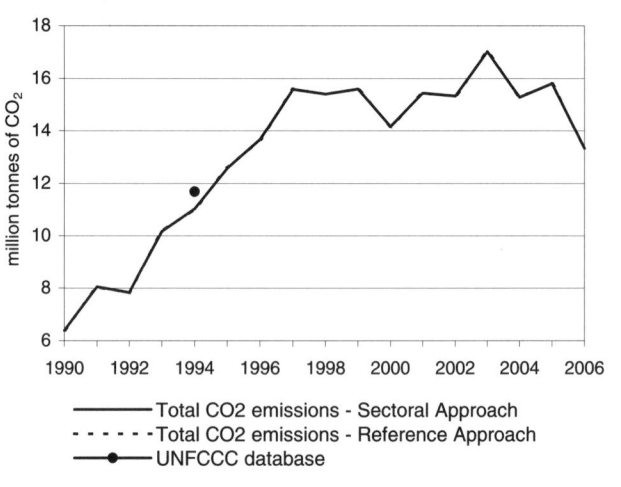

—— Total CO2 emissions - Sectoral Approach
- - - - Total CO2 emissions - Reference Approach
——●—— UNFCCC database

Figure 5. Electricity generation by fuel

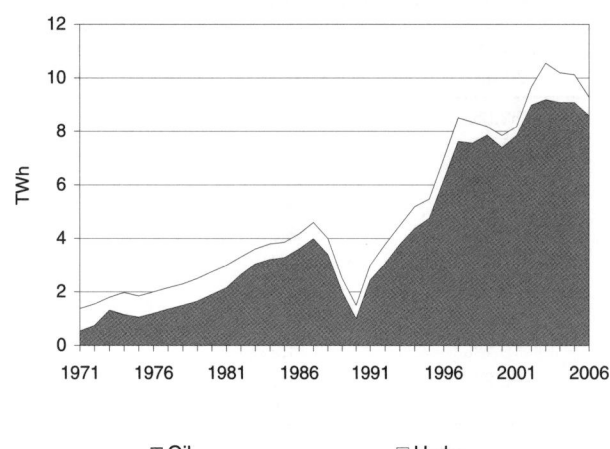

■ Oil   ☐ Hydro

Figure 6. Key indicators

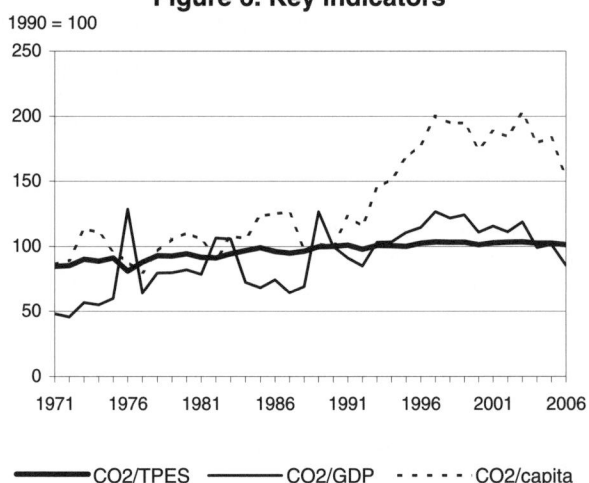

—— CO2/TPES   —— CO2/GDP   - - - - CO2/capita

Lebanon / Liban

Key indicators

	1990	1995	2000	2003	2004	2005	2006	% change 90-06
CO$_2$ Sectoral Approach (Mt of CO$_2$)	6.39	12.57	14.17	17.03	15.28	15.80	13.33	108.7%
CO$_2$ Reference Approach (Mt of CO$_2$)	6.41	12.57	14.17	17.03	15.28	15.80	13.33	108.0%
TPES (PJ)	97	190	212	249	226	233	199	106.0%
TPES (Mtoe)	2.31	4.54	5.06	5.96	5.39	5.57	4.76	106.0%
GDP (billion 2000 US$ using exch. rates)	8.40	14.94	16.82	18.89	20.30	20.50	20.50	143.9%
GDP (billion 2000 US$ using PPPs)	8.11	14.41	16.23	18.22	19.58	19.78	19.77	143.9%
Population (millions)	2.97	3.49	3.77	3.92	3.97	4.01	4.06	36.3%
CO$_2$ / TPES (t CO$_2$ per TJ)	66.0	66.1	66.9	68.3	67.7	67.7	66.9	1.3%
CO$_2$ / GDP (kg CO$_2$ per 2000 US$)	0.76	0.84	0.84	0.90	0.75	0.77	0.65	-14.5%
CO$_2$ / GDP (kg CO$_2$ per 2000 US$ PPP)	0.79	0.87	0.87	0.93	0.78	0.80	0.67	-14.5%
CO$_2$ / population (t CO$_2$ per capita)	2.15	3.60	3.76	4.35	3.85	3.94	3.29	53.0%

Ratios are based on the Sectoral Approach.

2006 CO$_2$ emissions by sector

million tonnes of CO$_2$	Coal/peat	Oil	Gas	Other *	Total	% change 90-06
Sectoral Approach	0.51	12.81	-	-	13.33	108.7%
Main activity producer elec. and heat	-	6.45	-	-	6.45	134.4%
Unallocated autoproducers	-	-	-	-	-	-
Other energy industries	-	-	-	-	-	-100.0%
Manufacturing industries and construction	0.51	0.92	-	-	1.44	344.4%
Transport	-	3.80	-	-	3.80	106.1%
of which: road	-	*3.80*	-	-	*3.80*	*106.1%*
Other sectors	-	1.64	-	-	1.64	12.8%
of which: residential	-	*1.64*	-	-	*1.64*	*12.8%*
Reference Approach	0.51	12.81	-	-	13.33	108.0%
Diff. due to losses and/or transformation	-	-	-	-	-	
Statistical differences	-	- 0.00	-	-	- 0.00	
Memo: international marine bunkers	-	*0.05*	-	-	*0.05*	*..*
Memo: international aviation	-	*0.33*	-	-	*0.33*	*71.7%*

* Other includes industrial waste and non-renewable municipal waste.

Key sources for CO$_2$ emissions from fuel combustion in 2006

IPCC source category	CO$_2$ emissions (Mt of CO$_2$)	% change 90-06	Level assessment (%) **	Cumulative total (%)
Main activity prod. elec. and heat - oil	6.45	134.4%	38.0	38.0
Road - oil	3.80	106.1%	22.4	60.4
Residential - oil	1.64	12.8%	9.6	70.0
Manufacturing industries - oil	0.92	185.7%	5.4	75.4
Manufacturing industries - coal/peat	0.51	x	3.0	78.5
-	-	-	-	-
-	-	-	-	-
-	-	-	-	-
-	-	-	-	-
-	-	-	-	-
-	-	-	-	-
Memo: total CO$_2$ from fuel combustion	*13.33*	*108.7%*	*78.5*	*78.5*

** Percent calculated using the total GHG estimate for CO$_2$, CH$_4$, N$_2$O, HFCs, PFCs and SF$_6$ excluding CO$_2$ emissions/removals from land use change and forestry.

Libya / Libye

Figure 1. CO$_2$ emissions by fuel

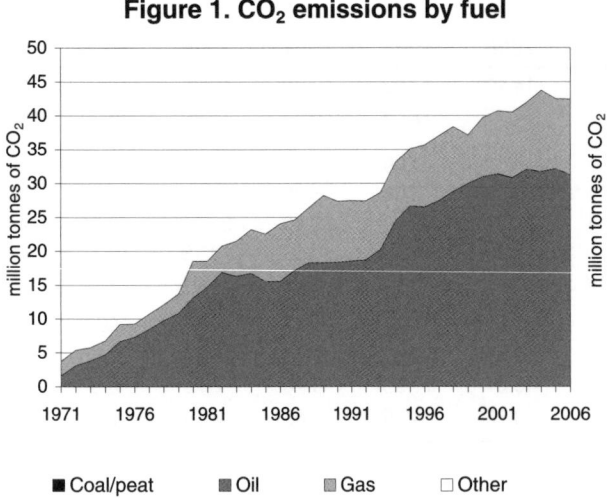

■ Coal/peat　■ Oil　■ Gas　□ Other

Figure 2. CO$_2$ emissions by sector

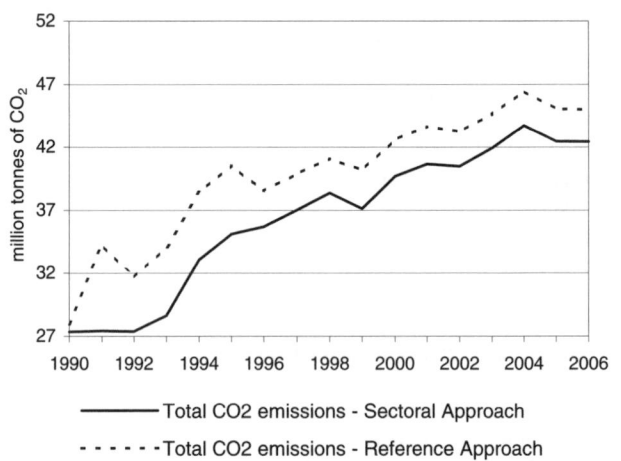

■ Electricity and heat　□ Other energy industries
■ Manuf. ind. and construction　■ Transport
□ Residential　■ Other

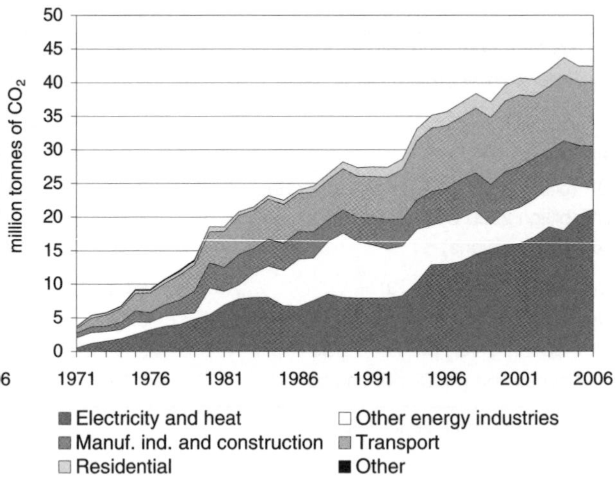

Figure 3. CO$_2$ emissions by sector

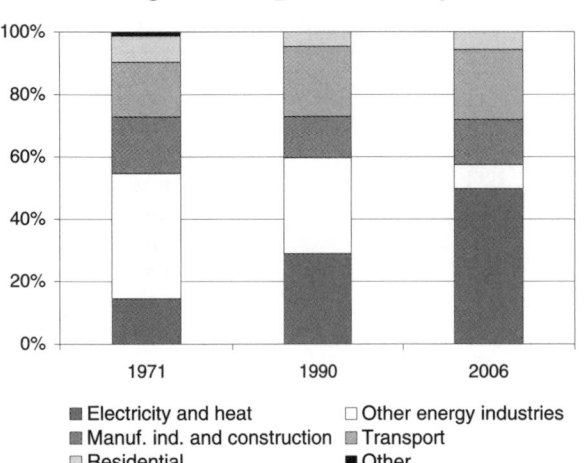

■ Electricity and heat　□ Other energy industries
■ Manuf. ind. and construction　■ Transport
□ Residential　■ Other

Figure 4. Reference vs Sectoral Approach

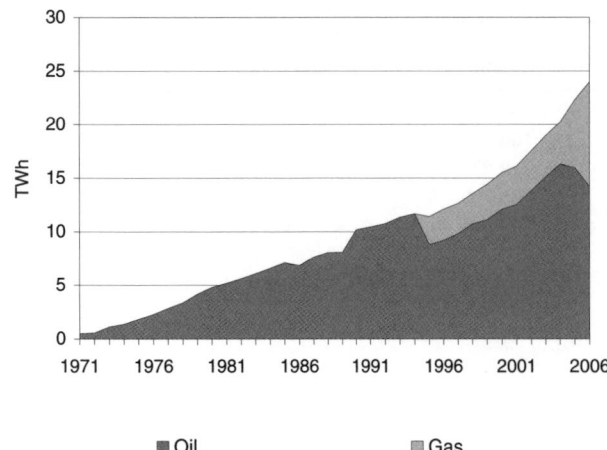

——— Total CO2 emissions - Sectoral Approach
- - - - - Total CO2 emissions - Reference Approach

Figure 5. Electricity generation by fuel

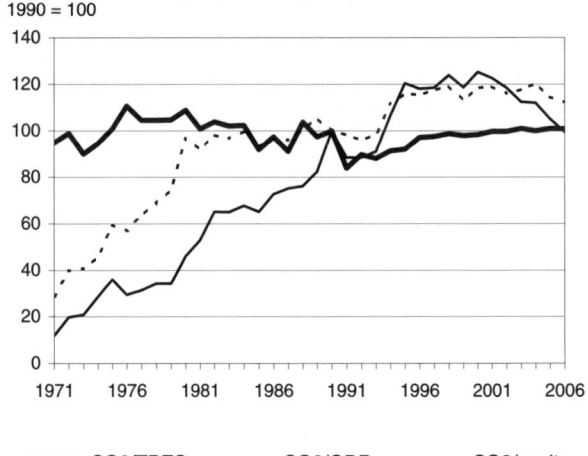

■ Oil　　　■ Gas

Figure 6. Key indicators

1990 = 100

——— CO2/TPES　——— CO2/GDP　- - - - CO2/capita

Libya / Libye
Key indicators

	1990	1995	2000	2003	2004	2005	2006	% change 90-06
CO$_2$ Sectoral Approach (Mt of CO$_2$)	27.35	35.12	39.69	41.93	43.71	42.47	42.44	55.2%
CO$_2$ Reference Approach (Mt of CO$_2$)	27.97	40.56	42.62	44.64	46.43	45.07	44.97	60.8%
TPES (PJ)	483	674	713	734	772	743	744	53.9%
TPES (Mtoe)	11.54	16.10	17.02	17.53	18.45	17.75	17.77	53.9%
GDP (billion 2000 US$ using exch. rates)	29.79	31.77	34.50	40.60	42.50	44.00	46.46	56.0%
GDP (billion 2000 US$ using PPPs)	40.48	43.18	46.89	55.18	57.76	59.80	63.15	56.0%
Population (millions)	4.36	4.83	5.35	5.68	5.80	5.92	6.04	38.4%
CO$_2$ / TPES (t CO$_2$ per TJ)	56.6	52.1	55.7	57.1	56.6	57.1	57.0	0.8%
CO$_2$ / GDP (kg CO$_2$ per 2000 US$)	0.92	1.11	1.15	1.03	1.03	0.97	0.91	-0.5%
CO$_2$ / GDP (kg CO$_2$ per 2000 US$ PPP)	0.68	0.81	0.85	0.76	0.76	0.71	0.67	-0.5%
CO$_2$ / population (t CO$_2$ per capita)	6.27	7.27	7.42	7.38	7.54	7.18	7.03	12.1%

Ratios are based on the Sectoral Approach.

2006 CO$_2$ emissions by sector

million tonnes of CO$_2$	Coal/peat	Oil	Gas	Other *	Total	% change 90-06
Sectoral Approach	-	**31.22**	**11.22**	-	**42.44**	**55.2%**
Main activity producer elec. and heat	-	15.29	5.79	-	21.08	166.3%
Unallocated autoproducers	-	..	-	-	-	-
Other energy industries	-	2.06	1.19	-	3.25	-61.3%
Manufacturing industries and construction	-	1.92	4.23	-	6.15	70.6%
Transport	-	9.53	-	-	9.53	55.6%
of which: road	-	9.52	-	-	9.52	55.6%
Other sectors	-	2.43	-	-	2.43	87.0%
of which: residential	-	2.43	-	-	2.43	87.0%
Reference Approach	-	**33.76**	**11.22**	-	**44.97**	**60.8%**
Diff. due to losses and/or transformation	-	2.53	-	-	2.53	
Statistical differences	-	-	-	-	-	
Memo: international marine bunkers	-	0.28	-	-	0.28	12.5%
Memo: international aviation	-	0.55	-	-	0.55	-13.5%

* Other includes industrial waste and non-renewable municipal waste.

Key sources for CO$_2$ emissions from fuel combustion in 2006

IPCC source category	CO$_2$ emissions (Mt of CO$_2$)	% change 90-06	Level assessment (%) **	Cumulative total (%)
Main activity prod. elec. and heat - oil	15.29	93.1%	26.8	26.8
Road - oil	9.52	55.6%	16.7	43.5
Main activity prod. elec. and heat - gas	5.79	x	10.2	53.7
Manufacturing industries - gas	4.23	65.8%	7.4	61.1
Residential - oil	2.43	87.0%	4.3	65.4
Other energy industries - oil	2.06	5.2%	3.6	69.0
Manufacturing industries - oil	1.92	82.2%	3.4	72.3
Other energy industries - gas	1.19	-81.5%	2.1	74.4
Other transport - oil	0.01	50.0%	0.0	74.5
-	-	-	-	-
-	-	-	-	-
Memo: total CO$_2$ from fuel combustion	42.44	55.2%	74.5	74.5

** Percent calculated using the total GHG estimate for CO$_2$, CH$_4$, N$_2$O, HFCs, PFCs and SF$_6$ excluding CO$_2$ emissions/removals from land use change and forestry.

Lithuania / Lituanie

Figure 1. CO$_2$ emissions by fuel

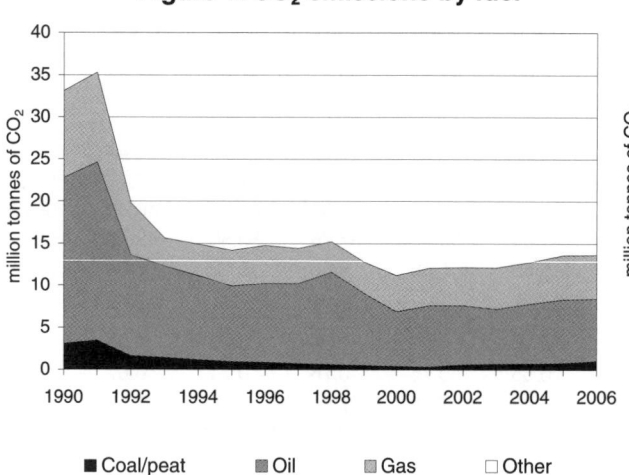

■ Coal/peat   ■ Oil   ■ Gas   □ Other

Figure 2. CO$_2$ emissions by sector

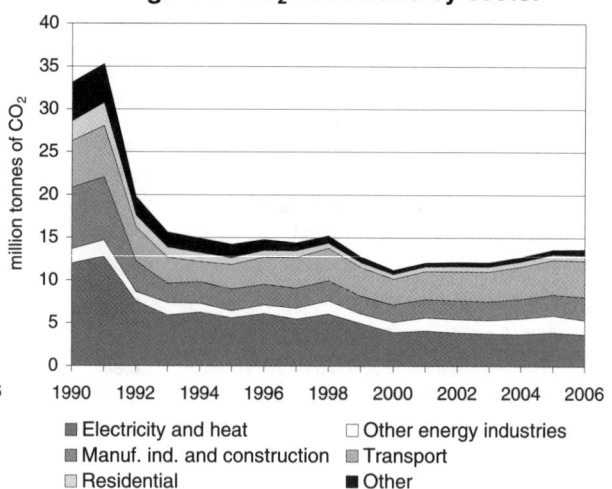

■ Electricity and heat   □ Other energy industries
■ Manuf. ind. and construction   ■ Transport
▨ Residential   ■ Other

Figure 3. CO$_2$ emissions by sector

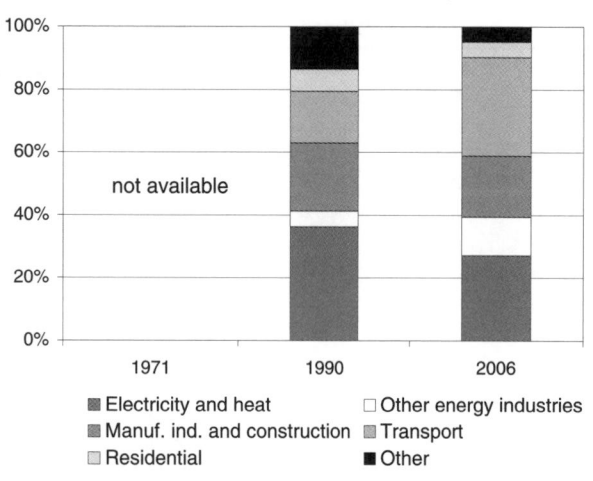

■ Electricity and heat   □ Other energy industries
■ Manuf. ind. and construction   ▨ Transport
▨ Residential   ■ Other

Figure 4. Reference vs Sectoral Approach

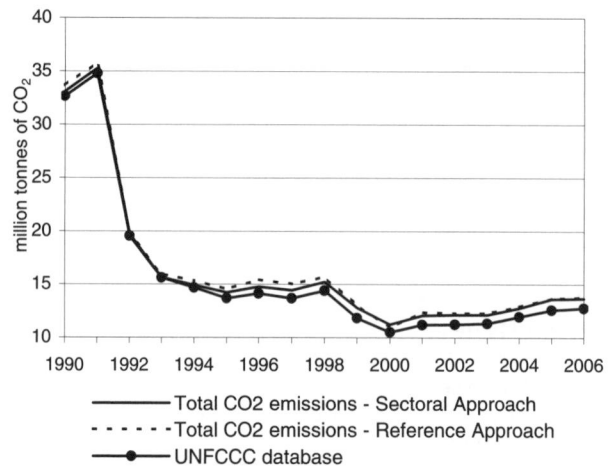

—— Total CO2 emissions - Sectoral Approach
- - - - Total CO2 emissions - Reference Approach
—●— UNFCCC database

Figure 5. Electricity generation by fuel

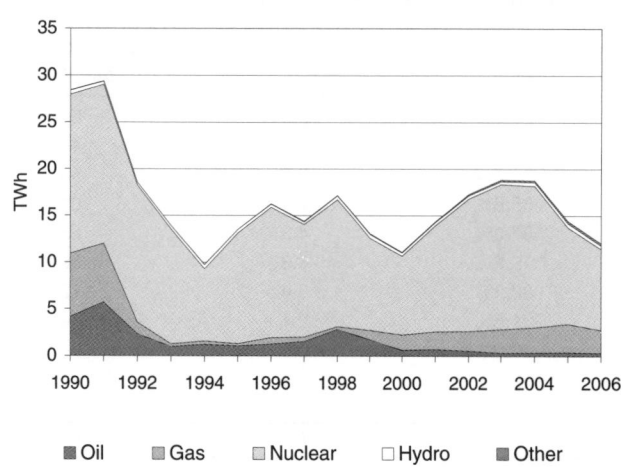

■ Oil   ▨ Gas   ▨ Nuclear   □ Hydro   ■ Other

Figure 6. Key indicators

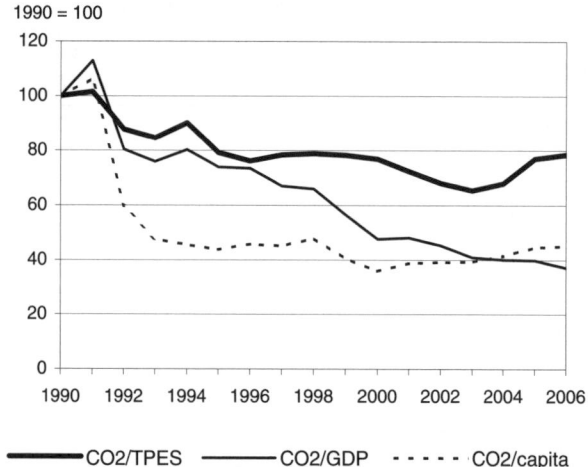

—— CO2/TPES   —— CO2/GDP   - - - - CO2/capita

Lithuania / Lituanie

Key indicators

	1990	1995	2000	2003	2004	2005	2006	% change 90-06
CO$_2$ Sectoral Approach (Mt of CO$_2$)	33.11	14.20	11.22	12.13	12.77	13.62	13.67	-58.7%
CO$_2$ Reference Approach (Mt of CO$_2$)	33.68	14.54	10.96	12.30	12.91	13.66	13.76	-59.2%
TPES (PJ)	680	368	300	382	386	364	358	-47.4%
TPES (Mtoe)	16.25	8.80	7.17	9.12	9.23	8.68	8.54	-47.4%
GDP (billion 2000 US$ using exch. rates)	16.04	9.30	11.42	14.36	15.41	16.58	17.82	11.1%
GDP (billion 2000 US$ using PPPs)	42.86	24.86	30.51	38.38	41.19	44.30	47.63	11.1%
Population (millions)	3.70	3.63	3.50	3.45	3.44	3.41	3.40	-8.2%
CO$_2$ / TPES (t CO$_2$ per TJ)	48.7	38.5	37.4	31.8	33.1	37.5	38.2	-21.5%
CO$_2$ / GDP (kg CO$_2$ per 2000 US$)	2.06	1.53	0.98	0.84	0.83	0.82	0.77	-62.9%
CO$_2$ / GDP (kg CO$_2$ per 2000 US$ PPP)	0.77	0.57	0.37	0.32	0.31	0.31	0.29	-62.8%
CO$_2$ / population (t CO$_2$ per capita)	8.95	3.91	3.21	3.51	3.72	3.99	4.03	-55.0%

Ratios are based on the Sectoral Approach.

2006 CO$_2$ emissions by sector

million tonnes of CO$_2$	Coal/peat	Oil	Gas	Other *	Total	% change 90-06
Sectoral Approach	**1.07**	**7.35**	**5.25**	**-**	**13.67**	**-58.7%**
Main activity producer elec. and heat	0.03	0.69	2.88	-	3.60	-67.2%
Unallocated autoproducers	0.01	0.01	0.09	-	0.11	-89.4%
Other energy industries	0.00	1.66	0.01	-	1.67	-0.6%
Manufacturing industries and construction	0.53	0.45	1.66	-	2.65	-63.0%
Transport	-	4.24	0.06	-	4.30	-21.3%
of which: road	*-*	*3.96*	*-*	*-*	*3.96*	*-22.1%*
Other sectors	0.50	0.30	0.54	-	1.34	-80.4%
of which: residential	*0.20*	*0.14*	*0.33*	*-*	*0.67*	*-71.2%*
Reference Approach	**1.07**	**7.41**	**5.27**	**-**	**13.76**	**-59.2%**
Diff. due to losses and/or transformation	0.00	0.06	0.03	-	0.09	
Statistical differences	- 0.00	0.00	0.00	-	0.00	
Memo: international marine bunkers	*-*	*0.44*	*-*	*-*	*0.44*	*46.7%*
Memo: international aviation	*-*	*0.16*	*-*	*-*	*0.16*	*-61.1%*

* Other includes industrial waste and non-renewable municipal waste.

Key sources for CO$_2$ emissions from fuel combustion in 2006

IPCC source category	CO$_2$ emissions (Mt of CO$_2$)	% change 90-06	Level assessment (%) **	Cumulative total (%)
Road - oil	3.96	-22.1%	16.4	16.4
Main activity prod. elec. and heat - gas	2.88	-46.8%	12.0	28.4
Manufacturing industries - gas	1.66	-45.9%	6.9	35.3
Other energy industries - oil	1.66	-1.0%	6.9	42.2
Main activity prod. elec. and heat - oil	0.69	-87.4%	2.9	45.0
Manufacturing industries - coal/peat	0.53	187.3%	2.2	47.2
Manufacturing industries - oil	0.45	-88.4%	1.9	49.1
Residential - gas	0.33	-36.5%	1.4	50.4
Non-specified other sectors - coal/peat	0.30	-77.2%	1.2	51.7
Other transport - oil	0.28	-26.6%	1.2	52.8
Non-specified other sectors - gas	0.21	-75.7%	0.9	53.7
Memo: total CO$_2$ from fuel combustion	*13.67*	*-58.7%*	*56.7*	*56.7*

** Percent calculated using the total GHG estimate for CO$_2$, CH$_4$, N$_2$O, HFCs, PFCs and SF$_6$ excluding CO$_2$ emissions/removals from land use change and forestry.

Luxembourg

Figure 1. CO$_2$ emissions by fuel

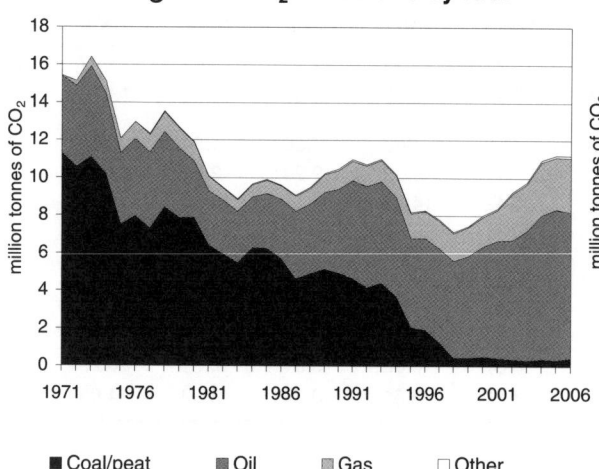

■ Coal/peat   ■ Oil   ▨ Gas   ☐ Other

Figure 2. CO$_2$ emissions by sector

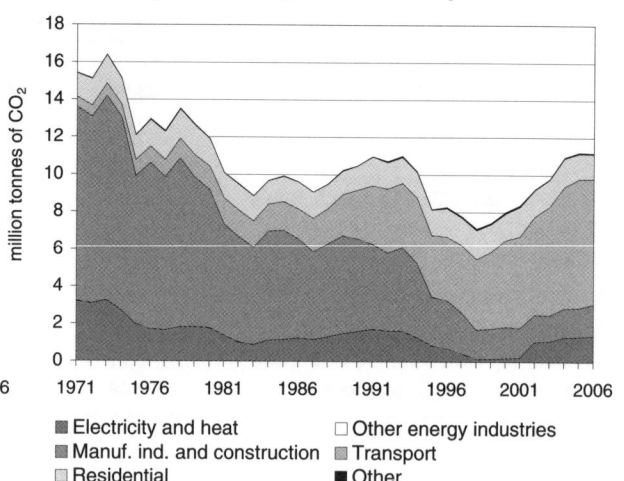

■ Electricity and heat   ☐ Other energy industries
▨ Manuf. ind. and construction   ▨ Transport
☐ Residential   ■ Other

Figure 3. CO$_2$ emissions by sector

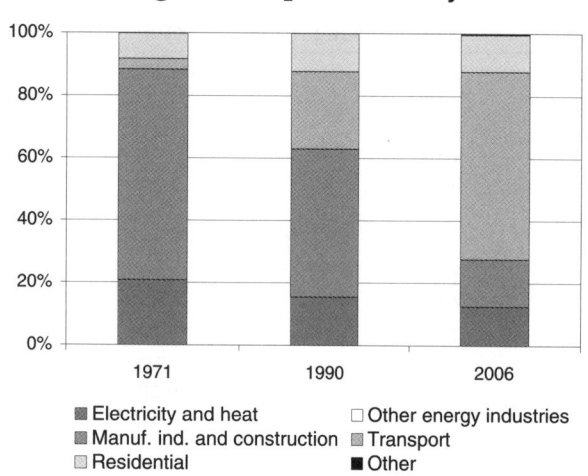

■ Electricity and heat   ☐ Other energy industries
▨ Manuf. ind. and construction   ▨ Transport
☐ Residential   ■ Other

Figure 4. Reference vs Sectoral Approach

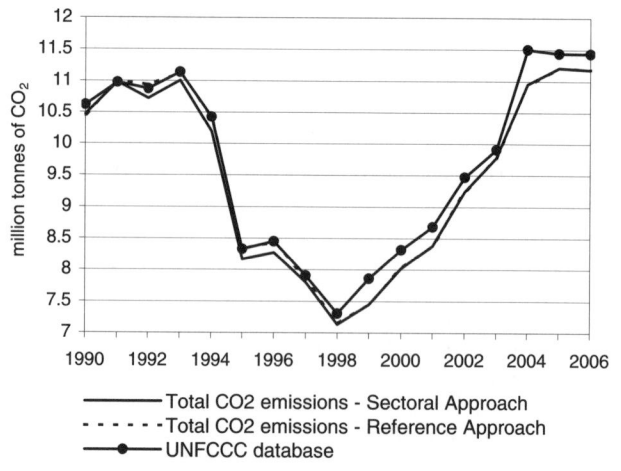

—— Total CO2 emissions - Sectoral Approach
- - - - Total CO2 emissions - Reference Approach
—●— UNFCCC database

Figure 5. Electricity generation by fuel

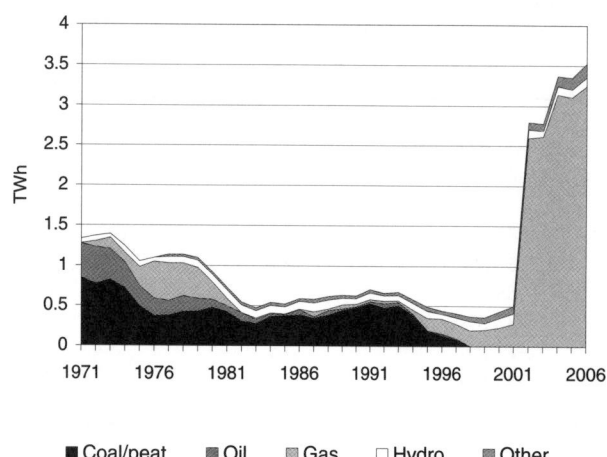

■ Coal/peat   ■ Oil   ▨ Gas   ☐ Hydro   ▨ Other

Figure 6. Key indicators

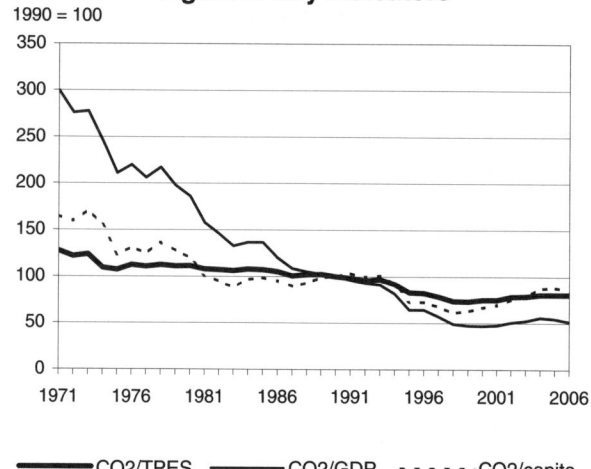

—— CO2/TPES   —— CO2/GDP   - - - - CO2/capita

Luxembourg

Key indicators

	1990	1995	2000	2003	2004	2005	2006	% change 90-06
CO$_2$ Sectoral Approach (Mt of CO$_2$)	10.47	8.17	8.02	9.78	10.95	11.21	11.18	6.8%
CO$_2$ Reference Approach (Mt of CO$_2$)	10.45	8.33	8.03	9.78	10.93	11.21	11.19	7.0%
TPES (PJ)	148	140	152	176	193	197	197	33.0%
TPES (Mtoe)	3.54	3.34	3.64	4.21	4.62	4.71	4.71	33.0%
GDP (billion 2000 US$ using exch. rates)	12.40	15.10	20.30	22.10	23.20	24.30	25.80	108.1%
GDP (billion 2000 US$ using PPPs)	14.30	17.36	23.38	25.48	26.72	28.06	29.78	108.2%
Population (millions)	0.38	0.41	0.44	0.45	0.46	0.47	0.47	23.8%
CO$_2$ / TPES (t CO$_2$ per TJ)	70.5	58.4	52.7	55.5	56.6	56.8	56.7	-19.7%
CO$_2$ / GDP (kg CO$_2$ per 2000 US$)	0.84	0.54	0.40	0.44	0.47	0.46	0.43	-48.7%
CO$_2$ / GDP (kg CO$_2$ per 2000 US$ PPP)	0.73	0.47	0.34	0.38	0.41	0.40	0.38	-48.7%
CO$_2$ / population (t CO$_2$ per capita)	27.40	19.92	18.27	21.64	23.92	24.11	23.64	-13.7%

Ratios are based on the Sectoral Approach.

2006 CO$_2$ emissions by sector

million tonnes of CO$_2$	Coal/peat	Oil	Gas	Other *	Total	% change 90-06
Sectoral Approach	**0.43**	**7.76**	**2.88**	**0.11**	**11.18**	**6.8%**
Main activity producer elec. and heat	-	-	1.03	0.11	1.14	+
Unallocated autoproducers	-	-	0.25	-	0.25	-83.7%
Other energy industries	-	-	-	-	-	-
Manufacturing industries and construction	0.43	0.24	1.02	-	1.69	-65.8%
Transport	-	6.71	-	-	6.71	157.9%
of which: road	-	*6.67*	-	-	*6.67*	*157.1%*
Other sectors	0.00	0.80	0.58	-	1.38	6.9%
of which: residential	*0.00*	*0.75*	*0.58*	-	*1.33*	*3.8%*
Reference Approach	**0.43**	**7.76**	**2.88**	**0.11**	**11.19**	**7.0%**
Diff. due to losses and/or transformation	-	-	-	-	-	
Statistical differences	0.00	0.00	0.00	-	0.00	
Memo: international marine bunkers	-	-	-	-	-	-
Memo: international aviation	-	*1.20*	-	-	*1.20*	*207.8%*

* Other includes industrial waste and non-renewable municipal waste.

Key sources for CO$_2$ emissions from fuel combustion in 2006

IPCC source category	CO$_2$ emissions (Mt of CO$_2$)	% change 90-06	Level assessment (%) **	Cumulative total (%)
Road - oil	6.67	157.1%	51.0	51.0
Main activity prod. elec. and heat - gas	1.03	x	7.9	58.9
Manufacturing industries - gas	1.02	56.3%	7.8	66.8
Residential - oil	0.75	-19.4%	5.7	72.5
Residential - gas	0.58	75.9%	4.4	76.9
Manufacturing industries - coal/peat	0.43	-87.4%	3.3	80.2
Unallocated autoproducers - gas	0.25	+	1.9	82.1
Manufacturing industries - oil	0.24	-72.2%	1.9	84.0
Main activity prod. elec. and heat - other	0.11	54.2%	0.8	84.8
Non-specified other sectors - oil	0.06	260.0%	0.4	85.2
Other transport - oil	0.04	431.1%	0.3	85.6
Memo: total CO$_2$ from fuel combustion	*11.18*	*6.8%*	*85.6*	*85.6*

** Percent calculated using the total GHG estimate for CO$_2$, CH$_4$, N$_2$O, HFCs, PFCs and SF$_6$ excluding CO$_2$ emissions/removals from land use change and forestry.

FYR of Macedonia / ex-République yougoslave de Macédoine

Figure 1. CO₂ emissions by fuel

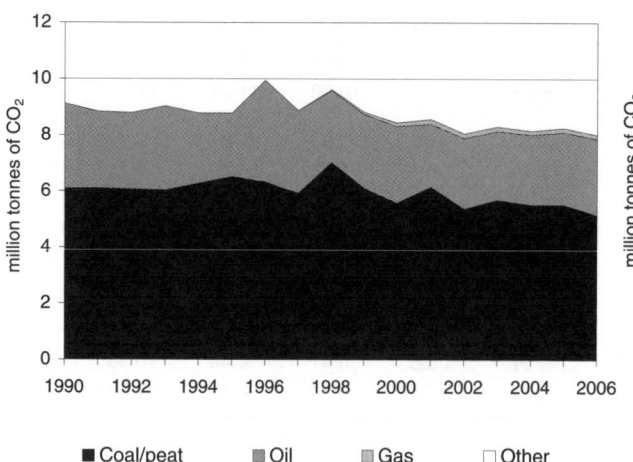

■ Coal/peat   ■ Oil   ■ Gas   □ Other

Figure 2. CO₂ emissions by sector

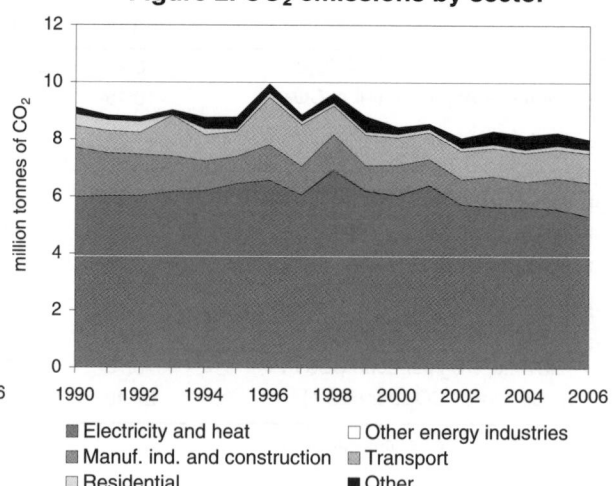

■ Electricity and heat   □ Other energy industries
■ Manuf. ind. and construction   ■ Transport
□ Residential   ■ Other

Figure 3. CO₂ emissions by sector

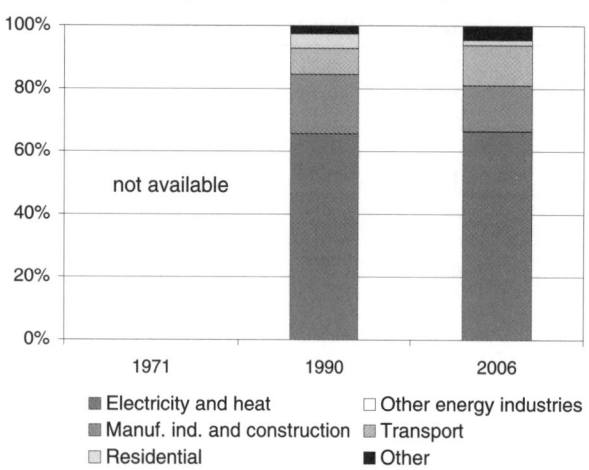

■ Electricity and heat   □ Other energy industries
■ Manuf. ind. and construction   ■ Transport
□ Residential   ■ Other

Figure 4. Reference vs Sectoral Approach

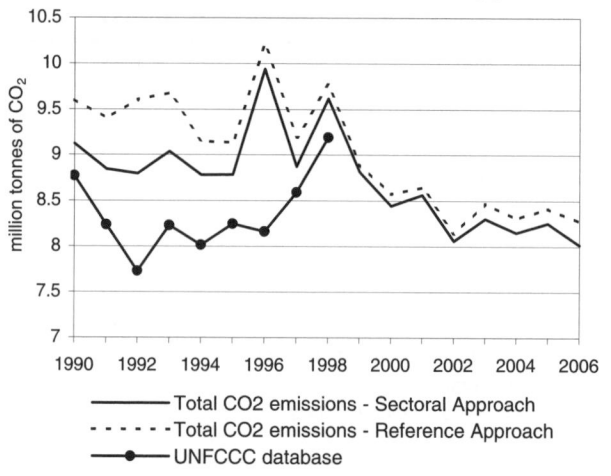

—— Total CO2 emissions - Sectoral Approach
- - - - Total CO2 emissions - Reference Approach
●—— UNFCCC database

Figure 5. Electricity generation by fuel

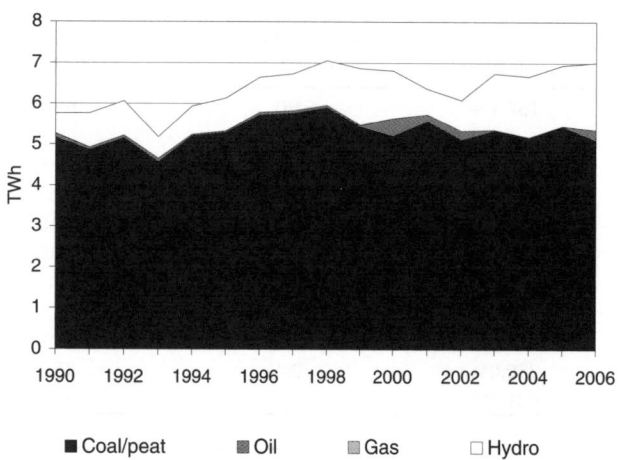

■ Coal/peat   ■ Oil   ■ Gas   □ Hydro

Figure 6. Key indicators

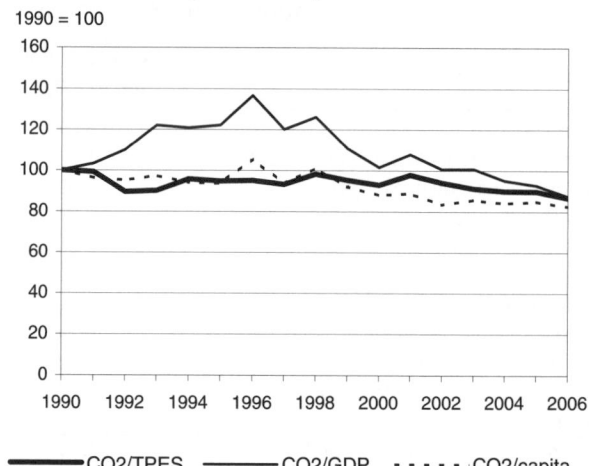

—— CO2/TPES   —— CO2/GDP   - - - - CO2/capita

FYR of Macedonia / ex-République yougoslave de Macédoine
Key indicators

	1990	1995	2000	2003	2004	2005	2006	% change 90-06
CO$_2$ Sectoral Approach (Mt of CO$_2$)	9.12	8.78	8.44	8.30	8.15	8.25	8.02	-12.1%
CO$_2$ Reference Approach (Mt of CO$_2$)	9.60	9.13	8.57	8.47	8.31	8.41	8.28	-13.8%
TPES (PJ)	114	116	113	113	113	115	116	1.6%
TPES (Mtoe)	2.72	2.76	2.71	2.71	2.70	2.74	2.76	1.6%
GDP (billion 2000 US$ using exch. rates)	3.93	3.10	3.59	3.55	3.70	3.84	3.95	0.5%
GDP (billion 2000 US$ using PPPs)	13.34	10.51	12.17	12.05	12.54	13.01	13.41	0.5%
Population (millions)	1.91	1.96	2.01	2.03	2.03	2.03	2.04	6.7%
CO$_2$ / TPES (t CO$_2$ per TJ)	80.2	76.0	74.4	73.2	72.2	72.0	69.4	-13.4%
CO$_2$ / GDP (kg CO$_2$ per 2000 US$)	2.32	2.83	2.35	2.34	2.21	2.15	2.03	-12.5%
CO$_2$ / GDP (kg CO$_2$ per 2000 US$ PPP)	0.68	0.84	0.69	0.69	0.65	0.63	0.60	-12.5%
CO$_2$ / population (t CO$_2$ per capita)	4.78	4.47	4.20	4.10	4.02	4.06	3.94	-17.6%

Ratios are based on the Sectoral Approach.

2006 CO$_2$ emissions by sector

million tonnes of CO$_2$	Coal/peat	Oil	Gas	Other *	Total	% change 90-06
Sectoral Approach	**5.15**	**2.71**	**0.16**	-	**8.02**	**-12.1%**
Main activity producer elec. and heat	4.62	0.39	0.04	-	5.05	-8.1%
Unallocated autoproducers	0.06	0.17	0.04	-	0.26	-44.8%
Other energy industries	-	0.01	-	-	0.01	x
Manufacturing industries and construction	0.44	0.65	0.08	-	1.17	-32.2%
Transport	-	1.02	0.00	-	1.02	34.9%
of which: road	-	*1.00*	*0.00*	-	*1.00*	*36.2%*
Other sectors	0.03	0.47	0.00	-	0.50	-23.7%
of which: residential	*0.01*	*0.12*	-	-	*0.14*	*-67.5%*
Reference Approach	**5.20**	**2.92**	**0.16**	-	**8.28**	**-13.8%**
Diff. due to losses and/or transformation	-	0.22	0.00	-	0.22	
Statistical differences	0.04	- 0.00	0.00	-	0.04	
Memo: international marine bunkers	-	-	-	-	-	-
Memo: international aviation	-	*0.02*	-	-	*0.02*	x

* Other includes industrial waste and non-renewable municipal waste.

Key sources for CO$_2$ emissions from fuel combustion in 2006

IPCC source category	CO$_2$ emissions (Mt of CO$_2$)	% change 90-06	Level assessment (%) **	Cumulative total (%)
Main activity prod. elec. and heat - coal/peat	4.62	-13.3%	46.8	46.8
Road - oil	1.00	36.1%	10.1	56.9
Manufacturing industries - oil	0.65	-45.2%	6.6	63.5
Manufacturing industries - coal/peat	0.44	-18.1%	4.5	68.0
Main activity prod. elec. and heat - oil	0.39	128.6%	4.0	72.0
Non-specified other sectors - oil	0.35	62.4%	3.5	75.5
Unallocated autoproducers - oil	0.17	-43.6%	1.7	77.2
Residential - oil	0.12	-69.3%	1.2	78.5
Manufacturing industries - gas	0.08	x	0.8	79.3
Unallocated autoproducers - coal/peat	0.06	-67.6%	0.6	79.8
Main activity prod. elec. and heat - gas	0.04	x	0.4	80.2
Memo: total CO$_2$ from fuel combustion	*8.02*	*-12.1%*	*81.2*	*81.2*

** Percent calculated using the total GHG estimate for CO$_2$, CH$_4$, N$_2$O, HFCs, PFCs and SF$_6$ excluding CO$_2$ emissions/removals from land use change and forestry.

Malaysia / Malaisie

Figure 1. CO_2 emissions by fuel

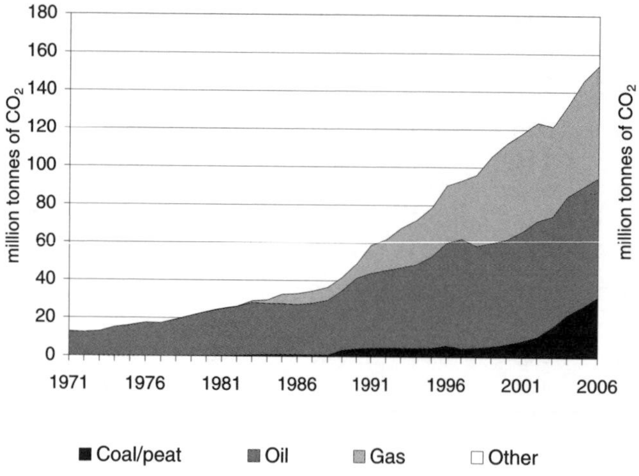

million tonnes of CO2
Coal/peat
Oil
Gas
Other

Figure 2. CO_2 emissions by sector

million tonnes of CO2
Electricity and heat
Manuf. ind. and construction
Residential
Other energy industries
Transport
Other

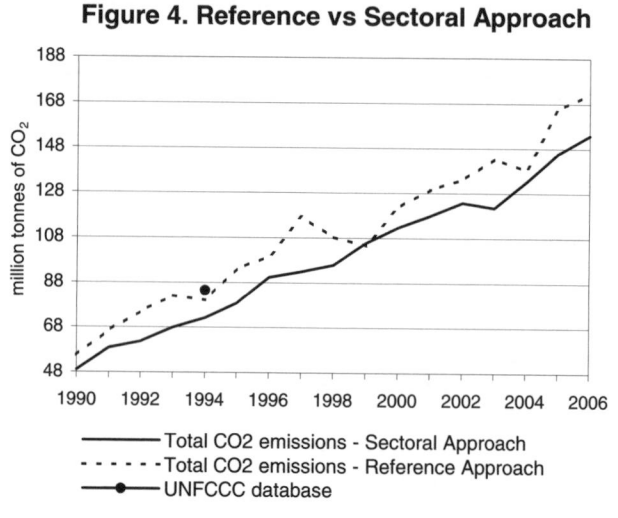

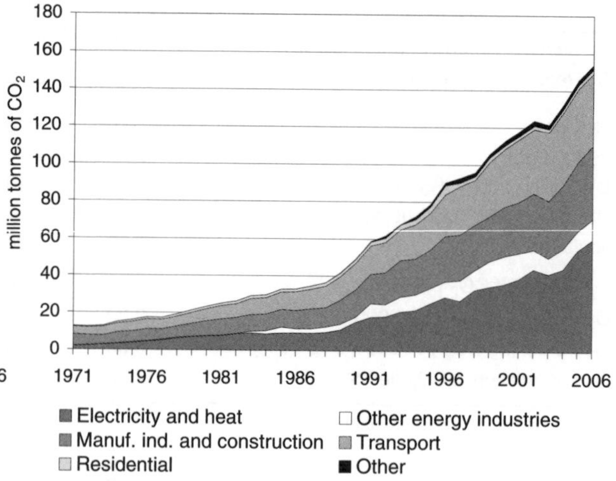

Figure 3. CO_2 emissions by sector

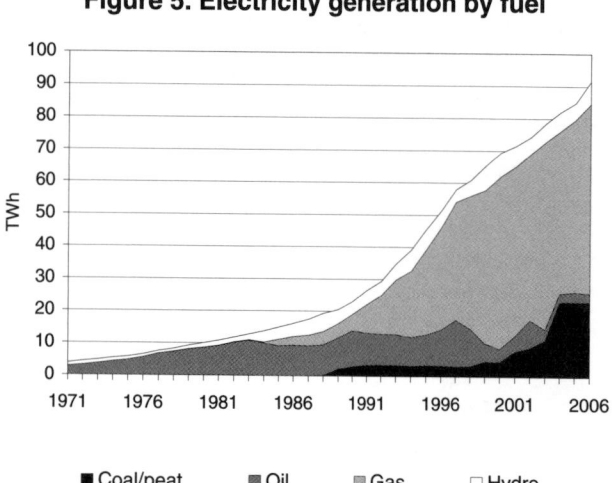

Electricity and heat
Manuf. ind. and construction
Residential
Other energy industries
Transport
Other

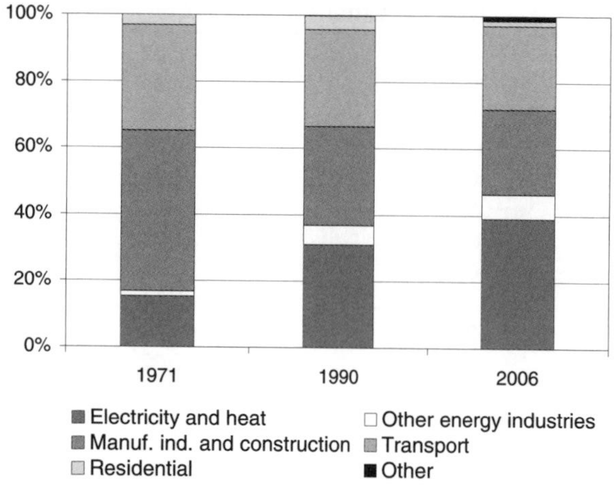

Figure 4. Reference vs Sectoral Approach

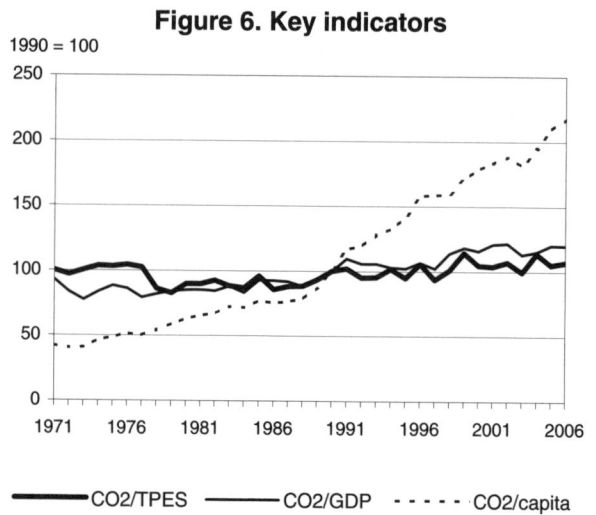

million tonnes of CO2
Total CO2 emissions - Sectoral Approach
Total CO2 emissions - Reference Approach
UNFCCC database

Figure 5. Electricity generation by fuel

TWh
Coal/peat
Oil
Gas
Hydro

Figure 6. Key indicators

1990 = 100
CO2/TPES
CO2/GDP
CO2/capita

Malaysia / Malaisie

Key indicators

	1990	1995	2000	2003	2004	2005	2006	% change 90-06
CO$_2$ Sectoral Approach (Mt of CO$_2$)	48.99	78.73	112.67	121.53	132.96	145.77	153.95	214.3%
CO$_2$ Reference Approach (Mt of CO$_2$)	55.41	94.05	121.73	143.42	138.19	165.55	172.32	211.0%
TPES (PJ)	976	1 654	2 146	2 434	2 329	2 760	2 861	193.0%
TPES (Mtoe)	23.32	39.51	51.26	58.14	55.64	65.93	68.33	193.0%
GDP (billion 2000 US$ using exch. rates)	45.46	71.48	90.32	99.73	106.95	112.46	119.11	162.0%
GDP (billion 2000 US$ using PPPs)	99.24	156.03	197.16	217.71	233.46	245.50	260.01	162.0%
Population (millions)	18.10	20.59	23.27	24.73	25.19	25.65	26.11	44.3%
CO$_2$ / TPES (t CO$_2$ per TJ)	50.2	47.6	52.5	49.9	57.1	52.8	53.8	7.3%
CO$_2$ / GDP (kg CO$_2$ per 2000 US$)	1.08	1.10	1.25	1.22	1.24	1.30	1.29	19.9%
CO$_2$ / GDP (kg CO$_2$ per 2000 US$ PPP)	0.49	0.50	0.57	0.56	0.57	0.59	0.59	19.9%
CO$_2$ / population (t CO$_2$ per capita)	2.71	3.82	4.84	4.91	5.28	5.68	5.90	117.9%

Ratios are based on the Sectoral Approach.

2006 CO$_2$ emissions by sector

million tonnes of CO$_2$	Coal/peat	Oil	Gas	Other *	Total	% change 90-06
Sectoral Approach	**31.84**	**62.99**	**59.13**	-	**153.95**	**214.3%**
Main activity producer elec. and heat	26.24	1.59	29.32	-	57.15	276.5%
Unallocated autoproducers	-	0.26	2.59	-	2.85	x
Other energy industries	-	1.03	10.28	-	11.31	299.7%
Manufacturing industries and construction	5.60	17.07	16.58	-	39.25	170.0%
Transport	-	38.44	0.29	-	38.74	170.9%
of which: road	-	*38.44*	-	-	*38.44*	*168.9%*
Other sectors	-	4.58	0.07	-	4.65	117.0%
of which: residential	-	*2.24*	*0.01*	-	*2.25*	*11.6%*
Reference Approach	**31.84**	**70.73**	**69.75**	-	**172.32**	**211.0%**
Diff. due to losses and/or transformation	-	7.65	5.88	-	13.53	
Statistical differences	0.00	0.09	4.74	-	4.83	
Memo: international marine bunkers	-	*0.16*	-	-	*0.16*	*-42.2%*
Memo: international aviation	-	*5.96*	-	-	*5.96*	*207.4%*

* Other includes industrial waste and non-renewable municipal waste.

Key sources for CO$_2$ emissions from fuel combustion in 2006

IPCC source category	CO$_2$ emissions (Mt of CO$_2$)	% change 90-06	Level assessment (%) **	Cumulative total (%)
Road - oil	38.44	168.9%	18.8	18.8
Main activity prod. elec. and heat - gas	29.32	822.1%	14.3	33.1
Main activity prod. elec. and heat - coal/peat	26.24	986.3%	12.8	45.9
Manufacturing industries - oil	17.07	56.4%	8.3	54.2
Manufacturing industries - gas	16.58	725.2%	8.1	62.3
Other energy industries - gas	10.28	324.9%	5.0	67.3
Manufacturing industries - coal/peat	5.60	247.1%	2.7	70.0
Unallocated autoproducers - gas	2.59	x	1.3	71.3
Non-specified other sectors - oil	2.34	+	1.1	72.4
Residential - oil	2.24	15.3%	1.1	73.5
Main activity prod. elec. and heat - oil	1.59	-83.4%	0.8	74.3
Memo: total CO$_2$ from fuel combustion	*153.95*	*214.3%*	*75.1*	*75.1*

** Percent calculated using the total GHG estimate for CO$_2$, CH$_4$, N$_2$O, HFCs, PFCs and SF$_6$ excluding CO$_2$ emissions/removals from land use change and forestry.

Malta / Malte

Figure 1. CO$_2$ emissions by fuel

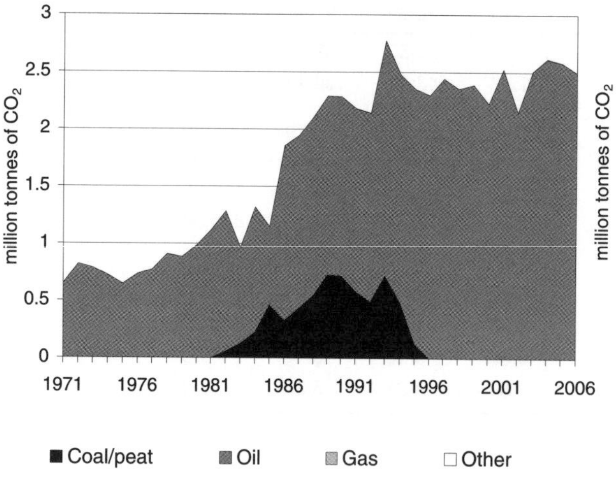

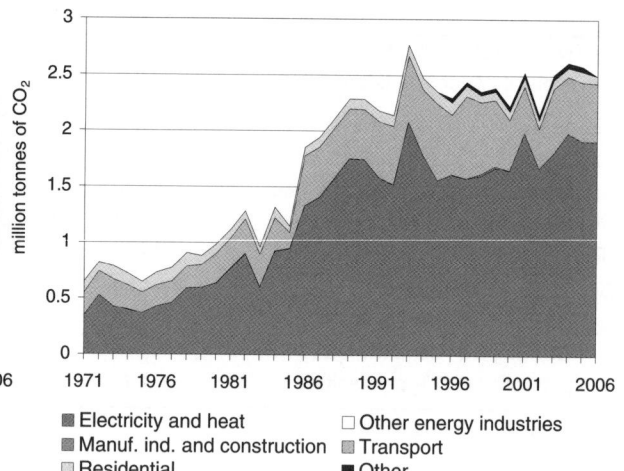

Coal/peat　　Oil　　Gas　　Other

Figure 2. CO$_2$ emissions by sector

Electricity and heat　　Other energy industries
Manuf. ind. and construction　　Transport
Residential　　Other

Figure 3. CO$_2$ emissions by sector

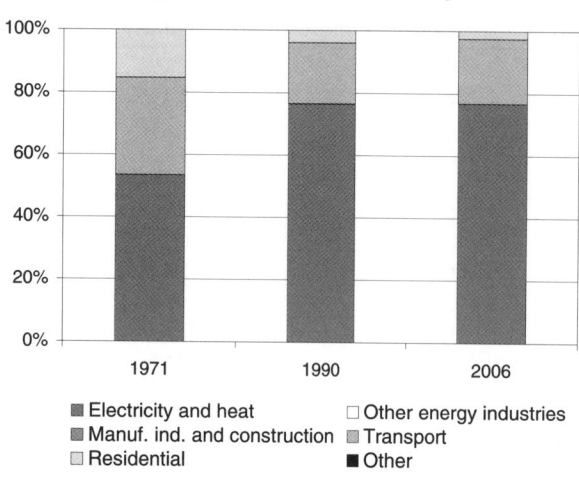

Electricity and heat　　Other energy industries
Manuf. ind. and construction　　Transport
Residential　　Other

Figure 4. Reference vs Sectoral Approach

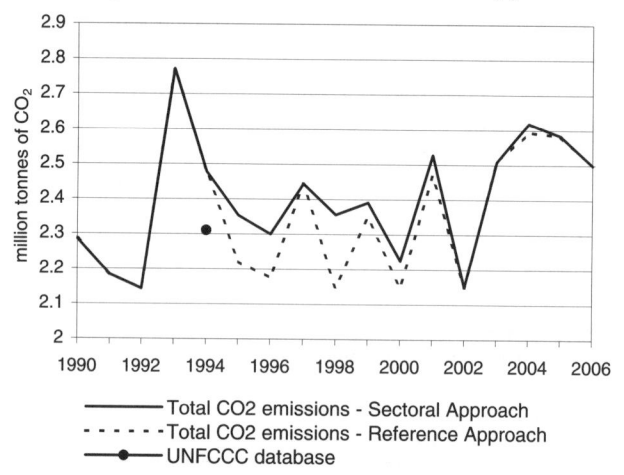

——— Total CO2 emissions - Sectoral Approach
- - - - Total CO2 emissions - Reference Approach
——●— UNFCCC database

Figure 5. Electricity generation by fuel

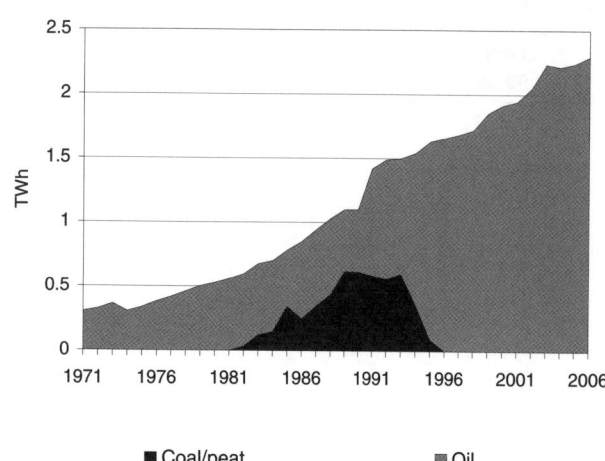

Coal/peat　　　　Oil

Figure 6. Key indicators

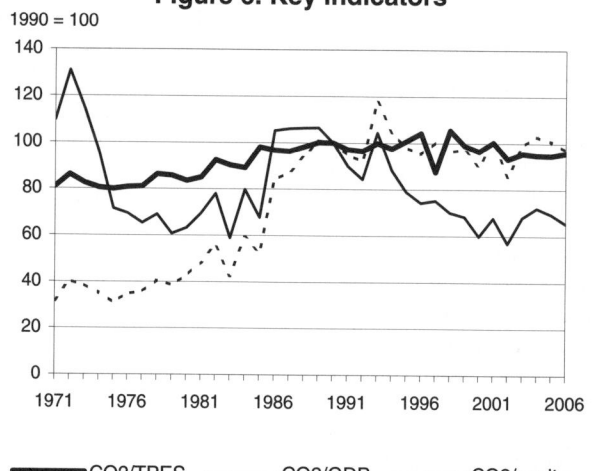

1990 = 100

CO2/TPES　　CO2/GDP　　- - - - CO2/capita

Malta / Malte

Key indicators

	1990	1995	2000	2003	2004	2005	2006	% change 90-06
CO$_2$ Sectoral Approach (Mt of CO$_2$)	2.29	2.35	2.23	2.51	2.62	2.58	2.50	9.3%
CO$_2$ Reference Approach (Mt of CO$_2$)	2.29	2.22	2.15	2.51	2.59	2.58	2.50	9.3%
TPES (PJ)	32	33	32	37	39	38	37	14.1%
TPES (Mtoe)	0.77	0.78	0.77	0.88	0.93	0.92	0.88	14.2%
GDP (billion 2000 US$ using exch. rates)	2.38	3.11	3.87	3.84	3.79	3.88	3.98	67.1%
GDP (billion 2000 US$ using PPPs)	4.23	5.52	6.88	6.83	6.72	6.89	7.06	67.2%
Population (millions)	0.36	0.38	0.39	0.40	0.40	0.40	0.41	12.8%
CO$_2$ / TPES (t CO$_2$ per TJ)	71.2	71.8	68.6	67.9	67.4	67.4	68.2	-4.2%
CO$_2$ / GDP (kg CO$_2$ per 2000 US$)	0.96	0.76	0.57	0.65	0.69	0.67	0.63	-34.6%
CO$_2$ / GDP (kg CO$_2$ per 2000 US$ PPP)	0.54	0.43	0.32	0.37	0.39	0.37	0.35	-34.6%
CO$_2$ / population (t CO$_2$ per capita)	6.35	6.22	5.71	6.29	6.53	6.40	6.15	-3.0%

Ratios are based on the Sectoral Approach.

2006 CO$_2$ emissions by sector

million tonnes of CO$_2$	Coal/peat	Oil	Gas	Other *	Total	% change 90-06
Sectoral Approach	-	**2.50**	-	-	**2.50**	**9.3%**
Main activity producer elec. and heat	-	1.92	-	-	1.92	9.7%
Unallocated autoproducers	-	-	-	-	-	-
Other energy industries	-	-	-	-	-	-
Manufacturing industries and construction	-	-	-	-	-	-100.0%
Transport	-	0.52	-	-	0.52	16.5%
of which: road	-	*0.52*	-	-	*0.52*	*16.5%*
Other sectors	-	0.06	-	-	0.06	-30.9%
of which: residential	-	*0.06*	-	-	*0.06*	*-30.9%*
Reference Approach	-	**2.50**	-	-	**2.50**	**9.3%**
Diff. due to losses and/or transformation	-	-	-	-	-	
Statistical differences	-	-	-	-	-	
Memo: international marine bunkers	-	*0.07*	-	-	*0.07*	*-24.3%*
Memo: international aviation	-	*0.23*	-	-	*0.23*	*7.1%*

* Other includes industrial waste and non-renewable municipal waste.

Key sources for CO$_2$ emissions from fuel combustion in 2006

IPCC source category	CO$_2$ emissions (Mt of CO$_2$)	% change 90-06	Level assessment (%) **	Cumulative total (%)
Main activity prod. elec. and heat - oil	1.92	86.3%	72.3	72.3
Road - oil	0.52	16.5%	19.6	91.9
Residential - oil	0.06	-30.9%	2.4	94.3
-	-	-	-	-
-	-	-	-	-
-	-	-	-	-
-	-	-	-	-
-	-	-	-	-
-	-	-	-	-
-	-	-	-	-
-	-	-	-	-
Memo: total CO$_2$ from fuel combustion	*2.50*	*9.3%*	*94.3*	*94.3*

** Percent calculated using the total GHG estimate for CO$_2$, CH$_4$, N$_2$O, HFCs, PFCs and SF$_6$ excluding CO$_2$ emissions/removals from land use change and forestry.

Mexico / Mexique

Figure 1. CO$_2$ emissions by fuel

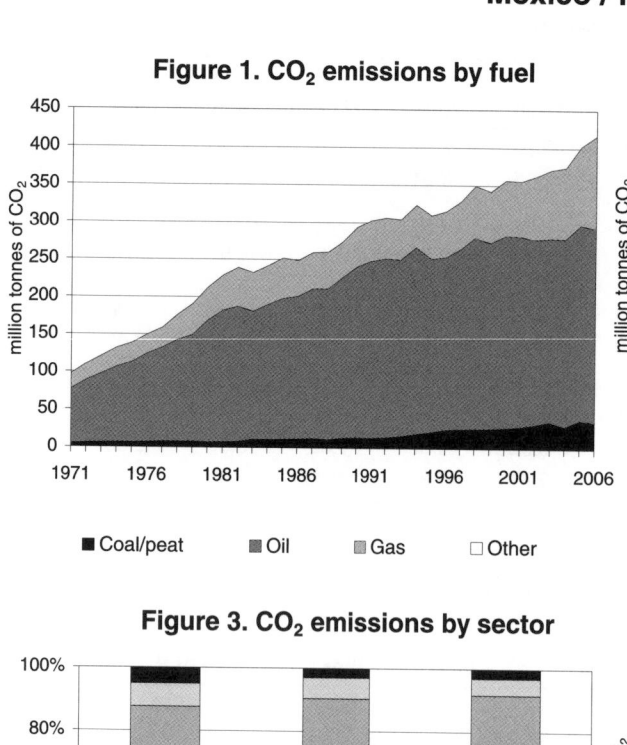

Figure 2. CO$_2$ emissions by sector

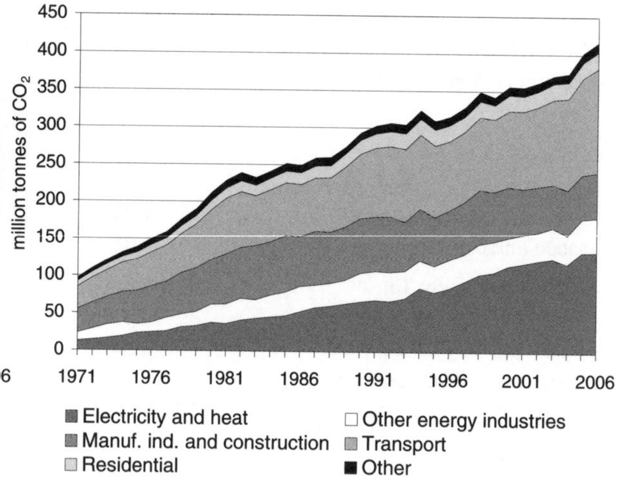

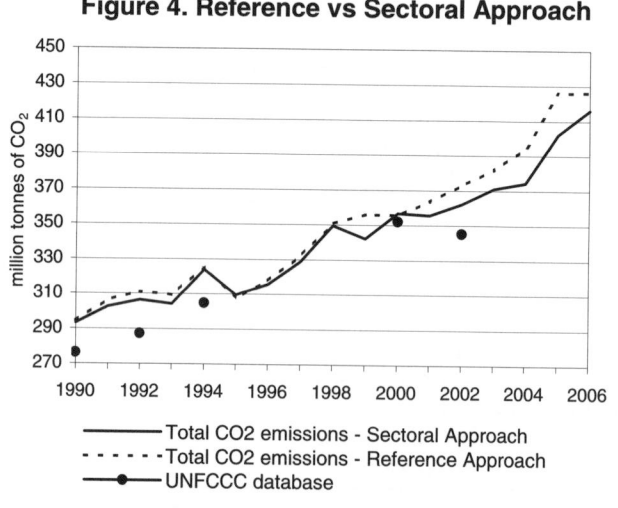

Figure 3. CO$_2$ emissions by sector

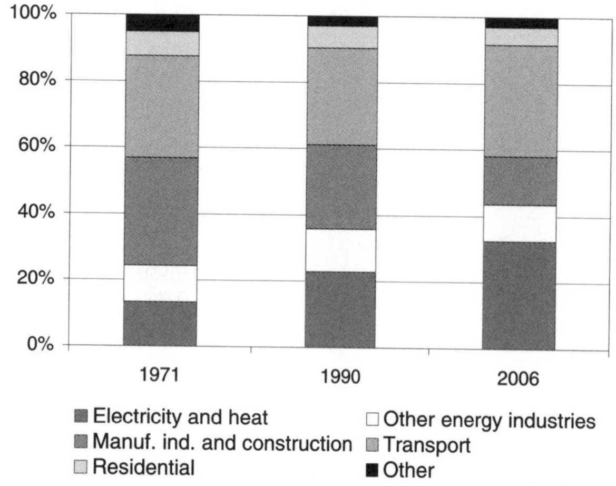

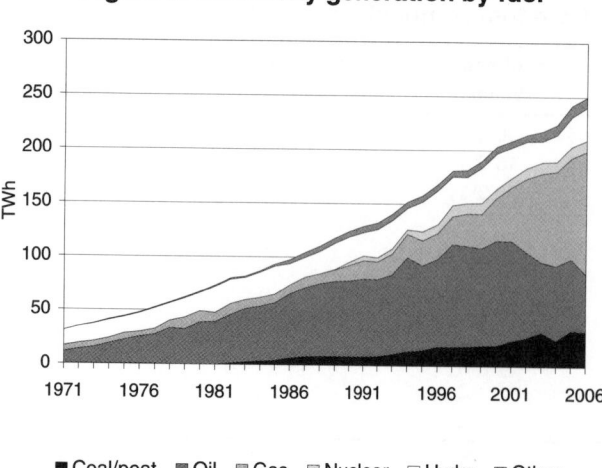

Figure 4. Reference vs Sectoral Approach

Figure 5. Electricity generation by fuel

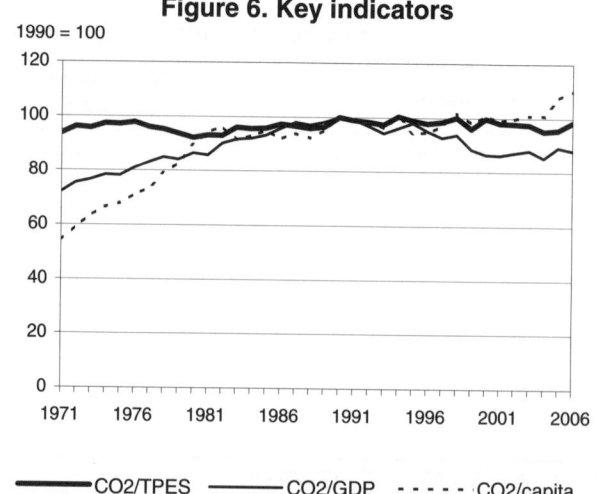

Figure 6. Key indicators

Mexico / Mexique

Key indicators

	1990	1995	2000	2003	2004	2005	2006	% change 90-06
CO$_2$ Sectoral Approach (Mt of CO$_2$)	292.94	309.56	356.76	370.97	374.32	402.20	416.26	42.1%
CO$_2$ Reference Approach (Mt of CO$_2$)	294.34	307.41	355.78	381.96	394.46	425.96	426.16	44.8%
TPES (PJ)	5 150	5 499	6 287	6 689	6 918	7 395	7 429	44.2%
TPES (Mtoe)	123.01	131.34	150.16	159.75	165.23	176.64	177.43	44.2%
GDP (billion 2000 US$ using exch. rates)	412.80	445.30	580.80	593.20	617.90	635.20	665.50	61.2%
GDP (billion 2000 US$ using PPPs)	639.17	689.55	899.28	918.52	956.74	983.55	1 030.48	61.2%
Population (millions)	81.25	91.12	98.26	101.87	102.87	103.83	104.75	28.9%
CO$_2$ / TPES (t CO$_2$ per TJ)	56.9	56.3	56.7	55.5	54.1	54.4	56.0	-1.5%
CO$_2$ / GDP (kg CO$_2$ per 2000 US$)	0.71	0.70	0.61	0.63	0.61	0.63	0.63	-11.9%
CO$_2$ / GDP (kg CO$_2$ per 2000 US$ PPP)	0.46	0.45	0.40	0.40	0.39	0.41	0.40	-11.8%
CO$_2$ / population (t CO$_2$ per capita)	3.61	3.40	3.63	3.64	3.64	3.87	3.97	10.2%

Ratios are based on the Sectoral Approach.

2006 CO$_2$ emissions by sector

million tonnes of CO$_2$	Coal/peat	Oil	Gas	Other *	Total	% change 90-06
Sectoral Approach	**35.65**	**257.67**	**122.93**	**-**	**416.26**	**42.1%**
Main activity producer elec. and heat	27.57	40.42	45.43	-	113.42	69.7%
Unallocated autoproducers	0.89	3.77	17.05	-	21.71	x
Other energy industries	0.10	18.02	27.87	-	46.00	20.7%
Manufacturing industries and construction	7.10	25.60	27.76	-	60.46	-18.2%
Transport	-	137.41	2.35	-	139.76	62.8%
of which: road	*-*	*132.63*	*0.05*	*-*	*132.67*	*58.3%*
Other sectors	-	32.44	2.47	-	34.91	23.4%
of which: residential	*-*	*20.21*	*1.97*	*-*	*22.18*	*15.5%*
Reference Approach	**34.74**	**279.64**	**111.77**	**-**	**426.16**	**44.8%**
Diff. due to losses and/or transformation	- 0.20	14.10	-	-	13.91	
Statistical differences	- 0.72	7.87	- 11.16	-	- 4.01	
Memo: international marine bunkers	*-*	*2.71*	*-*	*-*	*2.71*	*33.8%*
Memo: international aviation	*-*	*8.45*	*-*	*-*	*8.45*	*54.3%*

* Other includes industrial waste and non-renewable municipal waste.

Key sources for CO$_2$ emissions from fuel combustion in 2006

IPCC source category	CO$_2$ emissions (Mt of CO$_2$)	% change 90-06	Level assessment (%) **	Cumulative total (%)
Road - oil	132.63	58.2%	20.5	20.5
Main activity prod. elec. and heat - gas	45.43	466.5%	7.0	27.5
Main activity prod. elec. and heat - oil	40.42	-21.7%	6.2	33.8
Other energy industries - gas	27.87	115.7%	4.3	38.1
Manufacturing industries - gas	27.76	-5.1%	4.3	42.4
Main activity prod. elec. and heat - coal/peat	27.57	285.0%	4.3	46.6
Manufacturing industries - oil	25.60	-32.2%	4.0	50.6
Residential - oil	20.21	16.7%	3.1	53.7
Other energy industries - oil	18.02	-28.0%	2.8	56.5
Unallocated autoproducers - gas	17.05	x	2.6	59.1
Non-specified other sectors - oil	12.23	34.7%	1.9	61.0
Memo: total CO$_2$ from fuel combustion	*416.26*	*42.1%*	*64.4*	*64.4*

** Percent calculated using the total GHG estimate for CO$_2$, CH$_4$, N$_2$O, HFCs, PFCs and SF$_6$ excluding CO$_2$ emissions/removals from land use change and forestry.

Republic of Moldova / République de Moldavie

Figure 1. CO$_2$ emissions by fuel

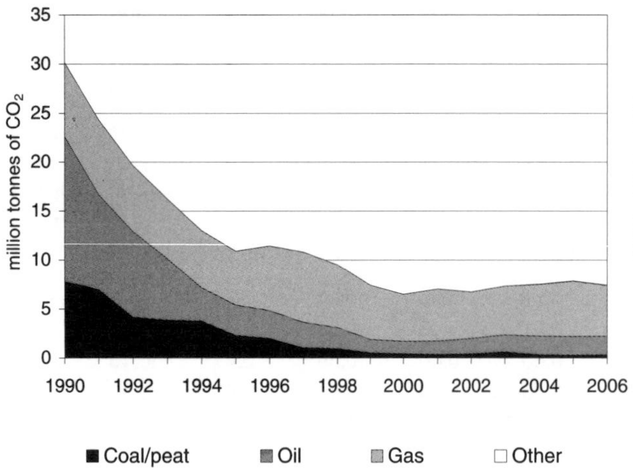

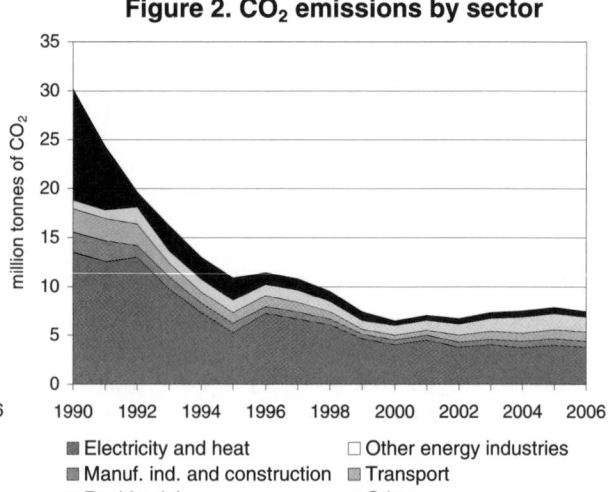

■ Coal/peat   ■ Oil   ▨ Gas   ☐ Other

Figure 2. CO$_2$ emissions by sector

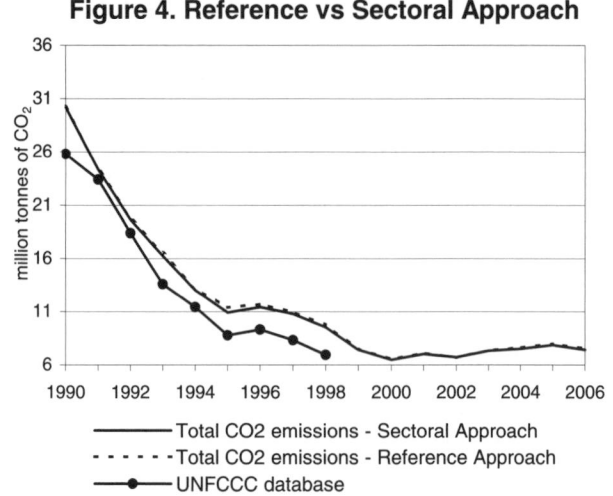

■ Electricity and heat   ☐ Other energy industries
■ Manuf. ind. and construction   ▨ Transport
☐ Residential   ■ Other

Figure 3. CO$_2$ emissions by sector

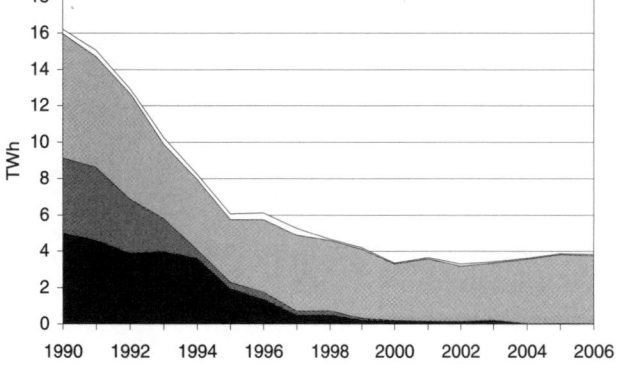

■ Electricity and heat   ☐ Other energy industries
■ Manuf. ind. and construction   ▨ Transport
☐ Residential   ■ Other

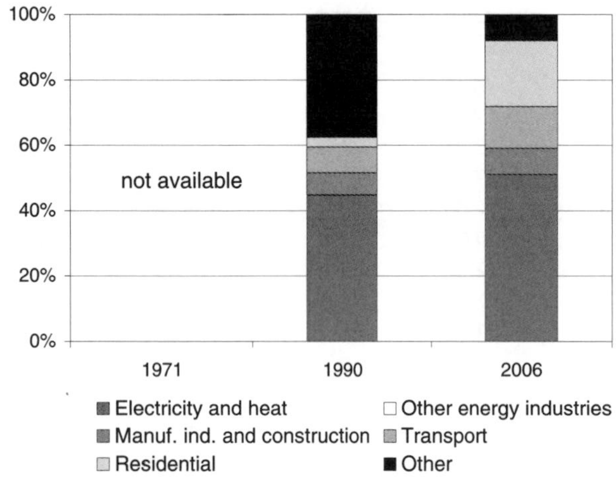

Figure 4. Reference vs Sectoral Approach

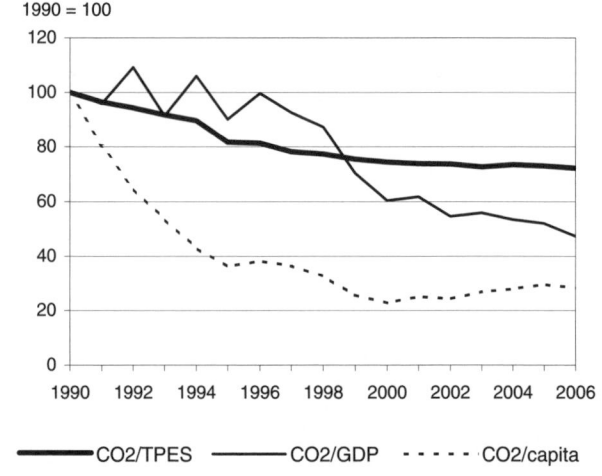

—— Total CO2 emissions - Sectoral Approach
····· Total CO2 emissions - Reference Approach
—●— UNFCCC database

Figure 5. Electricity generation by fuel

■ Coal/peat   ■ Oil   ▨ Gas   ☐ Hydro

Figure 6. Key indicators

1990 = 100

—— CO2/TPES   —— CO2/GDP   ····· CO2/capita

Republic of Moldova / République de Moldavie

Key indicators

	1990	1995	2000	2003	2004	2005	2006	% change 90-06
CO$_2$ Sectoral Approach (Mt of CO$_2$)	30.18	10.92	6.48	7.32	7.51	7.86	7.42	-75.4%
CO$_2$ Reference Approach (Mt of CO$_2$)	30.24	11.38	6.54	7.35	7.62	7.99	7.54	-75.1%
TPES (PJ)	416	184	120	139	141	149	142	-65.9%
TPES (Mtoe)	9.94	4.40	2.87	3.32	3.37	3.55	3.39	-65.9%
GDP (billion 2000 US$ using exch. rates)	3.62	1.45	1.29	1.57	1.69	1.81	1.89	-47.9%
GDP (billion 2000 US$ using PPPs)	15.81	6.34	5.63	6.87	7.37	7.93	8.27	-47.7%
Population (millions)	4.39	4.38	4.15	3.98	3.93	3.88	3.83	-12.7%
CO$_2$ / TPES (t CO$_2$ per TJ)	72.5	59.3	54.0	52.7	53.2	52.9	52.4	-27.8%
CO$_2$ / GDP (kg CO$_2$ per 2000 US$)	8.34	7.52	5.03	4.66	4.45	4.33	3.94	-52.8%
CO$_2$ / GDP (kg CO$_2$ per 2000 US$ PPP)	1.91	1.72	1.15	1.07	1.02	0.99	0.90	-52.9%
CO$_2$ / population (t CO$_2$ per capita)	6.88	2.49	1.56	1.84	1.91	2.03	1.94	-71.8%

Ratios are based on the Sectoral Approach.

2006 CO$_2$ emissions by sector

million tonnes of CO$_2$	Coal/peat	Oil	Gas	Other *	Total	% change 90-06
Sectoral Approach	**0.33**	**1.88**	**5.19**	**0.02**	**7.42**	**-75.4%**
Main activity producer elec. and heat	-	0.05	3.45	-	3.50	-74.0%
Unallocated autoproducers	0.01	-	0.25	0.02	0.28	x
Other energy industries	-	-	-	-	-	-100.0%
Manufacturing industries and construction	0.01	0.04	0.55	-	0.60	-70.7%
Transport	-	0.80	0.15	-	0.95	-60.4%
of which: road	-	0.70	0.02	-	0.73	-69.2%
Other sectors	0.31	0.99	0.80	-	2.09	-82.9%
of which: residential	0.16	0.77	0.57	-	1.50	71.2%
Reference Approach	**0.33**	**1.89**	**5.28**	**0.02**	**7.54**	**-75.1%**
Diff. due to losses and/or transformation	-	0.00	0.10	-	0.10	
Statistical differences	0.00	0.01	0.00	-	0.01	
Memo: international marine bunkers	-	..	-	-	..	..
Memo: international aviation	-	0.04	-	-	0.04	-83.3%

* Other includes industrial waste and non-renewable municipal waste.

Key sources for CO$_2$ emissions from fuel combustion in 2006

IPCC source category	CO$_2$ emissions (Mt of CO$_2$)	% change 90-06	Level assessment (%) **	Cumulative total (%)
Main activity prod. elec. and heat - gas	3.45	-34.9%	29.6	29.6
Residential - oil	0.77	110.2%	6.6	36.2
Road - oil	0.70	-69.9%	6.0	42.2
Residential - gas	0.57	12.0%	4.9	47.1
Manufacturing industries - gas	0.55	-55.5%	4.7	51.8
Unallocated autoproducers - gas	0.25	x	2.1	53.9
Non-specified other sectors - gas	0.22	-57.1%	1.9	55.9
Non-specified other sectors - oil	0.22	-97.3%	1.9	57.8
Residential - coal/peat	0.16	x	1.4	59.1
Non-specified other sectors - coal/peat	0.15	-94.3%	1.3	60.4
Other transport - gas	0.12	+	1.1	61.5
Memo: total CO$_2$ from fuel combustion	7.42	-75.4%	63.7	63.7

** Percent calculated using the total GHG estimate for CO$_2$, CH$_4$, N$_2$O, HFCs, PFCs and SF$_6$ excluding CO$_2$ emissions/removals from land use change and forestry.

Mongolia / Mongolie

Figure 1. CO$_2$ emissions by fuel

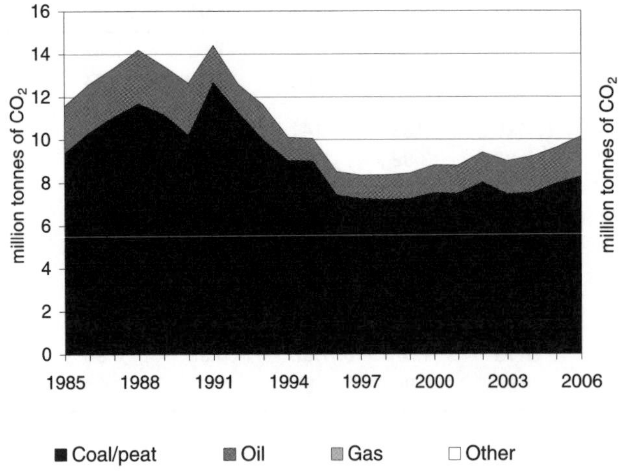

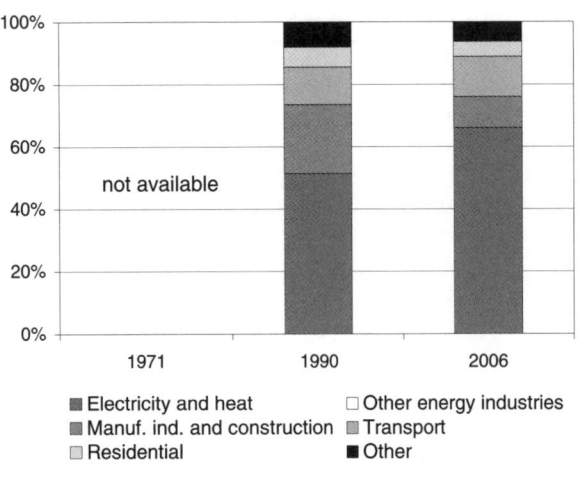

Figure 2. CO$_2$ emissions by sector

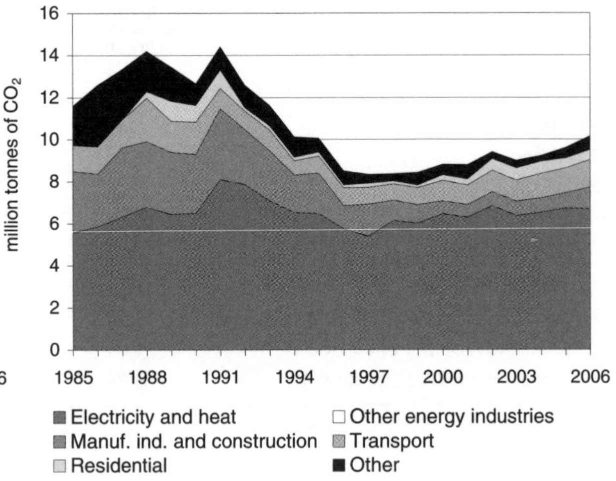

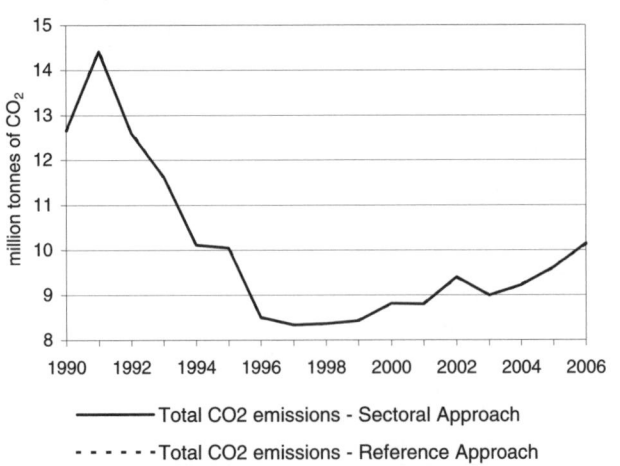

Figure 3. CO$_2$ emissions by sector

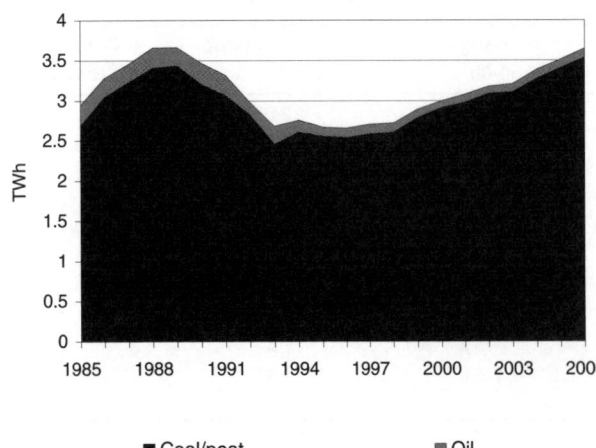

Figure 4. Reference vs Sectoral Approach

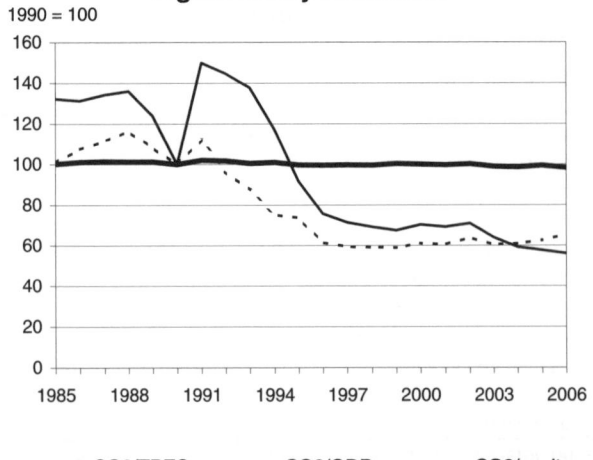

Figure 5. Electricity generation by fuel

Figure 6. Key indicators

Mongolia / Mongolie

Key indicators

	1990	1995	2000	2003	2004	2005	2006	% change 90-06
CO$_2$ Sectoral Approach (Mt of CO$_2$)	12.66	10.05	8.81	8.99	9.21	9.61	10.15	-19.8%
CO$_2$ Reference Approach (Mt of CO$_2$)	12.66	10.05	8.81	8.99	9.21	9.61	10.15	-19.8%
TPES (PJ)	143	114	100	103	106	109	117	-18.4%
TPES (Mtoe)	3.42	2.73	2.38	2.46	2.53	2.61	2.79	-18.4%
GDP (billion 2000 US$ using exch. rates)	0.95	0.82	0.94	1.05	1.17	1.25	1.36	42.8%
GDP (billion 2000 US$ using PPPs)	3.68	3.19	3.65	4.09	4.53	4.85	5.26	42.9%
Population (millions)	2.11	2.28	2.40	2.48	2.52	2.55	2.59	22.7%
CO$_2$ / TPES (t CO$_2$ per TJ)	88.4	88.1	88.3	87.3	87.1	87.8	86.8	-1.7%
CO$_2$ / GDP (kg CO$_2$ per 2000 US$)	13.34	12.22	9.37	8.53	7.90	7.69	7.49	-43.8%
CO$_2$ / GDP (kg CO$_2$ per 2000 US$ PPP)	3.44	3.15	2.41	2.20	2.04	1.98	1.93	-43.9%
CO$_2$ / population (t CO$_2$ per capita)	6.01	4.42	3.68	3.62	3.66	3.76	3.93	-34.7%

Ratios are based on the Sectoral Approach.

2006 CO$_2$ emissions by sector

million tonnes of CO$_2$	Coal/peat	Oil	Gas	Other *	Total	% change 90-06
Sectoral Approach	**8.29**	**1.86**	-	-	**10.15**	**-19.8%**
Main activity producer elec. and heat	6.56	0.12	-	-	6.69	2.9%
Unallocated autoproducers	-	-	-	-	-	-
Other energy industries	-	-	-	-	-	-
Manufacturing industries and construction	0.50	0.53	-	-	1.02	-63.4%
Transport	0.17	1.13	-	-	1.30	-14.6%
of which: road	-	0.91	-	-	0.91	-17.5%
Other sectors	1.05	0.08	-	-	1.13	-38.1%
of which: residential	0.49	-	-	-	0.49	-39.6%
Reference Approach	**8.29**	**1.86**	-	-	**10.15**	**-19.8%**
Diff. due to losses and/or transformation	-	-	-	-	-	
Statistical differences	-	-	-	-	-	
Memo: international marine bunkers	-	..	-	-	..	..
Memo: international aviation	-	0.13	-	-	0.13	925.0%

* Other includes industrial waste and non-renewable municipal waste.

Key sources for CO$_2$ emissions from fuel combustion in 2006

IPCC source category	CO$_2$ emissions (Mt of CO$_2$)	% change 90-06	Level assessment (%) **	Cumulative total (%)
Main activity prod. elec. and heat - coal/peat	6.56	6.3%	17.1	17.1
Road - oil	0.91	-17.5%	2.4	19.5
Non-specified other sectors - coal/peat	0.57	-39.0%	1.5	21.0
Manufacturing industries - oil	0.53	-18.7%	1.4	22.4
Manufacturing industries - coal/peat	0.50	-76.9%	1.3	23.7
Residential - coal/peat	0.49	-39.6%	1.3	24.9
Other transport - oil	0.22	-14.8%	0.6	25.5
Other transport - coal/peat	0.17	6.1%	0.5	26.0
Main activity prod. elec. and heat - oil	0.12	-61.9%	0.3	26.3
Non-specified other sectors - oil	0.08	-16.7%	0.2	26.5
-	-	-	-	-
Memo: total CO$_2$ from fuel combustion	10.15	-19.8%	26.5	26.5

** Percent calculated using the total GHG estimate for CO$_2$, CH$_4$, N$_2$O, HFCs, PFCs and SF$_6$ excluding CO$_2$ emissions/removals from land use change and forestry.

Morocco / Maroc

Figure 1. CO$_2$ emissions by fuel

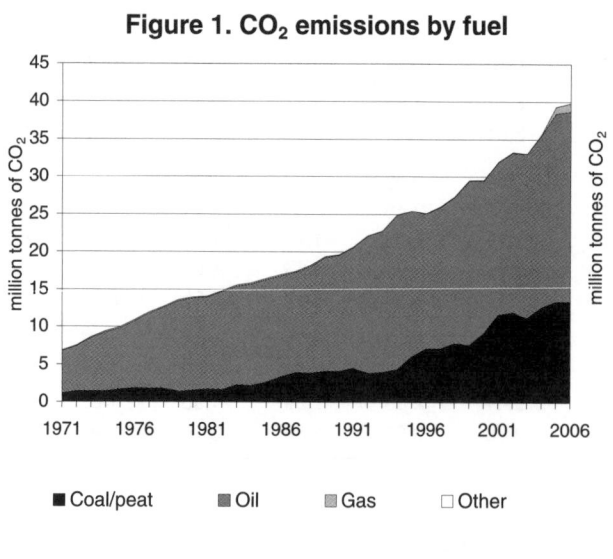

■ Coal/peat ■ Oil ▨ Gas □ Other

Figure 2. CO$_2$ emissions by sector

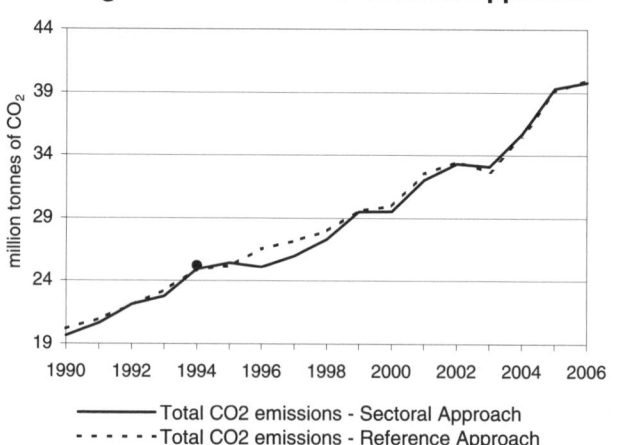

■ Electricity and heat □ Other energy industries
▨ Manuf. ind. and construction ▨ Transport
▨ Residential ■ Other

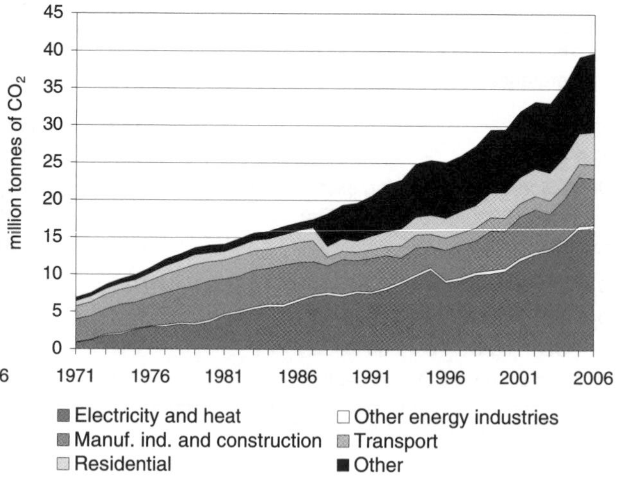

Figure 3. CO$_2$ emissions by sector

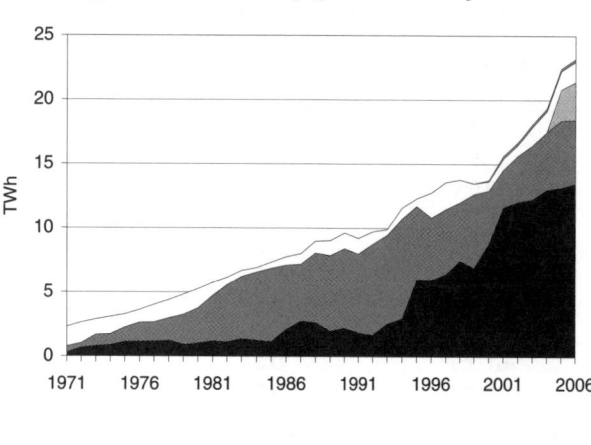

■ Electricity and heat □ Other energy industries
▨ Manuf. ind. and construction ▨ Transport
▨ Residential ■ Other

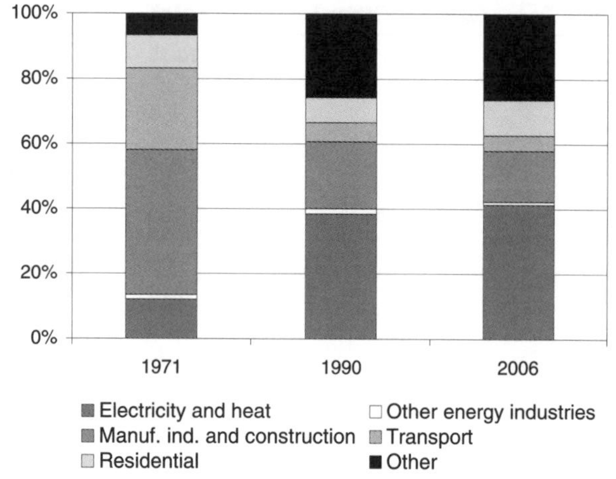

Figure 4. Reference vs Sectoral Approach

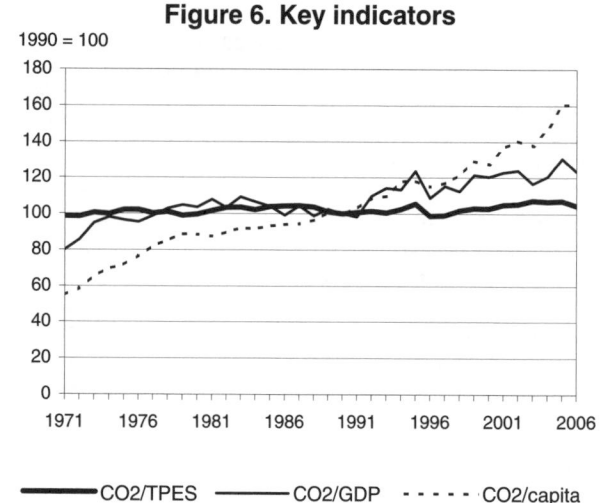

—— Total CO2 emissions - Sectoral Approach
- - - - Total CO2 emissions - Reference Approach
—●— UNFCCC database

Figure 5. Electricity generation by fuel

■ Coal/peat ■ Oil ▨ Gas □ Hydro ▨ Other

Figure 6. Key indicators

1990 = 100

—— CO2/TPES —— CO2/GDP - - - - CO2/capita

Morocco / Maroc

Key indicators

	1990	1995	2000	2003	2004	2005	2006	% change 90-06
CO$_2$ Sectoral Approach (Mt of CO$_2$)	19.64	25.43	29.53	33.10	35.68	39.32	39.80	102.6%
CO$_2$ Reference Approach (Mt of CO$_2$)	20.16	25.17	29.96	32.69	35.54	39.13	40.02	98.5%
TPES (PJ)	302	370	441	474	513	564	585	93.9%
TPES (Mtoe)	7.21	8.84	10.54	11.32	12.26	13.46	13.98	93.9%
GDP (billion 2000 US$ using exch. rates)	26.72	27.97	33.33	38.58	40.22	40.91	43.88	64.3%
GDP (billion 2000 US$ using PPPs)	80.70	84.49	100.68	116.54	121.48	123.57	132.55	64.3%
Population (millions)	24.17	26.44	28.47	29.52	29.84	30.14	30.50	26.2%
CO$_2$ / TPES (t CO$_2$ per TJ)	65.1	68.7	66.9	69.8	69.5	69.8	68.0	4.5%
CO$_2$ / GDP (kg CO$_2$ per 2000 US$)	0.74	0.91	0.89	0.86	0.89	0.96	0.91	23.4%
CO$_2$ / GDP (kg CO$_2$ per 2000 US$ PPP)	0.24	0.30	0.29	0.28	0.29	0.32	0.30	23.4%
CO$_2$ / population (t CO$_2$ per capita)	0.81	0.96	1.04	1.12	1.20	1.30	1.31	60.6%

Ratios are based on the Sectoral Approach.

2006 CO$_2$ emissions by sector

million tonnes of CO$_2$	Coal/peat	Oil	Gas	Other *	Total	% change 90-06
Sectoral Approach	**13.46**	**25.23**	**1.12**	-	**39.80**	**102.6%**
Main activity producer elec. and heat	11.47	1.81	0.99	-	14.27	120.0%
Unallocated autoproducers	-	2.15	-	-	2.15	104.1%
Other energy industries	-	0.38	-	-	0.38	19.0%
Manufacturing industries and construction	1.99	4.10	0.13	-	6.22	54.0%
Transport	-	1.87	-	-	1.87	59.9%
of which: road	-	*1.19*	-	-	*1.19*	*1.8%*
Other sectors	-	14.92	-	-	14.92	126.9%
of which: residential	-	*4.35*	-	-	*4.35*	*189.4%*
Reference Approach	**15.06**	**23.84**	**1.12**	-	**40.02**	**98.5%**
Diff. due to losses and/or transformation	-	0.35	-	-	0.35	
Statistical differences	1.60	- 1.73	-	-	- 0.14	
Memo: international marine bunkers	-	*0.04*	-	-	*0.04*	*-34.9%*
Memo: international aviation	-	*1.32*	-	-	*1.32*	*67.5%*

* Other includes industrial waste and non-renewable municipal waste.

Key sources for CO$_2$ emissions from fuel combustion in 2006

IPCC source category	CO$_2$ emissions (Mt of CO$_2$)	% change 90-06	Level assessment (%) **	Cumulative total (%)
Main activity prod. elec. and heat - coal/peat	11.47	317.3%	15.4	15.4
Non-specified other sectors - oil	10.56	108.3%	14.2	29.7
Residential - oil	4.35	189.4%	5.9	35.5
Manufacturing industries - oil	4.10	60.4%	5.5	41.0
Unallocated autoproducers - oil	2.15	104.1%	2.9	43.9
Manufacturing industries - coal/peat	1.99	44.1%	2.7	46.6
Main activity prod. elec. and heat - oil	1.81	-51.6%	2.4	49.0
Road - oil	1.19	1.8%	1.6	50.7
Main activity prod. elec. and heat - gas	0.99	x	1.3	52.0
Other transport - oil	0.68	x	0.9	52.9
Other energy industries - oil	0.38	19.0%	0.5	53.4
Memo: total CO$_2$ from fuel combustion	*39.80*	*102.6%*	*53.6*	*53.6*

** Percent calculated using the total GHG estimate for CO$_2$, CH$_4$, N$_2$O, HFCs, PFCs and SF$_6$ excluding CO$_2$ emissions/removals from land use change and forestry.

Mozambique

Figure 1. CO₂ emissions by fuel

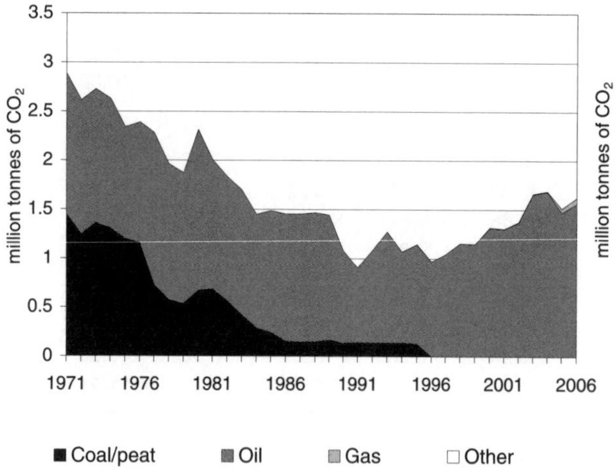

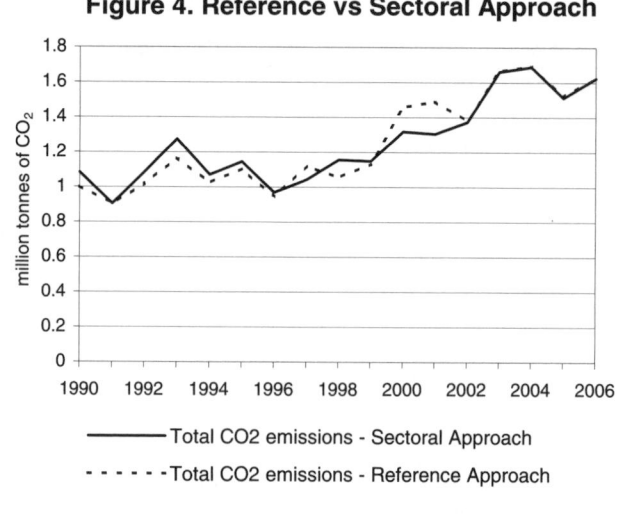

- Coal/peat
- Oil
- Gas
- Other

Figure 2. CO₂ emissions by sector

- Electricity and heat
- Other energy industries
- Manuf. ind. and construction
- Transport
- Residential
- Other

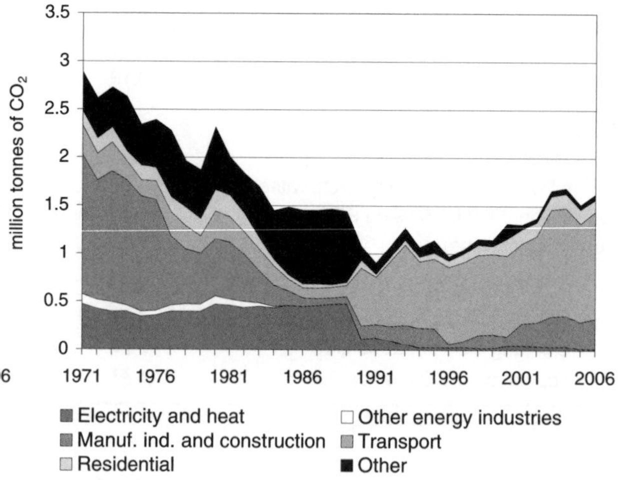

Figure 3. CO₂ emissions by sector

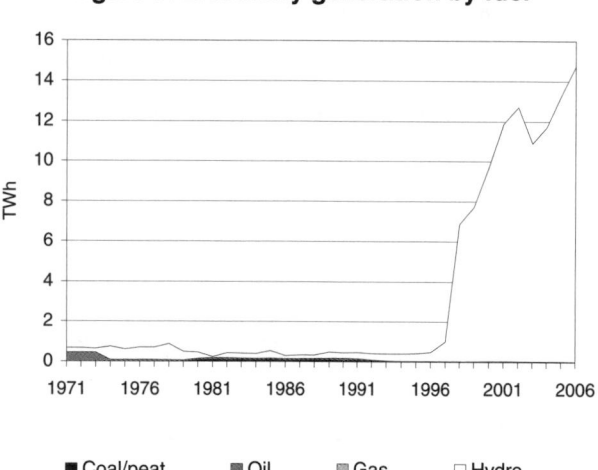

- Electricity and heat
- Other energy industries
- Manuf. ind. and construction
- Transport
- Residential
- Other

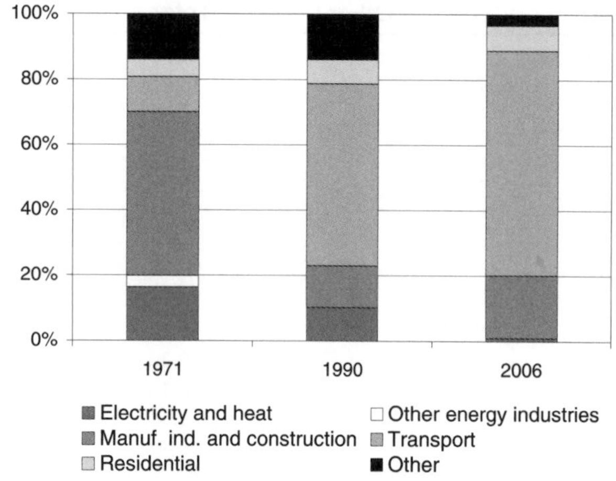

Figure 4. Reference vs Sectoral Approach

———— Total CO2 emissions - Sectoral Approach

- - - - - Total CO2 emissions - Reference Approach

Figure 5. Electricity generation by fuel

- Coal/peat
- Oil
- Gas
- Hydro

Figure 6. Key indicators

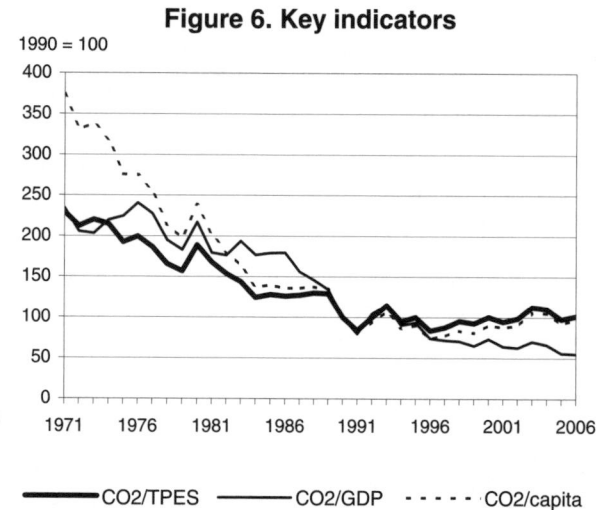

1990 = 100

———— CO2/TPES ———— CO2/GDP - - - - - CO2/capita

Mozambique

Key indicators

	1990	1995	2000	2003	2004	2005	2006	% change 90-06
CO$_2$ Sectoral Approach (Mt of CO$_2$)	1.08	1.14	1.32	1.66	1.69	1.51	1.62	50.0%
CO$_2$ Reference Approach (Mt of CO$_2$)	1.00	1.10	1.46	1.66	1.69	1.52	1.63	62.7%
TPES (PJ)	250	264	302	339	353	358	369	47.6%
TPES (Mtoe)	5.97	6.30	7.22	8.11	8.42	8.54	8.80	47.6%
GDP (billion 2000 US$ using exch. rates)	2.28	2.58	3.78	4.99	5.36	5.70	6.18	171.1%
GDP (billion 2000 US$ using PPPs)	8.64	9.77	14.31	18.90	20.31	21.58	23.41	171.2%
Population (millions)	13.54	15.94	18.19	19.61	20.08	20.53	20.97	54.8%
CO$_2$ / TPES (t CO$_2$ per TJ)	4.3	4.3	4.4	4.9	4.8	4.2	4.4	1.6%
CO$_2$ / GDP (kg CO$_2$ per 2000 US$)	0.48	0.44	0.35	0.33	0.31	0.27	0.26	-44.7%
CO$_2$ / GDP (kg CO$_2$ per 2000 US$ PPP)	0.13	0.12	0.09	0.09	0.08	0.07	0.07	-44.7%
CO$_2$ / population (t CO$_2$ per capita)	0.08	0.07	0.07	0.08	0.08	0.07	0.08	-3.3%

Ratios are based on the Sectoral Approach.

2006 CO$_2$ emissions by sector

million tonnes of CO$_2$	Coal/peat	Oil	Gas	Other *	Total	% change 90-06
Sectoral Approach	-	**1.56**	**0.07**	-	**1.62**	**50.0%**
Main activity producer elec. and heat	-	0.01	0.01	-	0.02	-86.3%
Unallocated autoproducers	-	-	-	-	-	-
Other energy industries	-	-	-	-	-	-
Manufacturing industries and construction	-	0.25	0.06	-	0.31	123.0%
Transport	-	1.12	-	-	1.12	85.4%
of which: road	-	*1.02*	-	-	*1.02*	*92.9%*
Other sectors	-	0.18	0.00	-	0.18	-21.6%
of which: residential	-	*0.12*	*0.00*	-	*0.12*	*54.5%*
Reference Approach	-	**1.56**	**0.07**	-	**1.63**	**62.7%**
Diff. due to losses and/or transformation	-	-	-	-	-	
Statistical differences	-	0.00	0.00	-	0.00	
Memo: international marine bunkers	-	*0.01*	-	-	*0.01*	*-89.3%*
Memo: international aviation	-	*0.17*	-	-	*0.17*	*31.7%*

* Other includes industrial waste and non-renewable municipal waste.

Key sources for CO$_2$ emissions from fuel combustion in 2006

IPCC source category	CO$_2$ emissions (Mt of CO$_2$)	% change 90-06	Level assessment (%) **	Cumulative total (%)
Road - oil	1.02	92.9%	4.3	4.3
Manufacturing industries - oil	0.25	315.0%	1.1	5.4
Residential - oil	0.12	54.3%	0.5	5.9
Other transport - oil	0.10	33.3%	0.4	6.3
Manufacturing industries - gas	0.06	x	0.3	6.6
Non-specified other sectors - oil	0.06	-62.2%	0.2	6.8
Main activity prod. elec. and heat - oil	0.01	-82.4%	0.0	6.8
Main activity prod. elec. and heat - gas	0.01	x	0.0	6.9
Residential - gas	0.00	x	0.0	6.9
Non-specified other sectors - gas	0.00	x	0.0	6.9
-	-	-	-	-
Memo: total CO$_2$ from fuel combustion	*1.62*	*50.0%*	*6.9*	*6.9*

** Percent calculated using the total GHG estimate for CO$_2$, CH$_4$, N$_2$O, HFCs, PFCs and SF$_6$ excluding CO$_2$ emissions/removals from land use change and forestry.

Myanmar

Figure 1. CO₂ emissions by fuel

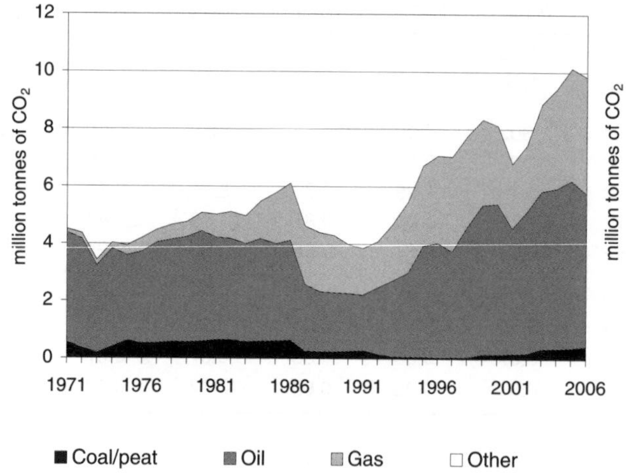

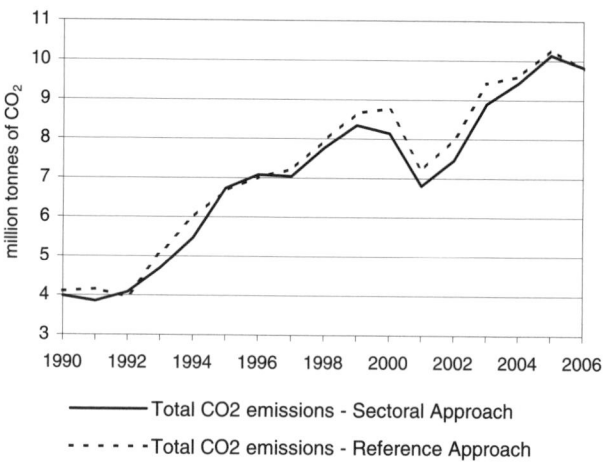

■ Coal/peat   ■ Oil   ■ Gas   □ Other

Figure 2. CO₂ emissions by sector

■ Electricity and heat   □ Other energy industries
■ Manuf. ind. and construction   ■ Transport
□ Residential   ■ Other

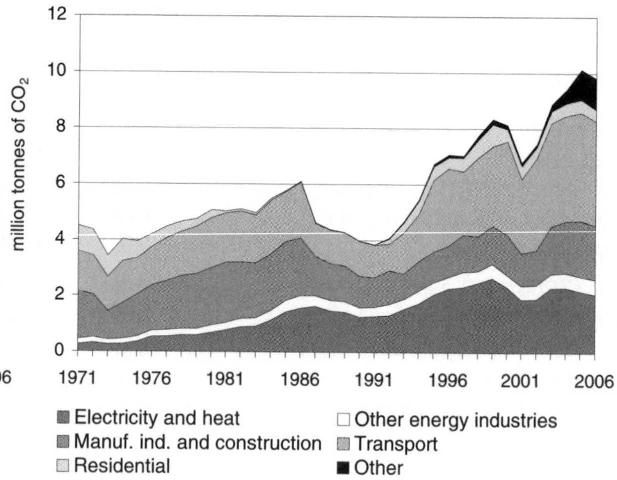

Figure 3. CO₂ emissions by sector

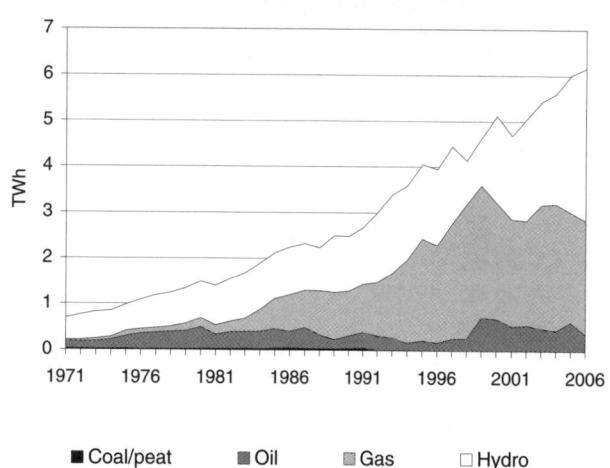

■ Electricity and heat   □ Other energy industries
■ Manuf. ind. and construction   ■ Transport
□ Residential   ■ Other

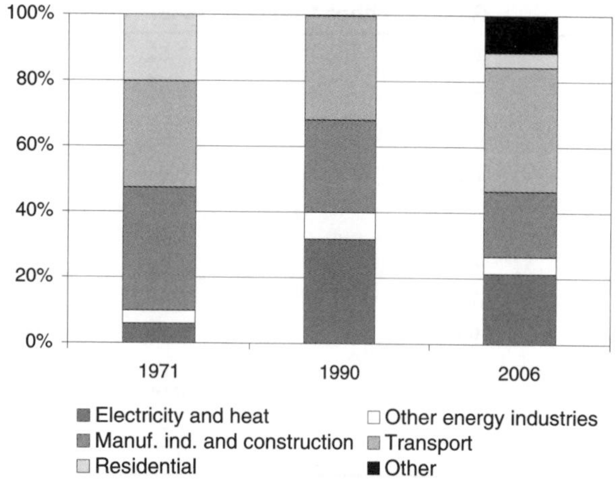

Figure 4. Reference vs Sectoral Approach

—— Total CO2 emissions - Sectoral Approach
- - - - - Total CO2 emissions - Reference Approach

Figure 5. Electricity generation by fuel

■ Coal/peat   ■ Oil   ■ Gas   □ Hydro

Figure 6. Key indicators

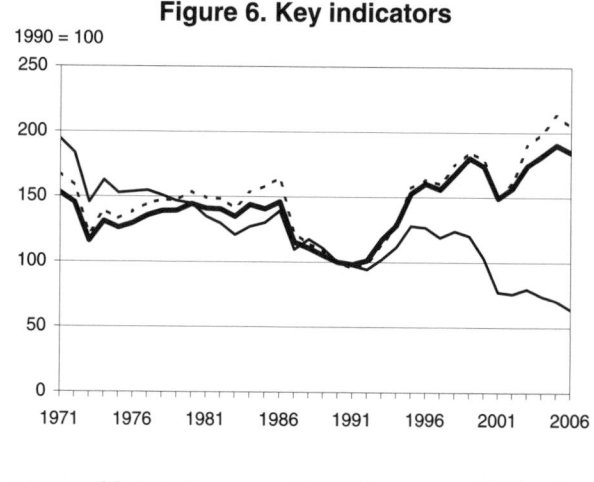

1990 = 100

—— CO2/TPES   —— CO2/GDP   - - - - CO2/capita

Myanmar
Key indicators

	1990	1995	2000	2003	2004	2005	2006	% change 90-06
CO_2 Sectoral Approach (Mt of CO_2)	3.98	6.73	8.13	8.89	9.43	10.14	9.83	146.9%
CO_2 Reference Approach (Mt of CO_2)	4.10	6.67	8.77	9.41	9.60	10.29	9.80	139.1%
TPES (PJ)	447	495	526	574	582	598	598	33.7%
TPES (Mtoe)	10.69	11.82	12.57	13.70	13.90	14.29	14.29	33.7%
GDP (billion 2000 US$ using exch. rates)	4.49	5.94	8.91	12.63	14.35	16.25	17.38	286.8%
GDP (billion 2000 US$ using PPPs)	27.18	35.89	53.85	76.39	86.78	98.24	105.11	286.8%
Population (millions)	40.15	43.13	45.88	47.17	47.57	47.97	48.38	20.5%
CO_2 / TPES (t CO_2 per TJ)	8.9	13.6	15.5	15.5	16.2	17.0	16.4	84.7%
CO_2 / GDP (kg CO_2 per 2000 US$)	0.89	1.13	0.91	0.70	0.66	0.62	0.57	-36.2%
CO_2 / GDP (kg CO_2 per 2000 US$ PPP)	0.15	0.19	0.15	0.12	0.11	0.10	0.09	-36.2%
CO_2 / population (t CO_2 per capita)	0.10	0.16	0.18	0.19	0.20	0.21	0.20	104.8%

Ratios are based on the Sectoral Approach.

2006 CO_2 emissions by sector

million tonnes of CO_2	Coal/peat	Oil	Gas	Other *	Total	% change 90-06
Sectoral Approach	**0.44**	**5.34**	**4.05**	**-**	**9.83**	**146.9%**
Main activity producer elec. and heat	-	0.29	1.80	-	2.08	65.1%
Unallocated autoproducers	-	-	-	-	-	-
Other energy industries	-	0.19	0.34	-	0.53	62.3%
Manufacturing industries and construction	0.34	0.53	1.07	-	1.94	73.8%
Transport	-	3.71	0.01	-	3.71	194.5%
of which: road	-	3.61	-	-	3.61	186.9%
Other sectors	0.10	0.62	0.84	-	1.56	+
of which: residential	-	0.43	-	-	0.43	+
Reference Approach	**0.44**	**5.31**	**4.05**	**-**	**9.80**	**139.1%**
Diff. due to losses and/or transformation	-	0.14	-	-	0.14	
Statistical differences	0.00	- 0.18	0.00	-	- 0.18	
Memo: international marine bunkers	-	0.01	-	-	0.01	x
Memo: international aviation	-	0.24	-	-	0.24	167.9%

* Other includes industrial waste and non-renewable municipal waste.

Key sources for CO_2 emissions from fuel combustion in 2006

IPCC source category	CO_2 emissions (Mt of CO_2)	% change 90-06	Level assessment (%) **	Cumulative total (%)
Road - oil	3.61	186.9%	3.7	3.7
Main activity prod. elec. and heat - gas	1.80	77.3%	1.8	5.5
Manufacturing industries - gas	1.07	136.2%	1.1	6.6
Non-specified other sectors - gas	0.84	x	0.9	7.5
Manufacturing industries - oil	0.53	19.0%	0.5	8.0
Residential - oil	0.43	+	0.4	8.5
Other energy industries - gas	0.34	43.7%	0.3	8.8
Manufacturing industries - coal/peat	0.34	56.7%	0.3	9.2
Main activity prod. elec. and heat - oil	0.29	42.9%	0.3	9.4
Other energy industries - oil	0.19	110.2%	0.2	9.6
Non-specified other sectors - oil	0.19	+	0.2	9.8
Memo: total CO_2 from fuel combustion	9.83	146.9%	10.0	10.0

** Percent calculated using the total GHG estimate for CO_2, CH_4, N_2O, HFCs, PFCs and SF_6 excluding CO_2 emissions/removals from land use change and forestry.

Namibia / Namibie

Figure 1. CO₂ emissions by fuel

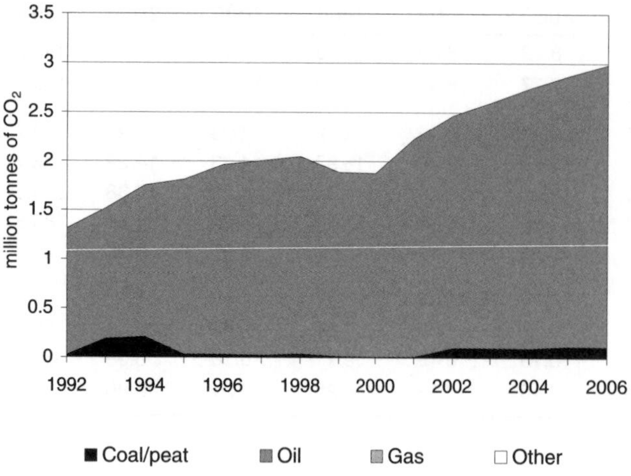

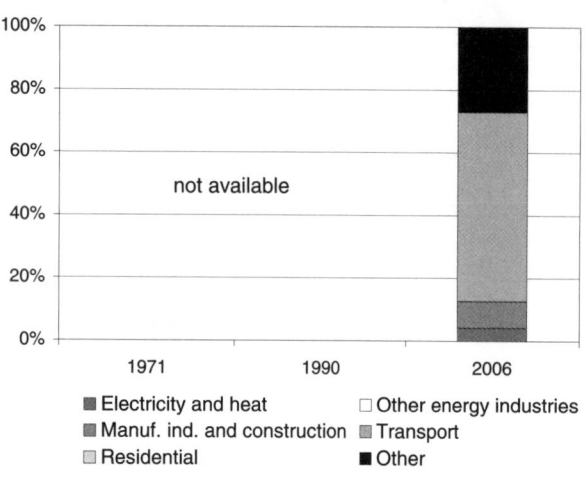

Figure 2. CO₂ emissions by sector

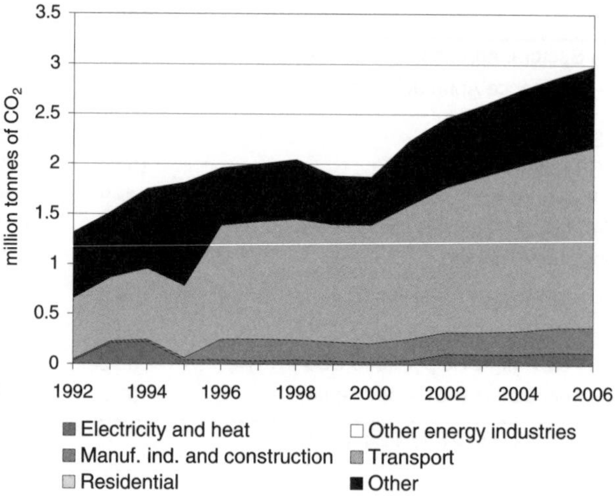

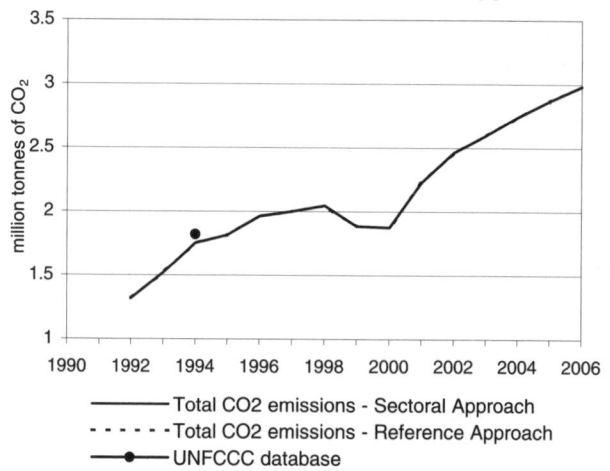

Figure 3. CO₂ emissions by sector

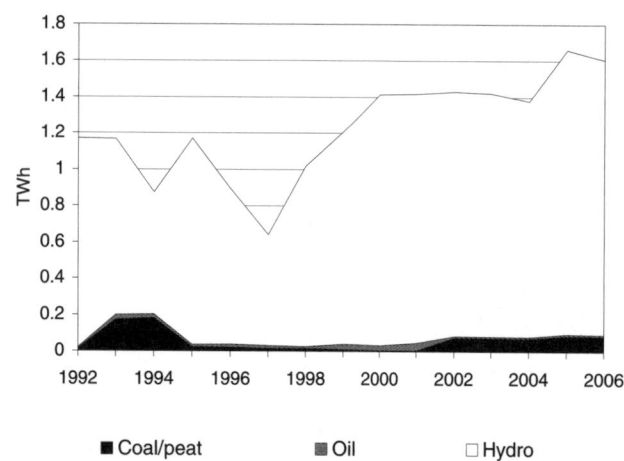

Figure 4. Reference vs Sectoral Approach

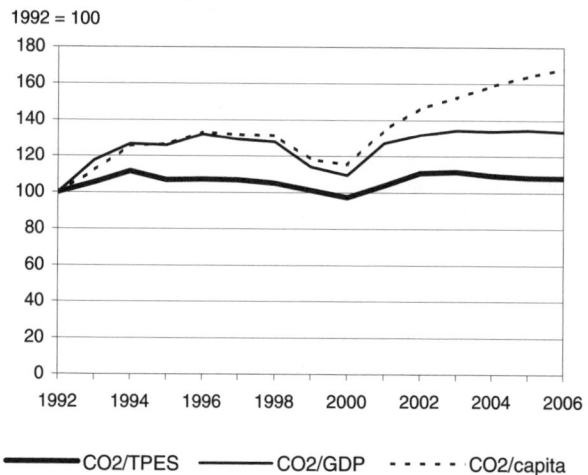

Figure 5. Electricity generation by fuel

Figure 6. Key indicators

Namibia / Namibie *

Key indicators

	1990	1995	2000	2003	2004	2005	2006	% change 90-06
CO$_2$ Sectoral Approach (Mt of CO$_2$)	..	1.81	1.87	2.60	2.74	2.87	2.98	..
CO$_2$ Reference Approach (Mt of CO$_2$)	..	1.81	1.87	2.60	2.74	2.87	2.98	..
TPES (PJ)	..	38	43	52	56	59	62	..
TPES (Mtoe)	..	0.91	1.03	1.25	1.34	1.42	1.48	..
GDP (billion 2000 US$ using exch. rates)	..	2.87	3.41	3.86	4.09	4.26	4.46	..
GDP (billion 2000 US$ using PPPs)	..	9.31	11.06	12.50	13.25	13.80	14.43	..
Population (millions)	..	1.66	1.88	1.97	1.99	2.02	2.05	..
CO$_2$ / TPES (t CO$_2$ per TJ)	..	47.7	43.4	49.7	48.8	48.3	48.3	..
CO$_2$ / GDP (kg CO$_2$ per 2000 US$)	..	0.63	0.55	0.67	0.67	0.67	0.67	..
CO$_2$ / GDP (kg CO$_2$ per 2000 US$ PPP)	..	0.19	0.17	0.21	0.21	0.21	0.21	..
CO$_2$ / population (t CO$_2$ per capita)	..	1.09	1.00	1.32	1.38	1.42	1.46	..

Ratios are based on the Sectoral Approach.
* Prior to 1991, data for Namibia were included in Other Africa.

2006 CO$_2$ emissions by sector

million tonnes of CO$_2$	Coal/peat	Oil	Gas	Other **	Total	% change 90-06
Sectoral Approach	**0.11**	**2.87**	-	-	**2.98**	..
Main activity producer elec. and heat	0.11	0.01	-	-	0.12	..
Unallocated autoproducers	-	-	-	-	-	..
Other energy industries	-	-	-	-	-	..
Manufacturing industries and construction	-	0.25	-	-	0.25	..
Transport	-	1.80	-	-	1.80	..
of which: road	-	*1.61*	-	-	*1.61*	..
Other sectors	-	0.81	-	-	0.81	..
of which: residential	-	-	-	-	-	..
Reference Approach	**0.11**	**2.87**	-	-	**2.98**	..
Diff. due to losses and/or transformation	-	-	-	-	-	
Statistical differences	-	-	-	-	-	
Memo: international marine bunkers	-	..	-	-	..	..
Memo: international aviation	-	..	-	-	..	..

** Other includes industrial waste and non-renewable municipal waste.

Key sources for CO$_2$ emissions from fuel combustion in 2006

IPCC source category	CO$_2$ emissions (Mt of CO$_2$)	% change 90-06	Level assessment (%) ***	Cumulative total (%)
Road - oil	1.61	..	13.5	13.5
Non-specified other sectors - oil	0.81	..	6.8	20.3
Manufacturing industries - oil	0.25	..	2.1	22.4
Other transport - oil	0.19	..	1.6	23.9
Main activity prod. elec. and heat - coal/peat	0.11	..	0.9	24.9
Main activity prod. elec. and heat - oil	0.01	..	0.1	25.0
-	-	..	-	-
-	-	..	-	-
-	-	..	-	-
-	-	..	-	-
-	-	..	-	-
Memo: total CO$_2$ from fuel combustion	2.98	..	25.0	25.0

*** Percent calculated using the total GHG estimate for CO$_2$, CH$_4$, N$_2$O, HFCs, PFCs and SF$_6$ excluding CO$_2$ emissions/removals from land use change and forestry.

Nepal / Népal

Figure 1. CO₂ emissions by fuel

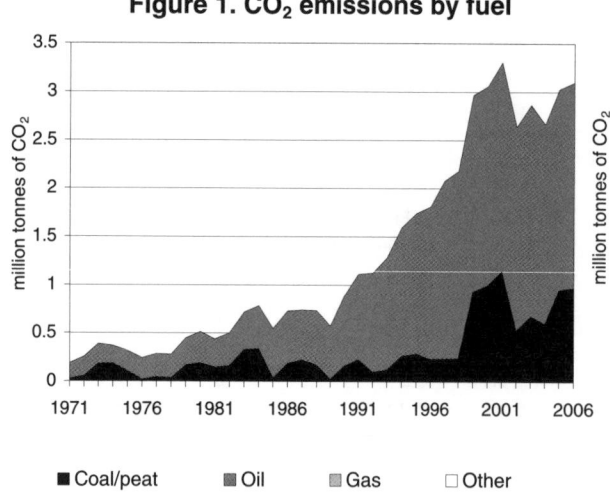

■ Coal/peat   ■ Oil   ■ Gas   □ Other

Figure 2. CO₂ emissions by sector

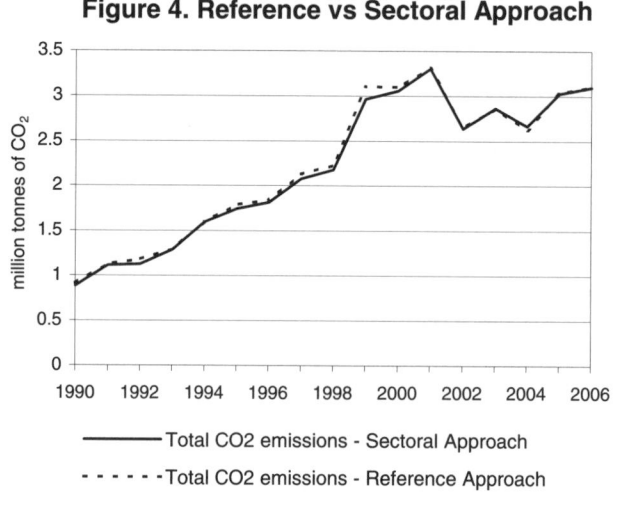

■ Electricity and heat   □ Other energy industries
■ Manuf. ind. and construction ■ Transport
□ Residential   ■ Other

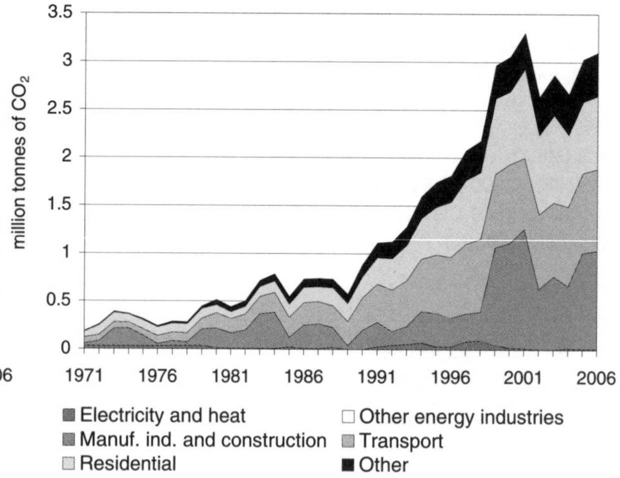

Figure 3. CO₂ emissions by sector

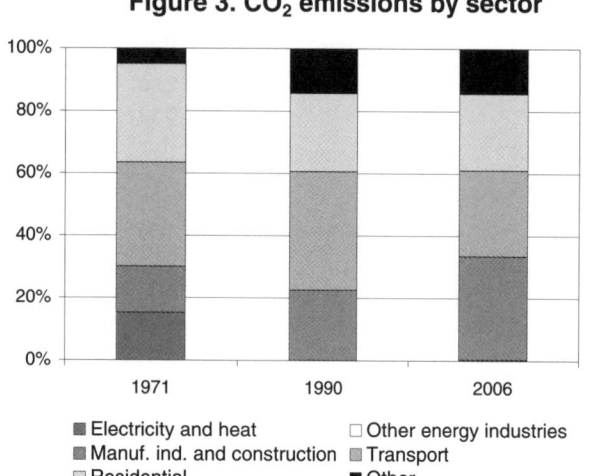

■ Electricity and heat   □ Other energy industries
■ Manuf. ind. and construction ■ Transport
□ Residential   ■ Other

Figure 4. Reference vs Sectoral Approach

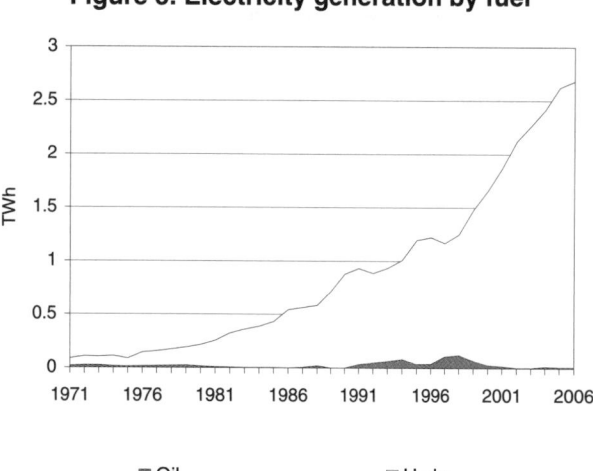

—— Total CO2 emissions - Sectoral Approach

- - - - Total CO2 emissions - Reference Approach

Figure 5. Electricity generation by fuel

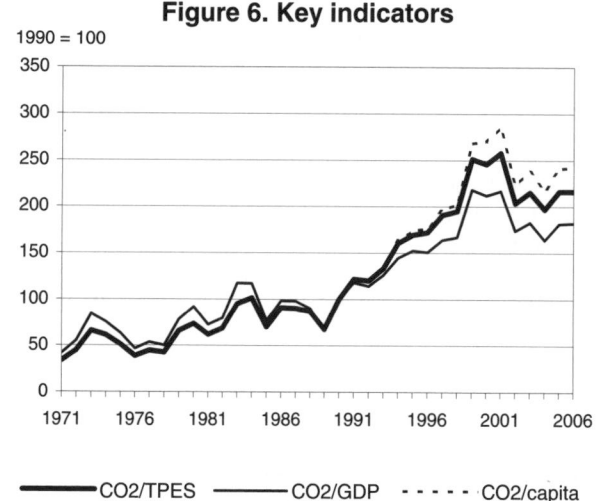

■ Oil   □ Hydro

Figure 6. Key indicators

1990 = 100

—— CO2/TPES   —— CO2/GDP   - - - - CO2/capita

Nepal / Népal

Key indicators

	1990	1995	2000	2003	2004	2005	2006	% change 90-06
CO$_2$ Sectoral Approach (Mt of CO$_2$)	0.88	1.74	3.06	2.87	2.67	3.03	3.10	250.5%
CO$_2$ Reference Approach (Mt of CO$_2$)	0.91	1.79	3.10	2.87	2.63	3.04	3.11	240.2%
TPES (PJ)	243	283	342	366	372	385	394	62.0%
TPES (Mtoe)	5.81	6.75	8.16	8.75	8.89	9.19	9.41	62.0%
GDP (billion 2000 US$ using exch. rates)	3.36	4.34	5.49	5.96	6.18	6.35	6.47	92.6%
GDP (billion 2000 US$ using PPPs)	19.81	25.59	32.38	35.15	36.45	37.44	38.14	92.5%
Population (millions)	19.11	21.67	24.42	26.02	26.55	27.09	27.64	44.6%
CO$_2$ / TPES (t CO$_2$ per TJ)	3.6	6.2	8.9	7.8	7.2	7.9	7.9	116.3%
CO$_2$ / GDP (kg CO$_2$ per 2000 US$)	0.26	0.40	0.56	0.48	0.43	0.48	0.48	82.0%
CO$_2$ / GDP (kg CO$_2$ per 2000 US$ PPP)	0.04	0.07	0.09	0.08	0.07	0.08	0.08	82.1%
CO$_2$ / population (t CO$_2$ per capita)	0.05	0.08	0.13	0.11	0.10	0.11	0.11	142.1%

Ratios are based on the Sectoral Approach.

2006 CO$_2$ emissions by sector

million tonnes of CO$_2$	Coal/peat	Oil	Gas	Other *	Total	% change 90-06
Sectoral Approach	**0.98**	**2.12**	-	-	**3.10**	**250.5%**
Main activity producer elec. and heat	-	0.01	-	-	0.01	x
Unallocated autoproducers	-	-	-	-	-	-
Other energy industries	-	-	-	-	-	-
Manufacturing industries and construction	0.97	0.05	-	-	1.03	413.1%
Transport	-	0.85	-	-	0.85	153.2%
of which: road	-	*0.85*	-	-	*0.85*	*153.2%*
Other sectors	0.00	1.21	-	-	1.21	247.6%
of which: residential	*0.00*	*0.76*	-	-	*0.77*	*245.6%*
Reference Approach	**0.98**	**2.13**	-	-	**3.11**	**240.2%**
Diff. due to losses and/or transformation	-	-	-	-	-	
Statistical differences	-	0.01	-	-	0.01	
Memo: international marine bunkers	-	-	-	-	-	-
Memo: international aviation	-	*0.19*	-	-	*0.19*	*293.3%*

* Other includes industrial waste and non-renewable municipal waste.

Key sources for CO$_2$ emissions from fuel combustion in 2006

IPCC source category	CO$_2$ emissions (Mt of CO$_2$)	% change 90-06	Level assessment (%) **	Cumulative total (%)
Manufacturing industries - coal/peat	0.97	497.1%	2.1	2.1
Road - oil	0.85	153.2%	1.8	3.9
Residential - oil	0.76	243.5%	1.6	5.5
Non-specified other sectors - oil	0.45	251.3%	1.0	6.5
Manufacturing industries - oil	0.05	43.9%	0.1	6.6
Main activity prod. elec. and heat - oil	0.01	x	0.0	6.6
Residential - coal/peat	0.00	x	0.0	6.6
-	-	-	-	-
-	-	-	-	-
-	-	-	-	-
-	-	-	-	-
Memo: total CO$_2$ from fuel combustion	*3.10*	*250.5%*	*6.6*	*6.6*

** Percent calculated using the total GHG estimate for CO$_2$, CH$_4$, N$_2$O, HFCs, PFCs and SF$_6$ excluding CO$_2$ emissions/removals from land use change and forestry.

Netherlands / Pays-Bas

Figure 1. CO$_2$ emissions by fuel

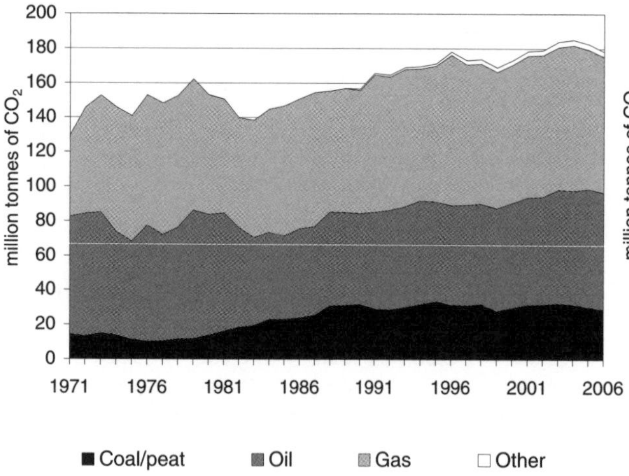

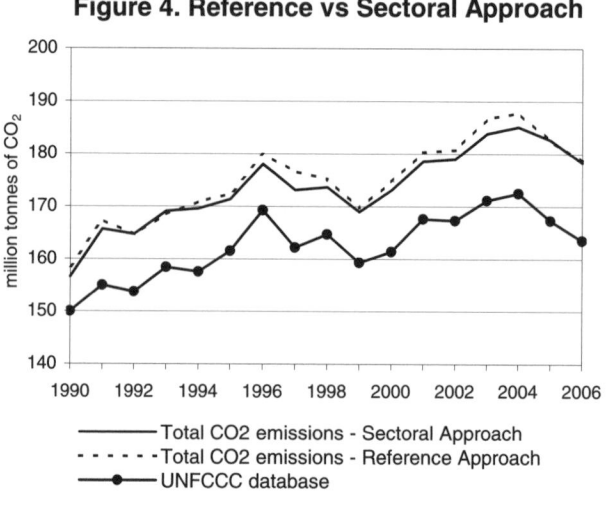

Figure 2. CO$_2$ emissions by sector

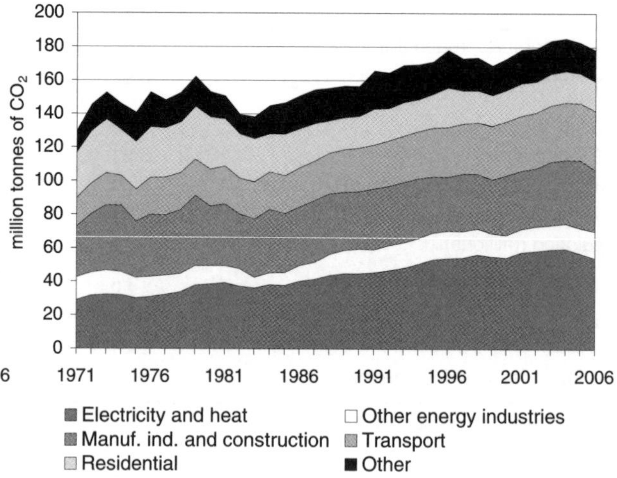

Figure 3. CO$_2$ emissions by sector

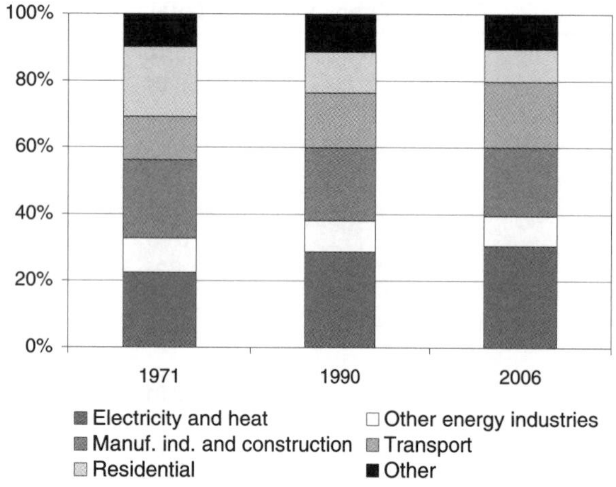

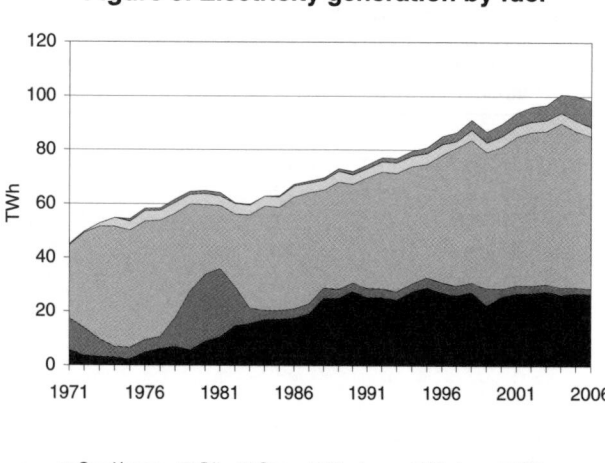

Figure 4. Reference vs Sectoral Approach

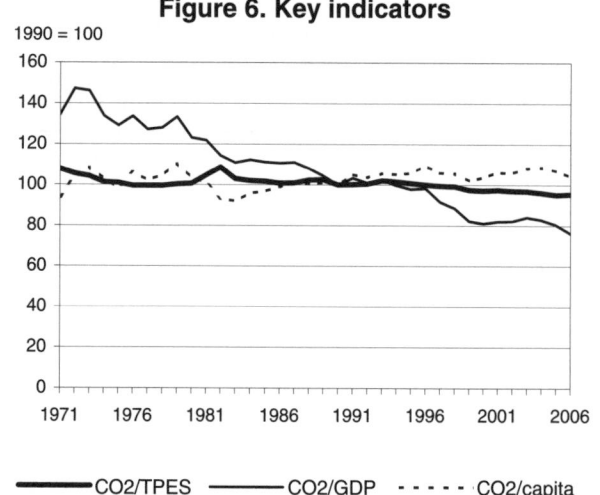

Figure 5. Electricity generation by fuel

Figure 6. Key indicators

Netherlands / Pays-Bas

Key indicators

	1990	1995	2000	2003	2004	2005	2006	% change 90-06
CO$_2$ Sectoral Approach (Mt of CO$_2$)	156.59	171.33	173.09	183.86	185.14	182.64	178.31	13.9%
CO$_2$ Reference Approach (Mt of CO$_2$)	158.50	172.32	174.75	186.74	187.82	182.57	178.66	12.7%
TPES (PJ)	2 810	3 058	3 199	3 409	3 461	3 449	3 354	19.4%
TPES (Mtoe)	67.12	73.03	76.40	81.41	82.66	82.38	80.12	19.4%
GDP (billion 2000 US$ using exch. rates)	282.00	315.80	385.10	394.10	402.90	409.00	421.30	49.4%
GDP (billion 2000 US$ using PPPs)	342.43	383.55	467.67	478.64	489.35	496.74	511.67	49.4%
Population (millions)	14.95	15.46	15.92	16.22	16.28	16.32	16.34	9.3%
CO$_2$ / TPES (t CO$_2$ per TJ)	55.7	56.0	54.1	53.9	53.5	53.0	53.2	-4.6%
CO$_2$ / GDP (kg CO$_2$ per 2000 US$)	0.56	0.54	0.45	0.47	0.46	0.45	0.42	-23.8%
CO$_2$ / GDP (kg CO$_2$ per 2000 US$ PPP)	0.46	0.45	0.37	0.38	0.38	0.37	0.35	-23.8%
CO$_2$ / population (t CO$_2$ per capita)	10.48	11.08	10.87	11.33	11.37	11.19	10.91	4.2%

Ratios are based on the Sectoral Approach.

2006 CO$_2$ emissions by sector

million tonnes of CO$_2$	Coal/peat	Oil	Gas	Other *	Total	% change 90-06
Sectoral Approach	**28.85**	**67.84**	**78.49**	**3.13**	**178.31**	**13.9%**
Main activity producer elec. and heat	23.76	0.33	22.27	-	46.36	22.9%
Unallocated autoproducers	0.09	1.31	3.43	3.13	7.95	12.3%
Other energy industries	0.50	12.18	3.37	-	16.05	8.6%
Manufacturing industries and construction	4.39	15.91	16.28	-	36.58	7.3%
Transport	-	35.22	0.00	-	35.22	36.2%
of which: road	*-*	*34.06*	*0.00*	*-*	*34.06*	*38.2%*
Other sectors	0.12	2.87	33.15	-	36.14	-2.5%
of which: residential	*0.03*	*0.26*	*17.22*	*-*	*17.51*	*-8.7%*
Reference Approach	**29.78**	**67.35**	**78.39**	**3.13**	**178.66**	**12.7%**
Diff. due to losses and/or transformation	0.93	- 0.03	- 0.10	-	0.81	
Statistical differences	- 0.00	- 0.45	0.00	0.00	- 0.45	
Memo: international marine bunkers	*-*	*55.26*	*-*	*-*	*55.26*	*61.1%*
Memo: international aviation	*-*	*10.81*	*-*	*-*	*10.81*	*151.8%*

* Other includes industrial waste and non-renewable municipal waste.

Key sources for CO$_2$ emissions from fuel combustion in 2006

IPCC source category	CO$_2$ emissions (Mt of CO$_2$)	% change 90-06	Level assessment (%) **	Cumulative total (%)
Road - oil	34.06	38.2%	15.3	15.3
Main activity prod. elec. and heat - coal/peat	23.76	-3.4%	10.7	26.0
Main activity prod. elec. and heat - gas	22.27	71.8%	10.0	36.0
Residential - gas	17.22	-6.3%	7.7	43.8
Manufacturing industries - gas	16.28	-13.4%	7.3	51.1
Non-specified other sectors - gas	15.92	7.4%	7.2	58.3
Manufacturing industries - oil	15.91	70.2%	7.2	65.4
Other energy industries - oil	12.18	4.0%	5.5	70.9
Manufacturing industries - coal/peat	4.39	-26.2%	2.0	72.9
Unallocated autoproducers - gas	3.43	-6.1%	1.5	74.4
Other energy industries - gas	3.37	41.5%	1.5	75.9
Memo: total CO$_2$ from fuel combustion	*178.31*	*13.9%*	*80.2*	*80.2*

** Percent calculated using the total GHG estimate for CO$_2$, CH$_4$, N$_2$O, HFCs, PFCs and SF$_6$ excluding CO$_2$ emissions/removals from land use change and forestry.

Netherlands Antilles / Antilles néerlandaises

Figure 1. CO₂ emissions by fuel

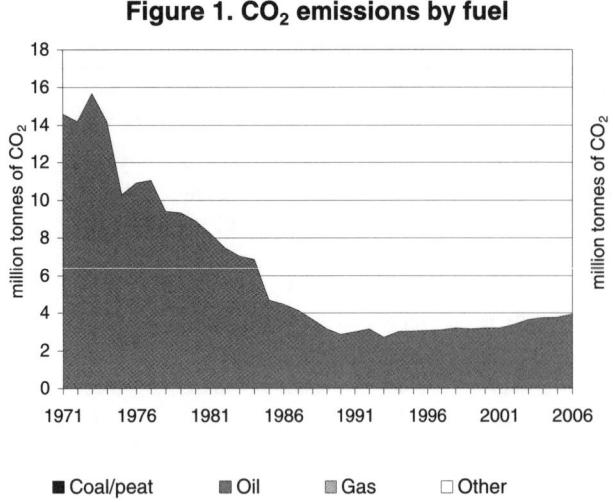

■ Coal/peat   ■ Oil   ▨ Gas   □ Other

Figure 2. CO₂ emissions by sector

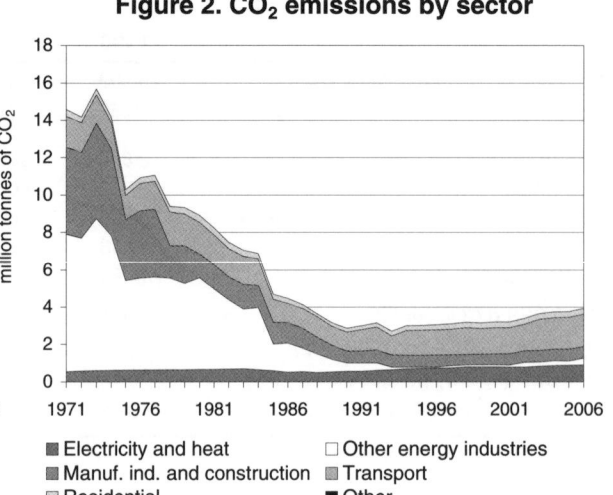

■ Electricity and heat   □ Other energy industries
■ Manuf. ind. and construction   ▨ Transport
▨ Residential   ■ Other

Figure 3. CO₂ emissions by sector

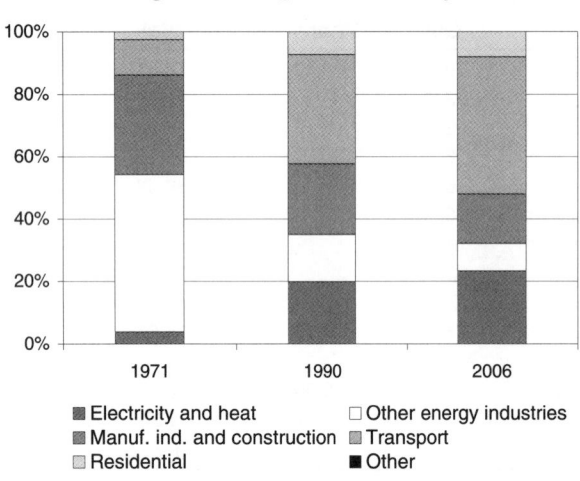

■ Electricity and heat   □ Other energy industries
■ Manuf. ind. and construction   ▨ Transport
▨ Residential   ■ Other

Figure 4. Reference vs Sectoral Approach

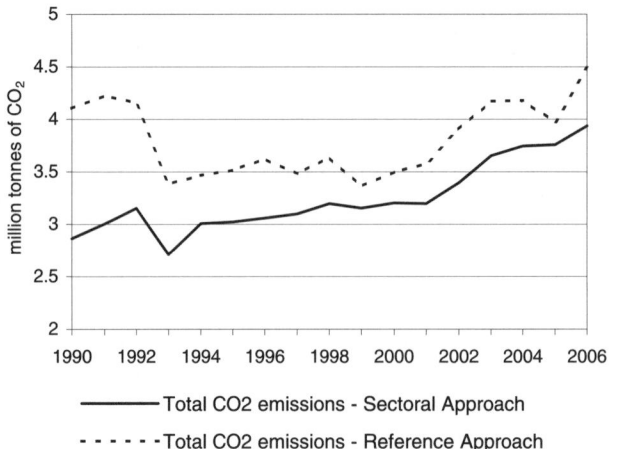

——— Total CO2 emissions - Sectoral Approach
- - - - - Total CO2 emissions - Reference Approach

Figure 5. Electricity generation by fuel

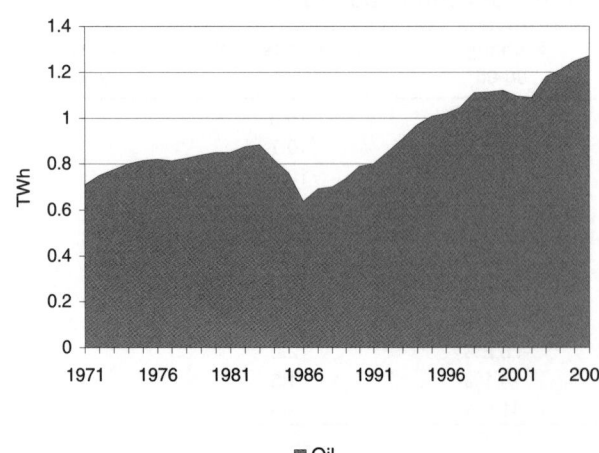

▨ Oil

Figure 6. Key indicators

1990 = 100

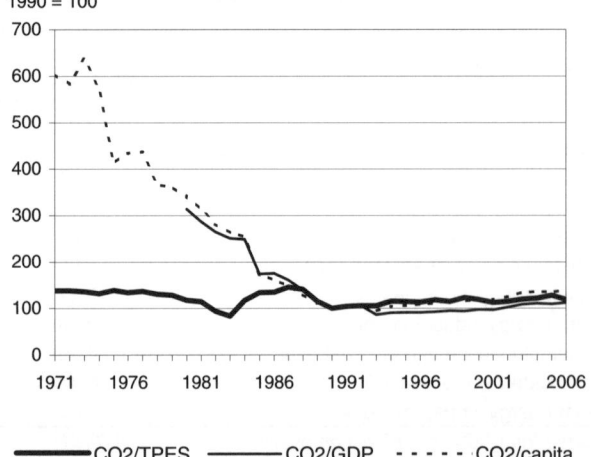

——CO2/TPES   ——CO2/GDP   - - - - CO2/capita

Netherlands Antilles / Antilles néerlandaises

Key indicators

	1990	1995	2000	2003	2004	2005	2006	% change 90-06
CO$_2$ Sectoral Approach (Mt of CO$_2$)	2.86	3.02	3.20	3.65	3.74	3.76	3.93	37.3%
CO$_2$ Reference Approach (Mt of CO$_2$) *	4.10	3.51	3.50	4.17	4.18	3.97	4.49	9.3%
TPES (PJ)	63	58	59	67	68	64	72	15.5%
TPES (Mtoe)	1.50	1.38	1.41	1.61	1.62	1.54	1.73	15.5%
GDP (billion 2000 US$ using exch. rates)	1.05	1.22	1.20	1.23	1.25	1.26	1.29	22.6%
GDP (billion 2000 US$ using PPPs)	2.36	2.74	2.71	2.77	2.80	2.84	2.89	22.6%
Population (millions)	0.19	0.19	0.18	0.18	0.18	0.19	0.19	-1.0%
CO$_2$ / TPES (t CO$_2$ per TJ)	45.7	52.3	54.3	54.3	55.3	58.3	54.3	18.9%
CO$_2$ / GDP (kg CO$_2$ per 2000 US$)	2.73	2.48	2.66	2.96	3.01	2.97	3.06	12.0%
CO$_2$ / GDP (kg CO$_2$ per 2000 US$ PPP)	1.21	1.10	1.18	1.32	1.34	1.32	1.36	12.0%
CO$_2$ / population (t CO$_2$ per capita)	15.00	15.83	17.69	20.07	20.34	20.19	20.81	38.8%

Ratios are based on the Sectoral Approach.

* The Reference Approach in 1990 overstates emissions since data for lubricants and bitumen (which store carbon) are not available.

2006 CO$_2$ emissions by sector

million tonnes of CO$_2$	Coal/peat	Oil	Gas	Other **	Total	% change 90-06
Sectoral Approach	-	**3.93**	-	-	**3.93**	37.3%
Main activity producer elec. and heat	-	0.45	-	-	0.45	61.1%
Unallocated autoproducers	-	0.46	-	-	0.46	60.6%
Other energy industries	-	0.35	-	-	0.35	-19.2%
Manufacturing industries and construction	-	0.62	-	-	0.62	-3.6%
Transport	-	1.73	-	-	1.73	72.2%
of which: road	-	*1.47*	-	-	*1.47*	*66.1%*
Other sectors	-	0.32	-	-	0.32	50.7%
of which: residential	-	*0.32*	-	-	*0.32*	*50.7%*
Reference Approach *	-	**4.49**	-	-	**4.49**	9.3%
Diff. due to losses and/or transformation	-	0.22	-	-	0.22	
Statistical differences	-	0.33	-	-	0.33	
Memo: international marine bunkers	-	*5.34*	-	-	*5.34*	*3.1%*
Memo: international aviation	-	*..*	-	-	*..*	*..*

** Other includes industrial waste and non-renewable municipal waste.

Key sources for CO$_2$ emissions from fuel combustion in 2006

IPCC source category	CO$_2$ emissions (Mt of CO$_2$)	% change 90-06	Level assessment (%) ***	Cumulative total (%)
Road - oil	1.47	66.1%	35.9	35.9
Manufacturing industries - oil	0.62	-3.6%	15.2	51.1
Unallocated autoproducers - oil	0.46	60.6%	11.3	62.4
Main activity prod. elec. and heat - oil	0.45	61.1%	10.9	73.3
Other energy industries - oil	0.35	-19.2%	8.6	81.9
Residential - oil	0.32	50.7%	7.7	89.6
Other transport - oil	0.26	118.5%	6.2	95.8
-	-	-	-	-
-	-	-	-	-
-	-	-	-	-
-	-	-	-	-
Memo: total CO$_2$ from fuel combustion	*3.93*	*37.3%*	*95.8*	*95.8*

*** Percent calculated using the total GHG estimate for CO$_2$, CH$_4$, N$_2$O, HFCs, PFCs and SF$_6$ excluding CO$_2$ emissions/removals from land use change and forestry.

New Zealand / Nouvelle-Zélande

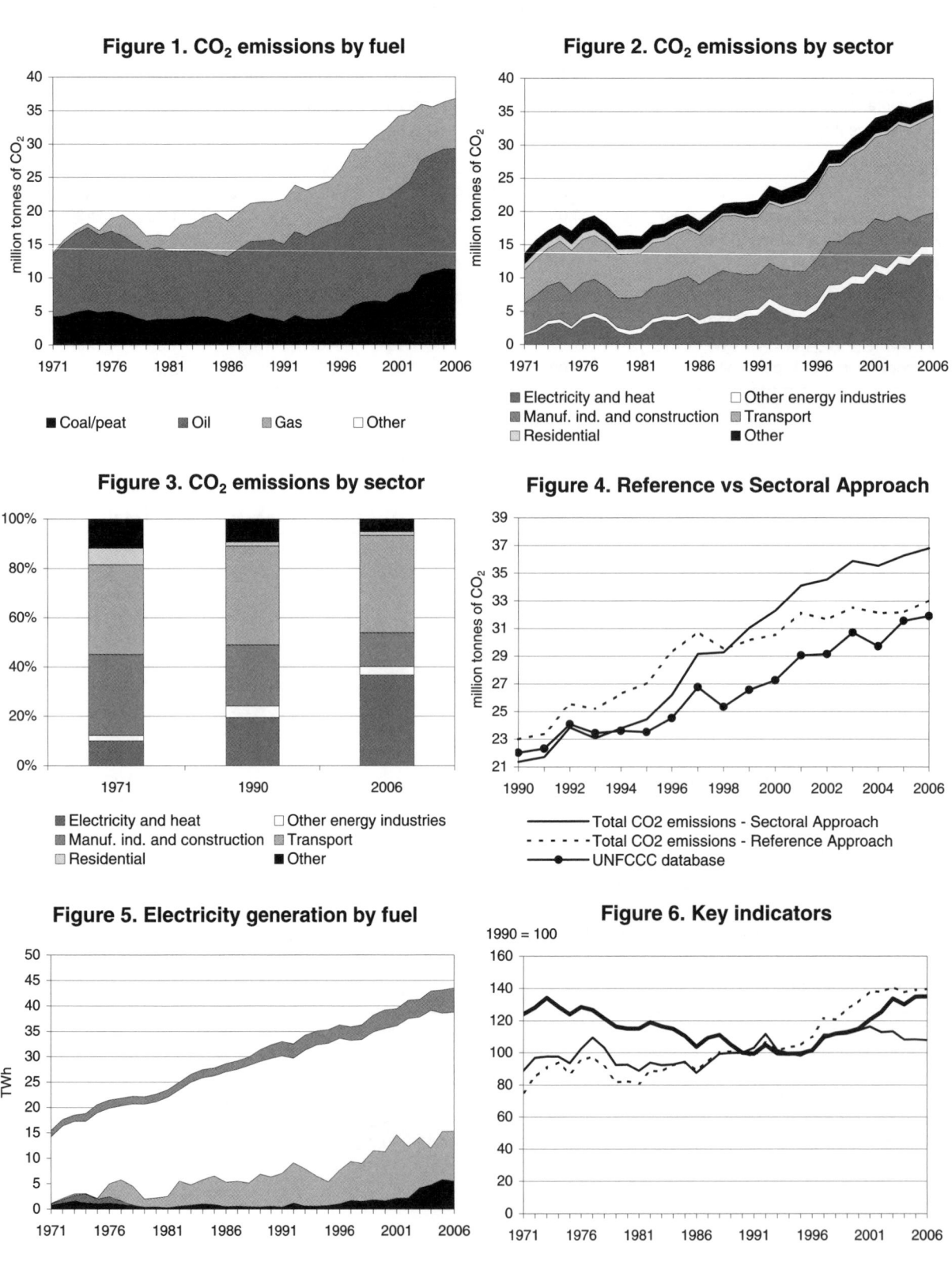

Figure 1. CO_2 emissions by fuel

■ Coal/peat ■ Oil ■ Gas □ Other

Figure 2. CO_2 emissions by sector

■ Electricity and heat □ Other energy industries
■ Manuf. ind. and construction ■ Transport
□ Residential ■ Other

Figure 3. CO_2 emissions by sector

■ Electricity and heat □ Other energy industries
■ Manuf. ind. and construction ■ Transport
□ Residential ■ Other

Figure 4. Reference vs Sectoral Approach

—— Total CO2 emissions - Sectoral Approach
- - - - Total CO2 emissions - Reference Approach
—●— UNFCCC database

Figure 5. Electricity generation by fuel

■ Coal/peat ■ Oil ■ Gas □ Hydro ■ Other

Figure 6. Key indicators

1990 = 100

—— CO2/TPES —— CO2/GDP - - - - CO2/capita

New Zealand / Nouvelle-Zélande

Key indicators

	1990	1995	2000	2003	2004	2005	2006	% change 90-06
CO$_2$ Sectoral Approach (Mt of CO$_2$)	21.37	24.42	32.27	35.90	35.54	36.27	36.80	72.2%
CO$_2$ Reference Approach (Mt of CO$_2$)	22.99	27.07	30.54	32.53	32.12	32.15	33.02	43.6%
TPES (PJ)	576	662	758	724	737	724	734	27.5%
TPES (Mtoe)	13.76	15.82	18.09	17.29	17.60	17.30	17.54	27.5%
GDP (billion 2000 US$ using exch. rates)	39.80	46.40	52.70	59.00	61.20	62.40	63.60	59.8%
GDP (billion 2000 US$ using PPPs)	60.57	70.59	80.11	89.76	93.07	94.92	96.72	59.7%
Population (millions)	3.36	3.68	3.86	4.01	4.06	4.10	4.14	23.2%
CO$_2$ / TPES (t CO$_2$ per TJ)	37.1	36.9	42.6	49.6	48.2	50.1	50.1	35.1%
CO$_2$ / GDP (kg CO$_2$ per 2000 US$)	0.54	0.53	0.61	0.61	0.58	0.58	0.58	7.7%
CO$_2$ / GDP (kg CO$_2$ per 2000 US$ PPP)	0.35	0.35	0.40	0.40	0.38	0.38	0.38	7.8%
CO$_2$ / population (t CO$_2$ per capita)	6.36	6.64	8.36	8.95	8.75	8.84	8.88	39.7%

Ratios are based on the Sectoral Approach.

2006 CO$_2$ emissions by sector

million tonnes of CO$_2$	Coal/peat	Oil	Gas	Other *	Total	% change 90-06
Sectoral Approach	**11.27**	**18.06**	**7.47**	-	**36.80**	**72.2%**
Main activity producer elec. and heat	4.82	0.02	3.93	-	8.77	163.1%
Unallocated autoproducers	4.36	-	0.37	-	4.72	483.0%
Other energy industries	-	1.01	0.26	-	1.26	25.9%
Manufacturing industries and construction	1.51	1.32	2.21	-	5.05	-4.6%
Transport	-	14.49	0.01	-	14.50	68.8%
of which: road	-	12.98	0.01	-	12.99	72.3%
Other sectors	0.58	1.22	0.69	-	2.49	6.0%
of which: residential	0.06	0.15	0.35	-	0.56	62.0%
Reference Approach	**8.26**	**17.48**	**7.28**	-	**33.02**	**43.6%**
Diff. due to losses and/or transformation	- 2.69	0.09	0.04	-	- 2.56	
Statistical differences	- 0.31	- 0.67	- 0.23	-	- 1.21	
Memo: international marine bunkers	-	0.95	-	-	0.95	-8.8%
Memo: international aviation	-	2.40	-	-	2.40	77.6%

* Other includes industrial waste and non-renewable municipal waste.

Key sources for CO$_2$ emissions from fuel combustion in 2006

IPCC source category	CO$_2$ emissions (Mt of CO$_2$)	% change 90-06	Level assessment (%) **	Cumulative total (%)
Road - oil	12.98	75.2%	15.7	15.7
Main activity prod. elec. and heat - coal/peat	4.82	901.8%	5.8	21.5
Unallocated autoproducers - coal/peat	4.36	460.7%	5.3	26.8
Main activity prod. elec. and heat - gas	3.93	38.3%	4.8	31.5
Manufacturing industries - gas	2.21	6.9%	2.7	34.2
Manufacturing industries - coal/peat	1.51	-29.8%	1.8	36.0
Other transport - oil	1.51	44.0%	1.8	37.9
Manufacturing industries - oil	1.32	24.3%	1.6	39.5
Non-specified other sectors - oil	1.06	-24.2%	1.3	40.7
Other energy industries - oil	1.01	22.4%	1.2	42.0
Non-specified other sectors - coal/peat	0.52	47.4%	0.6	42.6
Memo: total CO$_2$ from fuel combustion	36.80	72.2%	44.5	44.5

** Percent calculated using the total GHG estimate for CO$_2$, CH$_4$, N$_2$O, HFCs, PFCs and SF$_6$ excluding CO$_2$ emissions/removals from land use change and forestry.

Nicaragua

Figure 1. CO₂ emissions by fuel

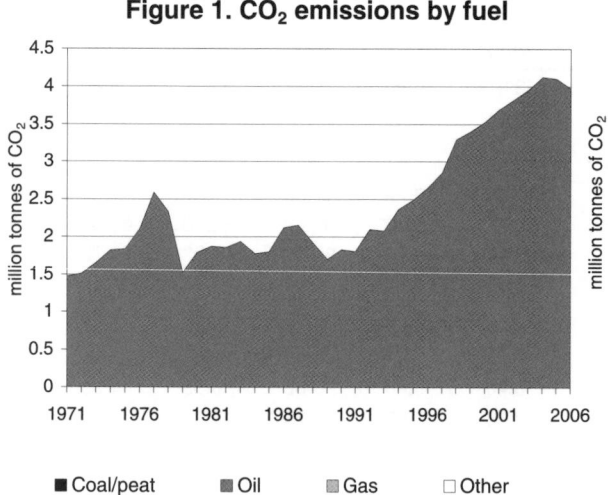

■ Coal/peat   ■ Oil   ■ Gas   □ Other

Figure 2. CO₂ emissions by sector

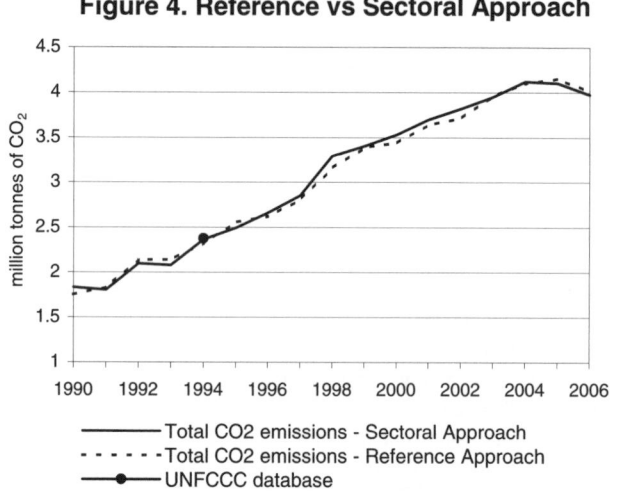

■ Electricity and heat   □ Other energy industries
■ Manuf. ind. and construction   ■ Transport
□ Residential   ■ Other

Figure 3. CO₂ emissions by sector

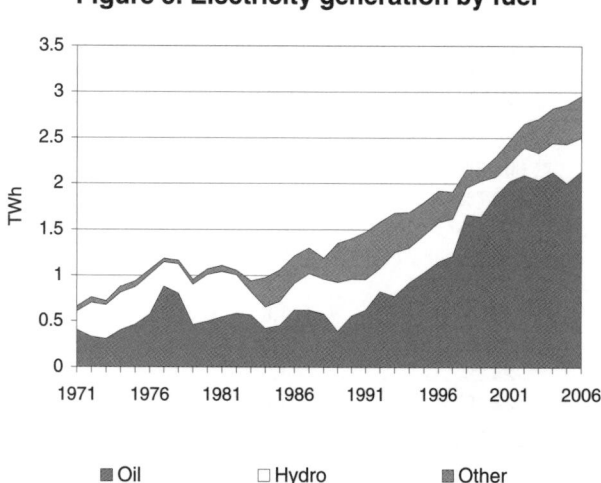

■ Electricity and heat   □ Other energy industries
■ Manuf. ind. and construction   ■ Transport
□ Residential   ■ Other

Figure 4. Reference vs Sectoral Approach

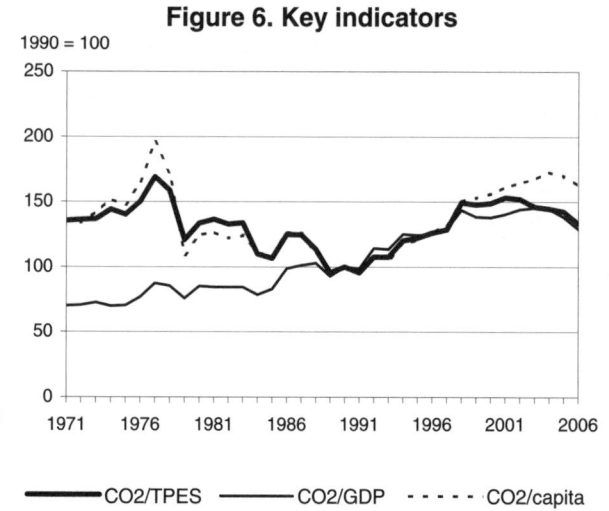

—— Total CO2 emissions - Sectoral Approach
- - - - Total CO2 emissions - Reference Approach
—●— UNFCCC database

Figure 5. Electricity generation by fuel

■ Oil   □ Hydro   ■ Other

Figure 6. Key indicators

1990 = 100

━━ CO2/TPES   —— CO2/GDP   - - - - CO2/capita

Nicaragua
Key indicators

	1990	1995	2000	2003	2004	2005	2006	% change 90-06
CO$_2$ Sectoral Approach (Mt of CO$_2$)	1.83	2.49	3.53	3.95	4.12	4.10	3.98	117.1%
CO$_2$ Reference Approach (Mt of CO$_2$)	1.75	2.55	3.44	3.97	4.10	4.15	4.02	129.7%
TPES (PJ)	89	99	115	131	138	140	145	62.9%
TPES (Mtoe)	2.12	2.36	2.75	3.13	3.30	3.34	3.45	62.9%
GDP (billion 2000 US$ using exch. rates)	2.82	3.08	3.94	4.19	4.40	4.58	4.75	68.3%
GDP (billion 2000 US$ using PPPs)	11.04	12.06	15.41	16.39	17.23	17.92	18.58	68.3%
Population (millions)	4.14	4.66	5.11	5.33	5.39	5.46	5.53	33.6%
CO$_2$ / TPES (t CO$_2$ per TJ)	20.7	25.2	30.7	30.2	29.9	29.4	27.5	33.2%
CO$_2$ / GDP (kg CO$_2$ per 2000 US$)	0.65	0.81	0.90	0.94	0.94	0.90	0.84	29.0%
CO$_2$ / GDP (kg CO$_2$ per 2000 US$ PPP)	0.17	0.21	0.23	0.24	0.24	0.23	0.21	29.0%
CO$_2$ / population (t CO$_2$ per capita)	0.44	0.53	0.69	0.74	0.76	0.75	0.72	62.5%

Ratios are based on the Sectoral Approach.

2006 CO$_2$ emissions by sector

million tonnes of CO$_2$	Coal/peat	Oil	Gas	Other *	Total	% change 90-06
Sectoral Approach	-	**3.98**	-	-	**3.98**	**117.1%**
Main activity producer elec. and heat	-	1.63	-	-	1.63	236.2%
Unallocated autoproducers	..	..	..	..	..	..
Other energy industries	-	-	-	-	-	-100.0%
Manufacturing industries and construction	-	0.53	-	-	0.53	60.7%
Transport	-	1.46	-	-	1.46	98.2%
of which: road	-	*1.42*	-	-	*1.42*	*102.6%*
Other sectors	-	0.36	-	-	0.36	76.6%
of which: residential	-	*0.09*	-	-	*0.09*	*76.0%*
Reference Approach	-	**4.02**	-	-	**4.02**	**129.7%**
Diff. due to losses and/or transformation	-	- 0.03	-	-	- 0.03	
Statistical differences	-	0.07	-	-	0.07	
Memo: international marine bunkers	-	*..*	-	-	*..*	*..*
Memo: international aviation	-	*0.05*	-	-	*0.05*	*-34.6%*

* Other includes industrial waste and non-renewable municipal waste.

Key sources for CO$_2$ emissions from fuel combustion in 2006

IPCC source category	CO$_2$ emissions (Mt of CO$_2$)	% change 90-06	Level assessment (%) **	Cumulative total (%)
Main activity prod. elec. and heat - oil	1.63	236.2%	11.7	11.7
Road - oil	1.42	102.6%	10.2	21.8
Manufacturing industries - oil	0.53	60.7%	3.8	25.6
Non-specified other sectors - oil	0.28	76.8%	2.0	27.6
Residential - oil	0.09	76.0%	0.6	28.2
Other transport - oil	0.04	16.1%	0.3	28.5
-	-	-	-	-
-	-	-	-	-
-	-	-	-	-
-	-	-	-	-
-	-	-	-	-
Memo: total CO$_2$ from fuel combustion	*3.98*	*117.1%*	*28.5*	*28.5*

** Percent calculated using the total GHG estimate for CO$_2$, CH$_4$, N$_2$O, HFCs, PFCs and SF$_6$ excluding CO$_2$ emissions/removals from land use change and forestry.

Nigeria / Nigéria

Figure 1. CO₂ emissions by fuel

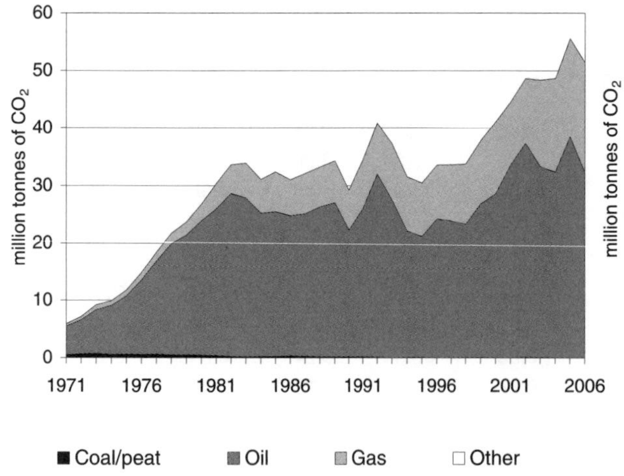

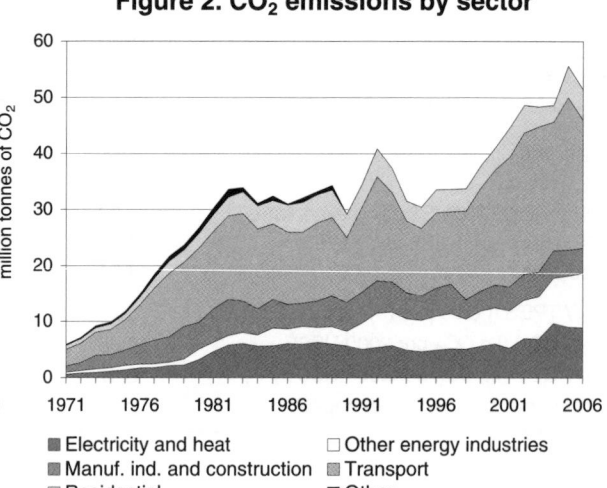

■ Coal/peat   ■ Oil   ▨ Gas   ☐ Other

Figure 2. CO₂ emissions by sector

■ Electricity and heat   ☐ Other energy industries
■ Manuf. ind. and construction ▨ Transport
▨ Residential   ■ Other

Figure 3. CO₂ emissions by sector

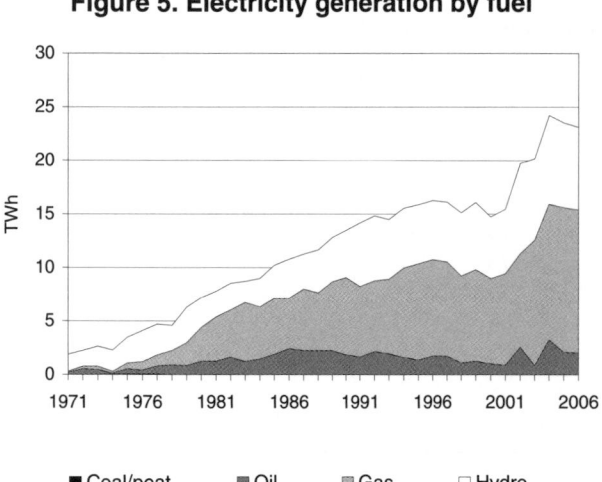

■ Electricity and heat   ☐ Other energy industries
■ Manuf. ind. and construction ▨ Transport
▨ Residential   ■ Other

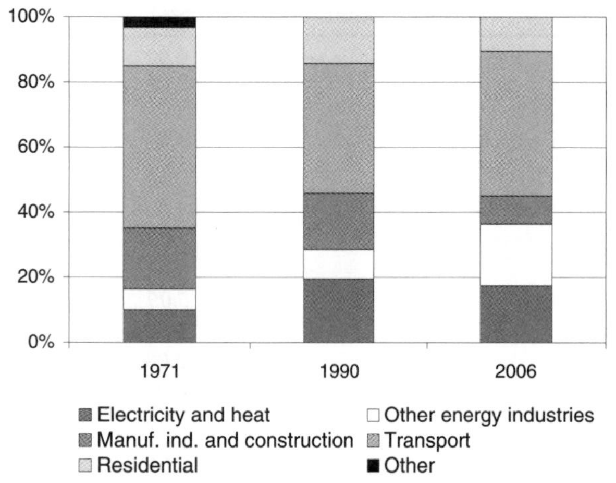

Figure 4. Reference vs Sectoral Approach

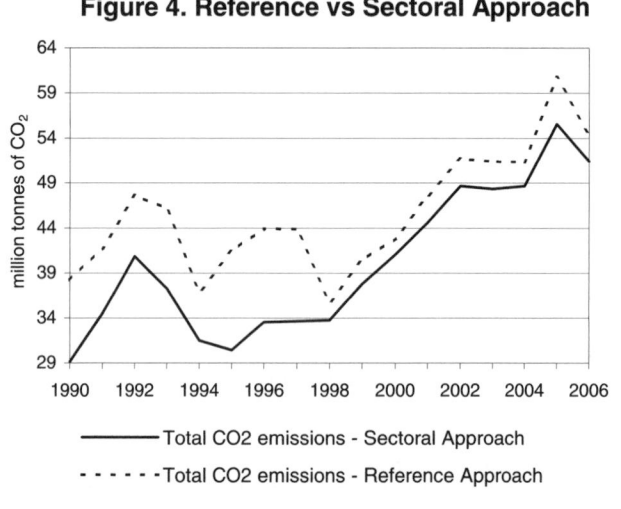

——— Total CO2 emissions - Sectoral Approach
- - - - Total CO2 emissions - Reference Approach

Figure 5. Electricity generation by fuel

■ Coal/peat   ■ Oil   ▨ Gas   ☐ Hydro

Figure 6. Key indicators

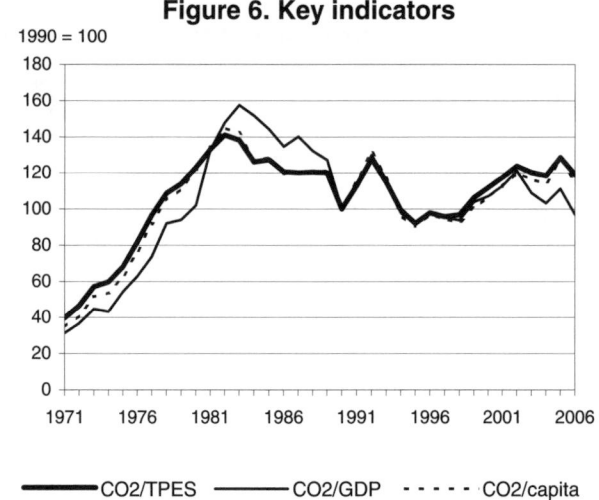

1990 = 100

——CO2/TPES   ——CO2/GDP   - - - - CO2/capita

Nigeria / Nigéria

Key indicators

	1990	1995	2000	2003	2004	2005	2006	% change 90-06
CO$_2$ Sectoral Approach (Mt of CO$_2$) *	29.16	30.41	41.07	48.34	48.64	55.57	51.42	76.3%
CO$_2$ Reference Approach (Mt of CO$_2$) *	38.23	41.46	42.85	51.40	51.34	60.77	54.38	42.2%
TPES (PJ)	2 969	3 367	3 738	4 096	4 177	4 398	4 399	48.2%
TPES (Mtoe)	70.90	80.42	89.27	97.84	99.77	105.04	105.07	48.2%
GDP (billion 2000 US$ using exch. rates)	34.98	39.54	45.98	53.29	56.54	59.99	63.53	81.6%
GDP (billion 2000 US$ using PPPs)	80.32	90.80	105.59	122.38	129.84	137.76	145.92	81.7%
Population (millions)	94.45	109.01	124.77	134.66	138.00	141.36	144.72	53.2%
CO$_2$ / TPES (t CO$_2$ per TJ)	9.8	9.0	11.0	11.8	11.6	12.6	11.7	19.0%
CO$_2$ / GDP (kg CO$_2$ per 2000 US$)	0.83	0.77	0.89	0.91	0.86	0.93	0.81	-2.9%
CO$_2$ / GDP (kg CO$_2$ per 2000 US$ PPP)	0.36	0.33	0.39	0.40	0.37	0.40	0.35	-2.9%
CO$_2$ / population (t CO$_2$ per capita)	0.31	0.28	0.33	0.36	0.35	0.39	0.36	15.1%

Ratios are based on the Sectoral Approach.
* The difference in the growth rate between the Sectoral and Reference Approaches is mainly due to statistical differences for some oil products in 1990.

2006 CO$_2$ emissions by sector

million tonnes of CO$_2$	Coal/peat	Oil	Gas	Other **	Total	% change 90-06
Sectoral Approach *	0.02	32.32	19.08	-	51.42	76.3%
Main activity producer elec. and heat	-	2.04	6.89	-	8.92	57.6%
Unallocated autoproducers	-	-	-	-	-	-
Other energy industries	-	1.09	8.66	-	9.75	268.3%
Manufacturing industries and construction	0.02	0.89	3.54	-	4.45	-11.8%
Transport	-	22.86	-	-	22.86	96.4%
of which: road	-	*22.73*	-	-	*22.73*	*99.1%*
Other sectors	-	5.43	-	-	5.43	30.5%
of which: residential	-	*5.43*	-	-	*5.43*	*30.5%*
Reference Approach *	0.02	33.34	21.03	-	54.38	42.2%
Diff. due to losses and/or transformation	-	1.03	2.18	-	3.21	
Statistical differences	-	- 0.01	- 0.23	-	- 0.24	
Memo: international marine bunkers	-	*1.91*	-	-	*1.91*	*228.0%*
Memo: international aviation	-	*0.71*	-	-	*0.71*	*-25.2%*

** Other includes industrial waste and non-renewable municipal waste.

Key sources for CO$_2$ emissions from fuel combustion in 2006

IPCC source category	CO$_2$ emissions (Mt of CO$_2$)	% change 90-06	Level assessment (%) ***	Cumulative total (%)
Road - oil	22.73	99.1%	11.0	11.0
Other energy industries - gas	8.66	776.4%	4.2	15.2
Main activity prod. elec. and heat - gas	6.89	63.2%	3.3	18.5
Residential - oil	5.43	30.5%	2.6	21.2
Manufacturing industries - gas	3.54	111.5%	1.7	22.9
Main activity prod. elec. and heat - oil	2.04	43.5%	1.0	23.9
Other energy industries - oil	1.09	-34.2%	0.5	24.4
Manufacturing industries - oil	0.89	-72.3%	0.4	24.8
Other transport - oil	0.13	-41.2%	0.1	24.9
Manufacturing industries - coal/peat	0.02	-87.5%	0.0	24.9
-	-	-	-	-
Memo: total CO$_2$ from fuel combustion	*51.42*	*76.3%*	*24.9*	*24.9*

*** Percent calculated using the total GHG estimate for CO$_2$, CH$_4$, N$_2$O, HFCs, PFCs and SF$_6$ excluding CO$_2$ emissions/removals from land use change and forestry.

Norway / Norvège *

Figure 1. CO₂ emissions by fuel

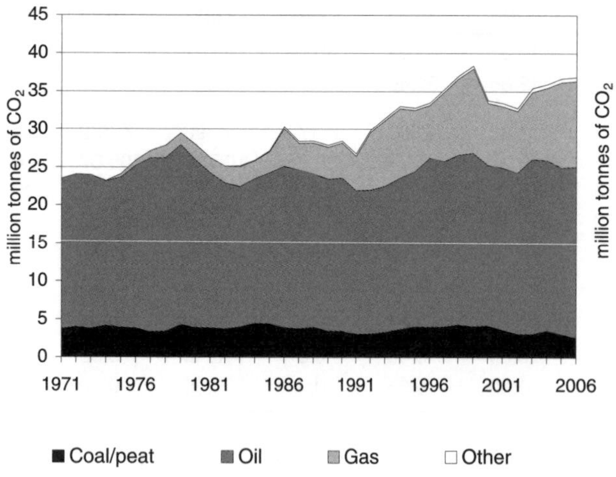

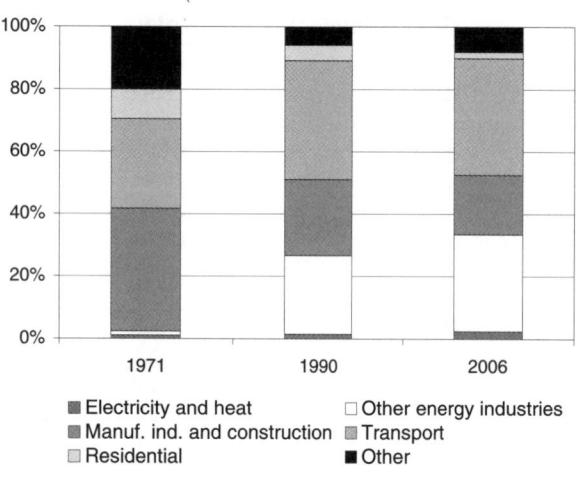

■ Coal/peat   ■ Oil   ▨ Gas   ☐ Other

Figure 2. CO₂ emissions by sector

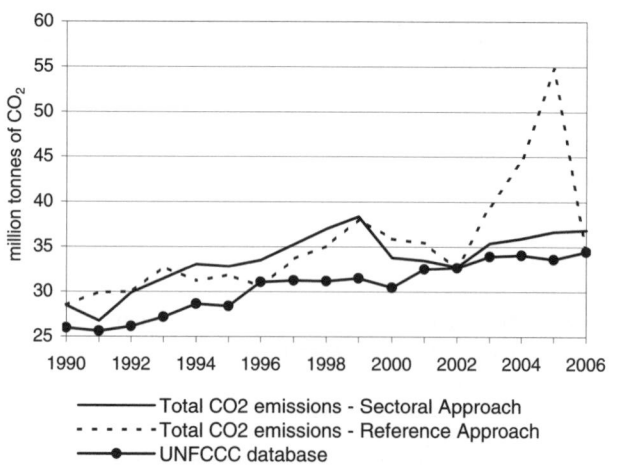

■ Electricity and heat   ☐ Other energy industries
▨ Manuf. ind. and construction   ▨ Transport
☐ Residential   ■ Other

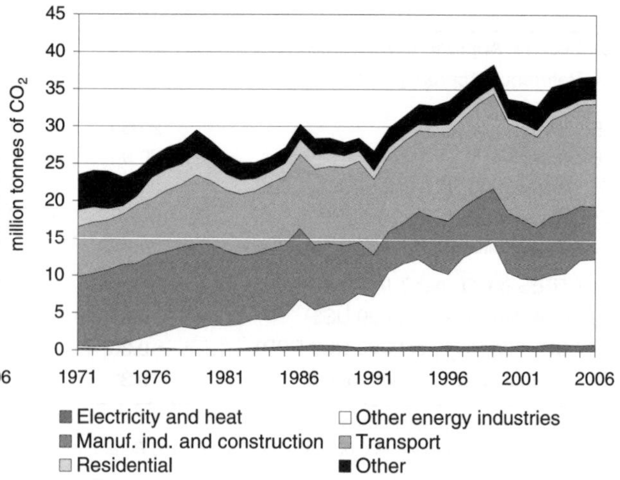

Figure 3. CO₂ emissions by sector

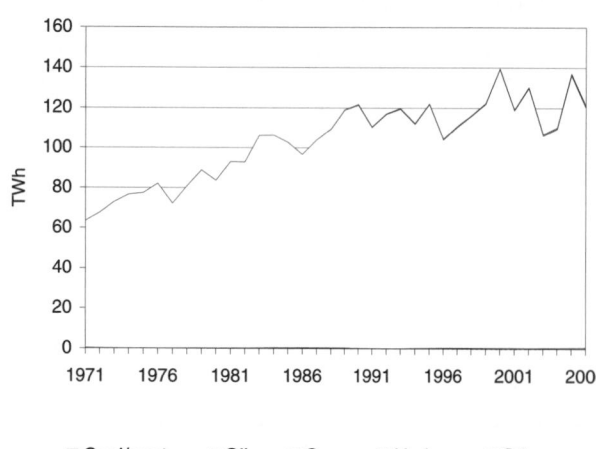

■ Electricity and heat   ☐ Other energy industries
▨ Manuf. ind. and construction   ▨ Transport
☐ Residential   ■ Other

Figure 4. Reference vs Sectoral Approach

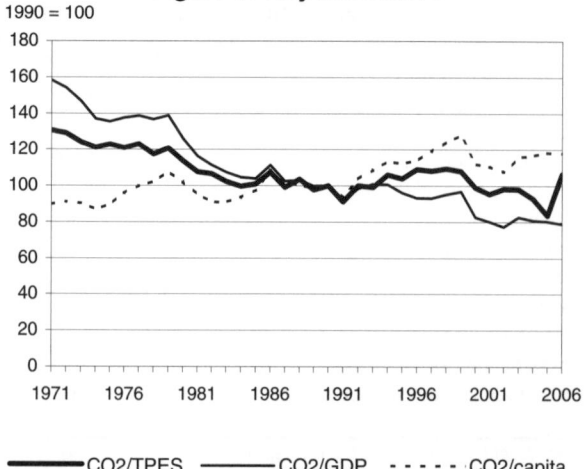

—— Total CO2 emissions - Sectoral Approach
----- Total CO2 emissions - Reference Approach
—●— UNFCCC database

Figure 5. Electricity generation by fuel

■ Coal/peat   ■ Oil   ▨ Gas   ☐ Hydro   ▨ Other

Figure 6. Key indicators

1990 = 100

——CO2/TPES   ——CO2/GDP   - - - - CO2/capita

* Large statistical differences for oil and gas cause discrepancies between the Sectoral and Reference Approaches; please see the note in Chapter 1.

Norway / Norvège

Key indicators

	1990	1995	2000	2003	2004	2005	2006	% change 90-06
CO_2 Sectoral Approach (Mt of CO_2) *	28.45	32.81	33.79	35.40	35.95	36.68	36.85	29.5%
CO_2 Reference Approach (Mt of CO_2) *	28.50	31.84	35.89	39.55	44.55	54.77	34.32	20.4%
TPES (PJ)	897	996	1 076	1 137	1 219	1 384	1 092	21.8%
TPES (Mtoe)	21.42	23.79	25.71	27.16	29.11	33.06	26.09	21.8%
GDP (billion 2000 US$ using exch. rates)	117.00	140.50	168.30	176.00	182.80	187.80	191.80	63.9%
GDP (billion 2000 US$ using PPPs)	112.64	135.25	162.06	169.47	176.02	180.84	184.73	64.0%
Population (millions)	4.24	4.36	4.49	4.57	4.59	4.62	4.66	9.9%
CO_2 / TPES (t CO_2 per TJ)	31.7	32.9	31.4	31.1	29.5	26.5	33.7	6.3%
CO_2 / GDP (kg CO_2 per 2000 US$)	0.24	0.23	0.20	0.20	0.20	0.20	0.19	-21.0%
CO_2 / GDP (kg CO_2 per 2000 US$ PPP)	0.25	0.24	0.21	0.21	0.20	0.20	0.20	-21.0%
CO_2 / population (t CO_2 per capita)	6.71	7.53	7.52	7.75	7.83	7.94	7.91	17.9%

Ratios are based on the Sectoral Approach.
* Large stastistical differences for oil and gas cause discrepancies between the Sectoral and Reference Approaches; please see note in Chapter 1.

2006 CO_2 emissions by sector

million tonnes of CO_2	Coal/peat	Oil	Gas	Other **	Total	% change 90-06
Sectoral Approach *	**2.63**	**22.44**	**11.27**	**0.51**	**36.85**	**29.5%**
Main activity producer elec. and heat	0.18	0.07	0.02	0.43	0.71	68.7%
Unallocated autoproducers	-	0.01	0.14	0.01	0.15	x
Other energy industries	-	1.77	9.72	-	11.49	60.1%
Manufacturing industries and construction	2.44	3.17	1.30	0.07	6.98	0.7%
Transport	-	13.77	0.03	-	13.79	27.4%
of which: road	-	*10.17*	*0.01*	-	*10.17*	*33.8%*
Other sectors	0.01	3.65	0.07	-	3.73	20.6%
of which: residential	*0.01*	*0.71*	*0.01*	-	*0.73*	*-47.8%*
Reference Approach *	**2.93**	**20.23**	**10.66**	**0.51**	**34.32**	**20.4%**
Diff. due to losses and/or transformation	0.16	- 1.22	-	-	- 1.06	
Statistical differences	0.14	- 0.99	- 0.61	- 0.00	- 1.46	
Memo: international marine bunkers	-	*1.56*	-	-	*1.56*	*12.3%*
Memo: international aviation	-	*1.11*	-	-	*1.11*	*-10.5%*

** Other includes industrial waste and non-renewable municipal waste.

Key sources for CO_2 emissions from fuel combustion in 2006

IPCC source category	CO_2 emissions (Mt of CO_2)	% change 90-06	Level assessment (%) ***	Cumulative total (%)
Road - oil	10.17	33.7%	18.2	18.2
Other energy industries - gas	9.72	110.5%	17.4	35.6
Other transport - oil	3.60	11.6%	6.4	42.0
Manufacturing industries - oil	3.17	-13.6%	5.7	47.7
Non-specified other sectors - oil	2.94	74.2%	5.3	53.0
Manufacturing industries - coal/peat	2.44	-25.0%	4.4	57.3
Other energy industries - oil	1.77	-30.8%	3.2	60.5
Manufacturing industries - gas	1.30	x	2.3	62.8
Residential - oil	0.71	-47.8%	1.3	64.1
Main activity prod. elec. and heat - other	0.43	75.5%	0.8	64.9
Main activity prod. elec. and heat - coal/peat	0.18	30.9%	0.3	65.2
Memo: total CO_2 from fuel combustion	*36.85*	*29.5%*	*65.9*	*65.9*

*** Percent calculated using the total GHG estimate for CO_2, CH_4, N_2O, HFCs, PFCs and SF_6 excluding CO_2 emissions/removals from land use change and forestry.

Oman

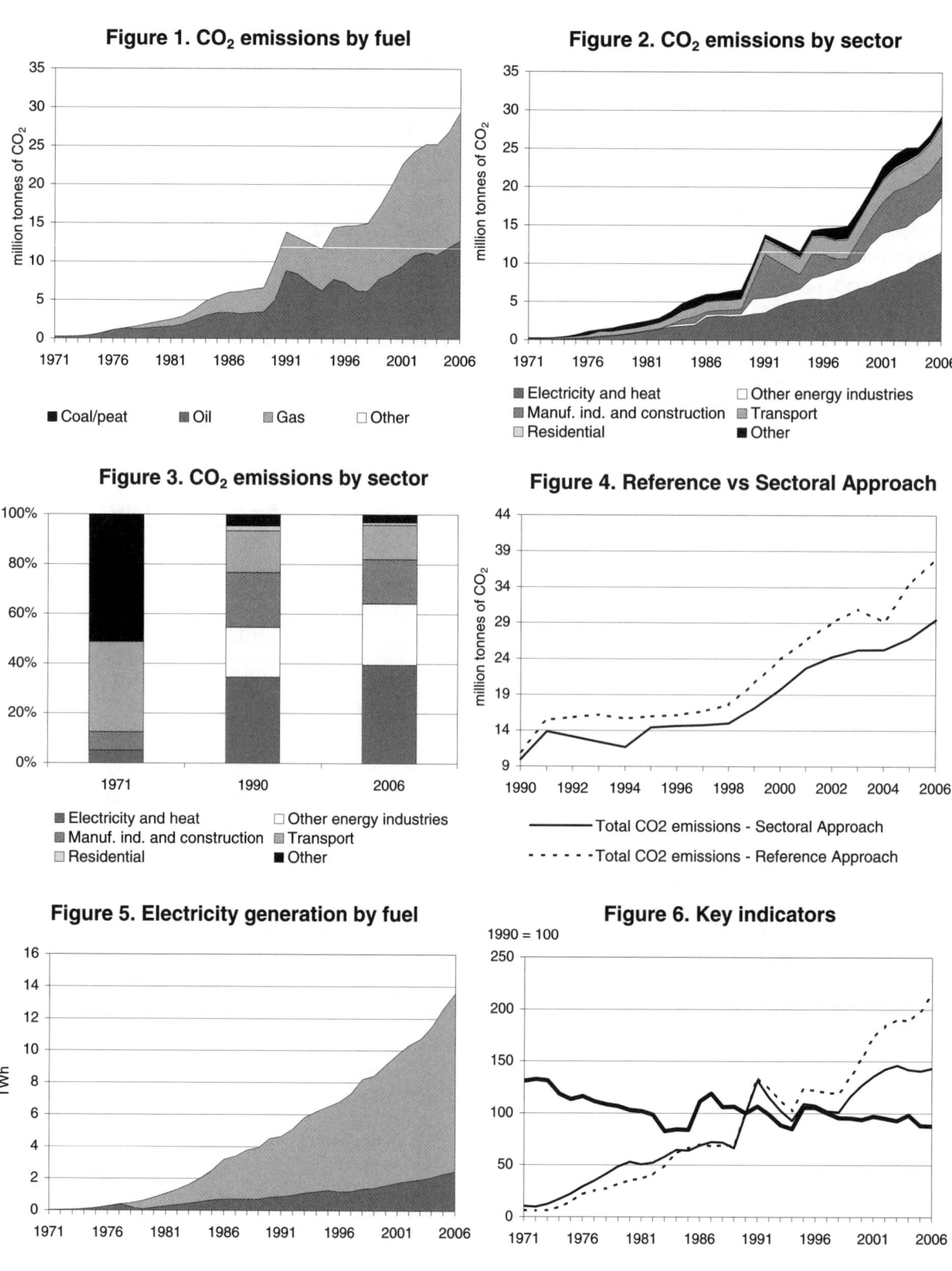

Figure 1. CO₂ emissions by fuel

■ Coal/peat   ■ Oil   ■ Gas   □ Other

Figure 2. CO₂ emissions by sector

■ Electricity and heat   □ Other energy industries
■ Manuf. ind. and construction   ■ Transport
□ Residential   ■ Other

Figure 3. CO₂ emissions by sector

■ Electricity and heat   □ Other energy industries
■ Manuf. ind. and construction   ■ Transport
□ Residential   ■ Other

Figure 4. Reference vs Sectoral Approach

—— Total CO2 emissions - Sectoral Approach
- - - - Total CO2 emissions - Reference Approach

Figure 5. Electricity generation by fuel

■ Oil   ■ Gas

Figure 6. Key indicators

1990 = 100

—— CO2/TPES   —— CO2/GDP   - - - - CO2/capita

Oman
Key indicators

	1990	1995	2000	2003	2004	2005	2006	% change 90-06
CO$_2$ Sectoral Approach (Mt of CO$_2$)	9.93	14.40	19.77	25.23	25.26	26.87	29.45	196.7%
CO$_2$ Reference Approach (Mt of CO$_2$)	10.99	15.95	23.94	30.89	29.18	34.54	38.01	245.9%
TPES (PJ)	191	263	405	523	495	587	646	238.1%
TPES (Mtoe)	4.56	6.28	9.67	12.49	11.83	14.02	15.42	238.1%
GDP (billion 2000 US$ using exch. rates)	12.65	16.83	19.87	22.02	22.71	24.37	26.22	107.2%
GDP (billion 2000 US$ using PPPs)	19.61	26.08	30.79	34.12	35.19	37.76	40.63	107.2%
Population (millions)	1.84	2.17	2.40	2.46	2.48	2.51	2.55	38.1%
CO$_2$ / TPES (t CO$_2$ per TJ)	52.0	54.8	48.8	48.2	51.0	45.8	45.6	-12.3%
CO$_2$ / GDP (kg CO$_2$ per 2000 US$)	0.78	0.86	0.99	1.15	1.11	1.10	1.12	43.1%
CO$_2$ / GDP (kg CO$_2$ per 2000 US$ PPP)	0.51	0.55	0.64	0.74	0.72	0.71	0.72	43.1%
CO$_2$ / population (t CO$_2$ per capita)	5.39	6.63	8.23	10.26	10.19	10.72	11.57	114.7%

Ratios are based on the Sectoral Approach.

2006 CO$_2$ emissions by sector

million tonnes of CO$_2$	Coal/peat	Oil	Gas	Other *	Total	% change 90-06
Sectoral Approach	-	**12.72**	**16.73**	-	**29.45**	**196.7%**
Main activity producer elec. and heat	-	2.39	9.24	-	11.63	239.0%
Unallocated autoproducers	-	-	-	-	-	-
Other energy industries	-	0.51	6.72	-	7.22	264.8%
Manufacturing industries and construction	-	4.65	0.62	-	5.27	141.1%
Transport	-	4.06	-	-	4.06	143.8%
of which: road	-	*4.06*	-	-	*4.06*	*143.8%*
Other sectors	-	1.10	0.15	-	1.26	90.0%
of which: residential	-	*0.30*	-	-	*0.30*	*54.5%*
Reference Approach	-	**13.64**	**24.37**	-	**38.01**	**245.9%**
Diff. due to losses and/or transformation	-	0.92	7.64	-	8.56	
Statistical differences	-	0.00	-	-	0.00	
Memo: international marine bunkers	-	*..*	-	-	*..*	*..*
Memo: international aviation	-	*1.25*	-	-	*1.25*	*34.1%*

* Other includes industrial waste and non-renewable municipal waste.

Key sources for CO$_2$ emissions from fuel combustion in 2006

IPCC source category	CO$_2$ emissions (Mt of CO$_2$)	% change 90-06	Level assessment (%) **	Cumulative total (%)
Main activity prod. elec. and heat - gas	9.24	261.3%	23.5	23.5
Other energy industries - gas	6.72	318.6%	17.1	40.6
Manufacturing industries - oil	4.65	191.8%	11.8	52.4
Road - oil	4.06	143.8%	10.3	62.7
Main activity prod. elec. and heat - oil	2.39	173.5%	6.1	68.8
Non-specified other sectors - oil	0.80	163.5%	2.0	70.8
Manufacturing industries - gas	0.62	4.4%	1.6	72.4
Other energy industries - oil	0.51	35.2%	1.3	73.7
Residential - oil	0.30	54.5%	0.8	74.4
Non-specified other sectors - gas	0.15	-5.4%	0.4	74.8
-	-	-	-	-
Memo: total CO$_2$ from fuel combustion	*29.45*	*196.7%*	*74.8*	*74.8*

** Percent calculated using the total GHG estimate for CO$_2$, CH$_4$, N$_2$O, HFCs, PFCs and SF$_6$ excluding CO$_2$ emissions/removals from land use change and forestry.

Pakistan

Figure 1. CO₂ emissions by fuel

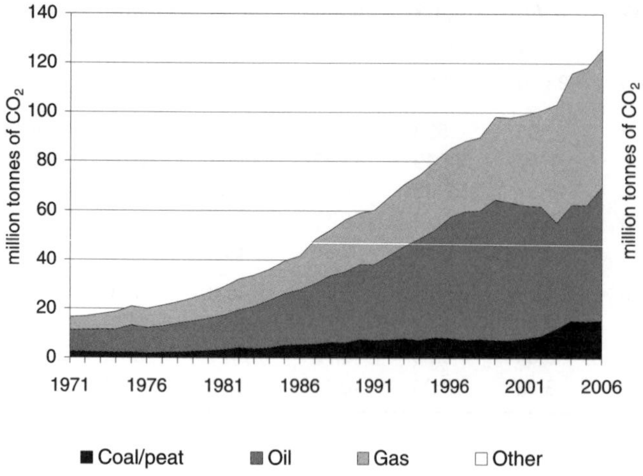

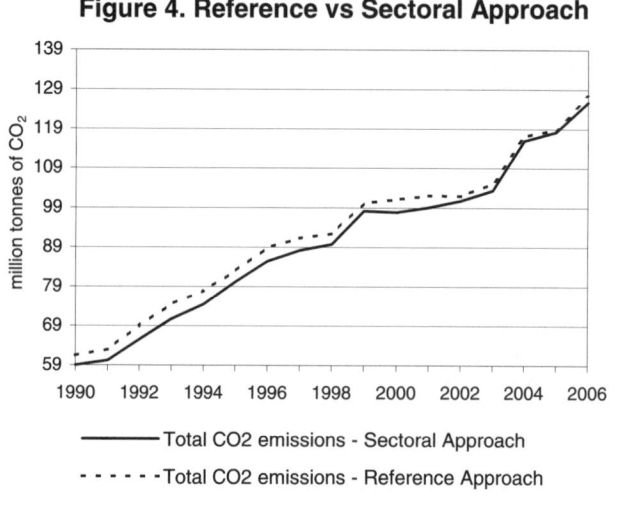

■ Coal/peat   ■ Oil   ▨ Gas   □ Other

Figure 2. CO₂ emissions by sector

■ Electricity and heat   □ Other energy industries
■ Manuf. ind. and construction ▨ Transport
▨ Residential   ■ Other

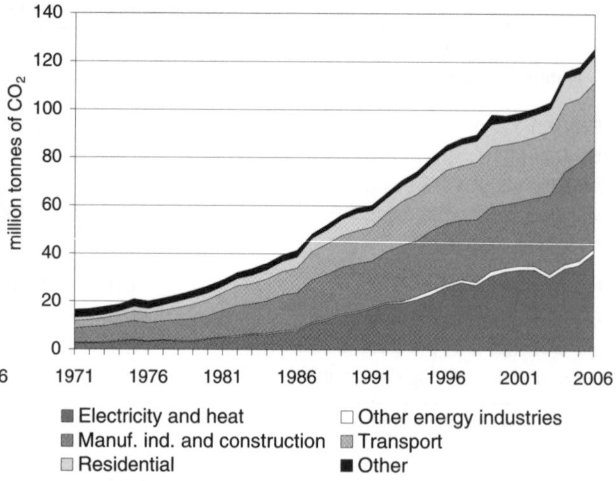

Figure 3. CO₂ emissions by sector

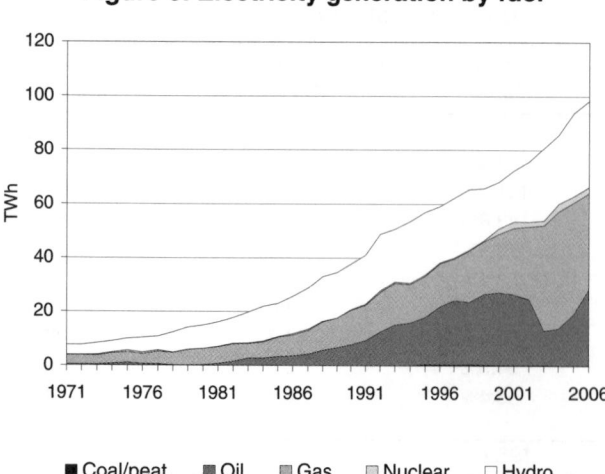

■ Electricity and heat   □ Other energy industries
■ Manuf. ind. and construction ▨ Transport
▨ Residential   ■ Other

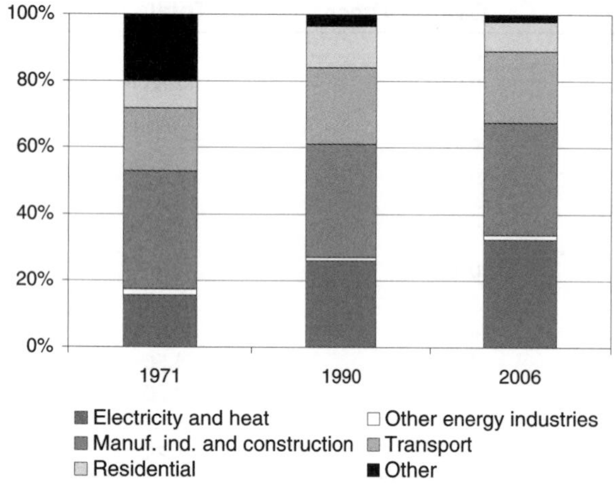

Figure 4. Reference vs Sectoral Approach

—— Total CO2 emissions - Sectoral Approach
- - - - Total CO2 emissions - Reference Approach

Figure 5. Electricity generation by fuel

■ Coal/peat   ■ Oil   ▨ Gas   ▨ Nuclear   □ Hydro

Figure 6. Key indicators

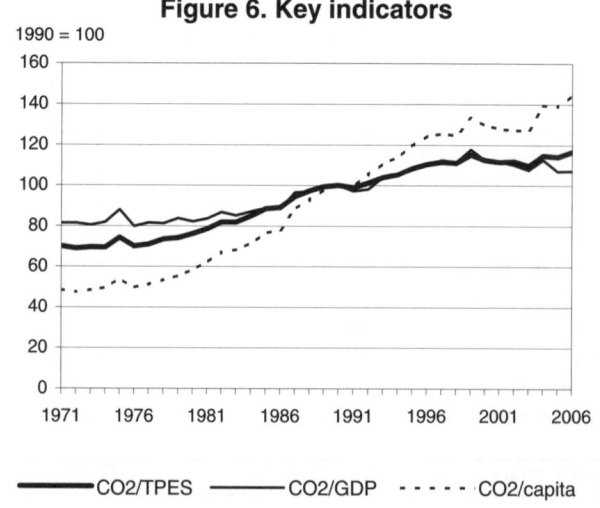

—— CO2/TPES   —— CO2/GDP   - - - - CO2/capita

Pakistan
Key indicators

	1990	1995	2000	2003	2004	2005	2006	% change 90-06
CO$_2$ Sectoral Approach (Mt of CO$_2$)	59.04	80.11	97.80	103.32	115.98	118.31	125.73	113.0%
CO$_2$ Reference Approach (Mt of CO$_2$)	61.40	82.90	101.04	105.12	117.12	118.93	127.33	107.4%
TPES (PJ)	1 818	2 274	2 678	2 898	3 110	3 192	3 320	82.6%
TPES (Mtoe)	43.42	54.32	63.95	69.22	74.29	76.23	79.29	82.6%
GDP (billion 2000 US$ using exch. rates)	49.82	62.46	73.32	80.93	86.89	93.22	99.03	98.8%
GDP (billion 2000 US$ using PPPs)	176.48	221.27	259.73	286.68	307.79	330.23	350.81	98.8%
Population (millions)	107.98	122.38	138.08	148.44	152.06	155.77	159.00	47.3%
CO$_2$ / TPES (t CO$_2$ per TJ)	32.5	35.2	36.5	35.6	37.3	37.1	37.9	16.6%
CO$_2$ / GDP (kg CO$_2$ per 2000 US$)	1.19	1.28	1.33	1.28	1.33	1.27	1.27	7.1%
CO$_2$ / GDP (kg CO$_2$ per 2000 US$ PPP)	0.33	0.36	0.38	0.36	0.38	0.36	0.36	7.1%
CO$_2$ / population (t CO$_2$ per capita)	0.55	0.65	0.71	0.70	0.76	0.76	0.79	44.6%

Ratios are based on the Sectoral Approach.

2006 CO$_2$ emissions by sector

million tonnes of CO$_2$	Coal/peat	Oil	Gas	Other *	Total	% change 90-06
Sectoral Approach	**15.34**	**54.28**	**56.12**	**-**	**125.73**	**113.0%**
Main activity producer elec. and heat	0.32	20.99	19.18	-	40.49	163.7%
Unallocated autoproducers	-	0.11	-	-	0.11	x
Other energy industries	-	1.18	0.70	-	1.88	231.2%
Manufacturing industries and construction	15.02	5.31	22.03	-	42.36	111.3%
Transport	-	23.98	2.93	-	26.91	97.2%
of which: road	-	*23.16*	-	-	*23.16*	*81.5%*
Other sectors	0.00	2.72	11.27	-	13.99	48.5%
of which: residential	*0.00*	*1.48*	*9.64*	-	*11.12*	*52.6%*
Reference Approach	**16.51**	**54.39**	**56.43**	**-**	**127.33**	**107.4%**
Diff. due to losses and/or transformation	0.17	0.18	0.31	-	0.66	
Statistical differences	1.00	- 0.07	0.00	-	0.93	
Memo: international marine bunkers	-	*0.32*	-	-	*0.32*	*203.8%*
Memo: international aviation	-	*2.72*	-	-	*2.72*	*94.9%*

* Other includes industrial waste and non-renewable municipal waste.

Key sources for CO$_2$ emissions from fuel combustion in 2006

IPCC source category	CO$_2$ emissions (Mt of CO$_2$)	% change 90-06	Level assessment (%) **	Cumulative total (%)
Road - oil	23.16	81.5%	7.1	7.1
Manufacturing industries - gas	22.03	162.3%	6.7	13.8
Main activity prod. elec. and heat - oil	20.99	204.4%	6.4	20.2
Main activity prod. elec. and heat - gas	19.18	128.6%	5.9	26.1
Manufacturing industries - coal/peat	15.02	102.1%	4.6	30.7
Residential - gas	9.64	177.8%	2.9	33.6
Manufacturing industries - oil	5.31	25.8%	1.6	35.2
Other transport - gas	2.93	+	0.9	36.1
Non-specified other sectors - gas	1.63	154.7%	0.5	36.6
Residential - oil	1.48	-61.1%	0.5	37.1
Non-specified other sectors - oil	1.24	-17.1%	0.4	37.5
Memo: total CO$_2$ from fuel combustion	*125.73*	*113.0%*	*38.4*	*38.4*

** Percent calculated using the total GHG estimate for CO$_2$, CH$_4$, N$_2$O, HFCs, PFCs and SF$_6$ excluding CO$_2$ emissions/removals from land use change and forestry.

Panama

Figure 1. CO₂ emissions by fuel

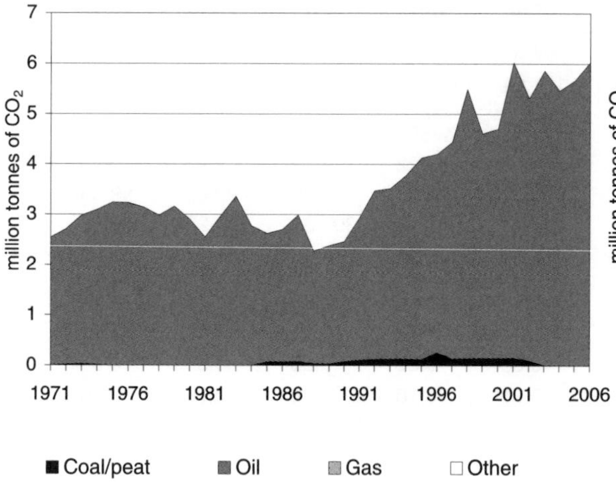

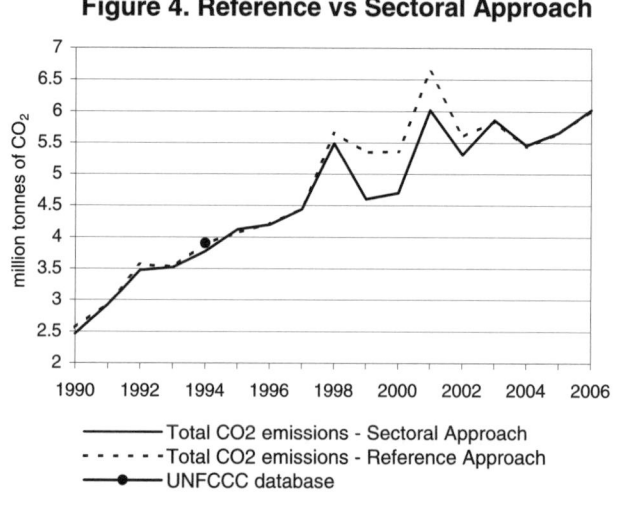

■ Coal/peat   ■ Oil   ■ Gas   □ Other

Figure 2. CO₂ emissions by sector

■ Electricity and heat   □ Other energy industries
■ Manuf. ind. and construction   ■ Transport
□ Residential   ■ Other

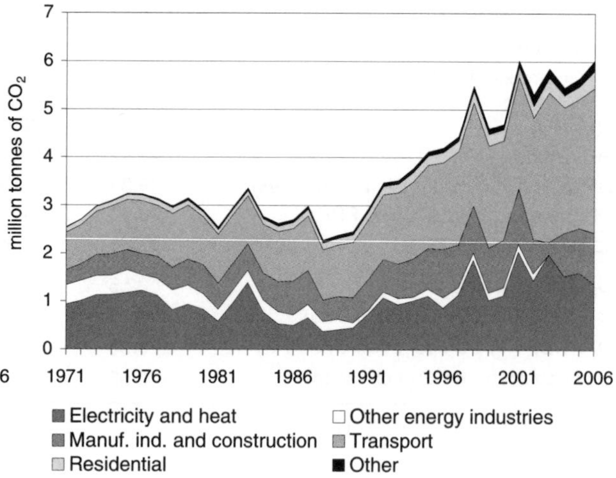

Figure 3. CO₂ emissions by sector

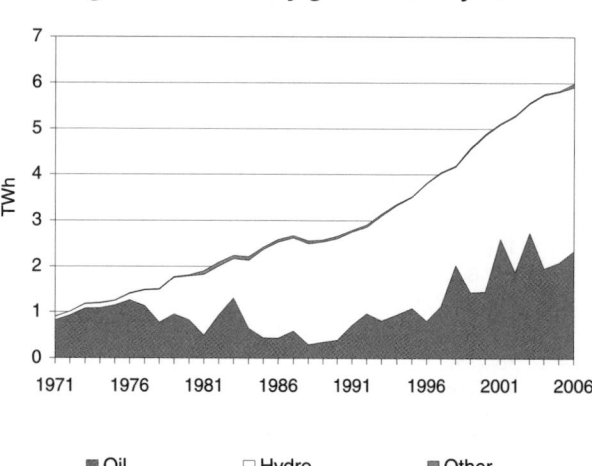

■ Electricity and heat   □ Other energy industries
■ Manuf. ind. and construction   ■ Transport
□ Residential   ■ Other

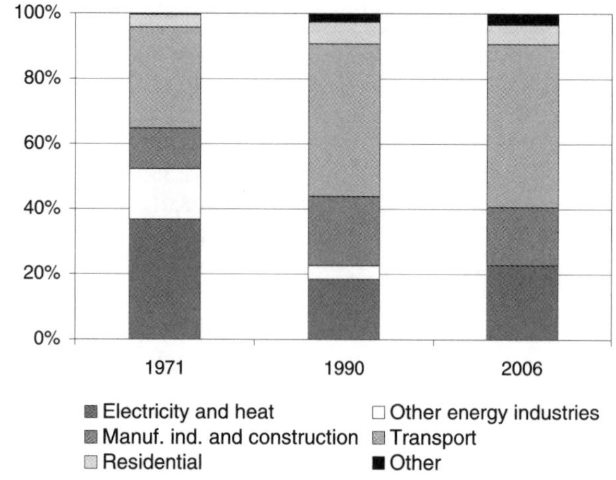

Figure 4. Reference vs Sectoral Approach

—— Total CO2 emissions - Sectoral Approach
- - - - Total CO2 emissions - Reference Approach
—●— UNFCCC database

Figure 5. Electricity generation by fuel

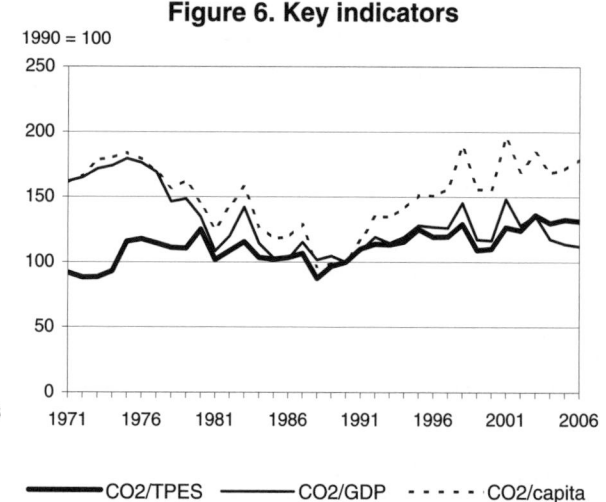

■ Oil   □ Hydro   ■ Other

Figure 6. Key indicators

1990 = 100

——CO2/TPES   ——CO2/GDP   - - - - CO2/capita

Panama

Key indicators

	1990	1995	2000	2003	2004	2005	2006	% change 90-06
CO$_2$ Sectoral Approach (Mt of CO$_2$)	2.46	4.12	4.70	5.86	5.46	5.66	6.02	144.6%
CO$_2$ Reference Approach (Mt of CO$_2$)	2.56	4.07	5.36	5.84	5.44	5.66	6.02	135.1%
TPES (PJ)	62	84	108	109	107	108	116	86.5%
TPES (Mtoe)	1.49	2.00	2.58	2.61	2.54	2.59	2.78	86.5%
GDP (billion 2000 US$ using exch. rates)	7.09	9.27	11.62	12.45	13.39	14.31	15.47	118.2%
GDP (billion 2000 US$ using PPPs)	10.89	14.23	17.84	19.12	20.56	21.98	23.76	118.2%
Population (millions)	2.41	2.67	2.95	3.12	3.18	3.23	3.29	36.4%
CO$_2$ / TPES (t CO$_2$ per TJ)	39.5	49.4	43.5	53.7	51.3	52.3	51.8	31.2%
CO$_2$ / GDP (kg CO$_2$ per 2000 US$)	0.35	0.44	0.40	0.47	0.41	0.40	0.39	12.1%
CO$_2$ / GDP (kg CO$_2$ per 2000 US$ PPP)	0.23	0.29	0.26	0.31	0.27	0.26	0.25	12.1%
CO$_2$ / population (t CO$_2$ per capita)	1.02	1.54	1.59	1.88	1.72	1.75	1.83	79.4%

Ratios are based on the Sectoral Approach.

2006 CO$_2$ emissions by sector

million tonnes of CO$_2$	Coal/peat	Oil	Gas	Other *	Total	% change 90-06
Sectoral Approach	-	**6.02**	-	-	**6.02**	**144.6%**
Main activity producer elec. and heat	-	1.22	-	-	1.22	200.9%
Unallocated autoproducers	-	0.15	-	-	0.15	214.3%
Other energy industries	-	-	-	-	-	-100.0%
Manufacturing industries and construction	-	1.07	-	-	1.07	105.5%
Transport	-	3.01	-	-	3.01	161.2%
of which: road	-	*1.32*	-	-	*1.32*	*103.8%*
Other sectors	-	0.57	-	-	0.57	148.1%
of which: residential	-	*0.36*	-	-	*0.36*	*118.8%*
Reference Approach	-	**6.02**	-	-	**6.02**	**135.1%**
Diff. due to losses and/or transformation	-	-	-	-	-	
Statistical differences	-	- 0.01	-	-	- 0.01	
Memo: international marine bunkers	-	..	-	-	..	..
Memo: international aviation	-	*0.01*	-	-	*0.01*	-

* Other includes industrial waste and non-renewable municipal waste.

Key sources for CO$_2$ emissions from fuel combustion in 2006

IPCC source category	CO$_2$ emissions (Mt of CO$_2$)	% change 90-06	Level assessment (%) **	Cumulative total (%)
Other transport - oil	1.70	234.1%	14.6	14.6
Road - oil	1.32	103.8%	11.3	26.0
Main activity prod. elec. and heat - oil	1.22	200.9%	10.5	36.5
Manufacturing industries - oil	1.07	140.9%	9.2	45.7
Residential - oil	0.36	118.8%	3.1	48.8
Non-specified other sectors - oil	0.21	220.4%	1.8	50.7
Unallocated autoproducers - oil	0.15	214.3%	1.3	51.9
-	-	-	-	-
-	-	-	-	-
-	-	-	-	-
-	-	-	-	-
Memo: total CO$_2$ from fuel combustion	*6.02*	*144.6%*	*51.9*	*51.9*

** Percent calculated using the total GHG estimate for CO$_2$, CH$_4$, N$_2$O, HFCs, PFCs and SF$_6$ excluding CO$_2$ emissions/removals from land use change and forestry.

Paraguay

Figure 1. CO_2 emissions by fuel

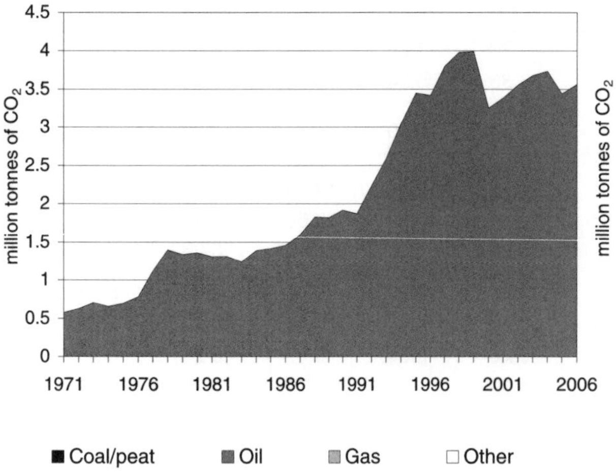
million tonnes of CO2
4.5
4
3.5
3
2.5
2
1.5
1
0.5
0
1971 1976 1981 1986 1991 1996 2001 2006
Coal/peat
Oil
Gas
Other

Figure 2. CO_2 emissions by sector

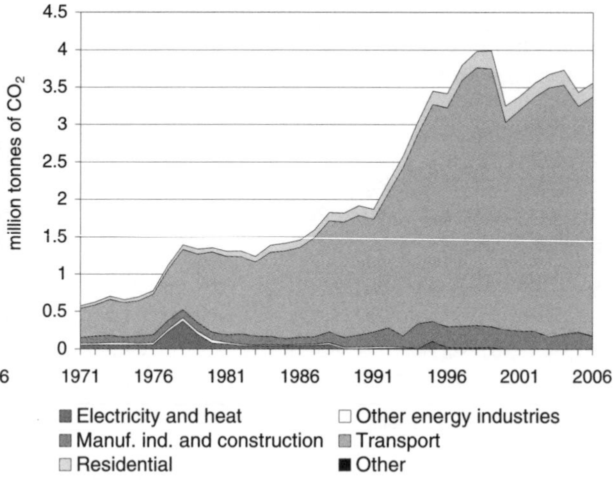
million tonnes of CO2
4.5
4
3.5
3
2.5
2
1.5
1
0.5
0
1971 1976 1981 1986 1991 1996 2001 2006
Electricity and heat
Other energy industries
Manuf. ind. and construction
Transport
Residential
Other

Figure 3. CO_2 emissions by sector

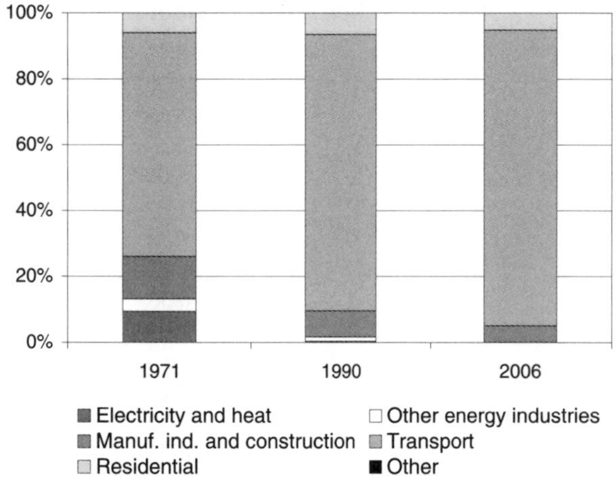
100%
80%
60%
40%
20%
0%
1971
1990
2006
Electricity and heat
Other energy industries
Manuf. ind. and construction
Transport
Residential
Other

Figure 4. Reference vs Sectoral Approach

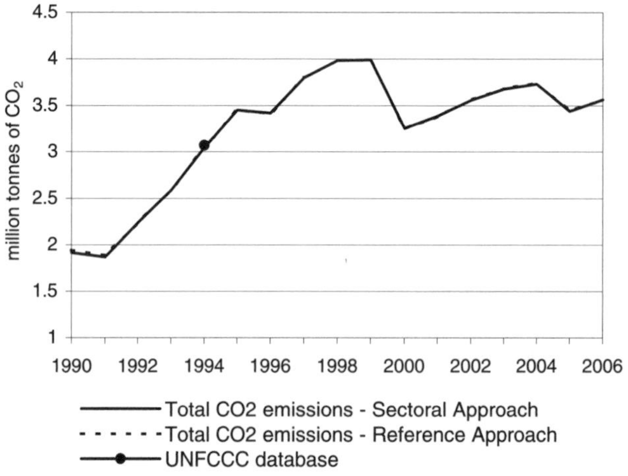
million tonnes of CO2
4.5
4
3.5
3
2.5
2
1.5
1
1990 1992 1994 1996 1998 2000 2002 2004 2006
Total CO2 emissions - Sectoral Approach
Total CO2 emissions - Reference Approach
UNFCCC database

Figure 5. Electricity generation by fuel

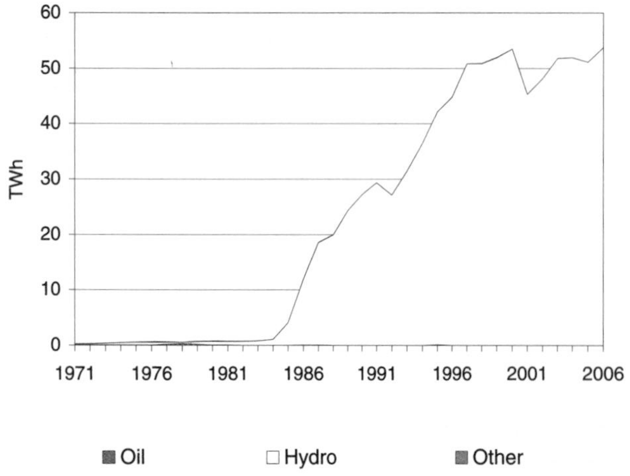
TWh
60
50
40
30
20
10
0
1971 1976 1981 1986 1991 1996 2001 2006
Oil
Hydro
Other

Figure 6. Key indicators

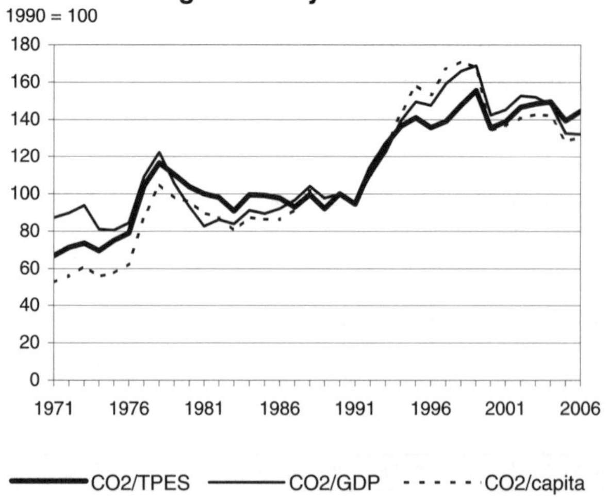
1990 = 100
180
160
140
120
100
80
60
40
20
0
1971 1976 1981 1986 1991 1996 2001 2006
CO2/TPES
CO2/GDP
CO2/capita

Paraguay
Key indicators

	1990	1995	2000	2003	2004	2005	2006	% change 90-06
CO$_2$ Sectoral Approach (Mt of CO$_2$)	1.91	3.45	3.25	3.68	3.73	3.44	3.56	86.1%
CO$_2$ Reference Approach (Mt of CO$_2$)	1.94	3.45	3.25	3.69	3.74	3.45	3.56	83.4%
TPES (PJ)	129	165	162	167	168	166	166	28.8%
TPES (Mtoe)	3.08	3.94	3.86	3.99	4.02	3.97	3.97	28.8%
GDP (billion 2000 US$ using exch. rates)	5.93	7.14	7.07	7.49	7.80	8.03	8.34	40.8%
GDP (billion 2000 US$ using PPPs)	18.67	22.49	22.27	23.59	24.57	25.29	26.28	40.8%
Population (millions)	4.22	4.80	5.35	5.68	5.79	5.90	6.02	42.6%
CO$_2$ / TPES (t CO$_2$ per TJ)	14.8	20.9	20.1	22.0	22.2	20.7	21.4	44.5%
CO$_2$ / GDP (kg CO$_2$ per 2000 US$)	0.32	0.48	0.46	0.49	0.48	0.43	0.43	32.2%
CO$_2$ / GDP (kg CO$_2$ per 2000 US$ PPP)	0.10	0.15	0.15	0.16	0.15	0.14	0.14	32.2%
CO$_2$ / population (t CO$_2$ per capita)	0.45	0.72	0.61	0.65	0.64	0.58	0.59	30.5%

Ratios are based on the Sectoral Approach.

2006 CO$_2$ emissions by sector

million tonnes of CO$_2$	Coal/peat	Oil	Gas	Other *	Total	% change 90-06
Sectoral Approach	-	3.56	-	-	3.56	86.1%
Main activity producer elec. and heat	-	-	-	-	-	-100.0%
Unallocated autoproducers	..	..	..	..	..	..
Other energy industries	-	-	-	-	-	-100.0%
Manufacturing industries and construction	-	0.18	-	-	0.18	16.5%
Transport	-	3.20	-	-	3.20	99.4%
of which: road	-	*3.15*	-	-	*3.15*	*101.4%*
Other sectors	-	0.19	-	-	0.19	47.4%
of which: residential	-	*0.19*	-	-	*0.19*	*47.4%*
Reference Approach	-	3.56	-	-	3.56	83.4%
Diff. due to losses and/or transformation	-	-	-	-	-	
Statistical differences	-	-	-	-	-	
Memo: international marine bunkers	-	-	-	-	-	-
Memo: international aviation		*0.07*	-	-	*0.07*	*125.2%*

* Other includes industrial waste and non-renewable municipal waste.

Key sources for CO$_2$ emissions from fuel combustion in 2006

IPCC source category	CO$_2$ emissions (Mt of CO$_2$)	% change 90-06	Level assessment (%) **	Cumulative total (%)
Road - oil	3.15	101.4%	9.0	9.0
Residential - oil	0.19	47.4%	0.5	9.6
Manufacturing industries - oil	0.18	16.5%	0.5	10.1
Other transport - oil	0.05	25.1%	0.1	10.2
-	-	-	-	-
-	-	-	-	-
-	-	-	-	-
-	-	-	-	-
-	-	-	-	-
-	-	-	-	-
-	-	-	-	-
Memo: total CO$_2$ from fuel combustion	*3.56*	*86.1%*	*10.2*	*10.2*

** Percent calculated using the total GHG estimate for CO$_2$, CH$_4$, N$_2$O, HFCs, PFCs and SF$_6$ excluding CO$_2$ emissions/removals from land use change and forestry.

Peru / Pérou

Figure 1. CO$_2$ emissions by fuel

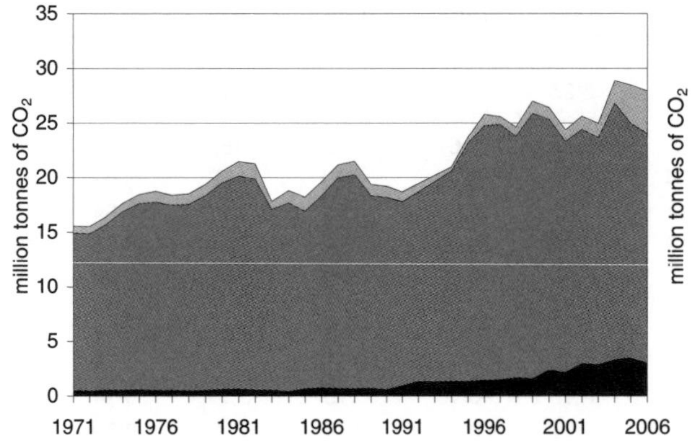

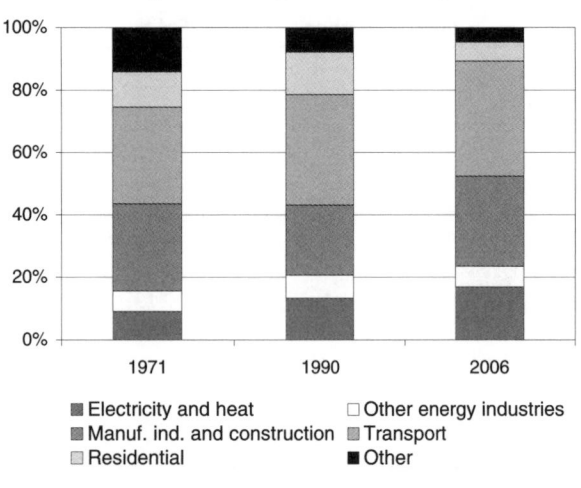

■ Coal/peat   ■ Oil   ▨ Gas   ☐ Other

Figure 2. CO$_2$ emissions by sector

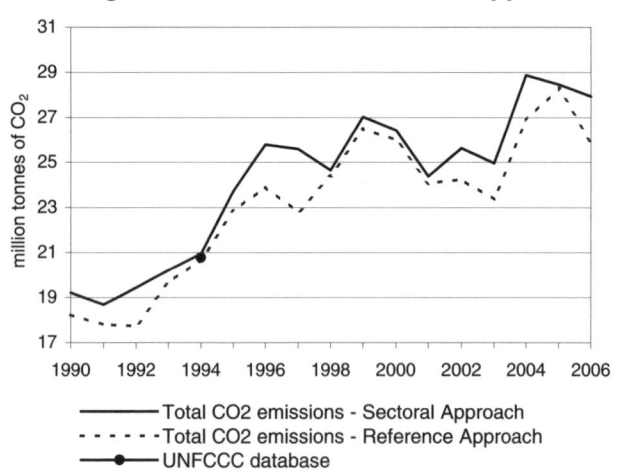

■ Electricity and heat   ☐ Other energy industries
■ Manuf. ind. and construction ▨ Transport
☐ Residential   ■ Other

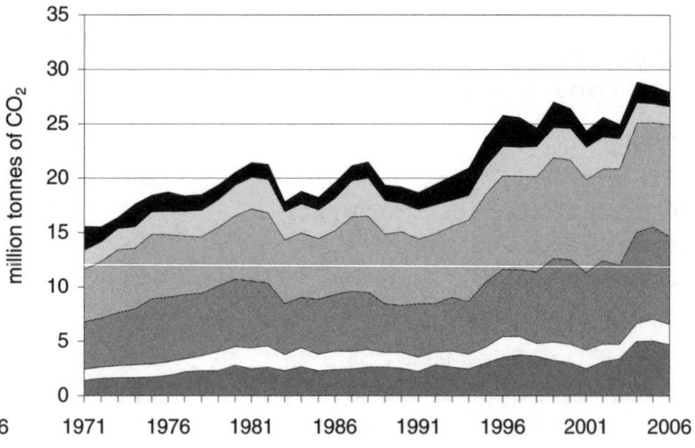

Figure 3. CO$_2$ emissions by sector

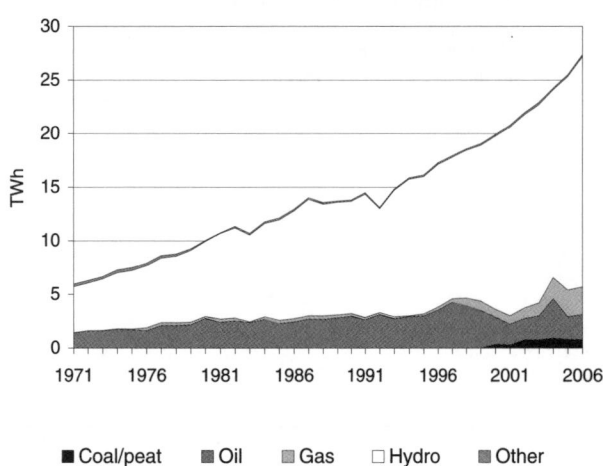

■ Electricity and heat   ☐ Other energy industries
■ Manuf. ind. and construction ▨ Transport
☐ Residential   ■ Other

Figure 4. Reference vs Sectoral Approach

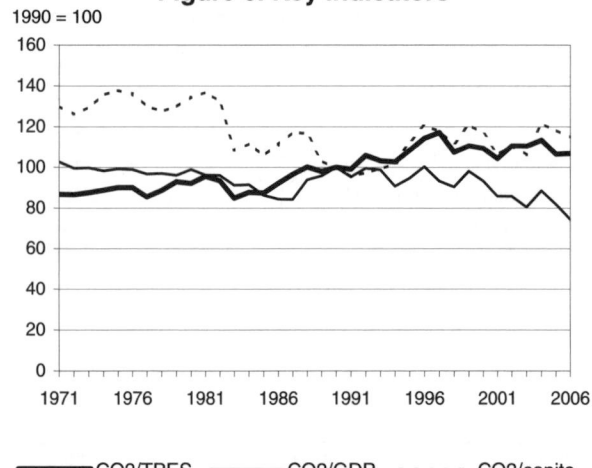

——— Total CO2 emissions - Sectoral Approach
- - - - Total CO2 emissions - Reference Approach
—●— UNFCCC database

Figure 5. Electricity generation by fuel

■ Coal/peat   ■ Oil   ▨ Gas   ☐ Hydro   ▨ Other

Figure 6. Key indicators

1990 = 100

━━ CO2/TPES   ——— CO2/GDP   - - - - CO2/capita

Peru / Pérou
Key indicators

	1990	1995	2000	2003	2004	2005	2006	% change 90-06
CO$_2$ Sectoral Approach (Mt of CO$_2$)	19.21	23.72	26.43	24.96	28.88	28.46	27.93	45.4%
CO$_2$ Reference Approach (Mt of CO$_2$)	18.22	22.83	25.98	23.37	26.88	28.30	25.88	42.0%
TPES (PJ)	417	475	525	491	553	580	567	36.2%
TPES (Mtoe)	9.95	11.34	12.53	11.72	13.20	13.85	13.55	36.2%
GDP (billion 2000 US$ using exch. rates)	36.09	47.13	53.29	58.35	61.39	65.35	70.60	95.6%
GDP (billion 2000 US$ using PPPs)	83.02	108.42	122.59	134.22	141.23	150.34	162.41	95.6%
Population (millions)	21.76	23.86	25.66	26.64	26.96	27.27	27.59	26.8%
CO$_2$ / TPES (t CO$_2$ per TJ)	46.1	49.9	50.4	50.9	52.2	49.1	49.2	6.8%
CO$_2$ / GDP (kg CO$_2$ per 2000 US$)	0.53	0.50	0.50	0.43	0.47	0.44	0.40	-25.7%
CO$_2$ / GDP (kg CO$_2$ per 2000 US$ PPP)	0.23	0.22	0.22	0.19	0.20	0.19	0.17	-25.7%
CO$_2$ / population (t CO$_2$ per capita)	0.88	0.99	1.03	0.94	1.07	1.04	1.01	14.7%

Ratios are based on the Sectoral Approach.

2006 CO$_2$ emissions by sector

million tonnes of CO$_2$	Coal/peat	Oil	Gas	Other *	Total	% change 90-06
Sectoral Approach	**2.98**	**21.07**	**3.89**	**-**	**27.93**	**45.4%**
Main activity producer elec. and heat	0.91	1.05	2.18	-	4.14	414.4%
Unallocated autoproducers	-	0.43	0.14	-	0.57	-67.0%
Other energy industries	-	0.98	0.88	-	1.86	30.0%
Manufacturing industries and construction	2.05	5.35	0.65	-	8.05	86.8%
Transport	-	10.29	-	-	10.29	51.3%
of which: road	-	*10.22*	-	-	*10.22*	*56.1%*
Other sectors	0.02	2.96	0.04	-	3.02	-26.9%
of which: residential	-	*1.69*	*0.00*	-	*1.69*	*-34.9%*
Reference Approach	**3.19**	**18.78**	**3.91**	**-**	**25.88**	**42.0%**
Diff. due to losses and/or transformation	0.23	- 0.67	-	-	- 0.44	
Statistical differences	- 0.02	- 1.62	0.02	-	- 1.62	
Memo: international marine bunkers	-	*0.31*	-	-	*0.31*	*800.0%*
Memo: international aviation	-	*1.43*	-	-	*1.43*	*121.6%*

* Other includes industrial waste and non-renewable municipal waste.

Key sources for CO$_2$ emissions from fuel combustion in 2006

IPCC source category	CO$_2$ emissions (Mt of CO$_2$)	% change 90-06	Level assessment (%) **	Cumulative total (%)
Road - oil	10.22	56.1%	14.3	14.3
Manufacturing industries - oil	5.35	44.8%	7.5	21.8
Main activity prod. elec. and heat - gas	2.18	x	3.1	24.9
Manufacturing industries - coal/peat	2.05	270.1%	2.9	27.8
Residential - oil	1.69	-31.7%	2.4	30.1
Non-specified other sectors - oil	1.27	-17.0%	1.8	31.9
Main activity prod. elec. and heat - oil	1.05	30.6%	1.5	33.4
Other energy industries - oil	0.98	39.9%	1.4	34.8
Main activity prod. elec. and heat - coal/peat	0.91	x	1.3	36.0
Other energy industries - gas	0.88	20.4%	1.2	37.3
Manufacturing industries - gas	0.65	999.6%	0.9	38.2
Memo: total CO$_2$ from fuel combustion	*27.93*	*45.4%*	*39.2*	*39.2*

** Percent calculated using the total GHG estimate for CO$_2$, CH$_4$, N$_2$O, HFCs, PFCs and SF$_6$ excluding CO$_2$ emissions/removals from land use change and forestry.

Philippines

Figure 1. CO₂ emissions by fuel

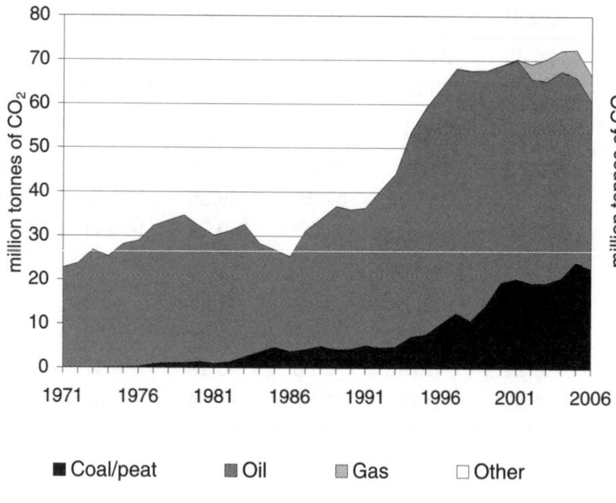

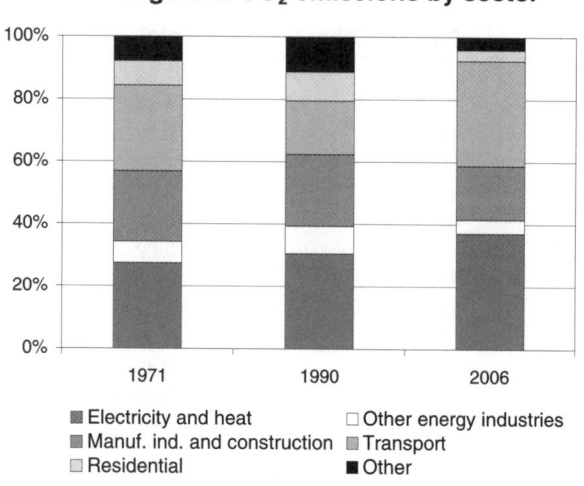

■ Coal/peat   ■ Oil   ■ Gas   □ Other

Figure 2. CO₂ emissions by sector

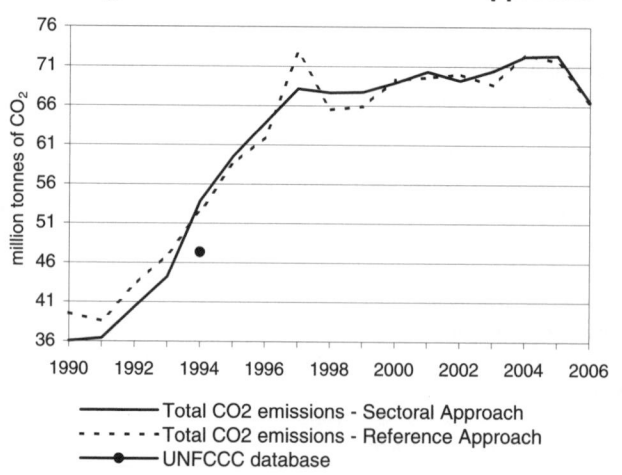

■ Electricity and heat   □ Other energy industries
■ Manuf. ind. and construction   ■ Transport
□ Residential   ■ Other

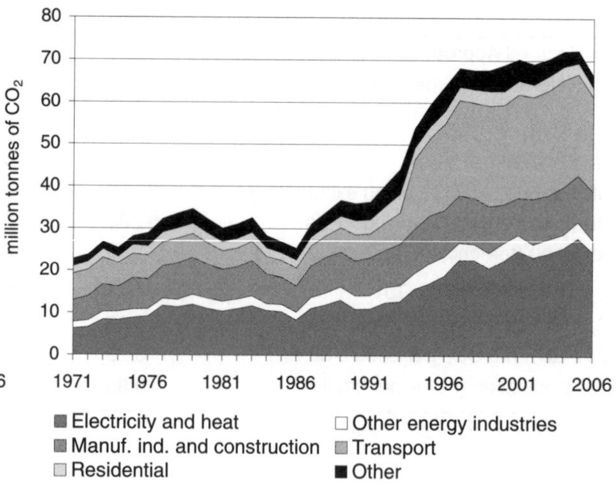

Figure 3. CO₂ emissions by sector

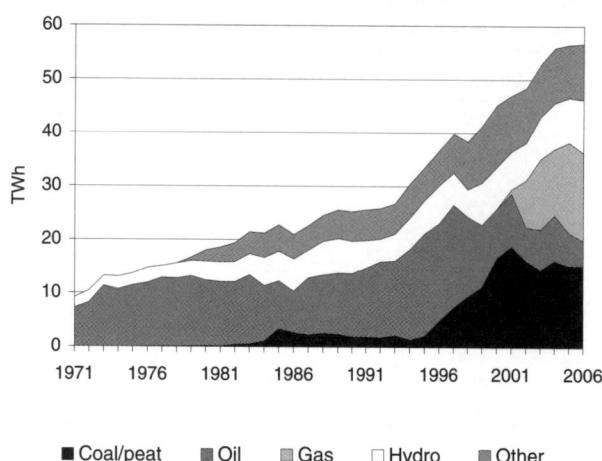

■ Electricity and heat   □ Other energy industries
■ Manuf. ind. and construction   ■ Transport
□ Residential   ■ Other

Figure 4. Reference vs Sectoral Approach

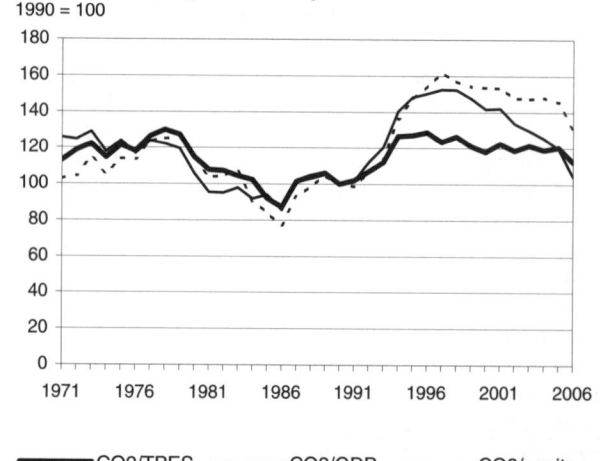

—— Total CO2 emissions - Sectoral Approach
- - - - Total CO2 emissions - Reference Approach
——●—— UNFCCC database

Figure 5. Electricity generation by fuel

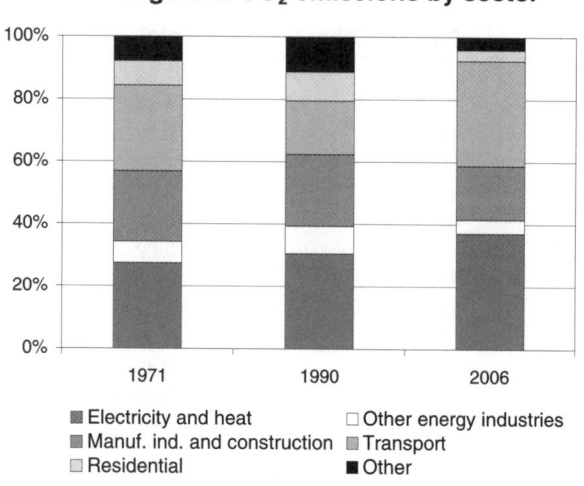

■ Coal/peat   ■ Oil   ■ Gas   □ Hydro   ■ Other

Figure 6. Key indicators

1990 = 100

—— CO2/TPES   —— CO2/GDP   - - - - CO2/capita

Philippines
Key indicators

	1990	1995	2000	2003	2004	2005	2006	% change 90-06
CO$_2$ Sectoral Approach (Mt of CO$_2$)	36.05	59.46	68.92	70.41	72.25	72.39	66.50	84.5%
CO$_2$ Reference Approach (Mt of CO$_2$)	39.56	58.53	69.34	68.64	72.58	71.60	66.35	67.7%
TPES (PJ)	1 095	1 422	1 776	1 762	1 844	1 827	1 799	64.2%
TPES (Mtoe)	26.16	33.96	42.42	42.08	44.03	43.64	42.97	64.2%
GDP (billion 2000 US$ using exch. rates)	56.23	62.59	75.91	84.66	89.90	94.37	99.43	76.8%
GDP (billion 2000 US$ using PPPs)	226.29	251.89	305.50	340.71	361.78	379.77	400.16	76.8%
Population (millions)	61.23	68.59	76.21	81.17	82.87	84.57	86.26	40.9%
CO$_2$ / TPES (t CO$_2$ per TJ)	32.9	41.8	38.8	40.0	39.2	39.6	37.0	12.3%
CO$_2$ / GDP (kg CO$_2$ per 2000 US$)	0.64	0.95	0.91	0.83	0.80	0.77	0.67	4.3%
CO$_2$ / GDP (kg CO$_2$ per 2000 US$ PPP)	0.16	0.24	0.23	0.21	0.20	0.19	0.17	4.3%
CO$_2$ / population (t CO$_2$ per capita)	0.59	0.87	0.90	0.87	0.87	0.86	0.77	30.9%

Ratios are based on the Sectoral Approach.

2006 CO$_2$ emissions by sector

million tonnes of CO$_2$	Coal/peat	Oil	Gas	Other *	Total	% change 90-06
Sectoral Approach	**22.77**	**37.91**	**5.82**	-	**66.50**	**84.5%**
Main activity producer elec. and heat	15.76	3.10	5.82	-	24.68	133.8%
Unallocated autoproducers	..	..	..	..	..	..
Other energy industries	1.16	1.75	-	-	2.91	-8.5%
Manufacturing industries and construction	5.85	5.56	-	-	11.41	37.8%
Transport	-	22.38	-	-	22.38	261.3%
of which: road	-	*17.98*	-	-	*17.98*	*243.1%*
Other sectors	-	5.13	-	-	5.13	-30.8%
of which: residential	-	*2.35*	-	-	*2.35*	*-29.4%*
Reference Approach	**22.44**	**38.08**	**5.82**	-	**66.35**	**67.7%**
Diff. due to losses and/or transformation	0.03	- 0.19	-	-	- 0.16	
Statistical differences	- 0.36	0.37	-	-	0.01	
Memo: international marine bunkers	-	*0.40*	-	-	*0.40*	*8.3%*
Memo: international aviation	-	*2.53*	-	-	*2.53*	*59.8%*

* Other includes industrial waste and non-renewable municipal waste.

Key sources for CO$_2$ emissions from fuel combustion in 2006

IPCC source category	CO$_2$ emissions (Mt of CO$_2$)	% change 90-06	Level assessment (%) **	Cumulative total (%)
Road - oil	17.98	243.1%	13.0	13.0
Main activity prod. elec. and heat - coal/peat	15.76	771.3%	11.4	24.5
Manufacturing industries - coal/peat	5.85	195.8%	4.2	28.7
Main activity prod. elec. and heat - gas	5.82	x	4.2	32.9
Manufacturing industries - oil	5.56	-11.8%	4.0	37.0
Other transport - oil	4.39	361.7%	3.2	40.1
Main activity prod. elec. and heat - oil	3.10	-64.6%	2.2	42.4
Non-specified other sectors - oil	2.78	-32.0%	2.0	44.4
Residential - oil	2.35	-29.4%	1.7	46.1
Other energy industries - oil	1.75	-33.8%	1.3	47.4
Other energy industries - coal/peat	1.16	116.0%	0.8	48.2
Memo: total CO$_2$ from fuel combustion	*66.50*	*84.5%*	*48.2*	*48.2*

** Percent calculated using the total GHG estimate for CO$_2$, CH$_4$, N$_2$O, HFCs, PFCs and SF$_6$ excluding CO$_2$ emissions/removals from land use change and forestry.

Poland / Pologne

Figure 1. CO$_2$ emissions by fuel

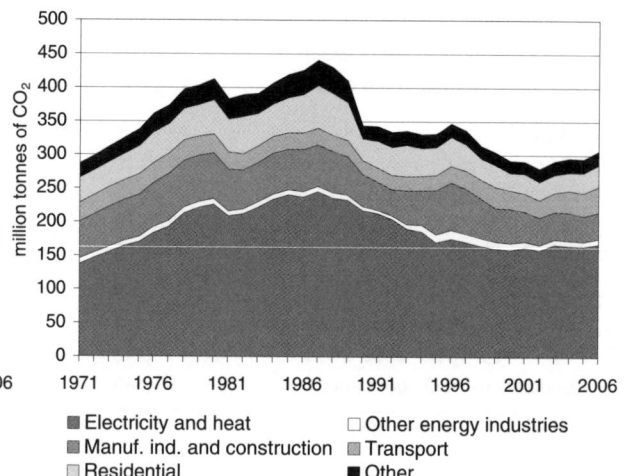

■ Coal/peat   ■ Oil   ■ Gas   □ Other

Figure 2. CO$_2$ emissions by sector

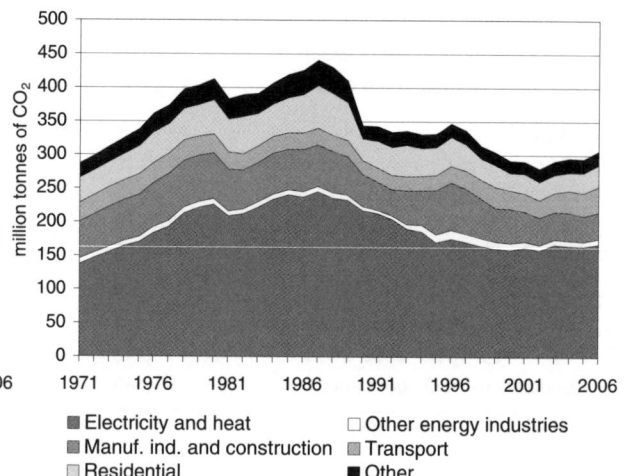

■ Electricity and heat   □ Other energy industries
■ Manuf. ind. and construction   ■ Transport
□ Residential   ■ Other

Figure 3. CO$_2$ emissions by sector

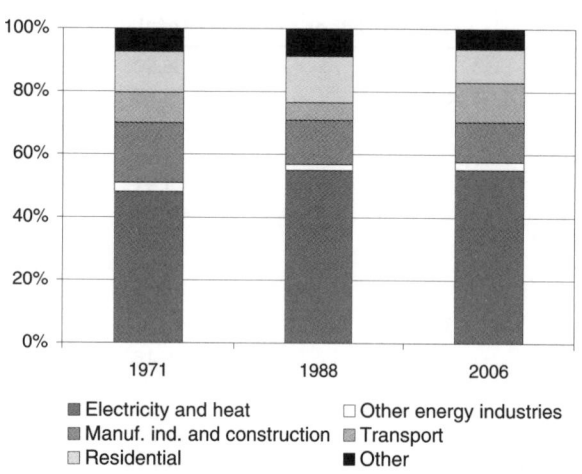

■ Electricity and heat   □ Other energy industries
■ Manuf. ind. and construction   ■ Transport
□ Residential   ■ Other

Figure 4. Reference vs Sectoral Approach

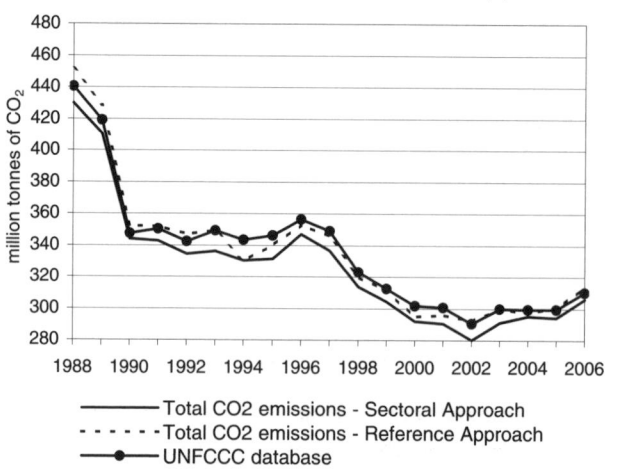

—— Total CO2 emissions - Sectoral Approach
- - - - Total CO2 emissions - Reference Approach
—●— UNFCCC database

Figure 5. Electricity generation by fuel

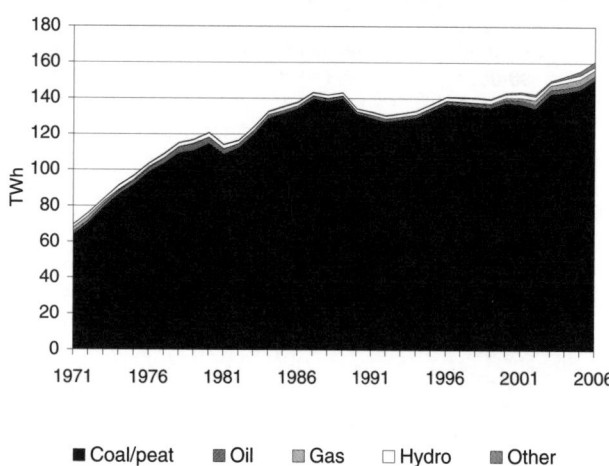

■ Coal/peat   ■ Oil   ■ Gas   □ Hydro   ■ Other

Figure 6. Key indicators

1988 = 100

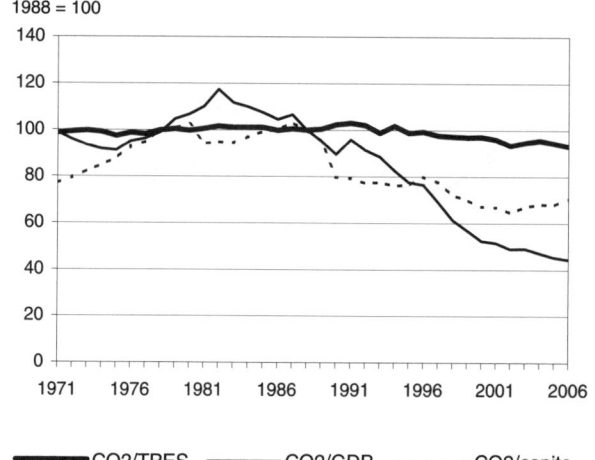

—— CO2/TPES   —— CO2/GDP   - - - - CO2/capita

Poland / Pologne *

Key indicators

	1988	1990	1995	2003	2004	2005	2006	% change 88-06
CO$_2$ Sectoral Approach (Mt of CO$_2$)	429.78	343.93	331.46	291.19	295.16	294.20	305.96	-28.8%
CO$_2$ Reference Approach (Mt of CO$_2$)	451.45	352.26	340.18	299.64	297.73	300.56	313.88	-30.5%
TPES (PJ)	5 347	4 181	4 176	3 827	3 840	3 881	4 091	-23.5%
TPES (Mtoe)	127.72	99.87	99.75	91.40	91.71	92.69	97.72	-23.5%
GDP (billion 2000 US$ using exch. rates)	132.19	118.20	131.60	182.60	192.40	199.40	211.60	60.1%
GDP (billion 2000 US$ using PPPs)	311.89	278.62	310.26	430.60	453.61	470.02	498.83	59.9%
Population (millions)	37.86	38.03	38.28	38.20	38.18	38.16	38.13	0.7%
CO$_2$ / TPES (t CO$_2$ per TJ)	80.4	82.3	79.4	76.1	76.9	75.8	74.8	-7.0%
CO$_2$ / GDP (kg CO$_2$ per 2000 US$)	3.25	2.91	2.52	1.59	1.53	1.48	1.45	-55.5%
CO$_2$ / GDP (kg CO$_2$ per 2000 US$ PPP)	1.38	1.23	1.07	0.68	0.65	0.63	0.61	-55.5%
CO$_2$ / population (t CO$_2$ per capita)	11.35	9.04	8.66	7.62	7.73	7.71	8.02	-29.3%

Ratios are based on the Sectoral Approach.
* According to the provisions of Article 4.6 of the Convention and Decisions 9/CP.2 and 11/CP.4, Poland is allowed to use 1988 as the base year.

2006 CO$_2$ emissions by sector

million tonnes of CO$_2$	Coal/peat	Oil	Gas	Other **	Total	% change 88-06
Sectoral Approach	**215.95**	**60.16**	**27.04**	**2.81**	**305.96**	**-28.8%**
Main activity producer elec. and heat	153.99	0.64	2.62	0.00	157.25	-5.5%
Unallocated autoproducers	8.86	1.31	0.33	0.56	11.06	-84.0%
Other energy industries	2.91	2.99	2.11	0.03	8.04	-0.8%
Manufacturing industries and construction	20.37	6.41	9.89	2.22	38.89	-36.1%
Transport	-	37.42	0.75	-	38.18	59.7%
of which: road	-	*36.66*	-	-	*36.66*	*80.3%*
Other sectors	29.82	11.39	11.33	-	52.54	-48.1%
of which: residential	*22.50*	*2.23*	*7.74*	-	*32.47*	*-48.4%*
Reference Approach	**221.76**	**61.89**	**27.42**	**2.81**	**313.88**	**-30.5%**
Diff. due to losses and/or transformation	1.40	1.86	0.29	-	3.54	
Statistical differences	4.42	- 0.13	0.09	- 0.00	4.37	
Memo: international marine bunkers	-	*0.93*	-	-	*0.93*	*-46.5%*
Memo: international aviation	-	*1.27*	-	-	*1.27*	*13.3%*

** Other includes industrial waste and non-renewable municipal waste.

Key sources for CO$_2$ emissions from fuel combustion in 2006

IPCC source category	CO$_2$ emissions (Mt of CO$_2$)	% change 88-06	Level assessment (%) ***	Cumulative total (%)
Main activity prod. elec. and heat - coal/peat	153.99	-6.6%	38.9	38.9
Road - oil	36.66	80.3%	9.3	48.1
Residential - coal/peat	22.50	-60.4%	5.7	53.8
Manufacturing industries - coal/peat	20.37	-50.5%	5.1	59.0
Manufacturing industries - gas	9.89	-12.9%	2.5	61.5
Non-specified other sectors - oil	9.16	135.9%	2.3	63.8
Unallocated autoproducers - coal/peat	8.86	-86.0%	2.2	66.0
Residential - gas	7.74	35.2%	2.0	68.0
Non-specified other sectors - coal/peat	7.32	-78.1%	1.8	69.8
Manufacturing industries - oil	6.41	-1.2%	1.6	71.4
Non-specified other sectors - gas	3.60	374.2%	0.9	72.3
Memo: total CO$_2$ from fuel combustion	*305.96*	*-28.8%*	*77.2*	*77.2*

*** Percent calculated using the total GHG estimate for CO$_2$, CH$_4$, N$_2$O, HFCs, PFCs and SF$_6$ excluding CO$_2$ emissions/removals from land use change and forestry.

Portugal

Figure 1. CO₂ emissions by fuel

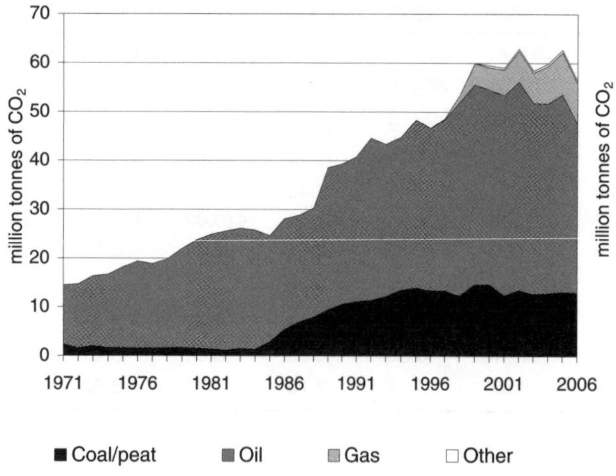

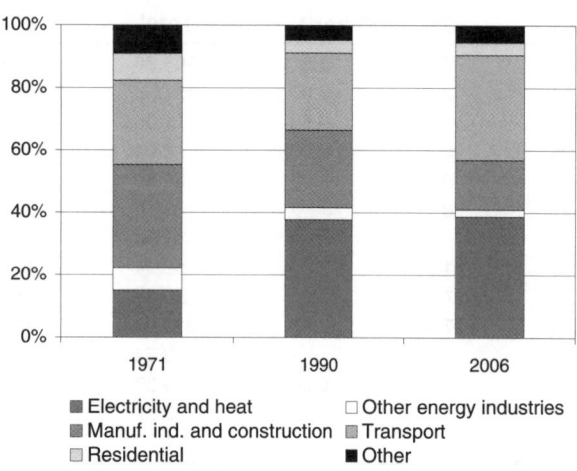

Figure 2. CO₂ emissions by sector

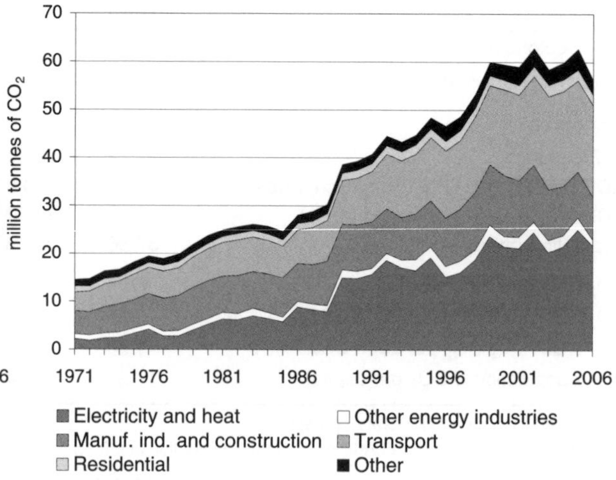

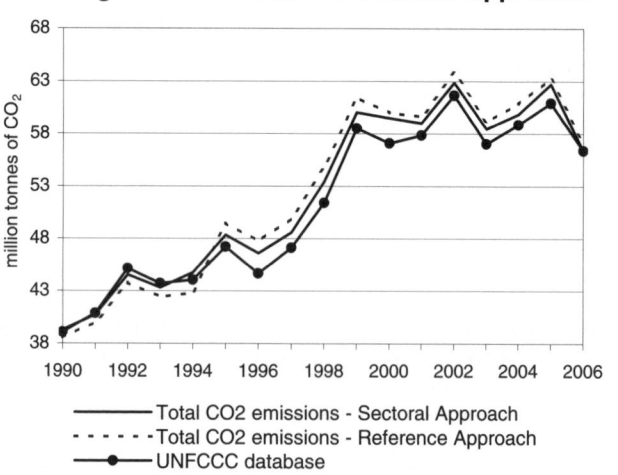

Figure 3. CO₂ emissions by sector

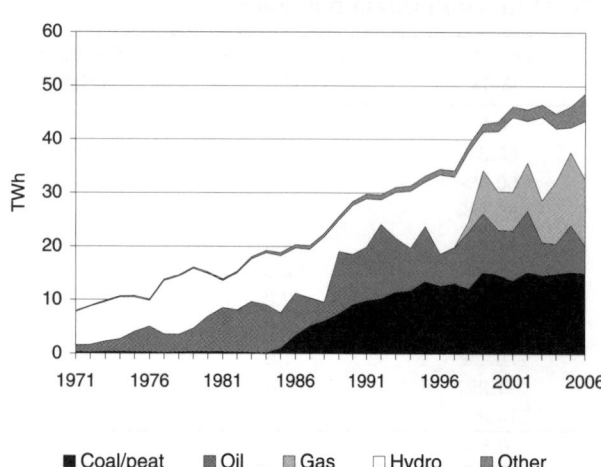

Figure 4. Reference vs Sectoral Approach

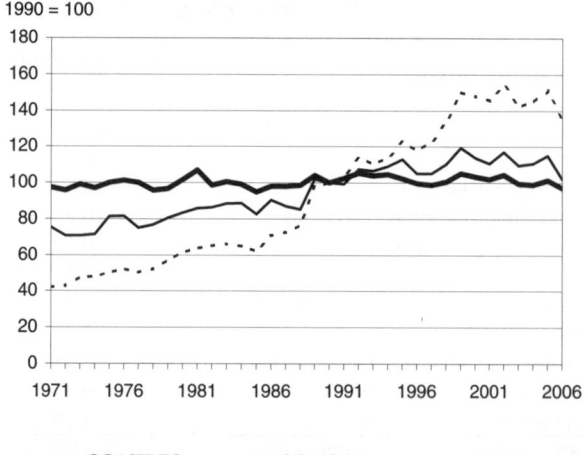

Figure 5. Electricity generation by fuel

Figure 6. Key indicators

Portugal
Key indicators

	1990	1995	2000	2003	2004	2005	2006	% change 90-06
CO$_2$ Sectoral Approach (Mt of CO$_2$)	39.28	48.33	59.49	58.44	59.85	62.71	56.33	43.4%
CO$_2$ Reference Approach (Mt of CO$_2$)	38.54	49.45	60.00	59.13	60.90	63.31	57.12	48.2%
TPES (PJ)	722	867	1 057	1 079	1 111	1 137	1 065	47.5%
TPES (Mtoe)	17.24	20.71	25.24	25.76	26.53	27.15	25.43	47.5%
GDP (billion 2000 US$ using exch. rates)	84.70	92.20	112.70	114.90	116.60	117.50	118.90	40.4%
GDP (billion 2000 US$ using PPPs)	131.30	142.88	174.53	177.96	180.65	181.98	184.16	40.3%
Population (millions)	10.00	10.03	10.23	10.44	10.50	10.55	10.58	5.9%
CO$_2$ / TPES (t CO$_2$ per TJ)	54.4	55.7	56.3	54.2	53.9	55.2	52.9	-2.8%
CO$_2$ / GDP (kg CO$_2$ per 2000 US$)	0.46	0.52	0.53	0.51	0.51	0.53	0.47	2.2%
CO$_2$ / GDP (kg CO$_2$ per 2000 US$ PPP)	0.30	0.34	0.34	0.33	0.33	0.34	0.31	2.2%
CO$_2$ / population (t CO$_2$ per capita)	3.93	4.82	5.82	5.60	5.70	5.94	5.32	35.4%

Ratios are based on the Sectoral Approach.

2006 CO$_2$ emissions by sector

million tonnes of CO$_2$	Coal/peat	Oil	Gas	Other *	Total	% change 90-06
Sectoral Approach	**12.95**	**34.61**	**8.28**	**0.48**	**56.33**	**43.4%**
Main activity producer elec. and heat	12.85	2.46	3.86	-	19.16	34.7%
Unallocated autoproducers	-	1.09	1.10	0.48	2.67	355.3%
Other energy industries	-	1.05	0.21	-	1.26	-17.9%
Manufacturing industries and construction	0.11	6.54	2.25	-	8.90	-8.6%
Transport	-	18.96	0.02	-	18.98	96.1%
of which: road	-	*18.27*	*0.02*	-	*18.30*	*102.4%*
Other sectors	-	4.52	0.85	-	5.37	52.1%
of which: residential	-	*1.75*	*0.47*	-	*2.22*	*36.5%*
Reference Approach	**12.85**	**35.29**	**8.50**	**0.48**	**57.12**	**48.2%**
Diff. due to losses and/or transformation	-	0.37	0.22	-	0.59	
Statistical differences	- 0.11	0.30	0.00	-	0.20	
Memo: international marine bunkers	-	*2.00*	-	-	*2.00*	*4.6%*
Memo: international aviation	-	*2.28*	-	-	*2.28*	*53.0%*

* Other includes industrial waste and non-renewable municipal waste.

Key sources for CO$_2$ emissions from fuel combustion in 2006

IPCC source category	CO$_2$ emissions (Mt of CO$_2$)	% change 90-06	Level assessment (%) **	Cumulative total (%)
Road - oil	18.27	102.1%	22.1	22.1
Main activity prod. elec. and heat - coal/peat	12.85	63.1%	15.5	37.6
Manufacturing industries - oil	6.54	-11.1%	7.9	45.5
Main activity prod. elec. and heat - gas	3.86	x	4.7	50.2
Non-specified other sectors - oil	2.77	48.0%	3.3	53.6
Main activity prod. elec. and heat - oil	2.46	-61.3%	3.0	56.5
Manufacturing industries - gas	2.25	x	2.7	59.2
Residential - oil	1.75	14.3%	2.1	61.4
Unallocated autoproducers - gas	1.10	x	1.3	62.7
Unallocated autoproducers - oil	1.09	173.9%	1.3	64.0
Other energy industries - oil	1.05	-29.9%	1.3	65.3
Memo: total CO$_2$ from fuel combustion	*56.33*	*43.4%*	*68.1*	*68.1*

** Percent calculated using the total GHG estimate for CO$_2$, CH$_4$, N$_2$O, HFCs, PFCs and SF$_6$ excluding CO$_2$ emissions/removals from land use change and forestry.

Qatar

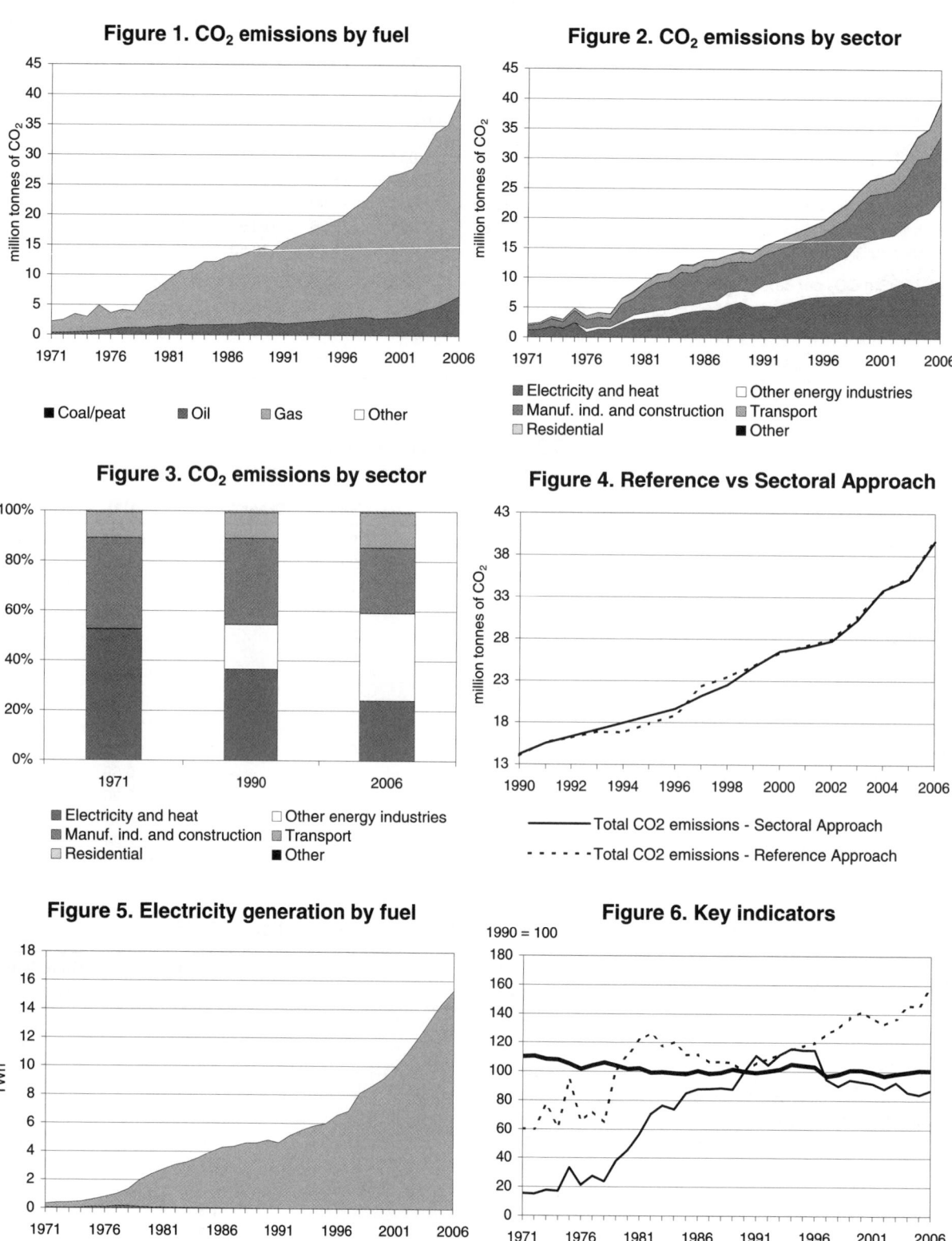

Figure 1. CO₂ emissions by fuel

Figure 2. CO₂ emissions by sector

Figure 3. CO₂ emissions by sector

Figure 4. Reference vs Sectoral Approach

Figure 5. Electricity generation by fuel

Figure 6. Key indicators

Qatar
Key indicators

	1990	1995	2000	2003	2004	2005	2006	% change 90-06
CO_2 Sectoral Approach (Mt of CO_2)	14.19	18.78	26.52	30.23	33.84	35.20	39.67	179.6%
CO_2 Reference Approach (Mt of CO_2)	13.97	17.85	26.40	30.67	33.82	35.42	39.87	185.3%
TPES (PJ)	273	347	506	590	654	672	758	178.0%
TPES (Mtoe)	6.52	8.28	12.08	14.10	15.62	16.05	18.12	178.0%
GDP (billion 2000 US$ using exch. rates)	8.82	10.18	17.76	20.34	24.57	26.07	28.36	221.5%
GDP (billion 2000 US$ using PPPs)	7.90	9.12	15.91	18.22	22.01	23.35	25.40	221.5%
Population (millions)	0.47	0.53	0.62	0.73	0.76	0.80	0.82	75.8%
CO_2 / TPES (t CO_2 per TJ)	52.0	54.2	52.5	51.2	51.8	52.4	52.3	0.6%
CO_2 / GDP (kg CO_2 per 2000 US$)	1.61	1.85	1.49	1.49	1.38	1.35	1.40	-13.0%
CO_2 / GDP (kg CO_2 per 2000 US$ PPP)	1.80	2.06	1.67	1.66	1.54	1.51	1.56	-13.0%
CO_2 / population (t CO_2 per capita)	30.38	35.71	42.99	41.59	44.30	44.22	48.32	59.1%

Ratios are based on the Sectoral Approach.

2006 CO_2 emissions by sector

million tonnes of CO_2	Coal/peat	Oil	Gas	Other *	Total	% change 90-06
Sectoral Approach	-	6.59	33.08	-	39.67	179.6%
Main activity producer elec. and heat	-	-	2.88	-	2.88	139.2%
Unallocated autoproducers	-	-	6.71	-	6.71	68.5%
Other energy industries	-	0.54	13.34	-	13.88	449.5%
Manufacturing industries and construction	-	0.27	10.14	-	10.42	111.6%
Transport	-	5.59	-	-	5.59	283.3%
of which: road	-	5.59	-	-	5.59	283.3%
Other sectors	-	0.19	-	-	0.19	106.0%
of which: residential	-	0.19	-	-	0.19	106.0%
Reference Approach	-	6.79	33.08	-	39.87	185.3%
Diff. due to losses and/or transformation	-	0.10	-	-	0.10	
Statistical differences	-	0.10	0.00	-	0.10	
Memo: international marine bunkers	-	..	-	-	..	..
Memo: international aviation	-	1.82	-	-	1.82	430.3%

* Other includes industrial waste and non-renewable municipal waste.

Key sources for CO_2 emissions from fuel combustion in 2006

IPCC source category	CO_2 emissions (Mt of CO_2)	% change 90-06	Level assessment (%) **	Cumulative total (%)
Other energy industries - gas	13.34	511.1%	28.8	28.8
Manufacturing industries - gas	10.14	111.8%	21.9	50.7
Unallocated autoproducers - gas	6.71	68.5%	14.5	65.1
Road - oil	5.59	283.3%	12.1	77.2
Main activity prod. elec. and heat - gas	2.88	139.2%	6.2	83.4
Other energy industries - oil	0.54	57.6%	1.2	84.6
Manufacturing industries - oil	0.27	104.0%	0.6	85.2
Residential - oil	0.19	106.0%	0.4	85.6
-	-	-	-	-
-	-	-	-	-
-	-	-	-	-
Memo: total CO_2 from fuel combustion	39.67	179.6%	85.6	85.6

** Percent calculated using the total GHG estimate for CO_2, CH_4, N_2O, HFCs, PFCs and SF_6 excluding CO_2 emissions/removals from land use change and forestry.

Romania / Roumanie

Figure 1. CO₂ emissions by fuel

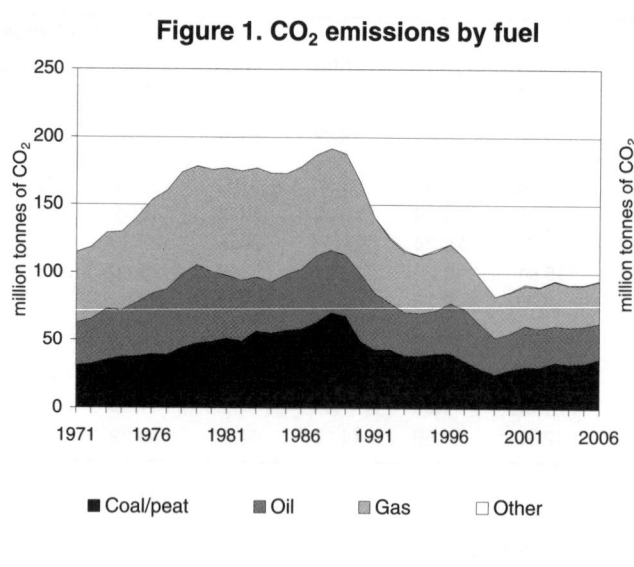

Coal/peat ■ Oil ■ Gas □ Other

Figure 2. CO₂ emissions by sector

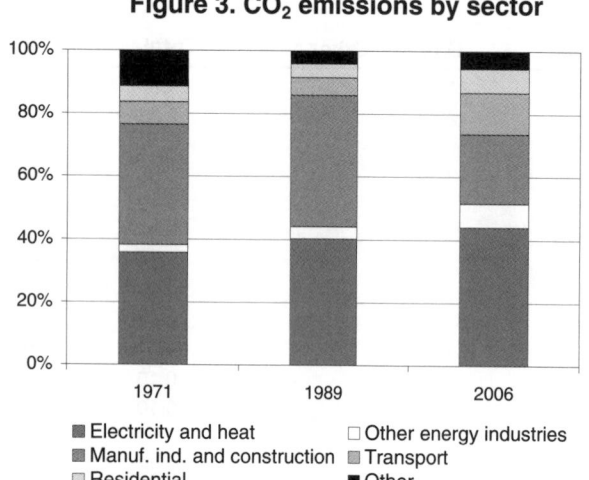

■ Electricity and heat □ Other energy industries
■ Manuf. ind. and construction ■ Transport
□ Residential ■ Other

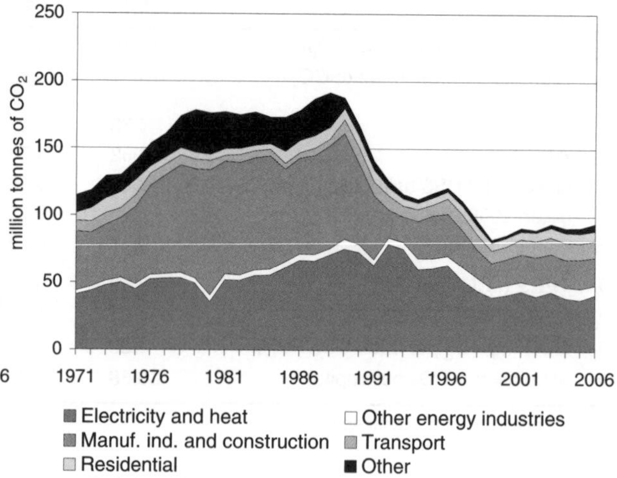

Figure 3. CO₂ emissions by sector

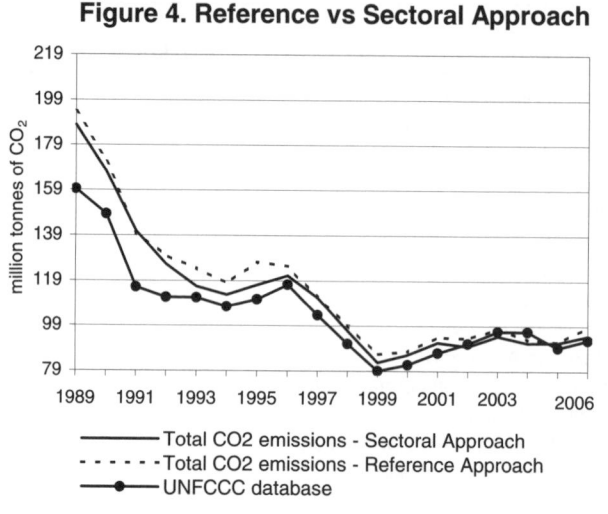

■ Electricity and heat □ Other energy industries
■ Manuf. ind. and construction ■ Transport
□ Residential ■ Other

Figure 4. Reference vs Sectoral Approach

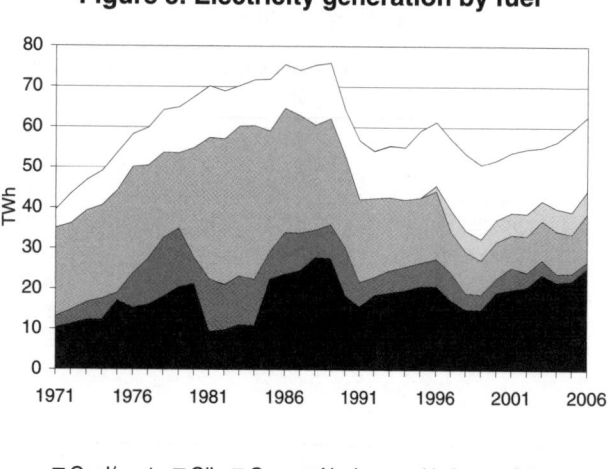

——— Total CO2 emissions - Sectoral Approach
- - - - Total CO2 emissions - Reference Approach
—●— UNFCCC database

Figure 5. Electricity generation by fuel

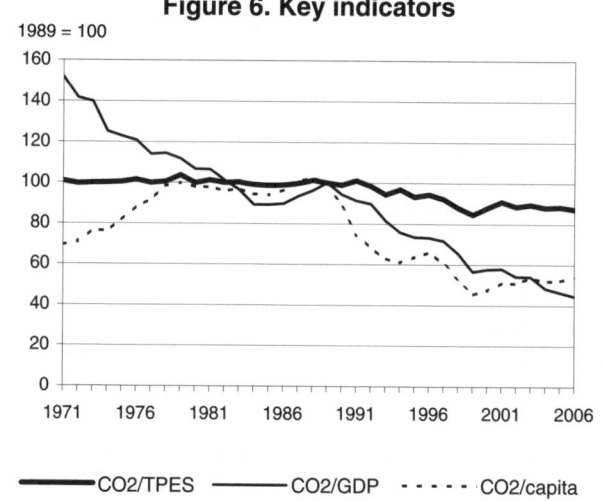

■ Coal/peat ■ Oil ■ Gas □ Nuclear □ Hydro ■ Other

Figure 6. Key indicators

1989 = 100

——— CO2/TPES ——— CO2/GDP - - - - CO2/capita

Romania / Roumanie *

Key indicators

	1989	1990	1995	2003	2004	2005	2006	% change 89-06
CO₂ Sectoral Approach (Mt of CO₂)	187.82	167.08	117.07	94.44	91.53	91.70	94.68	-49.6%
CO₂ Reference Approach (Mt of CO₂)	193.68	171.76	127.17	97.73	92.93	91.94	98.56	-49.1%
TPES (PJ)	2 907	2 616	1 946	1 635	1 612	1 608	1 681	-42.2%
TPES (Mtoe)	69.44	62.49	46.47	39.06	38.50	38.40	40.15	-42.2%
GDP (billion 2000 US$ using exch. rates)	46.60	43.99	39.50	43.30	46.94	48.86	52.63	12.9%
GDP (billion 2000 US$ using PPPs)	166.36	157.05	141.03	154.59	167.58	174.45	187.88	12.9%
Population (millions)	23.15	23.21	22.68	21.74	21.69	21.63	21.59	-6.7%
CO₂ / TPES (t CO₂ per TJ)	64.6	63.9	60.2	57.8	56.8	57.0	56.3	-12.8%
CO₂ / GDP (kg CO₂ per 2000 US$)	4.03	3.80	2.96	2.18	1.95	1.88	1.80	-55.4%
CO₂ / GDP (kg CO₂ per 2000 US$ PPP)	1.13	1.06	0.83	0.61	0.55	0.53	0.50	-55.4%
CO₂ / population (t CO₂ per capita)	8.11	7.20	5.16	4.34	4.22	4.24	4.39	-45.9%

Ratios are based on the Sectoral Approach.
* According to the provisions of Article 4.6 of the Convention and Decisions 9/CP.2 and 11/CP.4, Romania is allowed to use 1989 as the base year.

2006 CO₂ emissions by sector

million tonnes of CO₂	Coal/peat	Oil	Gas	Other **	Total	% change 89-06
Sectoral Approach	**36.54**	**26.85**	**30.92**	**0.37**	**94.68**	**-49.6%**
Main activity producer elec. and heat	26.89	1.94	9.37	-	38.20	-44.6%
Unallocated autoproducers	2.17	0.61	0.59	0.00	3.37	-47.9%
Other energy industries	0.61	4.66	1.79	0.15	7.21	-1.4%
Manufacturing industries and construction	6.79	4.60	9.35	0.20	20.94	-73.3%
Transport	-	12.37	0.07	-	12.44	18.6%
of which: road	-	*11.97*	-	-	*11.97*	*33.3%*
Other sectors	0.08	2.68	9.75	0.01	12.52	-22.5%
of which: residential	*0.04*	*1.27*	*5.95*	-	*7.26*	*-12.8%*
Reference Approach	**38.42**	**26.21**	**33.57**	**0.37**	**98.56**	**-49.1%**
Diff. due to losses and/or transformation	1.84	- 1.69	2.06	-	2.20	
Statistical differences	0.03	1.05	0.59	- 0.00	1.68	
Memo: international marine bunkers	-	..	-	-	..	..
Memo: international aviation	-	*0.40*	-	-	*0.40*	*-45.7%*

** Other includes industrial waste and non-renewable municipal waste.

Key sources for CO₂ emissions from fuel combustion in 2006

IPCC source category	CO₂ emissions (Mt of CO₂)	% change 89-06	Level assessment (%) ***	Cumulative total (%)
Main activity prod. elec. and heat - coal/peat	26.89	-22.7%	17.0	17.0
Road - oil	11.97	33.3%	7.5	24.5
Main activity prod. elec. and heat - gas	9.37	-57.9%	5.9	30.4
Manufacturing industries - gas	9.35	-79.5%	5.9	36.3
Manufacturing industries - coal/peat	6.79	-69.6%	4.3	40.6
Residential - gas	5.95	17.3%	3.8	44.4
Other energy industries - oil	4.66	-26.6%	2.9	47.3
Manufacturing industries - oil	4.60	-55.7%	2.9	50.2
Non-specified other sectors - gas	3.80	91.5%	2.4	52.6
Unallocated autoproducers - coal/peat	2.17	-66.4%	1.4	54.0
Main activity prod. elec. and heat - oil	1.94	-83.8%	1.2	55.2
Memo: total CO₂ from fuel combustion	*94.68*	*-49.6%*	*59.7*	*59.7*

*** Percent calculated using the total GHG estimate for CO₂, CH₄, N₂O, HFCs, PFCs and SF₆ excluding CO₂ emissions/removals from land use change and forestry.

Russia / Russie

Figure 1. CO_2 emissions by fuel

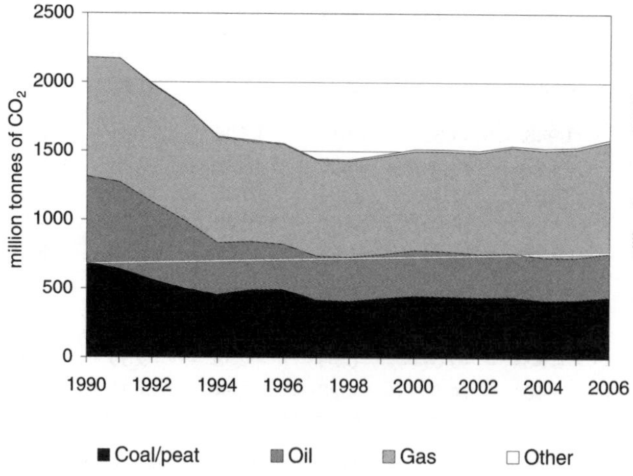

million tonnes of CO2
2500
2000
1500
1000
500
0
1990
1992
1994
1996
1998
2000
2002
2004
2006
Coal/peat
Oil
Gas
Other

Figure 2. CO_2 emissions by sector

million tonnes of CO2
2500
2000
1500
1000
500
0
1990
1992
1994
1996
1998
2000
2002
2004
2006
Electricity and heat
Other energy industries
Manuf. ind. and construction
Transport
Residential
Other

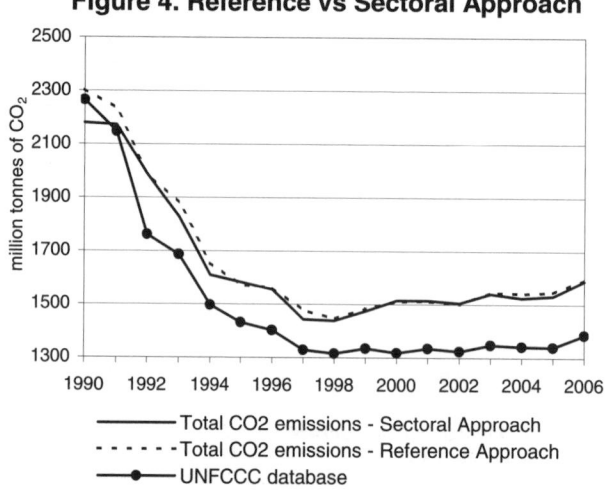

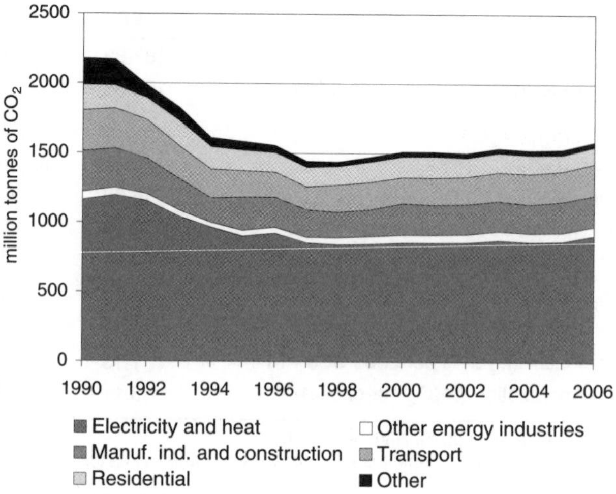

Figure 3. CO_2 emissions by sector

100%
80%
60%
40%
20%
0%
not available
1971
1990
2006
Electricity and heat
Other energy industries
Manuf. ind. and construction
Transport
Residential
Other

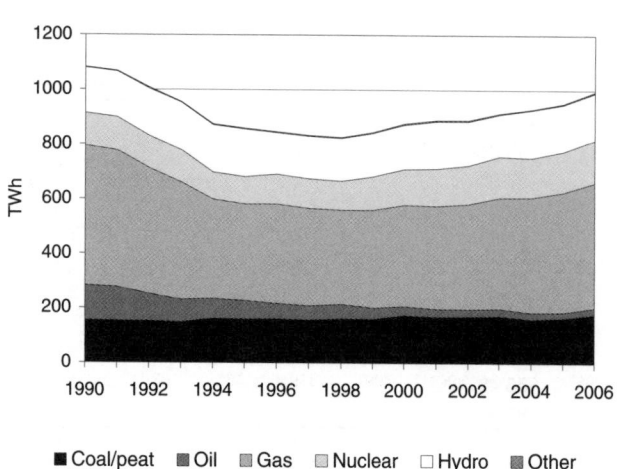

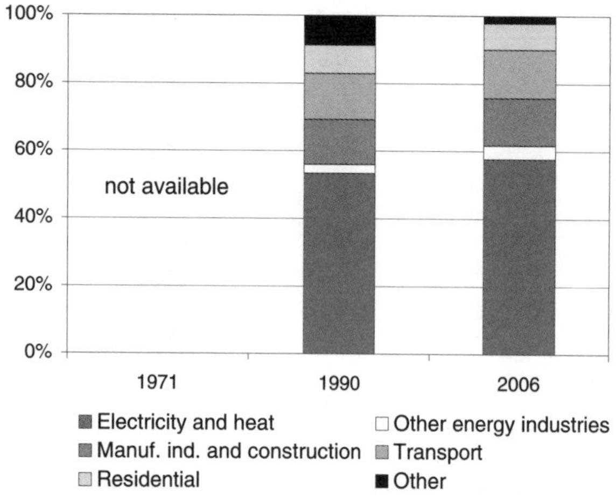

Figure 4. Reference vs Sectoral Approach

million tonnes of CO2
2500
2300
2100
1900
1700
1500
1300
1990
1992
1994
1996
1998
2000
2002
2004
2006
Total CO2 emissions - Sectoral Approach
Total CO2 emissions - Reference Approach
UNFCCC database

Figure 5. Electricity generation by fuel

TWh
1200
1000
800
600
400
200
0
1990
1992
1994
1996
1998
2000
2002
2004
2006
Coal/peat
Oil
Gas
Nuclear
Hydro
Other

Figure 6. Key indicators

1990 = 100
140
120
100
80
60
40
20
0
1990
1992
1994
1996
1998
2000
2002
2004
2006
CO2/TPES
CO2/GDP
CO2/capita

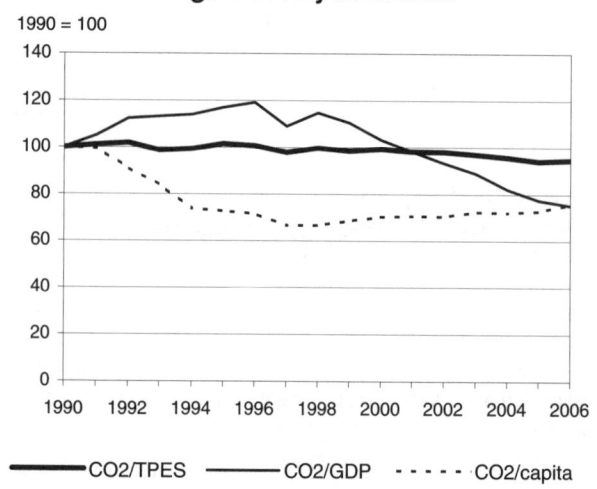

Russia / Russie

Key indicators

	1990	1995	2000	2003	2004	2005	2006	% change 90-06
CO$_2$ Sectoral Approach (Mt of CO$_2$)	2 179.9	1 582.9	1 513.8	1 540.0	1 524.1	1 531.2	1 587.2	-27.2%
CO$_2$ Reference Approach (Mt of CO$_2$)	2 302.6	1 573.1	1 510.7	1 544.3	1 540.6	1 545.0	1 595.3	-30.7%
TPES (PJ)	36 798	26 329	25 732	26 814	26 892	27 483	28 311	-23.1%
TPES (Mtoe)	878.9	628.9	614.6	640.4	642.3	656.4	676.2	-23.1%
GDP (billion 2000 US$ using exch. rates)	385.9	239.7	259.7	306.6	328.7	349.8	373.2	-3.3%
GDP (billion 2000 US$ using PPPs)	1 523.6	946.5	1 025.4	1 210.7	1 297.9	1 381.0	1 473.5	-3.3%
Population (millions)	148.3	148.1	146.3	144.6	143.9	143.2	142.5	-3.9%
CO$_2$ / TPES (t CO$_2$ per TJ)	59.2	60.1	58.8	57.4	56.7	55.7	56.1	-5.4%
CO$_2$ / GDP (kg CO$_2$ per 2000 US$)	5.65	6.60	5.83	5.02	4.64	4.38	4.25	-24.7%
CO$_2$ / GDP (kg CO$_2$ per 2000 US$ PPP)	1.43	1.67	1.48	1.27	1.17	1.11	1.08	-24.7%
CO$_2$ / population (t CO$_2$ per capita)	14.70	10.69	10.35	10.65	10.60	10.70	11.14	-24.2%

Ratios are based on the Sectoral Approach.

2006 CO$_2$ emissions by sector

million tonnes of CO$_2$	Coal/peat	Oil	Gas	Other *	Total	% change 90-06
Sectoral Approach	**444.6**	**321.0**	**804.5**	**17.1**	**1 587.2**	**-27.2%**
Main activity producer elec. and heat	221.1	20.6	305.6	0.1	547.4	-52.9%
Unallocated autoproducers	132.4	34.1	185.3	14.3	366.0	x
Other energy industries	3.4	35.8	24.9	1.4	65.5	15.6%
Manufacturing industries and construction	66.7	46.4	107.8	1.3	222.2	-24.0%
Transport	-	148.8	78.4	-	227.2	-23.3%
of which: road	*-*	*119.7*	*0.1*	*-*	*119.7*	*-21.4%*
Other sectors	21.0	35.3	102.4	0.1	158.8	-57.4%
of which: residential	*12.0*	*18.3*	*92.4*	*-*	*122.8*	*-32.5%*
Reference Approach	**417.2**	**338.8**	**821.3**	**18.0**	**1 595.3**	**-30.7%**
Diff. due to losses and/or transformation	- 27.4	17.8	16.9	0.9	8.1	
Statistical differences	- 0.0	- 0.0	- 0.0	-	- 0.0	
Memo: international marine bunkers	*-*	*..*	*-*	*-*	*..*	*..*
Memo: international aviation	*-*	*16.1*	*-*	*-*	*16.1*	*-38.8%*

* Other includes industrial waste and non-renewable municipal waste.

Key sources for CO$_2$ emissions from fuel combustion in 2006

IPCC source category	CO$_2$ emissions (Mt of CO$_2$)	% change 90-06	Level assessment (%) **	Cumulative total (%)
Main activity prod. elec. and heat - gas	305.6	-42.6%	12.8	12.8
Main activity prod. elec. and heat - coal/peat	221.1	-48.8%	9.2	22.0
Unallocated autoproducers - gas	185.3	x	7.7	29.8
Unallocated autoproducers - coal/peat	132.4	x	5.5	35.3
Road - oil	119.7	-20.1%	5.0	40.3
Manufacturing industries - gas	107.8	3.3%	4.5	44.8
Residential - gas	92.4	-16.1%	3.9	48.7
Other transport - gas	78.4	1.8%	3.3	51.9
Manufacturing industries - coal/peat	66.7	-34.6%	2.8	54.7
Manufacturing industries - oil	46.4	-46.0%	1.9	56.7
Other energy industries - oil	35.8	-7.4%	1.5	58.2
Memo: total CO$_2$ from fuel combustion	*1 587.2*	*-27.2%*	*66.3*	*66.3*

** Percent calculated using the total GHG estimate for CO$_2$, CH$_4$, N$_2$O, HFCs, PFCs and SF$_6$ excluding CO$_2$ emissions/removals from land use change and forestry.

Saudi Arabia / Arabie saoudite

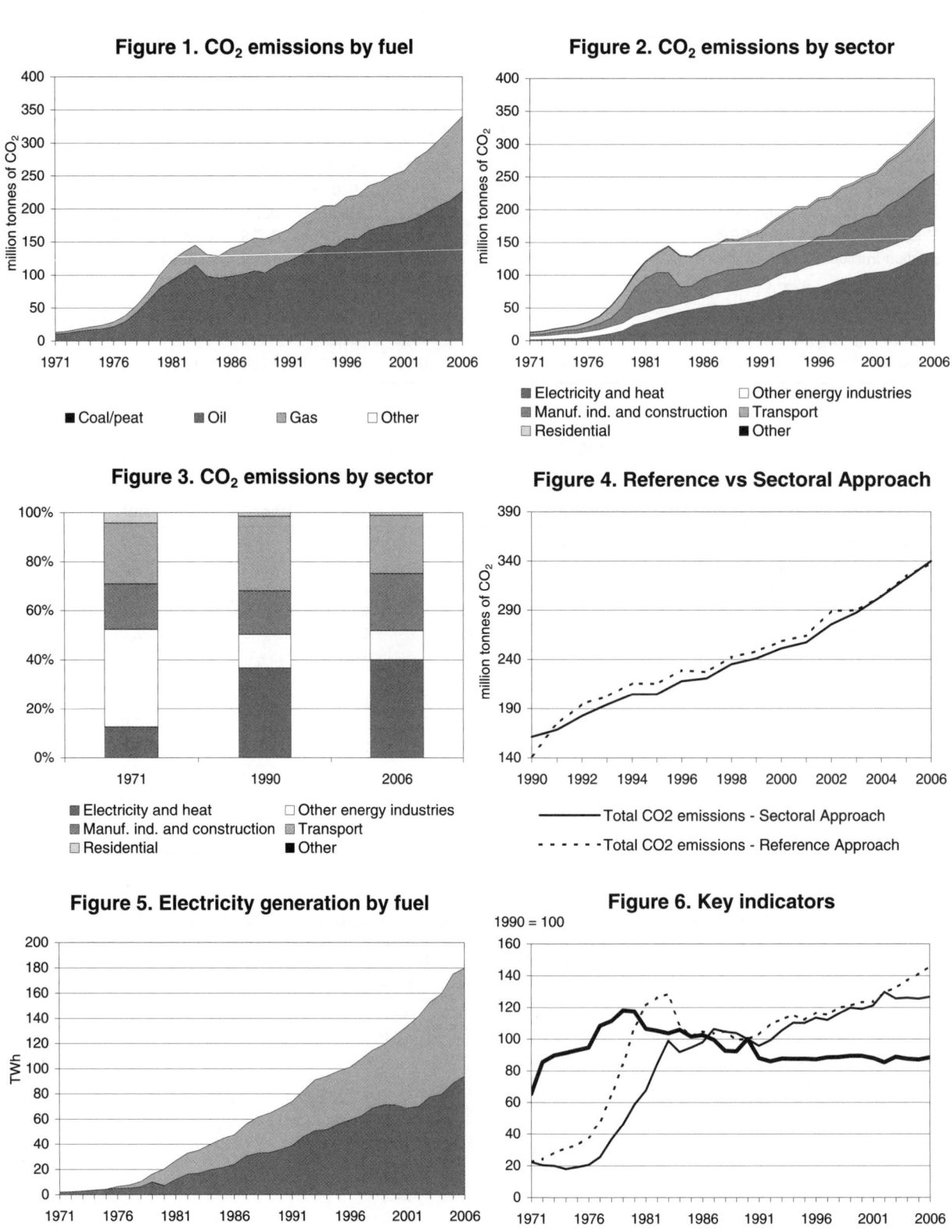

Figure 1. CO₂ emissions by fuel

■ Coal/peat　■ Oil　▨ Gas　□ Other

Figure 2. CO₂ emissions by sector

■ Electricity and heat　□ Other energy industries
■ Manuf. ind. and construction　▨ Transport
▨ Residential　■ Other

Figure 3. CO₂ emissions by sector

■ Electricity and heat　□ Other energy industries
■ Manuf. ind. and construction　▨ Transport
▨ Residential　■ Other

Figure 4. Reference vs Sectoral Approach

——— Total CO2 emissions - Sectoral Approach
- - - - - Total CO2 emissions - Reference Approach

Figure 5. Electricity generation by fuel

■ Oil　▨ Gas

Figure 6. Key indicators

1990 = 100

——— CO2/TPES　——— CO2/GDP　- - - - CO2/capita

Saudi Arabia / Arabie saoudite

Key indicators

	1990	1995	2000	2003	2004	2005	2006	% change 90-06
CO$_2$ Sectoral Approach (Mt of CO$_2$)	161.41	204.53	251.11	287.47	303.64	321.92	340.03	110.7%
CO$_2$ Reference Approach (Mt of CO$_2$)	141.94	215.24	258.34	289.80	304.03	324.41	337.56	137.8%
TPES (PJ)	2 568	3 721	4 471	5 150	5 524	5 883	6 117	138.2%
TPES (Mtoe)	61.33	88.87	106.80	123.01	131.93	140.50	146.11	138.2%
GDP (billion 2000 US$ using exch. rates)	144.13	166.00	188.44	204.25	215.00	229.10	239.64	66.3%
GDP (billion 2000 US$ using PPPs)	214.80	247.40	280.85	304.40	320.44	341.44	357.15	66.3%
Population (millions)	16.38	18.51	20.66	22.05	22.53	23.12	23.68	44.6%
CO$_2$ / TPES (t CO$_2$ per TJ)	62.9	55.0	56.2	55.8	55.0	54.7	55.6	-11.6%
CO$_2$ / GDP (kg CO$_2$ per 2000 US$)	1.12	1.23	1.33	1.41	1.41	1.41	1.42	26.7%
CO$_2$ / GDP (kg CO$_2$ per 2000 US$ PPP)	0.75	0.83	0.89	0.94	0.95	0.94	0.95	26.7%
CO$_2$ / population (t CO$_2$ per capita)	9.85	11.05	12.15	13.03	13.48	13.92	14.36	45.7%

Ratios are based on the Sectoral Approach.

2006 CO$_2$ emissions by sector

million tonnes of CO$_2$	Coal/peat	Oil	Gas	Other *	Total	% change 90-06
Sectoral Approach	-	**226.69**	**113.34**	-	**340.03**	**110.7%**
Main activity producer elec. and heat	-	68.49	43.73	-	112.22	181.8%
Unallocated autoproducers	-	1.65	21.93	-	23.58	22.9%
Other energy industries	-	16.94	23.37	-	40.31	82.9%
Manufacturing industries and construction	-	54.87	24.31	-	79.19	175.1%
Transport	-	81.06	-	-	81.06	65.3%
of which: road	-	79.25	-	-	79.25	68.6%
Other sectors	-	3.67	-	-	3.67	46.1%
of which: residential	-	3.67	-	-	3.67	46.1%
Reference Approach	-	**224.22**	**113.34**	-	**337.56**	**137.8%**
Diff. due to losses and/or transformation	-	- 2.47	-	-	- 2.47	
Statistical differences	-	-	0.00	-	0.00	
Memo: international marine bunkers	-	8.27	-	-	8.27	44.1%
Memo: international aviation	-	5.43	-	-	5.43	-11.7%

* Other includes industrial waste and non-renewable municipal waste.

Key sources for CO$_2$ emissions from fuel combustion in 2006

IPCC source category	CO$_2$ emissions (Mt of CO$_2$)	% change 90-06	Level assessment (%) **	Cumulative total (%)
Road - oil	79.25	68.6%	18.6	18.6
Main activity prod. elec. and heat - oil	68.49	142.0%	16.1	34.6
Manufacturing industries - oil	54.87	160.4%	12.9	47.5
Main activity prod. elec. and heat - gas	43.73	279.3%	10.3	57.7
Manufacturing industries - gas	24.31	215.1%	5.7	63.4
Other energy industries - gas	23.37	128.5%	5.5	68.9
Unallocated autoproducers - gas	21.93	26.5%	5.1	74.1
Other energy industries - oil	16.94	43.4%	4.0	78.0
Residential - oil	3.67	46.1%	0.9	78.9
Other transport - oil	1.81	-11.7%	0.4	79.3
Unallocated autoproducers - oil	1.65	-11.3%	0.4	79.7
Memo: total CO$_2$ from fuel combustion	340.03	110.7%	79.7	79.7

** Percent calculated using the total GHG estimate for CO$_2$, CH$_4$, N$_2$O, HFCs, PFCs and SF$_6$ excluding CO$_2$ emissions/removals from land use change and forestry.

Senegal / Sénégal

Figure 1. CO$_2$ emissions by fuel

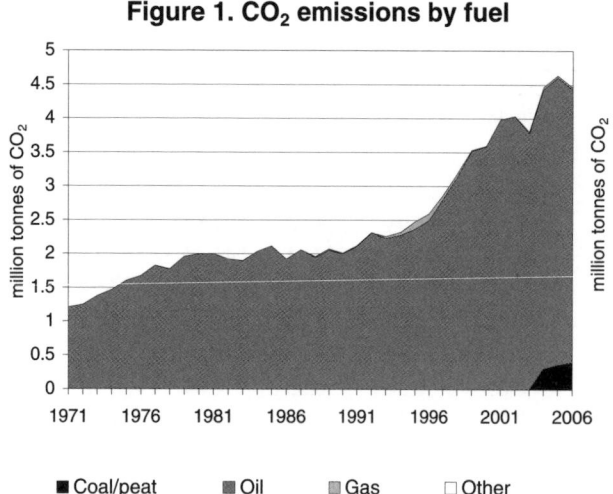

- Coal/peat
- Oil
- Gas
- Other

Figure 2. CO$_2$ emissions by sector

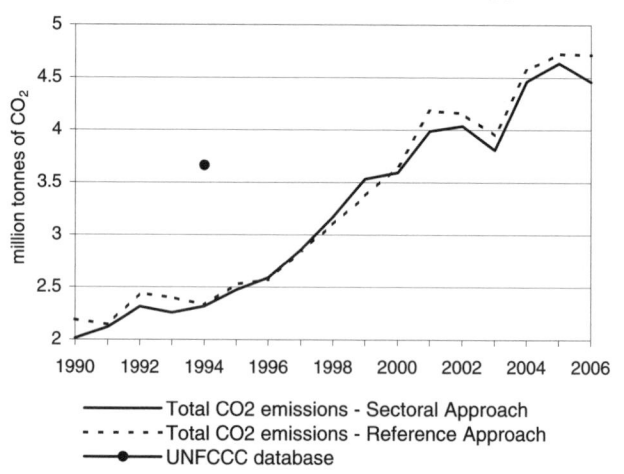

- Electricity and heat
- Other energy industries
- Manuf. ind. and construction
- Transport
- Residential
- Other

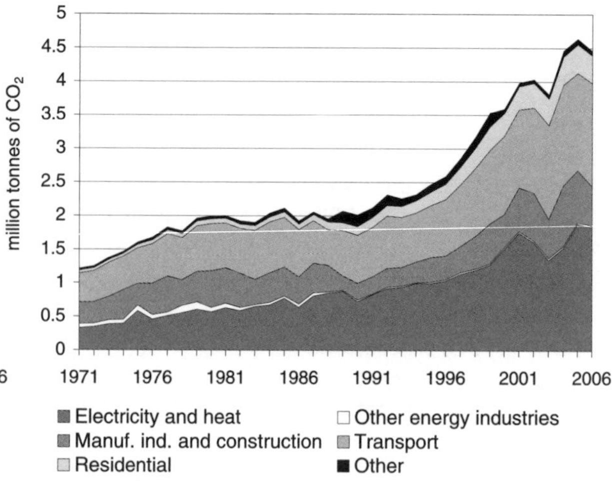

Figure 3. CO$_2$ emissions by sector

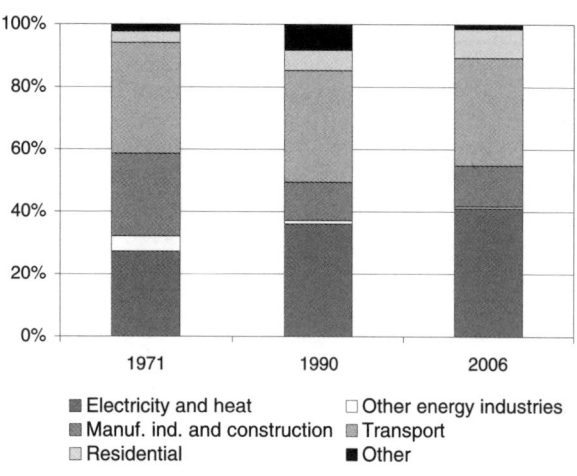

- Electricity and heat
- Other energy industries
- Manuf. ind. and construction
- Transport
- Residential
- Other

Figure 4. Reference vs Sectoral Approach

- Total CO2 emissions - Sectoral Approach
- Total CO2 emissions - Reference Approach
- UNFCCC database

Figure 5. Electricity generation by fuel

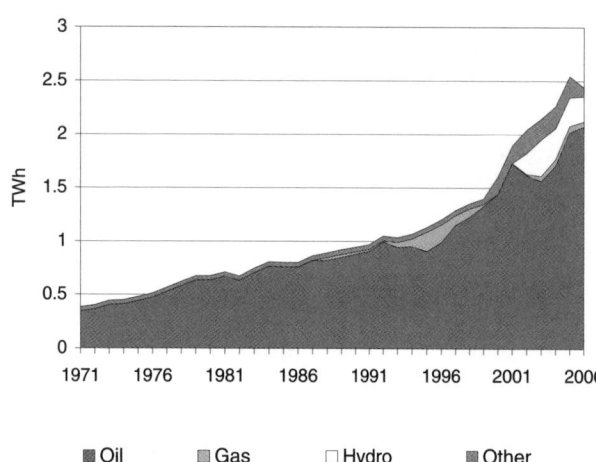

- Oil
- Gas
- Hydro
- Other

Figure 6. Key indicators

1990 = 100

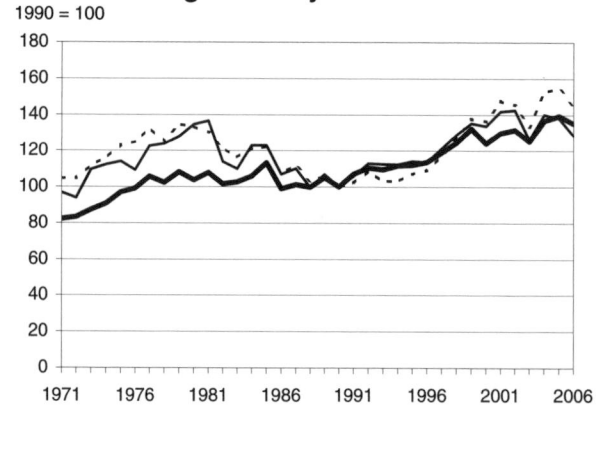

- CO2/TPES
- CO2/GDP
- CO2/capita

Senegal / Sénégal

Key indicators

	1990	1995	2000	2003	2004	2005	2006	% change 90-06
CO$_2$ Sectoral Approach (Mt of CO$_2$)	2.01	2.47	3.59	3.81	4.46	4.64	4.46	121.6%
CO$_2$ Reference Approach (Mt of CO$_2$)	2.19	2.53	3.65	3.95	4.57	4.73	4.72	115.6%
TPES (PJ)	77	84	111	116	125	127	126	63.9%
TPES (Mtoe)	1.84	2.02	2.65	2.78	2.98	3.04	3.02	63.9%
GDP (billion 2000 US$ using exch. rates)	3.27	3.52	4.37	4.91	5.18	5.47	5.65	72.5%
GDP (billion 2000 US$ using PPPs)	11.05	11.90	14.77	16.58	17.51	18.46	19.07	72.6%
Population (millions)	7.90	9.05	10.33	11.18	11.47	11.77	12.07	52.9%
CO$_2$ / TPES (t CO$_2$ per TJ)	26.1	29.3	32.4	32.7	35.7	36.4	35.3	35.2%
CO$_2$ / GDP (kg CO$_2$ per 2000 US$)	0.61	0.70	0.82	0.78	0.86	0.85	0.79	28.4%
CO$_2$ / GDP (kg CO$_2$ per 2000 US$ PPP)	0.18	0.21	0.24	0.23	0.26	0.25	0.23	28.4%
CO$_2$ / population (t CO$_2$ per capita)	0.25	0.27	0.35	0.34	0.39	0.39	0.37	44.9%

Ratios are based on the Sectoral Approach.

2006 CO$_2$ emissions by sector

million tonnes of CO$_2$	Coal/peat	Oil	Gas	Other *	Total	% change 90-06
Sectoral Approach	0.40	4.03	0.02	-	4.46	121.6%
Main activity producer elec. and heat	-	1.63	0.02	-	1.65	131.7%
Unallocated autoproducers	-	0.18	-	-	0.18	+
Other energy industries	-	0.03	-	-	0.03	14.3%
Manufacturing industries and construction	0.40	0.18	-	-	0.58	138.3%
Transport	-	1.54	-	-	1.54	112.9%
of which: road	-	*1.46*	-	-	*1.46*	*121.1%*
Other sectors	-	0.48	-	-	0.48	61.6%
of which: residential	-	*0.41*	-	-	*0.41*	*220.9%*
Reference Approach	0.40	4.29	0.02	-	4.72	115.6%
Diff. due to losses and/or transformation	-	0.03	-	-	0.03	
Statistical differences	-	0.23	-	-	0.23	
Memo: international marine bunkers	-	*0.24*	-	-	*0.24*	*115.0%*
Memo: international aviation	-	*0.80*	-	-	*0.80*	*75.9%*

* Other includes industrial waste and non-renewable municipal waste.

Key sources for CO$_2$ emissions from fuel combustion in 2006

IPCC source category	CO$_2$ emissions (Mt of CO$_2$)	% change 90-06	Level assessment (%) **	Cumulative total (%)
Main activity prod. elec. and heat - oil	1.63	132.5%	7.4	7.4
Road - oil	1.46	121.1%	6.6	14.0
Residential - oil	0.41	220.9%	1.9	15.9
Manufacturing industries - coal/peat	0.40	x	1.8	17.7
Manufacturing industries - oil	0.18	-25.4%	0.8	18.5
Unallocated autoproducers - oil	0.18	+	0.8	19.3
Other transport - oil	0.08	24.8%	0.3	19.7
Non-specified other sectors - oil	0.07	-60.2%	0.3	20.0
Other energy industries - oil	0.03	14.3%	0.1	20.1
Main activity prod. elec. and heat - gas	0.02	86.5%	0.1	20.2
-	-	-	-	-
Memo: total CO$_2$ from fuel combustion	*4.46*	*121.6%*	*20.2*	*20.2*

** Percent calculated using the total GHG estimate for CO$_2$, CH$_4$, N$_2$O, HFCs, PFCs and SF$_6$ excluding CO$_2$ emissions/removals from land use change and forestry.

Serbia / Serbie

Figure 1. CO₂ emissions by fuel

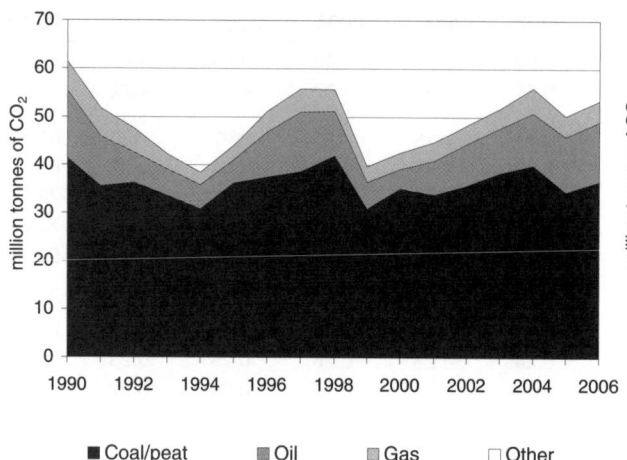

Figure 2. CO₂ emissions by sector

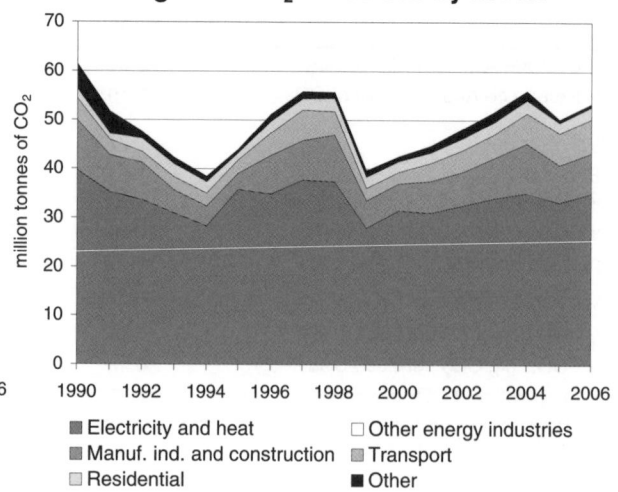

Figure 3. CO₂ emissions by sector

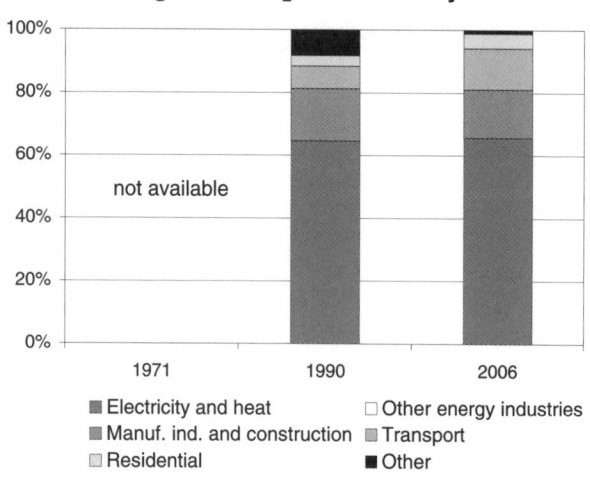

Figure 4. Reference vs Sectoral Approach

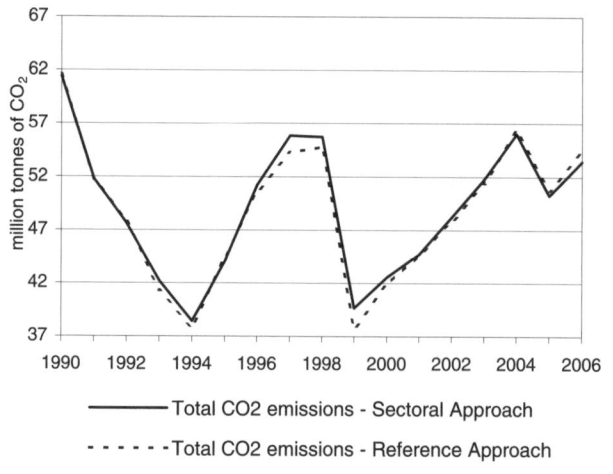

Figure 5. Electricity generation by fuel

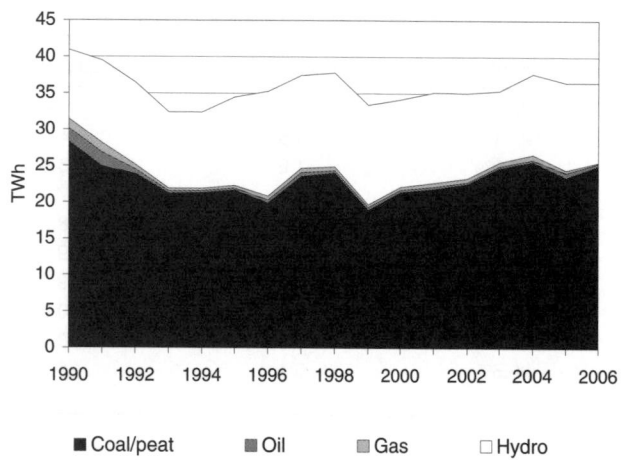

Figure 6. Key indicators

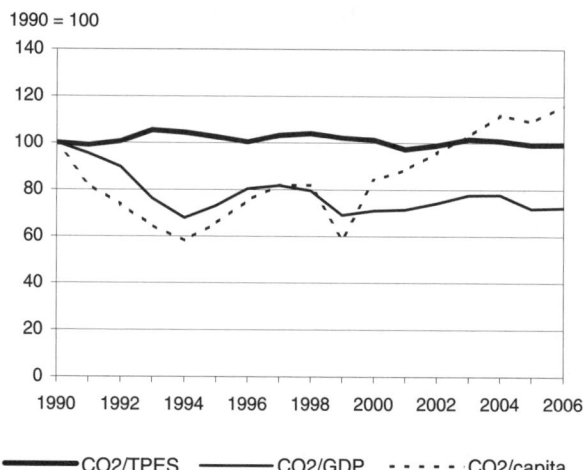

Serbia / Serbie *

Key indicators

	1990	1995	2000	2003	2004	2005	2006	% change 90-06
CO$_2$ Sectoral Approach (Mt of CO$_2$)	61.44	44.01	42.54	51.77	56.03	50.23	53.43	-13.0%
CO$_2$ Reference Approach (Mt of CO$_2$)	61.58	44.41	41.88	51.42	56.37	50.74	54.35	-11.7%
TPES (PJ)	816	570	559	678	738	673	715	-12.4%
TPES (Mtoe)	19.49	13.62	13.34	16.19	17.63	16.08	17.07	-12.4%
GDP (billion 2000 US$ using exch. rates)	10.15	9.94	9.91	11.02	11.90	11.56	12.23	20.4%
GDP (billion 2000 US$ using PPPs)	37.38	36.61	36.48	40.57	43.82	42.56	45.01	20.4%
Population (millions)	9.93	10.86	8.19	8.12	8.08	7.44	7.44	-25.1%
CO$_2$ / TPES (t CO$_2$ per TJ)	75.3	77.2	76.2	76.4	75.9	74.6	74.8	-0.7%
CO$_2$ / GDP (kg CO$_2$ per 2000 US$)	6.05	4.43	4.29	4.70	4.71	4.35	4.37	-27.8%
CO$_2$ / GDP (kg CO$_2$ per 2000 US$ PPP)	1.64	1.20	1.17	1.28	1.28	1.18	1.19	-27.8%
CO$_2$ / population (t CO$_2$ per capita)	6.19	4.05	5.20	6.38	6.93	6.75	7.18	16.1%

Ratios are based on the Sectoral Approach.

* Data for Serbia include Montenegro until 2004 and Kosovo until 1999.

2006 CO$_2$ emissions by sector

million tonnes of CO$_2$	Coal/peat	Oil	Gas	Other **	Total	% change 90-06
Sectoral Approach	**36.60**	**12.46**	**4.35**	**0.02**	**53.43**	**-13.0%**
Main activity producer elec. and heat	30.41	0.78	0.96	-	32.15	-19.0%
Unallocated autoproducers	1.40	1.05	0.43	0.02	2.90	x
Other energy industries	-	-	-	-	-	-
Manufacturing industries and construction	2.51	3.25	2.46	-	8.22	-19.4%
Transport	0.00	7.02	-	-	7.02	58.7%
of which: road	-	7.02	-	-	7.02	58.6%
Other sectors	2.28	0.36	0.50	-	3.14	-55.9%
of which: residential	1.93	0.08	0.50	-	2.51	24.8%
Reference Approach	**36.34**	**13.64**	**4.35**	**0.02**	**54.35**	**-11.7%**
Diff. due to losses and/or transformation	0.66	1.18	-	-	1.84	
Statistical differences	- 0.92	0.00	- 0.00	-	- 0.92	
Memo: international marine bunkers	-	..	-	-	..	..
Memo: international aviation	-	0.16	-	-	0.16	-62.9%

** Other includes industrial waste and non-renewable municipal waste.

Key sources for CO$_2$ emissions from fuel combustion in 2006

IPCC source category	CO$_2$ emissions (Mt of CO$_2$)	% change 90-06	Level assessment (%) ***	Cumulative total (%)
Main activity prod. elec. and heat - coal/peat	30.41	-18.9%	45.3	45.3
Road - oil	7.02	58.6%	10.4	55.7
Manufacturing industries - oil	3.25	-52.4%	4.8	60.5
Manufacturing industries - coal/peat	2.51	62.1%	3.7	64.3
Manufacturing industries - gas	2.46	35.4%	3.7	67.9
Residential - coal/peat	1.93	4.0%	2.9	70.8
Unallocated autoproducers - coal/peat	1.40	x	2.1	72.9
Unallocated autoproducers - oil	1.05	x	1.6	74.5
Main activity prod. elec. and heat - gas	0.96	81.3%	1.4	75.9
Main activity prod. elec. and heat - oil	0.78	-54.1%	1.2	77.1
Residential - gas	0.50	x	0.7	77.8
Memo: total CO$_2$ from fuel combustion	53.43	-13.0%	79.5	79.5

*** Percent calculated using the total GHG estimate for CO$_2$, CH$_4$, N$_2$O, HFCs, PFCs and SF$_6$ excluding CO$_2$ emissions/removals from land use change and forestry.

Singapore / Singapour

Figure 1. CO₂ emissions by fuel

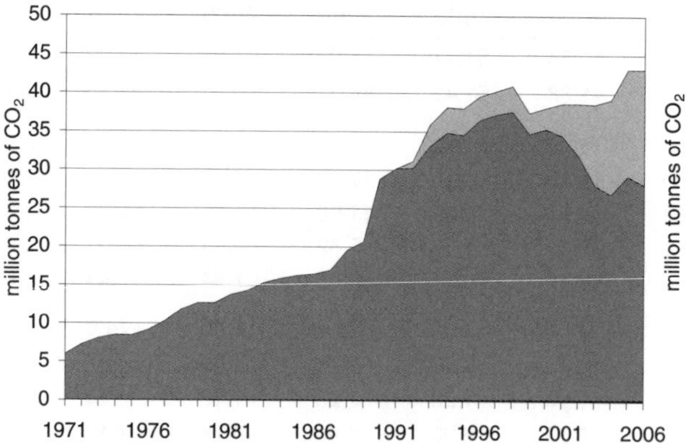

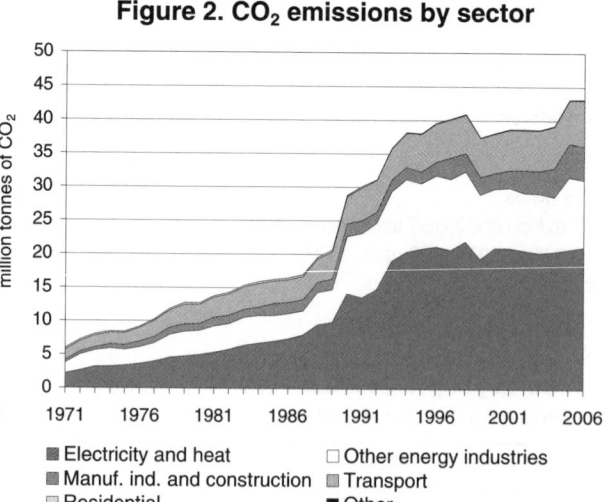

Figure 2. CO₂ emissions by sector

Figure 3. CO₂ emissions by sector

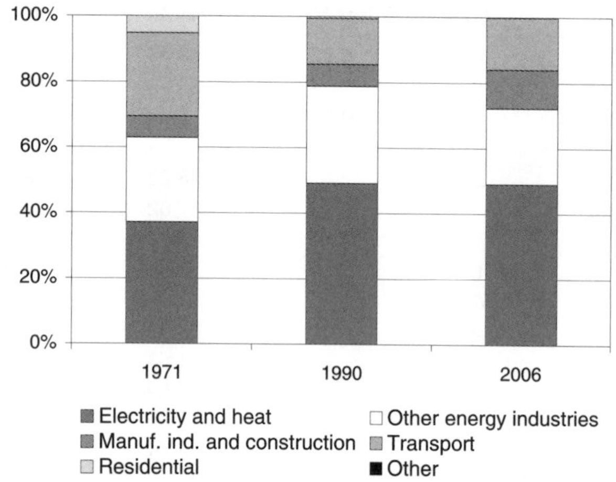

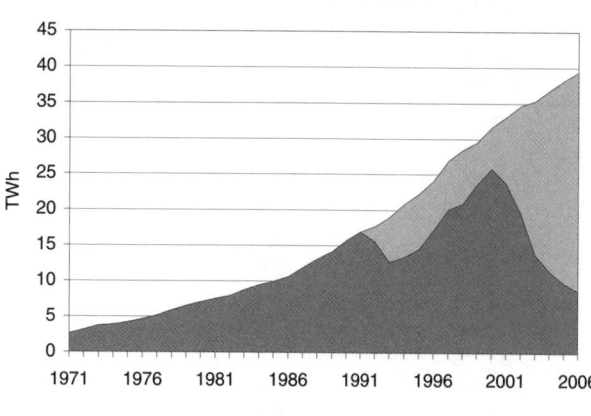

Figure 4. Reference vs Sectoral Approach

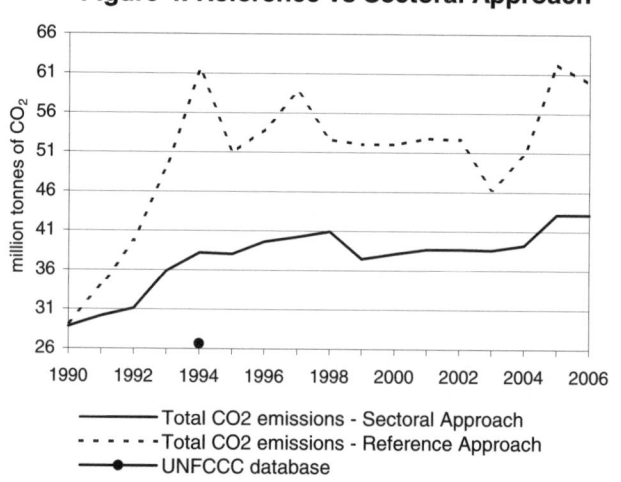

Figure 5. Electricity generation by fuel

Figure 6. Key indicators

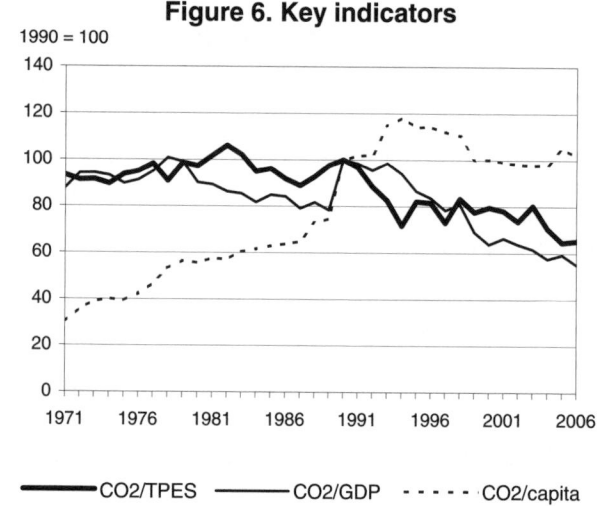

Singapore / Singapour

Key indicators

	1990	1995	2000	2003	2004	2005	2006	% change 90-06
CO$_2$ Sectoral Approach (Mt of CO$_2$)	28.80	38.03	38.13	38.62	39.23	43.13	43.13	49.8%
CO$_2$ Reference Approach (Mt of CO$_2$)	29.26	50.91	51.99	46.37	50.62	62.27	59.92	104.7%
TPES (PJ)	559	900	931	934	1 080	1 297	1 284	129.6%
TPES (Mtoe)	13.36	21.49	22.24	22.31	25.79	30.97	30.67	129.6%
GDP (billion 2000 US$ using exch. rates)	44.66	68.23	92.72	97.19	105.75	112.75	121.63	172.3%
GDP (billion 2000 US$ using PPPs)	45.66	69.76	94.79	99.37	108.11	115.27	124.35	172.3%
Population (millions)	3.05	3.53	4.03	4.19	4.24	4.34	4.48	47.2%
CO$_2$ / TPES (t CO$_2$ per TJ)	51.5	42.3	41.0	41.4	36.3	33.3	33.6	-34.8%
CO$_2$ / GDP (kg CO$_2$ per 2000 US$)	0.64	0.56	0.41	0.40	0.37	0.38	0.35	-45.0%
CO$_2$ / GDP (kg CO$_2$ per 2000 US$ PPP)	0.63	0.55	0.40	0.39	0.36	0.37	0.35	-45.0%
CO$_2$ / population (t CO$_2$ per capita)	9.45	10.79	9.47	9.23	9.26	9.93	9.62	1.8%

Ratios are based on the Sectoral Approach.

2006 CO$_2$ emissions by sector

million tonnes of CO$_2$	Coal/peat	Oil	Gas	Other *	Total	% change 90-06
Sectoral Approach	**0.25**	**27.87**	**15.01**	-	**43.13**	**49.8%**
Main activity producer elec. and heat	-	6.14	15.01	-	21.14	51.2%
Unallocated autoproducers	..	..	..	..	..	..
Other energy industries	-	10.00	-	-	10.00	17.1%
Manufacturing industries and construction	0.14	4.92	-	-	5.07	164.5%
Transport	-	6.81	-	-	6.81	69.3%
of which: road	-	*6.81*	-	-	*6.81*	*69.3%*
Other sectors	0.10	-	-	-	0.10	-42.3%
of which: residential	*0.10*	-	-	-	*0.10*	*-42.3%*
Reference Approach	**0.02**	**44.89**	**15.01**	-	**59.92**	**104.7%**
Diff. due to losses and/or transformation	- 0.23	17.01	-	-	16.79	
Statistical differences	-	0.00	-	-	0.00	
Memo: international marine bunkers	-	*86.35*	-	-	*86.35*	*155.0%*
Memo: international aviation	-	*10.54*	-	-	*10.54*	*87.2%*

* Other includes industrial waste and non-renewable municipal waste.

Key sources for CO$_2$ emissions from fuel combustion in 2006

IPCC source category	CO$_2$ emissions (Mt of CO$_2$)	% change 90-06	Level assessment (%) **	Cumulative total (%)
Main activity prod. elec. and heat - gas	15.01	x	27.8	27.8
Other energy industries - oil	10.00	17.1%	18.6	46.4
Road - oil	6.81	69.3%	12.6	59.0
Main activity prod. elec. and heat - oil	6.14	-56.1%	11.4	70.4
Manufacturing industries - oil	4.92	167.3%	9.1	79.6
Manufacturing industries - coal/peat	0.14	94.1%	0.3	79.8
Residential - coal/peat	0.10	50.9%	0.2	80.0
-	-	-	-	-
-	-	-	-	-
-	-	-	-	-
-	-	-	-	-
Memo: total CO$_2$ from fuel combustion	*43.13*	*49.8%*	*80.0*	*80.0*

** Percent calculated using the total GHG estimate for CO$_2$, CH$_4$, N$_2$O, HFCs, PFCs and SF$_6$ excluding CO$_2$ emissions/removals from land use change and forestry.

Slovak Republic / République slovaque

Figure 1. CO₂ emissions by fuel

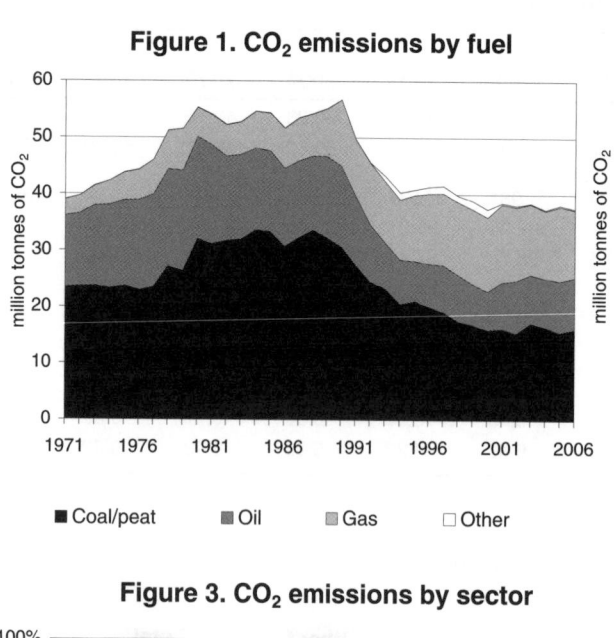

■ Coal/peat   ■ Oil   ■ Gas   □ Other

Figure 2. CO₂ emissions by sector

■ Electricity and heat   □ Other energy industries
■ Manuf. ind. and construction   ■ Transport
□ Residential   ■ Other

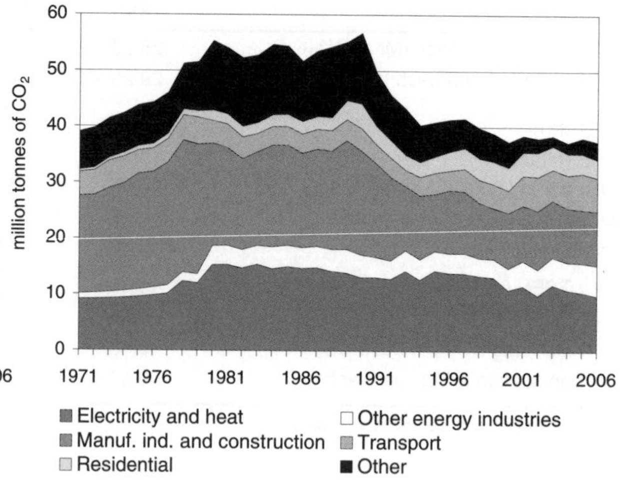

Figure 3. CO₂ emissions by sector

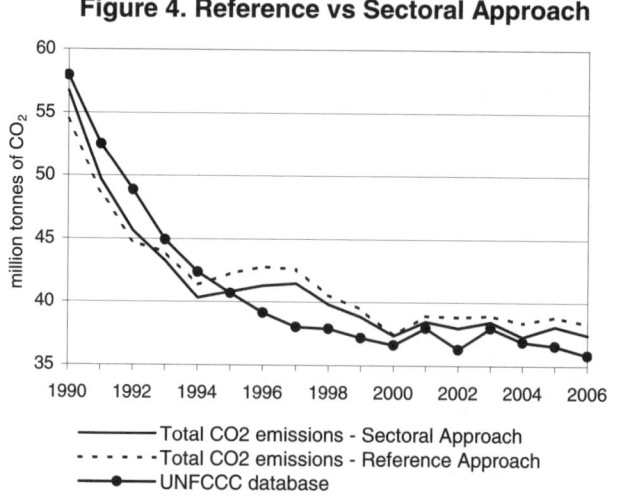

■ Electricity and heat   □ Other energy industries
■ Manuf. ind. and construction   ■ Transport
□ Residential   ■ Other

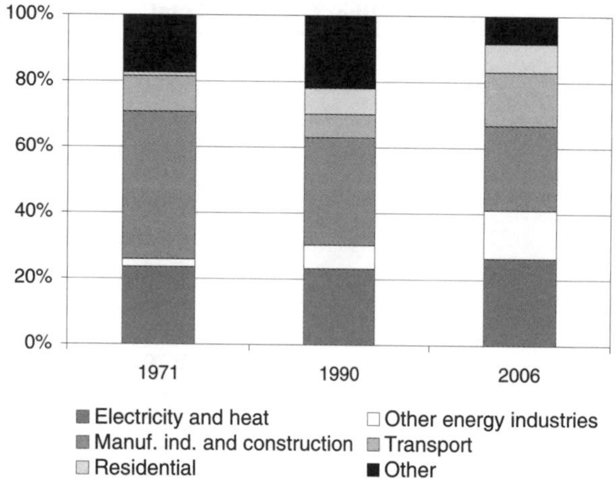

Figure 4. Reference vs Sectoral Approach

—— Total CO2 emissions - Sectoral Approach
- - - - Total CO2 emissions - Reference Approach
—●— UNFCCC database

Figure 5. Electricity generation by fuel

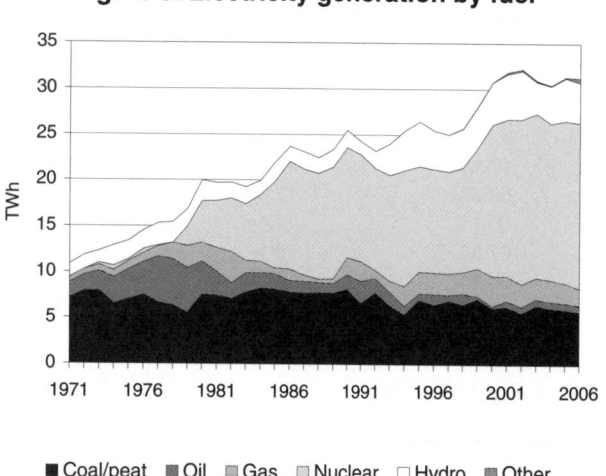

■ Coal/peat   ■ Oil   ■ Gas   ■ Nuclear   □ Hydro   ■ Other

Figure 6. Key indicators

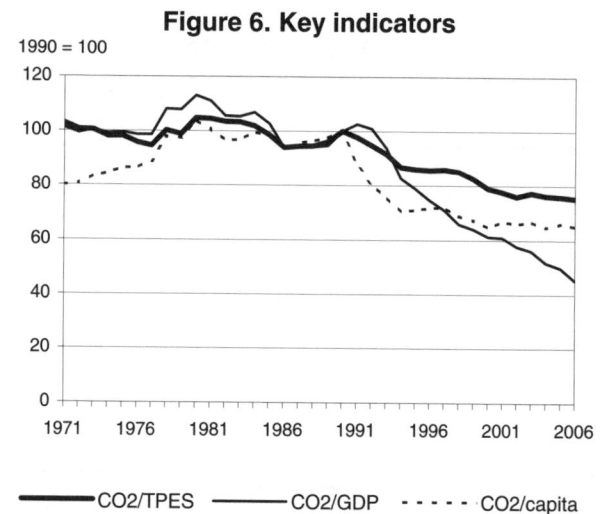

1990 = 100

—— CO2/TPES   —— CO2/GDP   - - - - CO2/capita

Slovak Republic / République slovaque
Key indicators

	1990	1995	2000	2003	2004	2005	2006	% change 90-06
CO$_2$ Sectoral Approach (Mt of CO$_2$)	56.73	40.83	37.37	38.45	37.28	38.10	37.45	-34.0%
CO$_2$ Reference Approach (Mt of CO$_2$)	54.44	42.26	37.42	38.96	38.38	38.85	38.31	-29.6%
TPES (PJ)	892	746	744	782	770	790	782	-12.4%
TPES (Mtoe)	21.32	17.82	17.77	18.67	18.38	18.87	18.68	-12.4%
GDP (billion 2000 US$ using exch. rates)	18.95	17.30	20.40	22.90	24.10	25.60	27.70	46.2%
GDP (billion 2000 US$ using PPPs)	54.79	50.11	59.37	66.46	70.06	74.29	80.43	46.8%
Population (millions)	5.30	5.36	5.40	5.38	5.38	5.39	5.39	1.8%
CO$_2$ / TPES (t CO$_2$ per TJ)	63.6	54.7	50.2	49.2	48.5	48.2	47.9	-24.7%
CO$_2$ / GDP (kg CO$_2$ per 2000 US$)	2.99	2.36	1.83	1.68	1.55	1.49	1.35	-54.8%
CO$_2$ / GDP (kg CO$_2$ per 2000 US$ PPP)	1.04	0.81	0.63	0.58	0.53	0.51	0.47	-55.0%
CO$_2$ / population (t CO$_2$ per capita)	10.71	7.61	6.92	7.15	6.93	7.07	6.95	-35.1%

Ratios are based on the Sectoral Approach.

2006 CO$_2$ emissions by sector

million tonnes of CO$_2$	Coal/peat	Oil	Gas	Other *	Total	% change 90-06
Sectoral Approach	**16.18**	**9.13**	**11.96**	**0.18**	**37.45**	**-34.0%**
Main activity producer elec. and heat	6.02	0.03	2.13	0.00	8.19	-24.6%
Unallocated autoproducers	0.93	0.31	0.35	0.10	1.70	-23.3%
Other energy industries	3.48	1.62	0.39	0.01	5.49	33.0%
Manufacturing industries and construction	5.23	1.60	2.73	0.07	9.63	-47.9%
Transport	-	5.09	0.97	-	6.06	49.7%
of which: road	-	*5.07*	-	-	*5.07*	*25.4%*
Other sectors	0.52	0.48	5.40	0.00	6.40	-62.3%
of which: residential	*0.20*	*0.04*	*3.00*	-	*3.24*	*-27.0%*
Reference Approach	**17.36**	**8.43**	**12.32**	**0.19**	**38.31**	**-29.6%**
Diff. due to losses and/or transformation	0.97	- 0.53	0.35	0.01	0.81	
Statistical differences	0.21	- 0.16	0.00	- 0.00	0.05	
Memo: international marine bunkers	-	-	-	-	-	-
Memo: international aviation	-	*0.12*	-	-	*0.12*	..

* Other includes industrial waste and non-renewable municipal waste.

Key sources for CO$_2$ emissions from fuel combustion in 2006

IPCC source category	CO$_2$ emissions (Mt of CO$_2$)	% change 90-06	Level assessment (%) **	Cumulative total (%)
Main activity prod. elec. and heat - coal/peat	6.02	-26.2%	11.9	11.9
Manufacturing industries - coal/peat	5.23	-37.4%	10.3	22.3
Road - oil	5.07	25.4%	10.0	32.3
Other energy industries - coal/peat	3.48	1.8%	6.9	39.2
Residential - gas	3.00	17.6%	5.9	45.1
Manufacturing industries - gas	2.73	-12.3%	5.4	50.5
Non-specified other sectors - gas	2.40	-31.1%	4.7	55.3
Main activity prod. elec. and heat - gas	2.13	3.7%	4.2	59.5
Other energy industries - oil	1.62	260.3%	3.2	62.7
Manufacturing industries - oil	1.60	-77.2%	3.2	65.9
Other transport - gas	0.97	x	1.9	67.8
Memo: total CO$_2$ from fuel combustion	*37.45*	*-34.0%*	*74.1*	*74.1*

** Percent calculated using the total GHG estimate for CO$_2$, CH$_4$, N$_2$O, HFCs, PFCs and SF$_6$ excluding CO$_2$ emissions/removals from land use change and forestry.

Slovenia / Slovénie

Figure 1. CO_2 emissions by fuel

million tonnes of CO2
18
16
14
12
10
8
6
4
2
0
1986
1991
1996
2001
2006
Coal/peat
Oil
Gas
Other

Figure 2. CO_2 emissions by sector

million tonnes of CO2
18
16
14
12
10
8
6
4
2
0
1986
1991
1996
2001
2006
Electricity and heat
Manuf. ind. and construction
Residential
Other energy industries
Transport
Other

Figure 3. CO_2 emissions by sector

100%
80%
60%
40%
20%
0%
not available
1971
1990
2006
Electricity and heat
Manuf. ind. and construction
Residential
Other energy industries
Transport
Other

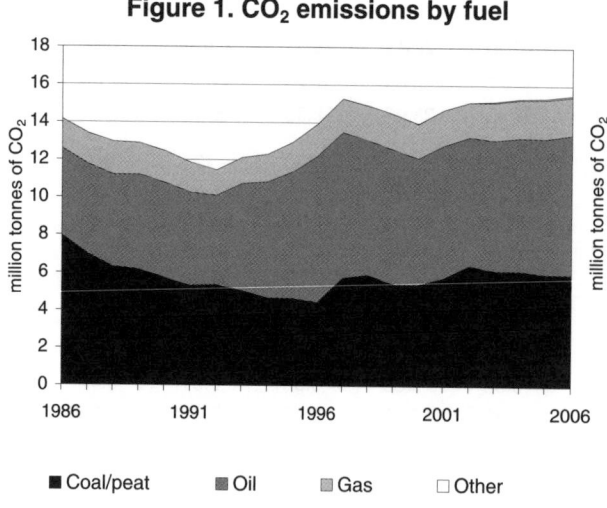

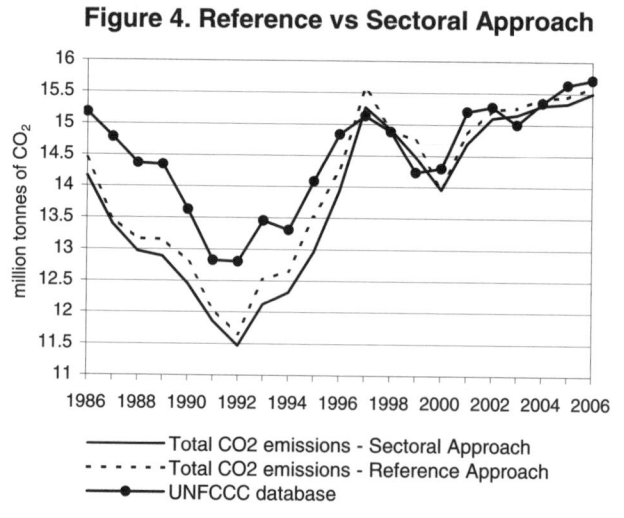

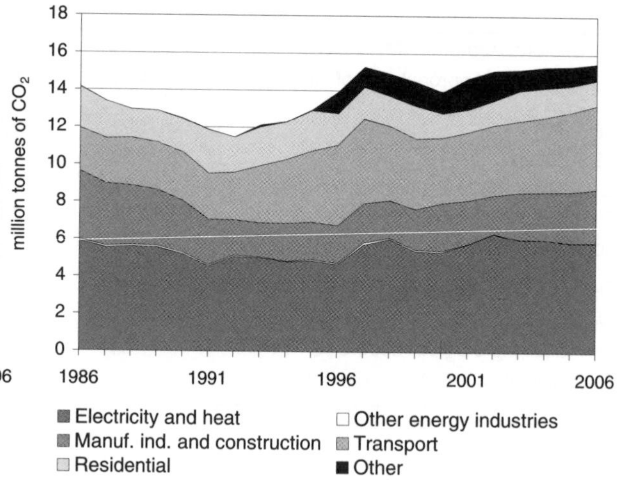

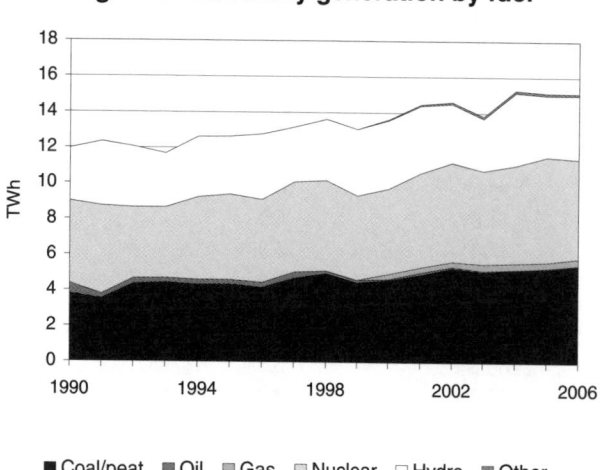

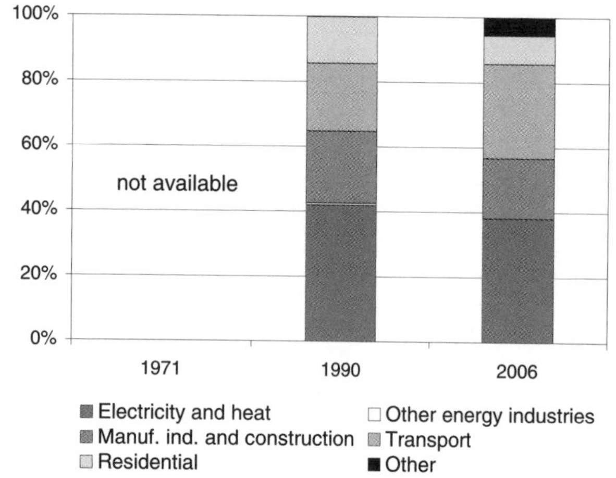

Figure 4. Reference vs Sectoral Approach

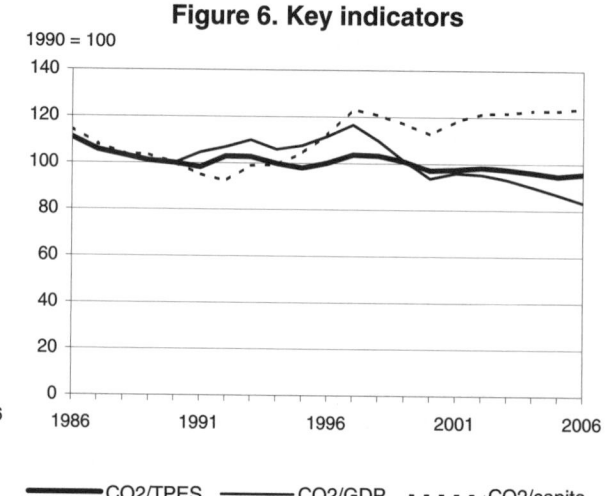

million tonnes of CO2
16
15.5
15
14.5
14
13.5
13
12.5
12
11.5
11
1986
1988
1990
1992
1994
1996
1998
2000
2002
2004
2006
Total CO2 emissions - Sectoral Approach
Total CO2 emissions - Reference Approach
UNFCCC database

Figure 5. Electricity generation by fuel

TWh
18
16
14
12
10
8
6
4
2
0
1990
1994
1998
2002
2006
Coal/peat
Oil
Gas
Nuclear
Hydro
Other

Figure 6. Key indicators

1990 = 100
140
120
100
80
60
40
20
0
1986
1991
1996
2001
2006
CO2/TPES
CO2/GDP
CO2/capita

Slovenia / Slovénie *

Key indicators

	1986	1990	1995	2003	2004	2005	2006	% change 86-06
CO$_2$ Sectoral Approach (Mt of CO$_2$)	14.16e	12.46	12.96	15.15	15.30	15.34	15.50	9.4%
CO$_2$ Reference Approach (Mt of CO$_2$)	14.44e	12.83	13.52	15.26	15.41	15.44	15.60	8.1%
TPES (PJ)	239e	234	248	292	298	304	304	27.0%
TPES (Mtoe)	5.72e	5.58	5.93	6.96	7.13	7.26	7.26	27.0%
GDP (billion 2000 US$ using exch. rates)	..	16.11	15.58	21.05	21.99	22.87	24.07	0.0%
GDP (billion 2000 US$ using PPPs)	..	27.94	27.01	36.51	38.12	39.66	41.73	0.0%
Population (millions)	1.98e	2.00	1.99	2.00	2.00	2.00	2.01	1.3%
CO$_2$ / TPES (t CO$_2$ per TJ)	59.1e	53.3	52.2	52.0	51.3	50.5	51.0	-13.8%
CO$_2$ / GDP (kg CO$_2$ per 2000 US$)	..	0.77	0.83	0.72	0.70	0.67	0.64	0.0%
CO$_2$ / GDP (kg CO$_2$ per 2000 US$ PPP)	..	0.45	0.48	0.42	0.40	0.39	0.37	0.0%
CO$_2$ / population (t CO$_2$ per capita)	7.15e	6.23	6.51	7.59	7.66	7.66	7.72	8.0%

Ratios are based on the Sectoral Approach.

* According to the provisions of Article 4.6 of the Convention and Decisions 9/CP.2 and 11/CP.4, Slovenia is allowed to use 1986 as the base year.

2006 CO$_2$ emissions by sector

million tonnes of CO$_2$	Coal/peat	Oil	Gas	Other **	Total	% change 86-06
Sectoral Approach	**5.97**	**7.44**	**2.01**	**0.07**	**15.50**	**9.4%**
Main activity producer elec. and heat	5.51	0.04	0.25	-	5.80	17.9%
Unallocated autoproducers	0.04	0.01	0.04	0.00	0.10	-90.2%
Other energy industries	-	-	0.01	-	0.01	-88.3%
Manufacturing industries and construction	0.42	0.90	1.46	0.07	2.85	-22.1%
Transport	-	4.51	-	-	4.51	95.9%
of which: road	-	4.47	-	-	4.47	97.1%
Other sectors	-	1.98	0.25	-	2.23	0.0%
of which: residential	-	1.14	0.22	-	1.36	-38.7%
Reference Approach	**6.08**	**7.44**	**2.01**	**0.07**	**15.60**	**8.1%**
Diff. due to losses and/or transformation	-	-	-	-	-	
Statistical differences	0.11	0.00	- 0.00	-	0.11	
Memo: international marine bunkers	-	0.09	-	-	0.09	x
Memo: international aviation	-	0.07	-	-	0.07	-25.0%

** Other includes industrial waste and non-renewable municipal waste.

Key sources for CO$_2$ emissions from fuel combustion in 2006

IPCC source category	CO$_2$ emissions (Mt of CO$_2$)	% change 86-06	Level assessment (%) ***	Cumulative total (%)
Main activity prod. elec. and heat - coal/peat	5.51	..	27.0	27.0
Road - oil	4.47	..	21.9	49.0
Manufacturing industries - gas	1.46	..	7.2	56.1
Residential - oil	1.14	..	5.6	61.7
Manufacturing industries - oil	0.90	..	4.4	66.2
Non-specified other sectors - oil	0.84	..	4.1	70.3
Manufacturing industries - coal/peat	0.42	..	2.1	72.3
Main activity prod. elec. and heat - gas	0.25	..	1.2	73.5
Residential - gas	0.22	..	1.1	74.6
Manufacturing industries -other	0.07	..	0.3	75.0
Main activity prod. elec. and heat - oil	0.04	..	0.2	75.2
Memo: total CO$_2$ from fuel combustion	15.50	9.4%	76.0	76.0

*** Percent calculated using the total GHG estimate for CO$_2$, CH$_4$, N$_2$O, HFCs, PFCs and SF$_6$ excluding CO$_2$ emissions/removals from land use change and forestry.

South Africa / Afrique du Sud

Figure 1. CO₂ emissions by fuel

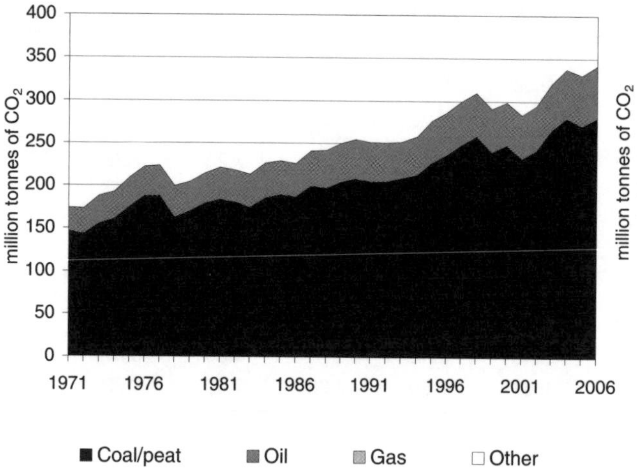

Coal/peat ■ Oil ■ Gas ■ Other □

Figure 2. CO₂ emissions by sector

■ Electricity and heat □ Other energy industries
■ Manuf. ind. and construction ■ Transport
□ Residential ■ Other

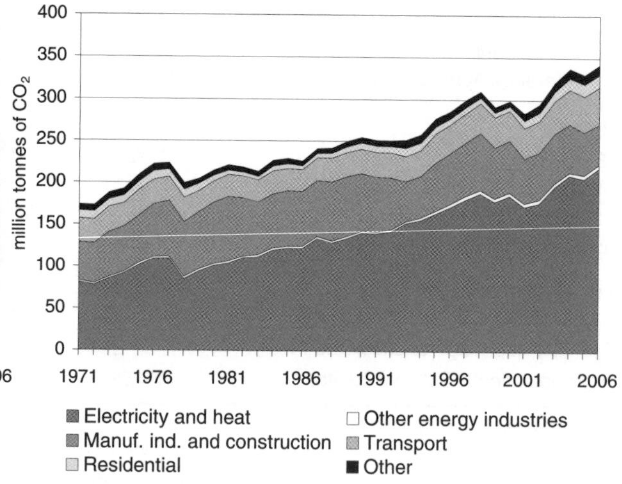

Figure 3. CO₂ emissions by sector

■ Electricity and heat □ Other energy industries
■ Manuf. ind. and construction ■ Transport
□ Residential ■ Other

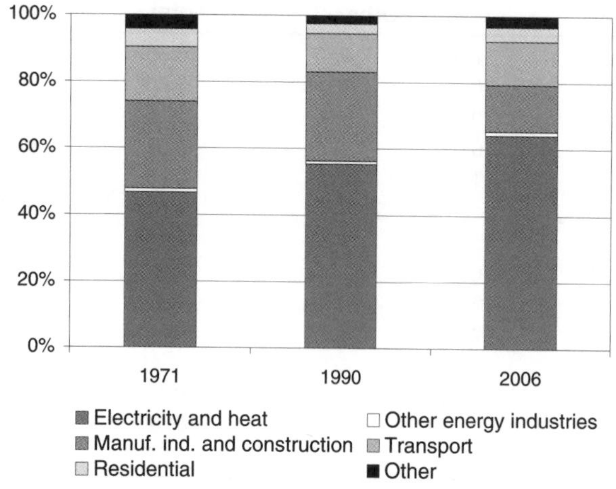

Figure 4. Reference vs Sectoral Approach

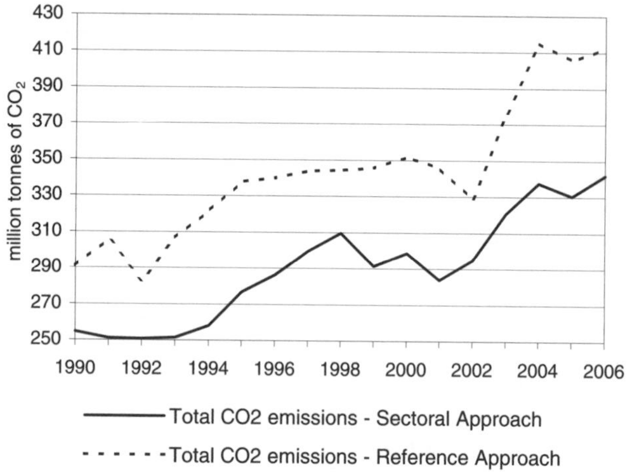

——— Total CO2 emissions - Sectoral Approach
- - - - - Total CO2 emissions - Reference Approach

Figure 5. Electricity generation by fuel

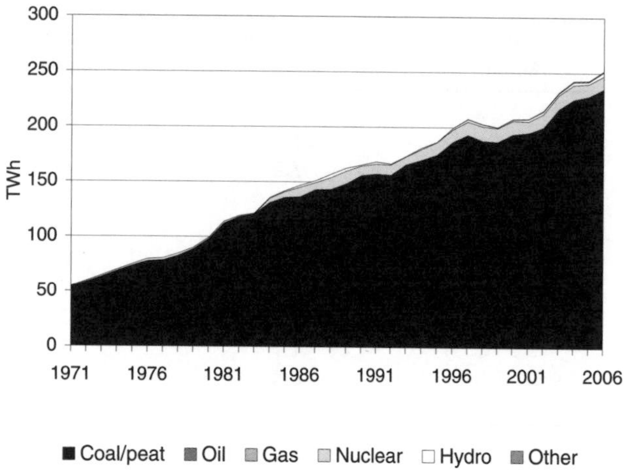

■ Coal/peat ■ Oil ■ Gas □ Nuclear □ Hydro ■ Other

Figure 6. Key indicators

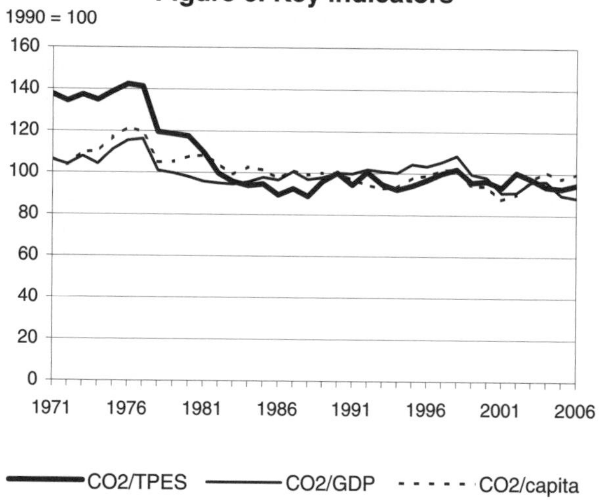

—— CO2/TPES —— CO2/GDP - - - - CO2/capita

South Africa / Afrique du Sud

Key indicators

	1990	1995	2000	2003	2004	2005	2006	% change 90-06
CO$_2$ Sectoral Approach (Mt of CO$_2$)	254.61	276.77	298.56	320.79	337.53	330.36	341.96	34.3%
CO$_2$ Reference Approach (Mt of CO$_2$)	291.09	337.67	351.78	375.31	414.97	405.64	412.37	41.7%
TPES (PJ)	3 820	4 416	4 659	4 945	5 413	5 344	5 435	42.3%
TPES (Mtoe)	91.23	105.48	111.27	118.11	129.29	127.64	129.81	42.3%
GDP (billion 2000 US$ using exch. rates)	110.95	115.81	132.88	145.76	153.00	160.79	168.81	52.2%
GDP (billion 2000 US$ using PPPs)	321.98	336.11	385.64	423.03	444.03	466.65	489.92	52.2%
Population (millions)	35.20	39.12	44.00	45.80	46.35	46.89	47.39	34.6%
CO$_2$ / TPES (t CO$_2$ per TJ)	66.7	62.7	64.1	64.9	62.4	61.8	62.9	-5.6%
CO$_2$ / GDP (kg CO$_2$ per 2000 US$)	2.29	2.39	2.25	2.20	2.21	2.05	2.03	-11.7%
CO$_2$ / GDP (kg CO$_2$ per 2000 US$ PPP)	0.79	0.82	0.77	0.76	0.76	0.71	0.70	-11.7%
CO$_2$ / population (t CO$_2$ per capita)	7.23	7.07	6.79	7.00	7.28	7.05	7.22	-0.2%

Ratios are based on the Sectoral Approach.

2006 CO$_2$ emissions by sector

million tonnes of CO$_2$	Coal/peat	Oil	Gas	Other *	Total	% change 90-06
Sectoral Approach	**280.45**	**61.45**	**0.05**	**-**	**341.96**	**34.3%**
Main activity producer elec. and heat	208.18	-	0.05	-	208.23	57.7%
Unallocated autoproducers	10.67	-	0.00	-	10.67	24.6%
Other energy industries	-	4.54	-	-	4.54	93.7%
Manufacturing industries and construction	42.95	4.96	-	-	47.91	-29.9%
Transport	-	44.40	-	-	44.40	52.1%
of which: road	-	*40.96*	-	-	*40.96*	*46.7%*
Other sectors	18.65	7.55	-	-	26.19	85.6%
of which: residential	*12.37*	*2.42*	-	-	*14.79*	*95.3%*
Reference Approach	**360.96**	**42.49**	**8.92**	**-**	**412.37**	**41.7%**
Diff. due to losses and/or transformation	80.16	- 19.05	8.87	-	69.98	
Statistical differences	0.35	0.09	-	-	0.44	
Memo: international marine bunkers	-	*8.38*	-	-	*8.38*	*40.7%*
Memo: international aviation	-	*2.21*	-	-	*2.21*	*91.5%*

* Other includes industrial waste and non-renewable municipal waste.

Key sources for CO$_2$ emissions from fuel combustion in 2006

IPCC source category	CO$_2$ emissions (Mt of CO$_2$)	% change 90-06	Level assessment (%) **	Cumulative total (%)
Main activity prod. elec. and heat - coal/peat	208.18	57.7%	47.2	47.2
Manufacturing industries - coal/peat	42.95	-26.0%	9.7	56.9
Road - oil	40.96	46.7%	9.3	66.2
Residential - coal/peat	12.37	114.8%	2.8	69.0
Unallocated autoproducers - coal/peat	10.67	24.6%	2.4	71.4
Non-specified other sectors - coal/peat	6.28	71.1%	1.4	72.8
Non-specified other sectors - oil	5.12	78.5%	1.2	74.0
Manufacturing industries - oil	4.96	-52.1%	1.1	75.1
Other energy industries - oil	4.54	96.6%	1.0	76.2
Other transport - oil	3.44	220.3%	0.8	76.9
Residential - oil	2.42	33.5%	0.5	77.5
Memo: total CO$_2$ from fuel combustion	*341.96*	*34.3%*	*77.5*	*77.5*

** Percent calculated using the total GHG estimate for CO$_2$, CH$_4$, N$_2$O, HFCs, PFCs and SF$_6$ excluding CO$_2$ emissions/removals from land use change and forestry.

Spain / Espagne

Figure 1. CO₂ emissions by fuel

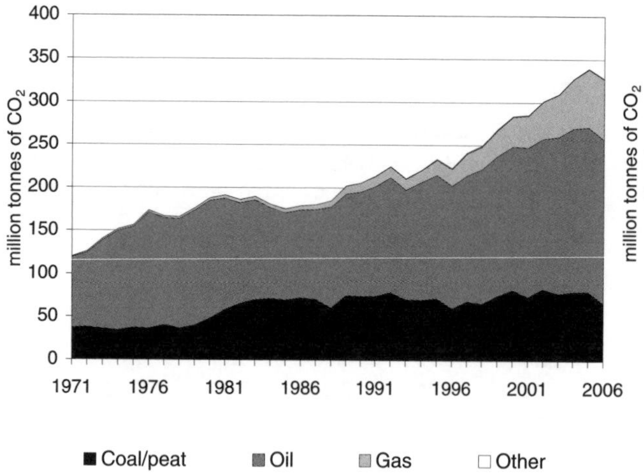

Coal/peat ■ Oil ■ Gas ■ Other □

Figure 2. CO₂ emissions by sector

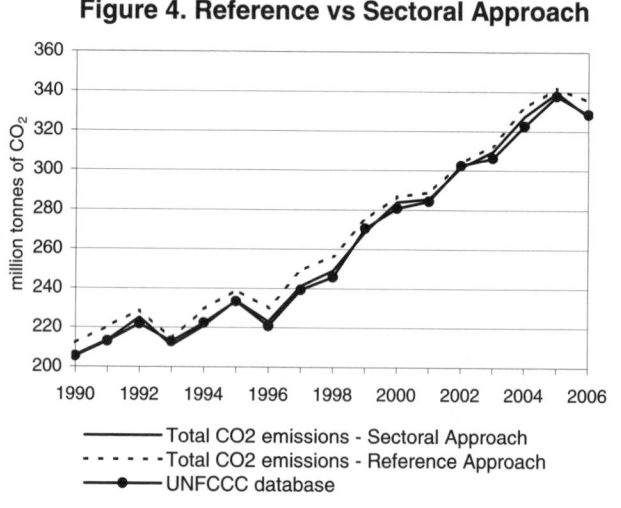

Electricity and heat ■ Other energy industries □
Manuf. ind. and construction ■ Transport ■
Residential □ Other ■

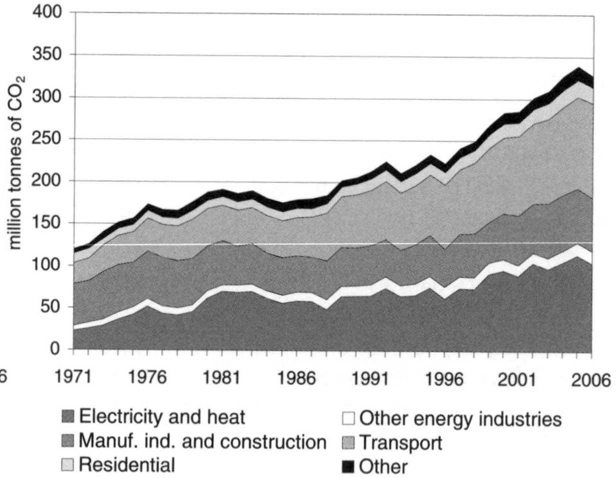

Figure 3. CO₂ emissions by sector

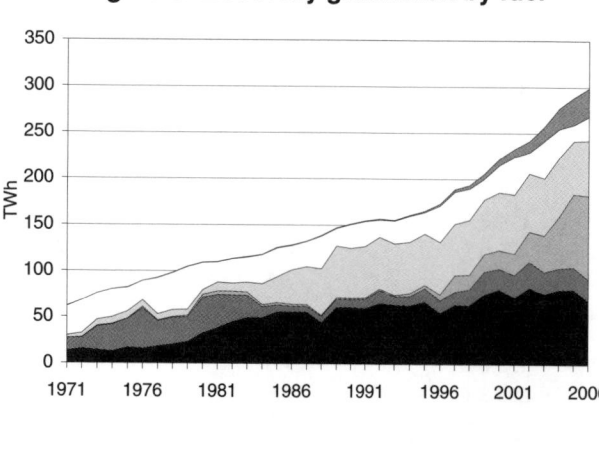

Electricity and heat ■ Other energy industries □
Manuf. ind. and construction ■ Transport ■
Residential □ Other ■

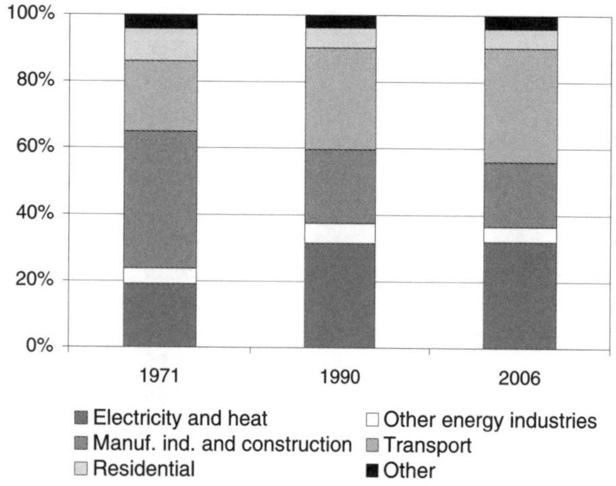

Figure 4. Reference vs Sectoral Approach

Total CO2 emissions - Sectoral Approach
Total CO2 emissions - Reference Approach
UNFCCC database

Figure 5. Electricity generation by fuel

Coal/peat ■ Oil ■ Gas ■ Nuclear □ Hydro □ Other ■

Figure 6. Key indicators

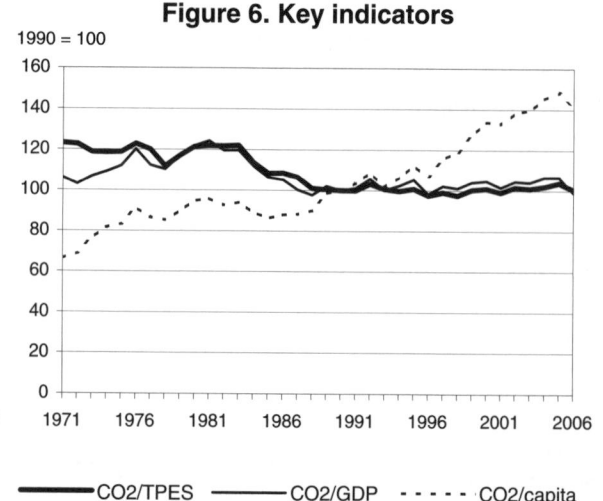

1990 = 100

CO2/TPES —— CO2/GDP —— CO2/capita - - - -

Spain / Espagne

Key indicators

	1990	1995	2000	2003	2004	2005	2006	% change 90-06
CO$_2$ Sectoral Approach (Mt of CO$_2$)	205.85	233.67	283.87	309.61	327.45	339.48	327.65	59.2%
CO$_2$ Reference Approach (Mt of CO$_2$)	212.09	239.18	286.67	312.97	332.06	341.91	335.53	58.2%
TPES (PJ)	3 819	4 306	5 219	5 694	5 952	6 068	6 052	58.5%
TPES (Mtoe)	91.21	102.85	124.66	136.01	142.17	144.93	144.56	58.5%
GDP (billion 2000 US$ using exch. rates)	440.60	474.90	580.70	637.30	658.10	681.90	708.20	60.7%
GDP (billion 2000 US$ using PPPs)	650.69	701.21	857.48	941.06	971.80	1 006.95	1 045.82	60.7%
Population (millions)	39.01	39.39	40.26	42.01	42.69	43.40	44.07	13.0%
CO$_2$ / TPES (t CO$_2$ per TJ)	53.9	54.3	54.4	54.4	55.0	55.9	54.1	0.4%
CO$_2$ / GDP (kg CO$_2$ per 2000 US$)	0.47	0.49	0.49	0.49	0.50	0.50	0.46	-1.0%
CO$_2$ / GDP (kg CO$_2$ per 2000 US$ PPP)	0.32	0.33	0.33	0.33	0.34	0.34	0.31	-1.0%
CO$_2$ / population (t CO$_2$ per capita)	5.28	5.93	7.05	7.37	7.67	7.82	7.44	40.9%

Ratios are based on the Sectoral Approach.

2006 CO$_2$ emissions by sector

million tonnes of CO$_2$	Coal/peat	Oil	Gas	Other *	Total	% change 90-06
Sectoral Approach	**66.59**	**190.32**	**69.97**	**0.78**	**327.65**	**59.2%**
Main activity producer elec. and heat	57.91	11.76	24.49	0.78	94.94	51.7%
Unallocated autoproducers	0.72	2.61	6.36	-	9.69	380.6%
Other energy industries	1.39	13.71	-	-	15.10	21.0%
Manufacturing industries and construction	5.50	28.09	29.71	-	63.30	39.2%
Transport	-	112.33	-	-	112.33	78.5%
of which: road	*-*	*97.71*	*-*	*-*	*97.71*	*85.2%*
Other sectors	1.07	21.83	9.40	-	32.30	58.5%
of which: residential	*0.85*	*10.94*	*7.05*	*-*	*18.84*	*50.8%*
Reference Approach	**69.20**	**193.42**	**72.13**	**0.78**	**335.53**	**58.2%**
Diff. due to losses and/or transformation	0.00	3.03	0.48	-	3.51	
Statistical differences	2.62	0.07	1.69	-	4.37	
Memo: international marine bunkers	*-*	*26.11*	*-*	*-*	*26.11*	*127.9%*
Memo: international aviation	*-*	*9.57*	*-*	*-*	*9.57*	*188.3%*

* Other includes industrial waste and non-renewable municipal waste.

Key sources for CO$_2$ emissions from fuel combustion in 2006

IPCC source category	CO$_2$ emissions (Mt of CO$_2$)	% change 90-06	Level assessment (%) **	Cumulative total (%)
Road - oil	97.71	85.2%	22.6	22.6
Main activity prod. elec. and heat - coal/peat	57.91	3.1%	13.4	36.0
Manufacturing industries - gas	29.71	248.5%	6.9	42.9
Manufacturing industries - oil	28.09	20.8%	6.5	49.4
Main activity prod. elec. and heat - gas	24.49	+	5.7	55.0
Other transport - oil	14.62	43.6%	3.4	58.4
Other energy industries - oil	13.71	29.5%	3.2	61.6
Main activity prod. elec. and heat - oil	11.76	96.8%	2.7	64.3
Residential - oil	10.94	10.2%	2.5	66.8
Non-specified other sectors - oil	10.89	48.3%	2.5	69.4
Residential - gas	7.05	678.4%	1.6	71.0
Memo: total CO$_2$ from fuel combustion	*327.65*	*59.2%*	*75.8*	*75.8*

** Percent calculated using the total GHG estimate for CO$_2$, CH$_4$, N$_2$O, HFCs, PFCs and SF$_6$ excluding CO$_2$ emissions/removals from land use change and forestry.

Sri Lanka

Figure 1. CO$_2$ emissions by fuel

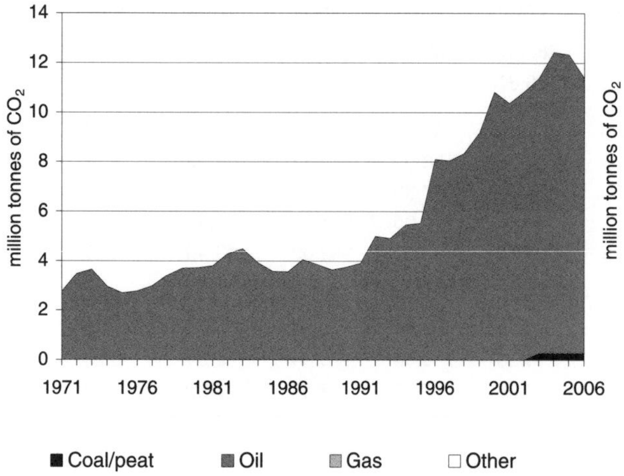

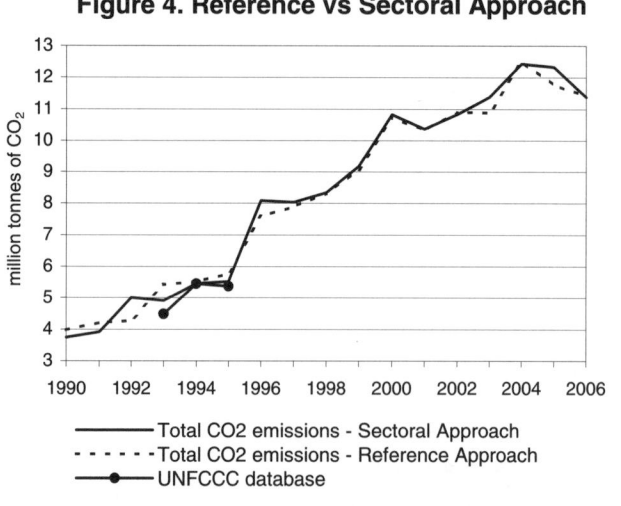

■ Coal/peat ■ Oil ■ Gas □ Other

Figure 2. CO$_2$ emissions by sector

■ Electricity and heat □ Other energy industries
■ Manuf. ind. and construction ■ Transport
□ Residential ■ Other

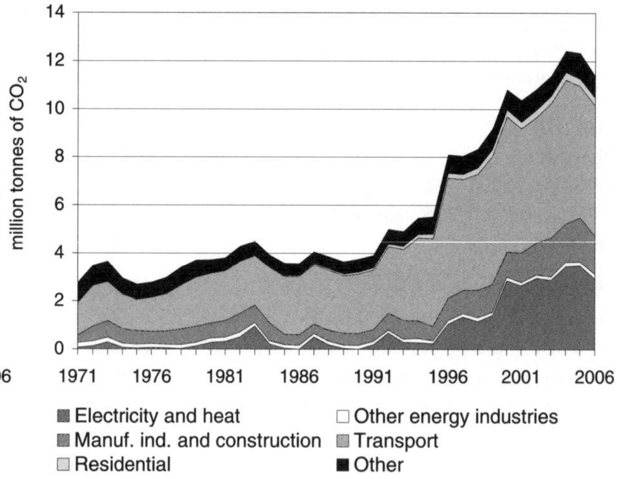

Figure 3. CO$_2$ emissions by sector

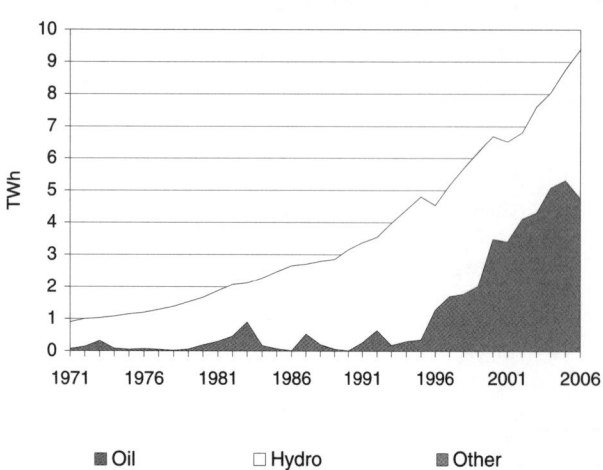

■ Electricity and heat □ Other energy industries
■ Manuf. ind. and construction ■ Transport
□ Residential ■ Other

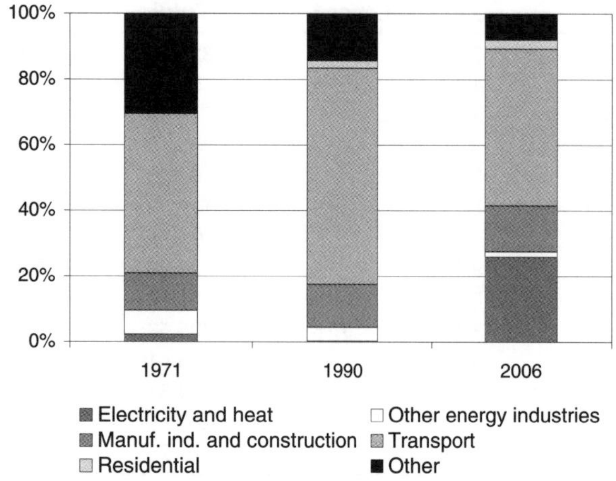

Figure 4. Reference vs Sectoral Approach

—— Total CO2 emissions - Sectoral Approach
- - - - Total CO2 emissions - Reference Approach
—●— UNFCCC database

Figure 5. Electricity generation by fuel

■ Oil □ Hydro ■ Other

Figure 6. Key indicators

1990 = 100

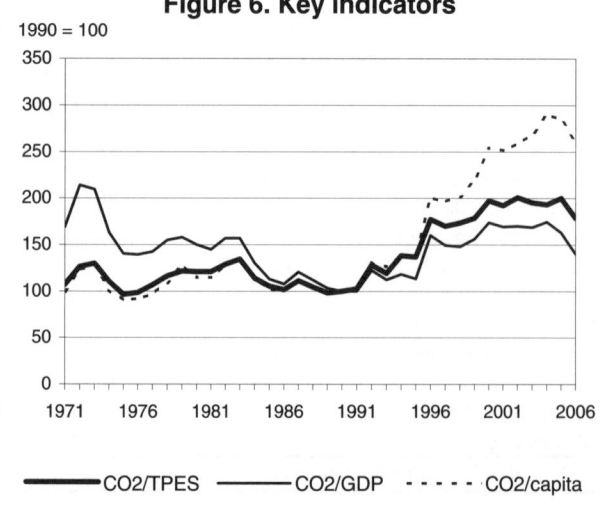

—— CO2/TPES —— CO2/GDP - - - - CO2/capita

Sri Lanka

Key indicators

	1990	1995	2000	2003	2004	2005	2006	% change 90-06
CO$_2$ Sectoral Approach (Mt of CO$_2$)	3.74	5.52	10.82	11.38	12.43	12.33	11.39	204.2%
CO$_2$ Reference Approach (Mt of CO$_2$)	3.98	5.77	10.72	10.88	12.52	11.77	11.43	187.3%
TPES (PJ)	231	249	338	360	397	380	393	70.3%
TPES (Mtoe)	5.52	5.95	8.08	8.59	9.48	9.09	9.39	70.3%
GDP (billion 2000 US$ using exch. rates)	9.82	12.78	16.33	17.72	18.69	19.82	21.27	116.6%
GDP (billion 2000 US$ using PPPs)	40.09	52.14	66.66	72.34	76.28	80.88	86.82	116.6%
Population (millions)	17.02	18.14	19.36	19.25	19.46	19.67	19.89	16.9%
CO$_2$ / TPES (t CO$_2$ per TJ)	16.2	22.2	32.0	31.7	31.3	32.4	29.0	78.6%
CO$_2$ / GDP (kg CO$_2$ per 2000 US$)	0.38	0.43	0.66	0.64	0.67	0.62	0.54	40.5%
CO$_2$ / GDP (kg CO$_2$ per 2000 US$ PPP)	0.09	0.11	0.16	0.16	0.16	0.15	0.13	40.4%
CO$_2$ / population (t CO$_2$ per capita)	0.22	0.30	0.56	0.59	0.64	0.63	0.57	160.3%

Ratios are based on the Sectoral Approach.

2006 CO$_2$ emissions by sector

million tonnes of CO$_2$	Coal/peat	Oil	Gas	Other *	Total	% change 90-06
Sectoral Approach	**0.26**	**11.13**	-	-	**11.39**	**204.2%**
Main activity producer elec. and heat	-	2.95	-	-	2.95	+
Unallocated autoproducers	-	-	-	-	-	-
Other energy industries	-	0.18	-	-	0.18	15.2%
Manufacturing industries and construction	0.26	1.34	-	-	1.60	227.8%
Transport	-	5.43	-	-	5.43	119.7%
of which: road	-	*4.65*	-	-	*4.65*	*111.3%*
Other sectors	-	1.23	-	-	1.23	98.4%
of which: residential	-	*0.32*	-	-	*0.32*	*285.4%*
Reference Approach	**0.26**	**11.16**	-	-	**11.43**	**187.3%**
Diff. due to losses and/or transformation	-	0.01	-	-	0.01	
Statistical differences	-	0.03	-	-	0.03	
Memo: international marine bunkers	-	*0.43*	-	-	*0.43*	*-64.1%*
Memo: international aviation	-	*0.37*	-	-	*0.37*	*..*

* Other includes industrial waste and non-renewable municipal waste.

Key sources for CO$_2$ emissions from fuel combustion in 2006

IPCC source category	CO$_2$ emissions (Mt of CO$_2$)	% change 90-06	Level assessment (%) **	Cumulative total (%)
Road - oil	4.65	111.3%	18.3	18.3
Main activity prod. elec. and heat - oil	2.95	+	11.6	29.8
Manufacturing industries - oil	1.34	185.5%	5.3	35.1
Non-specified other sectors - oil	0.91	69.6%	3.6	38.7
Other transport - oil	0.78	188.4%	3.0	41.7
Residential - oil	0.32	285.4%	1.3	43.0
Manufacturing industries - coal/peat	0.26	+	1.0	44.0
Other energy industries - oil	0.18	15.2%	0.7	44.7
-	-	-	-	-
-	-	-	-	-
-	-	-	-	-
Memo: total CO$_2$ from fuel combustion	*11.39*	*204.2%*	*44.7*	*44.7*

** Percent calculated using the total GHG estimate for CO$_2$, CH$_4$, N$_2$O, HFCs, PFCs and SF$_6$ excluding CO$_2$ emissions/removals from land use change and forestry.

Sudan / Soudan

Figure 1. CO$_2$ emissions by fuel

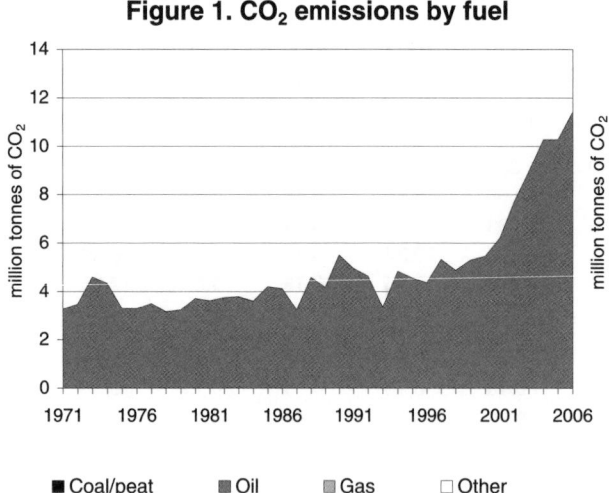

■ Coal/peat ■ Oil ■ Gas □ Other

Figure 2. CO$_2$ emissions by sector

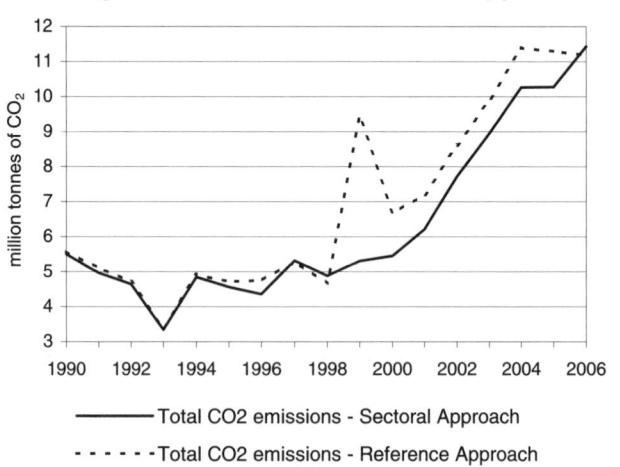

■ Electricity and heat □ Other energy industries
■ Manuf. ind. and construction ■ Transport
□ Residential ■ Other

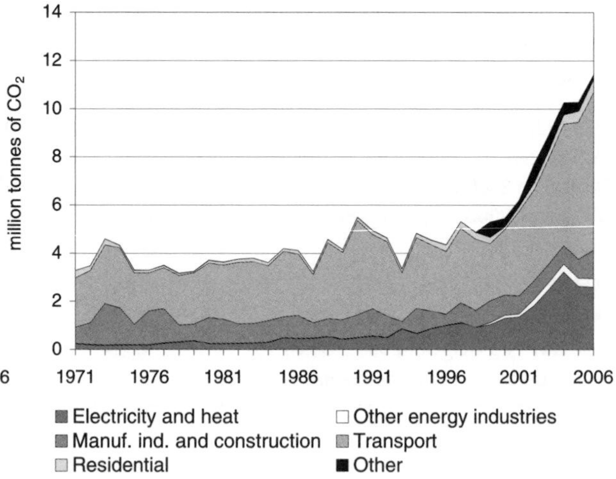

Figure 3. CO$_2$ emissions by sector

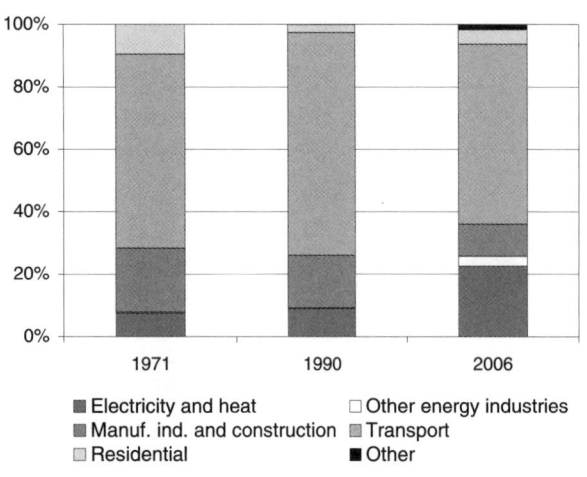

■ Electricity and heat □ Other energy industries
■ Manuf. ind. and construction ■ Transport
□ Residential ■ Other

Figure 4. Reference vs Sectoral Approach

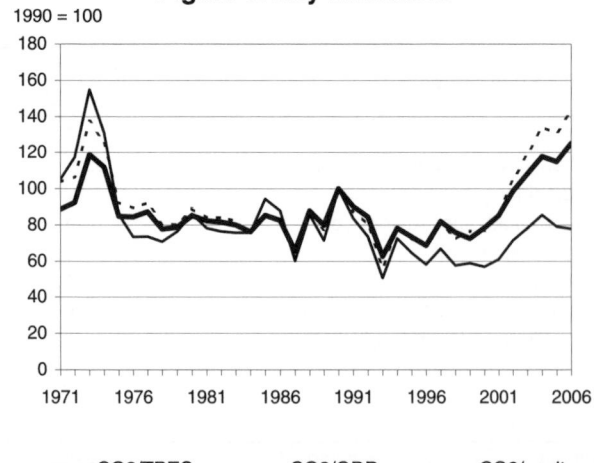

—— Total CO2 emissions - Sectoral Approach
- - - - - Total CO2 emissions - Reference Approach

Figure 5. Electricity generation by fuel

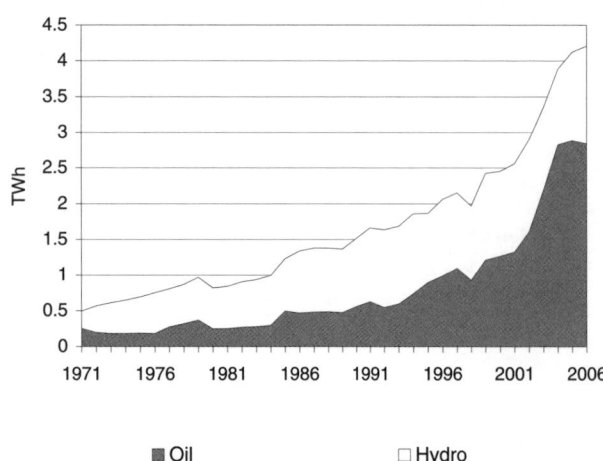

■ Oil □ Hydro

Figure 6. Key indicators

1990 = 100

—— CO2/TPES —— CO2/GDP - - - - - CO2/capita

Sudan / Soudan

Key indicators

	1990	1995	2000	2003	2004	2005	2006	% change 90-06
CO$_2$ Sectoral Approach (Mt of CO$_2$)	5.50	4.56	5.45	8.94	10.27	10.28	11.43	107.7%
CO$_2$ Reference Approach (Mt of CO$_2$)	5.58	4.71	6.68	9.90	11.39	11.30	11.18	100.6%
TPES (PJ)	446	503	564	670	708	725	742	66.1%
TPES (Mtoe)	10.66	12.01	13.48	16.01	16.90	17.32	17.71	66.1%
GDP (billion 2000 US$ using exch. rates)	7.10	9.11	12.37	14.74	15.51	16.75	18.93	166.6%
GDP (billion 2000 US$ using PPPs)	28.46	36.51	49.57	59.09	62.16	67.14	75.86	166.6%
Population (millions)	25.93	29.49	33.35	35.44	36.15	36.90	37.71	45.4%
CO$_2$ / TPES (t CO$_2$ per TJ)	12.3	9.1	9.7	13.3	14.5	14.2	15.4	25.0%
CO$_2$ / GDP (kg CO$_2$ per 2000 US$)	0.78	0.50	0.44	0.61	0.66	0.61	0.60	-22.1%
CO$_2$ / GDP (kg CO$_2$ per 2000 US$ PPP)	0.19	0.12	0.11	0.15	0.17	0.15	0.15	-22.1%
CO$_2$ / population (t CO$_2$ per capita)	0.21	0.15	0.16	0.25	0.28	0.28	0.30	42.9%

Ratios are based on the Sectoral Approach.

2006 CO$_2$ emissions by sector

million tonnes of CO$_2$	Coal/peat	Oil	Gas	Other *	Total	% change 90-06
Sectoral Approach	-	**11.43**	-	-	**11.43**	**107.7%**
Main activity producer elec. and heat	-	2.58	-	-	2.58	424.6%
Unallocated autoproducers	-	-	-	-	-	-
Other energy industries	-	0.36	-	-	0.36	+
Manufacturing industries and construction	-	1.18	-	-	1.18	26.8%
Transport	-	6.58	-	-	6.58	67.7%
of which: road	-	6.54	-	-	6.54	66.7%
Other sectors	-	0.73	-	-	0.73	397.8%
of which: residential	-	0.53	-	-	0.53	274.7%
Reference Approach	-	**11.18**	-	-	**11.18**	**100.6%**
Diff. due to losses and/or transformation	-	0.42	-	-	0.42	
Statistical differences	-	- 0.66	-	-	- 0.66	
Memo: international marine bunkers	-	0.03	-	-	0.03	14.3%
Memo: international aviation	-	0.69	-	-	0.69	631.3%

* Other includes industrial waste and non-renewable municipal waste.

Key sources for CO$_2$ emissions from fuel combustion in 2006

IPCC source category	CO$_2$ emissions (Mt of CO$_2$)	% change 90-06	Level assessment (%) **	Cumulative total (%)
Road - oil	6.54	66.7%	4.7	4.7
Main activity prod. elec. and heat - oil	2.58	424.6%	1.8	6.5
Manufacturing industries - oil	1.18	26.8%	0.8	7.4
Residential - oil	0.53	274.7%	0.4	7.7
Other energy industries - oil	0.36	+	0.3	8.0
Non-specified other sectors - oil	0.20	+	0.1	8.1
Other transport - oil	0.04	x	0.0	8.2
-	-	-	-	-
-	-	-	-	-
-	-	-	-	-
-	-	-	-	-
Memo: total CO$_2$ from fuel combustion	11.43	107.7%	8.2	8.2

** Percent calculated using the total GHG estimate for CO$_2$, CH$_4$, N$_2$O, HFCs, PFCs and SF$_6$ excluding CO$_2$ emissions/removals from land use change and forestry.

Sweden / Suède

Figure 1. CO_2 emissions by fuel

million tonnes of CO2
Coal/peat
Oil
Gas
Other

Figure 2. CO_2 emissions by sector

million tonnes of CO2
Electricity and heat
Manuf. ind. and construction
Residential
Other energy industries
Transport
Other

Figure 3. CO_2 emissions by sector

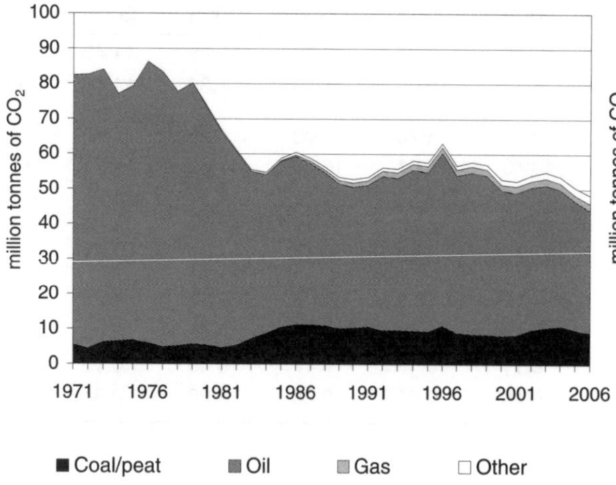

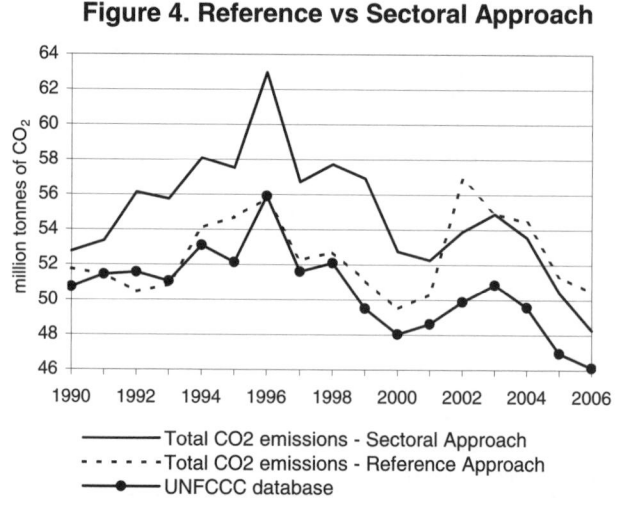

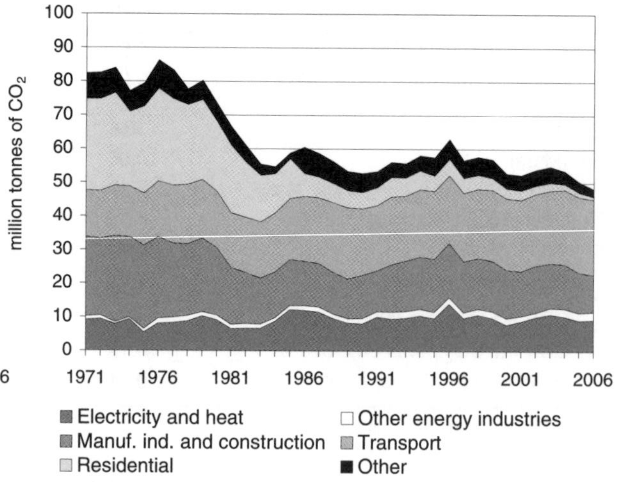

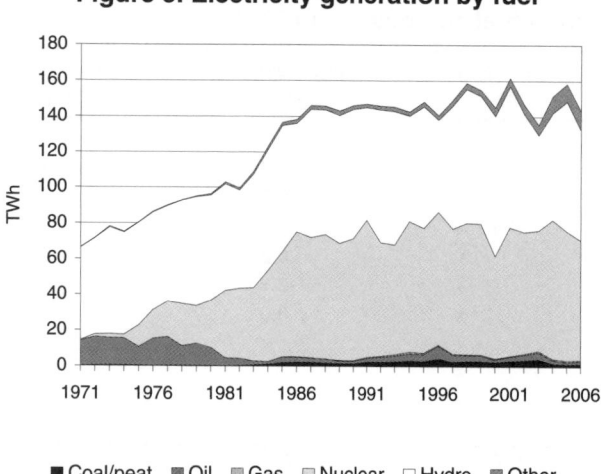

Electricity and heat
Manuf. ind. and construction
Residential
Other energy industries
Transport
Other

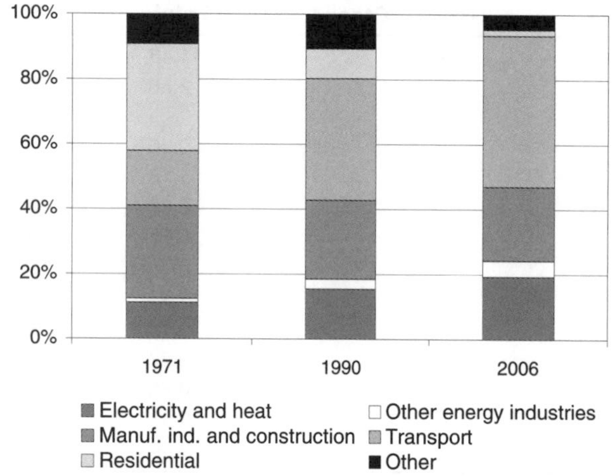

Figure 4. Reference vs Sectoral Approach

million tonnes of CO2
Total CO2 emissions - Sectoral Approach
Total CO2 emissions - Reference Approach
UNFCCC database

Figure 5. Electricity generation by fuel

TWh
Coal/peat
Oil
Gas
Nuclear
Hydro
Other

Figure 6. Key indicators

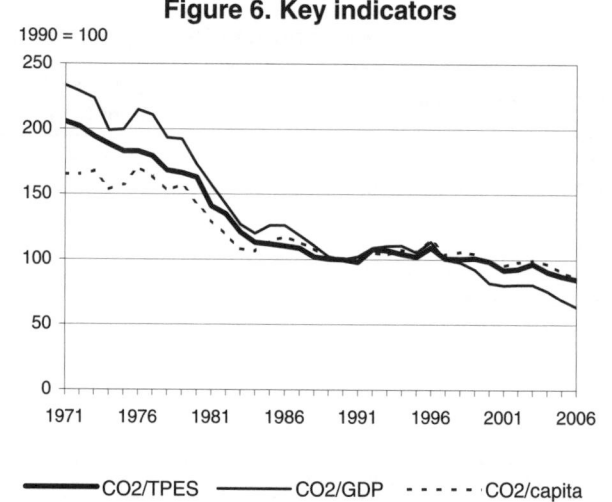

1990 = 100
CO2/TPES
CO2/GDP
CO2/capita

Sweden / Suède
Key indicators

	1990	1995	2000	2003	2004	2005	2006	% change 90-06
CO$_2$ Sectoral Approach (Mt of CO$_2$)	52.75	57.52	52.76	54.90	53.56	50.42	48.27	-8.5%
CO$_2$ Reference Approach (Mt of CO$_2$)	51.76	54.69	49.47	54.93	54.45	51.35	50.45	-2.5%
TPES (PJ)	1 991	2 132	2 020	2 141	2 228	2 185	2 148	7.9%
TPES (Mtoe)	47.56	50.92	48.26	51.13	53.21	52.20	51.31	7.9%
GDP (billion 2000 US$ using exch. rates)	201.30	208.40	245.60	259.00	269.70	278.60	290.00	44.1%
GDP (billion 2000 US$ using PPPs)	201.61	208.74	245.99	259.46	270.17	279.08	290.49	44.1%
Population (millions)	8.56	8.83	8.87	8.96	8.99	9.03	9.08	6.1%
CO$_2$ / TPES (t CO$_2$ per TJ)	26.5	27.0	26.1	25.6	24.0	23.1	22.5	-15.2%
CO$_2$ / GDP (kg CO$_2$ per 2000 US$)	0.26	0.28	0.21	0.21	0.20	0.18	0.17	-36.5%
CO$_2$ / GDP (kg CO$_2$ per 2000 US$ PPP)	0.26	0.28	0.21	0.21	0.20	0.18	0.17	-36.5%
CO$_2$ / population (t CO$_2$ per capita)	6.16	6.52	5.95	6.13	5.96	5.58	5.32	-13.8%

Ratios are based on the Sectoral Approach.

2006 CO$_2$ emissions by sector

million tonnes of CO$_2$	Coal/peat	Oil	Gas	Other *	Total	% change 90-06
Sectoral Approach	**8.96**	**34.96**	**1.99**	**2.36**	**48.27**	**-8.5%**
Main activity producer elec. and heat	4.39	1.30	0.50	2.36	8.55	10.0%
Unallocated autoproducers	0.44	0.29	0.02	-	0.74	129.5%
Other energy industries	0.31	2.08	0.01	-	2.40	47.6%
Manufacturing industries and construction	3.75	6.16	1.06	-	10.97	-14.2%
Transport	-	22.39	0.05	-	22.44	13.5%
of which: road	-	21.05	0.05	-	21.11	18.5%
Other sectors	0.07	2.75	0.35	-	3.17	-69.7%
of which: residential	0.05	0.77	0.08	-	0.90	-81.5%
Reference Approach	**10.37**	**35.66**	**2.06**	**2.36**	**50.45**	**-2.5%**
Diff. due to losses and/or transformation	2.60	2.85	0.01	-	5.45	
Statistical differences	- 1.18	- 2.15	0.06	-	- 3.27	
Memo: international marine bunkers	-	6.57	-	-	6.57	214.1%
Memo: international aviation	-	1.96	-	-	1.96	82.2%

* Other includes industrial waste and non-renewable municipal waste.

Key sources for CO$_2$ emissions from fuel combustion in 2006

IPCC source category	CO$_2$ emissions (Mt of CO$_2$)	% change 90-06	Level assessment (%) **	Cumulative total (%)
Road - oil	21.05	18.2%	31.0	31.0
Manufacturing industries - oil	6.16	-18.6%	9.1	40.1
Main activity prod. elec. and heat - coal/peat	4.39	-16.1%	6.5	46.5
Manufacturing industries - coal/peat	3.75	-18.8%	5.5	52.1
Main activity prod. elec. and heat - other	2.36	147.2%	3.5	55.5
Other energy industries - oil	2.08	56.8%	3.1	58.6
Non-specified other sectors - oil	1.98	-62.8%	2.9	61.5
Other transport - oil	1.33	-31.6%	2.0	63.5
Main activity prod. elec. and heat - oil	1.30	14.3%	1.9	65.4
Manufacturing industries - gas	1.06	79.9%	1.6	67.0
Residential - oil	0.77	-83.8%	1.1	68.1
Memo: total CO$_2$ from fuel combustion	48.27	-8.5%	71.1	71.1

** Percent calculated using the total GHG estimate for CO$_2$, CH$_4$, N$_2$O, HFCs, PFCs and SF$_6$ excluding CO$_2$ emissions/removals from land use change and forestry.

Switzerland / Suisse

Figure 1. CO₂ emissions by fuel

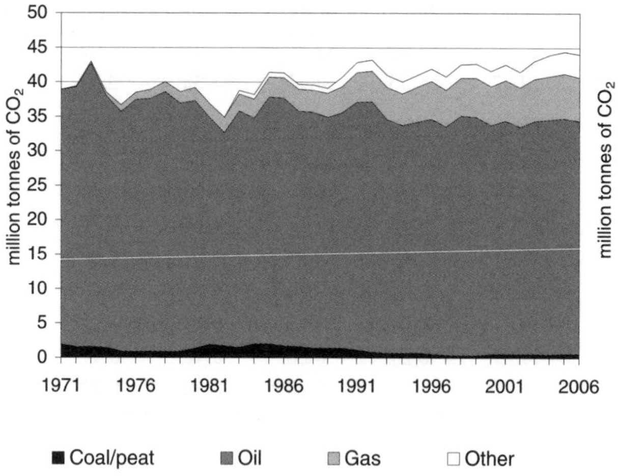

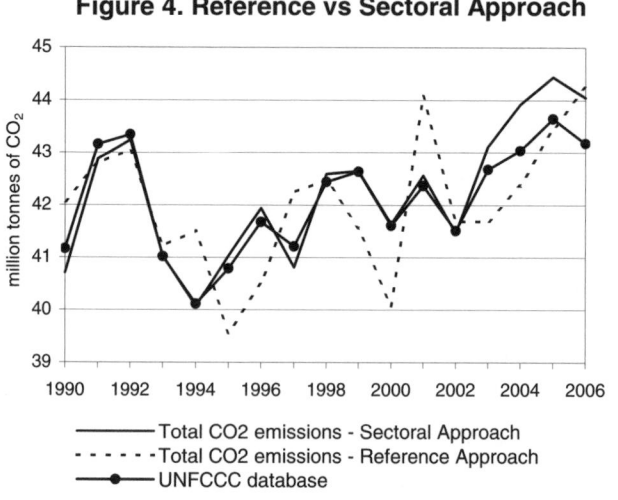

■ Coal/peat   ■ Oil   ■ Gas   ☐ Other

Figure 2. CO₂ emissions by sector

■ Electricity and heat   ☐ Other energy industries
■ Manuf. ind. and construction   ■ Transport
☐ Residential   ■ Other

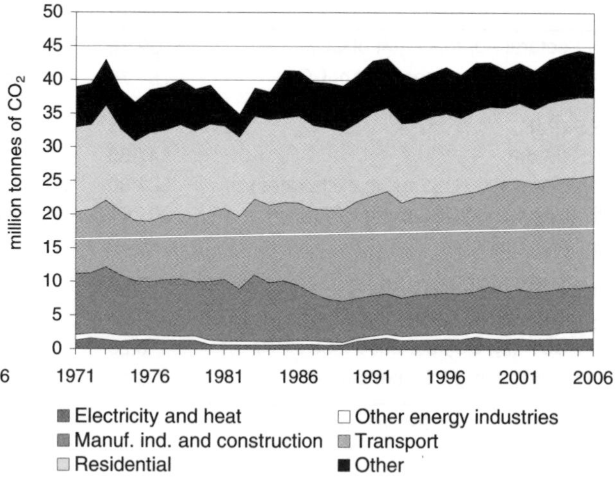

Figure 3. CO₂ emissions by sector

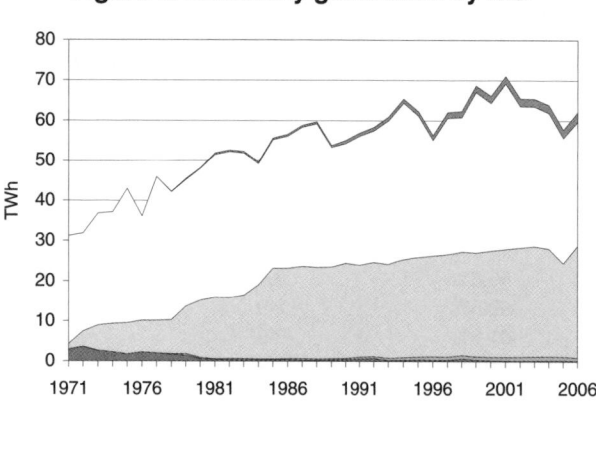

■ Electricity and heat   ☐ Other energy industries
■ Manuf. ind. and construction   ■ Transport
☐ Residential   ■ Other

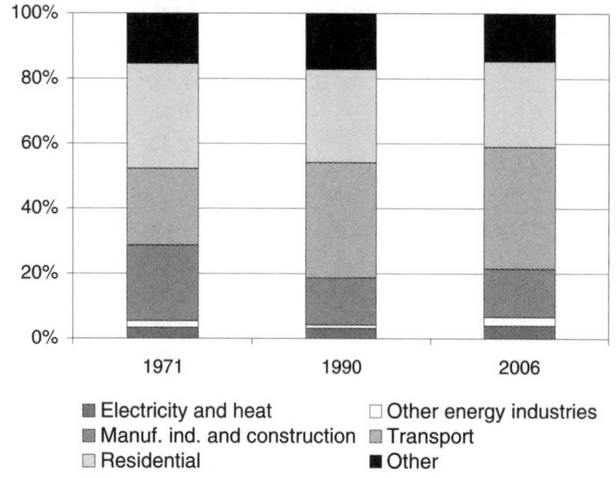

Figure 4. Reference vs Sectoral Approach

—— Total CO2 emissions - Sectoral Approach
- - - - Total CO2 emissions - Reference Approach
—●— UNFCCC database

Figure 5. Electricity generation by fuel

■ Coal/peat   ■ Oil   ■ Gas   ■ Nuclear   ☐ Hydro   ■ Other

Figure 6. Key indicators

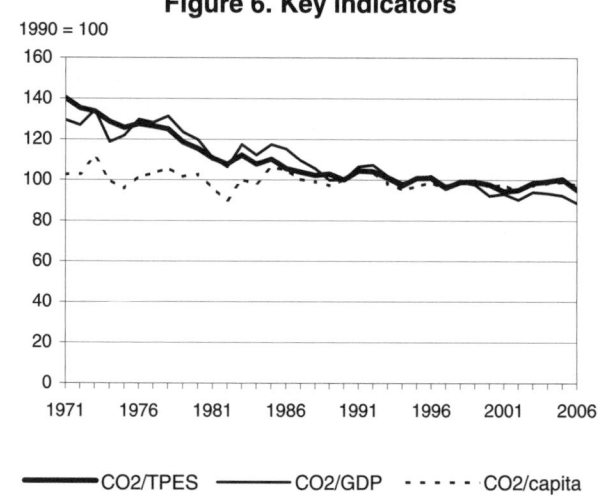

1990 = 100

—— CO2/TPES   —— CO2/GDP   - - - - CO2/capita

Switzerland / Suisse

Key indicators

	1990	1995	2000	2003	2004	2005	2006	% change 90-06
CO$_2$ Sectoral Approach (Mt of CO$_2$)	40.71	41.03	41.64	43.11	43.92	44.44	44.05	8.2%
CO$_2$ Reference Approach (Mt of CO$_2$)	42.06	39.56	40.07	41.68	42.37	43.46	44.25	5.2%
TPES (PJ)	1 038	1 040	1 088	1 119	1 130	1 130	1 181	13.7%
TPES (Mtoe)	24.80	24.84	26.00	26.72	26.99	27.00	28.21	13.7%
GDP (billion 2000 US$ using exch. rates)	224.80	225.90	249.90	253.40	259.80	266.10	274.70	22.2%
GDP (billion 2000 US$ using PPPs)	204.77	205.79	227.68	230.87	236.72	242.45	250.30	22.2%
Population (millions)	6.80	7.08	7.21	7.41	7.45	7.50	7.56	11.2%
CO$_2$ / TPES (t CO$_2$ per TJ)	39.2	39.5	38.3	38.5	38.9	39.3	37.3	-4.9%
CO$_2$ / GDP (kg CO$_2$ per 2000 US$)	0.18	0.18	0.17	0.17	0.17	0.17	0.16	-11.4%
CO$_2$ / GDP (kg CO$_2$ per 2000 US$ PPP)	0.20	0.20	0.18	0.19	0.19	0.18	0.18	-11.5%
CO$_2$ / population (t CO$_2$ per capita)	5.99	5.80	5.78	5.82	5.89	5.92	5.83	-2.7%

Ratios are based on the Sectoral Approach.

2006 CO$_2$ emissions by sector

million tonnes of CO$_2$	Coal/peat	Oil	Gas	Other *	Total	% change 90-06
Sectoral Approach	**0.63**	**33.78**	**6.28**	**3.37**	**44.05**	**8.2%**
Main activity producer elec. and heat	-	0.01	0.08	-	0.09	-79.3%
Unallocated autoproducers	-	0.08	0.19	1.36	1.63	99.4%
Other energy industries	-	1.18	-	-	1.18	190.4%
Manufacturing industries and construction	0.43	2.92	2.02	1.16	6.53	10.3%
Transport	-	16.47	-	-	16.47	14.4%
of which: road	-	16.26	-	-	16.26	17.3%
Other sectors	0.20	13.12	3.98	0.85	18.15	-3.1%
of which: residential	0.20	9.14	2.29	-	11.63	-0.6%
Reference Approach	**0.62**	**33.93**	**6.32**	**3.37**	**44.25**	**5.2%**
Diff. due to losses and/or transformation	- 0.01	0.41	0.05	-	0.45	
Statistical differences	0.00	- 0.25	-	- 0.00	- 0.25	
Memo: international marine bunkers	-	0.03	-	-	0.03	-50.0%
Memo: international aviation	-	3.68	-	-	3.68	22.6%

* Other includes industrial waste and non-renewable municipal waste.

Key sources for CO$_2$ emissions from fuel combustion in 2006

IPCC source category	CO$_2$ emissions (Mt of CO$_2$)	% change 90-06	Level assessment (%) **	Cumulative total (%)
Road - oil	16.26	17.3%	30.1	30.1
Residential - oil	9.14	-10.5%	16.9	47.0
Non-specified other sectors - oil	3.98	-36.1%	7.4	54.3
Manufacturing industries - oil	2.92	14.6%	5.4	59.7
Residential - gas	2.29	61.7%	4.2	64.0
Manufacturing industries - gas	2.02	47.7%	3.7	67.7
Non-specified other sectors - gas	1.69	112.0%	3.1	70.8
Unallocated autoproducers - other	1.36	105.0%	2.5	73.3
Other energy industries - oil	1.18	190.4%	2.2	75.5
Manufacturing industries -other	1.16	65.2%	2.1	77.7
Non-specified other sectors - other	0.85	x	1.6	79.2
Memo: total CO$_2$ from fuel combustion	44.05	8.2%	81.4	81.4

** Percent calculated using the total GHG estimate for CO$_2$, CH$_4$, N$_2$O, HFCs, PFCs and SF$_6$ excluding CO$_2$ emissions/removals from land use change and forestry.

Syria / Syrie

Figure 1. CO$_2$ emissions by fuel

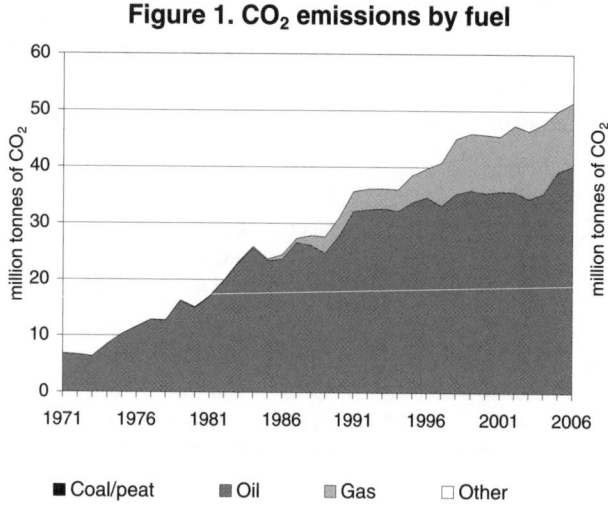

Legend: ■ Coal/peat ■ Oil ■ Gas □ Other

Figure 2. CO$_2$ emissions by sector

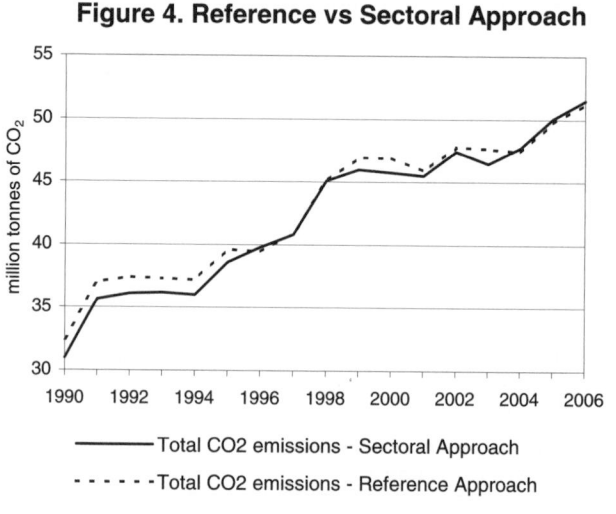

Legend: ■ Electricity and heat   □ Other energy industries   ■ Manuf. ind. and construction   ■ Transport   ■ Residential   ■ Other

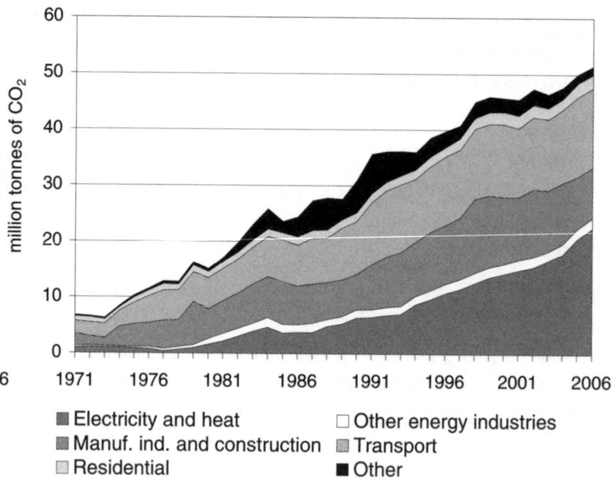

Figure 3. CO$_2$ emissions by sector

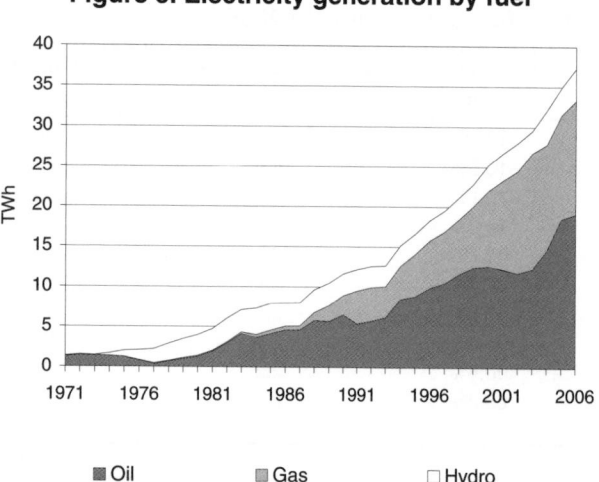

Legend: ■ Electricity and heat   □ Other energy industries   ■ Manuf. ind. and construction   ■ Transport   ■ Residential   ■ Other

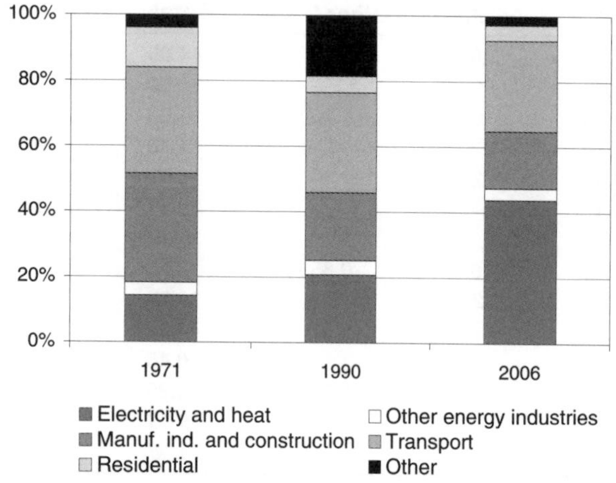

Figure 4. Reference vs Sectoral Approach

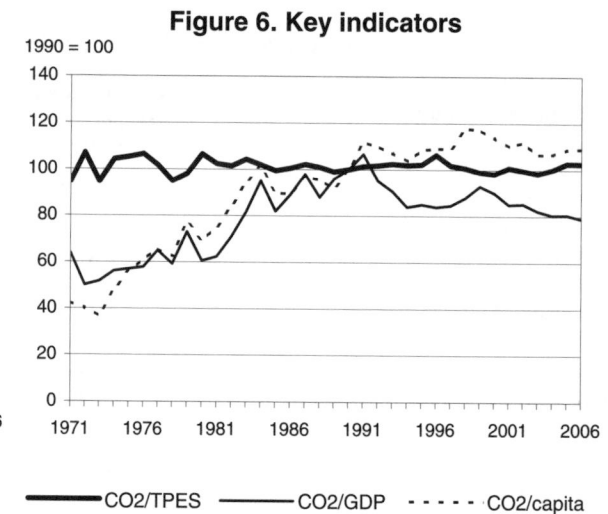

Legend: —— Total CO2 emissions - Sectoral Approach
----- Total CO2 emissions - Reference Approach

Figure 5. Electricity generation by fuel

Legend: ■ Oil   ■ Gas   □ Hydro

Figure 6. Key indicators

1990 = 100

Legend: —— CO2/TPES   —— CO2/GDP   ----- CO2/capita

Syria / Syrie
Key indicators

	1990	1995	2000	2003	2004	2005	2006	% change 90-06
CO$_2$ Sectoral Approach (Mt of CO$_2$)	30.98	38.61	45.76	46.45	47.72	50.05	51.50	66.2%
CO$_2$ Reference Approach (Mt of CO$_2$)	32.44	39.60	46.92	47.64	47.41	49.77	51.22	57.9%
TPES (PJ)	489	596	735	745	753	769	792	62.0%
TPES (Mtoe)	11.68	14.24	17.57	17.80	17.99	18.37	18.92	62.0%
GDP (billion 2000 US$ using exch. rates)	11.77	17.26	19.33	21.48	22.54	23.60	24.78	110.5%
GDP (billion 2000 US$ using PPPs)	32.38	47.48	53.17	59.10	62.01	64.93	68.18	110.5%
Population (millions)	12.72	14.61	16.51	17.89	18.39	18.89	19.41	52.6%
CO$_2$ / TPES (t CO$_2$ per TJ)	63.4	64.7	62.2	62.3	63.3	65.1	65.0	2.6%
CO$_2$ / GDP (kg CO$_2$ per 2000 US$)	2.63	2.24	2.37	2.16	2.12	2.12	2.08	-21.0%
CO$_2$ / GDP (kg CO$_2$ per 2000 US$ PPP)	0.96	0.81	0.86	0.79	0.77	0.77	0.76	-21.0%
CO$_2$ / population (t CO$_2$ per capita)	2.44	2.64	2.77	2.60	2.60	2.65	2.65	9.0%

Ratios are based on the Sectoral Approach.

2006 CO$_2$ emissions by sector

million tonnes of CO$_2$	Coal/peat	Oil	Gas	Other *	Total	% change 90-06
Sectoral Approach	**0.01**	**40.30**	**11.19**	**-**	**51.50**	**66.2%**
Main activity producer elec. and heat	-	13.74	7.70	-	21.44	292.1%
Unallocated autoproducers	-	1.09	-	-	1.09	14.3%
Other energy industries	-	1.53	0.33	-	1.85	34.1%
Manufacturing industries and construction	0.01	6.25	2.73	-	8.98	40.7%
Transport	-	14.24	-	-	14.24	50.3%
of which: road	-	13.62	-	-	13.62	43.7%
Other sectors	-	3.45	0.43	-	3.89	-46.9%
of which: residential	-	2.41	-	-	2.41	53.9%
Reference Approach	**0.01**	**40.02**	**11.19**	**-**	**51.22**	**57.9%**
Diff. due to losses and/or transformation	0.01	- 0.29	-	-	- 0.28	
Statistical differences	-	-	-	-	-	
Memo: international marine bunkers	-	..	-	-	..	..
Memo: international aviation	-	0.32	-	-	0.32	-62.9%

* Other includes industrial waste and non-renewable municipal waste.

Key sources for CO$_2$ emissions from fuel combustion in 2006

IPCC source category	CO$_2$ emissions (Mt of CO$_2$)	% change 90-06	Level assessment (%) **	Cumulative total (%)
Main activity prod. elec. and heat - oil	13.74	229.1%	19.1	19.1
Road - oil	13.62	43.7%	19.0	38.1
Main activity prod. elec. and heat - gas	7.70	495.0%	10.7	48.8
Manufacturing industries - oil	6.25	-2.1%	8.7	57.5
Manufacturing industries - gas	2.73	x	3.8	61.3
Residential - oil	2.41	53.9%	3.4	64.6
Other energy industries - oil	1.53	24.0%	2.1	66.8
Unallocated autoproducers - oil	1.09	14.3%	1.5	68.3
Non-specified other sectors - oil	1.04	-73.9%	1.5	69.7
Other transport - oil	0.63	x	0.9	70.6
Non-specified other sectors - gas	0.43	-75.3%	0.6	71.2
Memo: total CO$_2$ from fuel combustion	51.50	66.2%	71.7	71.7

** Percent calculated using the total GHG estimate for CO$_2$, CH$_4$, N$_2$O, HFCs, PFCs and SF$_6$ excluding CO$_2$ emissions/removals from land use change and forestry.

Tajikistan / Tadjikistan

Figure 1. CO$_2$ emissions by fuel

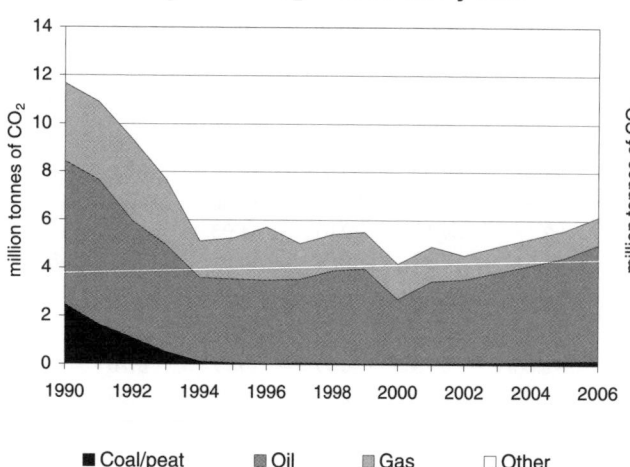

■ Coal/peat   ■ Oil   ■ Gas   □ Other

Figure 2. CO$_2$ emissions by sector

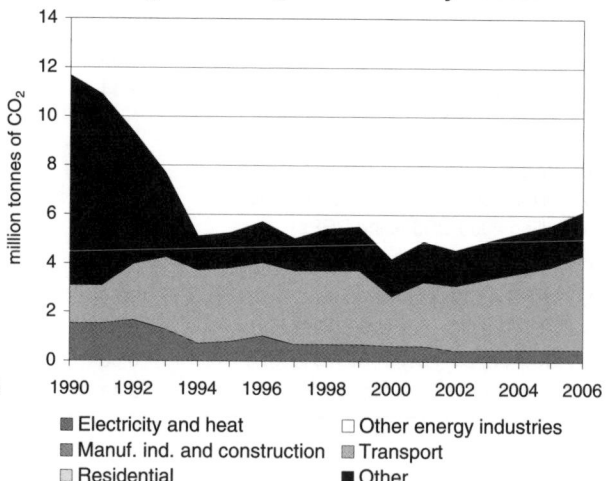

■ Electricity and heat   □ Other energy industries
■ Manuf. ind. and construction   ■ Transport
■ Residential   ■ Other

Figure 3. CO$_2$ emissions by sector

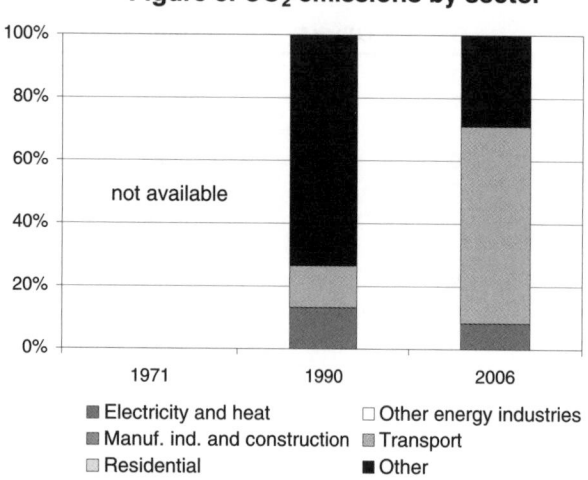

■ Electricity and heat   □ Other energy industries
■ Manuf. ind. and construction   ■ Transport
■ Residential   ■ Other

Figure 4. Reference vs Sectoral Approach

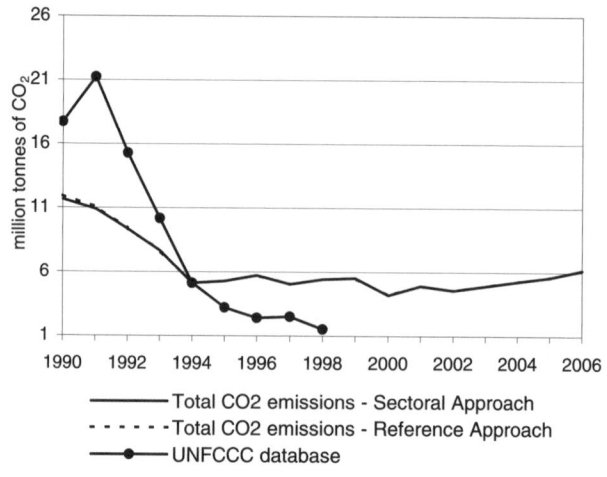

—— Total CO2 emissions - Sectoral Approach
- - - - Total CO2 emissions - Reference Approach
—●— UNFCCC database

Figure 5. Electricity generation by fuel

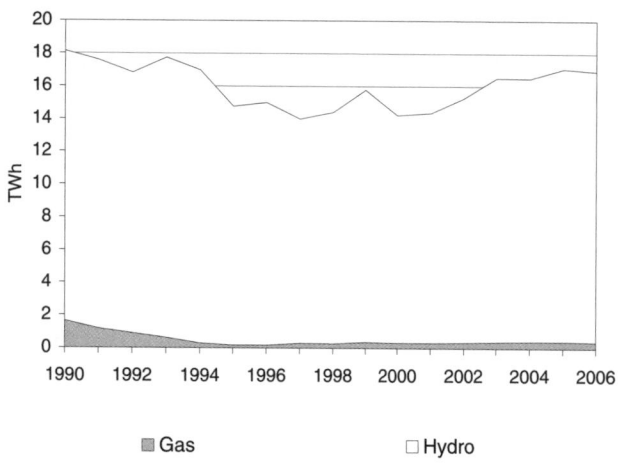

■ Gas   □ Hydro

Figure 6. Key indicators

1990 = 100

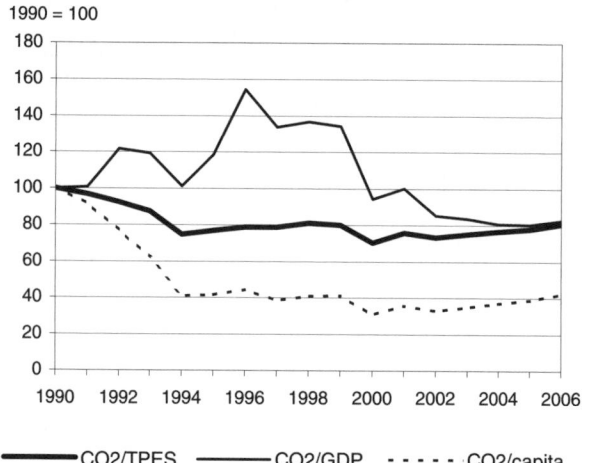

—— CO2/TPES   —— CO2/GDP   - - - - CO2/capita

Tajikistan / Tadjikistan

Key indicators

	1990	1995	2000	2003	2004	2005	2006	% change 90-06
CO$_2$ Sectoral Approach (Mt of CO$_2$)	11.67	5.26	4.19	4.92	5.26	5.58	6.15	-47.3%
CO$_2$ Reference Approach (Mt of CO$_2$)	11.93	5.26	4.19	4.92	5.27	5.59	6.15	-48.4%
TPES (PJ)	233	137	119	131	137	143	152	-34.8%
TPES (Mtoe)	5.57	3.27	2.85	3.13	3.27	3.42	3.64	-34.8%
GDP (billion 2000 US$ using exch. rates)	2.57	0.98	0.98	1.30	1.44	1.53	1.64	-36.3%
GDP (billion 2000 US$ using PPPs)	13.10	4.98	4.99	6.61	7.31	7.80	8.36	-36.2%
Population (millions)	5.30	5.77	6.17	6.39	6.47	6.55	6.64	25.2%
CO$_2$ / TPES (t CO$_2$ per TJ)	50.0	38.4	35.2	37.6	38.4	38.9	40.4	-19.2%
CO$_2$ / GDP (kg CO$_2$ per 2000 US$)	4.53	5.37	4.28	3.79	3.66	3.64	3.75	-17.3%
CO$_2$ / GDP (kg CO$_2$ per 2000 US$ PPP)	0.89	1.06	0.84	0.74	0.72	0.72	0.74	-17.4%
CO$_2$ / population (t CO$_2$ per capita)	2.20	0.91	0.68	0.77	0.81	0.85	0.93	-57.9%

Ratios are based on the Sectoral Approach.

2006 CO$_2$ emissions by sector

million tonnes of CO$_2$	Coal/peat	Oil	Gas	Other *	Total	% change 90-06
Sectoral Approach	**0.19**	**4.82**	**1.14**	**-**	**6.15**	**-47.3%**
Main activity producer elec. and heat	-	-	0.50	-	0.50	-67.0%
Unallocated autoproducers	-	-	-	-	-	-
Other energy industries	-	-	-	-	-	-
Manufacturing industries and construction	-	-	-	-	-	-
Transport	-	3.85	-	-	3.85	148.0%
of which: road	-	3.85	-	-	3.85	148.0%
Other sectors	0.19	0.97	0.64	-	1.79	-79.2%
of which: residential	-	-	-	-	-	-
Reference Approach	**0.19**	**4.82**	**1.14**	**-**	**6.15**	**-48.4%**
Diff. due to losses and/or transformation	-	0.00	-	-	0.00	
Statistical differences	-	-	- 0.00	-	- 0.00	
Memo: international marine bunkers	-	-	-	-	-	-
Memo: international aviation	-	0.01	-	-	0.01	..

* Other includes industrial waste and non-renewable municipal waste.

Key sources for CO$_2$ emissions from fuel combustion in 2006

IPCC source category	CO$_2$ emissions (Mt of CO$_2$)	% change 90-06	Level assessment (%) **	Cumulative total (%)
Road - oil	3.85	148.0%	34.0	34.0
Non-specified other sectors - oil	0.97	-78.0%	8.5	42.5
Non-specified other sectors - gas	0.64	-62.8%	5.6	48.2
Main activity prod. elec. and heat - gas	0.50	-67.0%	4.4	52.6
Non-specified other sectors - coal/peat	0.19	-92.5%	1.6	54.2
-	-	-	-	-
-	-	-	-	-
-	-	-	-	-
-	-	-	-	-
-	-	-	-	-
-	-	-	-	-
Memo: total CO$_2$ from fuel combustion	6.15	-47.3%	54.2	54.2

** Percent calculated using the total GHG estimate for CO$_2$, CH$_4$, N$_2$O, HFCs, PFCs and SF$_6$ excluding CO$_2$ emissions/removals from land use change and forestry.

United Republic of Tanzania / République unie de Tanzanie

Figure 1. CO$_2$ emissions by fuel

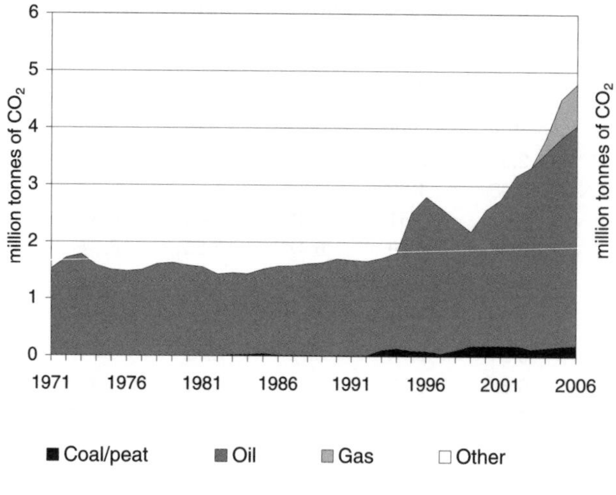

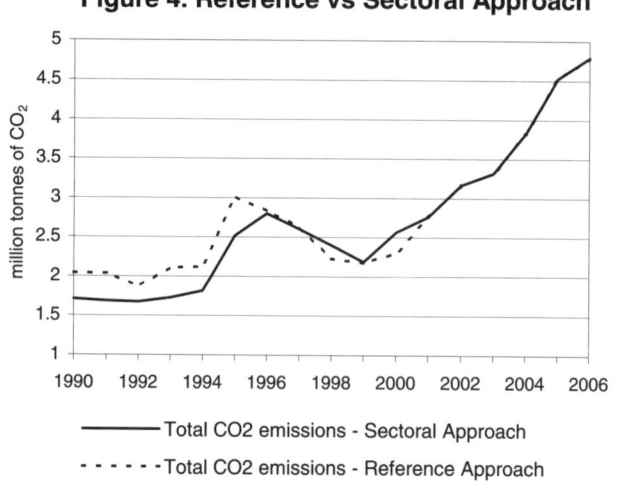

■ Coal/peat   ■ Oil   ■ Gas   □ Other

Figure 2. CO$_2$ emissions by sector

■ Electricity and heat   □ Other energy industries
■ Manuf. ind. and construction ■ Transport
□ Residential   ■ Other

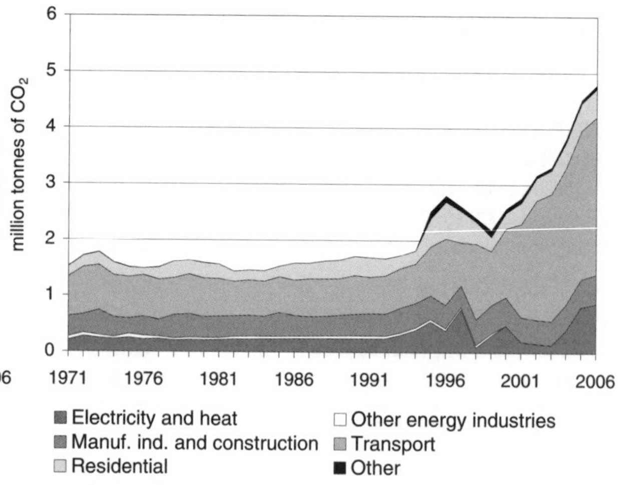

Figure 3. CO$_2$ emissions by sector

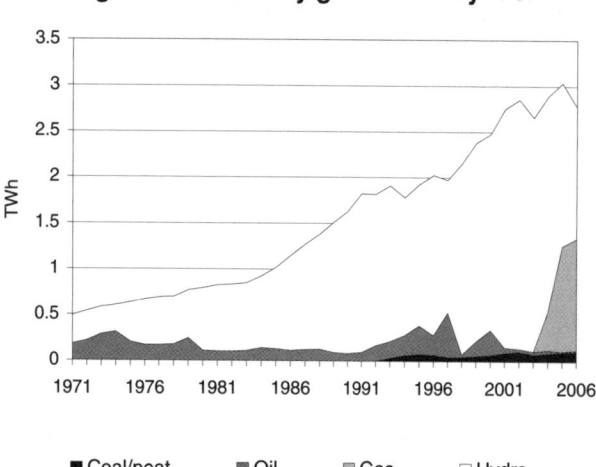

■ Electricity and heat   □ Other energy industries
■ Manuf. ind. and construction ■ Transport
□ Residential   ■ Other

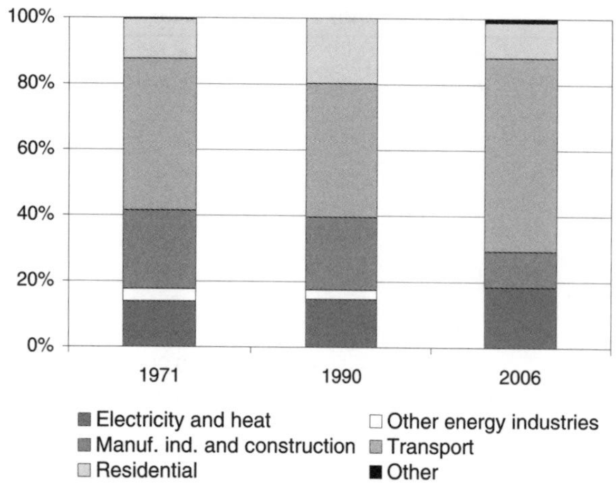

Figure 4. Reference vs Sectoral Approach

——— Total CO2 emissions - Sectoral Approach

- - - - Total CO2 emissions - Reference Approach

Figure 5. Electricity generation by fuel

■ Coal/peat   ■ Oil   ■ Gas   □ Hydro

Figure 6. Key indicators

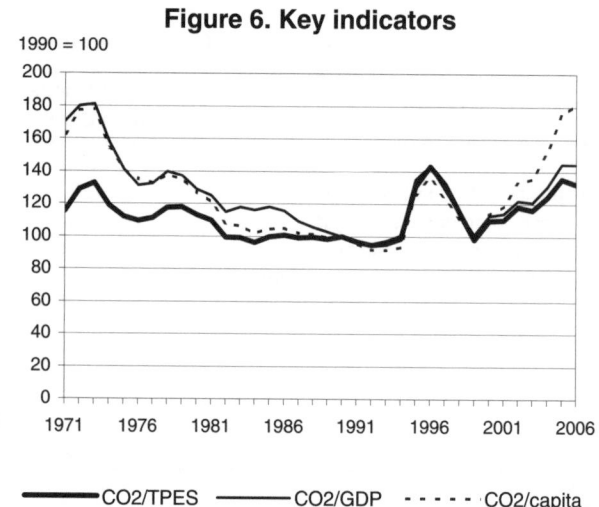

1990 = 100

━━━ CO2/TPES   ——— CO2/GDP   - - - - CO2/capita

United Republic of Tanzania / République unie de Tanzanie
Key indicators

	1990	1995	2000	2003	2004	2005	2006	% change 90-06
CO$_2$ Sectoral Approach (Mt of CO$_2$)	1.71	2.52	2.57	3.32	3.82	4.52	4.79	180.6%
CO$_2$ Reference Approach (Mt of CO$_2$)	2.04	3.01	2.30	3.32	3.82	4.52	4.79	134.5%
TPES (PJ)	411	464	563	687	741	804	871	112.1%
TPES (Mtoe)	9.81	11.09	13.45	16.40	17.69	19.21	20.81	112.1%
GDP (billion 2000 US$ using exch. rates)	6.80	7.43	9.08	10.93	11.67	12.46	13.20	94.1%
GDP (billion 2000 US$ using PPPs)	13.20	14.43	17.63	21.22	22.65	24.19	25.64	94.2%
Population (millions)	25.49	29.90	33.85	36.55	37.51	38.48	39.46	54.8%
CO$_2$ / TPES (t CO$_2$ per TJ)	4.2	5.4	4.6	4.8	5.2	5.6	5.5	32.3%
CO$_2$ / GDP (kg CO$_2$ per 2000 US$)	0.25	0.34	0.28	0.30	0.33	0.36	0.36	44.5%
CO$_2$ / GDP (kg CO$_2$ per 2000 US$ PPP)	0.13	0.17	0.15	0.16	0.17	0.19	0.19	44.5%
CO$_2$ / population (t CO$_2$ per capita)	0.07	0.08	0.08	0.09	0.10	0.12	0.12	81.3%

Ratios are based on the Sectoral Approach.

2006 CO$_2$ emissions by sector

million tonnes of CO$_2$	Coal/peat	Oil	Gas	Other *	Total	% change 90-06
Sectoral Approach	**0.19**	**3.86**	**0.73**	-	**4.79**	**180.6%**
Main activity producer elec. and heat	-	0.03	0.73	-	0.76	206.3%
Unallocated autoproducers	0.12	-	-	-	0.12	x
Other energy industries	-	-	-	-	-	-100.0%
Manufacturing industries and construction	0.07	0.45	-	-	0.52	37.9%
Transport	-	2.81	-	-	2.81	305.9%
of which: road	-	*2.81*	-	-	*2.81*	*305.9%*
Other sectors	-	0.58	-	-	0.58	70.3%
of which: residential	-	*0.52*	-	-	*0.52*	*52.5%*
Reference Approach	**0.19**	**3.86**	**0.73**	-	**4.79**	**134.5%**
Diff. due to losses and/or transformation	-	-	-	-	-	
Statistical differences	-	-	-	-	-	
Memo: international marine bunkers	-	*0.07*	-	-	*0.07*	*-11.5%*
Memo: international aviation	-	*0.28*	-	-	*0.28*	*26.0%*

* Other includes industrial waste and non-renewable municipal waste.

Key sources for CO$_2$ emissions from fuel combustion in 2006

IPCC source category	CO$_2$ emissions (Mt of CO$_2$)	% change 90-06	Level assessment (%) **	Cumulative total (%)
Road - oil	2.81	305.9%	3.6	3.6
Main activity prod. elec. and heat - gas	0.73	x	0.9	4.6
Residential - oil	0.52	52.5%	0.7	5.3
Manufacturing industries - oil	0.45	21.7%	0.6	5.8
Unallocated autoproducers - coal/peat	0.12	x	0.2	6.0
Manufacturing industries - coal/peat	0.07	629.5%	0.1	6.1
Non-specified other sectors - oil	0.06	x	0.1	6.2
Main activity prod. elec. and heat - oil	0.03	-89.7%	0.0	6.2
-	-	-	-	-
-	-	-	-	-
-	-	-	-	-
Memo: total CO$_2$ from fuel combustion	4.79	180.6%	6.2	6.2

** Percent calculated using the total GHG estimate for CO$_2$, CH$_4$, N$_2$O, HFCs, PFCs and SF$_6$ excluding CO$_2$ emissions/removals from land use change and forestry.

Thailand / Thailande

Figure 1. CO$_2$ emissions by fuel

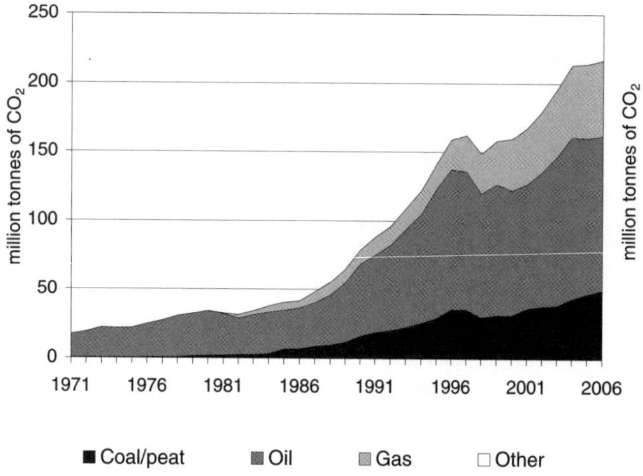

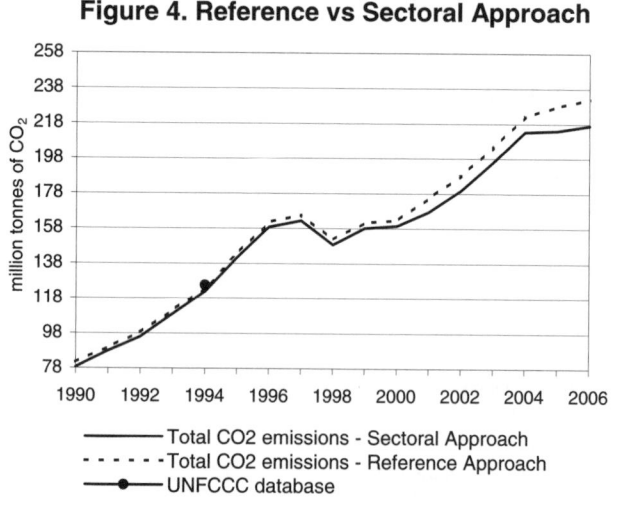

■ Coal/peat   ■ Oil   ■ Gas   □ Other

Figure 2. CO$_2$ emissions by sector

■ Electricity and heat   □ Other energy industries
■ Manuf. ind. and construction ■ Transport
□ Residential   ■ Other

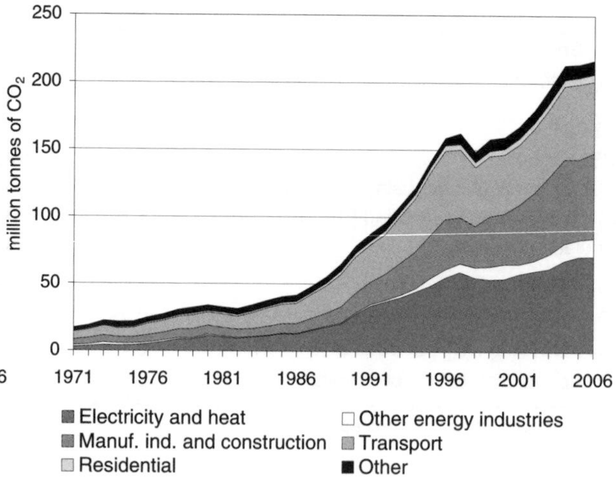

Figure 3. CO$_2$ emissions by sector

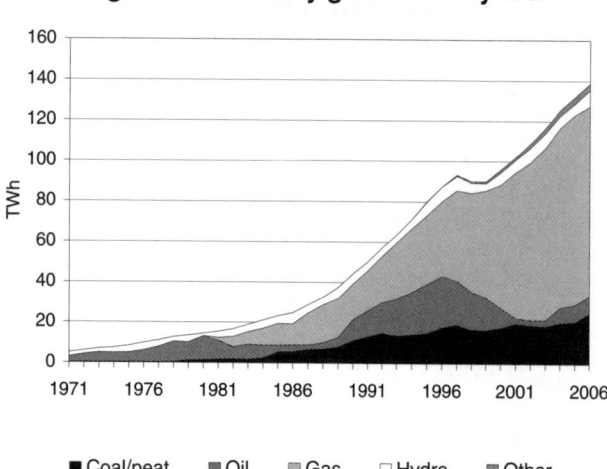

■ Electricity and heat   □ Other energy industries
■ Manuf. ind. and construction ■ Transport
□ Residential   ■ Other

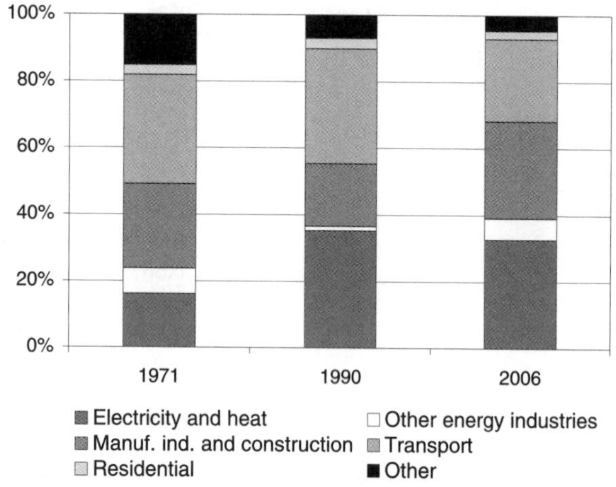

Figure 4. Reference vs Sectoral Approach

—— Total CO2 emissions - Sectoral Approach
- - - Total CO2 emissions - Reference Approach
——●—— UNFCCC database

Figure 5. Electricity generation by fuel

■ Coal/peat   ■ Oil   ■ Gas   □ Hydro   ■ Other

Figure 6. Key indicators

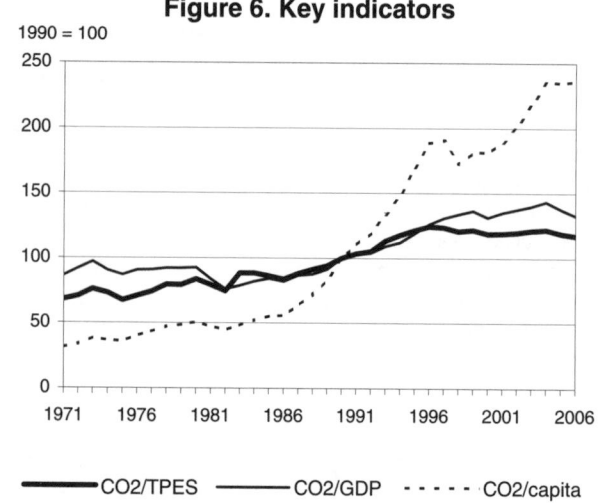

1990 = 100

—— CO2/TPES   —— CO2/GDP   - - - CO2/capita

Thailand / Thailande

Key indicators

	1990	1995	2000	2003	2004	2005	2006	% change 90-06
CO$_2$ Sectoral Approach (Mt of CO$_2$)	78.59	141.26	159.46	195.99	213.43	214.15	217.01	176.1%
CO$_2$ Reference Approach (Mt of CO$_2$)	81.36	143.49	162.88	204.66	222.35	227.94	232.14	185.3%
TPES (PJ)	1 839	2 720	3 141	3 783	4 092	4 214	4 329	135.5%
TPES (Mtoe)	43.91	64.98	75.03	90.35	97.73	100.65	103.39	135.5%
GDP (billion 2000 US$ using exch. rates)	79.36	120.01	122.73	141.48	150.37	157.11	164.95	107.9%
GDP (billion 2000 US$ using PPPs)	251.14	379.77	388.38	447.73	475.85	497.19	522.01	107.9%
Population (millions)	54.29	57.52	60.67	62.13	62.57	63.00	63.44	16.9%
CO$_2$ / TPES (t CO$_2$ per TJ)	42.8	51.9	50.8	51.8	52.2	50.8	50.1	17.3%
CO$_2$ / GDP (kg CO$_2$ per 2000 US$)	0.99	1.18	1.30	1.39	1.42	1.36	1.32	32.8%
CO$_2$ / GDP (kg CO$_2$ per 2000 US$ PPP)	0.31	0.37	0.41	0.44	0.45	0.43	0.42	32.9%
CO$_2$ / population (t CO$_2$ per capita)	1.45	2.46	2.63	3.15	3.41	3.40	3.42	136.3%

Ratios are based on the Sectoral Approach.

2006 CO$_2$ emissions by sector

million tonnes of CO$_2$	Coal/peat	Oil	Gas	Other *	Total	% change 90-06
Sectoral Approach	49.79	112.15	55.08	-	217.01	176.1%
Main activity producer elec. and heat	16.94	6.27	39.58	-	62.80	126.9%
Unallocated autoproducers	3.31	0.03	4.76	-	8.09	x
Other energy industries	-	7.66	6.16	-	13.82	+
Manufacturing industries and construction	29.54	29.41	4.40	-	63.35	328.4%
Transport	-	53.27	0.18	-	53.44	97.1%
of which: road	-	52.75	0.18	-	52.93	106.1%
Other sectors	-	15.51	-	-	15.51	93.4%
of which: residential	-	5.32	-	-	5.32	116.2%
Reference Approach	50.07	119.92	62.15	-	232.14	185.3%
Diff. due to losses and/or transformation	0.01	7.66	7.04	-	14.71	
Statistical differences	0.27	0.12	0.03	-	0.41	
Memo: international marine bunkers	-	5.26	-	-	5.26	208.9%
Memo: international aviation	-	10.70	-	-	10.70	91.4%

* Other includes industrial waste and non-renewable municipal waste.

Key sources for CO$_2$ emissions from fuel combustion in 2006

IPCC source category	CO$_2$ emissions (Mt of CO$_2$)	% change 90-06	Level assessment (%) **	Cumulative total (%)
Road - oil	52.75	105.5%	15.3	15.3
Main activity prod. elec. and heat - gas	39.58	342.9%	11.5	26.8
Manufacturing industries - coal/peat	29.54	438.5%	8.6	35.4
Manufacturing industries - oil	29.41	233.6%	8.5	43.9
Main activity prod. elec. and heat - coal/peat	16.94	60.2%	4.9	48.8
Non-specified other sectors - oil	10.19	83.3%	3.0	51.8
Other energy industries - oil	7.66	+	2.2	54.0
Main activity prod. elec. and heat - oil	6.27	-23.1%	1.8	55.8
Other energy industries - gas	6.16	+	1.8	57.6
Residential - oil	5.32	116.2%	1.5	59.1
Unallocated autoproducers - gas	4.76	x	1.4	60.5
Memo: total CO$_2$ from fuel combustion	217.01	176.1%	63.0	63.0

** Percent calculated using the total GHG estimate for CO$_2$, CH$_4$, N$_2$O, HFCs, PFCs and SF$_6$ excluding CO$_2$ emissions/removals from land use change and forestry.

Togo

Figure 1. CO$_2$ emissions by fuel

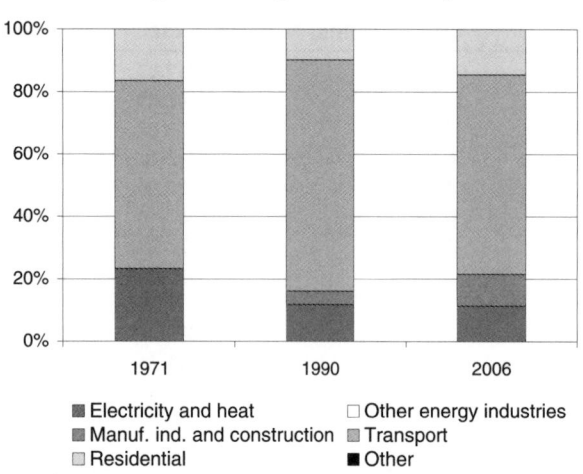

■ Coal/peat   ■ Oil   ■ Gas   □ Other

Figure 2. CO$_2$ emissions by sector

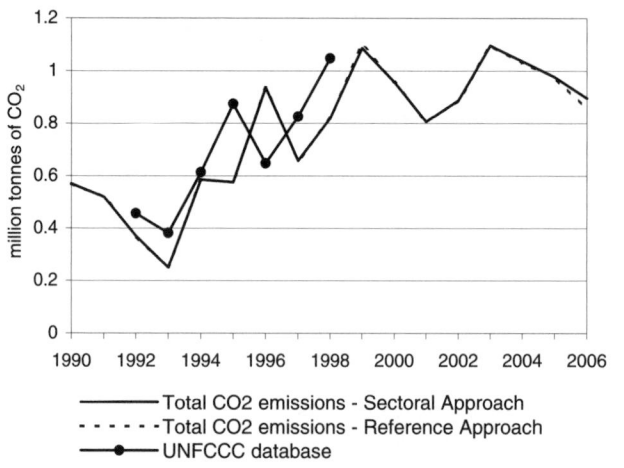

■ Electricity and heat   □ Other energy industries
■ Manuf. ind. and construction   ■ Transport
□ Residential   ■ Other

Figure 3. CO$_2$ emissions by sector

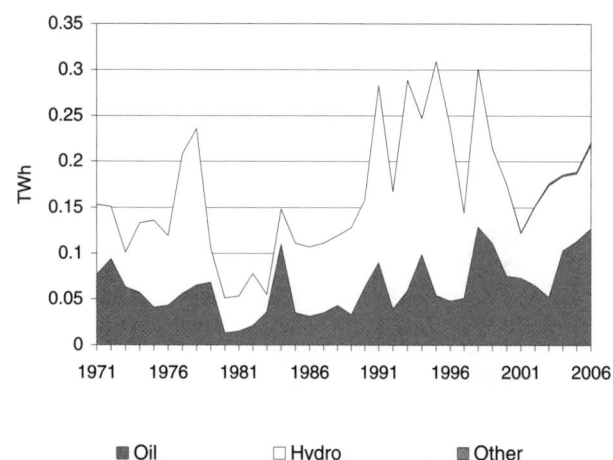

■ Electricity and heat   □ Other energy industries
■ Manuf. ind. and construction   ■ Transport
□ Residential   ■ Other

Figure 4. Reference vs Sectoral Approach

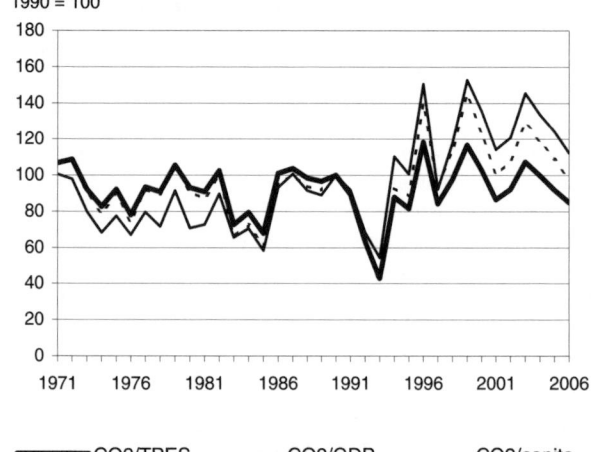

—— Total CO2 emissions - Sectoral Approach
----- Total CO2 emissions - Reference Approach
—●— UNFCCC database

Figure 5. Electricity generation by fuel

■ Oil   □ Hydro   ■ Other

Figure 6. Key indicators

1990 = 100

—— CO2/TPES   —— CO2/GDP   ----- CO2/capita

Togo

Key indicators

	1990	1995	2000	2003	2004	2005	2006	% change 90-06
CO$_2$ Sectoral Approach (Mt of CO$_2$)	0.57	0.57	0.96	1.10	1.04	0.98	0.90	57.3%
CO$_2$ Reference Approach (Mt of CO$_2$)	0.57	0.57	0.96	1.10	1.03	0.98	0.85	50.1%
TPES (PJ)	54	67	89	98	99	101	101	85.2%
TPES (Mtoe)	1.30	1.61	2.12	2.33	2.37	2.42	2.40	85.2%
GDP (billion 2000 US$ using exch. rates)	1.07	1.08	1.33	1.42	1.46	1.48	1.50	40.2%
GDP (billion 2000 US$ using PPPs)	5.87	5.89	7.28	7.77	8.01	8.11	8.23	40.3%
Population (millions)	3.96	4.52	5.40	5.91	6.07	6.24	6.41	61.8%
CO$_2$ / TPES (t CO$_2$ per TJ)	10.5	8.5	10.8	11.2	10.5	9.6	8.9	-15.0%
CO$_2$ / GDP (kg CO$_2$ per 2000 US$)	0.53	0.53	0.72	0.77	0.71	0.66	0.60	12.2%
CO$_2$ / GDP (kg CO$_2$ per 2000 US$ PPP)	0.10	0.10	0.13	0.14	0.13	0.12	0.11	12.2%
CO$_2$ / population (t CO$_2$ per capita)	0.14	0.13	0.18	0.19	0.17	0.16	0.14	-2.8%

Ratios are based on the Sectoral Approach.

2006 CO$_2$ emissions by sector

million tonnes of CO$_2$	Coal/peat	Oil	Gas	Other *	Total	% change 90-06
Sectoral Approach	-	**0.90**	-	-	**0.90**	**57.3%**
Main activity producer elec. and heat	-	0.09	-	-	0.09	52.2%
Unallocated autoproducers	-	0.01	-	-	0.01	50.0%
Other energy industries	-	-	-	-	-	-
Manufacturing industries and construction	-	0.09	-	-	0.09	271.5%
Transport	-	0.57	-	-	0.57	35.6%
of which: road	-	0.57	-	-	0.57	35.6%
Other sectors	-	0.13	-	-	0.13	133.1%
of which: residential	-	0.13	-	-	0.13	133.1%
Reference Approach	-	**0.85**	-	-	**0.85**	**50.1%**
Diff. due to losses and/or transformation	-	-	-	-	-	
Statistical differences	-	- 0.04	-	-	- 0.04	
Memo: international marine bunkers	-	0.01	-	-	0.01	..
Memo: international aviation	-	0.11	-	-	0.11	3.0%

* Other includes industrial waste and non-renewable municipal waste.

Key sources for CO$_2$ emissions from fuel combustion in 2006

IPCC source category	CO$_2$ emissions (Mt of CO$_2$)	% change 90-06	Level assessment (%) **	Cumulative total (%)
Road - oil	0.57	35.6%	5.9	5.9
Residential - oil	0.13	133.1%	1.3	7.2
Main activity prod. elec. and heat - oil	0.09	52.2%	0.9	8.2
Manufacturing industries - oil	0.09	271.5%	0.9	9.1
Unallocated autoproducers - oil	0.01	50.0%	0.1	9.2
-	-	-	-	-
-	-	-	-	-
-	-	-	-	-
-	-	-	-	-
-	-	-	-	-
-	-	-	-	-
Memo: total CO$_2$ from fuel combustion	0.90	57.3%	9.2	9.2

** Percent calculated using the total GHG estimate for CO$_2$, CH$_4$, N$_2$O, HFCs, PFCs and SF$_6$ excluding CO$_2$ emissions/removals from land use change and forestry.

Trinidad and Tobago / Trinité-et-Tobago

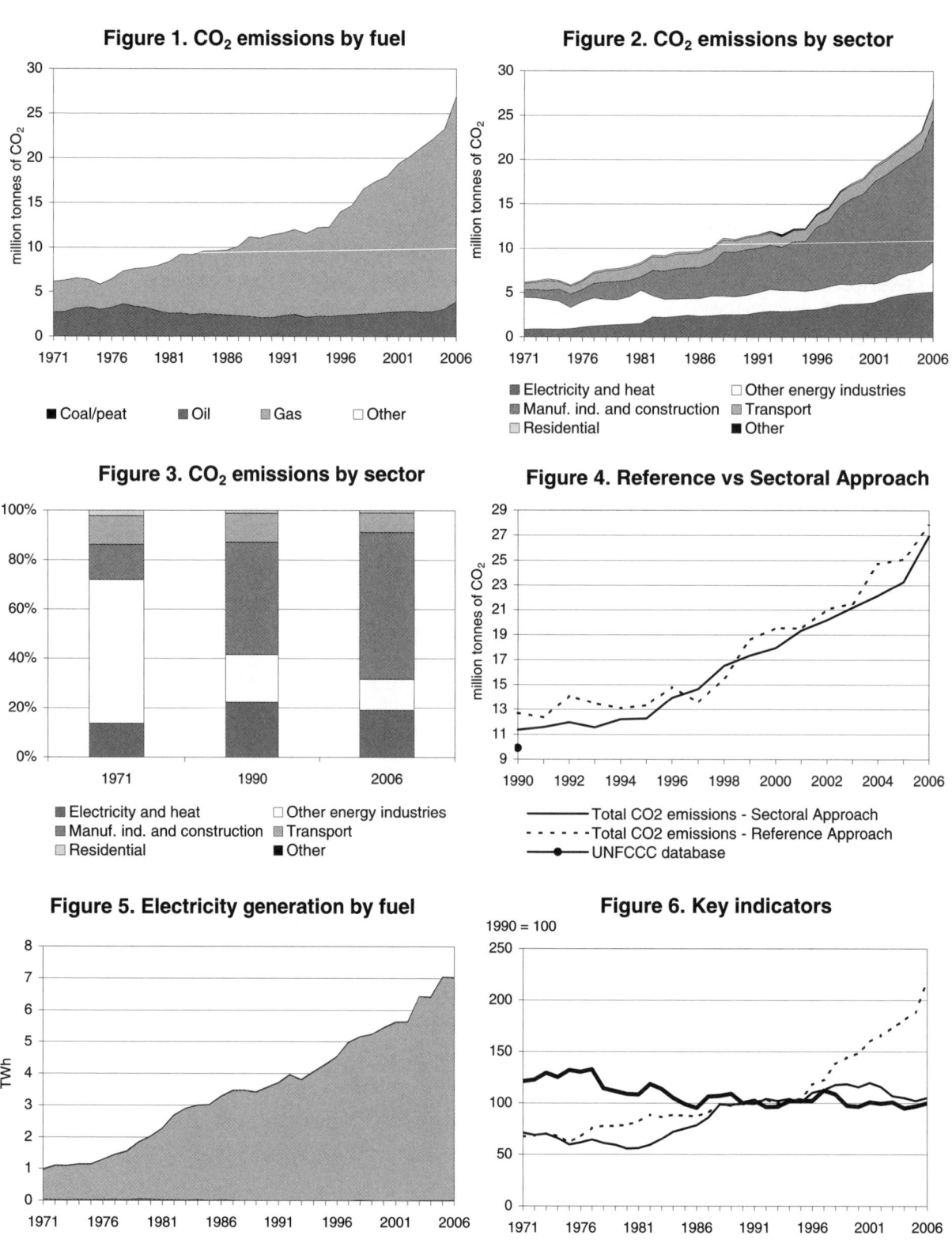

Figure 1. CO$_2$ emissions by fuel

■ Coal/peat   ■ Oil   ▨ Gas   ☐ Other

Figure 2. CO$_2$ emissions by sector

■ Electricity and heat   ☐ Other energy industries
▨ Manuf. ind. and construction   ▨ Transport
▨ Residential   ■ Other

Figure 3. CO$_2$ emissions by sector

■ Electricity and heat   ☐ Other energy industries
■ Manuf. ind. and construction   ▨ Transport
▨ Residential   ■ Other

Figure 4. Reference vs Sectoral Approach

—— Total CO2 emissions - Sectoral Approach
- - - - Total CO2 emissions - Reference Approach
●—— UNFCCC database

Figure 5. Electricity generation by fuel

■ Oil   ▨ Gas   ▨ Other

Figure 6. Key indicators

1990 = 100

—— CO2/TPES   —— CO2/GDP   - - - - CO2/capita

Trinidad and Tobago / Trinité-et-Tobago

Key indicators

	1990	1995	2000	2003	2004	2005	2006	% change 90-06
CO$_2$ Sectoral Approach (Mt of CO$_2$)	11.37	12.27	17.94	21.18	22.15	23.26	26.94	136.9%
CO$_2$ Reference Approach (Mt of CO$_2$)	12.71	13.34	19.56	21.54	24.71	25.09	27.78	118.6%
TPES (PJ)	253	266	413	466	519	533	599	136.9%
TPES (Mtoe)	6.04	6.35	9.86	11.12	12.39	12.74	14.30	136.9%
GDP (billion 2000 US$ using exch. rates)	5.97	6.40	8.15	10.39	11.07	11.95	13.44	125.1%
GDP (billion 2000 US$ using PPPs)	8.55	9.16	11.68	14.88	15.86	17.11	19.25	125.1%
Population (millions)	1.22	1.27	1.30	1.32	1.32	1.32	1.33	8.5%
CO$_2$ / TPES (t CO$_2$ per TJ)	45.0	46.1	43.5	45.5	42.7	43.6	45.0	0.0%
CO$_2$ / GDP (kg CO$_2$ per 2000 US$)	1.90	1.92	2.20	2.04	2.00	1.95	2.00	5.2%
CO$_2$ / GDP (kg CO$_2$ per 2000 US$ PPP)	1.33	1.34	1.54	1.42	1.40	1.36	1.40	5.3%
CO$_2$ / population (t CO$_2$ per capita)	9.29	9.66	13.79	16.11	16.79	17.57	20.28	118.3%

Ratios are based on the Sectoral Approach.

2006 CO$_2$ emissions by sector

million tonnes of CO$_2$	Coal/peat	Oil	Gas	Other *	Total	% change 90-06
Sectoral Approach	-	**3.90**	**23.04**	-	**26.94**	**136.9%**
Main activity producer elec. and heat	-	0.01	5.07	-	5.08	111.0%
Unallocated autoproducers	-	-	0.02	-	0.02	-81.8%
Other energy industries	-	1.12	2.28	-	3.40	55.4%
Manufacturing industries and construction	-	0.37	15.66	-	16.03	209.7%
Transport	-	2.13	-	-	2.13	60.2%
of which: road	-	*2.13*	-	-	*2.13*	*66.0%*
Other sectors	-	0.27	-	-	0.27	91.7%
of which: residential	-	*0.27*	-	-	*0.27*	*91.7%*
Reference Approach	-	**4.75**	**23.04**	-	**27.78**	**118.6%**
Diff. due to losses and/or transformation	-	1.88	-	-	1.88	
Statistical differences	-	- 1.03	-	-	- 1.03	
Memo: international marine bunkers	-	*0.85*	-	-	*0.85*	*680.6%*
Memo: international aviation	-	*0.22*	-	-	*0.22*	*14.5%*

* Other includes industrial waste and non-renewable municipal waste.

Key sources for CO$_2$ emissions from fuel combustion in 2006

IPCC source category	CO$_2$ emissions (Mt of CO$_2$)	% change 90-06	Level assessment (%) **	Cumulative total (%)
Manufacturing industries - gas	15.66	221.0%	49.6	49.6
Main activity prod. elec. and heat - gas	5.07	110.9%	16.1	65.7
Other energy industries - gas	2.28	22.4%	7.2	72.9
Road - oil	2.13	66.0%	6.8	79.7
Other energy industries - oil	1.12	242.8%	3.6	83.2
Manufacturing industries - oil	0.37	24.3%	1.2	84.4
Residential - oil	0.27	91.7%	0.8	85.2
Unallocated autoproducers - gas	0.02	-81.8%	0.1	85.3
Main activity prod. elec. and heat - oil	0.01	200.1%	0.0	85.3
-	-	-	-	-
-	-	-	-	-
Memo: total CO$_2$ from fuel combustion	*26.94*	*136.9%*	*85.3*	*85.3*

** Percent calculated using the total GHG estimate for CO$_2$, CH$_4$, N$_2$O, HFCs, PFCs and SF$_6$ excluding CO$_2$ emissions/removals from land use change and forestry.

Tunisia / Tunisie

Figure 1. CO₂ emissions by fuel

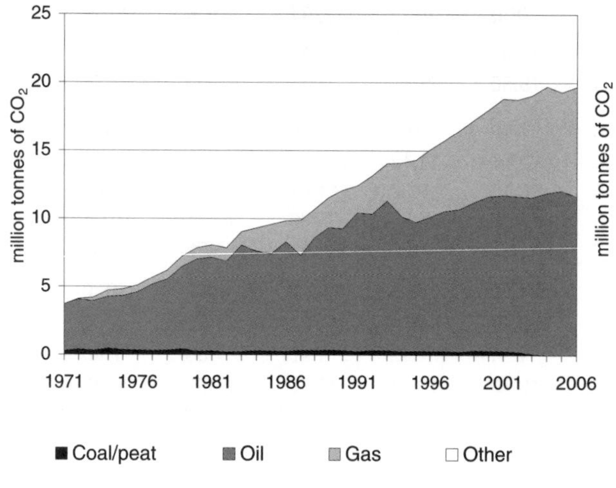

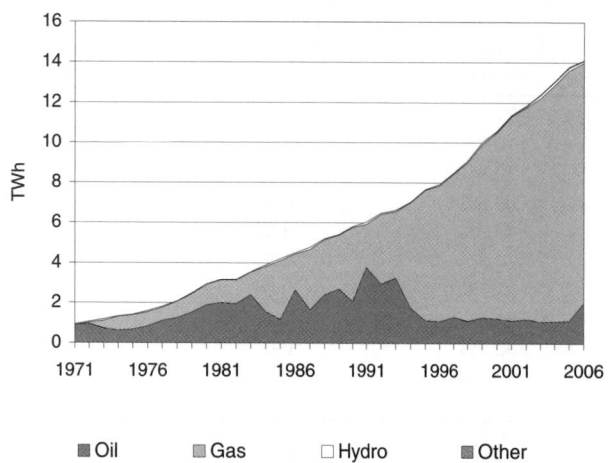

■ Coal/peat ■ Oil ■ Gas □ Other

Figure 2. CO₂ emissions by sector

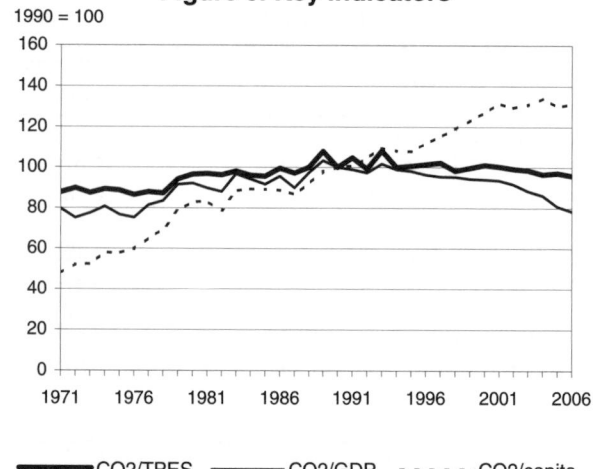

■ Electricity and heat □ Other energy industries
■ Manuf. ind. and construction ■ Transport
□ Residential ■ Other

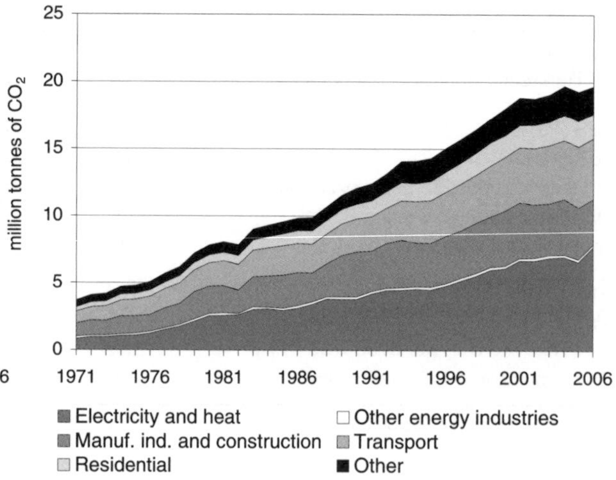

Figure 3. CO₂ emissions by sector

■ Electricity and heat □ Other energy industries
■ Manuf. ind. and construction ■ Transport
□ Residential ■ Other

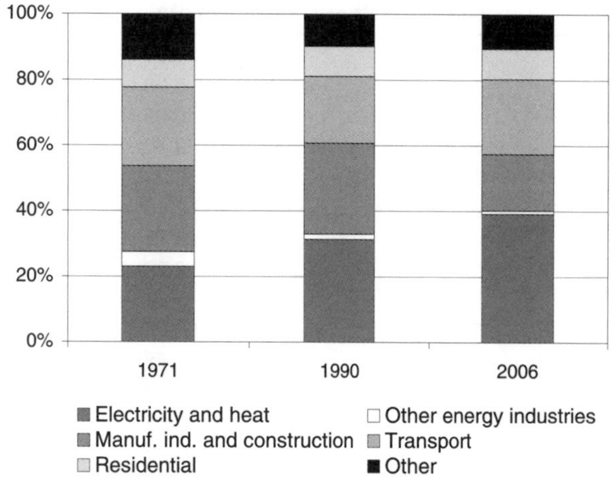

Figure 4. Reference vs Sectoral Approach

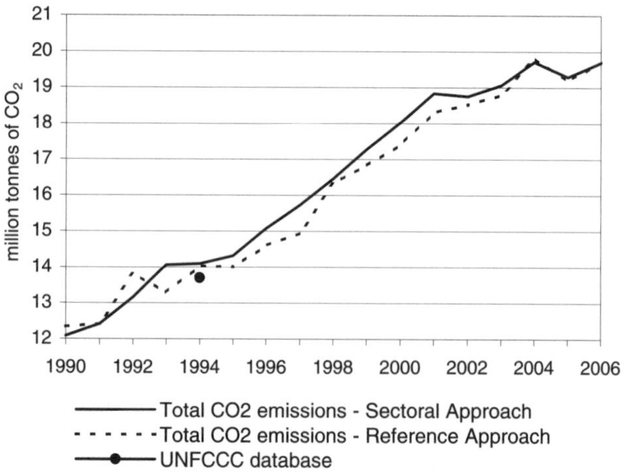

—— Total CO2 emissions - Sectoral Approach
------ Total CO2 emissions - Reference Approach
——●—— UNFCCC database

Figure 5. Electricity generation by fuel

■ Oil ■ Gas □ Hydro ■ Other

Figure 6. Key indicators

1990 = 100

—— CO2/TPES —— CO2/GDP ----- CO2/capita

Tunisia / Tunisie

Key indicators

	1990	1995	2000	2003	2004	2005	2006	% change 90-06
CO$_2$ Sectoral Approach (Mt of CO$_2$)	12.08	14.32	18.02	19.07	19.72	19.29	19.70	63.0%
CO$_2$ Reference Approach (Mt of CO$_2$)	12.34	14.01	17.41	18.81	19.83	19.19	19.72	59.9%
TPES (PJ)	215	254	318	345	364	354	366	70.1%
TPES (Mtoe)	5.14	6.05	7.59	8.24	8.70	8.45	8.74	70.1%
GDP (billion 2000 US$ using exch. rates)	12.24	14.79	19.44	21.89	23.21	24.19	25.45	108.0%
GDP (billion 2000 US$ using PPPs)	37.79	45.69	60.05	67.61	71.69	74.72	78.61	108.0%
Population (millions)	8.15	8.96	9.56	9.84	9.93	10.03	10.13	24.2%
CO$_2$ / TPES (t CO$_2$ per TJ)	56.1	56.5	56.7	55.3	54.1	54.5	53.8	-4.1%
CO$_2$ / GDP (kg CO$_2$ per 2000 US$)	0.99	0.97	0.93	0.87	0.85	0.80	0.77	-21.6%
CO$_2$ / GDP (kg CO$_2$ per 2000 US$ PPP)	0.32	0.31	0.30	0.28	0.28	0.26	0.25	-21.6%
CO$_2$ / population (t CO$_2$ per capita)	1.48	1.60	1.88	1.94	1.99	1.92	1.95	31.3%

Ratios are based on the Sectoral Approach.

2006 CO$_2$ emissions by sector

million tonnes of CO$_2$	Coal/peat	Oil	Gas	Other *	Total	% change 90-06
Sectoral Approach	-	**11.64**	**8.06**	-	**19.70**	**63.0%**
Main activity producer elec. and heat	-	0.75	6.03	-	6.78	112.0%
Unallocated autoproducers	-	0.93	-	-	0.93	58.3%
Other energy industries	-	0.21	-	-	0.21	0.6%
Manufacturing industries and construction	-	1.90	1.48	-	3.38	1.2%
Transport	-	4.51	-	-	4.51	83.0%
of which: road	-	*4.51*	-	-	*4.51*	*85.4%*
Other sectors	-	3.35	0.55	-	3.90	70.0%
of which: residential	-	*1.37*	*0.44*	-	*1.81*	*64.4%*
Reference Approach	-	**11.68**	**8.04**	-	**19.72**	**59.9%**
Diff. due to losses and/or transformation	-	0.05	-	-	0.05	
Statistical differences	-	- 0.01	- 0.02	-	- 0.03	
Memo: international marine bunkers	-	*0.03*	-	-	*0.03*	*-58.3%*
Memo: international aviation	-	*0.65*	-	-	*0.65*	*14.4%*

* Other includes industrial waste and non-renewable municipal waste.

Key sources for CO$_2$ emissions from fuel combustion in 2006

IPCC source category	CO$_2$ emissions (Mt of CO$_2$)	% change 90-06	Level assessment (%) **	Cumulative total (%)
Main activity prod. elec. and heat - gas	6.03	191.5%	16.9	16.9
Road - oil	4.51	85.4%	12.6	29.5
Non-specified other sectors - oil	1.97	73.0%	5.5	35.0
Manufacturing industries - oil	1.90	-21.6%	5.3	40.3
Manufacturing industries - gas	1.48	148.6%	4.1	44.4
Residential - oil	1.37	35.8%	3.8	48.3
Unallocated autoproducers - oil	0.93	58.3%	2.6	50.9
Main activity prod. elec. and heat - oil	0.75	-33.3%	2.1	53.0
Residential - gas	0.44	404.8%	1.2	54.2
Other energy industries - oil	0.21	0.6%	0.6	54.8
Non-specified other sectors - gas	0.11	120.5%	0.3	55.1
Memo: total CO$_2$ from fuel combustion	*19.70*	*63.0%*	*55.1*	*55.1*

** Percent calculated using the total GHG estimate for CO$_2$, CH$_4$, N$_2$O, HFCs, PFCs and SF$_6$ excluding CO$_2$ emissions/removals from land use change and forestry.

Turkey / Turquie

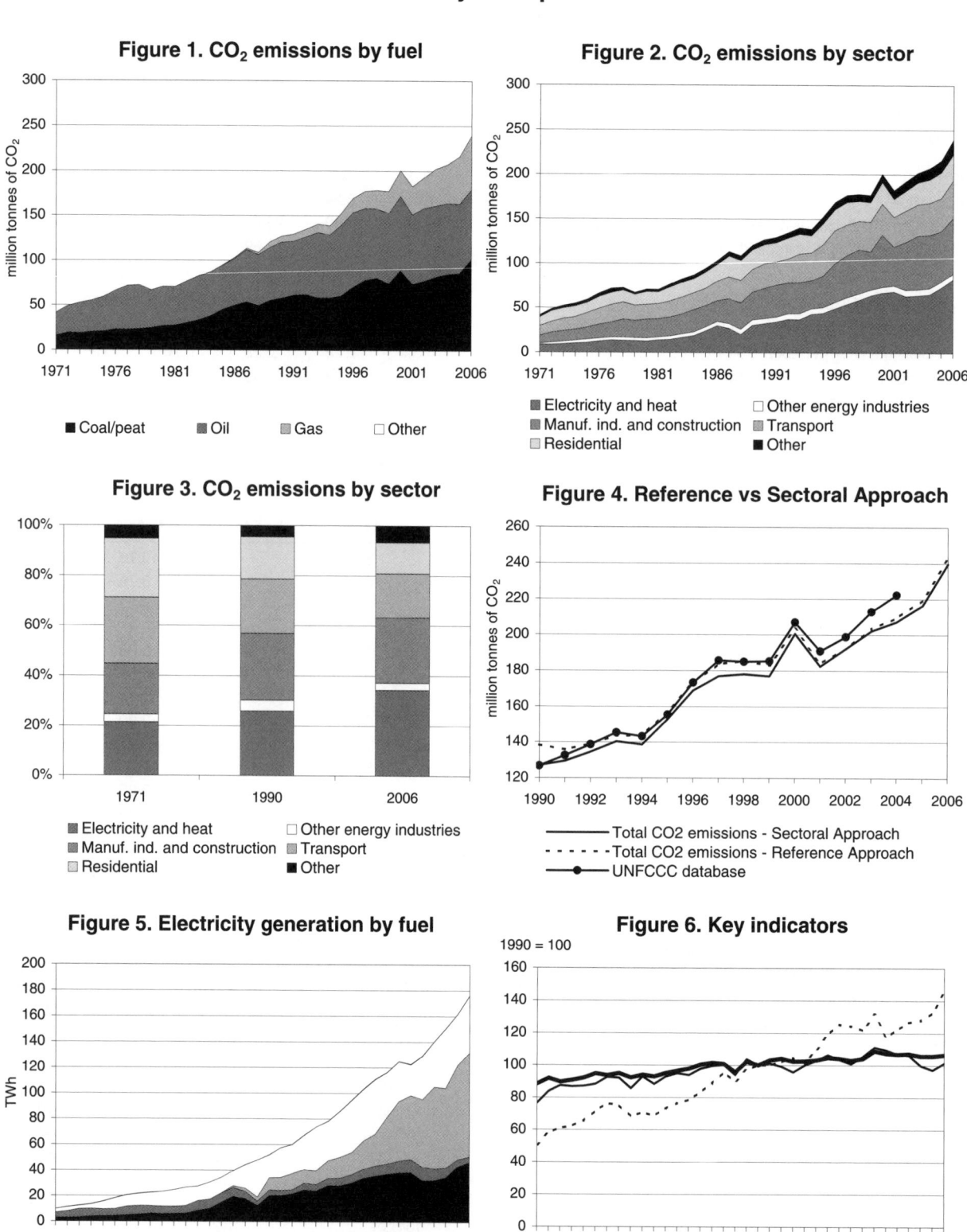

Figure 1. CO₂ emissions by fuel

■ Coal/peat   ■ Oil   ■ Gas   □ Other

Figure 2. CO₂ emissions by sector

■ Electricity and heat   □ Other energy industries
■ Manuf. ind. and construction   ■ Transport
□ Residential   ■ Other

Figure 3. CO₂ emissions by sector

■ Electricity and heat   □ Other energy industries
■ Manuf. ind. and construction   ■ Transport
□ Residential   ■ Other

Figure 4. Reference vs Sectoral Approach

—— Total CO2 emissions - Sectoral Approach
- - - - Total CO2 emissions - Reference Approach
—●— UNFCCC database

Figure 5. Electricity generation by fuel

■ Coal/peat   ■ Oil   ■ Gas   □ Hydro   ■ Other

Figure 6. Key indicators

1990 = 100

—— CO2/TPES   —— CO2/GDP   - - - - CO2/capita

Turkey / Turquie
Key indicators

	1990	1995	2000	2003	2004	2005	2006	% change 90-06
CO$_2$ Sectoral Approach (Mt of CO$_2$)	126.91	152.66	200.56	202.13	207.25	216.36	239.74	88.9%
CO$_2$ Reference Approach (Mt of CO$_2$)	138.20	157.28	203.48	203.45	209.50	219.65	242.61	75.5%
TPES (PJ)	2 216	2 588	3 218	3 296	3 426	3 578	3 936	77.6%
TPES (Mtoe)	52.94	61.81	76.87	78.73	81.83	85.46	94.00	77.6%
GDP (billion 2000 US$ using exch. rates)	140.20	164.20	199.30	210.50	229.30	246.20	261.20	86.3%
GDP (billion 2000 US$ using PPPs)	309.57	362.57	439.99	464.79	506.30	543.67	576.82	86.3%
Population (millions)	56.20	61.64	67.46	70.71	71.79	72.07	72.97	29.8%
CO$_2$ / TPES (t CO$_2$ per TJ)	57.3	59.0	62.3	61.3	60.5	60.5	60.9	6.4%
CO$_2$ / GDP (kg CO$_2$ per 2000 US$)	0.91	0.93	1.01	0.96	0.90	0.88	0.92	1.4%
CO$_2$ / GDP (kg CO$_2$ per 2000 US$ PPP)	0.41	0.42	0.46	0.43	0.41	0.40	0.42	1.4%
CO$_2$ / population (t CO$_2$ per capita)	2.26	2.48	2.97	2.86	2.89	3.00	3.29	45.5%

Ratios are based on the Sectoral Approach.

2006 CO$_2$ emissions by sector

million tonnes of CO$_2$	Coal/peat	Oil	Gas	Other *	Total	% change 90-06
Sectoral Approach	**101.75**	**77.34**	**60.53**	**0.13**	**239.74**	**88.9%**
Main activity producer elec. and heat	42.32	1.83	27.28	-	71.43	165.8%
Unallocated autoproducers	5.21	1.52	3.86	0.13	10.71	83.6%
Other energy industries	1.82	4.73	0.16	-	6.71	19.3%
Manufacturing industries and construction	42.30	12.35	8.01	-	62.65	85.8%
Transport	-	41.95	0.27	-	42.22	52.1%
of which: road	-	*36.60*	*0.01*	-	*36.60*	*45.4%*
Other sectors	10.10	14.96	20.95	-	46.01	69.8%
of which: residential	*10.10*	*5.27*	*14.45*	-	*29.81*	*40.2%*
Reference Approach	**105.11**	**76.80**	**60.58**	**0.13**	**242.61**	**75.5%**
Diff. due to losses and/or transformation	3.45	- 0.85	0.05	-	2.65	
Statistical differences	- 0.09	0.31	-	-	0.22	
Memo: international marine bunkers	-	*3.06*	-	-	*3.06*	*722.0%*
Memo: international aviation	-	*2.91*	-	-	*2.91*	*446.3%*

* Other includes industrial waste and non-renewable municipal waste.

Key sources for CO$_2$ emissions from fuel combustion in 2006

IPCC source category	CO$_2$ emissions (Mt of CO$_2$)	% change 90-06	Level assessment (%) **	Cumulative total (%)
Main activity prod. elec. and heat - coal/peat	42.32	103.6%	12.6	12.6
Manufacturing industries - coal/peat	42.30	117.0%	12.6	25.1
Road - oil	36.60	45.3%	10.9	36.0
Main activity prod. elec. and heat - gas	27.28	448.7%	8.1	44.1
Residential - gas	14.45	+	4.3	48.4
Manufacturing industries - oil	12.35	-3.5%	3.7	52.0
Residential - coal/peat	10.10	-17.5%	3.0	55.0
Non-specified other sectors - oil	9.69	65.9%	2.9	57.9
Manufacturing industries - gas	8.01	460.1%	2.4	60.3
Non-specified other sectors - gas	6.51	x	1.9	62.2
Other transport - oil	5.36	112.3%	1.6	63.8
Memo: total CO$_2$ from fuel combustion	*239.74*	*88.9%*	*71.1*	*71.1*

** Percent calculated using the total GHG estimate for CO$_2$, CH$_4$, N$_2$O, HFCs, PFCs and SF$_6$ excluding CO$_2$ emissions/removals from land use change and forestry.

Turkmenistan / Turkménistan

Figure 1. CO$_2$ emissions by fuel

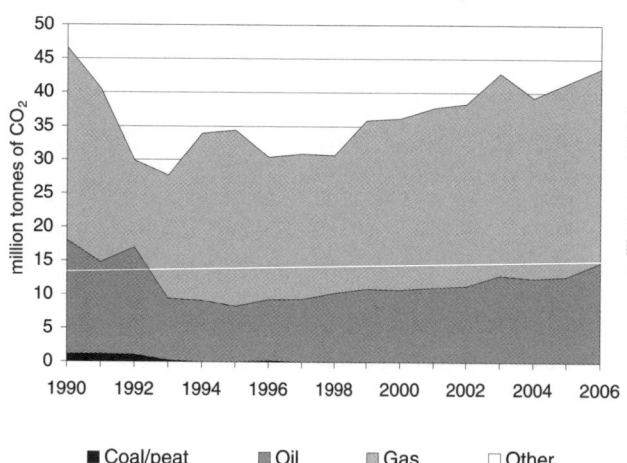

■ Coal/peat   ■ Oil   ■ Gas   ▢ Other

Figure 2. CO$_2$ emissions by sector

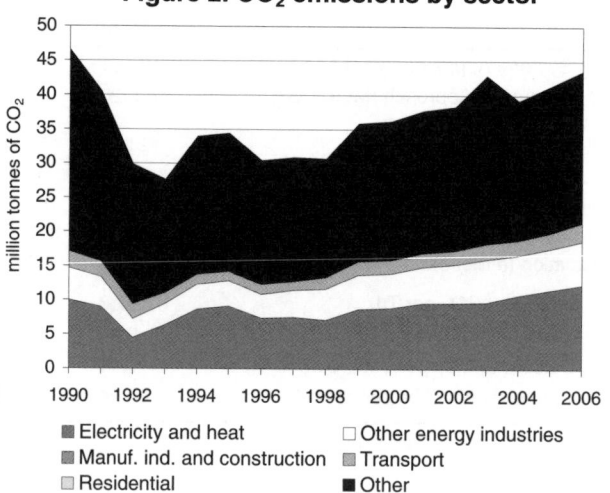

■ Electricity and heat   ▢ Other energy industries
■ Manuf. ind. and construction   ■ Transport
▢ Residential   ■ Other

Figure 3. CO$_2$ emissions by sector

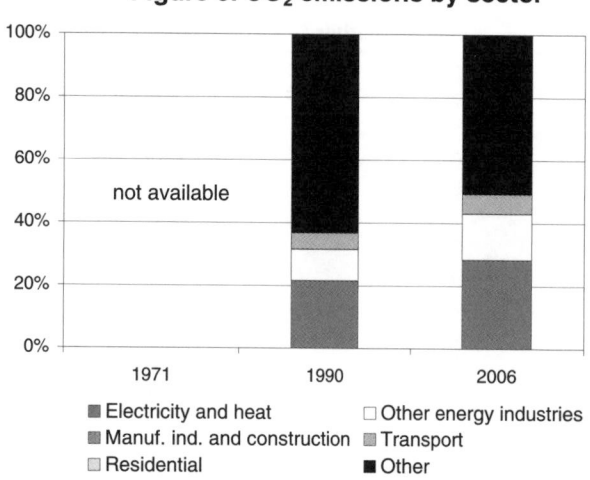

■ Electricity and heat   ▢ Other energy industries
■ Manuf. ind. and construction   ■ Transport
▢ Residential   ■ Other

Figure 4. Reference vs Sectoral Approach

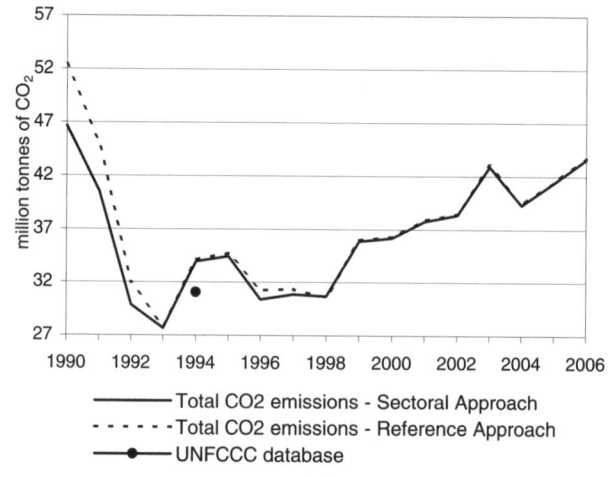

—— Total CO2 emissions - Sectoral Approach
----- Total CO2 emissions - Reference Approach
—●— UNFCCC database

Figure 5. Electricity generation by fuel

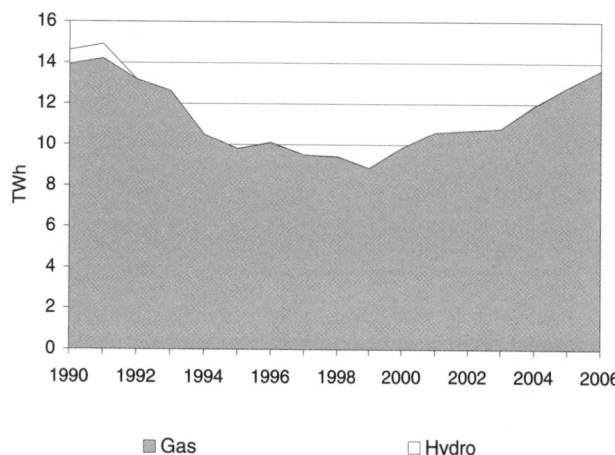

■ Gas   ▢ Hydro

Figure 6. Key indicators

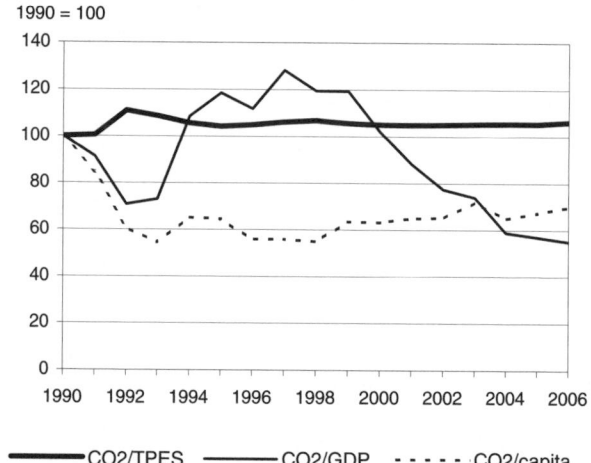

—— CO2/TPES   —— CO2/GDP   ----- CO2/capita

Turkmenistan / Turkménistan

Key indicators

	1990	1995	2000	2003	2004	2005	2006	% change 90-06
CO$_2$ Sectoral Approach (Mt of CO$_2$)	46.64	34.43	36.19	42.88	39.26	41.37	43.58	-6.6%
CO$_2$ Reference Approach (Mt of CO$_2$)	52.41	34.74	36.30	43.03	39.40	41.52	43.75	-16.5%
TPES (PJ)	822	582	607	719	655	692	723	-12.0%
TPES (Mtoe)	19.63	13.90	14.51	17.17	15.66	16.52	17.27	-12.0%
GDP (billion 2000 US$ using exch. rates)	3.74	2.33	2.85	4.65	5.34	5.82	6.34	69.5%
GDP (billion 2000 US$ using PPPs)	20.16	12.57	15.38	25.11	28.80	31.39	34.21	69.7%
Population (millions)	3.67	4.19	4.50	4.70	4.77	4.83	4.90	33.6%
CO$_2$ / TPES (t CO$_2$ per TJ)	56.7	59.2	59.6	59.6	59.9	59.8	60.3	6.2%
CO$_2$ / GDP (kg CO$_2$ per 2000 US$)	12.47	14.77	12.70	9.22	7.36	7.11	6.87	-44.9%
CO$_2$ / GDP (kg CO$_2$ per 2000 US$ PPP)	2.31	2.74	2.35	1.71	1.36	1.32	1.27	-44.9%
CO$_2$ / population (t CO$_2$ per capita)	12.71	8.21	8.04	9.13	8.24	8.56	8.90	-30.0%

Ratios are based on the Sectoral Approach.

2006 CO$_2$ emissions by sector

million tonnes of CO$_2$	Coal/peat	Oil	Gas	Other *	Total	% change 90-06
Sectoral Approach	-	**14.82**	**28.76**	-	**43.58**	**-6.6%**
Main activity producer elec. and heat	-	-	12.31	-	12.31	22.9%
Unallocated autoproducers	-	-	-	-	-	-
Other energy industries	-	3.53	2.86	-	6.39	36.1%
Manufacturing industries and construction	-	-	-	-	-	-
Transport	-	2.73	-	-	2.73	12.9%
of which: road	-	2.73	-	-	2.73	12.9%
Other sectors	-	8.56	13.60	-	22.15	-24.9%
of which: residential	-	-	-	-	-	-
Reference Approach	-	**14.99**	**28.76**	-	**43.75**	**-16.5%**
Diff. due to losses and/or transformation	-	0.17	-	-	0.17	
Statistical differences	-	-	-	-	-	
Memo: international marine bunkers	-	..	-	-	..	..
Memo: international aviation	-	..	-	-	..	..

* Other includes industrial waste and non-renewable municipal waste.

Key sources for CO$_2$ emissions from fuel combustion in 2006

IPCC source category	CO$_2$ emissions (Mt of CO$_2$)	% change 90-06	Level assessment (%) **	Cumulative total (%)
Non-specified other sectors - gas	13.60	-13.6%	19.2	19.2
Main activity prod. elec. and heat - gas	12.31	22.9%	17.4	36.6
Non-specified other sectors - oil	8.56	-32.1%	12.1	48.7
Other energy industries - oil	3.53	92.8%	5.0	53.7
Other energy industries - gas	2.86	-0.2%	4.0	57.7
Road - oil	2.73	12.9%	3.9	61.6
-	-	-	-	-
-	-	-	-	-
-	-	-	-	-
-	-	-	-	-
-	-	-	-	-
Memo: total CO$_2$ from fuel combustion	*43.58*	*-6.6%*	*61.6*	*61.6*

** Percent calculated using the total GHG estimate for CO$_2$, CH$_4$, N$_2$O, HFCs, PFCs and SF$_6$ excluding CO$_2$ emissions/removals from land use change and forestry.

Ukraine

Figure 1. CO₂ emissions by fuel

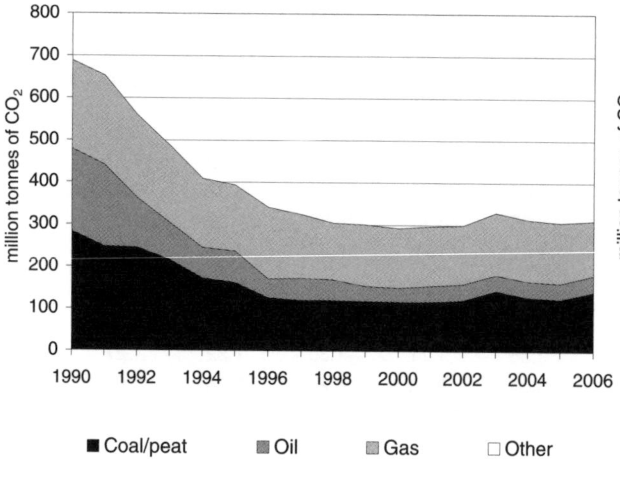

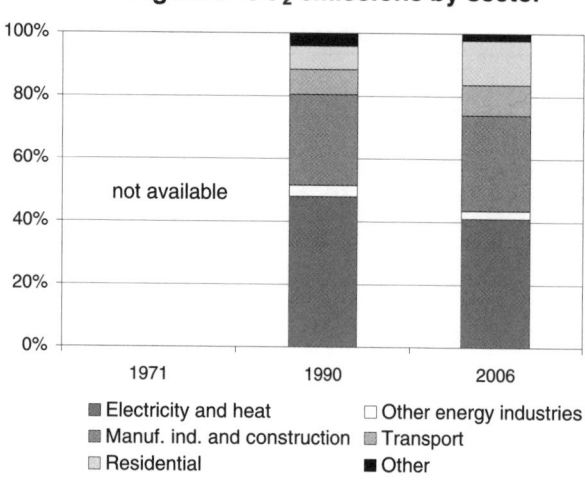

Coal/peat   Oil   Gas   Other

Figure 2. CO₂ emissions by sector

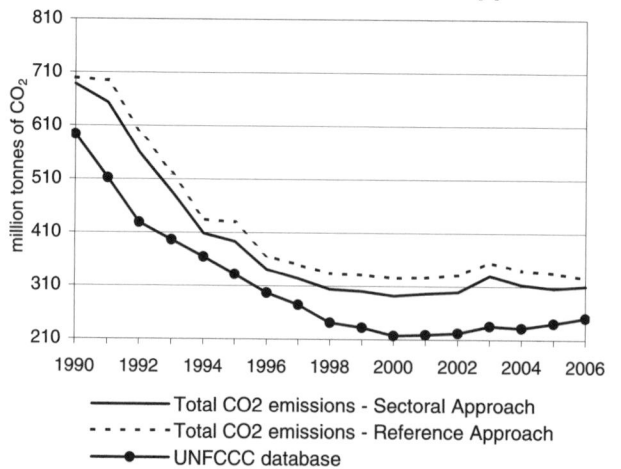

Electricity and heat   Other energy industries
Manuf. ind. and construction   Transport
Residential   Other

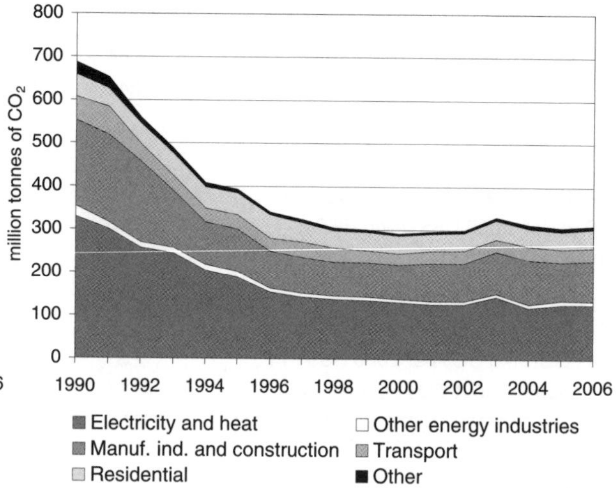

Figure 3. CO₂ emissions by sector

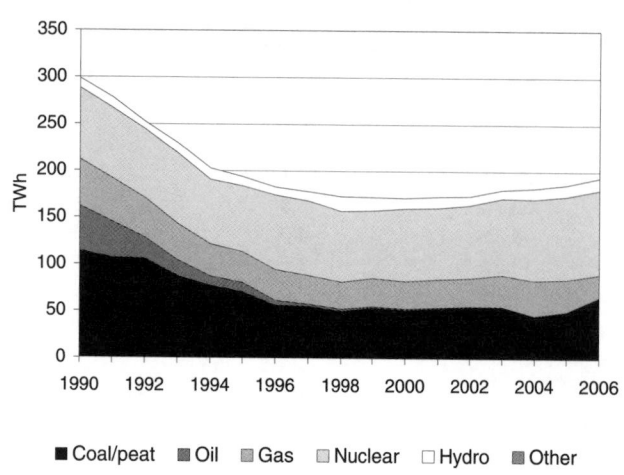

Electricity and heat   Other energy industries
Manuf. ind. and construction   Transport
Residential   Other

Figure 4. Reference vs Sectoral Approach

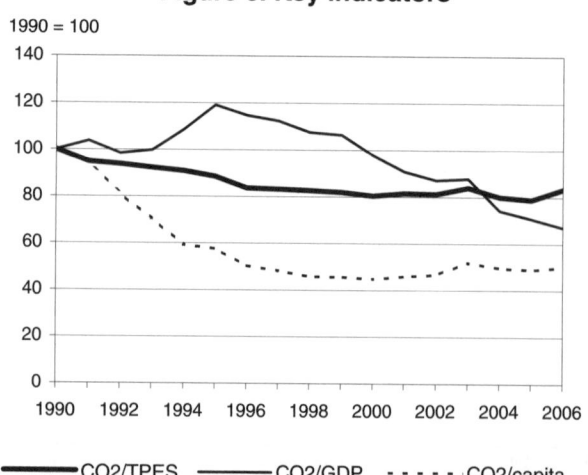

——— Total CO2 emissions - Sectoral Approach
- - - - - Total CO2 emissions - Reference Approach
——●—— UNFCCC database

Figure 5. Electricity generation by fuel

Coal/peat   Oil   Gas   Nuclear   Hydro   Other

Figure 6. Key indicators

1990 = 100

——— CO2/TPES   ——— CO2/GDP   - - - - CO2/capita

Ukraine
Key indicators

	1990	1995	2000	2003	2004	2005	2006	% change 90-06
CO$_2$ Sectoral Approach (Mt of CO$_2$)	687.86	392.78	291.96	329.55	312.61	306.02	310.29	-54.9%
CO$_2$ Reference Approach (Mt of CO$_2$)	699.10	428.82	325.75	355.26	339.67	335.36	325.72	-53.4%
TPES (PJ)	10 627	6 865	5 612	6 070	6 039	5 998	5 754	-45.9%
TPES (Mtoe)	253.82	163.97	134.04	144.99	144.25	143.26	137.43	-45.9%
GDP (billion 2000 US$ using exch. rates)	71.95	34.54	31.26	39.29	44.04	45.23	48.44	-32.7%
GDP (billion 2000 US$ using PPPs)	456.90	219.32	198.51	249.48	279.67	287.22	307.61	-32.7%
Population (millions)	51.89	51.51	49.18	47.81	47.45	47.11	46.79	-9.8%
CO$_2$ / TPES (t CO$_2$ per TJ)	64.7	57.2	52.0	54.3	51.8	51.0	53.9	-16.7%
CO$_2$ / GDP (kg CO$_2$ per 2000 US$)	9.56	11.37	9.34	8.39	7.10	6.77	6.41	-33.0%
CO$_2$ / GDP (kg CO$_2$ per 2000 US$ PPP)	1.51	1.79	1.47	1.32	1.12	1.07	1.01	-33.0%
CO$_2$ / population (t CO$_2$ per capita)	13.26	7.63	5.94	6.89	6.59	6.50	6.63	-50.0%

Ratios are based on the Sectoral Approach.

2006 CO$_2$ emissions by sector

million tonnes of CO$_2$	Coal/peat	Oil	Gas	Other *	Total	% change 90-06
Sectoral Approach	**140.97**	**39.33**	**129.98**	-	**310.29**	**-54.9%**
Main activity producer elec. and heat	65.52	0.72	42.08	-	108.32	-63.6%
Unallocated autoproducers	8.76	-	9.76	-	18.52	-41.0%
Other energy industries	3.37	1.97	2.83	-	8.17	-66.7%
Manufacturing industries and construction	54.74	7.34	32.13	-	94.21	-52.8%
Transport	0.00	23.20	6.87	-	30.07	-44.6%
of which: road	-	*21.52*	*0.15*	-	*21.67*	*-53.8%*
Other sectors	8.58	6.10	36.32	-	51.00	-36.4%
of which: residential	*7.20*	*1.77*	*34.78*	-	*43.75*	*-14.5%*
Reference Approach	**153.42**	**40.17**	**132.12**	-	**325.72**	**-53.4%**
Diff. due to losses and/or transformation	13.78	0.87	2.21	-	16.86	
Statistical differences	- 1.33	- 0.04	- 0.07	-	- 1.44	
Memo: international marine bunkers	-	..	-	-	..	..
Memo: international aviation	-	*0.99*	-	-	*0.99*	*-83.8%*

* Other includes industrial waste and non-renewable municipal waste.

Key sources for CO$_2$ emissions from fuel combustion in 2006

IPCC source category	CO$_2$ emissions (Mt of CO$_2$)	% change 90-06	Level assessment (%) **	Cumulative total (%)
Main activity prod. elec. and heat - coal/peat	65.52	-51.8%	13.0	13.0
Manufacturing industries - coal/peat	54.74	-48.1%	10.9	23.9
Main activity prod. elec. and heat - gas	42.08	-54.7%	8.4	32.3
Residential - gas	34.78	70.4%	6.9	39.2
Manufacturing industries - gas	32.13	-41.0%	6.4	45.6
Road - oil	21.52	-54.2%	4.3	49.9
Unallocated autoproducers - gas	9.76	-66.3%	1.9	51.8
Unallocated autoproducers - coal/peat	8.76	261.4%	1.7	53.6
Manufacturing industries - oil	7.34	-81.6%	1.5	55.1
Residential - coal/peat	7.20	-67.2%	1.4	56.5
Other transport - gas	6.72	x	1.3	57.8
Memo: total CO$_2$ from fuel combustion	*310.29*	*-54.9%*	*61.8*	*61.8*

** Percent calculated using the total GHG estimate for CO$_2$, CH$_4$, N$_2$O, HFCs, PFCs and SF$_6$ excluding CO$_2$ emissions/removals from land use change and forestry.

United Arab Emirates / Emirats arabes unis

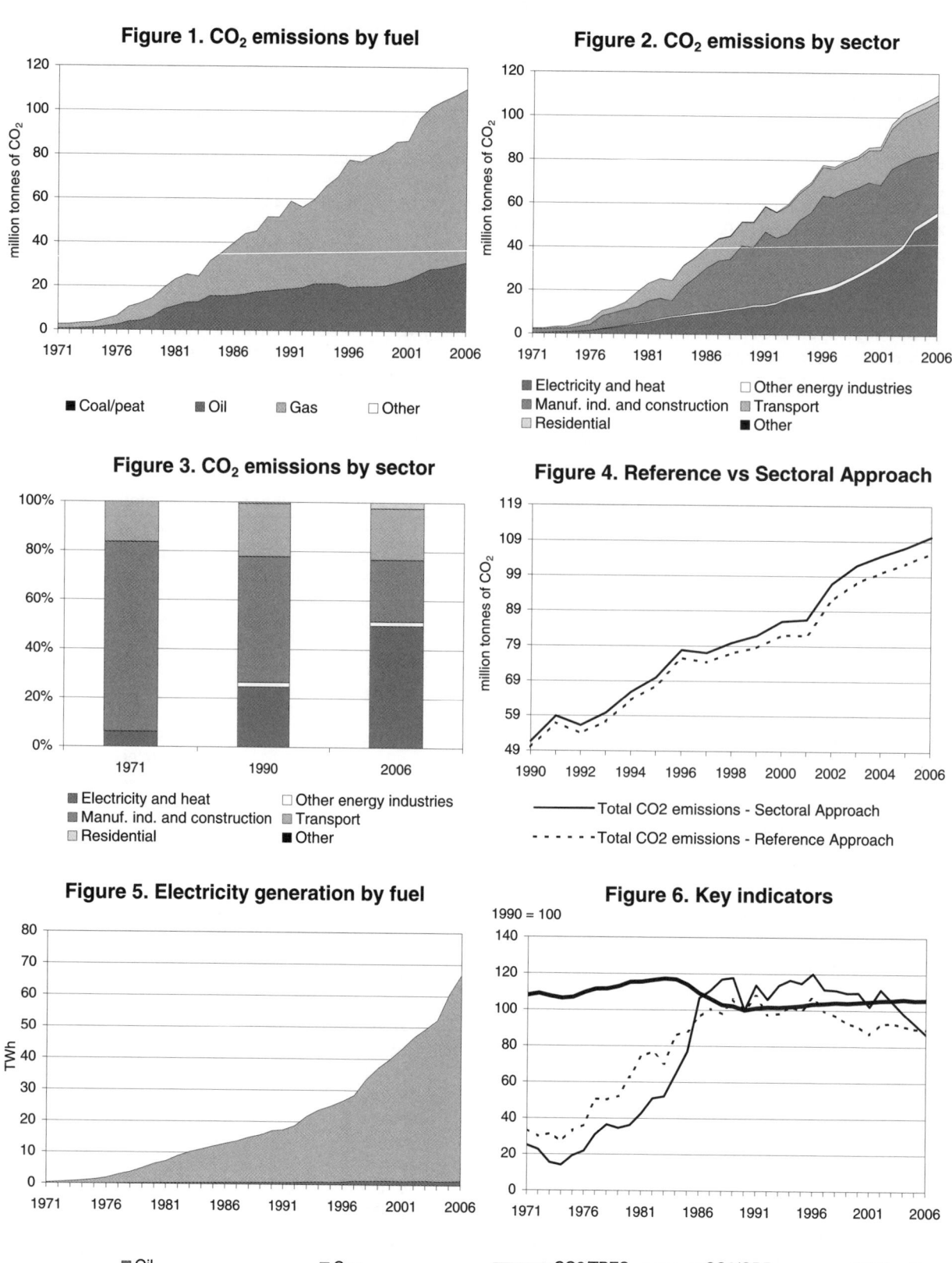

Figure 1. CO₂ emissions by fuel

■ Coal/peat   ■ Oil   ▨ Gas   □ Other

Figure 2. CO₂ emissions by sector

■ Electricity and heat   □ Other energy industries
■ Manuf. ind. and construction   ▨ Transport
▨ Residential   ■ Other

Figure 3. CO₂ emissions by sector

■ Electricity and heat   □ Other energy industries
■ Manuf. ind. and construction   ▨ Transport
▨ Residential   ■ Other

Figure 4. Reference vs Sectoral Approach

—— Total CO2 emissions - Sectoral Approach
----- Total CO2 emissions - Reference Approach

Figure 5. Electricity generation by fuel

■ Oil   ▨ Gas

Figure 6. Key indicators

1990 = 100

—— CO2/TPES   —— CO2/GDP   ----- CO2/capita

United Arab Emirates / Emirats arabes unis

Key indicators

	1990	1995	2000	2003	2004	2005	2006	% change 90-06
CO$_2$ Sectoral Approach (Mt of CO$_2$)	51.61	69.99	86.06	102.06	104.85	107.30	110.29	113.7%
CO$_2$ Reference Approach (Mt of CO$_2$)	49.89	67.65	82.12	97.34	100.04	102.69	105.65	111.7%
TPES (PJ)	971	1 284	1 550	1 819	1 860	1 913	1 963	102.3%
TPES (Mtoe)	23.18	30.66	37.02	43.46	44.42	45.69	46.89	102.3%
GDP (billion 2000 US$ using exch. rates)	46.40	54.82	70.59	87.50	95.99	104.15	114.25	146.3%
GDP (billion 2000 US$ using PPPs)	45.84	54.16	69.74	86.45	94.83	102.90	112.88	146.2%
Population (millions)	1.77	2.41	3.25	3.78	3.95	4.10	4.25	139.6%
CO$_2$ / TPES (t CO$_2$ per TJ)	53.2	54.5	55.5	56.1	56.4	56.1	56.2	5.7%
CO$_2$ / GDP (kg CO$_2$ per 2000 US$)	1.11	1.28	1.22	1.17	1.09	1.03	0.97	-13.2%
CO$_2$ / GDP (kg CO$_2$ per 2000 US$ PPP)	1.13	1.29	1.23	1.18	1.11	1.04	0.98	-13.2%
CO$_2$ / population (t CO$_2$ per capita)	29.11	29.03	26.50	27.01	26.56	26.14	25.96	-10.8%

Ratios are based on the Sectoral Approach.

2006 CO$_2$ emissions by sector

million tonnes of CO$_2$	Coal/peat	Oil	Gas	Other *	Total	% change 90-06
Sectoral Approach	-	**31.41**	**78.88**	-	**110.29**	**113.7%**
Main activity producer elec. and heat	-	1.62	53.13	-	54.75	331.2%
Unallocated autoproducers	-	-	-	-	-	-
Other energy industries	-	0.55	1.39	-	1.94	110.7%
Manufacturing industries and construction	-	3.44	24.36	-	27.81	4.9%
Transport	-	23.09	-	-	23.09	106.7%
of which: road	-	*23.09*	*-*	*-*	*23.09*	*106.7%*
Other sectors	-	2.71	-	-	2.71	799.0%
of which: residential	-	*2.71*	*-*	*-*	*2.71*	*799.0%*
Reference Approach	-	**26.77**	**78.88**	-	**105.65**	**111.7%**
Diff. due to losses and/or transformation	-	- 4.64	-	-	- 4.64	
Statistical differences	-	-	-	-	-	
Memo: international marine bunkers	-	*40.83*	*-*	*-*	*40.83*	*115.0%*
Memo: international aviation	-	*11.33*	*-*	*-*	*11.33*	*15.7%*

* Other includes industrial waste and non-renewable municipal waste.

Key sources for CO$_2$ emissions from fuel combustion in 2006

IPCC source category	CO$_2$ emissions (Mt of CO$_2$)	% change 90-06	Level assessment (%) **	Cumulative total (%)
Main activity prod. elec. and heat - gas	53.13	339.7%	34.8	34.8
Manufacturing industries - gas	24.36	19.4%	15.9	50.7
Road - oil	23.09	106.7%	15.1	65.8
Manufacturing industries - oil	3.44	-43.6%	2.3	68.1
Residential - oil	2.71	799.0%	1.8	69.8
Main activity prod. elec. and heat - oil	1.62	163.3%	1.1	70.9
Other energy industries - gas	1.39	121.3%	0.9	71.8
Other energy industries - oil	0.55	88.0%	0.4	72.2
-	-	-	-	-
-	-	-	-	-
-	-	-	-	-
Memo: total CO$_2$ from fuel combustion	*110.29*	*113.7%*	*72.2*	*72.2*

** Percent calculated using the total GHG estimate for CO$_2$, CH$_4$, N$_2$O, HFCs, PFCs and SF$_6$ excluding CO$_2$ emissions/removals from land use change and forestry.

United Kingdom / Royaume-Uni

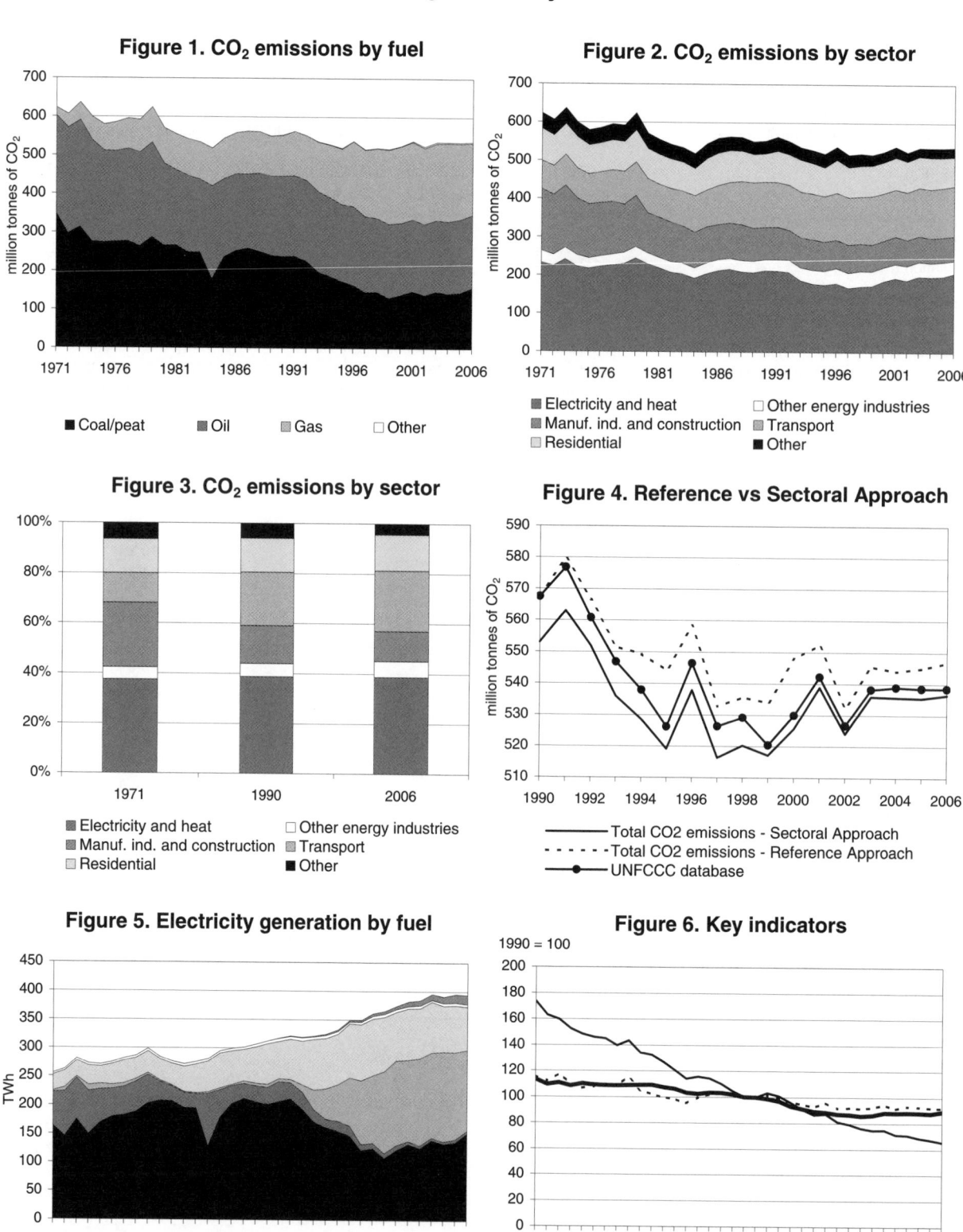

Figure 1. CO$_2$ emissions by fuel

Figure 2. CO$_2$ emissions by sector

Figure 3. CO$_2$ emissions by sector

Figure 4. Reference vs Sectoral Approach

Figure 5. Electricity generation by fuel

Figure 6. Key indicators

United Kingdom / Royaume-Uni

Key indicators

	1990	1995	2000	2003	2004	2005	2006	% change 90-06
CO$_2$ Sectoral Approach (Mt of CO$_2$)	552.97	519.07	525.56	535.91	535.62	535.42	536.48	-3.0%
CO$_2$ Reference Approach (Mt of CO$_2$)	567.72	544.15	547.95	545.47	543.96	544.91	546.81	-3.7%
TPES (PJ)	8 888	9 364	9 791	9 749	9 764	9 819	9 677	8.9%
TPES (Mtoe)	212.28	223.66	233.86	232.85	233.22	234.53	231.13	8.9%
GDP (billion 2000 US$ using exch. rates)	1 140.90	1 238.50	1 450.90	1 557.80	1 608.50	1 638.10	1 684.70	47.7%
GDP (billion 2000 US$ using PPPs)	1 184.16	1 285.42	1 505.88	1 616.82	1 669.50	1 700.20	1 748.59	47.7%
Population (millions)	57.24	58.03	58.89	59.55	59.83	60.22	60.53	5.8%
CO$_2$ / TPES (t CO$_2$ per TJ)	62.2	55.4	53.7	55.0	54.9	54.5	55.4	-10.9%
CO$_2$ / GDP (kg CO$_2$ per 2000 US$)	0.48	0.42	0.36	0.34	0.33	0.33	0.32	-34.3%
CO$_2$ / GDP (kg CO$_2$ per 2000 US$ PPP)	0.47	0.40	0.35	0.33	0.32	0.31	0.31	-34.3%
CO$_2$ / population (t CO$_2$ per capita)	9.66	8.95	8.93	9.00	8.95	8.89	8.86	-8.3%

Ratios are based on the Sectoral Approach.

2006 CO$_2$ emissions by sector

million tonnes of CO$_2$	Coal/peat	Oil	Gas	Other *	Total	% change 90-06
Sectoral Approach	**157.64**	**189.56**	**186.74**	**2.54**	**536.48**	**-3.0%**
Main activity producer elec. and heat	128.59	1.74	46.55	-	176.87	-11.6%
Unallocated autoproducers	12.82	1.37	13.58	2.36	30.13	125.2%
Other energy industries	4.93	15.12	14.54	-	34.59	17.5%
Manufacturing industries and construction	9.17	27.51	27.14	0.08	63.90	-23.5%
Transport	-	130.58	-	-	130.58	10.6%
of which: road	-	*118.06*	-	-	*118.06*	*10.7%*
Other sectors	2.12	13.24	84.94	0.10	100.40	-7.4%
of which: residential	*2.06*	*8.90*	*65.91*	*0.03*	*76.90*	*2.6%*
Reference Approach	**159.79**	**195.66**	**188.83**	**2.54**	**546.81**	**-3.7%**
Diff. due to losses and/or transformation	1.47	5.48	2.02	-	8.98	
Statistical differences	0.68	0.61	0.06	0.00	1.36	
Memo: international marine bunkers	-	*7.26*	-	-	*7.26*	*-7.5%*
Memo: international aviation	-	*33.66*	-	-	*33.66*	*122.4%*

* Other includes industrial waste and non-renewable municipal waste.

Key sources for CO$_2$ emissions from fuel combustion in 2006

IPCC source category	CO$_2$ emissions (Mt of CO$_2$)	% change 90-06	Level assessment (%) **	Cumulative total (%)
Main activity prod. elec. and heat - coal/peat	128.59	-28.7%	19.7	19.7
Road - oil	118.06	10.7%	18.1	37.7
Residential - gas	65.91	21.4%	10.1	47.8
Main activity prod. elec. and heat - gas ***	46.55	x	7.1	54.9
Manufacturing industries - oil	27.51	4.1%	4.2	59.1
Manufacturing industries - gas	27.14	1.5%	4.2	63.3
Non-specified other sectors - gas	19.02	23.7%	2.9	66.2
Other energy industries - oil	15.12	-24.3%	2.3	68.5
Other energy industries - gas	14.54	107.7%	2.2	70.7
Unallocated autoproducers - gas ***	13.58	421.7%	2.1	72.8
Unallocated autoproducers - coal/peat	12.82	67.6%	2.0	74.8
Memo: total CO$_2$ from fuel combustion	*536.48*	*-3.0%*	*82.1*	*82.1*

** Percent calculated using the total GHG estimate for CO$_2$, CH$_4$, N$_2$O, HFCs, PFCs and SF$_6$ excluding CO$_2$ emissions/removals from land use change and forestry.

*** For reasons of confidentiality, gas for main activity producer electricity is included in autoproducers for 1990.

United States / Etats-Unis

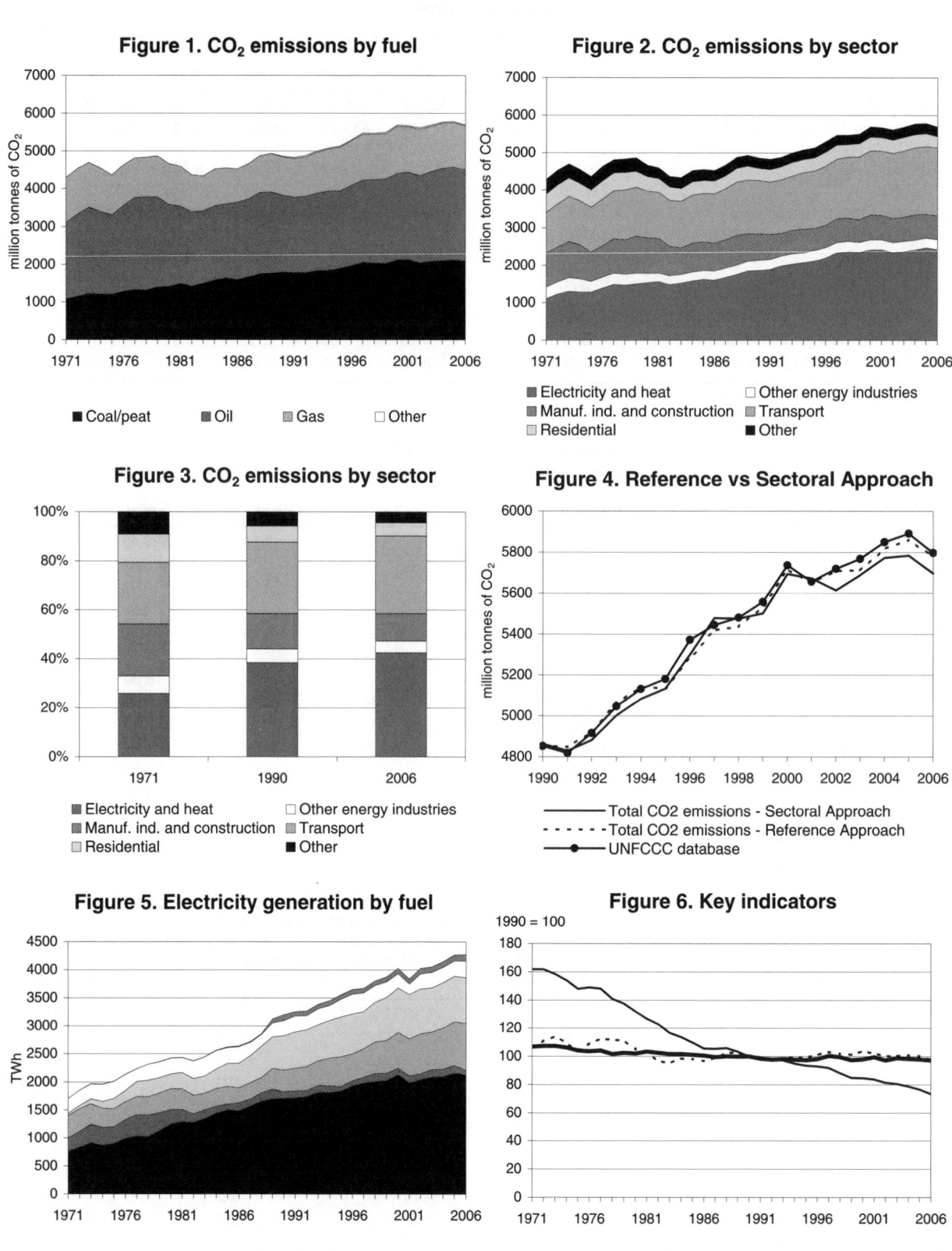

Figure 1. CO$_2$ emissions by fuel

■ Coal/peat   ■ Oil   ■ Gas   ☐ Other

Figure 2. CO$_2$ emissions by sector

■ Electricity and heat   ☐ Other energy industries
■ Manuf. ind. and construction   ■ Transport
☐ Residential   ■ Other

Figure 3. CO$_2$ emissions by sector

■ Electricity and heat   ☐ Other energy industries
■ Manuf. ind. and construction   ■ Transport
☐ Residential   ■ Other

Figure 4. Reference vs Sectoral Approach

—— Total CO2 emissions - Sectoral Approach
----- Total CO2 emissions - Reference Approach
—●— UNFCCC database

Figure 5. Electricity generation by fuel

■ Coal/peat   ■ Oil   ■ Gas   ■ Nuclear   ☐ Hydro   ■ Other

Figure 6. Key indicators

—— CO2/TPES   —— CO2/GDP   ----- CO2/capita

United States / Etats-Unis

Key indicators

	1990	1995	2000	2003	2004	2005	2006	% change 90-06
CO$_2$ Sectoral Approach (Mt of CO$_2$)	4 863.3	5 133.3	5 693.0	5 688.6	5 772.4	5 784.5	5 696.8	17.1%
CO$_2$ Reference Approach (Mt of CO$_2$)	4 853.7	5 134.9	5 715.2	5 711.5	5 817.0	5 860.7	5 780.1	19.1%
TPES (PJ)	80 649	87 371	96 403	95 504	97 467	98 050	97 163	20.5%
TPES (Mtoe)	1 926.3	2 086.8	2 302.6	2 281.1	2 328.0	2 341.9	2 320.7	20.5%
GDP (billion 2000 US$ using exch. rates)	7 055.0	7 972.8	9 764.8	10 249.8	10 623.9	10 950.6	11 265.2	59.7%
GDP (billion 2000 US$ using PPPs)	7 055.0	7 972.8	9 764.8	10 249.8	10 623.9	10 950.6	11 265.2	59.7%
Population (millions)	250.2	266.6	282.5	291.3	294.1	297.0	299.8	19.8%
CO$_2$ / TPES (t CO$_2$ per TJ)	60.3	58.8	59.1	59.6	59.2	59.0	58.6	-2.8%
CO$_2$ / GDP (kg CO$_2$ per 2000 US$)	0.69	0.64	0.58	0.56	0.54	0.53	0.51	-26.6%
CO$_2$ / GDP (kg CO$_2$ per 2000 US$ PPP)	0.69	0.64	0.58	0.56	0.54	0.53	0.51	-26.6%
CO$_2$ / population (t CO$_2$ per capita)	19.44	19.26	20.16	19.53	19.63	19.48	19.00	-2.3%

Ratios are based on the Sectoral Approach.

2006 CO$_2$ emissions by sector

million tonnes of CO$_2$	Coal/peat	Oil	Gas	Other *	Total	% change 90-06
Sectoral Approach	**2 090.0**	**2 410.9**	**1 169.4**	**26.5**	**5 696.8**	**17.1%**
Main activity producer elec. and heat	1 924.8	53.1	338.8	13.6	2 330.3	31.4%
Unallocated autoproducers	30.8	13.0	42.1	4.8	90.7	-1.5%
Other energy industries	13.2	156.7	99.2	-	269.1	-1.5%
Manufacturing industries and construction	115.9	243.1	266.3	7.4	632.7	-9.3%
Transport	-	1 776.1	33.2	-	1 809.3	27.4%
of which: road	-	*1 525.8*	*1.4*	-	*1 527.2*	*34.2%*
Other sectors	5.2	169.0	389.8	0.8	564.7	-6.9%
of which: residential	-	*71.4*	*238.0*	-	*309.3*	*-4.5%*
Reference Approach	**2 156.6**	**2 435.5**	**1 161.4**	**26.5**	**5 780.1**	**19.1%**
Diff. due to losses and/or transformation	8.3	- 14.8	- 2.8	-	- 9.3	
Statistical differences	58.3	39.4	- 5.2	0.0	92.6	
Memo: international marine bunkers	-	*88.2*	-	-	*88.2*	*-2.8%*
Memo: international aviation	-	*47.9*	-	-	*47.9*	*23.5%*

* Other includes industrial waste and non-renewable municipal waste.

Key sources for CO$_2$ emissions from fuel combustion in 2006

IPCC source category	CO$_2$ emissions (Mt of CO$_2$)	% change 90-06	Level assessment (%) **	Cumulative total (%)
Main activity prod. elec. and heat - coal/peat	1 924.8	25.5%	27.8	27.8
Road - oil	1 525.8	34.1%	22.1	49.9
Main activity prod. elec. and heat - gas	338.8	121.9%	4.9	54.8
Manufacturing industries - gas	266.3	-4.4%	3.8	58.6
Other transport - oil	250.2	1.7%	3.6	62.2
Manufacturing industries - oil	243.1	12.0%	3.5	65.8
Residential - gas	238.0	-0.7%	3.4	69.2
Other energy industries - oil	156.7	-5.8%	2.3	71.5
Non-specified other sectors - gas	151.8	6.0%	2.2	73.7
Manufacturing industries - coal/peat	115.9	-42.7%	1.7	75.3
Other energy industries - gas	99.2	-4.8%	1.4	76.8
Memo: total CO$_2$ from fuel combustion	*5 696.8*	*17.1%*	*82.4*	*82.4*

** Percent calculated using the total GHG estimate for CO$_2$, CH$_4$, N$_2$O, HFCs, PFCs and SF$_6$ excluding CO$_2$ emissions/removals from land use change and forestry.

Uruguay

Figure 1. CO$_2$ emissions by fuel

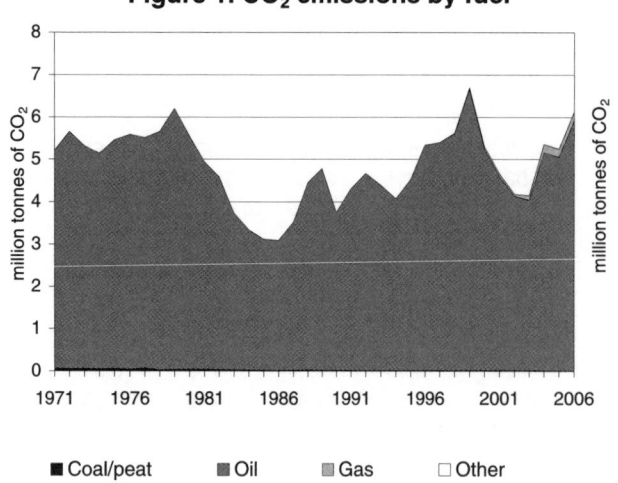

Coal/peat   Oil   Gas   Other

Figure 2. CO$_2$ emissions by sector

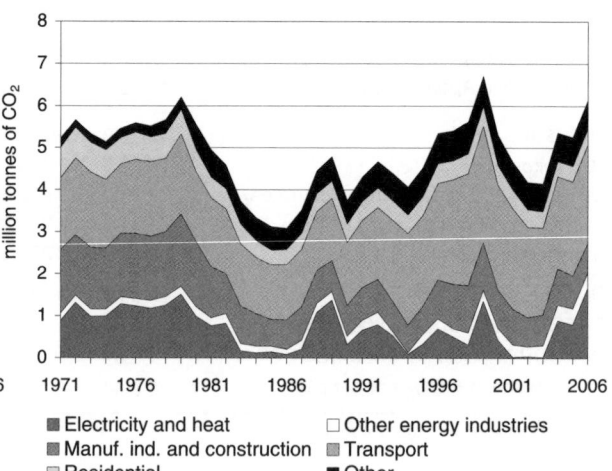

Electricity and heat   Other energy industries
Manuf. ind. and construction   Transport
Residential   Other

Figure 3. CO$_2$ emissions by sector

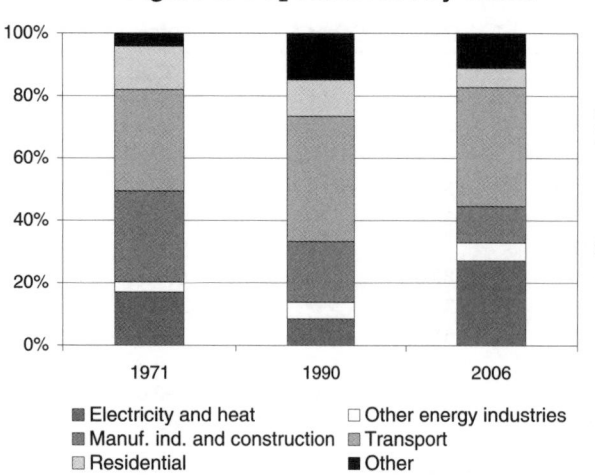

Electricity and heat   Other energy industries
Manuf. ind. and construction   Transport
Residential   Other

Figure 4. Reference vs Sectoral Approach

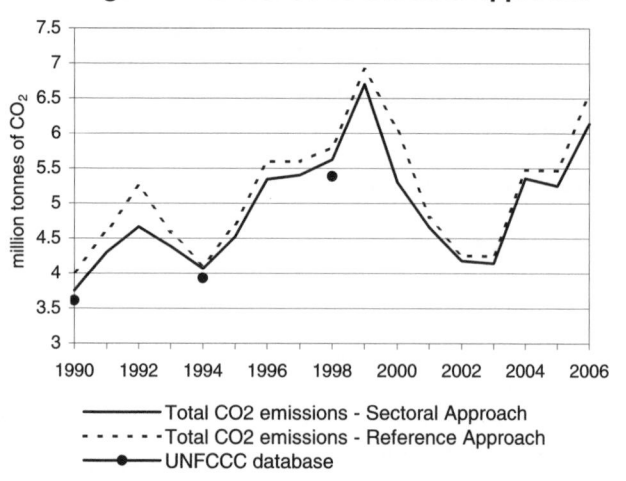

——— Total CO2 emissions - Sectoral Approach
- - - - Total CO2 emissions - Reference Approach
—●— UNFCCC database

Figure 5. Electricity generation by fuel

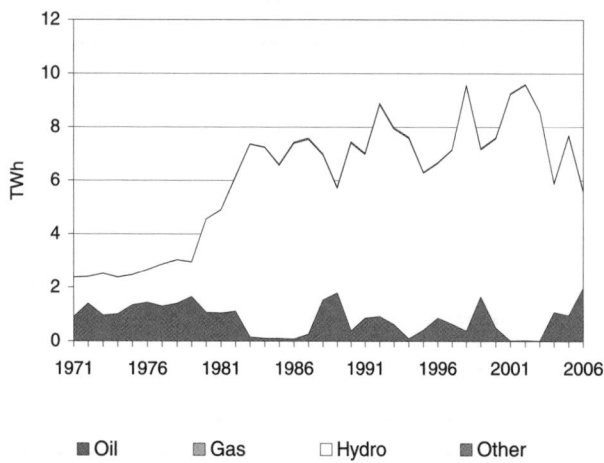

Oil   Gas   Hydro   Other

Figure 6. Key indicators

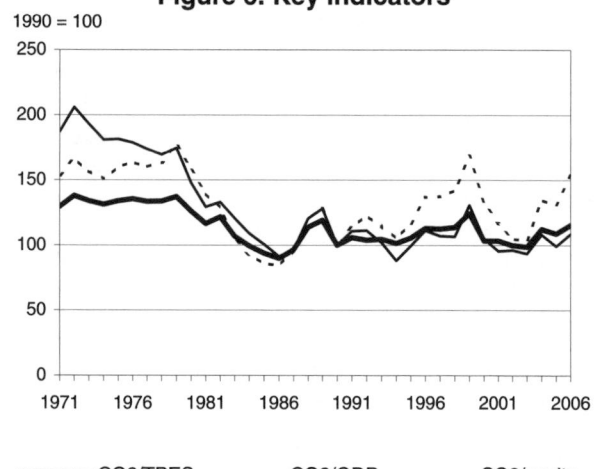

——CO2/TPES   ——CO2/GDP   - - - - CO2/capita

Uruguay
Key indicators

	1990	1995	2000	2003	2004	2005	2006	% change 90-06
CO$_2$ Sectoral Approach (Mt of CO$_2$)	3.75	4.52	5.30	4.15	5.36	5.25	6.14	63.8%
CO$_2$ Reference Approach (Mt of CO$_2$)	4.02	4.70	6.06	4.24	5.48	5.47	6.57	63.5%
TPES (PJ)	94	108	129	105	120	121	134	41.7%
TPES (Mtoe)	2.25	2.57	3.08	2.52	2.86	2.89	3.19	41.7%
GDP (billion 2000 US$ using exch. rates)	15.35	18.62	20.67	18.15	20.30	21.63	23.16	50.9%
GDP (billion 2000 US$ using PPPs)	21.75	26.38	29.28	25.72	28.76	30.64	32.79	50.8%
Population (millions)	3.11	3.22	3.30	3.30	3.30	3.31	3.31	6.7%
CO$_2$ / TPES (t CO$_2$ per TJ)	39.8	42.0	41.1	39.3	44.7	43.3	46.0	15.6%
CO$_2$ / GDP (kg CO$_2$ per 2000 US$)	0.24	0.24	0.26	0.23	0.26	0.24	0.27	8.6%
CO$_2$ / GDP (kg CO$_2$ per 2000 US$ PPP)	0.17	0.17	0.18	0.16	0.19	0.17	0.19	8.6%
CO$_2$ / population (t CO$_2$ per capita)	1.21	1.41	1.61	1.25	1.62	1.59	1.85	53.5%

Ratios are based on the Sectoral Approach.

2006 CO$_2$ emissions by sector

million tonnes of CO$_2$	Coal/peat	Oil	Gas	Other *	Total	% change 90-06
Sectoral Approach	**0.01**	**5.92**	**0.21**	**-**	**6.14**	**63.8%**
Main activity producer elec. and heat	-	1.66	-	-	1.66	462.2%
Unallocated autoproducers	-	-	0.00	-	0.00	-92.5%
Other energy industries	-	0.35	0.01	-	0.36	80.2%
Manufacturing industries and construction	0.01	0.56	0.14	-	0.71	-2.4%
Transport	-	2.34	-	-	2.34	55.7%
of which: road	-	*2.33*	-	-	*2.33*	*62.9%*
Other sectors	-	1.01	0.06	-	1.06	6.4%
of which: residential	-	*0.34*	*0.03*	-	*0.37*	*-15.5%*
Reference Approach	**0.01**	**6.32**	**0.24**	**-**	**6.57**	**63.5%**
Diff. due to losses and/or transformation	-	0.39	-	-	0.39	
Statistical differences	- 0.00	0.01	0.03	-	0.03	
Memo: international marine bunkers	-	*0.77*	-	-	*0.77*	*109.7%*
Memo: international aviation	-	*..*	-	-	*..*	*..*

* Other includes industrial waste and non-renewable municipal waste.

Key sources for CO$_2$ emissions from fuel combustion in 2006

IPCC source category	CO$_2$ emissions (Mt of CO$_2$)	% change 90-06	Level assessment (%) **	Cumulative total (%)
Road - oil	2.33	62.9%	5.8	5.8
Main activity prod. elec. and heat - oil	1.66	462.2%	4.1	9.9
Non-specified other sectors - oil	0.66	20.7%	1.6	11.5
Manufacturing industries - oil	0.56	-22.3%	1.4	12.9
Other energy industries - oil	0.35	73.8%	0.9	13.8
Residential - oil	0.34	-20.2%	0.9	14.6
Manufacturing industries - gas	0.14	x	0.3	15.0
Residential - gas	0.03	x	0.1	15.1
Non-specified other sectors - gas	0.03	x	0.1	15.1
Other energy industries - gas	0.01	x	0.0	15.2
Other transport - oil	0.01	-83.5%	0.0	15.2
Memo: total CO$_2$ from fuel combustion	*6.14*	*63.8%*	*15.2*	*15.2*

** Percent calculated using the total GHG estimate for CO$_2$, CH$_4$, N$_2$O, HFCs, PFCs and SF$_6$ excluding CO$_2$ emissions/removals from land use change and forestry.

Uzbekistan / Ouzbékistan

Figure 1. CO$_2$ emissions by fuel

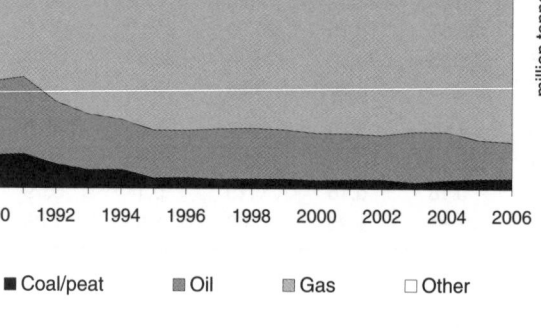

■ Coal/peat   ■ Oil   ■ Gas   □ Other

Figure 2. CO$_2$ emissions by sector

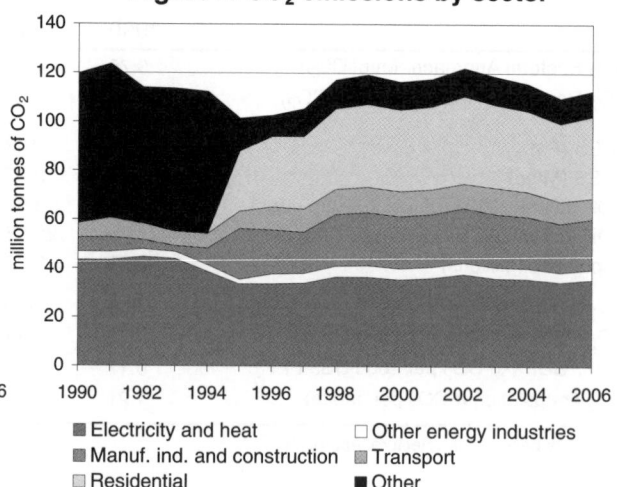

■ Electricity and heat   □ Other energy industries
■ Manuf. ind. and construction   ▨ Transport
▨ Residential   ■ Other

Figure 3. CO$_2$ emissions by sector

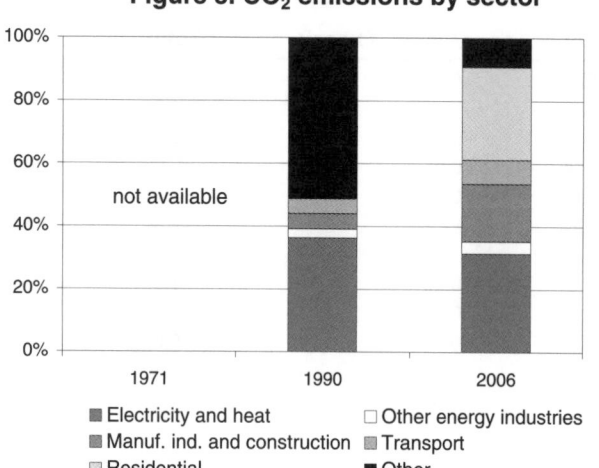

■ Electricity and heat   □ Other energy industries
■ Manuf. ind. and construction   ▨ Transport
▨ Residential   ■ Other

Figure 4. Reference vs Sectoral Approach

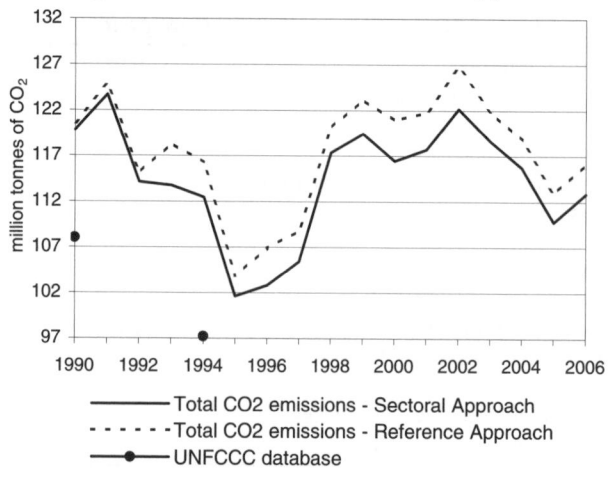

—— Total CO2 emissions - Sectoral Approach
- - - - Total CO2 emissions - Reference Approach
●—— UNFCCC database

Figure 5. Electricity generation by fuel

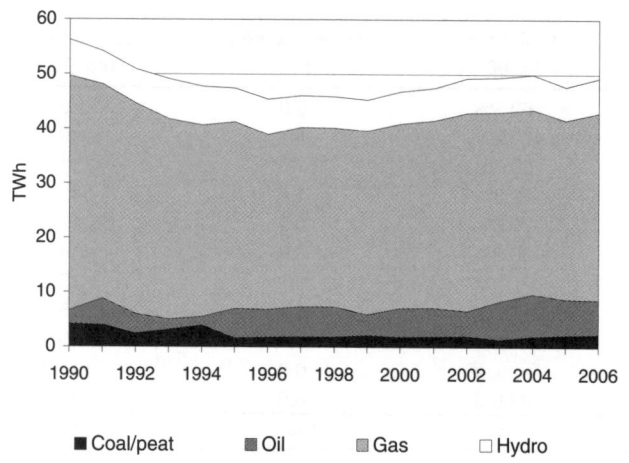

■ Coal/peat   ■ Oil   ▨ Gas   □ Hydro

Figure 6. Key indicators

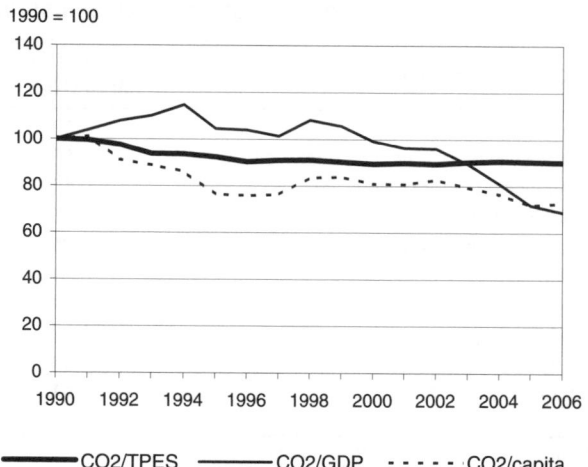

—— CO2/TPES   —— CO2/GDP   - - - - CO2/capita

Uzbekistan / Ouzbékistan

Key indicators

	1990	1995	2000	2003	2004	2005	2006	% change 90-06
CO$_2$ Sectoral Approach (Mt of CO$_2$)	119.83	101.59	116.46	118.61	115.72	109.77	112.86	-5.8%
CO$_2$ Reference Approach (Mt of CO$_2$)	120.58	103.83	120.93	121.88	118.84	112.94	116.19	-3.6%
TPES (PJ)	1 941	1 782	2 109	2 129	2 069	1 968	2 029	4.5%
TPES (Mtoe)	46.37	42.57	50.38	50.84	49.42	47.00	48.45	4.5%
GDP (billion 2000 US$ using exch. rates)	14.04	11.39	13.76	15.54	16.74	17.91	19.21	36.8%
GDP (billion 2000 US$ using PPPs)	37.68	30.56	36.92	41.69	44.90	48.04	51.55	36.8%
Population (millions)	20.51	22.79	24.65	25.57	25.86	26.17	26.54	29.4%
CO$_2$ / TPES (t CO$_2$ per TJ)	61.7	57.0	55.2	55.7	55.9	55.8	55.6	-9.9%
CO$_2$ / GDP (kg CO$_2$ per 2000 US$)	8.53	8.92	8.46	7.63	6.91	6.13	5.87	-31.2%
CO$_2$ / GDP (kg CO$_2$ per 2000 US$ PPP)	3.18	3.32	3.15	2.85	2.58	2.28	2.19	-31.2%
CO$_2$ / population (t CO$_2$ per capita)	5.84	4.46	4.72	4.64	4.47	4.20	4.25	-27.2%

Ratios are based on the Sectoral Approach.

2006 CO$_2$ emissions by sector

million tonnes of CO$_2$	Coal/peat	Oil	Gas	Other *	Total	% change 90-06
Sectoral Approach	**4.39**	**15.03**	**93.44**	-	**112.86**	**-5.8%**
Main activity producer elec. and heat	3.63	4.24	27.41	-	35.28	-18.7%
Unallocated autoproducers	-	0.02	0.06	-	0.09	x
Other energy industries	-	0.58	3.76	-	4.33	27.5%
Manufacturing industries and construction	0.21	1.84	18.56	-	20.61	252.9%
Transport	-	5.38	3.24	-	8.62	52.2%
of which: road	-	*4.45*	*0.14*	-	*4.60*	*-15.4%*
Other sectors	0.55	2.97	40.41	-	43.93	-28.6%
of which: residential	*0.06*	*0.05*	*33.38*	-	*33.49*	*x*
Reference Approach	**4.43**	**14.60**	**97.15**	-	**116.19**	**-3.6%**
Diff. due to losses and/or transformation	0.04	- 0.43	3.71	-	3.32	
Statistical differences	-	- 0.00	- 0.00	-	- 0.00	
Memo: international marine bunkers	-	-	-	-	-	-
Memo: international aviation	-	..	..	-	..	..

* Other includes industrial waste and non-renewable municipal waste.

Key sources for CO$_2$ emissions from fuel combustion in 2006

IPCC source category	CO$_2$ emissions (Mt of CO$_2$)	% change 90-06	Level assessment (%) **	Cumulative total (%)
Residential - gas	33.38	x	18.2	18.2
Main activity prod. elec. and heat - gas	27.41	1.0%	14.9	33.1
Manufacturing industries - gas	18.56	x	10.1	43.3
Non-specified other sectors - gas	7.03	-84.7%	3.8	47.1
Road - oil	4.45	-18.0%	2.4	49.5
Main activity prod. elec. and heat - oil	4.24	-43.4%	2.3	51.8
Other energy industries - gas	3.76	55.5%	2.0	53.9
Main activity prod. elec. and heat - coal/peat	3.63	-58.7%	2.0	55.8
Other transport - gas	3.10	x	1.7	57.5
Non-specified other sectors - oil	2.92	-72.4%	1.6	59.1
Manufacturing industries - oil	1.84	-68.5%	1.0	60.1
Memo: total CO$_2$ from fuel combustion	*112.86*	*-5.8%*	*61.5*	*61.5*

** Percent calculated using the total GHG estimate for CO$_2$, CH$_4$, N$_2$O, HFCs, PFCs and SF$_6$ excluding CO$_2$ emissions/removals from land use change and forestry.

Venezuela / Vénézuela

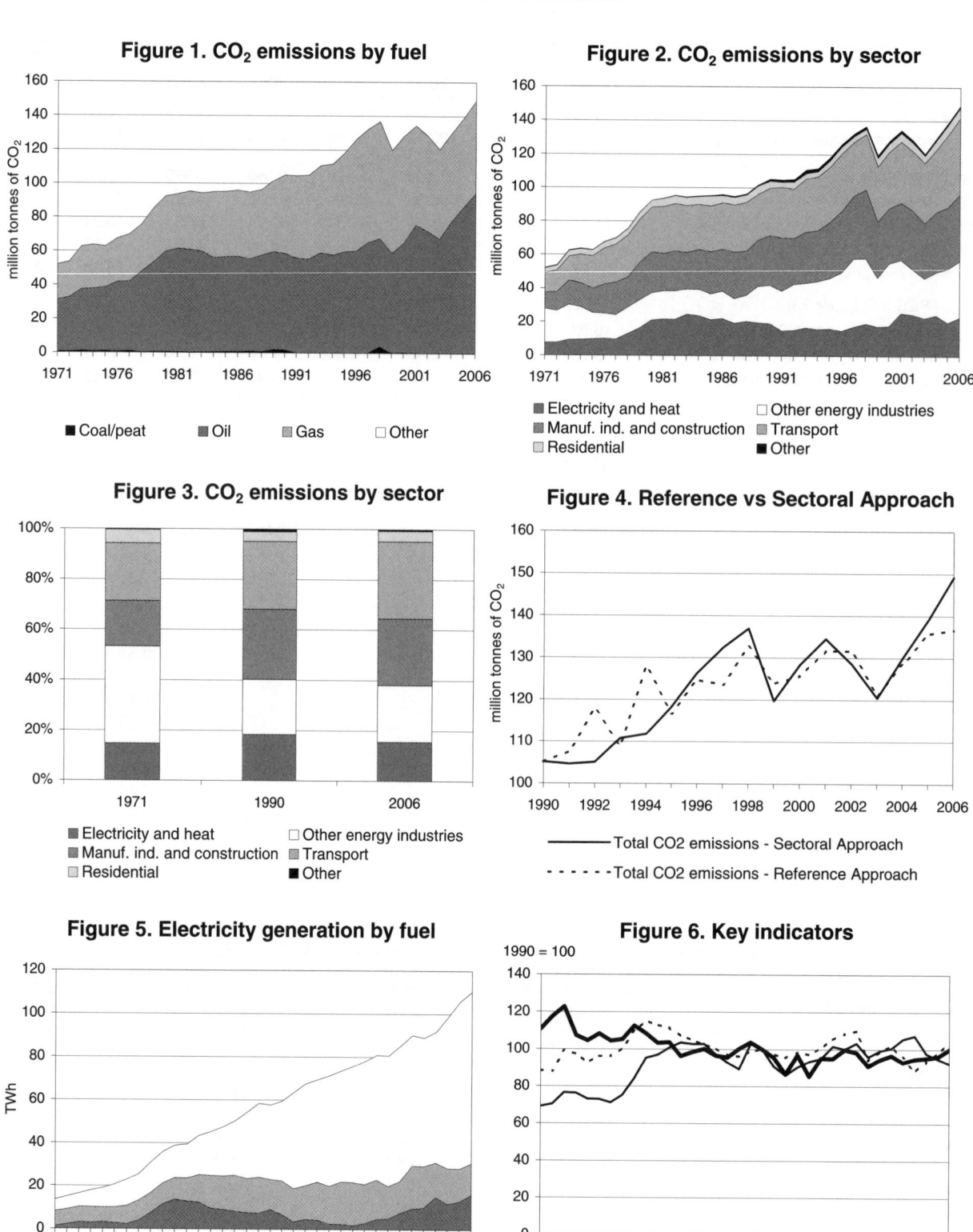

Figure 1. CO_2 emissions by fuel

■ Coal/peat ■ Oil ■ Gas ☐ Other

Figure 2. CO_2 emissions by sector

■ Electricity and heat   ☐ Other energy industries
■ Manuf. ind. and construction   ■ Transport
☐ Residential   ■ Other

Figure 3. CO_2 emissions by sector

■ Electricity and heat   ☐ Other energy industries
■ Manuf. ind. and construction   ■ Transport
☐ Residential   ■ Other

Figure 4. Reference vs Sectoral Approach

—— Total CO2 emissions - Sectoral Approach
- - - - - Total CO2 emissions - Reference Approach

Figure 5. Electricity generation by fuel

■ Oil   ■ Gas   ☐ Hydro

Figure 6. Key indicators

1990 = 100

—— CO2/TPES   —— CO2/GDP   - - - - - CO2/capita

Venezuela / Vénézuela

Key indicators

	1990	1995	2000	2003	2004	2005	2006	% change 90-06
CO$_2$ Sectoral Approach (Mt of CO$_2$)	105.10	118.29	128.31	120.49	129.94	139.07	149.20	42.0%
CO$_2$ Reference Approach (Mt of CO$_2$)	105.03	116.68	125.66	121.20	128.49	135.70	136.60	30.1%
TPES (PJ)	1 839	2 174	2 375	2 225	2 386	2 530	2 605	41.7%
TPES (Mtoe)	43.92	51.93	56.73	53.14	57.00	60.44	62.22	41.7%
GDP (billion 2000 US$ using exch. rates)	95.26	112.85	117.15	101.84	120.46	132.91	146.64	53.9%
GDP (billion 2000 US$ using PPPs)	113.85	134.86	140.00	121.70	143.95	158.83	175.24	53.9%
Population (millions)	19.75	22.04	24.31	25.67	26.13	26.58	27.02	36.8%
CO$_2$ / TPES (t CO$_2$ per TJ)	57.2	54.4	54.0	54.2	54.4	55.0	57.3	0.2%
CO$_2$ / GDP (kg CO$_2$ per 2000 US$)	1.10	1.05	1.10	1.18	1.08	1.05	1.02	-7.8%
CO$_2$ / GDP (kg CO$_2$ per 2000 US$ PPP)	0.92	0.88	0.92	0.99	0.90	0.88	0.85	-7.8%
CO$_2$ / population (t CO$_2$ per capita)	5.32	5.37	5.28	4.69	4.97	5.23	5.52	3.8%

Ratios are based on the Sectoral Approach.

2006 CO$_2$ emissions by sector

million tonnes of CO$_2$	Coal/peat	Oil	Gas	Other *	Total	% change 90-06
Sectoral Approach	**0.15**	**94.35**	**54.70**	-	**149.20**	**42.0%**
Main activity producer elec. and heat	-	12.36	9.63	-	21.99	44.3%
Unallocated autoproducers	-	-	1.01	-	1.01	-74.1%
Other energy industries	-	17.96	15.82	-	33.78	46.8%
Manufacturing industries and construction	0.15	14.33	24.98	-	39.46	34.3%
Transport	-	45.39	0.25	-	45.64	61.5%
of which: road	-	*45.35*	-	-	*45.35*	*60.6%*
Other sectors	-	4.31	3.00	-	7.31	38.5%
of which: residential	-	*3.93*	*2.30*	-	*6.23*	*50.5%*
Reference Approach	**0.15**	**81.77**	**54.67**	-	**136.60**	**30.1%**
Diff. due to losses and/or transformation	-	- 0.26	-	-	- 0.26	
Statistical differences	-	- 12.32	- 0.02	-	- 12.34	
Memo: international marine bunkers	-	*2.19*	-	-	*2.19*	*-12.2%*
Memo: international aviation	-	*2.13*	-	-	*2.13*	*108.1%*

* Other includes industrial waste and non-renewable municipal waste.

Key sources for CO$_2$ emissions from fuel combustion in 2006

IPCC source category	CO$_2$ emissions (Mt of CO$_2$)	% change 90-06	Level assessment (%) **	Cumulative total (%)
Road - oil	45.35	60.6%	17.9	17.9
Manufacturing industries - gas	24.98	38.2%	9.9	27.8
Other energy industries - oil	17.96	94.7%	7.1	34.9
Other energy industries - gas	15.82	14.7%	6.3	41.2
Manufacturing industries - oil	14.33	50.8%	5.7	46.8
Main activity prod. elec. and heat - oil	12.36	118.4%	4.9	51.7
Main activity prod. elec. and heat - gas	9.63	0.6%	3.8	55.5
Residential - oil	3.93	6.3%	1.6	57.1
Residential - gas	2.30	424.0%	0.9	58.0
Unallocated autoproducers - gas	1.01	-70.8%	0.4	58.4
Non-specified other sectors - gas	0.70	-28.3%	0.3	58.7
Memo: total CO$_2$ from fuel combustion	*149.20*	*42.0%*	*59.0*	*59.0*

** Percent calculated using the total GHG estimate for CO$_2$, CH$_4$, N$_2$O, HFCs, PFCs and SF$_6$ excluding CO$_2$ emissions/removals from land use change and forestry.

Vietnam / Viêt-Nam *

Figure 1. CO$_2$ emissions by fuel

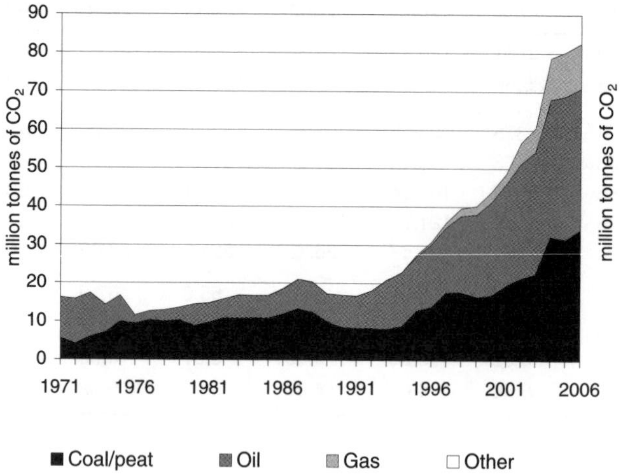

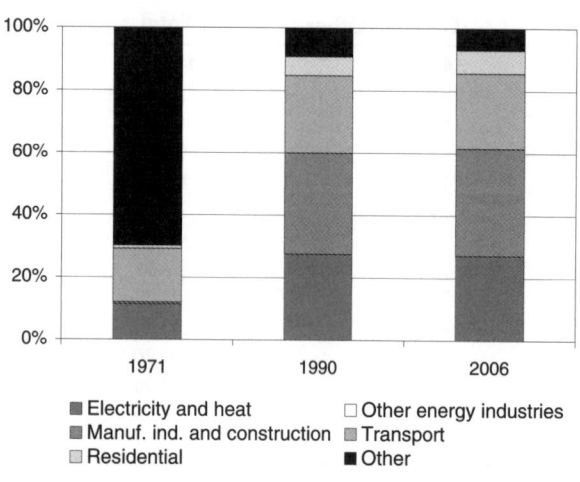

■ Coal/peat ■ Oil ■ Gas □ Other

Figure 2. CO$_2$ emissions by sector

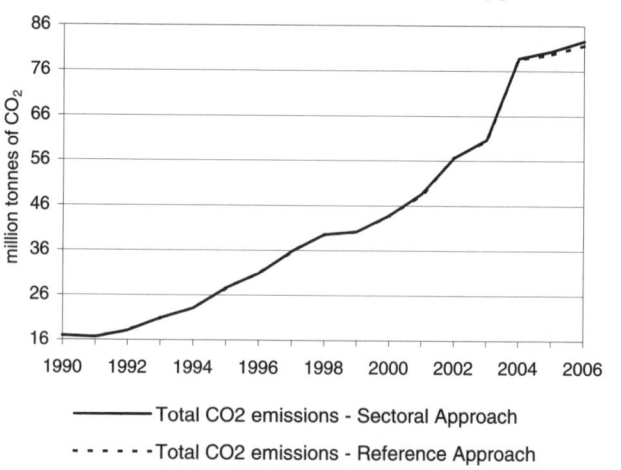

■ Electricity and heat   □ Other energy industries
■ Manuf. ind. and construction ■ Transport
□ Residential   ■ Other

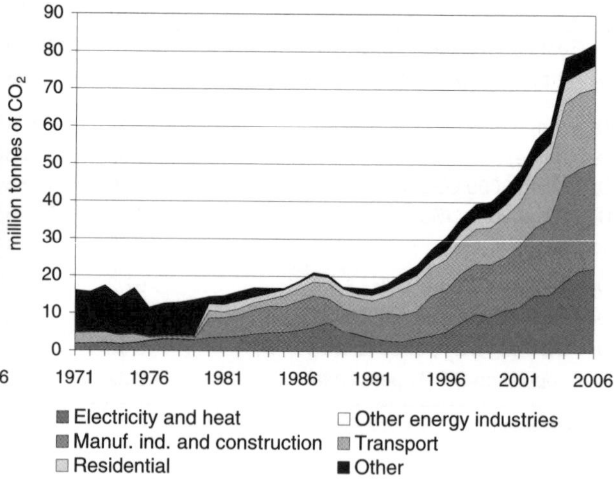

Figure 3. CO$_2$ emissions by sector

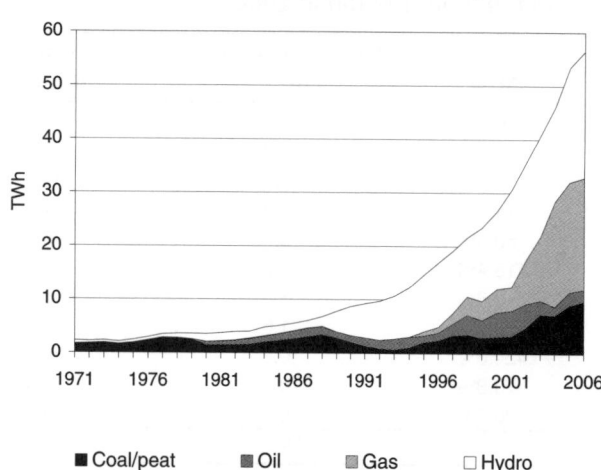

■ Electricity and heat   □ Other energy industries
■ Manuf. ind. and construction ■ Transport
□ Residential   ■ Other

Figure 4. Reference vs Sectoral Approach

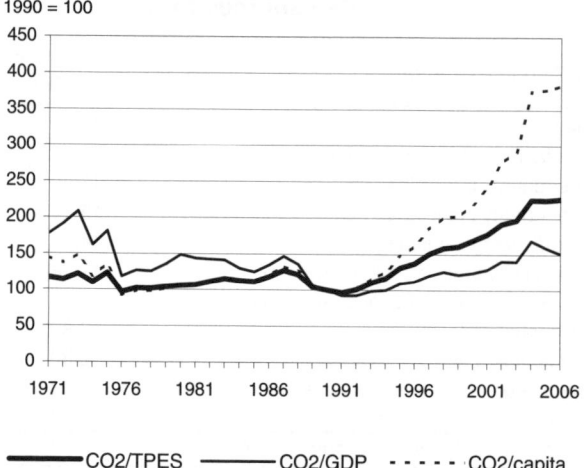

—— Total CO2 emissions - Sectoral Approach
- - - - - Total CO2 emissions - Reference Approach

Figure 5. Electricity generation by fuel

■ Coal/peat ■ Oil ■ Gas □ Hydro

Figure 6. Key indicators

1990 = 100

—— CO2/TPES —— CO2/GDP - - - - - CO2/capita

* A detailed sectoral breakdown is available starting in 1980.

Vietnam / Viêt-Nam

Key indicators

	1990	1995	2000	2003	2004	2005	2006	% change 90-06
CO$_2$ Sectoral Approach (Mt of CO$_2$)	16.95	27.51	43.81	60.63	78.79	80.35	82.62	387.4%
CO$_2$ Reference Approach (Mt of CO$_2$)	16.96	27.52	43.76	60.53	78.69	79.68	81.70	381.8%
TPES (PJ)	1 018	1 260	1 556	1 847	2 101	2 147	2 189	115.0%
TPES (Mtoe)	24.32	30.09	37.17	44.11	50.18	51.29	52.29	115.0%
GDP (billion 2000 US$ using exch. rates)	15.02	22.28	31.17	38.30	41.28	44.77	48.42	222.4%
GDP (billion 2000 US$ using PPPs)	76.30	113.18	158.37	194.59	209.75	227.43	246.00	222.4%
Population (millions)	66.20	72.98	77.64	80.90	82.03	83.11	84.11	27.1%
CO$_2$ / TPES (t CO$_2$ per TJ)	16.7	21.8	28.2	32.8	37.5	37.4	37.7	126.7%
CO$_2$ / GDP (kg CO$_2$ per 2000 US$)	1.13	1.24	1.41	1.58	1.91	1.80	1.71	51.2%
CO$_2$ / GDP (kg CO$_2$ per 2000 US$ PPP)	0.22	0.24	0.28	0.31	0.38	0.35	0.34	51.1%
CO$_2$ / population (t CO$_2$ per capita)	0.26	0.38	0.56	0.75	0.96	0.97	0.98	283.6%

Ratios are based on the Sectoral Approach.

2006 CO$_2$ emissions by sector

million tonnes of CO$_2$	Coal/peat	Oil	Gas	Other *	Total	% change 90-06
Sectoral Approach	**34.18**	**36.77**	**11.67**	-	**82.62**	**387.4%**
Main activity producer elec. and heat	8.25	0.90	11.06	-	20.21	333.8%
Unallocated autoproducers	0.72	1.09	0.37	-	2.18	x
Other energy industries	-	-	-	-	-	-
Manufacturing industries and construction	20.10	8.04	0.24	-	28.37	417.0%
Transport	-	19.88	-	-	19.88	372.6%
of which: road	-	*18.50*	-	-	*18.50*	*393.7%*
Other sectors	5.12	6.86	-	-	11.98	361.0%
of which: residential	*3.62*	*2.53*	-	-	*6.15*	*495.4%*
Reference Approach	**34.18**	**35.85**	**11.67**	-	**81.70**	**381.8%**
Diff. due to losses and/or transformation	-	- 0.92	-	-	- 0.92	
Statistical differences	- 0.00	0.00	-	-	- 0.00	
Memo: international marine bunkers	-	*..*	-	-	*..*	*..*
Memo: international aviation		*0.73*	-	-	*0.73*	*..*

* Other includes industrial waste and non-renewable municipal waste.

Key sources for CO$_2$ emissions from fuel combustion in 2006

IPCC source category	CO$_2$ emissions (Mt of CO$_2$)	% change 90-06	Level assessment (%) **	Cumulative total (%)
Manufacturing industries - coal/peat	20.10	402.7%	9.5	9.5
Road - oil	18.50	393.7%	8.7	18.2
Main activity prod. elec. and heat - gas	11.06	+	5.2	23.4
Main activity prod. elec. and heat - coal/peat	8.25	139.4%	3.9	27.3
Manufacturing industries - oil	8.04	439.3%	3.8	31.1
Non-specified other sectors - oil	4.33	249.1%	2.0	33.1
Residential - coal/peat	3.62	350.3%	1.7	34.8
Residential - oil	2.53	+	1.2	36.0
Non-specified other sectors - coal/peat	1.50	361.7%	0.7	36.7
Other transport - oil	1.38	240.2%	0.6	37.4
Unallocated autoproducers - oil	1.09	x	0.5	37.9
Memo: total CO$_2$ from fuel combustion	*82.62*	*387.4%*	*38.9*	*38.9*

** Percent calculated using the total GHG estimate for CO$_2$, CH$_4$, N$_2$O, HFCs, PFCs and SF$_6$ excluding CO$_2$ emissions/removals from land use change and forestry.

Yemen / Yémen

Figure 1. CO$_2$ emissions by fuel

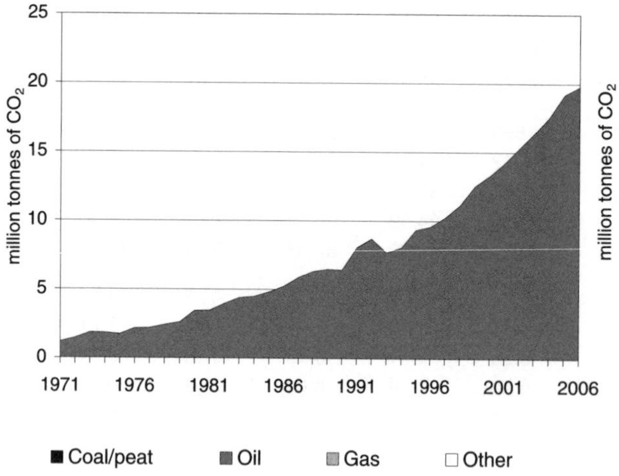

■ Coal/peat　　■ Oil　　■ Gas　　□ Other

Figure 2. CO$_2$ emissions by sector

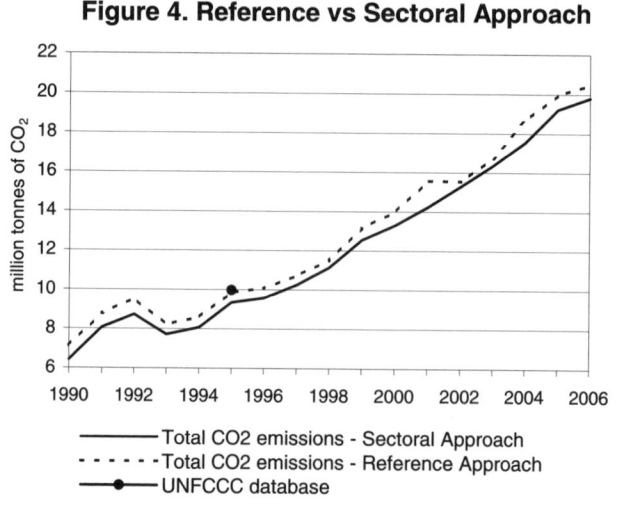

■ Electricity and heat　　□ Other energy industries
■ Manuf. ind. and construction　　■ Transport
□ Residential　　■ Other

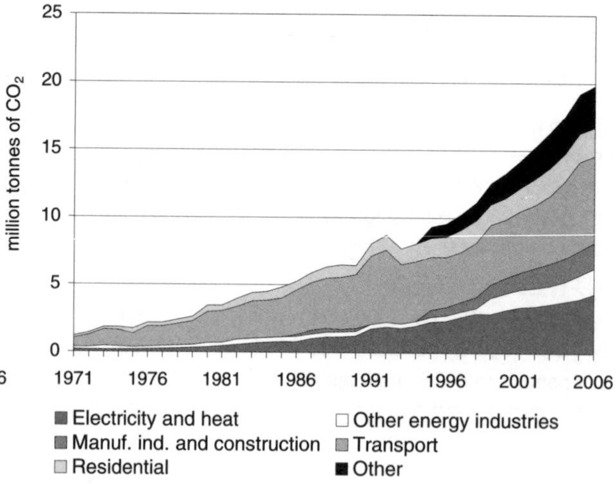

Figure 3. CO$_2$ emissions by sector

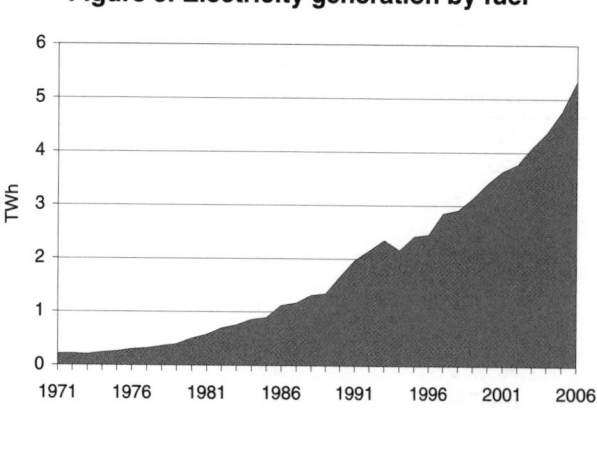

■ Electricity and heat　　□ Other energy industries
■ Manuf. ind. and construction　　■ Transport
□ Residential　　■ Other

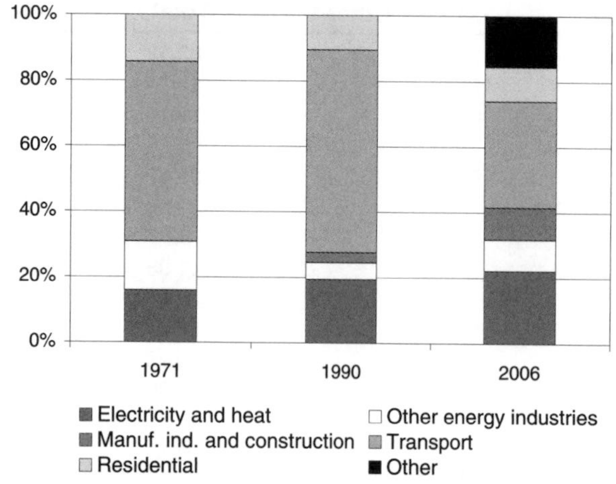

Figure 4. Reference vs Sectoral Approach

——— Total CO2 emissions - Sectoral Approach
- - - - Total CO2 emissions - Reference Approach
—●— UNFCCC database

Figure 5. Electricity generation by fuel

■ Oil

Figure 6. Key indicators

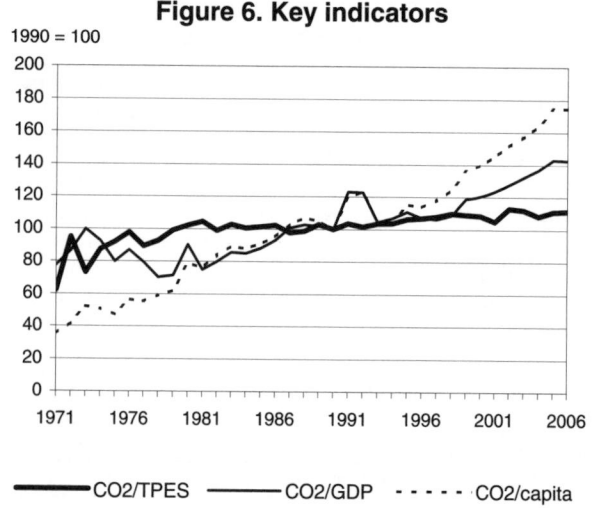

1990 = 100

——— CO2/TPES　　——— CO2/GDP　　- - - - CO2/capita

Yemen / Yémen

Key indicators

	1990	1995	2000	2003	2004	2005	2006	% change 90-06
CO$_2$ Sectoral Approach (Mt of CO$_2$)	6.43	9.34	13.29	16.35	17.55	19.21	19.80	207.9%
CO$_2$ Reference Approach (Mt of CO$_2$)	7.12	9.86	13.97	16.74	18.68	19.96	20.46	187.3%
TPES (PJ)	107	147	205	244	271	289	297	176.5%
TPES (Mtoe)	2.56	3.51	4.89	5.83	6.47	6.91	7.09	176.5%
GDP (billion 2000 US$ using exch. rates)	5.51	7.22	9.44	10.58	11.00	11.50	11.88	115.7%
GDP (billion 2000 US$ using PPPs)	8.60	11.28	14.74	16.52	17.18	17.96	18.56	115.7%
Population (millions)	12.31	15.52	18.18	19.88	20.48	21.10	21.73	76.5%
CO$_2$ / TPES (t CO$_2$ per TJ)	59.9	63.6	64.9	67.0	64.8	66.4	66.7	11.4%
CO$_2$ / GDP (kg CO$_2$ per 2000 US$)	1.17	1.29	1.41	1.55	1.60	1.67	1.67	42.7%
CO$_2$ / GDP (kg CO$_2$ per 2000 US$ PPP)	0.75	0.83	0.90	0.99	1.02	1.07	1.07	42.8%
CO$_2$ / population (t CO$_2$ per capita)	0.52	0.60	0.73	0.82	0.86	0.91	0.91	74.5%

Ratios are based on the Sectoral Approach.

2006 CO$_2$ emissions by sector

million tonnes of CO$_2$	Coal/peat	Oil	Gas	Other *	Total	% change 90-06
Sectoral Approach	-	**19.80**	-	-	**19.80**	207.9%
Main activity producer elec. and heat	-	3.85	-	-	3.85	318.7%
Unallocated autoproducers	-	0.54	-	-	0.54	69.2%
Other energy industries	-	1.88	-	-	1.88	455.7%
Manufacturing industries and construction	-	1.93	-	-	1.93	877.6%
Transport	-	6.42	-	-	6.42	61.6%
of which: road	-	*6.42*	-	-	*6.42*	*61.6%*
Other sectors	-	5.17	-	-	5.17	661.2%
of which: residential	-	*2.09*	-	-	*2.09*	*207.0%*
Reference Approach	-	**20.46**	-	-	**20.46**	187.3%
Diff. due to losses and/or transformation	-	0.45	-	-	0.45	
Statistical differences	-	0.21	-	-	0.21	
Memo: international marine bunkers	-	*0.39*	-	-	*0.39*	*-68.2%*
Memo: international aviation	-	*0.35*	-	-	*0.35*	*103.7%*

* Other includes industrial waste and non-renewable municipal waste.

Key sources for CO$_2$ emissions from fuel combustion in 2006

IPCC source category	CO$_2$ emissions (Mt of CO$_2$)	% change 90-06	Level assessment (%) **	Cumulative total (%)
Road - oil	6.42	61.6%	17.4	17.4
Main activity prod. elec. and heat - oil	3.85	318.7%	10.4	27.9
Non-specified other sectors - oil	3.09	x	8.4	36.2
Residential - oil	2.09	207.0%	5.7	41.9
Manufacturing industries - oil	1.93	877.6%	5.2	47.1
Other energy industries - oil	1.88	455.7%	5.1	52.3
Unallocated autoproducers - oil	0.54	69.2%	1.5	53.7
-	-	-	-	-
-	-	-	-	-
-	-	-	-	-
-	-	-	-	-
Memo: total CO$_2$ from fuel combustion	*19.80*	*207.9%*	*53.7*	*53.7*

** Percent calculated using the total GHG estimate for CO$_2$, CH$_4$, N$_2$O, HFCs, PFCs and SF$_6$ excluding CO$_2$ emissions/removals from land use change and forestry.

Zambia / Zambie

Figure 1. CO₂ emissions by fuel

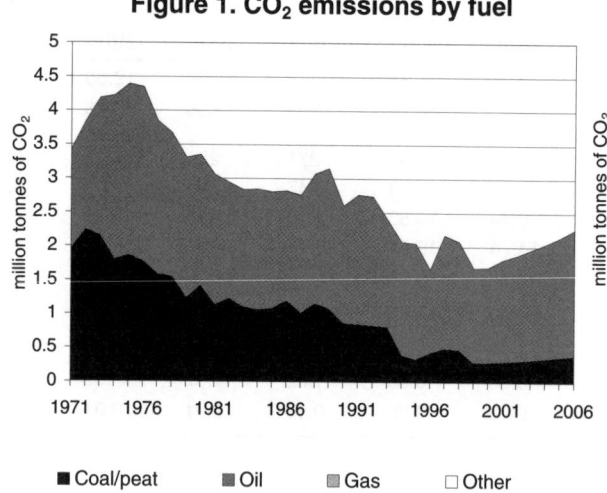

Coal/peat　　Oil　　Gas　　Other

Figure 2. CO₂ emissions by sector

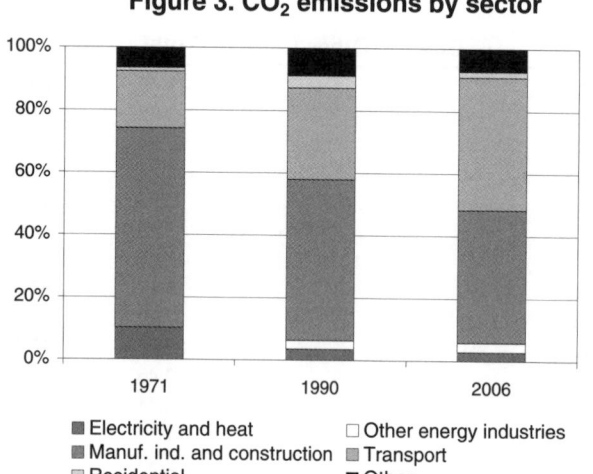

Electricity and heat　　Other energy industries
Manuf. ind. and construction　　Transport
Residential　　Other

Figure 3. CO₂ emissions by sector

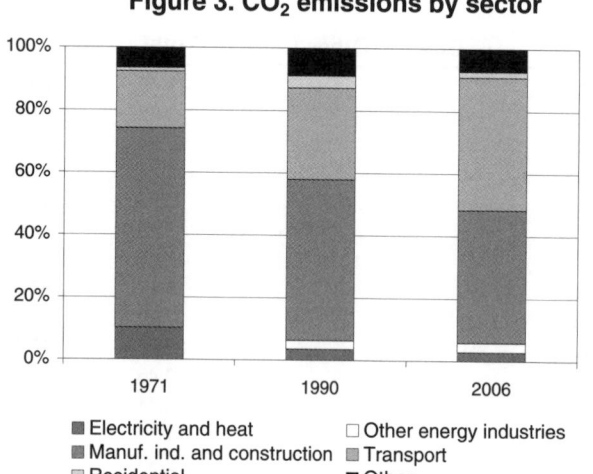

Electricity and heat　　Other energy industries
Manuf. ind. and construction　　Transport
Residential　　Other

Figure 4. Reference vs Sectoral Approach

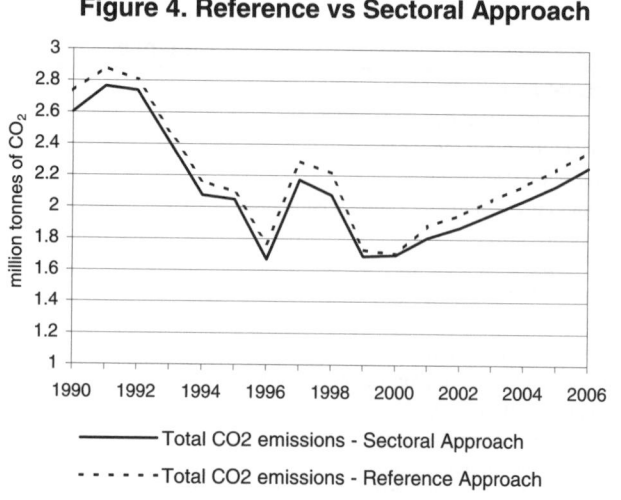

——— Total CO2 emissions - Sectoral Approach
- - - - Total CO2 emissions - Reference Approach

Figure 5. Electricity generation by fuel

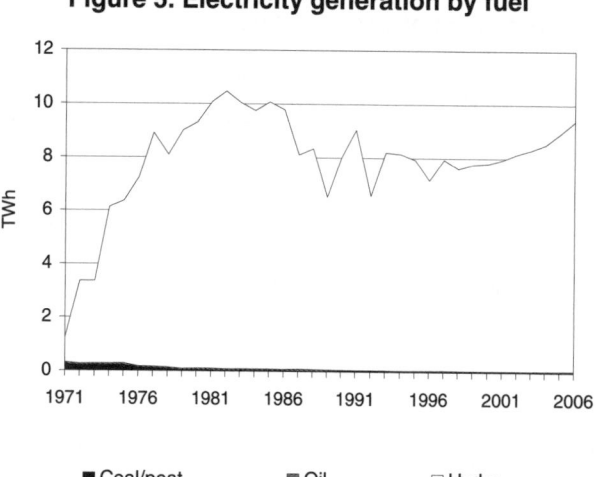

Coal/peat　　Oil　　Hydro

Figure 6. Key indicators

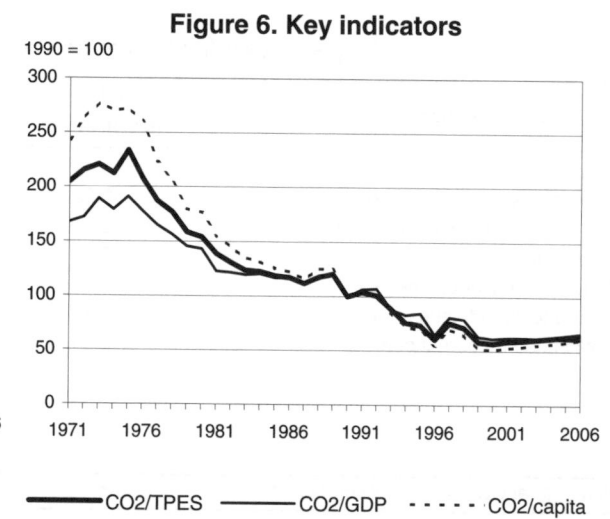

—— CO2/TPES　　—— CO2/GDP　　- - - - CO2/capita

Zambia / Zambie

Key indicators

	1990	1995	2000	2003	2004	2005	2006	% change 90-06
CO$_2$ Sectoral Approach (Mt of CO$_2$)	2.60	2.05	1.70	1.96	2.04	2.14	2.26	-13.3%
CO$_2$ Reference Approach (Mt of CO$_2$)	2.73	2.10	1.71	2.05	2.14	2.24	2.36	-13.7%
TPES (PJ)	229	245	263	284	291	298	306	33.7%
TPES (Mtoe)	5.46	5.86	6.27	6.78	6.94	7.12	7.31	33.8%
GDP (billion 2000 US$ using exch. rates)	3.03	2.82	3.24	3.69	3.89	4.09	4.34	43.2%
GDP (billion 2000 US$ using PPPs)	7.86	7.33	8.41	9.58	10.10	10.62	11.26	43.2%
Population (millions)	8.12	9.26	10.45	11.07	11.27	11.48	11.70	44.0%
CO$_2$ / TPES (t CO$_2$ per TJ)	11.4	8.3	6.5	6.9	7.0	7.2	7.4	-35.2%
CO$_2$ / GDP (kg CO$_2$ per 2000 US$)	0.86	0.73	0.52	0.53	0.53	0.52	0.52	-39.5%
CO$_2$ / GDP (kg CO$_2$ per 2000 US$ PPP)	0.33	0.28	0.20	0.20	0.20	0.20	0.20	-39.5%
CO$_2$ / population (t CO$_2$ per capita)	0.32	0.22	0.16	0.18	0.18	0.19	0.19	-39.8%

Ratios are based on the Sectoral Approach.

2006 CO$_2$ emissions by sector

million tonnes of CO$_2$	Coal/peat	Oil	Gas	Other *	Total	% change 90-06
Sectoral Approach	**0.39**	**1.86**	-	-	**2.26**	**-13.3%**
Main activity producer elec. and heat	-	0.03	-	-	0.03	28.5%
Unallocated autoproducers	0.03	0.00	-	-	0.04	-49.4%
Other energy industries	-	0.07	-	-	0.07	-8.5%
Manufacturing industries and construction	0.33	0.63	-	-	0.96	-28.5%
Transport	-	0.96	-	-	0.96	25.2%
of which: road	-	0.87	-	-	0.87	27.3%
Other sectors	0.03	0.18	-	-	0.21	-37.3%
of which: residential	-	0.04	-	-	0.04	-57.6%
Reference Approach	**0.39**	**1.97**	-	-	**2.36**	**-13.7%**
Diff. due to losses and/or transformation	-	0.10	-	-	0.10	
Statistical differences	0.00	- 0.00	-	-	- 0.00	
Memo: international marine bunkers	-	-	-	-	-	-
Memo: international aviation	-	0.17	-	-	0.17	-14.3%

* Other includes industrial waste and non-renewable municipal waste.

Key sources for CO$_2$ emissions from fuel combustion in 2006

IPCC source category	CO$_2$ emissions (Mt of CO$_2$)	% change 90-06	Level assessment (%) **	Cumulative total (%)
Road - oil	0.87	27.3%	2.8	2.8
Manufacturing industries - oil	0.63	0.6%	2.0	4.8
Manufacturing industries - coal/peat	0.33	-54.0%	1.1	5.9
Non-specified other sectors - oil	0.13	-11.7%	0.4	6.3
Other transport - oil	0.09	7.7%	0.3	6.6
Other energy industries - oil	0.07	-8.5%	0.2	6.8
Residential - oil	0.04	-57.6%	0.1	7.0
Unallocated autoproducers - coal/peat	0.03	-51.7%	0.1	7.1
Non-specified other sectors - coal/peat	0.03	-60.0%	0.1	7.2
Main activity prod. elec. and heat - oil	0.03	28.5%	0.1	7.3
Unallocated autoproducers - oil	0.00	-	0.0	7.3
Memo: total CO$_2$ from fuel combustion	2.26	-13.3%	7.3	7.3

** Percent calculated using the total GHG estimate for CO$_2$, CH$_4$, N$_2$O, HFCs, PFCs and SF$_6$ excluding CO$_2$ emissions/removals from land use change and forestry.

Zimbabwe

Figure 1. CO$_2$ emissions by fuel

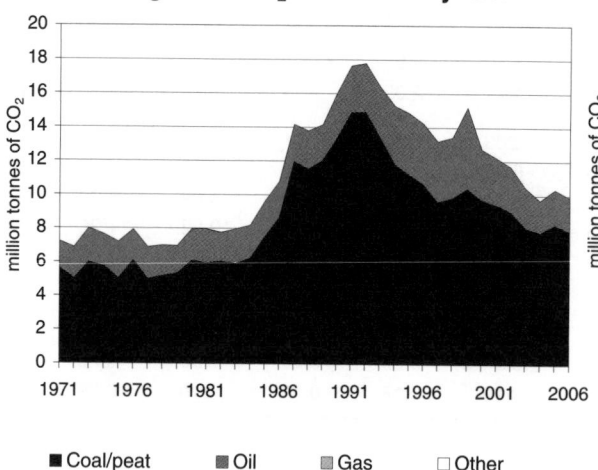

Figure 2. CO$_2$ emissions by sector

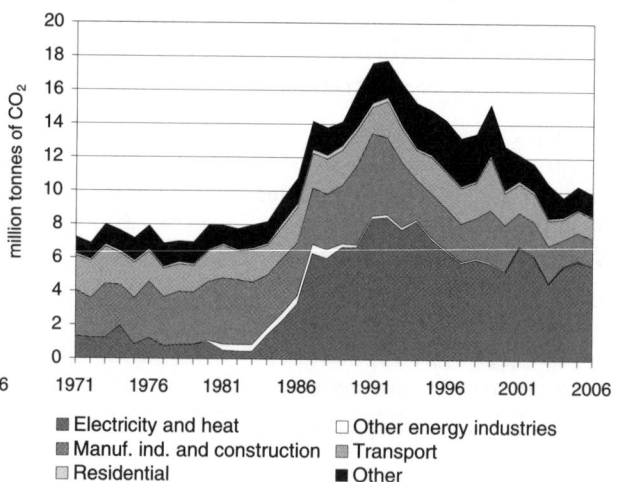

Figure 3. CO$_2$ emissions by sector

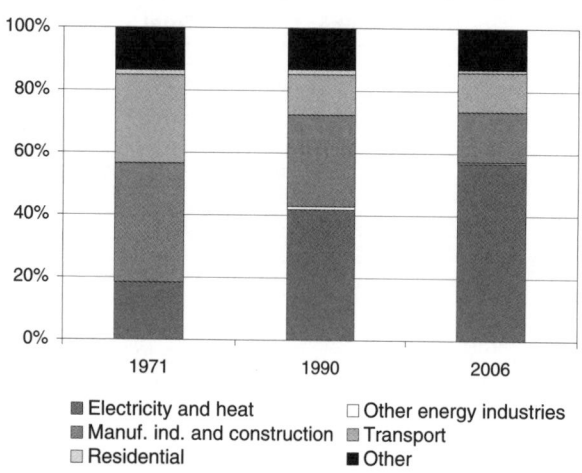

Figure 4. Reference vs Sectoral Approach

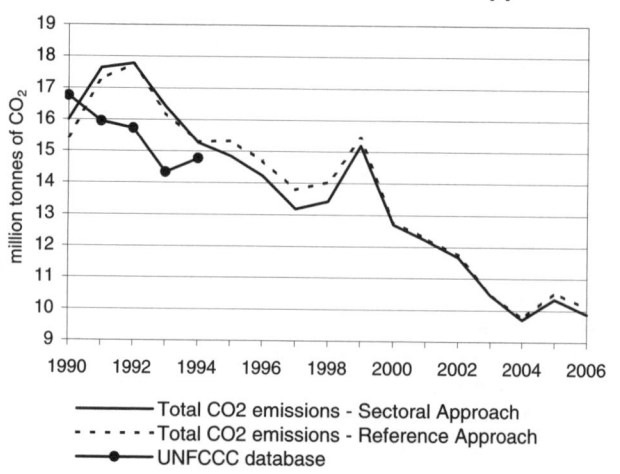

Figure 5. Electricity generation by fuel

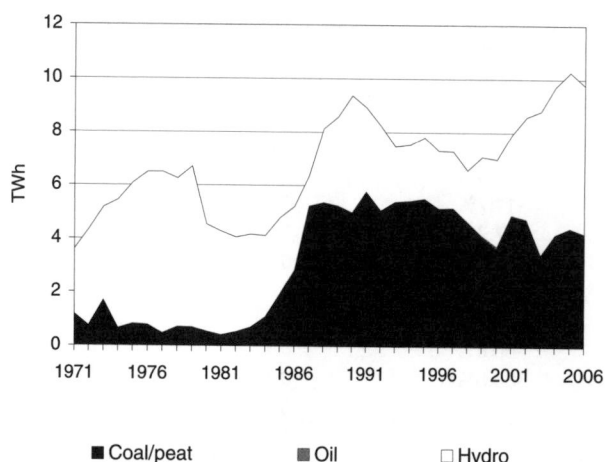

Figure 6. Key indicators

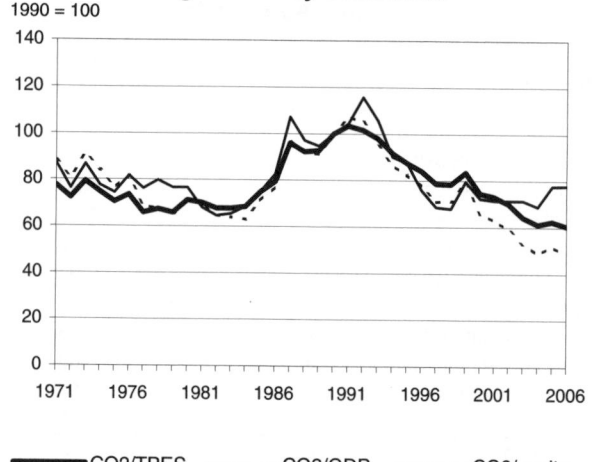

Zimbabwe

Key indicators

	1990	1995	2000	2003	2004	2005	2006	% change 90-06
CO$_2$ Sectoral Approach (Mt of CO$_2$)	16.00	14.85	12.71	10.47	9.70	10.36	9.88	-38.2%
CO$_2$ Reference Approach (Mt of CO$_2$)	15.44	15.33	12.79	10.53	9.76	10.58	10.09	-34.6%
TPES (PJ)	393	417	419	400	389	407	401	2.1%
TPES (Mtoe)	9.38	9.96	10.01	9.55	9.30	9.71	9.58	2.1%
GDP (billion 2000 US$ using exch. rates)	6.73	7.15	7.40	6.17	5.93	5.62	5.35	-20.6%
GDP (billion 2000 US$ using PPPs)	28.64	30.41	31.48	26.23	25.24	23.90	22.75	-20.6%
Population (millions)	10.49	11.79	12.66	12.94	13.03	13.12	13.23	26.1%
CO$_2$ / TPES (t CO$_2$ per TJ)	40.7	35.6	30.3	26.2	24.9	25.5	24.7	-39.5%
CO$_2$ / GDP (kg CO$_2$ per 2000 US$)	2.38	2.08	1.72	1.70	1.63	1.84	1.85	-22.2%
CO$_2$ / GDP (kg CO$_2$ per 2000 US$ PPP)	0.56	0.49	0.40	0.40	0.38	0.43	0.43	-22.2%
CO$_2$ / population (t CO$_2$ per capita)	1.53	1.26	1.00	0.81	0.74	0.79	0.75	-51.0%

Ratios are based on the Sectoral Approach.

2006 CO$_2$ emissions by sector

million tonnes of CO$_2$	Coal/peat	Oil	Gas	Other *	Total	% change 90-06
Sectoral Approach	**7.88**	**2.01**	-	-	**9.88**	**-38.2%**
Main activity producer elec. and heat	5.55	0.05	-	-	5.60	-16.2%
Unallocated autoproducers	-	-	-	-	-	-
Other energy industries	0.05	-	-	-	0.05	-67.3%
Manufacturing industries and construction	1.34	0.25	-	-	1.60	-66.1%
Transport	0.02	1.22	-	-	1.24	-40.2%
of which: road	-	*1.15*	-	-	*1.15*	*-12.9%*
Other sectors	0.91	0.49	-	-	1.40	-41.4%
of which: residential	*0.00*	*0.08*	-	-	*0.09*	*-64.5%*
Reference Approach	**8.08**	**2.01**	-	-	**10.09**	**-34.6%**
Diff. due to losses and/or transformation	0.33	-	-	-	0.33	
Statistical differences	- 0.12	0.00	-	-	- 0.12	
Memo: international marine bunkers	-	..	-	-	..	..
Memo: international aviation	-	*0.03*	-	-	*0.03*	*-89.9%*

* Other includes industrial waste and non-renewable municipal waste.

Key sources for CO$_2$ emissions from fuel combustion in 2006

IPCC source category	CO$_2$ emissions (Mt of CO$_2$)	% change 90-06	Level assessment (%) **	Cumulative total (%)
Main activity prod. elec. and heat - coal/peat	5.55	-16.9%	18.0	18.0
Manufacturing industries - coal/peat	1.34	-69.0%	4.3	22.3
Road - oil	1.15	-12.9%	3.7	26.0
Non-specified other sectors - coal/peat	0.91	-41.9%	3.0	29.0
Non-specified other sectors - oil	0.40	-30.3%	1.3	30.3
Manufacturing industries - oil	0.25	-31.5%	0.8	31.1
Residential - oil	0.08	-29.0%	0.3	31.4
Other transport - oil	0.07	-72.0%	0.2	31.6
Other energy industries - coal/peat	0.05	-67.3%	0.2	31.8
Main activity prod. elec. and heat - oil	0.05	x	0.2	31.9
Other transport - coal/peat	0.02	-96.1%	0.1	32.0
Memo: total CO$_2$ from fuel combustion	*9.88*	*-38.2%*	*32.0*	*32.0*

** Percent calculated using the total GHG estimate for CO$_2$, CH$_4$, N$_2$O, HFCs, PFCs and SF$_6$ excluding CO$_2$ emissions/removals from land use change and forestry.

PART III:

GREENHOUSE GAS EMISSIONS

PARTIE III :

EMISSIONS DE GAZ A EFFET DE SERRE

1. SHARES AND TRENDS IN GREENHOUSE GAS EMISSIONS

The information in Part III (with the exception of CO$_2$ emissions from fuel combustion) has been provided by Dr. Jos G.J. Olivier from the Netherlands Environmental Assessment Agency (PBL, formerly called MNP) based on the EDGAR 3.2 database, the 32FT2000 dataset and preliminary data from the EDGAR 4.0 dataset developed jointly by JRC and PBL as part of and in cooperation with the *Global Exchange and Interactions Activity* (GEIA) of IGBP and the *ACCENT Network of Excellence*. Country data have been provided for 1990, 1995, 2000 and 2005. Please see Chapter 2 for further details. Emission trends for gases and sources are provided in this discussion through 2005.

CO$_2$ emissions from fuel combustion constitute the majority of anthropogenic greenhouse (GHG) emissions. However, comprehensive analysis of emissions and emission trends considers other sources of CO$_2$ as well as other gases.

To complement work regarding the emissions of CO$_2$ from fuel combustion, the IEA elected to include the EDGAR data on other CO$_2$ sources and on five other greenhouse gases; CH$_4$, N$_2$O and the fluorinated gases (or "F-gases") HFCs, PFCs and SF$_6$. These gases are addressed by the Kyoto Protocol.

When considering comparative shares and trends in greenhouse gas emissions, data on gases and sources other than CO$_2$ from fuel combustion are much more uncertain. **Country-specific estimates of CO$_2$ from biomass burning and F-gas emissions are particularly difficult to ascertain.**

Shares by gas

The contribution of non-CO$_2$ gases to total emissions can be estimated by expressing the emissions of all the gases in CO$_2$-equivalent units. For a given gas, emissions expressed in mass are multiplied by its specific weighting factor, the Global Warming Potential (GWP), an estimate of the relative contribution of a kilogramme of that gas to global radiative forcing, as compared to the same amount of CO$_2$, integrated over a fixed period of time (e.g. 100 years).

The UN Framework Convention on Climate Change (UNFCCC), following the Second Assessment Report of the Intergovernmental Panel on Climate Change (IPCC), uses the 100-year GWPs of 21 for CH$_4$, 310 for N$_2$O and 23 900 for SF$_6$. For the most common HFCs, GWPs vary between 140 and 3 000 (1 300 for HFC-134a). For the by-product HFC-23, the GWP is 11 700. The GWPs for PFCs vary between 6 500 (CF$_4$) to 9 200 (C$_2$F$_6$). These two PFCs, the ones most commonly used, are also significant sources of by-product emissions. This chapter expresses all emission data in CO$_2$-equivalents using these GWP values.

In 2005, CO$_2$ contributed 74% of global greenhouse gas emissions, CH$_4$ about 15%, N$_2$O about 9% and the combined F-gases about 2% (Figure 1).

In 2005, the largest sources of GHG emissions were the sectors of energy (69%, mainly CO_2 fossil fuel use), and agriculture (14%, mainly CH_4 and N_2O, in comparable amounts). Other sources of GHGs were CO_2 from biomass burning (7%, mostly deforestation in Non-Annex I countries), and CO_2 from cement production (3%, of which 45% originated in China).

For **nitrous oxide** (N_2O), agriculture contributed 83% of emissions in 2005, mainly from synthetic fertilisers and animal waste dropped on soils (either as animal manure or by animals during grazing) and agricultural waste burning (see Figure 3). Another smaller source was N_2O from industry (5%), mostly in Annex I countries.

Figure 1. Global greenhouse gas emissions by gas/source in 2005

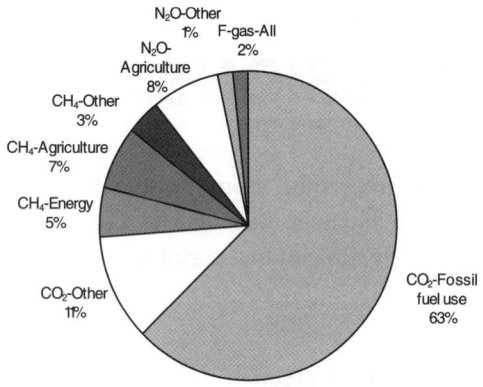

Figure 3. Global N₂O emissions in 2005

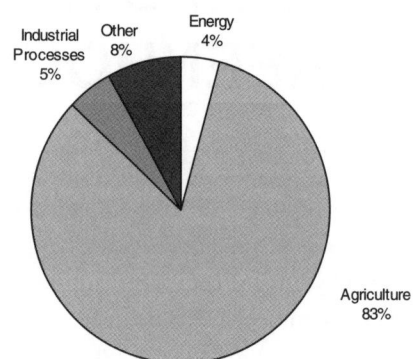

As seen in Figure 2, on an individual gas basis, the major global sources for **methane** (CH_4) in 2005 were:

- agriculture (44%), mainly from enteric fermentation by animals and animal waste, from rice cultivation and from savannah burning;

- energy production and transmission (34%), mainly from coal production and gas production and transmission;

- waste (18%), from landfills and wastewater.

For the **fluorinated gases** (see Figure 4), emissions are split between "use" and "by-products" because of the different ways they are produced. HFC use represented about half of the total in 2005, of which HFC 134a alone represented nearly half. Total by-product emissions of HFC contributed 19% and by-product emissions of PFCs another 10%. SF_6 use represented 16%, while PFC use represented the remaining 2%. Most F-gas emissions are emitted by Annex I countries.

Figure 2. Global CH₄ emissions in 2005

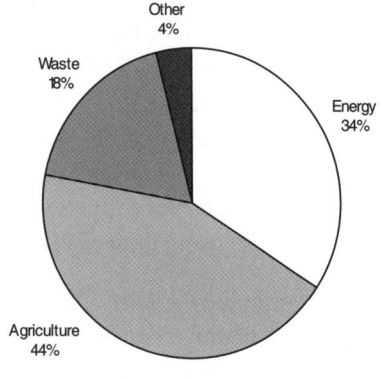

Figure 4. Global F-gas emissions in 2005

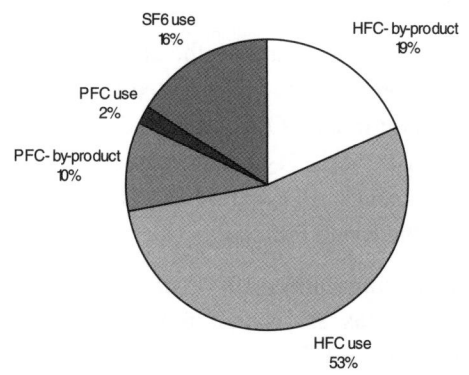

Shares by region

In 2005, most **methane** emissions originated in Non-Annex I regions such as Asia including China (37%) and Latin America (12%). Emissions from Annex I countries contributed 32%, largely driven by emissions from the former USSR and North America.

For methane, emissions from animals and their waste dominate sources in Latin America and South Asia, while emissions from rice cultivation are common in South, East and Southeast Asia. Coal production emissions are concentrated in East Asia (mainly China), North America, and EIT countries[1], while emissions from gas systems are concentrated in the former USSR and North America. Methane from landfills stems mainly from Annex I countries, whereas methane emissions from wastewater disposal originate predominantly in Non-Annex I countries.

Non-Annex I regions produced two-thirds of global **nitrous oxide** emissions in 2005: Asia including China (32%), Latin America (15%) and Africa (15%). N$_2$O emissions from Annex I countries contributed 32% to the global total, with most emissions originating in Annex II North America (13%) and Annex II Europe (10%).

Of all nitrous oxide sources, animal waste emissions occur predominantly in the Non-Annex I regions of Latin America, Africa and South Asia; N$_2$O from fertiliser use is largest in East Asia (mainly China) and Latin America followed by North America, Annex II Europe and South Asia (mainly India). N$_2$O emissions from crop production are largest in North America, Latin America, South Asia and East Asia. Industrial processes also emit significant volumes of N$_2$O.

The shares of Annex I countries in total CH$_4$ and total N$_2$O emissions were relatively low compared to their share in global CO$_2$ emissions (46%).

In 2005, most **fluorinated gas** emissions originated in Annex I countries, with Annex II North America contributing 39%, Annex II Europe 13%, Annex II Pacific 12% and the EIT countries 10%. Non-Annex I countries only contributed about 25% to global F-gas emissions.

Total greenhouse gas emission trends

Emissions related to fossil-fuels dominate the global trend in total greenhouse gas emissions. Between 1970 and 2005, global anthropogenic CO$_2$ emissions increased by about 90%, CH$_4$ by about 35%, N$_2$O by about 45% and the F-gases by about 500%. Total emissions of all greenhouse gases - weighted by their GWP - increased by about 80% since 1970.

According to the EDGAR 3.2 and 32FT2000 datasets, supplemented with preliminary EDGAR 4.0 data, global total greenhouse gas emissions increased by 26% during the 1990-2005 period (see Figure 5). A 29% growth in CO$_2$ emissions from fuel combustion drove much of this increase. Over the same period, CO$_2$ from biomass burning – based on satellite observations between 1997 and 2002 – is assumed to have increased by about 40%. Increases in CO$_2$ emissions from cement production (about 90%), N$_2$O emissions from agriculture (12%) and the F-gases (about 200%, mainly from HFC use) also contributed to the total increase. The F-gases, for which 1995 generally serves as base year, increased their share of global emissions from 0.8% in 1990 to 1.0% in 1995 and to 1.8% in 2005.

Between 2000 and 2005, emission trends for all sources except CO$_2$ emissions from fossil fuel combustion and fugitive sources and CO$_2$, N$_2$O and HFC-23 emissions from industrial processes were based on global total activity data and global emission factor trends (MNP, 2007).

---

1. In this chapter, economies in transition covers former USSR and Eastern European countries.

Figure 5. Trend in global greenhouse gas emissions 1970-2005

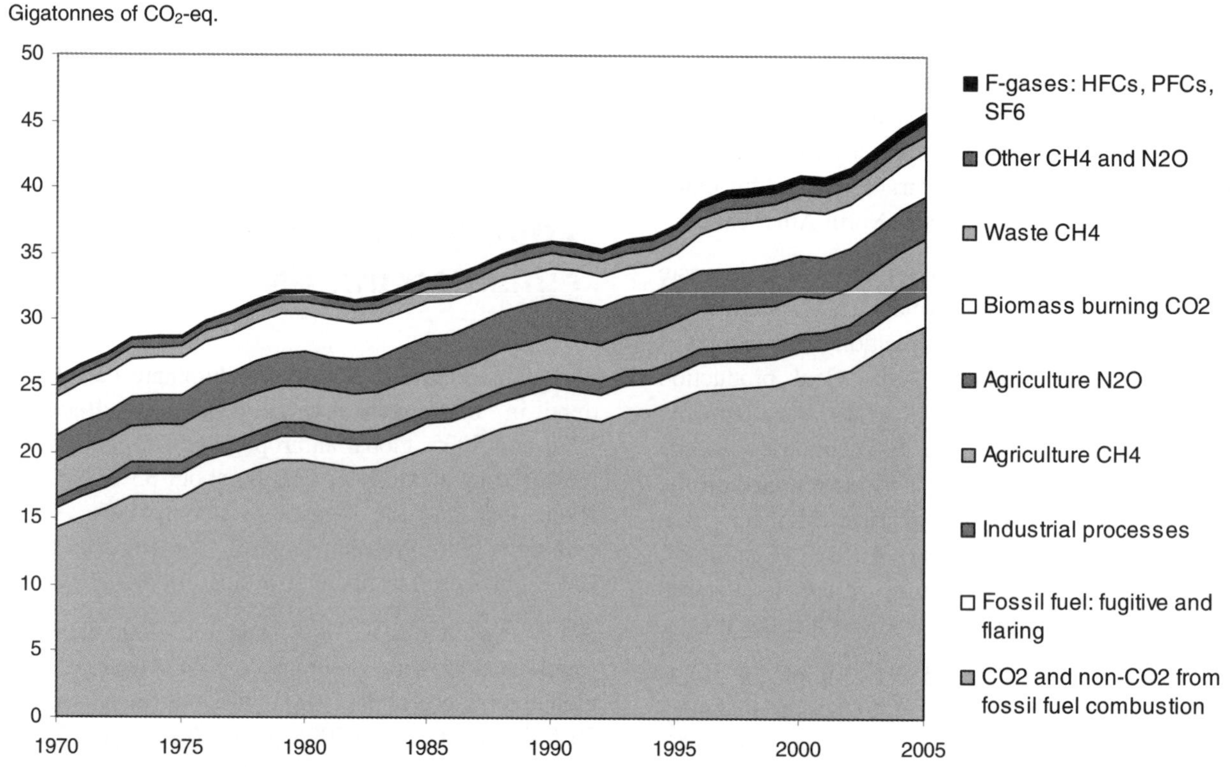
Gigatonnes of CO2-eq.
50
45
40
35
30
25
20
15
10
5
0
1970
1975
1980
1985
1990
1995
2000
2005
F-gases: HFCs, PFCs, SF6
Other CH4 and N2O
Waste CH4
Biomass burning CO2
Agriculture N2O
Agriculture CH4
Industrial processes
Fossil fuel: fugitive and flaring
CO2 and non-CO2 from fossil fuel combustion

Source: EDGAR 3.2, FT2000 and EDGAR 4.0.

CO_2 emission trends

Energy dominates the trend in CO_2 emissions, accounting for 85% of the global total CO_2 emissions in 2005. About 7% less in 1970, this share now varies between 90 and 99% in most Annex I countries. Within Non-Annex I countries, the energy share in CO_2 emissions varies more widely. Indeed, in some African, Latin American and Asian countries, it can be lower than 10%.

Over the 1990-2005 period, total fossil fuel combustion emissions of CO_2 increased about 29% worldwide (2% in Annex I countries and 86% in Non-Annex I countries). Emissions from electricity and heat production and from road transport dominated global trends. Between 1990 and 2005, CO_2 emissions from electricity and heat production increased by 27% for Annex II countries and by 64% in the rest of the world. Over the same period, road transport emissions rose 29% in Annex II countries and 62% in the other countries. By 2005, these two sectors together accounted for about 58% of global total CO_2 emissions from fuel combustion. The chapter "The Energy – Climate Challenge" at the beginning of the publication provides a more complete discussion of trends in energy-related CO_2 emissions.

In 2005, deforestation accounted for about 8% of CO_2 emissions (or 10% including unsustainable biofuel use). According to the FAO dataset of areas deforested in the 1970s and satellite observations in the late 1990s, the share of deforestation in global emissions was one-quarter less for the late 1990s than in 1970. In 2005, CO_2 emissions from cement production represent over 3% of total emissions worldwide. Between 1990 and 2005, CO_2 from cement production increased by about 100%, with the increase in China more than offsetting the decrease in the former USSR.

CH₄ emission trends

Between 1970 and 2005, global methane emissions rose about 35%. In the 1980s, emissions rose about 10%, driven by growth of emissions in the former USSR from gas production and transmission (see Figure 6). In addition, enteric fermentation by ruminants and wastewater disposal contributed to the increased emissions, particularly in Non-Annex I regions.

Emissions from rice cultivation are estimated to have decreased due to changes in types of rice and to other organic amendment practices. Furthermore, coal production shifted to incorporate more surface mining, which releases much less methane than underground mines. The economic decline of former USSR countries in the early 1990s strongly influenced global methane trends. The emissions from coal production, from gas transmission and from animals (enteric fermentation) decreased substantially between 1990 and 1995. It should be stressed, however, that detailed statistics for this region are rather uncertain in this period.

Based on country-specific trends of activity data and emission factors for the 1995-2000 period (Olivier et al., 2005; Van Aardenne et al., 2005) and global sector trends for 2000-2005 (MNP, 2007), global total methane emissions are estimated to have effectively increased by about 7% between 1990 and 2005.

Between 1990 and 2005, emissions in Non-Annex I countries increased about 25%, with the largest absolute growth ocurring in Asia, Latin America and Africa. Emissions in Annex I countries decreased by about 15%, mainly driven by the countries of the former Soviet Union. Annex II emissions as a whole decreased by almost 10%. Annex II Europe decreased by about 25%, mainly as a result of the policies of the United Kingdom and Germany. These two countries reduced their domestic coal production and increased methane recovery from coal mines, entailing a reduction in methane emissions from coal of more than 50%. In Annex II North America and Annex II Europe, methane emissions from landfills also decreased more than 15% due to enhanced methane recovery.

In the 1990s, emissions increased from gas production (particularly in the Middle East and North America), from waste handling sectors (particularly landfills in Latin America and wastewater in South Asia), from large-scale biomass burning in developing countries and from coal production in China. These increases were partly offset by decreases in fugitive emissions from coal production and methane emissions from animals in EIT countries.

Figure 6. Trends in global and regional CH₄ emissions

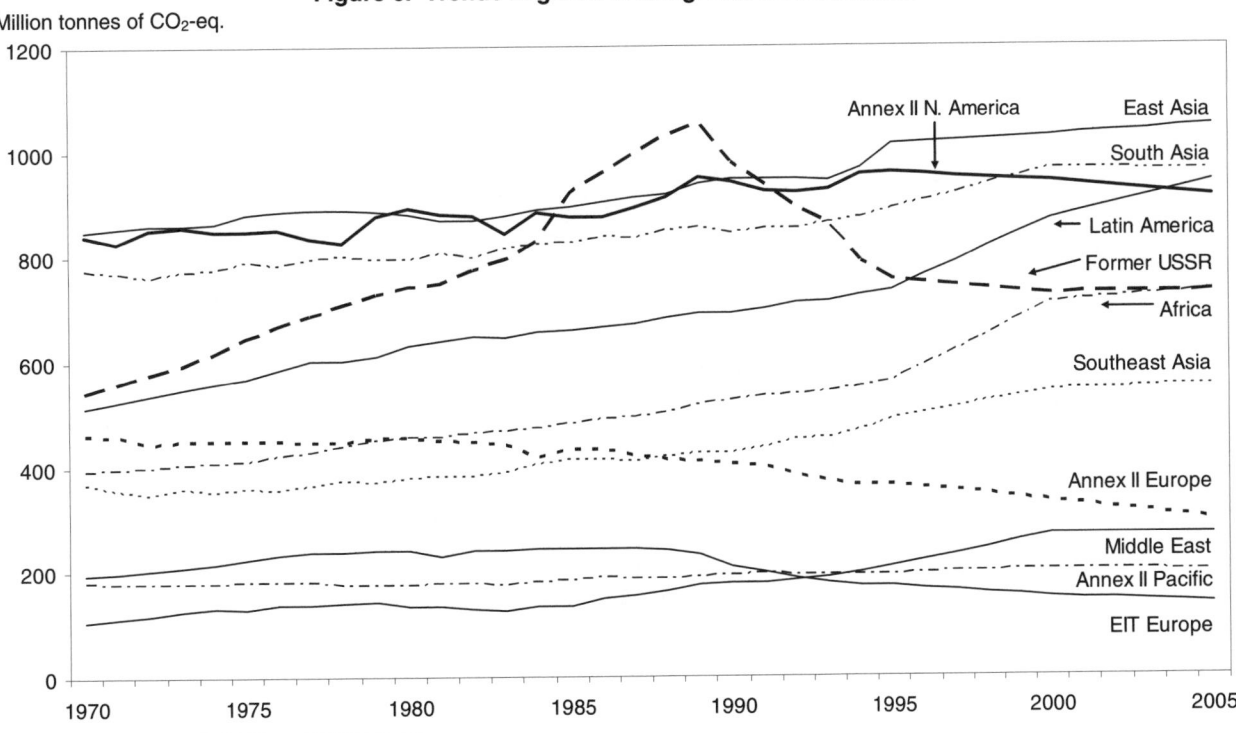

Source: EDGAR 3.2, FT2000 and EDGAR 4.0.

N_2O emission trends

Between 1970 and 2005, global emissions of N_2O increased by more than 50%. In the 1980s, increased use of synthetic fertilisers and manure from livestock caused agricultural emissions in South Asia and East Asia to increase by 2-3% annually. These regional emission trends continued into the 1990s (see Figure 7). Emissions from Latin America and Africa also increased in the 1990s, predominantly from the same sources and from deforestation.

In contrast, N_2O emissions from industrial processes have decreased by 30% during the 1980s. This decrease resulted from the gradual upgrade of global production facilities for nitric acid. In 1990 about 20% of the facilities were equipped for non-selective catalytic reduction limiting NO_x emissions while simultaneously reducing N_2O emissions.

During the 1980s, North America and Japan introduced catalytic converters in gasoline-fired cars to reduce emissions of precursors of tropospheric ozone. However, the catalytic converters contributed to the increase in N_2O emissions in these countries.

Based on country-specific trends of activity data and emission factors for the 1995-2000 period (Olivier et al., 2005; Van Aardenne et al., 2005) and global sector trends for 2000-2005 (MNP, 2007), global N_2O emissions are estimated to have increased by 14% between 1990 and 2005. The three-quarter reduction in industrial emissions from adipic acid manufacturing particularly limited this increase.

Between 1990 and 2005, emissions in Non-Annex I countries increased by about 30%, mainly in the agricultural sector in South Asia, East Asia and Latin America. This increase was partially offset by decreasing emissions in the former USSR countries (about -60%) and, to a lesser extent, in other EIT countries. In Annex II Europe, N_2O decreased by almost 10% since 1990, mainly due to emission abatement in the chemical industry and to a decrease in the use of nitrogen fertilisers.

When considering these trends, one should note that the uncertainties in annual emissions of most sources of N_2O are very large, e.g. the uncertainty for agricultural sources may sometimes exceed 100%.

Figure 7. Trends in global and regional N_2O emissions

Million tonnes of CO_2-eq

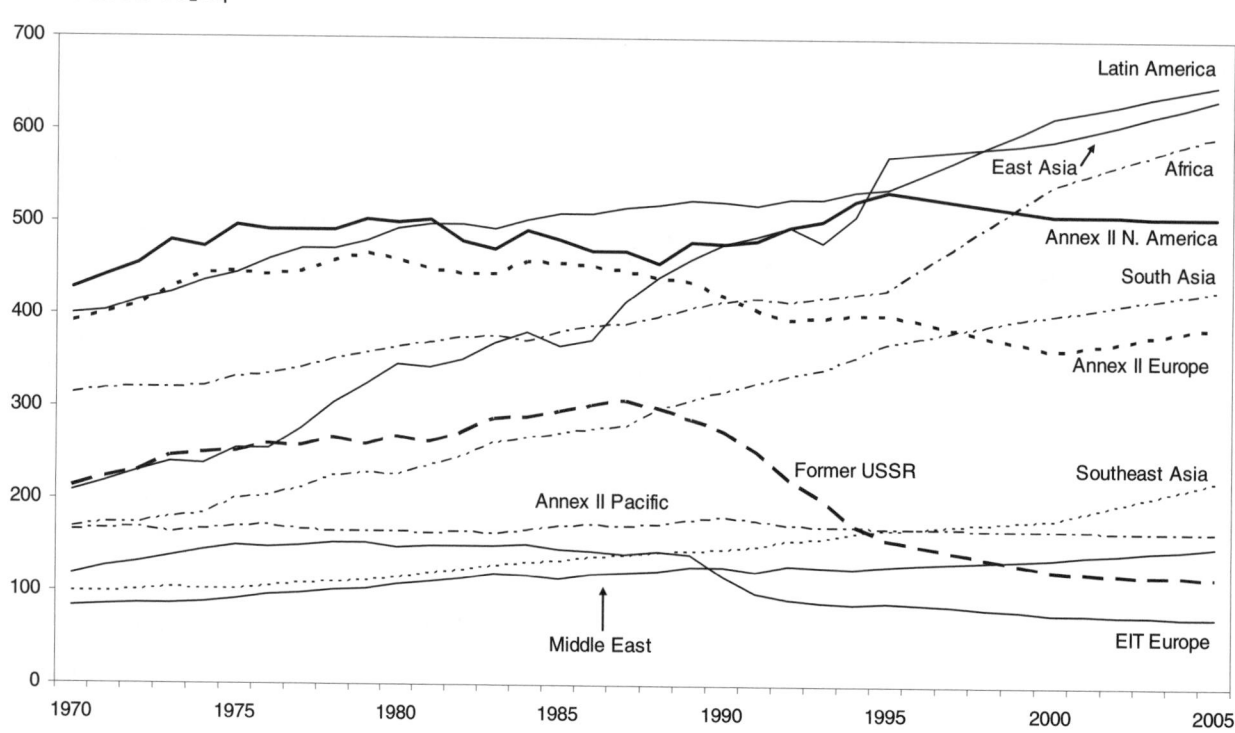

Source: EDGAR 3.2, FT2000 and EDGAR 4.0.

HFC, PFC and SF₆ emission trends

Between 1990 and 2005, the emissions of F-gases almost tripled, mainly due to an increase in HFC emissions: emissions of HFC in 2005 were more than 7 times higher than in 1990. During the same period, PFC emissions increased by 16% while SF₆ emissions increased by 10%. Annex I regions experienced large growth in F-gas emissions, with average increases on the order of 100-200%. In the Non-Annex I regions, total F-gas emission trends varied between 10% and 80%, with the largest absolute increases coming from China (included in East Asia).

Based on country-specific activity data and emission factor trends for the 1995-2005 period (Olivier et al., 2005; Van Aardenne et al., 2005) and global sector trends for 2000-2005 (MNP, 2007), global F-gas emissions increased more rapidly starting in 1995. The increase in HFC emissions (4 and ½ times higher) more than offset the 13% reduction in SF₆ emissions and the 6% reduction in PFC emissions. The reductions in SF₆ were mainly due to reductions in emissions from manufacture and use of switch-gear for the electricity sector. At present, global emissions of HFCs other than HFC-134a exceed emissions of HFC-134a, widely used for refrigeration and air-conditioning.

When considering these trends, one should note that the uncertainties in annual emissions of most sources of F-gases are very large, e.g. at a country level they may well exceed 100%. Therefore, the figures provided for individual countries should only be considered as order-of-magnitude estimates.

Figure 8. Trends in regional* F-gas emissions

Million tonnes of CO₂-eq.

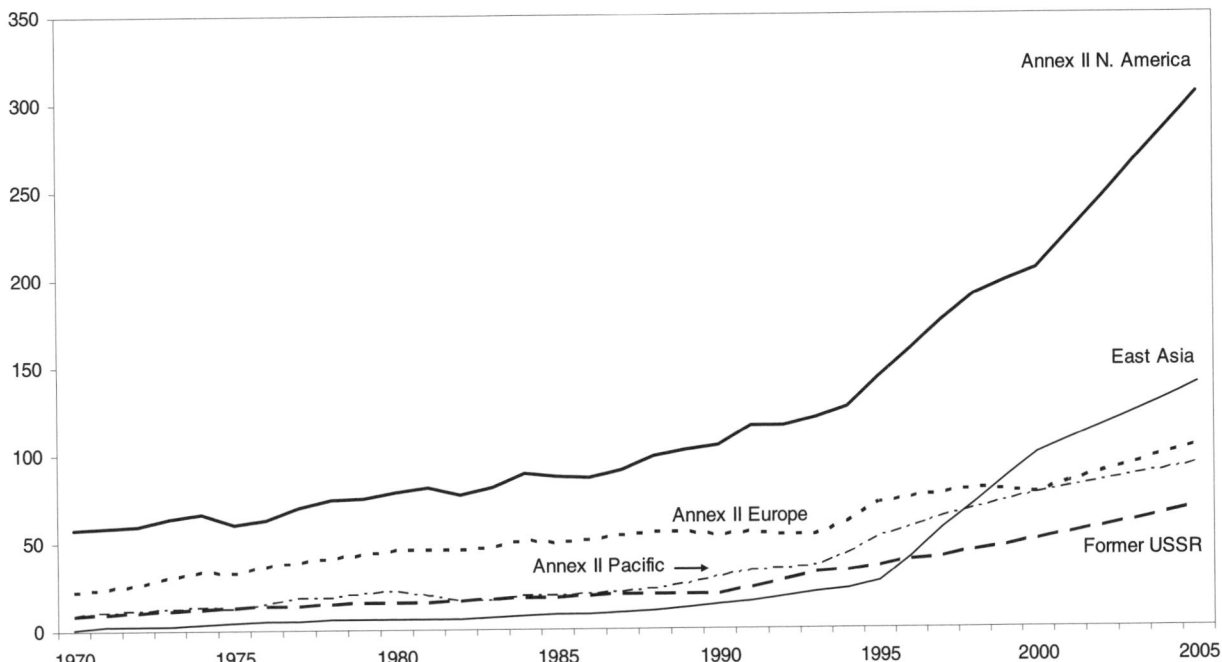

* Only regions with significant emissions of F-gases have been included in this figure.

Source: EDGAR 3.2, FT2000 and EDGAR 4.0.

2. SOURCES AND METHODS

When looking at GHG emission trends, limiting the emissions to CO$_2$ from fuel combustion means that the estimates give an incomplete picture of total greenhouse gas emissions. Therefore, to put the CO$_2$ emissions from fuel combustion into context, information has been added from the emissions model "EDGAR", developed by the Netherlands Environmental Assessment Agency (PBL, formerly known as MNP), the Joint Research Centre (JRC) and the Netherlands Organisation for Applied Scientific Research (TNO), to provide global anthropogenic emissions of greenhouse gases to be used as a reference database for policy applications.

The information in Part III (with the exception of CO$_2$ emissions from fossil fuel combustion) has been provided by Dr. Jos G.J. Olivier from PBL based on the EDGAR 3.2 and EDGAR 3.2 Fast Track 2000 (32FT2000) datasets, supplemented with prelimary EDGAR 4.0 data for selected sources. PBL and TNO (Dr. Tinus Pulles) are responsible for the calculation of the EDGAR 3.2 estimates and PBL and JRC (Dr. John A. van Aardenne) are responsible for the EDGAR 32FT2000 estimates for 2000 and for the EDGAR 4.0 data. Please see below for further details.

Background on PBL, JRC and TNO

The **Netherlands Environmental Assessment Agency** (PBL), is a government-funded agency that supports national and international policymakers by analysing spatial and social developments and environmental and spatial policies, which impact the human, plant and animal environment. PBL explores the future quality of this environment and advises on possible policy options and aims to contribute to the integrated spatial and ecological considerations for European and global policy-making. PBL provides independent integrated assessments on topics such as sustainable development, energy and climate change, biodiversity, spatial planning, transport, land use and air quality. PBL acts as an interface between science and policy and provides the Dutch government and international organisations such as EU/EEA, UN, OECD and the World Bank with sound, evidence-based assessments. PBL employs about 275 people and works in close collaboration with national and international partners, to assess future policies and the effects of policies already in place. PBL analyses interrelated environmental issues and their interaction with economic, spatial and social developments. This ranges from Dutch problems in the European and global context to global topics such as climate change, as well as European and global sustainability issues.

The **Joint Research Centre** (JRC) is a Directorate General of the European Commission (EC), which is a European centre of scientific and technical reference to support EU policies. JRC employs about 2000 people. The Institute for Environment and Sustainability (IES) is one of seven institutes of JRC, located in Ispra (Italy), whose aim is to provide scientific and technical support to European Union strategies for the protection of the environment, contributing to a sustainable development of Europe. The IES is engaged in five main fields of activity: global change; emissions, air quality and health; water; terrestrial and natural resources; and renewable energies. The IES covers the entire environmental sciences with particular competences in the field of earth observation and remote sensing. The main customers are several Directorates General of the European Commission. The IES has a core staff of about 250 and visiting staff of about 125.

The **Netherlands Organisation for Applied Scientific Research** (TNO) is an independent contract research organisation, whose main task is to apply technological knowledge with the aim of strengthening the innovative power of industry and government. TNO's activities are organised in five core areas with different areas of expertise, in which about 5000 people are employed. TNO Built Environment and Geosciences (TNO-BO) is an expert centre and contract research unit for businesses and government agencies in the field of sustainable development and environmentally oriented process innovation. This unit employs about 750 people, which are active in the following core areas: (a) sustainable development; (b) emissions to air and water and emissions from waste; (c) chain analysis to assess the effects at production and process levels; (d) evaluation of the environmental impact: the consequences of emissions for the environment; and (e) scenarios using scenario analysis. TNO has considerable expertise with emission inventories including national greenhouse gas inventories, CORINAIR and entity-level monitoring systems.

Both PBL and TNO participate in the Topic Centre on Air and Climate Change of the European Environmental Agency (EEA), whose aim is to support EU policy on air pollution and climate change, together with 12 other organisations in Europe. PBL has been designated to lead the Centre. TNO contributes significantly to the assessment of the EU data submissions from the member states to UNFCCC, UNECE/CLRTAP and the EU monitoring mechanism for greenhouse gas emissions. Both organisations were also involved in the work of the IPCC's National Greenhouse Gas Inventory Programme (NGGIP). The Institute for Environment and Sustainability of JRC cooperates with other European bodies like the European Environment Agency (EEA) and the European Space Agency (ESA), with authorities and other institutions in the EU member states and with international organizations such as UN-ECE, WHO, IPCC and NASA.

General note on EDGAR

The *Emission Database for Global Atmospheric Research,* in short the *EDGAR 3.2 system*, has been developed jointly by the Netherlands Organisation for Applied Scientific Research (TNO) and the Netherlands Environmental Assessment Agency (PBL, formerly known as MNP), which was part of the

National Institute of Public Health and the Environment (RIVM), with financial support from the Dutch Ministry of the Housing, Spatial Planning and Environment (VROM) and the Dutch National Research Programme on Global Air Pollution and Climate Change (NRP). The aim of the EDGAR system, which was started in 1992, is to provide global anthropogenic emissions of greenhouse gases CO$_2$, CH$_4$, N$_2$O, HFCs, PFCs and SF$_6$ and of precursor gases CO, NO$_x$, NMVOC and SO$_2$, per source category, both at country/region levels as well as on a 1x1 degree grid. It is meant to serve as a reference database for policy applications, e.g. to provide PBL's integrated global change model IMAGE 2 with emissions data and for assessments of potentials for emission reductions, as well as for scientific studies by providing gridded emissions as input for atmospheric models. The latter function is part of the *Global Exchange and Interactions Activity* (GEIA), that combines efforts to produce gridded inventories for all compounds relevant for the modeling activities within the *Analysis, Integration and Modeling of the Earth System* (AIMES) project of the *International Geosphere-Biosphere Programme* (IGBP) and of ACCENT, a Network of Excellence funded by the EC, 6th Framework Programme (FP6), Priority 1.1.6.3 Global Change and Ecosystems. EDGAR data have also been used in the Fourth Report of IPCC Working Group III, which was published in 2007 (IPCC, 2007).

Activity data were mostly taken from international statistical data sources and emission factors were selected mostly from international publications to ensure a consistent approach across countries. PBL, TNO and JRC have made all reasonable efforts to ensure that the information was generated correctly, but it is the responsibility of the EDGAR consortium to modify activity data when required to arrive at complete time series and for selecting the emission factors. It is stressed that the uncertainty in the resulting dataset at national level may be substantial, especially for methane and nitrous oxide, and even more so for the F-gases. The uncertainty is caused by the limited accuracy of international activity data used and in particular of emission factors selected for calculating emissions on a country level (Olivier et al., 1999, 2001; Olivier and Berdowski, 2001; Olivier, 2002; Olivier et al., 2005). However, since the methods used are comparable with IPCC methodologies (see below) and global totals comply with budgets used in atmospheric studies and the data were based on international information sources, this dataset provides a sound basis for comparability. For estimating the 2000 emissions a special Fast Track method was applied to estimate the emissions consistent with the detailed estimates made for 1995 (see below). For estimating the 2005 emissions per country an extrapolation method was applied to estimate for the most significant source categories the emissions consistent with the more detailed country-specific estimates made for 2000 (see below). Moreover, for some sources the country tables have been updated for all years using preliminary EDGAR 4.0 data: CO_2 emissions from fugitive sources (venting/flaring in oil and gas production) and industrial processes (cement and lime production) and N_2O and HFC-23 emissions from industrial processes.

Although this dataset has been constructed with great care, PBL, TNO and JRC do not accept any liability from using the data provided in this report including any inaccuracies or omissions in the data provided. For details on uncertainty and caveats identified in the dataset, as well as more detailed source category estimates, we refer to the EDGAR v4 website at http://edgar.jrc.it and EDGAR 3.2 FT2000 website at http://www.mnp.nl/edgar.

Source definitions

For carbon dioxide:

Fuel combustion refers to fossil fuel combustion and the unstored fraction of non-energy/feedstock use (IPCC Source/Sink Category 1A) estimated using the IPCC Sectoral Approach from the *Revised 1996 IPCC Guidelines*;

Fugitive refers to flaring of associated gas in oil and gas production (including indirect CO_2 from methane venting) (IPCC Source/Sink Category 1B);

Industrial Processes refers to cement production and lime production (IPCC Source/Sink Category 2); and

Other refers to direct emissions from tropical forest fires plus 10% of biofuel combustion emissions, which is the fraction assumed to be produced unsustainably (IPCC Source/Sink Category 5).

Please note that CO_2 emissions from decay (decomposition) of aboveground biomass that remains after logging and deforestation and CO_2 from peat fires and

decay of drained peat soils are not included. Also CO_2 from fossil fuel fires, notably coal fires, are excluded.

For methane:

Energy comprises production, handling, transmission and combustion of fossil fuels and biofuels (IPCC Source/Sink Categories 1A and 1B);

Agriculture comprises animals, animal waste, rice production, agricultural waste burning (non-energy, on-site) and savannah burning (IPCC Source/Sink Category 4);

Waste comprises landfills, wastewater treatment, human wastewater disposal and waste incineration (non-energy) (IPCC Source/Sink Category 6); and

Others includes industrial process emissions and tropical and temperate forest fires and other vegetation fires (IPCC Source/ Sink Categories 2 and 5).

For nitrous oxide:

Energy comprises combustion of fossil fuels and biofuels (IPCC Source/Sink Categories 1A and 1B);

Agriculture comprises fertiliser use (synthetic and animal manure), animal waste management, agricultural waste burning (non-energy, on-site) and savannah burning (IPCC Source/Sink Category 4);

Industrial Processes comprises non-combustion emissions from manufacturing of adipic acid and nitric acid (IPCC Source/Sink Category 2); and

Others includes N_2O usage, tropical and temperate forest fires and other vegetation fires, and human sewage discharge and waste incineration (non-energy) (IPCC Source/Sink Categories 3, 5 and 6).

For fluorinated gases:

HFC emissions comprise by-product emissions of HFC-23 from HCFC-22 manufacture and the use of HFCs (IPCC Source/Sink Categories 2E and 2F);

PFC emissions comprise by-product emissions of CF_4 and C_2F_6 from primary aluminium production and the use of PFCs, in particular for semiconductor manufacture (IPCC Source/Sink Categories 2C, 2E and 2F); and *SF₆ emissions* stem from various sources of SF_6 use, of which the largest is the use and manufacture of Gas Insulated Switchgear (GIS) used in the electricity distribution networks (IPCC Source/Sink Categories 2C and 2F).

Data sources and methodology for EDGAR 3.2 (1970-1995)

Energy / Fugitive / Biofuel

CO₂ emissions from fuel combustion were calculated by the International Energy Agency based on *Energy Balances of OECD Countries* and *Energy Balances of Non-OECD Countries* (IEA/OECD, 2005) using the Sectoral Approach from the *Revised 1996 IPCC Guidelines* (IPCC, 1997).

The data sources for **fugitive CO₂ emissions** and **CH₄ and N₂O from energy** are listed below. Data for fossil fuel production and use for 112 countries are taken from the IEA energy statistics for OECD and Non-OECD countries 1970-1995 (extended energy balances, in ktoe units) (IEA/OECD, 1997). For the countries of the former USSR a modified dataset was used to achieve a complete time series for the new countries for 1970-1995 of which the sum converges to the older dataset for the total former USSR. For another 71 countries, the aggregated IEA data for the regions 'Other America', 'Other Africa' and 'Other Asia' have been split using the sectoral IEA data per region and total production and consumption figures per country of hard coal, brown coal, gas and oil from UN energy statistics (UN, 1998). Note that the EDGAR 3.0 data are based on IEA statistics published in 1997 and thus may differ somewhat from more recent IEA datasets; in particular for countries of the former USSR since the IEA data have been updated considerably. Moreover, for estimating CH₄ emissions, hard coal and brown coal production data have been split into surface and underground mining based on various national reports.

Biofuel data for developing countries in 1990 have been based on Hall *et al.* (1994), with biofuel type splits from EDGAR 2.0 (Olivier et al., 1996, 1999), which includes vegetal waste used as fuel. Data for the time series 1970-1995 were based on the trend per country in urban and rural populations. However, for Latin American countries, biofuel statistics from OLADE were used (OLADE, 1999, personal communication). Fuelwood and charcoal consumption (also production) in Annex II and EIT countries were based on FAO (1998b), thereby replacing any IEA data for biofuel combustion in the 'Other sector' in these countries. For biofuel combustion in industry and power generation in Annex II countries, the data come from the IEA dataset (IEA, 1997). However these data were often not provided for all years and all countries.

Emission factors for CO₂, CH₄ and N₂O from fossil fuel production and use are described in Olivier et al. (1999), except for CO₂ from gas flaring/venting, which were based on data compiled by CDIAC (Marland, 1998, personal communication) from data collected by the U.S. Geological Survey and CH₄ from coal mining (Olivier, 2002). For N₂O from gasoline cars in road transport, the fraction of cars equipped with a catalytic converter was taken into account (based on data from Eurostat and others). The factors for biofuel combustion and charcoal production are based on a review made for the *Revised 1996 IPCC Guidelines*. For CO₂ from biofuels, it was assumed that 10% was produced unsustainably. For methane emissions from coal mining, the methane recovery for ten countries amounted to about 1 Tg in 1990 (of which about half was allocated to the United States and Germany). Recovery in 1995 was estimated at 2 Tg (Thakur et al., 1996; Bibler *et al.*, 1998; and national reports to Climate Convention; as described in Olivier, 2002).

Industrial processes

Production data of cement, nitric acid, iron and steel, and various chemicals were based on UN Industrial Commodity Statistics (UN, 1998). However, for many countries interpolations and extrapolations were necessary to arrive at complete time series per country for 1970-1995. Special attention had to be given to new EIT countries, in particular to former USSR countries, to match the older totals for the former countries. Cement production data were supplemented with data from the USGS. For adipic acid, production data were taken from SRI (1998) (smoothed and averaged); steel production was split into different technologies using data from IISI (1997), supplemented with UN data. For nitric acid, production data are primary based on UN statistics. However, since industry estimates of global total production are substantially higher, the data set has been expanded, first by adding countries not included in the UN nitric acid statistics, for which the amount of N in the production of nitrogen fertilisers according to FAO statistics was used as an estimate for nitric acid production, secondly by increasing the official UN production statistics of nitric acid by 40% to arrive at the estimated global industry total of about 55 Mt of HNO₃.

Global annual total production of HCFC-22 and consumption of HFC-134a are based on AFEAS (1997). Primary aluminium production statistics per country from UN (1998) were combined with smelters types characterised by one of five process types according to Aluminium Verlag (1998). Global consumption data of PFCs for semiconductors are taken from Mocella (1993) and for SF_6 per application from S&PS (1997) and Smythe (2000). These global totals were distribution over individual countries using related variables and statistics such as CFC consumption per country, per country semiconductor production and electricity use.

Emission factors for CO_2, CH_4 and N_2O are described in Olivier et al. (1999). Note that emissions of CO_2 from cement production are only a proxy for cement clinker production. The emission factors for NA production are based on IPCC (2000), assuming that in 1990, 20% of global total production is equipped with Non-Selective Catalytic Reduction (NSCR) technology, all in Annex II countries, and that for other plants the emission factor in 1990 is the average of the IPCC default for non-NSCR plants, whereas the emission factors for 1975 and before have been assumed to be equal to the IPCC default for "old plants". The emission factors for the F-gases were taken from various sources (Olivier and Bakker, 2000). We note that both the variables for distributing global total consumption and the emission factor may vary widely between different plants. This means the emissions at country level of the F-gases should more or less be considered as an order of magnitude estimate.

Solvent and other product use

For N_2O from the use of anaesthesia in hospitals, a fixed amount of N_2O per capita in Annex II countries was used, tentatively set at 25 g/cap/year, based on Kroeze (1994).

Agriculture

Activity data for livestock numbers were taken from FAO (2000), which were combined with information on animal waste generated per head in IPCC (1997) to estimate the total amount of animal waste. Net crop production was also taken from FAO (2000), with harvested areas of rice production split over different ecology types (rainfed, irrigated, deep water and upland) using the draft version of March 1977 the

RICE-ECO database of FAO (Van Gnuu, 1997, personal communication). In addition, the total harvested area of rice production in China was increased by 40%, due to recognition that official harvested rice area statistics of China are largely underestimating the actual area (Denier van der Gon, personal communication, 2000).

The fraction of agricultural waste associated with net crop production was based on a recent study by Smill (1999), whereas the fraction of agricultural residues burned on-site have been based on an analysis made by Bouwman (1997) and data reported in the Second National Communications. For Annex II countries 5% was assumed, for EIT countries 20% and for developing regions 30% - including amounts used as biofuel in developing countries, except for Annex II Europe, where a decreasing trend from 40% in 1970 to 5% in 1995 was assumed.

Emission factors for CH_4 and N_2O for enteric fermentation, animal waste (confined and outside), N-fixing crops were taken from the *Revised 1996 IPCC Guidelines*, where a 1x1 degree grid map for non-dairy cattle from Lerner et al. (1988) and the annual average temperature per grid cell from New et al. (1999) was used to calculate the fraction of the countries in the three climate zones (cold, temperate, warm). Other additional information, such as factors for indirect emissions of N_2O from agriculture, were taken from IPCC (1997) but were replaced by values updated in IPCC (2000). However, the emission factors for CH_4 from rice production in 1990 were taken from a review by Neue (1997); for the period 1970-1990 an emission factor improvement based on data of Denier van der Gon (1999, 2000) was assumed. For agricultural biomass burning the emission factors for CH_4 and N_2O were based on IPCC (1997).

Large-scale biomass burning

Biomass burning data (large-scale vegetation fires) were based on FAO reports providing ten-year or five-year averaged estimates per country of the change in forested areas for the 1970s, 1980s and the first half of the 1990s (FAO, 1993, 1995, 1998). Following the methodology described in the *Revised 1996 IPCC Guidelines*, these data were used as a proxy for estimating the amount of biomass being burned in tropical countries. Since there is no time-series data per country on this subject readily available, a smoothing function to construct a continuous time series per country for the 1970-1995 period was used. Tentatively, it was assumed that 50% of the biomass removed is burned. Given the uncertainty of this figure, the fraction oxidised is assumed to be 1. For Annex II and EIT countries, forest fire statistics for 1986-1997 have been included based on UN/ECE statistics of annual area burned (UN-ECE/FAO, 1996) combined with forest biomass densities per hectare from FAO (1995). There is a large uncertainty in the assumption for the carbon density of 0.5 and the fraction of carbon that is actually being burned of 0.5, and thus in the amount of burned carbon. The data selected, although often criticised for their limited accuracy are, however, well known and relatively well documented.

Emissions of CO$_2$ from deforestation and temperate vegetation fires are calculated according to IPCC (1997) and include only direct burning effects (thus no emissions due to decay of biomass). For large-scale biomass burning the emission factors for CH$_4$ and N$_2$O were also based on IPCC (1997), except for CH$_4$ from deforestation fires, where the GEIA value proposed by Veldt and Berdowski (1995) was used, and N$_2$O where post-burn emissions (Bouwman *et al.*, 1997) were used. The emission factors of CH$_4$ and N$_2$O used for temperate vegetation fires are the same that are used for other large-scale biomass burning activities. For accounting purposes, net CO$_2$ emissions from temperate vegetation fires and savannah fires have been assumed to be zero (organic carbon in a short cycle).

Waste handling

For solid waste generation, the 1970-1995 trend in activity data per country has been based on a fit with international waste generation figures per capita for 1990 - as published by IPCC and EPA and references mentioned therein - with per capita income per country. This fit was also used to estimate the activity data for 1990, for countries not mentioned in IPCC (1997) and in an EPA report by Adler (1994). Country-specific fractions of total MSW generated that is disposed of in landfills were based on IPCC (1997). For most countries it was assumed that this fraction has remained constant over time. Many other parameters, such as the fraction of Degradable Organic Carbon (DOC) were also based on the *Revised 1996 IPCC Guidelines*; in addition, many others were estimated through consultation of experts (Olivier et al., 2001). The methodology used for the calculation

of CH$_4$ emissions from landfills in EDGAR 3.0 is a *first order decay model* resembling the description in the *Revised 1996 IPCC Guidelines* of the more complex Tier 2 method, taking into account that the generation of methane from landfills is not an instantaneous process. Thus, the methodology calculates emissions in a specific year as the sum of delayed emissions from all MSW deposited in past years. A 40-year integration period was used, assuming emissions from MSW deposited more than 40 years ago are negligible. Based on national reports submitted to the Climate Convention, methane recovery amounts for eight OECD countries were included, amounting to about 2 Tg in 1990 and 4 Tg in 1995, about half of which was allocated to the United States (Olivier, 2002).

For domestic and industrial wastewater discharged in city sewers and subsequently treated by municipal Wastewater Treatment Plants (WWTP), an approach based on per capita organics loading and industrial wastewater generation was used, selected by Doorn et al. (1997), since information on domestic wastewater generation rates are very sparse and because it is essentially the same as the default IPCC methodology (IPCC, 1997). Estimates were based on population data from the UN (1999), whereas wastewater generation was based on industrial production statistics of the United Nations (1998) combined with wastewater generation rates of Doorn et al. (1997). It is well known that in OECD countries, which cover about 60% of this source, a large fraction of the methane generated in municipal WWTPs is generally recovered. Therefore methane recovery for municipal WWTPs in Annex II countries was assumed to be 75%, effectively reducing the total emissions of OECD countries in 1990 by 0.6 Tg.

For untreated domestic wastewater handling, treatment and disposal emission factors and other factors were based on Doorn et al. (1999), who distinguished disposal in septic tanks, latrines and sewers. The later was divided into sewage with municipal wastewater treatment and open sewers. Emission factors for CH$_4$ from domestic wastewater in latrines or open pits and septic tanks and from stagnant open sewers (untreated wastewater) were based on Doorn et al. (1999) following the same approach as for domestic WWTPs, but distinguishing national population into three population groups: rural and urban, with urban population further split into high and low income groups. For each of four municipal wastewater disposal types, region- and country-specific utilisation fractions were estimated for each of these three population categories. The emissions from open sewers were increased by 25% to account for the global amount of industrial wastewater annually discharged in municipal sewers. Globally, according to the assumptions of Doorn et al. (1999) this source of CH$_4$ appears to be as large as emissions from landfills.

For N$_2$O from human sewage the default IPCC methodology was used, with protein intake per country for various years from FAO (2000); for the small emissions of N$_2$O from DOC in wastewater from the meat processing industry the emission factor provided by Doorn et al. (1997) was used.

In addition, for domestic waste burning (i.e. by households for non-energetic purposes) a fixed amount per capita burned per year *by urban households* in less developed countries was used. In rural areas of the less-developed countries, it was assumed that there was no uncontrolled burning in addition to the agricultural residue burning and biofuel use that is already accounted for in other source categories. In contrast, for industrialised countries, it was assumed that domestic waste burning only occurs in rural areas, where waste incineration regulation is less well controlled.

Data sources and methodology for EDGAR 32FT2000 (2000)

In general, activity data for the year 2000 have been included following the EDGAR 3.2 method as described above. The selection of emission factors was based on the assumption of unchanged control technologies compared to 1995, resulting in application of the emission factors as included in version 3.2. However, to take into account emission reductions that have occurred due to control measures implemented since 1995, "implied" emission factors have been used for those countries for which information on emission reductions were available (mainly countries that were members of the OECD in 1990; hereafter referred to as "OECD"). Implied emission factors are constructed by division of annual emissions by activity selected for the extrapolation. In general these emission factors have been taken from the CRF emission data files which are part of the National Inventory Reports (NIR) to the UNFCCC (Olivier et al., 2005; Van Aardenne et al., 2005).

Energy / Fugitive / Biofuel

Activity data for **fossil fuel production and use** are taken from IEA statistics for OECD and Non-OECD (IEA/OECD, 2003) countries. For countries included in the aggregated IEA data for the three "other" regions the totals have been split into country data using population density figures from FAO (2005a). For other countries, for which no data are presented in the IEA statistics (mostly very small islands), the EDGAR 3.2 1990-1995 trend has been extrapolated to the year 2000. Data on hard coal and brown coal production have been split into surface and underground mining as included in EDGAR 3.2. Discontinuities with the EDGAR 3.2 data may be found due to (i) updated IEA energy statistics, in particular for former USSR countries and specific developing countries and (ii) distribution of country data included in the "other regions" of IEA using population statistics instead of data from the UN statistics applied in EDGAR 3.2.

Emission factors for 2000 have in general been taken from the EDGAR 3.2 data for 1995, except in OECD countries for which control measures have been included using so-called implied emission factors. This refers in particular to non-CO$_2$ combustion emissions from road transport, industrial combustion and power generation. Exceptions to the above-mentioned activity data and emission factors are gas flaring emissions, methane emissions from fossil fuel production and international shipping emissions. Gas flaring emissions have been calculated by combining the EDGAR 3.2 values for 1995 with the 1995-2000 CO$_2$ trends from CDIAC (Marland et al., 2003). For some countries, for which CDIAC did not report CO$_2$ flaring emissions in the year 2000 and for which it seems unrealistic that gas flaring did not occur (e.g. Nigeria, Norway and China), constant 1995 emissions have been applied. To calculate methane emissions from fossil fuel production and distribution country-specific trends reported to the UNFCCC have been used.

For **biofuel combustion** in the residential/commercial sector, to maintain consistency with the 1995 emissions data, the same trend estimation procedure was used as for EDGAR 3.2: for industrialised countries the total population trend was used; for developing countries the weighted trends of rural and urban population (see Olivier et al., 2001). However, for biofuel use in industry and power generation for the year 2000, data from IEA statistics for OECD and Non-OECD countries were used (IEA/OECD, 2003). Due to lack of data, for charcoal production and biofuel use in road transport, constant 1995 values have been applied. Under the assumption of unchanged control technologies in the production and use of biofuels, emission factors have been assumed to remain constant from 1995 to 2000.

Industrial processes / Solvent use

Production data on iron and steel (by technology) have been taken from IISI (2004). Production data of the non-ferrous industry are based on USGS (2004), while for PFCs from primary aluminium production the fractional contribution of different processes from EDGAR 3.2 has been applied. Industrial production data for the chemical industry are from the UN commodity statistics (UN, 2004). For those countries where no UN data were available, constant 1995 values are assumed. An exception was made for N$_2$O emissions from adipic acid and nitric acid manufacture from OECD countries, which were extrapolated from 1995 using the country-specific 1995-2000 trends reported to the UNFCCC. For the other industrial source categories the following data sources have been used: cement (USGS, 2004), paper and pulp (FAO, 2005b), food (FAO, 2005b) or constant values for countries with no data in FAO. For NMVOC from solvents, the trend in total population was used (FAO, 2005b). Emission factors have been assumed to remain constant from 1995 to 2000 except for country-specific trends of N$_2$O emissions from adipic acid manufacture in OECD countries which showed an average emission decrease of about 75%.

For the largest sources of HFC, PFC and SF$_6$ emissions, country-specific or OECD-average trends reported to the UNFCCC were used for OECD countries, while reported global total emissions, production or consumption trends were used as a proxy for Non-OECD countries. HFC-23 byproduct emissions from HCFC-22 manufacturing from OECD countries were extrapolated from 1995 using the country-specific 1995-2000 trend reported to the UNFCCC. For Non-OECD countries the global total HCFC-22 production trend reported by AFEAS (2005) of 0% was used. Emissions from HFC-134a use were dealt with in the same way, using a 1995-2000 trend factor of 2.7 for non-reporting OECD countries. For Non-OECD countries the global total HFC-134a emissions trend reported by AFEAS was used. For emissions from

other HFC use from OECD countries the same procedure was followed. PFC by-product emissions from aluminium production from OECD countries were extrapolated from 1995 using the country-specific 1995-2000 emission trend reported to the UNFCCC. For Non-OECD countries the 1995 emissions were extrapolated using the 1995-2000 trend of country-specific primary aluminium production reported by USGS. PFC emissions from semiconductor manufacture and from PFC use as solvent from OECD countries were extrapolated from 1995 using the country-specific 1995-2000 trend reported to the UNFCCC; for all other countries the reported OECD total trend was used. PFC emissions from all other sources were assumed to remain constant. SF$_6$ emissions from semiconductor manufacture and from use in magnesium production from OECD countries were extrapolated from 1995 using the country-specific 1995-2000 trend reported to the UNFCCC. For Non-OECD countries the global total consumption trend reported by RAND was used (Smythe, 2004), except for magnesium production where the UNFCCC trend for OECD countries was used as a proxy.

Agriculture

To calculate N$_2$O emissions from fertiliser application, the IFA nitrogen fertiliser consumption trend (FAO, 2005b) and the amount of animal waste used for fertiliser scaled with the livestock numbers from FAO (2005a) have been used. CH$_4$ emissions from rice cultivation and from ruminants are based on total harvest area trends and total cattle trend data, respectively, from FAO (2005b). Nitrous oxide emissions from confined animal waste have also been scaled to total cattle trend data from FAO (2005b). N$_2$O emissions from crop production and crop residues have been scaled using selected FAO crop data (FAO, 2005a). Indirect N$_2$O emissions from atmospheric deposition and from leaching and run-off are scaled to the trend in the sum of N$_2$O emissions from fertiliser application, confined animal waste and crop residues. Emissions from agricultural waste burning are discussed under large-scale biomass burning. All emission factors have been assumed to remain constant from 1995 to 2000.

Large-scale biomass burning

Large-scale biomass burning emissions have been taken from the *Global Fire Emissions Database* (GFED; Van der Werf et al., 2003), except for agricultural waste burning which was scaled to trends in the production of selected FAO crops (EDGAR 3.2 method). The ecosystem database of Olson et al. (1983) was aggregated into five classes: shrub/bush, forest, agriculture and other (e.g. urban regions/deserts). GFED 1.0 data in agricultural regions were attributed to savannah and grassland fires. There is an insignificant overlap with the EDGAR category for agricultural waste burning, which is presented separately with constant 1995 emissions. In addition, for N_2O the indirect post-burn emissions from tropical forest fires have been extrapolated using the calculated 1995-2000 trend in direct N_2O emissions from that source category. Given the structural difference in both activity data and emission factors of the GFED-based emission dataset and EDGAR 3.2 biomass burning emissions, four variants of large-scale biomass burning are included in the dataset. This allows for comparison with EDGAR 3.2 estimates for earlier years (Van Aardenne et al., 2005). Here the GFED with multi-year (1997-2002) averaged activity data and EDGAR 3.2 emission factors were used for 2000.

Waste handling

Landfill emissions (net CH_4) from OECD countries and a few EIT countries were extrapolated from 1995 onwards using the country-specific 1995-2000 trends reported to the UNFCCC. For Non-OECD countries, where methane recovery is assumed to be insignificant, the 1990-1995 emission trend was extrapolated since annual landfill emissions are less sensitive to recent changes in activity data as they are the sum of emissions from waste which was deposited several decades ago. Wastewater treatment and disposal emissions of net CH_4 have been extrapolated using the 1995-2000 trend of total national population, except for wastewater treatment by OECD countries for which country-specific 1995-2000 trends reported to the UNFCCC were used or the reported OECD total trend. N_2O from wastewater treatment from OECD countries and a few EIT countries was extrapolated using the country-specific 1995-2000 trend reported to the UNFCCC. For Non-OECD countries the 1995 emissions were extrapolated using the 1995-2000 trend of total national population. N_2O from wastewater disposal was extrapolated using the 1995-2000 trend of total national population. Finally, emissions from uncontrolled waste incineration were kept constant.

Data sources and methodology for 2005 (EDGAR 4.0, 1970-2005)

In general, emissions for the year 2005 have been estimated using either preliminary EDGAR 4.0 data for selected sources or extrapolations from 2000 for main sources. The latter was done using reported emission trends for Annex I countries (e.g. coal mining, landfills, F-gases), trends in key activity data (e.g. cattle numbers for livestock, population for landfills), and extrapolation using the 1995-2000 trend (N_2O from energy and agriculture). The smaller sources have been assumed to remain at the 2000 level (e.g. the three "Other" subcategories and SF_6 emissions).

To take into account emission reductions that have occurred due to control measures implemented since 2000, officially reported emissions were used for Annex I countries (mainly countries that were members of the OECD in 1990). These emission trends have been taken from the CRF emission data files which are part of the National Inventory Reports (NIR) to the UNFCCC.

For EDGAR 4.0 the same method as for EDGAR 3.2 as described above was applied, however, taking more explicitly into account changes of emission factors over time due to the application of control technology or other emission reduction measures.

Preliminary EDGAR 4.0 data have been used in the country tables for all years for fugitive CO_2 emissions from flaring/venting in oil and gas production (including indirect CO_2 from venting of methane) and for industrial processes: CO_2 emissions from cement and lime production, N_2O emissions from adipic acid and nitric acid production and HFC-23 by-product emissions from HCFC-22 manufacture.

We note that new EDGAR 4.0 estimates for all sources have been made for all years, some of which were not yet available at the time of printing of this report. For final data of the EDGAR 4.0 dataset, including more detailed source category estimates per country for the period 1970-2005 we refer to the EDGAR v4 website at http://edgar.jrc.it.

References

Adler, M.J. (1994). International anthropogenic methane emissions: estimates for 1990. EPA, Washington, DC, USA, EPA report no. 230-R-93-010, January 1994.

AFEAS (1997). Production, sales and atmospheric release of fluorocarbons through 1995. Alternative Fluorocarbons Environmental Acceptability Study (AFEAS) Program Office, Washington DC, USA. Also see: *http://www.afeas.org/production_and_sales.html*

AFEAS (2005). Production and sales data available through 2003. At website: *http://www.afeas.org/prodsales_download.html* on July 2005.

Aluminium Verlag (1998). Primary Aluminium Smelters and Producers of the World, Vol. 2, Compiled by R. Pawlek. Aluminium Verlag, Düsseldorf, Germany.

Bibler, C.J., Marshall, J.S. and R.C. Pilcher (1998). Status of worldwide coal mine methane emissions and use. *Int. J. of Coal Geology*, **35**, 283-310.

Bouwman, A.F., Lee, D.S., Asman, W.A.H., Dentener, F.J., Van Der Hoek, K.W. and J.G.J. Olivier (1997). A Global High-Resolution Emission Inventory for Ammonia, *Global Biogeochemical Cycles*, 11:4, 561-587.

Denier van der Gon, H. (1999). Changes in CH$_4$ emission from rice fields from 1960 to 1990s, The declining use of organic inputs in rice farming. *Global Biogeochemical Cycles*, 13, 1053-1062.

Denier van der Gon, H. (2000). Changes in CH$_4$ emission from rice fields from 1960 to 1990s, Impacts of modern rice technology. *Global Biogeochemical Cycles*, 14, 61-72.

Doorn, M.R.J., Strait, R.P., Barnard, W.R. and B. Eklund (1997). Estimates of global greenhouse gas emissions from industrial and domestic waste water treatment. Report no. NRMRL-RTP-086. R 8/18/97. Pechan & Ass., Durham.

Doorn, M.J. and D.S. Liles (1999). Quantification of methane emissions and discussion of nitrous oxide, and ammonia emissions from septic tanks, latrines, and stagnant open sewers in the world. EPA, Washington DC, USA. EPA report EPA-600/R-99-089, October 1999.

FAO (1993). Forest resources assessment 1990; Tropical countries. FAO, Rome. Report FP-112.

FAO (1995). Forest resources assessment 1990; Global analysis. FAO, Rome. Report FP 124.

FAO (1998). State of the Worlds Forests 1997. FAO, Rome.

FAO (1998b). FAOSTAT Forestry Data. Data downloaded from *http://faostat.fao.org*.

FAO (2000). FAOSTAT Agricultural Data.

FAO (2005a) FAOSTAT Forest Data (Annual time series on forested wood products).

FAO (2005b) FAOSTAT Agricultural Data (Annual time series on population).

Hall D.O., Rosillo-Calle F. and Woods J. (1994). Biomass utilization in households and industry: energy use and development, *Chemosphere* 29, 1099-1119.

IEA/OECD (1997). Energy Balances of OECD and Non-OECD Countries on-line data service, 1997. At *http://data.iea.org*.

IEA/OECD (2003). Energy Balances of OECD and Non-OECD Countries on-line data service, 2003. At *http://data.iea.org*.

IEA/OECD (2005). Energy Balances of OECD and Non-OECD Countries on-line data service, 2004. At *http://data.iea.org*.

IISI (1997). 1996 Steel Statistical Yearbook, International Iron and Steel Institute, Brussels.

IISI (2004). Steel statistical yearbook 2003. International Iron and Steel Institute, Brussels.

IPCC (1997). Revised 1996 IPCC Guidelines for National Greenhouse Gas Inventories. IPCC/OECD/IEA, Paris.

IPCC (2007). Climate Change 2007: Mitigation. Contribution of Working Group III to the Fourth Assessment Report of the Intergovernmental Panel on Climate Change [B. Metz, O.R. Davidson, P.R. Bosch, R. Dave, L.A. Meyer (eds)], Cambridge University Press, Cambridge, United Kingdom and New York, NY, USA. Available online at: *http://www.ipcc.ch/ipccreports/ar4-wg3.htm*.

IPCC (2000). Good Practice Guidance and Uncertainty Management in National Greenhouse Gas Inventories, IPCC-TSU NGGIP, Japan.

Kroeze, C. (1994). Nitrous oxide (N$_2$O). Emission inventory and options for control in the Netherlands. RIVM, Bilthoven. Report no. 773001 004.

Lerner, J., Matthews, E. and Fung, I. (1988). Methane emission from animals: a global high resolution database, *Global Biogeochemical Cycles* 2, 139-156.

Marland, G., T.A. Boden, and R. J. Andres. (2003). Global, Regional, and National Fossil Fuel CO$_2$ Emissions. In *Trends: A Compendium of Data on Global Change*. Carbon Dioxide Information Analysis Center (CDIAC), Oak Ridge National Laboratory, U.S. Department of Energy, Oak Ridge, Tenn., U.S.A.

MNP (2007). Environmental Data Compendium 2007. At *http://www.mnp.nl/mnc/index-en.html*.

Mocella, M.T. (1993). Production and Uses of C$_2$F$_6$. Proceedings of the *Workshop on Atmospheric effects, origins, and options for control of two potent greenhouse gases: CF$_4$ and C$_2$F$_6$*. US EPA, Global Change Division, April 21-22, Washington, D.C.

Neue, H.U. (1997). Fluxes of methane from rice fields and potential for mitigation. *Soil Use and Management*, 13, 258-267.

New, M.G., Hulme, M. and P.D. Jones (1999). Representing 20th century space-time climate variability. I: Development of a 1961-1990 mean monthly terrestrial climatology. *J. Climate*, 12, 829-856.

Olivier, J.G.J. and J. Bakker (2000). Historical global emission trends of the Kyoto gases HFCs, PFCs and SF$_6$. Proceedings of *"Conference on SF$_6$ and the Environment: Emission Reduction Strategies"*, November 2-3, San Diego. EPA, Washington DC, USA. Conference Proceedings published at *http://www.epa.gov/highgwp/electricpower-sf6/conf/ agenda_00.html*.

Olivier, J.G.J., Bouwman, A.F., Van der Maas, C.W.M., Berdowski, J.J.M., Veldt, C., Bloos, J.P.J., Visschedijk, A.J.H., Zandveld, P.Y.J. and Haverlag, J.L. (1996). Description of EDGAR Version 2.0: A set of global emission inventories of greenhouse gases and ozone depleting substances for all anthropogenic and most natural sources on a per country basis and on 1°x1° grid. RIVM, Bilthoven, December 1996. RIVM report nr. 771060 002 / TNO-MEP report nr. R96/119.

Olivier, J.G.J., Bouwman, A.F., Berdowski, J.J.M., Veldt, C., Bloos, J.P.J., Visschedijk, A.J.H., Van der Maas, C.W.M. and P.Y.J. Zandveld (1999). Sectoral emission inventories of greenhouse gases for 1990 on a per country basis as well as on 1° x 1°. *Environmental Science & Policy*, 2, 241-264.

Olivier, J.G.J., Berdowski, J.J.M., Peters, J.A.H.W., Bakker, J., Visschedijk, A.J.H. and J.P.J. Bloos (2001). Applications of EDGAR. Including a description of EDGAR 3.2: reference database with trend data for 1970-1995. RIVM, Bilthoven. RIVM report 773301 001/NRP report 410200 051. Available online at: *http://www.rivm.nl/bibliotheek/rapporten/ 410200051.html*.

Olivier, J.G.J. and J.J.M. Berdowski (2001). Global emissions sources and sinks. In: Berdowski, J., Guicherit, R. and B.J. Heij (eds.), *The Climate System*, pp. 33-78, A.A. Balkema Publishers/Swets & Zeitlinger Publishers, Lisse, The Netherlands, ISBN 90 5809 255 0.

Olivier (2002). *On the Quality of Global Emission Inventories, Approaches, Methodologies, Input Data and Uncertainties*, Thesis Utrecht University, Utrecht, ISBN 90 393 3103 0. Available online at: *http://www.library.uu.nl/digiarchief/dip/diss/2002-1025- 131210/inhoud.htm*.

Olivier, J.G.J., Van Aardenne, J.A., Dentener, F., Pagliari, V., Ganzeveld, L.N. and J.A.H.W. Peters (2005). Recent trends in global greenhouse gas emissions: regional trends 1970-2000 and spatial distribution of key sources in 2000. Env. Sc., 2 (2-3), 81-99. DOI: 10.1080/15693430500400345.

Olson, J. S., Watts, J. A. and L. J. Allison (1983). *Carbon in live vegetation of major world ecosystems*. Oak Ridge National Laboratory Technical Report ORNL-5862, Oak Ridge, Tennessee, USA.

Smill, V. (1999). Nitrogen in crop production: an account of global flows. *Global Biochemical Cycles*, 13, 647-662.

Smythe, K. D. (2000). Production and Distribution of SF$_6$ by End-Use Application. Proceedings of *"Conference on SF$_6$ and the Environment: Emission Reduction Strategies"*, San Diego, November 2-3, 2000. EPA, Washington DC, USA. Conference Proceedings published at *http://www.epa.gov/highgwp/ electricpower-sf6/conf/proceedings.html*.

Smythe, K. (2004). Trends in SF$_6$ Sales and End-Use Applications: 1961-2003. In: *Proceedings for the Conference on SF$_6$ and the Environment,* Scottsdale, Arizona, December 1-3, 2004. At website: *http://www.epa.gov/highgwp/electricpower-sf6/conf/ agenda_dec04.html.*

S&PS (1997). Sales of sulphur hexafluoride (SF$_6$) by end-use applications. Annual sales for 1961 through 1996. Sales projections for 1997 through 2000. Washington, USA, March 1997. Science & Policy Services (S&PS), now RAND.

SRI (1998). Adipic acid production data 1974-1997. SRI Consulting, Menlo Park, USA. Table dated January-1998, received 30-1-1998.

Thakur, P. C., H. G. Little and W. G. Karis (1996). Global Coalbed Methane Recovery and Use, in: Riemer, P. and A. Smith (eds.) (1996). *Proceedings of the International Energy Agency Greenhouse Gases Mitigation Options Conference,* Pergamon-Elsevier, 789-794.

UN (1998). Industrial commodity production statistics 1970-1995. UN Statistical Division, New York. Data file received 30-3-1998.

UN (1999). UN World Population Prospects, 1996 Revision. UN Population Division, New York.

UN (2004). Industrial commodity production statistics 1970-2001. UN Statistical Division, New York.

UN-ECE/FAO (1996). *Forest Fire Statistics 1993-1995.* United Nations Economic Commission for Europe & Food and Agriculture Organisation of the United Nations, Timber Bulletin, Vol. XLIX, No. 4, ECE/TIM/BULL/49/4, United Nations, 1996.

USGS (2004). U.S. Geological Survey Minerals Yearbook 2002, U.S. Geological Survey, Reston, Virginia.

Van Aardenne, J.A., Dentener, F.D., Olivier, J.G.J., Peters, J.A.H.W. and L.N. Ganzeveld (2005). The EDGAR 3.2 Fast Track 2000 dataset (32FT2000). Available from: *http://www.mnp.nl/edgar/model/ v32ft2000edgar/docv32ft2000/index.jsp.*

Van der Werf, G.R., Randerson, J.T., Collatz, G.J. and L. Giglio (2003). Carbon emissions from fires in tropical and subtropical ecosystems, *Global Change Biology,* 9, 547-562.

Veldt C. and Berdowski J.J.M. (1995). *GEIA - Note on the combustion of biomass fuels (Emission factors for CO, CH$_4$ and NMVOC).* TNO-MW, Delft. TNO Techn. Report R 94/218.

TOTAL GREENHOUSE GAS EMISSIONS

TOTAL DES EMISSIONS DE GAZ A EFFET DE SERRE

1990 Greenhouse gas emissions

Emissions de gaz à effet de serre pour 1990

millions de tonnes d'équivalent CO$_2$ selon le PRC-100

	CO$_2$						CH$_4$					
	Fuel comb.	Fugitive	Industrial processes	Other	Total	Share of energy	Energy	Agricult.	Waste	Other	Total	Share of energy
Monde *	**20 987.6**	**201.6**	**732.0**	**2 401.3**	**24 322.4**	**87.1%**	**2 268.6**	**2 821.7**	**1 098.5**	**148.5**	**6 337.4**	**35.8%**
Parties de l'Annexe I	13 907.1	49.9	346.1	56.0	14 359.2	97.2%	1 357.0	684.3	499.8	35.2	2 576.3	52.7%
Parties de l'Annexe II	9 809.8	21.4	226.6	41.8	10 099.7	97.3%	656.9	446.0	406.7	25.4	1 534.9	42.8%
Amérique du Nord	5 295.5	12.4	54.5	29.5	5 392.0	98.4%	502.6	167.8	255.0	15.3	940.7	53.4%
Europe	3 161.6	8.3	118.9	9.7	3 298.5	96.1%	113.8	177.5	107.8	6.0	405.2	28.1%
Pacifique	1 352.6	0.7	53.2	2.6	1 409.1	96.0%	40.6	100.6	43.8	4.1	189.1	21.4%
Annexe I EET	3 970.5	28.5	106.4	14.2	4 119.6	97.1%	696.2	220.5	88.0	9.6	1 014.4	68.6%
Parties non Annexe I	6 467.2	151.6	385.8	2 345.3	9 349.9	70.8%	911.6	2 137.4	598.7	113.3	3 761.0	24.2%
Parties Kyoto (Annexe I)	8 802.1	41.8	284.2	27.0	9 155.2	96.6%	879.5	506.1	262.6	24.2	1 672.4	52.6%
Soutes internat.	**613.3**	**-**	**-**	**-**	**613.3**	**100%**	**-**	**-**	**-**	**-**	**-**	**-**
Total Non-OCDE	**9 291.2**	**177.6**	**440.1**	**2 322.0**	**12 230.8**	**77.4%**	**1 492.1**	**2 271.8**	**634.4**	**119.9**	**4 518.2**	**33.0%**
Total OCDE	**11 083.2**	**24.0**	**291.9**	**79.3**	**11 478.3**	**96.8%**	**776.5**	**549.9**	**464.2**	**28.6**	**1 819.2**	**42.7%**
Canada	432.2	4.4	7.6	0.7	444.9	98.1%	35.3	18.7	24.7	4.4	83.0	42.5%
Mexique	292.9	2.6	16.7	35.2	347.4	85.1%	22.9	43.6	27.5	1.8	95.8	23.9%
Etats-Unis	4 863.3	8.1	47.0	28.8	4 947.1	98.5%	467.3	149.2	230.3	10.9	857.7	54.5%
OCDE Amérique du N.	**5 588.5**	**15.0**	**71.2**	**64.7**	**5 739.4**	**97.6%**	**525.4**	**211.5**	**282.5**	**17.1**	**1 036.5**	**50.7%**
Australie	259.8	0.4	4.4	0.6	265.1	98.1%	23.2	70.1	9.3	1.5	104.0	22.3%
Japon	1 071.4	0.0	48.5	2.0	1 121.9	95.5%	15.7	8.0	31.4	2.6	57.7	27.2%
Corée	229.3	-	16.9	1.5	247.7	92.6%	6.9	10.4	9.5	0.6	27.4	25.2%
Nouvelle-Zélande	21.4	0.3	0.4	0.0	22.1	98.1%	1.7	22.5	3.2	0.0	27.4	6.2%
OCDE Pacifique	**1 581.9**	**0.7**	**70.1**	**4.1**	**1656.8**	**95.5%**	**47.5**	**111.0**	**53.4**	**4.7**	**216.5**	**21.9%**
Autriche	56.6	-	3.7	0.3	60.5	93.5%	0.9	4.5	2.7	0.1	8.2	11.0%
Belgique	110.3	-	5.0	0.2	115.4	95.6%	1.6	5.5	2.8	0.3	10.2	15.4%
République tchèque	155.1	-	4.4	0.1	159.6	97.2%	12.3	5.9	3.9	0.2	22.2	55.1%
Danemark	50.4	0.2	0.9	0.1	51.7	98.0%	0.4	4.4	0.8	0.0	5.7	6.5%
Finlande	54.4	-	1.0	1.3	56.6	96.0%	0.6	2.5	4.3	0.1	7.4	7.4%
France	352.1	0.3	15.3	4.1	371.8	94.8%	10.3	35.2	10.3	0.9	56.7	18.2%
Allemagne	950.4	1.2	26.1	1.0	978.7	97.2%	52.2	35.3	21.4	0.9	109.9	47.5%
Grèce	70.1	0.1	6.9	0.2	77.3	90.8%	0.5	3.1	2.5	0.3	6.4	7.9%
Hongrie	68.5	-	2.6	0.3	71.4	96.0%	6.9	4.0	3.3	0.1	14.2	48.8%
Islande	1.9	-	0.1	0.0	1.9	97.1%	0.0	0.2	0.1	-	0.3	1.5%
Irlande	30.6	-	0.9	0.0	31.5	97.2%	0.8	9.3	1.4	0.0	11.6	6.9%
Italie	397.8	-	22.9	0.6	421.3	94.4%	4.8	19.0	17.7	0.9	42.3	11.3%
Luxembourg	10.5	-	0.3	0.0	10.8	97.0%	0.1	-	0.1	0.1	0.2	22.3%
Pays-Bas	156.6	0.8	1.8	0.1	159.3	98.8%	3.3	9.5	6.3	0.2	19.3	17.3%
Norvège	28.4	1.1	0.7	0.1	30.4	97.3%	2.9	2.1	2.7	0.0	7.6	37.8%
Pologne	343.9	-	8.6	0.2	352.7	97.5%	63.5	19.3	6.9	0.3	90.0	70.6%
Portugal	39.3	0.0	3.7	0.1	43.2	91.1%	0.2	3.8	2.7	0.7	7.4	3.2%
République slovaque	56.7	-	3.0	0.1	59.8	94.8%	3.2	2.9	1.3	0.1	7.5	42.4%
Espagne	205.8	0.2	14.8	0.4	221.3	93.1%	5.8	14.6	10.1	1.2	31.6	18.3%
Suède	52.8	0.1	2.9	0.8	56.5	93.4%	0.5	3.3	3.8	0.1	7.7	6.8%
Suisse	40.7	0.0	2.6	0.4	43.7	93.2%	0.3	3.3	1.1	0.0	4.8	6.6%
Turquie	126.9	0.0	13.1	-	140.0	90.7%	3.9	17.8	5.1	0.2	27.0	14.6%
Royaume-Uni	553.0	4.3	9.4	0.0	566.7	98.3%	28.6	21.8	17.0	0.4	67.7	42.2%
OCDE Europe	**3 912.8**	**8.3**	**150.5**	**10.5**	**4 082.1**	**96.1%**	**203.6**	**227.4**	**128.3**	**6.9**	**566.1**	**36.0%**
Union européenne - 27	4 063.1	7.1	146.7	11.3	4 228.3	96.3%	229.4	231.5	127.1	7.0	595.0	38.5%

* Total Monde inclue le total Non-OCDE, le total OCDE ainsi que les soutes internationales.
Sources: AIE, méthode sectorielle pour les émissions de CO$_2$ dues à la combustion d'énergie. Base de données EDGAR 3.2 pour les autres émissions.
En général, pour les émissions autres que celles de CO$_2$ dues à la combustion d'énergie, les estimations sont sujettes à une incertitude significativement plus grande.

1990 Greenhouse gas emissions
Emissions de gaz à effet de serre pour 1990

million tonnes of CO$_2$ equivalent using GWP-100

N$_2$O Energy	Agriculture	Industrial processes	Other	Total	Share of energy	HFCs	PFCs	SF$_6$	Total	Share of energy	
135.3	2 919.1	201.2	208.2	3 463.8	3.9%	74.2	80.5	113.4	34 391.7	68.6%	**World ***
66.8	1 098.3	192.8	75.1	1 433.0	4.7%	67.6	61.2	84.2	18 581.6	82.8%	*Annex I Parties*
52.4	783.1	153.6	67.9	1 057.1	5.0%	65.2	41.1	80.7	12 878.7	81.8%	*Annex II Parties*
36.1	342.3	47.1	37.8	463.4	7.8%	34.2	20.5	49.4	6 900.1	84.7%	*North America*
10.8	288.2	97.0	25.6	421.7	2.6%	19.8	15.5	18.1	4 178.7	78.8%	*Europe*
5.5	152.6	9.5	4.5	172.0	3.2%	11.3	5.2	13.1	1 799.8	77.8%	*Pacific*
13.9	272.0	39.0	6.7	331.7	4.2%	2.4	19.5	1.3	5 488.8	85.8%	*Annex I EIT*
68.5	1 820.8	8.4	133.1	2 030.8	3.4%	6.7	19.3	29.2	15 196.9	50.0%	*Non-Annex I Parties*
32.2	735.6	154.6	38.2	960.7	3.4%	33.9	47.1	37.9	11 907.3	81.9%	*Annex I Kyoto Parties*
-	-	-	-	-	-	-	-	-	613.3	100.0%	**Internat. bunkers**
78.2	1 973.1	52.5	136.0	2 239.8	3.5%	7.4	36.6	25.7	19 058.6	57.9%	**Non-OECD Total**
57.1	946.0	148.7	72.2	1 224.0	4.7%	66.8	43.9	87.7	14 719.9	81.1%	**OECD Total**
2.4	34.3	12.2	1.7	50.7	4.8%	0.5	6.9	5.4	591.4	80.2%	Canada
1.2	66.0	0.9	2.1	70.2	1.8%	0.7	0.5	0.6	515.4	62.0%	Mexico
33.7	308.0	34.9	36.1	412.7	8.2%	33.7	13.5	44.1	6 308.8	85.2%	United States
37.4	408.3	48.0	40.0	533.7	7.0%	34.9	21.0	50.1	7 415.6	83.2%	**OECD N. America**
1.3	103.9	0.6	0.3	106.1	1.2%	0.7	1.2	0.7	477.9	59.6%	Australia
4.1	14.9	8.9	4.1	32.0	12.9%	10.6	3.7	12.3	1 238.1	88.1%	Japan
0.8	7.8	0.9	0.1	9.5	8.0%	0.9	0.5	4.1	290.0	81.7%	Korea
0.1	33.8	0.0	0.0	33.9	0.2%	0.0	0.3	0.1	83.8	27.9%	New Zealand
6.2	160.3	10.4	4.5	181.5	3.4%	12.1	5.7	17.2	2 089.8	78.3%	**OECD Pacific**
0.2	4.7	0.8	0.1	5.7	2.8%	0.0	1.0	0.3	75.6	76.2%	Austria
0.3	6.1	3.6	1.3	11.2	2.4%	0.0	0.0	0.1	137.0	81.8%	Belgium
0.5	8.9	1.1	0.3	10.7	4.7%	0.0	0.0	0.0	192.6	87.2%	Czech Republic
0.2	8.1	1.0	0.7	10.0	2.0%	0.0	0.0	0.2	67.6	75.8%	Denmark
0.3	3.8	1.5	0.4	6.0	4.5%	0.0	0.0	0.2	70.3	78.5%	Finland
1.2	59.5	21.7	6.1	88.4	1.3%	5.4	1.3	4.1	527.7	69.0%	France
3.7	57.0	8.9	7.9	77.5	4.8%	2.9	1.5	6.8	1 177.3	85.6%	Germany
0.3	11.9	0.7	0.2	13.1	2.3%	0.6	0.1	0.1	97.5	72.8%	Greece
0.2	8.3	3.2	0.3	11.9	1.8%	0.0	0.7	0.0	98.3	77.0%	Hungary
0.0	0.4	0.0	0.0	0.4	1.7%	-	0.8	0.0	3.5	54.2%	Iceland
0.0	11.1	0.9	0.6	12.8	0.8%	0.0	0.0	0.1	56.0	56.3%	Ireland
1.0	27.4	6.7	0.5	35.6	2.7%	2.3	0.5	2.0	503.9	80.1%	Italy
0.0	-	0.0	0.0	0.0	43.0%	0.0	-	0.0	11.1	95.1%	Luxembourg
0.4	11.0	6.4	1.6	19.3	1.9%	3.3	2.3	0.4	203.9	79.0%	Netherlands
0.1	2.9	2.1	0.2	5.3	2.0%	0.0	4.2	0.8	48.3	67.4%	Norway
1.4	25.3	4.4	0.5	31.6	4.4%	0.0	0.4	0.0	474.8	86.1%	Poland
0.1	5.9	0.6	0.3	6.9	2.1%	0.0	0.0	0.1	57.7	68.9%	Portugal
0.2	3.4	0.5	0.5	4.7	3.4%	0.0	0.0	0.0	71.9	83.5%	Slovak Republic
0.7	31.0	2.3	1.3	35.3	2.0%	2.3	1.6	0.5	292.6	72.6%	Spain
0.3	4.7	0.8	0.5	6.3	4.3%	0.0	0.7	0.3	71.5	75.0%	Sweden
0.2	2.7	0.2	0.1	3.2	6.8%	0.0	0.2	0.5	52.4	78.7%	Switzerland
0.4	43.3	0.1	0.5	44.3	0.9%	0.0	0.6	2.3	214.2	61.3%	Turkey
1.8	39.9	22.9	3.8	68.5	2.7%	3.0	1.2	1.6	708.8	82.9%	United Kingdom
13.5	377.3	90.3	27.7	508.8	2.7%	19.8	17.2	20.5	5 214.5	79.4%	**OECD Europe**
14.0	365.9	96.1	27.8	503.8	2.8%	19.8	13.5	16.9	5 377.3	80.2%	*European Union - 27*

* Total World includes Non-OECD total, OECD total as well as international bunkers.
Sources: IEA, Sectoral Approach for CO$_2$ emissions from fuel combustion. EDGAR 3.2 database for other emissions. In general, estimates for emissions other than CO$_2$ from fuel combustion are subject to significantly larger uncertainties.

1990 Greenhouse gas emissions

Emissions de gaz à effet de serre pour 1990

millions de tonnes d'équivalent CO$_2$ selon le PRC-100

	CO$_2$						CH$_4$					
	Fuel comb.	Fugitive	Industrial processes	Other	Total	Share of energy	Energy	Agricult.	Waste	Other	Total	Share of energy
Total Non-OCDE	**9 291.2**	**177.6**	**440.1**	**2 322.0**	**12 230.8**	**77.4%**	**1 492.1**	**2 271.8**	**634.4**	**119.9**	**4 518.2**	**33.0%**
Algérie	54.8	8.7	3.2	4.2	70.8	89.6%	11.4	3.6	3.4	0.2	18.6	61.2%
Angola	4.1	1.8	0.2	13.8	19.8	29.5%	2.9	9.0	1.0	0.7	13.6	21.5%
Bénin	0.3	-	0.1	2.6	3.1	8.3%	0.4	1.6	0.5	0.1	2.7	16.0%
Botswana	2.9	-	-	0.3	3.2	91.1%	0.0	0.1	0.0	-	0.1	11.3%
Cameroun	2.7	-	0.3	16.6	19.6	13.7%	2.1	6.0	1.5	0.9	10.5	20.2%
Congo	0.7	-	0.0	9.0	9.7	7.2%	1.3	0.5	0.3	0.5	2.7	48.1%
Rép. dém. du Congo	3.0	0.2	0.3	157.0	160.5	2.0%	2.9	11.9	4.2	8.8	27.7	10.4%
Côte d'Ivoire	2.6	-	0.2	5.4	8.3	31.8%	1.0	2.7	1.5	0.2	5.4	18.8%
Egypte	79.2	2.2	7.0	4.2	92.6	87.9%	7.8	9.1	6.4	0.0	23.2	33.4%
Erythrée	..	-	0.0	0.3	..	..	0.2	1.6	0.3	-	2.1	11.0%
Ethiopie	2.2	-	0.2	12.1	14.5	15.3%	3.7	30.6	4.4	0.4	39.1	9.3%
Gabon	0.9	3.4	0.1	23.3	27.6	15.5%	1.5	0.2	0.1	1.3	3.1	46.6%
Ghana	2.7	-	0.3	9.8	12.9	21.0%	0.7	2.3	1.8	0.5	5.3	13.8%
Kenya	6.3	-	0.8	4.8	11.9	53.3%	3.0	13.9	2.5	0.0	19.4	15.7%
Libye	27.4	7.2	1.5	0.2	36.3	95.2%	6.9	1.0	0.8	-	8.7	79.1%
Maroc	19.6	-	2.7	2.0	24.3	80.7%	0.6	5.2	3.2	0.1	9.1	6.2%
Mozambique	1.1	-	0.0	10.4	11.5	9.4%	1.6	5.8	1.5	0.5	9.4	17.5%
Namibie	..	-	0.0	1.6	..	..	0.2	3.9	0.2	0.1	4.3	3.7%
Nigéria	29.2	38.4	1.5	34.7	103.7	65.1%	28.2	20.2	10.6	0.6	59.7	47.3%
Sénégal	2.0	-	0.2	3.3	5.6	36.0%	0.2	4.2	0.9	0.2	5.6	4.5%
Afrique du Sud	254.6	-	4.6	8.9	268.1	95.0%	27.4	16.3	8.2	0.4	52.3	52.4%
Soudan	5.5	-	0.1	29.5	35.1	15.7%	8.5	27.5	2.6	1.2	39.8	21.4%
Rép. unie de Tanzanie	1.7	-	0.3	23.0	25.0	6.8%	5.7	17.8	2.6	0.7	26.9	21.3%
Togo	0.6	-	0.2	1.7	2.4	23.5%	0.3	1.0	0.4	0.1	1.8	18.3%
Tunisie	12.1	0.0	2.6	0.8	15.5	77.8%	1.0	1.6	1.2	0.0	3.7	26.3%
Zambie	2.6	-	0.4	18.4	21.4	12.2%	0.8	7.1	0.9	1.0	9.8	8.2%
Zimbabwe	16.0	-	0.5	4.2	20.7	77.3%	2.4	7.1	1.2	0.2	10.8	22.2%
Autres pays d'Afrique	14.7	-	0.5	78.9	94.0	15.6%	12.1	82.5	12.1	3.6	110.2	10.9%
Afrique	**549.3**	**61.8**	**27.8**	**481.2**	**1 120.1**	**54.6%**	**134.9**	**294.5**	**74.2**	**22.2**	**525.8**	**25.7%**
Bahrein	11.7	0.0	0.1	0.0	11.8	99.2%	1.5	0.0	0.1	-	1.6	93.0%
Rép. islamique d'Iran	175.3	21.8	7.6	7.2	211.9	93.0%	27.1	17.9	9.4	0.3	54.7	49.6%
Irak	52.8	8.0	6.5	0.9	68.2	89.2%	4.9	3.1	3.2	-	11.1	44.1%
Israël	33.6	-	1.6	0.0	35.2	95.5%	0.1	0.5	0.4	0.0	1.0	7.4%
Jordanie	9.2	-	0.9	0.2	10.3	89.5%	0.1	0.3	0.7	0.0	1.1	11.4%
Koweit	24.3	1.3	0.4	0.1	26.2	98.0%	6.3	0.1	0.4	-	6.8	92.8%
Liban	6.4	-	0.5	0.4	7.3	87.8%	0.1	0.1	0.5	0.0	0.7	11.6%
Oman	9.9	1.4	0.0	0.1	11.4	99.2%	1.4	0.3	0.3	0.0	2.0	71.4%
Qatar	14.2	-	0.1	0.0	14.3	99.0%	2.0	0.1	0.1	0.0	2.2	91.3%
Arabie saoudite	161.4	0.5	5.9	0.6	168.4	96.1%	35.2	1.8	2.7	0.0	39.7	88.6%
Syrie	31.0	4.1	1.5	1.0	37.6	93.3%	1.5	2.4	1.8	0.0	5.8	26.1%
Emirats arabes unis	51.6	2.0	1.6	0.2	55.4	96.8%	18.5	0.3	0.3	-	19.1	97.0%
Yémen	6.4	-	0.4	0.5	7.3	88.1%	1.1	1.9	1.6	-	4.6	23.9%
Moyen-Orient	**587.9**	**39.1**	**27.1**	**11.2**	**665.3**	**94.2%**	**99.9**	**28.7**	**21.5**	**0.4**	**150.6**	**66.4%**
Albanie	6.2	0.0	0.3	0.2	6.8	92.5%	0.4	1.5	0.3	0.0	2.2	18.5%
Bosnie-Herzégovine	23.6	0.7	0.2	0.0	24.5	99.4%	0.3	1.3	0.4	0.0	2.0	15.1%
Bulgarie	74.9	-	3.5	0.1	78.5	95.4%	3.0	4.7	1.8	0.0	9.6	31.7%
Croatie	21.6	3.1	1.5	0.3	26.3	93.5%	1.5	1.5	0.9	0.0	4.0	39.1%
Chypre	3.8	-	0.6	-	4.4	87.2%	0.0	0.1	0.1	0.0	0.3	3.4%
Gibraltar	0.2	-	-	-	0.2	100.0%	0.0	-	0.0	-	0.0	7.2%
ex-RY de Macédoine	9.1	0.3	0.3	0.2	10.0	94.5%	0.2	0.6	0.2	0.1	1.2	18.9%
Malte	2.3	-	0.0	0.0	2.3	99.8%	0.0	0.0	0.0	-	0.1	3.3%
Roumanie	167.1	-	4.7	0.5	172.3	97.0%	24.0	14.1	3.9	0.2	42.3	56.8%
Serbie	61.4	3.6	2.2	0.0	67.3	96.7%	1.5	10.1	1.2	0.1	12.9	11.3%
Slovénie	12.5	-	0.8	0.1	13.3	93.6%	0.3	1.0	0.4	0.0	1.7	16.6%
Europe Non-OCDE	**382.8**	**7.6**	**14.0**	**1.4**	**405.7**	**96.2%**	**31.3**	**35.0**	**9.4**	**0.5**	**76.2**	**41.1%**

1990 Greenhouse gas emissions

Emissions de gaz à effet de serre pour 1990

million tonnes of CO$_2$ equivalent using GWP-100

| | N$_2$O | | | | | HFCs | PFCs | SF$_6$ | Total | | |
| | | Industrial processes | | | Share of energy | Industrial processes | | | | Share of energy | |
Energy	Agriculture	Industrial processes	Other	Total	Share of energy				Total	Share of energy	
78.2	**1 973.1**	**52.5**	**136.0**	**2 239.8**	**3.5%**	**7.4**	**36.6**	**25.7**	**19 058.6**	**57.9%**	**Non-OECD Total**
0.2	8.0	0.4	0.2	8.8	2.3%	-	-	0.2	98.4	76.2%	Algeria
0.1	4.1	-	0.9	5.1	2.9%	-	-	0.0	38.5	23.2%	Angola
0.1	1.9	-	0.1	2.1	2.9%	-	-	0.0	7.9	9.5%	Benin
0.0	4.4	-	0.0	4.4	0.9%	-	-	0.0	7.8	38.5%	Botswana
0.2	7.1	-	1.0	8.3	1.9%	-	0.8	0.0	39.2	12.6%	Cameroon
0.0	0.2	-	0.6	0.8	4.0%	-	-	0.0	13.2	15.2%	Congo
0.4	8.5	-	10.5	19.4	2.1%	-	-	0.0	207.6	3.1%	Dem. Rep. of Congo
0.2	2.0	-	0.3	2.5	6.5%	-	-	0.0	16.1	23.6%	Côte d'Ivoire
0.5	15.0	1.4	0.0	17.0	3.2%	0.0	1.4	0.9	135.0	66.4%	Egypt
0.0	1.3	-	0.0	1.3	2.8%	-	-	0.0	..	..	Eritrea
0.6	49.7	-	0.4	50.7	1.2%	-	-	0.0	104.3	6.2%	Ethiopia
0.0	0.2	-	1.6	1.9	1.8%	-	-	0.0	32.6	17.7%	Gabon
0.1	3.8	-	0.6	4.5	2.6%	-	0.2	0.0	22.9	15.5%	Ghana
0.5	21.3	-	0.0	21.8	2.2%	-	-	0.0	53.1	18.6%	Kenya
0.1	2.8	-	0.0	2.9	3.3%	-	-	0.1	48.0	86.6%	Libya
0.1	14.2	-	0.1	14.4	0.7%	-	-	0.0	47.8	42.5%	Morocco
0.3	2.1	-	0.6	2.9	8.5%	-	-	0.0	23.9	12.5%	Mozambique
0.0	4.1	-	0.1	4.2	0.6%	-	-	0.0	..		Namibia
2.7	24.7	-	0.7	28.1	9.6%	-	-	0.1	191.6	51.4%	Nigeria
0.1	6.0	-	0.2	6.2	1.0%	-	-	0.0	17.4	13.4%	Senegal
1.4	23.3	1.0	0.8	26.5	5.3%	0.0	0.1	1.3	348.3	81.4%	South Africa
0.9	37.1	-	1.4	39.4	2.4%	-	-	0.0	114.3	13.1%	Sudan
1.1	21.3	-	0.9	23.3	4.9%	-	-	0.0	75.2	11.4%	United Rep. of Tanzania
0.1	1.9	-	0.1	2.0	2.6%	-	-	0.0	6.2	15.3%	Togo
0.1	3.7	0.4	0.0	4.3	1.9%	0.0	-	0.0	23.5	55.9%	Tunisia
0.1	3.5	-	1.2	4.8	2.9%	-	-	0.0	36.0	9.8%	Zambia
0.2	8.0	0.5	0.2	9.0	2.6%	-	-	0.0	40.5	46.0%	Zimbabwe
1.7	92.5	-	4.3	98.5	1.7%	-	-	0.0	302.7	9.4%	Other Africa
11.9	**372.6**	**3.7**	**26.8**	**415.0**	**2.9%**	**0.0**	**2.5**	**2.7**	**2 066.0**	**36.7%**	**Africa**
0.0	0.0	-	0.0	0.1	49.3%	-	1.9	0.0	15.3	86.1%	Bahrain
0.7	47.3	0.3	0.3	48.6	1.4%	-	0.1	2.1	317.4	70.9%	Islamic Rep. of Iran
0.2	6.3	-	0.0	6.6	3.7%	-	-	0.4	86.3	76.4%	Iraq
0.1	1.5	0.3	0.0	1.9	5.7%	0.0	0.0	0.8	38.9	86.8%	Israel
0.0	1.1	-	0.0	1.2	3.5%	-	-	0.0	12.5	74.8%	Jordan
0.1	0.2	-	0.0	0.2	25.8%	-	-	0.2	33.5	95.7%	Kuwait
0.0	0.7	-	0.0	0.7	4.3%	-	-	0.0	8.7	74.4%	Lebanon
0.0	0.8	-	0.0	0.9	2.9%	-	-	0.0	14.3	89.4%	Oman
0.0	0.2	-	0.0	0.2	9.1%	-	-	0.0	16.7	97.0%	Qatar
0.4	7.8	-	0.0	8.2	5.2%	-	-	2.3	218.6	90.3%	Saudi Arabia
0.1	7.5	0.2	0.0	7.9	1.9%	-	-	0.0	51.2	71.7%	Syria
0.1	0.8	-	0.0	0.9	9.4%	-	0.1	0.2	75.7	95.5%	United Arab Emirates
0.1	5.0	-	0.0	5.1	1.1%	-	-	0.0	17.0	44.6%	Yemen
2.0	**79.3**	**0.8**	**0.4**	**82.5**	**2.4%**	**0.0**	**2.0**	**5.9**	**906.3**	**80.4%**	**Middle East**
0.0	2.3	-	0.0	2.3	1.7%	0.0	-	0.0	11.3	59.2%	Albania
0.1	1.1	-	0.0	1.1	4.9%	0.0	0.5	0.0	28.1	87.9%	Bosnia-Herzegovina
0.2	9.5	3.4	0.2	13.2	1.6%	0.0	-	0.0	101.3	77.1%	Bulgaria
0.1	2.3	0.9	0.1	3.4	2.8%	0.0	0.7	0.0	34.4	76.5%	Croatia
0.0	0.5	-	0.0	0.5	3.1%	-	-	0.0	5.2	74.1%	Cyprus
0.0	-	-	-	0.0	100.0%	-	-	0.0	0.2	96.8%	Gibraltar
0.1	0.8	-	0.0	0.9	6.2%	0.0	-	0.0	12.0	80.4%	FYR of Macedonia
0.0	0.0	-	0.0	0.1	17.2%	-	-	0.0	2.4	94.4%	Malta
0.4	19.2	4.8	0.3	24.7	1.5%	0.0	1.5	0.0	240.8	79.5%	Romania
0.3	8.0	0.7	0.1	9.1	3.2%	0.0	0.3	0.0	89.5	74.6%	Serbia
0.0	1.0	-	0.1	1.1	4.4%	0.0	0.6	0.0	16.7	76.6%	Slovenia
1.2	**44.8**	**9.7**	**0.8**	**56.5**	**2.1%**	**0.0**	**3.5**	**0.0**	**541.9**	**78.0%**	**Non-OECD Europe**

1990 Greenhouse gas emissions

Emissions de gaz à effet de serre pour 1990

millions de tonnes d'équivalent CO₂ selon le PRC-100

	CO₂						CH₄					
	Fuel comb.	Fugitive	Industrial processes	Other	Total	Share of energy	Energy	Agricult.	Waste	Other	Total	Share of energy
Arménie	20.5	-	0.7	0.2	21.4	95.7%	1.9	0.7	0.5	0.0	3.1	60.5%
Azerbaïdjan	62.7	3.0	0.5	0.4	66.6	98.7%	9.5	4.0	1.0	0.0	14.5	65.5%
Bélarus	114.8	-	1.9	0.2	116.9	98.2%	6.3	11.2	1.7	0.0	19.2	32.5%
Estonie	36.2	-	0.6	0.1	36.9	98.1%	1.0	1.3	0.4	0.0	2.6	36.6%
Géorgie	28.7	0.0	0.3	0.3	29.2	98.1%	2.6	2.4	0.8	0.0	5.8	44.7%
Kazakhstan	236.4	0.3	5.1	0.1	241.9	97.9%	29.4	23.0	2.5	0.4	55.3	53.2%
Kirghizistan	22.7	0.0	0.7	0.2	23.7	95.9%	0.4	3.8	0.5	-	4.7	8.0%
Lettonie	18.4	-	0.7	0.3	19.3	95.1%	1.3	2.4	0.6	0.0	4.3	31.2%
Lituanie	33.1	-	1.9	0.3	35.3	93.8%	3.3	3.8	0.7	0.0	7.7	42.1%
République de Moldavie	30.2	-	1.3	0.2	31.7	95.2%	2.0	2.1	0.6	0.0	4.8	42.5%
Russie	2 179.9	21.8	53.2	9.0	2 263.9	97.3%	473.7	98.7	51.9	7.1	631.4	75.0%
Tadjikistan	11.7	-	0.6	0.3	12.5	93.0%	0.4	2.7	0.6	-	3.7	10.3%
Turkménistan	46.6	0.1	0.6	0.2	47.5	98.3%	30.0	2.7	0.5	0.0	33.2	90.4%
Ukraine	687.9	0.1	17.7	2.7	708.4	97.1%	94.7	40.6	9.6	1.5	146.4	64.7%
Ouzbékistan	119.8	0.0	3.6	1.1	124.6	96.2%	27.7	11.5	2.4	-	41.6	66.6%
Ex-URSS	**3 649.5**	**25.3**	**89.5**	**15.5**	**3 779.8**	**97.2%**	**684.2**	**210.9**	**74.3**	**9.0**	**978.4**	**69.9%**
Argentine	100.4	5.3	1.8	27.5	135.0	78.3%	7.3	63.0	10.2	1.6	82.1	8.9%
Bolivie	5.4	0.8	0.3	74.0	80.5	7.7%	0.6	9.4	1.3	4.2	15.6	3.7%
Brésil	192.7	2.3	17.0	465.1	677.1	28.8%	9.3	204.8	44.8	26.8	285.7	3.2%
Chili	31.9	0.4	2.0	9.5	43.8	73.8%	2.5	5.9	5.3	0.5	14.2	17.7%
Colombie	45.0	0.8	4.1	50.0	99.9	45.8%	6.4	31.4	8.6	2.7	49.2	13.0%
Costa Rica	2.6	-	0.3	7.0	9.9	26.3%	0.1	2.6	0.6	0.4	3.7	3.9%
Cuba	27.6	-	2.0	3.9	33.5	82.4%	0.2	6.8	2.7	0.1	9.9	2.2%
République dominicaine	7.6	-	0.6	3.3	11.5	66.6%	0.2	3.4	1.5	0.2	5.3	3.5%
Equateur	13.2	1.7	0.9	33.9	49.6	30.0%	1.6	6.5	2.2	1.9	12.2	13.1%
El Salvador	2.2	-	0.3	0.8	3.3	65.8%	0.2	1.5	1.0	0.0	2.7	8.8%
Guatemala	3.3	-	0.5	12.9	16.7	19.8%	0.7	2.9	1.6	0.7	5.9	12.3%
Haïti	0.9	-	0.2	0.5	1.6	58.3%	0.2	1.7	1.0	0.0	2.9	7.7%
Honduras	2.1	-	0.2	10.7	13.0	16.5%	0.3	3.3	0.8	0.6	5.0	6.5%
Jamaïque	7.2	-	0.3	2.9	10.4	69.2%	0.0	0.5	0.5	0.2	1.2	2.1%
Antilles néerlandaises	2.9	-	-	0.0	2.9	99.2%	0.0	0.0	0.1	-	0.1	34.8%
Nicaragua	1.8	-	0.1	21.6	23.5	7.8%	0.2	2.5	0.7	1.2	4.7	4.8%
Panama	2.5	-	0.2	11.9	14.5	16.9%	0.1	1.7	0.5	0.7	3.0	3.4%
Paraguay	1.9	-	0.2	18.7	20.9	9.2%	0.3	9.5	0.9	1.0	11.7	2.9%
Pérou	19.2	0.4	1.1	47.3	68.0	28.8%	1.5	7.5	5.6	2.6	17.3	8.7%
Trinité-et-Tobago	11.4	2.5	0.3	0.5	14.6	94.6%	2.0	0.1	0.4	0.0	2.5	77.6%
Uruguay	3.7	-	0.2	0.3	4.3	86.5%	0.1	12.9	1.1	0.0	14.1	0.7%
Vénézuela	105.1	7.5	3.0	83.5	199.1	56.6%	14.3	15.9	6.5	4.8	41.5	34.4%
Autres Amérique Latine	12.4	-	1.1	8.1	21.7	57.5%	0.5	2.3	2.0	0.4	5.2	10.4%
Amérique latine	**603.1**	**21.6**	**36.5**	**894.0**	**1 555.2**	**40.2%**	**48.8**	**396.2**	**99.9**	**50.6**	**595.6**	**8.2%**
Bangladesh	13.6	-	0.2	18.8	32.6	41.7%	8.9	58.8	13.8	0.1	81.6	10.9%
Brunei Darussalam	3.4	0.1	0.0	0.6	4.1	83.3%	1.6	0.0	0.0	0.0	1.6	94.5%
Cambodge	..	..	..	..	..	..	..	..	..	..	..	..
Taipei chinois	113.9	-	8.7	1.9	124.4	91.5%	1.9	-	3.3	0.2	5.4	35.9%
Inde	589.3	10.0	23.4	102.3	724.9	82.7%	82.3	425.8	116.6	0.8	625.4	13.2%
Indonésie	140.2	9.1	8.1	217.9	375.4	39.8%	63.8	78.3	27.3	10.8	180.2	35.4%
Rép. pop. dém. de Corée	114.0	-	7.9	2.4	124.3	91.7%	2.0	4.6	3.1	0.1	9.8	20.3%
Malaisie	49.0	3.1	2.9	93.2	148.1	35.1%	8.8	4.9	2.7	4.9	21.3	41.5%
Mongolie	12.7	-	0.3	0.2	13.2	95.7%	0.1	6.3	0.3	0.6	7.4	1.9%
Myanmar	4.0	0.0	0.2	75.8	80.0	5.0%	3.4	27.0	5.7	4.0	40.2	8.6%
Népal	0.9	-	0.1	9.7	10.7	8.3%	2.8	28.1	2.6	0.3	33.8	8.4%
Pakistan	59.0	-	3.7	19.4	82.1	71.9%	10.7	55.8	16.0	0.3	82.8	12.9%
Philippines	36.1	-	3.2	64.0	103.2	34.9%	4.8	21.9	9.0	3.2	38.8	12.3%
Singapour	28.8	-	0.9	-	29.7	96.9%	0.1	0.0	0.6	-	0.7	11.8%
Sri Lanka	3.7	-	0.3	4.1	8.1	46.2%	1.2	6.6	2.4	0.1	10.3	11.5%
Thaïlande	78.6	-	9.1	42.6	130.4	60.3%	3.5	55.3	7.8	2.3	68.9	5.1%
Viêt-Nam	17.0	-	1.7	29.1	47.8	35.5%	5.5	37.2	9.2	1.2	53.0	10.3%
Autres pays d'Asie	10.5	0.1	0.1	109.7	120.5	8.8%	3.4	20.9	4.9	4.6	33.7	10.0%
Asie	**1 274.6**	**22.3**	**70.9**	**791.8**	**2 159.6**	**60.1%**	**204.8**	**831.6**	**225.1**	**33.6**	**1 295.1**	**15.8%**
Rép. populaire de Chine	2 211.0	-	173.4	126.9	2 511.3	88.0%	288.1	474.9	128.8	3.5	895.4	32.2%
Hong Kong, Chine	33.1	-	0.9	0.0	34.0	97.3%	0.0	0.0	1.1	-	1.2	2.7%
Chine	**2 244.0**	**-**	**174.3**	**126.9**	**2 545.3**	**88.2%**	**288.2**	**474.9**	**129.9**	**3.5**	**896.5**	**32.1%**

1990 Greenhouse gas emissions

Emissions de gaz à effet de serre pour 1990

million tonnes of CO$_2$ equivalent using GWP-100

		N$_2$O				HFCs	PFCs	SF$_6$	Total		
Energy	Agriculture	Industrial processes	Other	Total	Share of energy	Industrial processes			Total	Share of energy	
0.1	0.8	-	0.0	0.9	6.4%	0.0	-	-	25.4	88.2%	Armenia
0.1	3.9	-	0.0	4.1	2.9%	0.0	0.2	-	85.4	88.3%	Azerbaijan
0.4	11.5	3.1	0.3	15.3	2.8%	0.0	-	-	151.4	80.2%	Belarus
0.2	1.4	-	0.0	1.6	10.7%	0.0	-	0.0	41.2	90.7%	Estonia
0.1	2.6	0.7	0.0	3.4	1.7%	0.0	-	-	38.4	81.6%	Georgia
0.7	22.6	-	0.3	23.6	2.8%	0.0	-	-	320.8	83.2%	Kazakhstan
0.1	4.1	-	0.0	4.2	1.6%	0.0	-	-	32.6	71.0%	Kyrgyzstan
0.1	2.5	-	0.1	2.7	3.6%	0.0	-	-	26.3	75.3%	Latvia
0.3	3.8	-	0.1	4.2	6.8%	0.0	-	-	47.2	77.7%	Lithuania
0.2	3.0	-	0.1	3.3	4.8%	0.0	-	-	39.7	81.4%	Republic of Moldova
7.6	114.6	4.0	3.0	129.2	5.9%	2.4	15.8	1.2	3 043.9	88.1%	Russia
0.0	3.1	-	0.0	3.1	1.3%	0.0	0.1	-	19.4	62.2%	Tajikistan
0.1	3.9	0.1	0.0	4.2	1.9%	0.0	-	-	84.9	90.5%	Turkmenistan
2.1	53.3	13.0	0.9	69.4	3.1%	0.0	0.1	-	924.2	84.9%	Ukraine
0.2	14.0	0.1	0.0	14.3	1.3%	0.0	-	-	180.5	81.8%	Uzbekistan
12.1	**245.3**	**21.0**	**4.9**	**283.4**	**4.3%**	**2.4**	**16.1**	**1.2**	**5 061.3**	**86.4%**	**Former USSR**
0.2	62.9	0.1	1.9	65.1	0.3%	0.1	1.5	0.3	284.0	39.8%	Argentina
0.0	9.2	-	5.1	14.3	0.3%	-	-	0.0	110.4	6.2%	Bolivia
2.0	188.0	4.0	33.8	227.8	0.9%	0.9	3.2	1.2	1 195.8	17.2%	Brazil
0.2	7.3	0.0	0.6	8.2	2.9%	-	-	0.0	66.2	53.0%	Chile
0.4	17.4	0.1	3.3	21.1	1.8%	0.0	-	0.2	170.4	30.8%	Colombia
0.0	2.8	0.1	0.5	3.4	1.4%	-	-	0.0	17.1	16.4%	Costa Rica
0.3	12.4	0.7	0.3	13.6	2.1%	0.0	-	0.0	57.0	49.3%	Cuba
0.1	3.9	-	0.2	4.1	1.6%	-	-	0.0	20.9	37.8%	Dominican Republic
0.1	6.4	-	2.3	8.8	1.1%	-	-	0.0	70.6	23.4%	Ecuador
0.1	2.0	-	0.0	2.0	3.3%	-	-	0.0	8.1	30.6%	El Salvador
0.2	3.8	-	0.8	4.8	3.2%	-	-	0.0	27.4	15.3%	Guatemala
0.0	2.4	-	0.0	2.5	1.8%	-	-	0.0	7.0	17.4%	Haiti
0.1	2.8	-	0.7	3.6	2.4%	-	-	0.0	21.6	11.8%	Honduras
0.0	1.0	-	0.2	1.2	2.0%	-	-	0.0	12.8	56.4%	Jamaica
0.0	0.0	-	0.0	0.0	44.6%	-	-	0.0	3.0	96.7%	Netherlands Antilles
0.1	2.2	-	1.5	3.8	1.6%	-	-	0.0	32.0	6.6%	Nicaragua
0.0	1.7	-	0.8	2.5	1.1%	-	-	0.0	20.0	12.9%	Panama
0.1	8.7	-	1.2	10.0	0.8%	-	-	0.0	42.5	5.5%	Paraguay
0.2	10.8	0.2	3.1	14.3	1.6%	0.0	-	0.0	99.5	21.4%	Peru
0.0	0.3	-	0.0	0.3	3.5%	-	-	0.0	17.5	90.4%	Trinidad and Tobago
0.0	15.1	-	0.0	15.2	0.2%	-	-	0.0	33.6	11.5%	Uruguay
0.2	15.8	0.0	5.7	21.7	0.8%	0.5	0.6	0.3	263.6	48.2%	Venezuela
0.2	3.8	-	0.4	4.5	5.4%	-	0.3	0.0	31.6	41.8%	Other Latin America
4.6	**380.5**	**5.2**	**62.4**	**452.8**	**1.0%**	**1.5**	**5.5**	**2.0**	**2 612.6**	**26.0%**	**Latin America**
1.7	20.6	-	0.1	22.4	7.5%	-	-	0.0	136.6	17.7%	Bangladesh
0.0	0.0	-	0.0	0.1	11.8%	-	-	0.0	5.8	85.6%	Brunei Darussalam
..	..	..	..	..	-	..	..	..	..	..	Cambodia
0.6	0.0	0.1	0.0	0.7	77.7%	-	-	0.0	130.6	89.1%	Chinese Taipei
12.5	211.0	1.1	0.6	225.2	5.6%	0.8	1.7	5.5	1 583.6	43.8%	India
3.6	43.4	0.1	13.0	60.2	6.0%	-	0.2	1.2	617.2	35.1%	Indonesia
0.7	8.5	-	0.0	9.2	8.0%	-	-	0.3	143.6	81.3%	DPR of Korea
1.0	4.8	-	5.9	11.6	8.3%	-	-	1.0	182.0	34.0%	Malaysia
0.0	9.9	-	0.1	10.0	0.3%	-	-	-	30.6	41.9%	Mongolia
0.6	9.0	-	4.8	14.4	4.2%	-	-	0.0	134.6	6.0%	Myanmar
0.5	4.8	-	0.3	5.7	9.2%	-	-	0.0	50.2	8.5%	Nepal
1.6	52.8	0.6	0.4	55.4	2.9%	-	-	0.7	221.0	32.3%	Pakistan
1.1	13.1	-	3.7	18.0	6.4%	-	-	0.1	160.1	26.2%	Philippines
0.1	0.1	-	0.0	0.2	69.7%	0.0	0.1	0.3	31.1	93.4%	Singapore
0.2	2.0	-	0.1	2.4	9.4%	-	-	0.0	20.8	24.8%	Sri Lanka
0.5	18.1	-	2.8	21.3	2.4%	-	-	1.6	222.2	37.2%	Thailand
1.0	11.6	-	1.4	13.9	6.8%	-	-	0.0	114.7	20.4%	Vietnam
0.6	17.4	-	5.5	23.5	2.4%	-	0.3	1.9	179.9	8.1%	Other Asia
26.4	**427.0**	**2.0**	**38.9**	**494.3**	**5.3%**	**0.8**	**2.3**	**12.6**	**3 964.6**	**38.5%**	**Asia**
19.8	423.5	10.0	1.8	455.2	4.4%	2.8	4.6	1.2	3 870.5	65.1%	People's Rep. of China
0.2	0.0	-	0.0	0.2	84.2%	-	-	0.0	35.4	94.1%	Hong Kong, China
20.0	**423.6**	**10.0**	**1.8**	**455.4**	**4.4%**	**2.8**	**4.6**	**1.2**	**3 905.8**	**65.3%**	**China**

1995 Greenhouse gas emissions

Emissions de gaz à effet de serre pour 1995

millions de tonnes d'équivalent CO$_2$ selon le PRC-100

	CO$_2$						CH$_4$					
	Fuel comb.	Fugitive	Industrial processes	Other	Total	Share of energy	Energy	Agricult.	Waste	Other	Total	Share of energy
Monde *	**21 829.0**	**196.3**	**891.9**	**2 195.7**	**25 112.9**	**87.7%**	**2 202.9**	**2 816.0**	**1 168.9**	**152.5**	**6 340.3**	**34.7%**
Parties de l'Annexe I	*13 194.6*	*38.7*	*295.7*	*59.9*	*13 588.8*	*97.4%*	*1 179.9*	*607.1*	*488.2*	*50.1*	*2 325.3*	*50.7%*
Parties de l'Annexe II	*10 213.9*	*28.6*	*221.7*	*44.7*	*10 508.9*	*97.5%*	*638.9*	*434.5*	*391.9*	*45.7*	*1 510.9*	*42.3%*
Amérique du Nord	*5 598.4*	*20.0*	*58.8*	*31.4*	*5 708.7*	*98.4%*	*501.6*	*178.3*	*241.3*	*36.9*	*958.0*	*52.4%*
Europe	*3 149.2*	*7.9*	*107.5*	*9.9*	*3 274.5*	*96.4%*	*93.7*	*160.8*	*105.0*	*5.0*	*364.5*	*25.7%*
Pacifique	*1 466.3*	*0.6*	*55.4*	*3.3*	*1 525.7*	*96.1%*	*43.6*	*95.4*	*45.6*	*3.8*	*188.4*	*23.1%*
Annexe I EET	*2 828.0*	*9.9*	*56.3*	*15.1*	*2 909.2*	*97.5%*	*537.7*	*156.2*	*90.8*	*4.2*	*788.9*	*68.2%*
Parties non Annexe I	*7 946.5*	*157.6*	*596.2*	*2 135.8*	*10 836.1*	*74.8%*	*1 023.0*	*2 208.9*	*680.8*	*102.4*	*4 015.1*	*25.5%*
Parties Kyoto (Annexe I)	*7 849.1*	*23.0*	*225.2*	*29.1*	*8 126.4*	*96.9%*	*713.1*	*424.1*	*265.4*	*45.2*	*1 447.7*	*49.3%*
Soutes internat.	**688.0**	-	-	-	**688.0**	**100%**	-	-	-	-	-	-
Total Non-OCDE	**9 545.5**	**163.8**	**591.1**	**2 117.9**	**12 418.3**	**78.2%**	**1 455.0**	**2 290.8**	**711.8**	**103.7**	**4 561.3**	**31.9%**
Total OCDE	**11 595.5**	**32.4**	**300.8**	**77.8**	**12 006.6**	**96.8%**	**747.9**	**525.3**	**457.1**	**48.8**	**1 779.1**	**42.0%**
Canada	465.1	4.5	7.0	0.9	477.5	98.3%	44.0	20.5	25.9	32.2	122.6	35.9%
Mexique	309.6	3.7	17.4	29.6	360.3	86.9%	22.8	41.8	32.3	1.5	98.4	23.2%
Etats-Unis	5 133.3	15.5	51.9	30.5	5 231.2	98.4%	457.5	157.8	215.4	4.7	835.4	54.8%
OCDE Amérique du N.	**5 908.0**	**23.8**	**76.3**	**61.0**	**6 069.0**	**97.7%**	**524.4**	**220.0**	**273.6**	**38.4**	**1 056.5**	**49.6%**
Australie	285.2	0.3	4.4	0.8	290.7	98.2%	25.2	65.6	9.4	1.3	101.5	24.8%
Japon	1 156.7	0.1	50.6	2.4	1 209.8	95.6%	16.6	8.1	33.5	2.5	60.6	27.3%
Corée	364.8	-	27.9	2.1	394.9	92.4%	4.5	10.3	11.7	0.9	27.3	16.5%
Nouvelle-Zélande	24.4	0.3	0.4	0.1	25.2	97.9%	1.9	21.7	2.7	0.0	26.3	7.1%
OCDE Pacifique	**1 831.1**	**0.6**	**83.3**	**5.5**	**1920.6**	**95.4%**	**48.1**	**105.6**	**57.3**	**4.7**	**215.7**	**22.3%**
Autriche	59.2	-	3.2	0.5	62.9	94.1%	1.0	4.2	2.9	0.1	8.2	11.9%
Belgique	120.9	-	5.3	0.2	126.5	95.6%	1.1	5.5	3.0	0.3	9.9	11.3%
République tchèque	123.5	-	3.3	0.1	126.9	97.3%	8.9	3.6	3.5	0.2	16.2	55.0%
Danemark	57.6	0.3	1.4	0.2	59.5	97.3%	0.6	4.3	0.9	0.0	5.7	9.7%
Finlande	56.0	-	0.7	1.6	58.3	96.0%	0.5	2.1	4.5	0.1	7.3	7.4%
France	353.7	0.3	12.0	2.0	368.0	96.2%	8.3	32.7	8.6	0.6	50.1	16.5%
Allemagne	869.3	1.1	25.8	1.3	897.4	97.0%	40.4	27.6	23.8	0.9	92.6	43.6%
Grèce	75.8	0.0	6.9	0.3	83.0	91.4%	0.5	3.1	2.7	0.2	6.5	8.2%
Hongrie	58.8	-	1.8	0.5	61.0	96.2%	6.4	2.4	3.4	0.0	12.2	52.5%
Islande	1.9	-	0.0	0.0	2.0	98.0%	0.0	0.2	0.1	-	0.3	1.5%
Irlande	33.0	-	0.8	0.0	33.8	97.6%	0.7	9.7	1.5	0.0	11.9	6.1%
Italie	409.7	-	19.3	0.7	429.6	95.4%	5.4	15.6	18.6	0.4	40.1	13.5%
Luxembourg	8.2	-	0.4	0.0	8.5	95.7%	0.1	-	0.1	0.0	0.2	30.8%
Pays-Bas	171.3	0.4	1.7	0.2	173.6	98.9%	3.7	8.9	5.6	0.2	18.3	20.1%
Norvège	32.8	0.8	0.9	0.2	34.7	97.0%	5.1	2.1	2.9	0.0	10.1	50.3%
Pologne	331.5	-	8.8	0.5	340.8	97.3%	60.3	14.6	7.6	0.2	82.7	72.9%
Portugal	48.3	0.1	3.9	0.1	52.4	92.4%	0.2	3.6	2.9	0.9	7.5	2.0%
République slovaque	40.8	-	2.2	0.1	43.1	94.7%	2.8	1.7	1.3	0.1	5.9	47.4%
Espagne	233.7	0.2	14.2	0.7	248.7	94.0%	5.2	13.7	11.3	0.9	31.0	16.8%
Suède	57.5	0.1	1.4	1.1	60.1	95.8%	0.5	3.2	3.9	0.1	7.7	6.8%
Suisse	41.0	0.0	2.0	0.5	43.6	94.2%	0.3	3.2	1.2	0.0	4.7	7.4%
Turquie	152.7	0.1	17.7	0.2	170.7	89.5%	3.3	16.5	5.5	0.1	25.5	13.0%
Royaume-Uni	519.1	4.6	7.7	0.3	531.7	98.5%	20.2	21.2	10.6	0.4	52.3	38.6%
OCDE Europe	**3 856.4**	**8.1**	**141.2**	**11.3**	**4 017.0**	**96.2%**	**175.4**	**199.6**	**126.2**	**5.7**	**507.0**	**34.6%**
Union européenne - 27	*3 857.9*	*7.1*	*127.7*	*12.2*	*4 004.9*	*96.5%*	*187.7*	*193.6*	*124.6*	*5.8*	*511.6*	*36.7%*

* Total Monde inclue le total Non-OCDE, le total OCDE ainsi que les soutes internationales.

Sources: AIE, méthode sectorielle pour les émissions de CO$_2$ dues à la combustion d'énergie. Base de données EDGAR 3.2 pour les autres émissions. En général, pour les émissions autres que celles de CO2 dues à la combustion d'énergie, les estimations sont sujettes à une incertitude significativement plus grande.

1995 Greenhouse gas emissions

Emissions de gaz à effet de serre pour 1995

million tonnes of CO$_2$ equivalent using GWP-100

Energy	Agriculture	Industrial processes	Other	Total	Share of energy	HFCs	PFCs	SF$_6$	Total	Share of energy	
		N$_2$O				HFCs	PFCs	SF$_6$	Total		
							Industrial processes		Total		
144.5	**2 985.2**	**188.7**	**210.6**	**3 529.0**	**4.1%**	**120.1**	**98.6**	**143.5**	**35 344.5**	**69.0%**	**World ***
111.2	1 484.8	251.3	153.0	2 000.2	5.6%	110.6	79.3	111.9	18 216.0	79.7%	Annex I Parties
101.0	1 288.4	220.2	149.7	1 759.2	5.7%	105.3	54.1	102.0	14 040.4	78.2%	Annex II Parties
38.0	369.3	44.1	57.3	508.7	7.5%	55.4	26.8	58.4	7 315.9	84.2%	North America
56.4	782.2	165.5	88.2	1 092.3	5.2%	31.9	13.4	24.2	4 800.8	68.9%	Europe
6.5	136.9	10.6	4.1	158.2	4.1%	18.0	14.0	19.5	1 923.7	78.9%	Pacific
9.7	158.2	25.5	2.8	196.2	5.0%	5.2	24.5	8.5	3 932.7	86.1%	Annex I EIT
33.3	1 500.4	- 62.6	57.7	1 528.8	2.2%	9.5	19.3	31.6	16 440.4	55.7%	Non-Annex I Parties
75.0	1 110.7	202.1	101.2	1 489.0	5.0%	56.5	59.6	58.3	11 237.5	77.1%	Annex I Kyoto Parties
-	-	-	-	-	-	-	-	-	688.0	100.0%	**Internat. bunkers**
83.2	2 059.2	48.5	118.8	2 309.7	3.6%	12.1	40.9	36.5	19 378.8	58.0%	**Non-OECD Total**
61.2	926.0	140.2	91.8	1 219.3	5.0%	108.0	57.7	107.0	15 277.6	81.4%	**OECD Total**
2.5	41.1	2.8	6.3	52.7	4.8%	1.4	7.7	6.2	668.0	77.3%	Canada
1.3	61.0	1.5	2.1	65.9	1.9%	0.9	0.3	0.5	526.4	64.1%	Mexico
35.5	328.2	41.3	51.1	456.0	7.8%	54.0	19.1	52.2	6 647.9	84.9%	United States
39.3	**430.3**	**45.6**	**59.4**	**574.5**	**6.8%**	**56.3**	**27.1**	**58.9**	**7 842.3**	**82.8%**	**OECD N. America**
1.7	92.0	1.1	0.3	95.1	1.8%	1.4	1.2	1.0	490.9	63.6%	Australia
4.7	13.7	9.5	3.8	31.7	14.9%	16.4	12.4	18.3	1 349.4	87.3%	Japan
1.0	8.9	3.1	0.1	13.1	7.8%	1.1	1.8	3.0	441.1	84.0%	Korea
0.1	31.2	0.0	0.0	31.4	0.3%	0.1	0.3	0.1	83.4	31.9%	New Zealand
7.5	**145.8**	**13.7**	**4.3**	**171.3**	**4.4%**	**19.1**	**15.7**	**22.5**	**2 364.8**	**79.8%**	**OECD Pacific**
0.3	4.5	0.8	0.1	5.6	4.5%	0.3	0.1	0.3	77.4	78.1%	Austria
0.4	6.3	0.6	1.6	8.8	4.0%	0.4	0.0	0.3	145.8	83.9%	Belgium
0.4	5.4	1.0	0.2	6.9	5.7%	0.2	0.0	0.0	150.3	88.4%	Czech Republic
0.2	6.6	0.9	0.8	8.6	2.9%	0.3	0.0	0.2	74.3	79.1%	Denmark
0.3	3.4	1.4	0.5	5.6	5.1%	0.1	0.0	0.2	71.6	79.4%	Finland
1.3	58.8	9.6	6.5	76.1	1.7%	3.3	1.4	4.2	503.2	72.2%	France
3.7	50.0	10.8	5.1	69.6	5.3%	6.9	2.2	10.7	1 079.5	84.7%	Germany
0.4	12.0	0.6	0.2	13.2	2.8%	0.9	0.1	0.1	103.8	74.0%	Greece
0.2	5.8	1.4	0.2	7.5	2.3%	0.2	0.3	0.0	81.3	80.4%	Hungary
0.0	0.4	0.2	0.0	0.6	1.3%	0.0	0.0	0.0	3.0	65.9%	Iceland
0.1	12.2	0.8	0.6	13.8	0.9%	0.1	0.1	0.1	59.9	56.6%	Ireland
1.1	27.2	7.5	0.5	36.4	3.2%	5.0	0.4	2.3	513.8	81.0%	Italy
0.0	0.4	0.0	0.0	0.5	7.0%	0.0	0.0	0.0	9.2	89.6%	Luxembourg
0.5	10.7	6.9	1.9	20.0	2.4%	4.7	0.9	0.4	217.9	80.7%	Netherlands
0.1	3.0	1.7	0.3	5.1	2.8%	0.1	3.6	0.9	54.3	71.5%	Norway
1.4	22.2	5.4	0.4	29.4	4.6%	0.2	0.5	0.0	453.6	86.7%	Poland
0.2	5.9	0.8	0.5	7.4	2.4%	0.1	0.0	0.1	67.6	72.1%	Portugal
0.1	2.3	0.6	0.2	3.2	3.2%	0.1	0.0	0.0	52.3	83.6%	Slovak Republic
0.9	28.4	2.2	3.7	35.1	2.5%	3.7	1.8	0.7	321.0	74.7%	Spain
0.3	4.8	0.8	0.5	6.5	5.4%	0.2	0.7	0.6	75.8	77.2%	Sweden
0.3	2.6	0.2	0.1	3.2	8.8%	0.3	0.1	0.6	52.5	79.4%	Switzerland
0.5	38.2	5.6	0.6	44.8	1.1%	0.0	0.6	1.4	242.9	64.5%	Turkey
1.9	38.9	21.1	3.9	65.8	2.8%	5.6	1.9	2.4	659.7	82.7%	United Kingdom
14.4	**350.0**	**80.8**	**28.2**	**473.4**	**3.0%**	**32.6**	**14.9**	**25.7**	**5 070.6**	**80.0%**	**OECD Europe**
14.5	327.4	79.6	27.7	449.1	3.2%	32.4	12.1	22.9	5 033.0	80.8%	European Union - 27

* Total World includes Non-OECD total, OECD total as well as international bunkers.
Sources: IEA, Sectoral Approach for CO$_2$ emissions from fuel combustion. EDGAR 3.2 database for other emissions. In general, estimates for emissions other than CO$_2$ from fuel combustion are subject to significantly larger uncertainties.

1995 Greenhouse gas emissions

Emissions de gaz à effet de serre pour 1995

millions de tonnes d'équivalent CO$_2$ selon le PRC-100

	CO$_2$						CH$_4$					
	Fuel Comb.	Fugitive	Industrial processes	Other	Total	Share of energy	Energy	Agricult.	Waste	Other	Total	Share of energy
Total Non-OCDE	**9 545.5**	**163.8**	**591.1**	**2 117.9**	**12 418.3**	**78.2%**	**1 455.0**	**2 290.8**	**711.8**	**103.7**	**4 561.3**	**31.9%**
Algérie	59.3	15.6	3.1	3.5	81.5	91.9%	12.5	3.5	3.9	0.2	20.2	62.2%
Angola	4.0	1.7	0.1	16.0	21.9	26.3%	3.2	9.1	1.2	0.8	14.4	22.4%
Bénin	0.2	-	0.2	2.5	2.9	7.5%	0.5	1.8	0.6	0.1	3.0	16.0%
Botswana	3.3	-	-	-	3.3	100.0%	0.0	0.1	0.0	-	0.1	11.5%
Cameroun	2.5	4.4	0.3	17.2	24.4	28.3%	1.8	6.2	1.8	0.9	10.8	16.8%
Congo	0.5	-	0.0	10.2	10.8	4.9%	1.4	0.5	0.4	0.6	2.9	48.2%
Rép. dém. du Congo	2.1	0.2	0.1	158.8	161.1	1.4%	3.4	12.0	5.1	8.8	29.3	11.7%
Côte d'Ivoire	3.2	-	0.2	2.4	5.8	54.8%	1.2	2.9	1.8	0.0	5.9	20.2%
Egypte	84.0	2.1	7.6	4.6	98.3	87.6%	9.2	10.9	7.1	0.0	27.3	33.6%
Erythrée	0.8	-	0.0	0.4	1.2	65.5%	0.3	1.6	0.3	-	2.2	11.4%
Ethiopie	2.3	-	0.3	14.5	17.2	13.7%	4.2	31.9	5.3	0.5	41.9	10.1%
Gabon	1.3	3.2	0.1	20.1	24.7	18.5%	1.9	0.2	0.2	1.1	3.5	56.2%
Ghana	3.3	-	0.7	9.2	13.2	25.1%	0.8	3.0	2.1	0.5	6.5	12.9%
Kenya	7.3	-	0.8	5.2	13.3	54.8%	3.4	13.1	3.0	0.0	19.5	17.5%
Libye	35.1	3.4	1.3	0.3	40.1	96.0%	7.0	0.8	1.0	-	8.7	79.7%
Maroc	25.4	-	3.2	1.3	29.9	85.2%	0.7	4.8	3.6	0.1	9.1	7.2%
Mozambique	1.1	-	0.1	10.1	11.3	10.1%	1.9	5.8	1.9	0.4	10.1	19.3%
Namibie	1.8	-	0.0	1.6	3.4	53.7%	0.2	3.7	0.2	0.1	4.1	4.3%
Nigéria	30.4	47.7	0.8	38.0	116.9	66.8%	32.1	24.5	12.8	0.6	70.0	45.8%
Sénégal	2.5	-	0.3	3.4	6.2	40.2%	0.3	4.7	1.1	0.2	6.2	4.6%
Afrique du Sud	276.8	-	4.9	5.1	286.8	96.5%	29.0	15.6	8.8	0.2	53.6	54.0%
Soudan	4.6	-	0.1	26.6	31.3	14.6%	9.2	29.2	3.0	0.9	42.4	21.7%
Rép. unie de Tanzanie	2.5	-	0.4	22.3	25.2	10.0%	6.6	18.5	3.1	0.6	28.8	23.0%
Togo	0.6	-	0.2	1.6	2.4	24.4%	0.4	1.0	0.5	0.1	1.9	19.3%
Tunisie	14.3	0.3	2.9	0.8	18.3	79.8%	1.1	1.9	1.3	0.0	4.3	26.3%
Zambie	2.0	-	0.3	15.4	17.7	11.6%	0.9	7.4	1.0	0.8	10.1	8.7%
Zimbabwe	14.8	-	0.5	4.1	19.4	76.4%	2.7	5.9	1.4	0.1	10.0	26.6%
Autres pays d'Afrique	17.0	-	0.6	81.7	99.3	17.1%	13.0	83.9	13.9	3.7	114.5	11.4%
Afrique	**603.2**	**78.6**	**29.1**	**476.7**	**1 187.7**	**57.4%**	**148.9**	**304.8**	**86.5**	**21.2**	**561.4**	**26.5%**
Bahrein	11.6	-	0.1	0.0	11.7	99.0%	1.6	0.0	0.1	-	1.7	92.3%
Rép. islamique d'Iran	249.4	22.5	8.4	7.0	287.3	94.6%	36.5	19.4	11.2	0.3	67.3	54.1%
Irak	71.8	0.1	8.9	1.0	81.8	87.8%	2.3	2.9	3.5	-	8.7	26.4%
Israël	46.3	-	2.5	0.0	48.9	94.8%	0.1	0.5	0.5	0.0	1.1	8.4%
Jordanie	12.1	-	1.7	0.3	14.1	86.1%	0.2	0.4	0.8	0.0	1.4	12.2%
Koweit	41.0	1.0	1.0	0.1	43.1	97.5%	6.9	0.1	0.4	-	7.4	93.7%
Liban	12.6	-	1.7	0.6	14.9	84.2%	0.1	0.2	0.6	0.0	0.9	12.6%
Oman	14.4	0.7	0.0	0.1	15.2	99.4%	1.8	0.3	0.4	0.0	2.4	72.7%
Qatar	18.8	-	0.3	0.0	19.1	98.4%	2.5	0.1	0.2	0.0	2.8	91.1%
Arabie saoudite	204.5	0.5	7.8	0.6	213.4	96.1%	45.5	2.1	3.2	0.0	50.7	89.7%
Syrie	38.6	3.9	2.2	1.1	45.8	92.8%	2.1	2.2	2.1	0.0	6.4	32.6%
Emirats arabes unis	70.0	0.7	3.0	0.2	73.9	95.7%	25.6	0.3	0.4	-	26.3	97.2%
Yémen	9.3	-	0.5	0.6	10.5	89.2%	1.8	1.9	2.1	-	5.8	31.7%
Moyen-Orient	**800.4**	**29.4**	**38.2**	**11.6**	**879.6**	**94.3%**	**127.0**	**30.3**	**25.4**	**0.4**	**183.0**	**69.4%**
Albanie	1.9	-	0.1	0.2	2.1	86.6%	0.2	1.8	0.4	0.0	2.3	8.7%
Bosnie-Herzégovine	3.3	-	0.1	0.0	3.5	96.8%	0.5	0.6	0.3	0.0	1.4	34.0%
Bulgarie	53.4	-	1.4	0.2	55.0	97.1%	2.6	2.0	1.8	0.1	6.5	40.0%
Croatie	15.8	-	1.0	0.4	17.1	92.3%	1.5	1.1	0.8	0.0	3.4	42.7%
Chypre	5.2	-	0.5	0.0	5.7	91.1%	0.0	0.1	0.1	0.0	0.3	3.7%
Gibraltar	0.3	-	-	0.0	0.3	100.0%	0.0	-	0.0	-	0.0	11.7%
ex-RY de Macédoine	8.8	-	0.3	0.3	9.3	94.0%	0.3	0.9	0.3	0.0	1.4	18.2%
Malte	2.4	-	0.0	0.0	2.4	99.8%	0.0	0.0	0.0	-	0.1	3.5%
Roumanie	117.1	-	3.4	0.7	121.1	96.7%	15.8	9.1	3.9	0.2	29.0	54.5%
Serbie	44.0	-	1.2	0.0	45.2	97.4%	1.2	7.1	1.3	0.0	9.6	12.1%
Slovénie	13.0	-	1.1	0.1	14.2	91.4%	0.3	0.9	0.5	0.0	1.6	17.3%
Europe Non-OCDE	**265.1**	**-**	**9.0**	**1.8**	**276.0**	**96.1%**	**22.3**	**23.6**	**9.5**	**0.3**	**55.6**	**40.0%**

1995 Greenhouse gas emissions

Emissions de gaz à effet de serre pour 1995

million tonnes of CO$_2$ equivalent using GWP-100

N$_2$O Energy	Agriculture	Industrial processes	Other	Total	Share of energy	HFCs	PFCs	SF$_6$	Total	Share of energy	
						Industrial processes			Total		
83.2	**2 059.2**	**48.5**	**118.8**	**2 309.7**	**3.6%**	**12.1**	**40.9**	**36.5**	**19 378.8**	**58.0%**	**Non-OECD Total**
0.2	7.8	0.1	0.1	8.3	2.8%	-	-	0.1	110.1	79.6%	Algeria
0.2	4.3	-	1.0	5.5	3.1%	-	-	0.0	41.8	21.9%	Angola
0.1	2.2	-	0.1	2.4	2.9%	-	-	0.0	8.4	9.2%	Benin
0.0	4.3	-	0.0	4.3	0.9%	-	-	0.0	7.8	43.4%	Botswana
0.2	7.6	-	1.1	8.8	2.0%	-	0.7	0.0	44.6	19.9%	Cameroon
0.0	0.2	-	0.7	0.9	4.0%	-	-	0.0	14.7	13.5%	Congo
0.5	8.9	-	10.6	19.9	2.5%	-	-	0.0	210.3	2.9%	Dem. Rep. of Congo
0.2	2.4	-	0.1	2.6	7.1%	-	-	0.0	14.4	32.0%	Côte d'Ivoire
0.6	18.9	3.2	0.0	22.7	2.5%	0.0	0.5	0.8	149.6	64.1%	Egypt
0.0	1.4	-	0.0	1.4	2.9%	-	-	0.0	4.8	22.2%	Eritrea
0.7	51.7	-	0.6	52.9	1.3%	-	-	0.0	112.0	6.5%	Ethiopia
0.0	0.3	-	1.4	1.7	2.2%	-	-	0.0	29.8	21.9%	Gabon
0.1	6.0	-	0.5	6.7	2.0%	-	0.2	0.0	26.4	16.2%	Ghana
0.5	19.7	-	0.0	20.2	2.7%	-	-	0.0	53.1	21.2%	Kenya
0.1	2.1	-	0.0	2.3	5.4%	-	-	0.3	51.4	88.7%	Libya
0.1	13.3	-	0.1	13.5	1.0%	-	-	0.0	52.5	49.9%	Morocco
0.3	2.1	-	0.5	2.9	10.0%	-	-	0.0	24.3	13.9%	Mozambique
0.0	3.6	-	0.1	3.7	0.7%	-	-	0.0	11.2	17.9%	Namibia
3.0	27.9	-	0.7	31.6	9.6%	-	-	0.1	218.7	51.8%	Nigeria
0.1	7.2	-	0.2	7.5	1.0%	0.0	-	0.0	19.8	14.3%	Senegal
1.6	21.1	2.9	0.4	26.0	6.1%	0.4	0.1	0.9	367.9	83.5%	South Africa
1.0	40.1	-	1.1	42.2	2.4%	-	-	0.0	115.8	12.7%	Sudan
1.3	22.2	-	0.7	24.3	5.5%	-	-	0.0	78.3	13.4%	United Rep. of Tanzania
0.1	1.9	-	0.1	2.1	2.9%	-	-	0.0	6.3	15.9%	Togo
0.1	4.2	0.4	0.0	4.7	1.9%	0.0	-	0.0	27.3	57.9%	Tunisia
0.2	3.8	0.5	1.0	5.4	2.9%	-	-	0.0	33.3	9.3%	Zambia
0.2	6.4	-	0.2	6.8	3.7%	0.0	-	0.0	36.2	49.0%	Zimbabwe
1.8	93.3	-	4.4	99.5	0.9%	0.0	-	0.0	313.3	10.1%	Other Africa
13.4	**384.6**	**7.2**	**25.6**	**430.8**	**3.1%**	**0.4**	**1.5**	**2.3**	**2 184.1**	**38.6%**	**Africa**
0.0	0.0	-	0.0	0.1	43.2%	-	0.2	0.0	13.7	96.8%	Bahrain
0.8	51.3	0.4	0.3	52.7	1.4%	-	0.1	1.3	408.8	75.6%	Islamic Rep. of Iran
0.3	5.7	-	0.0	5.9	4.3%	-	-	0.4	96.8	76.8%	Iraq
0.2	1.6	-	0.0	1.7	8.9%	0.1	0.1	0.6	52.5	88.7%	Israel
0.1	1.4	-	0.0	1.5	3.6%	0.0	-	0.0	16.9	73.0%	Jordan
0.1	0.2	-	0.0	0.3	27.3%	-	-	0.4	51.1	95.9%	Kuwait
0.1	0.9	-	0.0	1.0	5.3%	-	-	0.0	16.8	75.6%	Lebanon
0.0	0.9	-	0.0	0.9	2.8%	-	-	0.0	18.5	91.1%	Oman
0.0	0.3	-	0.0	0.3	6.8%	-	-	0.0	22.2	96.2%	Qatar
0.5	7.6	-	0.0	8.1	5.8%	-	-	1.4	273.7	91.7%	Saudi Arabia
0.2	7.8	0.1	0.0	8.2	2.1%	-	-	0.0	60.5	74.1%	Syria
0.1	1.3	-	0.0	1.4	7.3%	-	0.1	0.3	102.0	94.5%	United Arab Emirates
0.1	4.8	-	0.0	4.9	1.5%	-	-	0.0	21.2	53.2%	Yemen
2.2	**83.8**	**0.5**	**0.4**	**87.0**	**2.6%**	**0.1**	**0.5**	**4.5**	**1 154.8**	**83.0%**	**Middle East**
0.0	1.9	-	0.0	1.9	1.4%	0.0	-	0.0	6.4	32.5%	Albania
0.0	0.6	-	0.0	0.6	8.0%	0.0	0.1	0.0	5.7	68.8%	Bosnia-Herzegovina
0.3	4.1	2.9	0.0	7.4	4.7%	0.1	-	0.0	69.0	81.7%	Bulgaria
0.2	2.0	0.8	0.0	3.1	5.3%	0.0	0.3	0.0	23.9	72.9%	Croatia
0.0	0.5	-	0.0	0.6	3.5%	-	-	0.0	6.6	79.5%	Cyprus
0.0	-	-	-	0.0	100.0%	-	-	0.0	0.3	98.2%	Gibraltar
0.1	1.1	-	0.0	1.2	5.5%	0.0	-	0.0	11.9	76.2%	FYR of Macedonia
0.0	0.1	-	0.0	0.1	15.1%	-	-	0.0	2.5	94.0%	Malta
0.3	12.3	3.6	0.2	16.4	1.8%	0.0	1.3	0.0	167.7	79.4%	Romania
0.2	5.9	0.4	0.0	6.6	3.4%	0.1	0.1	0.0	61.6	73.7%	Serbia
0.0	1.0	-	0.0	1.1	4.4%	0.0	0.3	0.0	17.2	77.4%	Slovenia
1.3	**29.6**	**7.7**	**0.4**	**38.9**	**3.2%**	**0.3**	**2.0**	**0.1**	**372.9**	**77.4%**	**Non-OECD Europe**

1995 Greenhouse gas emissions

Emissions de gaz à effet de serre pour 1995

millions de tonnes d'équivalent CO$_2$ selon le PRC-100

	CO$_2$						CH$_4$					
	Fuel Comb.	Fugitive	Industrial processes	Other	Total	Share of energy	Energy	Agricult.	Waste	Other	Total	Share of energy
Arménie	3.4	-	0.1	0.1	3.6	94.4%	0.6	0.6	0.5	0.0	1.7	33.7%
Azerbaïdjan	30.9	-	0.1	0.2	31.1	99.1%	5.5	3.4	1.0	0.0	9.9	55.7%
Bélarus	59.4	-	0.9	0.2	60.6	98.1%	6.0	8.8	1.9	0.0	16.6	35.9%
Estonie	16.0	-	0.2	0.1	16.4	97.9%	0.5	0.8	0.4	0.0	1.6	28.4%
Géorgie	7.1	-	0.1	0.1	7.2	97.4%	0.7	1.6	0.8	0.0	3.1	22.8%
Kazakhstan	167.0	1.1	1.4	0.1	169.7	99.1%	17.9	21.5	2.6	0.2	42.1	42.4%
Kirghizistan	4.6	-	0.2	0.1	4.9	94.6%	0.5	3.1	0.6	-	4.1	11.3%
Lettonie	8.8	-	0.1	0.3	9.2	95.4%	0.7	1.0	0.5	0.0	2.2	30.6%
Lituanie	14.2	-	0.4	0.3	14.9	95.2%	1.2	2.1	0.7	0.0	4.0	30.6%
République de Moldavie	10.9	-	0.0	0.1	11.1	98.7%	1.3	1.8	0.6	-	3.6	34.4%
Russie	1 582.9	9.9	25.0	10.4	1 628.2	97.8%	371.4	70.1	53.9	2.7	498.1	74.6%
Tadjikistan	5.3	-	0.0	0.1	5.4	96.7%	0.5	2.6	0.6	-	3.8	13.7%
Turkménistan	34.4	-	0.2	0.1	34.8	99.1%	15.6	3.1	0.6	0.0	19.2	81.0%
Ukraine	392.8	0.0	6.7	1.3	400.8	98.0%	58.6	31.8	9.8	0.7	100.9	58.1%
Ouzbékistan	101.6	-	1.9	0.5	104.0	97.7%	31.5	10.9	2.8	-	45.2	69.7%
Ex-URSS	**2 439.3**	**11.0**	**37.4**	**14.0**	**2 501.7**	**97.9%**	**512.3**	**163.1**	**77.2**	**3.6**	**756.3**	**67.7%**
Argentine	115.3	4.0	2.8	13.3	135.4	88.1%	10.3	63.6	11.9	0.8	86.6	11.9%
Bolivie	8.2	1.9	0.4	71.1	81.6	12.4%	0.7	9.9	1.6	4.1	16.3	4.4%
Brésil	238.4	2.3	18.2	369.0	627.9	38.3%	9.2	217.4	53.6	21.4	301.6	3.0%
Chili	39.1	0.3	2.4	6.2	48.0	82.0%	1.9	6.5	7.8	0.3	16.4	11.5%
Colombie	58.0	0.7	5.5	41.1	105.4	55.7%	7.9	33.2	10.4	2.2	53.7	14.8%
Costa Rica	4.4	-	0.5	6.2	11.1	40.1%	0.1	2.2	0.8	0.3	3.4	2.0%
Cuba	22.1	-	0.9	3.6	26.5	83.1%	0.2	5.4	2.8	0.1	8.6	2.8%
République dominicaine	11.4	-	0.7	2.8	14.9	76.2%	0.2	3.5	1.7	0.1	5.6	3.9%
Equateur	16.3	1.5	1.1	29.5	48.4	36.7%	2.1	7.7	2.6	1.7	14.1	14.6%
El Salvador	4.7	-	0.5	1.1	6.3	74.9%	0.4	1.6	1.1	0.0	3.1	12.5%
Guatemala	6.0	-	0.7	13.1	19.7	30.4%	0.8	2.6	1.8	0.7	5.8	13.0%
Haiti	0.9	-	0.2	0.5	1.6	56.9%	0.2	1.8	1.1	0.0	3.2	7.7%
Honduras	3.9	-	0.2	10.2	14.2	27.3%	0.3	2.8	1.0	0.5	4.7	7.1%
Jamaïque	8.4	-	0.4	2.1	10.9	77.0%	0.0	0.6	0.5	0.1	1.3	2.4%
Antilles néerlandaises	3.0	-	-	0.0	3.0	99.2%	0.0	0.0	0.1	-	0.1	35.8%
Nicaragua	2.5	-	0.2	23.9	26.6	9.4%	0.3	2.6	0.8	1.3	5.0	5.1%
Panama	4.1	-	0.3	11.9	16.4	25.2%	0.1	1.7	0.6	0.7	3.1	3.6%
Paraguay	3.4	-	0.4	16.6	20.4	16.9%	0.3	9.4	1.1	0.9	11.7	2.7%
Pérou	23.7	0.4	1.9	41.5	67.5	35.7%	1.6	8.3	6.5	2.3	18.7	8.4%
Trinité-et-Tobago	12.3	2.0	0.3	0.4	14.9	95.1%	2.2	0.1	0.6	0.0	2.9	75.5%
Uruguay	4.5	-	0.3	0.3	5.1	88.6%	0.1	15.3	1.2	0.0	16.7	0.6%
Vénézuéla	118.3	12.3	3.5	75.2	209.3	62.4%	19.6	17.5	8.0	4.3	49.4	39.7%
Autres Amérique Latine	13.4	-	1.0	7.8	22.2	60.2%	0.6	2.7	2.2	0.3	5.7	9.9%
Amérique latine	**722.3**	**25.3**	**42.4**	**747.5**	**1 537.5**	**48.6%**	**59.1**	**416.4**	**119.9**	**42.3**	**637.7**	**9.3%**
Bangladesh	20.5	-	0.2	18.0	38.7	52.9%	9.9	59.7	15.0	0.0	84.6	11.6%
Brunei Darussalam	4.7	1.0	0.0	0.8	6.5	87.5%	1.9	0.0	0.1	0.0	2.0	94.7%
Cambodge	1.4	-	-	26.5	27.9	5.0%	0.8	9.0	1.4	1.7	12.8	5.9%
Taipei chinois	158.7	-	10.8	1.9	171.4	92.6%	2.4	-	3.7	0.2	6.2	38.0%
Inde	782.6	3.0	33.7	101.9	921.1	85.3%	94.4	431.8	128.7	0.5	655.5	14.4%
Indonésie	192.2	9.6	11.6	207.5	421.0	47.9%	85.5	86.8	32.3	10.1	214.7	39.8%
Rép. pop. dém. de Corée	74.9	-	8.4	2.6	85.8	87.2%	1.9	4.7	3.4	0.1	10.0	18.8%
Malaisie	78.7	5.4	5.3	94.4	183.8	45.8%	11.3	5.1	3.0	4.9	24.4	46.5%
Mongolie	10.1	-	0.1	0.3	10.4	96.6%	0.1	7.1	0.4	0.6	8.2	1.8%
Myanmar	6.7	0.0	0.3	75.0	82.0	8.2%	3.9	35.6	6.2	3.9	49.6	7.8%
Népal	1.7	-	0.1	10.4	12.3	14.2%	3.2	27.7	2.9	0.3	34.1	9.5%
Pakistan	80.1	-	3.9	20.0	104.0	77.0%	12.3	61.3	18.6	0.3	92.5	13.3%
Philippines	59.5	-	5.2	58.9	123.6	48.1%	5.1	26.5	10.0	2.8	44.5	11.5%
Singapour	38.0	-	1.6	-	39.6	96.0%	0.4	0.0	0.7	-	1.1	35.1%
Sri Lanka	5.5	-	0.4	3.8	9.8	56.5%	1.2	6.8	2.5	0.1	10.7	11.6%
Thaïlande	141.3	-	17.1	32.2	190.6	74.1%	4.9	58.1	8.4	1.7	73.1	6.7%
Viêt-Nam	27.5	0.5	3.3	29.9	61.2	45.8%	6.8	41.0	10.2	1.2	59.1	11.4%
Autres pays d'Asie	9.3	-	0.1	74.6	84.1	11.1%	3.3	12.1	4.6	3.8	23.8	14.0%
Asie	**1 693.4**	**19.5**	**102.3**	**758.6**	**2 573.8**	**66.6%**	**249.2**	**873.3**	**252.0**	**32.3**	**1 406.9**	**17.7%**
Rép. populaire de Chine	2 985.9	-	332.6	107.6	3 426.1	87.2%	336.2	479.1	140.0	3.6	958.9	35.1%
Hong Kong, Chine	35.9	-	-	-	35.9	100.0%	0.0	0.0	1.3	-	1.3	2.8%
Chine	**3 021.8**	**-**	**332.6**	**107.6**	**3 462.0**	**87.3%**	**336.3**	**479.1**	**141.3**	**3.6**	**960.2**	**35.0%**

1995 Greenhouse gas emissions

Emissions de gaz à effet de serre pour 1995

million tonnes of CO$_2$ equivalent using GWP-100

N$_2$O						HFCs	PFCs	SF$_6$	Total		
Energy	Agriculture	Industrial processes	Other	Total	Share of energy	Industrial processes			Total	Share of energy	
0.0	0.5	-	0.0	0.5	3.5%	0.0	-	-	5.9	68.1%	Armenia
0.3	2.8	-	0.0	3.1	9.5%	0.0	0.0	-	44.1	83.0%	Azerbaijan
0.2	7.7	2.3	0.1	10.4	1.8%	0.1	-	-	87.7	74.8%	Belarus
0.1	0.7	-	0.0	0.8	10.0%	0.0	-	0.0	18.8	88.1%	Estonia
0.0	1.3	0.5	0.0	1.8	1.1%	0.0	-	-	12.1	64.1%	Georgia
0.7	17.5	-	0.1	18.3	3.9%	0.0	-	-	230.1	81.1%	Kazakhstan
0.0	3.0	-	0.0	3.1	0.9%	0.0	-	-	12.1	42.2%	Kyrgyzstan
0.1	1.1	-	0.0	1.1	5.2%	0.0	-	-	12.6	75.7%	Latvia
0.1	1.8	-	0.0	1.9	3.8%	0.0	-	-	20.8	74.3%	Lithuania
0.0	2.3	-	0.0	2.4	1.7%	0.1	-	-	17.2	71.1%	Republic of Moldova
4.9	56.6	2.5	1.0	65.0	7.5%	4.0	21.9	8.4	2 225.5	88.5%	Russia
0.0	2.3	-	0.0	2.3	1.1%	0.0	0.1	-	11.6	50.1%	Tajikistan
0.0	3.7	0.3	0.0	4.1	1.1%	0.1	-	-	58.1	86.1%	Turkmenistan
1.4	30.3	4.6	0.3	36.6	3.7%	0.2	0.1	-	538.6	84.1%	Ukraine
0.2	10.2	0.0	0.0	10.4	1.8%	0.2	-	-	159.8	83.4%	Uzbekistan
8.0	**141.8**	**10.3**	**1.7**	**161.9**	**5.0%**	**4.6**	**22.1**	**8.4**	**3 455.0**	**86.0%**	**Former USSR**
0.3	66.0	0.1	0.9	67.2	0.4%	0.2	0.1	0.2	289.7	44.8%	Argentina
0.1	10.1	-	4.9	15.0	0.3%	-	-	0.0	112.9	9.6%	Bolivia
2.3	207.0	6.8	28.4	244.5	0.9%	1.2	2.9	1.0	1 179.1	21.4%	Brazil
0.3	8.6	0.2	0.3	9.4	3.1%	-	-	0.0	73.9	56.3%	Chile
0.5	18.0	0.2	2.6	21.3	2.3%	0.0	-	0.1	180.6	37.2%	Colombia
0.0	2.8	0.2	0.4	3.4	1.1%	-	-	0.0	17.9	25.4%	Costa Rica
0.2	7.7	0.7	0.3	8.9	2.3%	0.0	-	0.0	44.1	51.0%	Cuba
0.1	4.0	-	0.2	4.2	1.8%	-	-	0.0	24.8	47.2%	Dominican Republic
0.1	7.8	-	2.0	9.9	1.1%	-	-	0.0	72.4	27.5%	Ecuador
0.1	1.9	-	0.0	2.1	5.2%	-	-	0.0	11.4	45.5%	El Salvador
0.2	4.1	-	0.8	5.1	3.2%	-	-	0.0	30.6	22.6%	Guatemala
0.0	2.5	-	0.0	2.6	1.9%	-	-	0.0	7.4	16.3%	Haiti
0.1	2.7	-	0.7	3.5	2.5%	-	-	0.0	22.4	19.2%	Honduras
0.0	1.0	-	0.1	1.2	3.4%	-	-	0.0	13.4	63.1%	Jamaica
0.0	0.0	-	0.0	0.0	51.3%	-	-	0.0	3.2	96.7%	Netherlands Antilles
0.1	2.3	-	1.6	4.0	1.7%	-	-	0.0	35.6	7.9%	Nicaragua
0.0	1.8	-	0.8	2.6	1.5%	-	-	0.0	22.1	19.3%	Panama
0.1	8.8	-	1.1	9.9	0.9%	-	-	0.0	42.0	9.2%	Paraguay
0.3	11.9	0.2	2.7	15.0	1.7%	0.0	-	0.0	101.3	25.6%	Peru
0.0	0.2	-	0.0	0.3	4.9%	-	-	0.0	18.1	90.6%	Trinidad and Tobago
0.0	16.4	-	0.0	16.5	0.2%	0.0	-	0.0	38.3	12.2%	Uruguay
0.2	17.5	0.0	5.2	22.9	1.0%	0.6	0.3	0.2	282.7	53.2%	Venezuela
0.3	3.8	-	0.4	4.5	6.1%	-	0.1	0.0	32.6	43.7%	Other Latin America
5.3	**407.0**	**8.3**	**53.5**	**474.1**	**1.1%**	**2.1**	**3.4**	**1.7**	**2 656.5**	**30.6%**	**Latin America**
1.8	27.5	-	0.0	29.3	6.1%	-	-	0.0	152.6	21.0%	Bangladesh
0.0	0.0	-	0.0	0.1	16.9%	-	-	0.0	8.5	88.7%	Brunei Darussalam
0.1	2.4	-	1.8	4.3	3.3%				45.0	5.1%	Cambodia
0.8	0.0	0.2	0.0	1.0	78.8%	-	-	0.0	178.6	90.6%	Chinese Taipei
14.3	240.5	1.4	0.0	256.2	5.6%	1.0	1.5	4.6	1 839.9	48.6%	India
3.9	50.4	0.2	12.1	66.6	5.9%	-	0.3	0.7	703.3	41.4%	Indonesia
0.6	7.8	-	0.0	8.4	7.1%	-	-	0.7	105.0	73.6%	DPR of Korea
1.1	5.3	0.1	5.9	12.4	8.8%	-	0.0	0.5	221.1	43.7%	Malaysia
0.0	12.4	-	0.1	12.5	0.2%				31.2	32.8%	Mongolia
0.6	10.5	-	4.7	15.8	4.1%	-	-	0.0	147.5	7.6%	Myanmar
0.6	5.4	-	0.3	6.3	9.5%	-	-	0.0	52.7	10.6%	Nepal
1.8	65.2	0.6	0.3	67.9	2.7%	-	-	0.6	265.0	35.6%	Pakistan
1.3	13.9	0.0	3.3	18.5	6.8%	-	-	0.3	186.9	35.2%	Philippines
0.2	0.0	0.9	0.0	1.1	13.9%	0.1	0.3	0.4	42.7	90.4%	Singapore
0.2	2.3	-	0.1	2.7	9.1%	-	-	0.0	23.1	30.3%	Sri Lanka
0.7	20.9	-	2.0	23.7	3.0%	-	-	0.9	288.2	51.0%	Thailand
1.1	18.0	-	1.4	20.5	5.2%	-	-	0.0	140.9	25.4%	Vietnam
0.6	19.9	-	4.7	25.2	2.3%	0.0	1.3	2.0	136.4	9.7%	Other Asia
29.7	**502.6**	**3.4**	**37.0**	**572.7**	**5.2%**	**1.0**	**3.4**	**10.8**	**4 568.6**	**43.6%**	**Asia**
23.2	509.7	11.2	0.2	544.2	4.3%	3.4	8.1	8.4	4 949.2	67.6%	People's Rep. of China
0.2	0.0	-	0.0	0.2	93.8%	-	-	0.3	37.7	95.8%	Hong Kong, China
23.4	**509.7**	**11.2**	**0.2**	**544.5**	**4.3%**	**3.4**	**8.1**	**8.7**	**4 986.9**	**67.8%**	**China**

2000 Greenhouse gas emissions

Emissions de gaz à effet de serre pour 2000

millions de tonnes d'équivalent CO$_2$ selon le PRC-100

	CO$_2$						CH$_4$					
	Fuel comb.	Fugitive	Industrial processes	Other	Total	Share of energy	Energy	Agricult.	Waste	Other	Total	Share of energy
Monde *	**23 508.5**	**179.0**	**994.1**	**3 310.0**	**27 991.7**	**84.6%**	**2 354.5**	**2 896.9**	**1 221.1**	**268.1**	**6 740.6**	**34.9%**
Parties de l'Annexe I	*13 778.8*	*28.6*	*305.1*	*52.4*	*14 164.9*	*97.5%*	*1 192.9*	*547.7*	*467.2*	*40.2*	*2 248.0*	*53.1%*
Parties de l'Annexe II	*11 018.7*	*19.7*	*233.0*	*38.3*	*11 309.6*	*97.6%*	*662.1*	*422.3*	*367.6*	*24.9*	*1 476.8*	*44.8%*
Amérique du Nord	*6 225.6*	*9.6*	*66.3*	*20.4*	*6 321.9*	*98.6%*	*524.3*	*172.6*	*232.4*	*12.0*	*941.3*	*55.7%*
Europe	*3 229.7*	*9.2*	*115.2*	*12.5*	*3 366.7*	*96.2%*	*89.0*	*149.6*	*91.3*	*3.4*	*333.3*	*26.7%*
Pacifique	*1 563.3*	*0.9*	*51.5*	*5.4*	*1 621.0*	*96.5%*	*48.8*	*100.1*	*43.9*	*9.4*	*202.2*	*24.1%*
Annexe I EET	*2 559.6*	*8.7*	*53.8*	*13.9*	*2 635.9*	*97.4%*	*526.9*	*110.5*	*93.5*	*15.2*	*746.0*	*70.6%*
Parties non Annexe I	*8 922.0*	*150.5*	*689.0*	*3 257.6*	*13 019.1*	*69.7%*	*1 161.6*	*2 349.2*	*753.9*	*227.9*	*4 492.5*	*25.9%*
Parties Kyoto (Annexe I)	*7 830.0*	*23.4*	*227.2*	*32.6*	*8 113.2*	*96.8%*	*705.6*	*373.3*	*253.7*	*32.7*	*1 365.3*	*51.7%*
Soutes internat.	**807.7**	-	-	-	**807.7**	**100%**	-	-	-	-	-	-
Total Non-OCDE	**10 187.3**	**150.6**	**680.4**	**3 206.2**	**14 224.5**	**72.7%**	**1 591.6**	**2 385.6**	**780.6**	**237.0**	**4 994.8**	**31.9%**
Total OCDE	**12 513.5**	**28.5**	**313.7**	**103.8**	**12 959.5**	**96.8%**	**762.9**	**511.3**	**440.5**	**31.1**	**1 745.8**	**43.7%**
Canada	532.6	4.6	8.1	1.0	546.4	98.3%	48.1	20.2	27.0	4.7	99.9	48.2%
Mexique	356.8	8.6	20.5	63.3	449.2	81.3%	26.7	45.8	37.0	4.6	114.1	23.4%
Etats-Unis	5 693.0	5.0	58.2	19.4	5 775.5	98.7%	476.2	152.4	205.4	7.3	841.4	56.6%
OCDE Amérique du N.	**6 582.4**	**18.2**	**86.8**	**83.8**	**6 771.1**	**97.5%**	**551.0**	**218.4**	**269.4**	**16.6**	**1 055.4**	**52.2%**
Australie	338.7	0.6	4.8	2.8	346.9	97.8%	28.3	71.5	9.6	6.7	116.0	24.4%
Japon	1 192.4	0.0	46.1	2.2	1 240.8	96.1%	17.4	7.4	31.9	2.7	59.5	29.3%
Corée	431.3	-	25.5	0.9	457.7	94.2%	5.8	9.5	13.7	0.9	29.9	19.4%
Nouvelle-Zélande	32.3	0.2	0.5	0.3	33.3	97.6%	3.1	21.2	2.4	0.0	26.7	11.5%
OCDE Pacifique	**1 994.6**	**0.9**	**77.0**	**6.3**	**2078.7**	**96.0%**	**54.6**	**109.7**	**57.6**	**10.3**	**232.1**	**23.5%**
Autriche	62.0	-	3.4	0.5	65.8	94.2%	1.1	3.8	2.4	0.1	7.5	14.1%
Belgique	127.3	-	4.8	0.2	132.3	96.2%	1.3	5.1	2.3	0.3	9.0	14.4%
République tchèque	121.6	-	2.9	0.1	124.7	97.6%	9.3	2.9	3.1	0.2	15.4	60.4%
Danemark	49.9	0.4	1.1	0.4	51.8	97.2%	0.8	4.0	0.9	-	5.7	14.2%
Finlande	53.9	-	0.9	1.0	55.9	96.4%	0.6	1.8	3.9	0.1	6.3	8.8%
France	375.8	0.4	11.8	3.7	391.7	96.0%	6.2	32.4	8.2	0.5	47.3	13.1%
Allemagne	827.1	1.0	22.3	1.8	852.2	97.2%	36.8	25.6	12.9	0.9	76.3	48.3%
Grèce	87.4	0.0	7.7	0.3	95.4	91.7%	0.7	2.9	3.4	0.0	7.1	10.1%
Hongrie	55.3	-	2.0	0.3	57.6	95.9%	5.9	2.4	3.6	0.1	11.8	49.6%
Islande	2.1	-	0.1	0.0	2.2	96.8%	0.0	0.2	0.1	-	0.3	1.6%
Irlande	41.2	-	1.4	-	42.6	96.8%	0.9	1.2	1.4	0.0	3.5	25.6%
Italie	424.7	-	21.9	0.9	447.4	94.9%	7.0	15.6	18.4	0.5	41.6	16.9%
Luxembourg	8.0	-	0.4	0.0	8.4	95.4%	0.1	0.0	0.1	0.0	0.2	37.0%
Pays-Bas	173.1	0.3	1.7	0.4	175.5	98.8%	3.6	8.0	4.7	0.2	16.5	22.1%
Norvège	33.8	1.4	1.0	0.2	36.3	96.8%	7.7	1.9	3.1	0.0	12.6	60.8%
Pologne	292.0	-	9.2	0.6	301.8	96.7%	46.3	12.2	8.3	0.2	67.0	69.1%
Portugal	59.5	0.0	5.3	0.1	64.9	91.7%	0.6	3.7	2.7	0.1	7.1	8.1%
République slovaque	37.4	0.0	2.1	0.0	39.5	94.6%	2.9	1.3	1.3	0.1	5.5	52.3%
Espagne	283.9	0.2	20.0	0.7	304.7	93.2%	5.0	16.2	14.9	0.3	36.4	13.8%
Suède	52.8	0.1	1.7	1.0	55.6	95.1%	0.4	2.8	3.6	0.1	6.9	6.2%
Suisse	41.6	0.0	1.9	0.6	44.2	94.3%	0.4	2.9	1.1	0.0	4.4	8.3%
Turquie	200.6	0.2	18.4	0.1	219.3	91.6%	3.9	14.9	6.1	0.2	25.2	15.6%
Royaume-Uni	525.6	5.4	8.0	0.8	539.8	98.4%	15.8	21.4	7.1	0.4	44.7	35.3%
OCDE Europe	**3 936.5**	**9.4**	**149.9**	**13.7**	**4 109.6**	**96.0%**	**157.3**	**183.2**	**113.6**	**4.2**	**458.3**	**34.3%**
Union européenne - 27	*3 841.6*	*7.8*	*136.6*	*16.7*	*4 002.7*	*96.2%*	*163.5*	*176.7*	*111.3*	*4.2*	*455.7*	*35.9%*

* Total Monde inclue le total Non-OCDE, le total OCDE ainsi que les soutes internationales.
Sources: AIE, méthode sectorielle pour les émissions de CO$_2$ dues à la combustion d'énergie. Base de données EDGAR 32FT2000 pour les autres émissions. En général, pour les émissions autres que celles de CO$_2$ dues à la combustion d'énergie, les estimations sont sujettes à une incertitude significativement plus grande.

2000 Greenhouse gas emissions

Emissions de gaz à effet de serre pour 2000

million tonnes of CO$_2$ equivalent using GWP-100

N$_2$O						HFCs	PFCs	SF$_6$	Total		
Energy	Agriculture	Industrial processes	Other	Total	Share of energy	Industrial processes			Total	Share of energy	
153.2	3 105.8	181.2	321.6	3 761.8	4.1%	323.8	108.1	124.7	39 050.6	67.1%	World *
68.2	965.0	132.6	95.8	1 261.7	5.4%	243.3	80.6	91.9	18 090.5	83.3%	Annex I Parties
58.9	796.6	98.0	90.7	1 044.2	5.6%	223.8	51.0	82.6	14 188.1	82.9%	Annex II Parties
37.6	377.3	29.5	58.2	502.6	7.5%	142.6	22.8	39.0	7 970.2	85.3%	North America
13.6	277.3	62.8	26.9	380.6	3.6%	47.1	10.7	19.3	4 157.6	80.4%	Europe
7.6	142.0	5.7	5.6	161.0	4.7%	34.2	17.5	24.3	2 060.3	78.7%	Pacific
8.7	128.3	29.8	4.6	171.3	5.1%	18.4	29.0	8.5	3 609.2	86.0%	Annex I EIT
85.0	2 140.7	48.6	225.8	2 500.1	3.4%	80.5	27.5	32.7	20 152.4	51.2%	Non-Annex I Parties
32.5	583.1	98.0	38.7	752.3	4.3%	106.1	61.8	56.7	10 455.4	82.2%	Annex I Kyoto Parties
-	-	-	-	-	-	-	-	-	807.7	100.0%	Internat. bunkers
89.3	2 162.4	61.8	224.5	2 537.9	3.5%	91.8	52.9	38.0	21 939.8	54.8%	Non-OECD Total
64.0	943.4	119.4	97.2	1 223.9	5.2%	232.0	55.2	86.7	16 303.1	82.0%	OECD Total
2.6	42.8	2.1	1.8	49.3	5.3%	6.5	4.6	4.6	711.4	82.7%	Canada
1.4	64.4	1.0	5.0	71.8	1.9%	2.8	0.2	0.3	638.5	61.6%	Mexico
35.0	334.5	27.4	56.4	453.3	7.7%	136.0	18.2	34.4	7 258.8	85.5%	United States
39.0	441.7	30.5	63.2	574.5	6.8%	145.4	23.0	39.3	8 608.7	83.5%	OECD N. America
2.2	100.0	1.4	1.5	105.1	2.1%	2.8	1.1	0.7	572.6	64.6%	Australia
5.3	12.6	4.3	4.1	26.2	20.2%	31.0	16.3	23.5	1 397.3	87.0%	Japan
1.3	8.4	6.5	0.0	16.2	8.0%	2.5	2.8	2.8	511.9	85.6%	Korea
0.1	29.5	0.0	0.0	29.6	0.4%	0.4	0.2	0.1	90.3	39.5%	New Zealand
8.9	150.4	12.2	5.6	177.1	5.0%	36.7	20.4	27.1	2 572.1	80.0%	OECD Pacific
0.2	4.2	0.9	0.1	5.4	4.1%	1.0	0.1	0.2	80.0	79.1%	Austria
0.4	6.3	0.6	1.7	9.0	4.9%	1.1	0.0	0.2	151.7	85.1%	Belgium
0.4	5.2	1.0	0.2	6.7	6.0%	0.4	0.0	0.0	147.3	89.2%	Czech Republic
0.2	6.2	1.0	0.8	8.3	3.0%	0.7	0.0	0.1	66.6	77.1%	Denmark
0.3	3.3	1.3	0.4	5.3	6.1%	0.4	0.0	0.2	68.1	80.5%	Finland
1.7	59.5	10.0	6.2	77.4	2.1%	7.2	2.0	2.9	528.4	72.7%	France
3.6	50.8	5.7	5.3	65.3	5.5%	10.5	2.2	9.3	1 015.9	85.5%	Germany
0.5	12.0	0.6	0.2	13.2	3.5%	1.1	0.1	0.1	116.9	75.8%	Greece
0.1	6.2	1.8	0.2	8.3	1.8%	0.5	0.2	0.0	78.5	78.1%	Hungary
0.0	0.4	0.2	0.0	0.6	1.5%	0.0	0.0	0.0	3.2	66.9%	Iceland
0.1	11.8	0.8	0.7	13.4	1.1%	0.4	0.5	0.1	60.4	69.9%	Ireland
1.4	26.7	8.2	0.5	36.8	3.8%	8.2	0.7	1.6	536.3	80.8%	Italy
0.0	-	0.0	0.0	0.1	56.7%	0.1	0.0	0.0	8.7	93.2%	Luxembourg
0.6	9.6	5.9	1.9	18.0	3.2%	3.1	0.7	0.3	214.1	83.0%	Netherlands
0.2	2.7	1.7	0.3	4.8	3.2%	0.2	0.7	1.0	55.6	77.3%	Norway
1.2	20.5	5.6	0.4	27.6	4.2%	0.7	0.3	0.0	397.6	85.4%	Poland
0.2	5.8	0.7	0.4	7.1	3.2%	0.4	0.0	0.1	79.6	75.8%	Portugal
0.1	1.9	0.7	0.2	2.9	2.7%	0.1	0.0	0.0	48.1	83.9%	Slovak Republic
1.2	34.4	2.1	3.7	41.4	2.8%	5.2	0.9	0.5	389.0	74.6%	Spain
0.4	4.7	0.8	0.4	6.4	6.5%	0.6	0.5	0.5	70.4	76.2%	Sweden
0.3	2.4	0.2	0.1	3.0	10.3%	0.9	0.1	0.4	52.9	80.0%	Switzerland
0.6	40.2	4.8	0.6	46.1	1.4%	1.1	0.6	0.9	293.2	70.0%	Turkey
2.2	36.5	22.1	4.4	65.2	3.4%	6.0	2.1	1.8	659.6	83.2%	United Kingdom
16.1	351.2	76.7	28.3	472.3	3.4%	49.9	11.9	20.3	5 122.2	80.4%	OECD Europe
16.0	325.1	74.9	27.8	443.8	3.6%	48.6	12.1	18.1	4 981.0	80.9%	European Union - 27

* Total World includes Non-OECD total, OECD total as well as international bunkers.
Sources: IEA, Sectoral Approach for CO$_2$ emissions from fuel combustion. EDGAR 32FT2000 database for other emissions. In general, estimates for emissions other than CO$_2$ from fuel combustion are subject to significantly larger uncertainties.

2000 Greenhouse gas emissions

Emissions de gaz à effet de serre pour 2000

millions de tonnes d'équivalent CO$_2$ selon le PRC-100

	CO$_2$						CH$_4$					
	Fuel comb.	Fugitive	Industrial processes	Other	Total	Share of energy	Energy	Agricult.	Waste	Other	Total	Share of energy
Total Non-OCDE	**10 187.3**	**150.6**	**680.4**	**3 206.2**	**14 224.5**	**72.7%**	**1 591.6**	**2 385.6**	**780.6**	**237.0**	**4 994.8**	**31.9%**
Algérie	66.6	11.1	4.2	2.0	83.9	92.7%	16.1	3.7	4.3	0.1	24.2	66.5%
Angola	5.2	1.7	0.2	227.1	234.2	3.0%	4.3	14.4	1.4	16.8	36.9	11.7%
Bénin	1.4	-	0.1	18.7	20.3	7.0%	0.4	2.0	0.7	1.4	4.6	9.4%
Botswana	4.2	-	-	-	4.2	100.0%	0.9	2.9	0.3	0.2	4.2	20.8%
Cameroun	2.8	3.5	0.4	26.4	33.2	19.1%	2.7	8.4	2.1	1.8	15.0	18.1%
Congo	0.6	-	0.0	23.8	24.4	2.4%	2.9	0.7	0.5	1.7	5.7	49.8%
Rép. dém. du Congo	2.1	0.2	0.1	370.7	373.1	0.6%	3.9	12.9	5.9	27.2	49.9	7.7%
Côte d'Ivoire	6.1	-	0.3	115.4	121.9	5.0%	1.7	3.1	1.9	8.5	15.2	11.3%
Egypte	110.2	1.6	12.5	5.0	129.4	86.4%	10.3	12.3	7.9	0.1	30.5	33.7%
Erythrée	0.6	-	0.0	0.3	0.9	65.2%	0.2	2.1	0.4	-	2.6	7.0%
Ethiopie	3.2	-	0.4	7.4	11.0	29.0%	4.8	32.4	6.1	-	43.3	11.1%
Gabon	1.4	3.1	0.1	1.9	6.6	68.8%	1.6	0.1	0.2	0.1	2.0	80.5%
Ghana	5.1	-	1.0	14.3	20.4	25.2%	0.9	4.2	2.4	1.0	8.5	10.9%
Kenya	8.9	-	0.6	5.6	15.0	59.3%	3.7	11.9	3.4	-	19.0	19.3%
Libye	39.7	1.9	1.7	0.3	43.6	95.5%	6.6	0.8	1.1	0.0	8.5	78.1%
Maroc	29.5	-	4.0	0.4	34.0	86.9%	1.5	14.8	1.8	3.4	21.5	6.8%
Mozambique	1.3	-	0.1	23.6	25.1	5.3%	0.2	4.0	0.4	-	4.6	4.3%
Namibie	1.9	-	0.0	0.3	2.2	86.6%	0.2	3.3	0.2	0.0	3.7	5.4%
Nigéria	41.1	31.3	1.2	46.8	120.4	60.1%	35.7	25.6	14.8	1.2	77.2	46.2%
Sénégal	3.6	-	0.5	0.7	4.8	75.7%	0.3	4.7	1.2	-	6.2	4.9%
Afrique du Sud	298.6	-	5.0	5.2	308.7	96.7%	32.2	13.9	9.4	3.3	58.8	54.7%
Soudan	5.5	-	0.1	21.7	27.3	20.0%	14.5	48.0	3.4	-	65.9	22.0%
Rép. unie de Tanzanie	2.6	-	0.4	52.0	55.0	4.7%	8.0	21.6	3.5	2.8	35.9	22.3%
Togo	1.0	-	0.3	7.3	8.6	11.1%	0.4	1.4	0.5	0.5	2.8	14.8%
Tunisie	18.0	0.3	3.2	0.7	22.2	82.4%	1.4	1.7	1.4	0.0	4.5	31.2%
Zambie	1.7	-	0.3	43.8	45.8	3.7%	1.0	11.5	1.1	3.1	16.8	5.7%
Zimbabwe	12.7	-	0.5	1.9	15.1	84.4%	2.6	6.5	1.5	0.0	10.6	24.3%
Autres pays d'Afrique	18.9	1.8	0.8	161.5	183.0	11.3%	14.7	86.8	19.8	9.3	130.6	11.3%
Afrique	**694.4**	**56.6**	**38.1**	**1 184.7**	**1 973.8**	**38.0%**	**173.5**	**355.5**	**97.6**	**82.4**	**709.1**	**24.5%**
Bahrein	14.1	-	0.0	0.0	14.2	99.5%	1.8	0.0	0.1	-	2.0	92.8%
Rép. islamique d'Iran	304.8	24.2	13.4	2.6	345.1	95.3%	61.5	19.7	12.4	0.0	93.6	65.7%
Irak	75.9	1.8	1.0	1.0	79.8	97.4%	5.3	1.4	3.9	0.0	10.7	49.8%
Israël	55.5	-	3.6	0.0	59.1	93.8%	0.1	0.5	0.6	0.0	1.1	9.6%
Jordanie	14.3	-	1.3	0.2	15.8	90.5%	0.2	0.4	1.0	-	1.6	13.3%
Koweit	50.2	1.0	0.8	-	51.9	98.5%	10.5	0.1	0.5	-	11.1	94.5%
Liban	14.2	-	1.4	0.2	15.7	90.1%	0.1	0.2	0.6	0.0	0.9	12.8%
Oman	19.8	1.9	0.6	0.1	22.3	96.8%	3.2	0.5	0.4	-	4.2	77.9%
Qatar	26.5	-	0.5	0.0	27.1	98.0%	4.9	0.1	0.2	0.0	5.2	94.5%
Arabie saoudite	251.1	1.1	9.2	0.3	261.7	96.4%	58.3	1.1	3.8	-	63.1	92.4%
Syrie	45.8	0.8	2.4	0.6	49.6	94.0%	2.7	2.5	2.4	0.0	7.7	35.1%
Emirats arabes unis	86.1	3.1	3.1	0.2	92.4	96.5%	33.2	0.5	0.5	-	34.2	97.2%
Yémen	13.3	-	0.7	0.6	14.6	91.1%	4.0	2.2	2.5	-	8.7	46.0%
Moyen-Orient	**971.5**	**33.8**	**38.1**	**5.8**	**1 049.2**	**95.8%**	**186.0**	**29.2**	**28.9**	**0.1**	**244.1**	**76.2%**
Albanie	3.2	-	0.1	0.2	3.4	92.3%	0.2	1.7	0.4	0.0	2.3	10.6%
Bosnie-Herzégovine	13.7	-	0.2	0.0	13.9	98.5%	1.5	0.9	0.4	0.0	2.8	52.3%
Bulgarie	42.0	-	2.1	0.6	44.8	93.8%	2.0	2.0	1.9	0.1	6.0	32.8%
Croatie	17.7	-	1.6	0.4	19.7	89.7%	1.6	1.0	0.8	0.0	3.4	47.3%
Chypre	6.3	-	0.7	0.0	7.0	90.0%	0.0	0.2	0.1	-	0.3	4.4%
Gibraltar	0.4	-	-	-	0.4	100.0%	0.0	-	0.0	-	0.0	46.1%
ex-RY de Macédoine	8.4	-	0.3	0.3	9.0	93.6%	0.2	0.7	0.3	0.0	1.2	17.6%
Malte	2.2	-	0.0	0.0	2.2	99.8%	0.0	0.0	0.1	-	0.1	2.7%
Roumanie	86.3	-	3.0	1.1	90.4	95.5%	12.9	7.6	3.9	0.1	24.4	52.6%
Serbie	42.5	-	1.4	0.0	44.0	96.8%	1.1	5.1	1.4	0.1	7.7	14.4%
Slovénie	14.0	-	1.6	0.2	15.7	88.7%	0.3	0.8	0.5	-	1.6	21.1%
Europe Non-OCDE	**236.6**	**-**	**10.9**	**2.9**	**250.4**	**94.5%**	**19.9**	**20.1**	**9.7**	**0.4**	**50.0**	**39.7%**

2000 Greenhouse gas emissions

Emissions de gaz à effet de serre pour 2000

million tonnes of CO$_2$ equivalent using GWP-100

Energy	Agriculture	Industrial processes	Other	Total	Share of energy	HFCs	PFCs	SF$_6$	Total	Share of energy	
		N$_2$O				HFCs	PFCs	SF$_6$	Total		
						Industrial processes					
89.3	2 162.4	61.8	224.5	2 537.9	3.5%	91.8	52.9	38.0	21 939.8	54.8%	**Non-OECD Total**
0.3	8.5	0.6	0.0	9.4	3.2%	0.1	-	0.1	117.7	80.0%	Algeria
0.2	6.6	-	17.9	24.8	0.9%	0.0	-	0.0	295.9	3.9%	Angola
0.1	2.7	-	1.4	4.2	1.4%	-	-	0.0	29.0	6.5%	Benin
0.0	3.2	-	0.0	3.3	1.4%	-	-	0.0	11.7	43.8%	Botswana
0.2	9.7	-	2.0	11.8	1.7%	-	0.9	0.0	60.9	15.2%	Cameroon
0.0	0.3	-	1.9	2.2	1.7%	0.0	-	0.0	32.3	10.8%	Congo
0.6	8.9	-	29.0	38.5	1.5%	-	-	-	461.5	1.5%	Dem. Rep. of Congo
0.2	2.7	-	9.0	11.9	1.8%	-	-	0.0	149.0	5.4%	Côte d'Ivoire
0.7	21.2	3.3	0.0	25.2	2.7%	0.1	0.7	0.9	186.8	65.7%	Egypt
0.0	1.8	-	0.0	1.8	1.6%	-	-	0.0	5.3	15.3%	Eritrea
0.8	56.7	-	0.0	57.5	1.4%	0.0	-	0.0	111.7	7.8%	Ethiopia
0.0	0.3	-	0.1	0.4	10.3%	0.0	-	0.0	9.0	68.7%	Gabon
0.2	7.5	-	1.0	8.6	1.8%	0.0	0.2	0.0	37.7	16.5%	Ghana
0.6	19.0	-	0.0	19.6	3.1%	-	-	0.0	53.6	24.6%	Kenya
0.1	2.0	-	0.0	2.2	6.8%	-	-	0.3	54.5	88.8%	Libya
0.2	9.4	-	3.6	13.2	1.8%	-	-	0.0	68.6	45.5%	Morocco
0.0	7.7	-	0.0	7.8	0.5%	0.0	-	0.0	37.5	4.1%	Mozambique
0.0	4.1	-	0.0	4.1	0.8%	-	-	0.0	9.9	21.2%	Namibia
3.4	30.8	-	1.3	35.4	9.6%	0.1	-	0.1	233.2	47.8%	Nigeria
0.1	8.6	-	0.0	8.6	1.0%	-	-	0.0	19.6	20.3%	Senegal
1.7	22.6	1.5	1.0	26.8	6.5%	0.3	0.5	1.0	396.1	83.9%	South Africa
2.1	48.0	-	0.0	50.1	4.3%	-	-	0.0	143.4	15.4%	Sudan
1.6	24.4	-	3.0	29.0	5.6%	-	-	0.0	119.9	10.2%	United Rep. of Tanzania
0.1	3.1	-	0.5	3.7	1.8%	-	-	0.0	15.1	9.5%	Togo
0.1	5.3	0.4	0.0	5.8	1.8%	-	-	0.0	32.5	60.8%	Tunisia
0.2	5.3	0.5	3.4	9.3	1.9%	0.0	-	0.0	71.8	3.9%	Zambia
0.3	7.9	-	0.0	8.2	3.3%	-	-	0.0	33.8	46.0%	Zimbabwe
2.3	108.0	-	9.4	119.7	1.9%	0.0	-	0.0	433.3	8.7%	Other Africa
16.3	436.0	6.2	84.6	543.1	3.0%	0.6	2.3	2.4	3 231.3	29.1%	**Africa**
0.0	0.0	-	0.0	0.1	49.1%	-	0.2	0.0	16.4	97.4%	Bahrain
0.9	57.6	0.5	0.0	58.9	1.5%	-	0.2	1.4	499.1	78.4%	Islamic Rep. of Iran
0.3	4.6	-	0.0	4.9	5.5%	-	-	0.5	95.8	86.9%	Iraq
0.2	1.5	-	0.0	1.8	12.4%	0.8	0.2	0.7	63.7	87.7%	Israel
0.1	1.3	-	0.0	1.3	4.6%	0.0	-	0.0	18.7	77.8%	Jordan
0.1	0.3	-	0.0	0.4	22.4%	0.2	-	0.4	64.0	96.5%	Kuwait
0.1	0.9	-	0.0	1.0	5.6%	-	-	0.0	17.6	81.3%	Lebanon
0.0	1.0	-	0.0	1.0	3.0%	0.0	-	0.0	27.5	90.5%	Oman
0.0	0.3	-	0.0	0.3	9.7%	-	-	0.0	32.5	96.7%	Qatar
0.5	7.4	-	0.0	7.9	6.8%	0.1	-	1.5	334.3	93.1%	Saudi Arabia
0.2	8.4	0.2	0.0	8.8	2.2%	-	-	0.0	66.0	75.0%	Syria
0.2	1.8	-	0.0	2.0	11.0%	-	0.2	0.3	129.1	95.0%	United Arab Emirates
0.1	5.8	-	0.0	5.9	1.3%	-	-	0.0	29.2	59.5%	Yemen
2.7	90.8	0.7	0.0	94.2	2.8%	1.1	0.7	4.8	1 394.0	85.7%	**Middle East**
0.0	1.6	-	0.0	1.6	2.0%	0.0	-	0.0	7.4	46.5%	Albania
0.2	0.8	-	0.0	1.0	17.4%	0.1	0.8	0.0	18.6	82.3%	Bosnia-Herzegovina
0.3	4.0	1.7	0.1	6.0	5.2%	0.1	-	0.0	56.9	77.8%	Bulgaria
0.3	2.2	0.9	0.0	3.3	8.3%	0.0	0.1	0.0	26.6	73.6%	Croatia
0.0	0.6	-	0.0	0.6	4.1%	0.1	-	0.0	8.0	79.0%	Cyprus
0.0	-	-	-	0.0	100.0%	-	-	-	0.4	98.7%	Gibraltar
0.1	0.9	-	0.0	0.9	6.6%	0.1	-	0.0	11.3	77.4%	FYR of Macedonia
0.0	0.0	-	0.0	0.1	15.9%	-	-	0.0	2.4	93.9%	Malta
0.3	10.1	3.4	0.2	13.9	2.2%	0.1	1.6	0.0	130.4	76.2%	Romania
0.3	4.8	0.5	0.0	5.6	4.7%	1.9	0.5	0.0	59.7	73.6%	Serbia
0.1	1.0	-	0.0	1.1	6.5%	0.2	0.1	0.0	18.7	76.8%	Slovenia
1.5	25.8	6.4	0.4	34.2	4.5%	2.6	3.1	0.0	340.4	75.8%	**Non-OECD Europe**

2000 Greenhouse gas emissions

Emissions de gaz à effet de serre pour 2000

millions de tonnes d'équivalent CO$_2$ selon le PRC-100

	CO$_2$						CH$_4$					
	Fuel comb.	Fugitive	Industrial processes	Other	Total	Share of energy	Energy	Agricult.	Waste	Other	Total	Share of energy
Arménie	3.4	-	0.1	0.1	3.6	94.3%	0.6	1.0	0.5	0.0	2.1	28.1%
Azerbaïdjan	28.2	12.6	0.1	0.2	41.0	99.3%	5.2	4.4	1.0	0.0	10.6	49.2%
Bélarus	55.2	-	1.4	0.2	56.8	97.2%	7.1	7.0	2.0	0.0	16.2	44.1%
Estonie	14.5	-	0.2	0.2	14.9	97.4%	0.5	0.5	0.4	0.0	1.3	38.6%
Géorgie	4.4	-	0.2	1.2	5.8	75.7%	1.3	2.0	0.8	0.0	4.1	31.4%
Kazakhstan	130.2	1.1	1.0	0.1	132.4	99.1%	13.9	8.3	2.8	0.6	25.6	54.2%
Kirghizistan	4.6	-	0.3	0.1	4.9	92.8%	0.4	2.3	0.6	0.0	3.2	11.4%
Lettonie	6.8	-	0.2	0.7	7.7	88.6%	0.9	0.7	0.6	0.0	2.2	41.2%
Lituanie	11.2	-	0.3	1.0	12.5	89.6%	1.6	1.6	0.7	0.0	3.9	41.2%
République de Moldavie	6.5	-	0.1	0.2	6.8	94.8%	1.1	1.0	0.6	0.0	2.7	41.1%
Russie	1 513.8	8.6	22.0	7.2	1 551.7	98.1%	381.6	48.2	55.8	13.2	498.8	76.5%
Tadjikistan	4.2	-	0.0	0.0	4.2	99.0%	0.3	2.1	0.7	0.0	3.1	10.7%
Turkménistan	36.2	-	0.2	0.0	36.4	99.3%	18.9	2.4	0.6	0.0	21.9	86.0%
Ukraine	292.0	0.0	5.3	1.3	298.6	97.8%	53.2	18.0	9.9	1.1	82.1	64.7%
Ouzbékistan	116.5	-	1.9	0.5	118.8	98.0%	36.1	9.6	3.2	0.0	48.9	73.8%
Ex-URSS	**2 227.5**	**22.3**	**33.3**	**13.1**	**2 296.2**	**98.0%**	**522.7**	**109.1**	**80.2**	**15.0**	**727.0**	**71.9%**
Argentine	132.9	1.1	4.5	2.9	141.5	94.8%	12.2	57.9	13.5	7.2	90.8	13.5%
Bolivie	7.6	0.5	0.5	200.9	209.6	3.9%	0.8	9.2	1.9	14.9	26.8	2.8%
Brésil	303.4	5.1	24.1	770.6	1 103.2	28.0%	12.7	240.9	61.9	58.8	374.4	3.4%
Chili	53.2	0.3	2.5	1.9	57.9	92.4%	2.4	5.7	10.0	0.5	18.5	12.8%
Colombie	60.7	1.0	5.8	63.3	130.8	47.2%	9.7	32.5	12.0	4.6	58.7	16.5%
Costa Rica	4.6	-	0.6	0.1	5.2	87.1%	0.0	1.8	0.9	-	2.8	1.3%
Cuba	24.8	0.2	0.9	1.3	27.1	92.1%	0.6	6.1	2.9	-	9.6	6.4%
République dominicaine	17.4	-	1.5	0.4	19.4	89.9%	0.2	3.5	1.9	-	5.6	4.3%
Equateur	18.5	1.5	1.4	1.1	22.5	89.0%	2.1	6.8	3.0	0.0	12.0	17.5%
El Salvador	5.2	-	0.5	0.8	6.6	79.3%	0.4	1.3	1.2	-	2.9	13.8%
Guatemala	8.8	-	0.9	27.8	37.6	23.5%	1.0	3.8	2.1	2.0	8.9	11.5%
Haïti	1.4	-	0.2	0.5	2.1	66.8%	0.2	2.3	1.2	-	3.7	6.5%
Honduras	4.4	-	0.5	0.6	5.6	79.3%	0.3	3.0	1.2	-	4.5	6.9%
Jamaïque	9.8	-	0.5	0.1	10.3	94.6%	0.0	0.5	0.6	-	1.1	3.3%
Antilles néerlandaises	3.2	-	-	0.0	3.2	99.3%	0.0	0.0	0.1	-	0.1	38.4%
Nicaragua	3.5	-	0.2	0.6	4.4	80.4%	0.3	4.8	0.9	-	6.1	5.0%
Panama	4.7	-	0.4	0.3	5.3	87.9%	0.1	1.9	0.7	-	2.7	4.8%
Paraguay	3.3	-	0.4	25.2	28.8	11.3%	0.3	12.7	1.2	3.5	17.7	1.7%
Pérou	26.4	0.3	2.0	23.5	52.2	51.2%	1.4	9.8	7.4	1.7	20.3	6.8%
Trinité-et-Tobago	17.9	4.3	0.4	0.0	22.7	98.1%	3.0	0.0	0.8	-	3.8	78.1%
Uruguay	5.3	-	0.4	0.2	5.8	90.7%	0.1	14.0	1.4	0.1	15.6	0.7%
Vénézuela	128.3	3.4	4.5	70.2	206.5	63.8%	27.6	20.5	9.5	5.2	62.9	43.9%
Autres Amérique Latine	14.4		1.1	17.7	33.2	43.3%	0.7	3.4	2.3	1.2	7.6	8.7%
Amérique latine	**859.8**	**17.7**	**53.8**	**1 210.2**	**2 141.5**	**41.0%**	**76.3**	**442.6**	**138.6**	**99.7**	**757.1**	**10.1%**
Bangladesh	25.2	-	1.8	31.7	58.6	43.0%	10.7	63.5	16.8	1.0	91.9	11.6%
Brunei Darussalam	4.6	0.7	0.1	4.3	9.7	54.6%	1.7	0.0	0.1	0.3	2.1	80.5%
Cambodge	2.4	-	-	8.1	10.5	23.1%	0.8	9.1	1.6	1.9	13.4	6.0%
Taipei chinois	215.0	-	9.3	1.9	226.2	95.0%	2.7	0.0	1.2	0.3	4.2	64.4%
Inde	976.5	3.3	47.6	136.2	1 163.7	84.2%	104.7	473.6	141.1	2.9	722.4	14.5%
Indonésie	264.6	9.3	13.9	208.3	496.1	55.2%	81.2	92.2	36.6	13.1	223.1	36.4%
Rép. pop. dém. de Corée	68.8	-	2.0	2.6	73.4	93.8%	3.1	3.9	3.5	0.1	10.6	29.2%
Malaisie	112.7	5.9	5.7	31.6	155.9	76.1%	14.6	5.6	3.4	1.7	25.3	57.7%
Mongolie	8.8	-	0.1	0.3	9.1	96.4%	0.1	8.4	0.4	0.2	9.2	1.6%
Myanmar	8.1	0.2	0.2	106.0	114.5	7.3%	4.1	41.0	6.7	7.4	59.3	6.9%
Népal	3.1	-	0.2	6.4	9.6	31.9%	3.7	29.0	3.3	0.0	36.1	10.4%
Pakistan	97.8	-	4.9	16.9	119.6	81.8%	15.6	67.8	21.3	0.1	104.7	14.9%
Philippines	68.9	-	5.9	7.7	82.5	83.5%	3.6	29.9	11.1	0.0	44.6	8.0%
Singapour	38.1	-	0.6	-	38.7	98.5%	0.4	0.1	0.8	-	1.3	31.1%
Sri Lanka	10.8	-	0.5	2.3	13.6	79.4%	1.3	6.3	2.7	-	10.2	12.3%
Thaïlande	159.5	-	13.0	33.5	205.9	77.4%	7.4	58.3	9.1	2.3	77.1	9.6%
Viêt-Nam	43.8	0.7	7.3	17.9	69.7	63.9%	13.4	46.7	11.0	0.6	71.6	18.7%
Autres pays d'Asie	11.1	-	0.2	57.1	68.4	16.3%	3.1	15.2	5.0	2.5	25.8	12.0%
Asie	**2 120.0**	**20.1**	**113.2**	**672.6**	**2 925.8**	**73.1%**	**272.1**	**950.6**	**275.6**	**34.4**	**1 532.8**	**17.8%**
Rép. populaire de Chine	3 037.9	-	392.4	116.9	3 547.2	85.6%	340.7	478.4	149.5	5.2	973.7	35.0%
Hong Kong, Chine	39.7	-	0.6	0.0	40.4	98.4%	0.5	0.0	0.6	-	1.0	44.2%
Chine	**3 077.6**	**-**	**393.1**	**116.9**	**3 587.6**	**85.8%**	**341.1**	**478.4**	**150.0**	**5.2**	**974.8**	**35.0%**

2000 Greenhouse gas emissions

Emissions de gaz à effet de serre pour 2000

million tonnes of CO$_2$ equivalent using GWP-100

Energy	Agriculture	Industrial processes	Other	Total	Share of energy	HFCs	PFCs	SF$_6$	Total	Share of energy	
				N$_2$O		**Industrial processes**			**Total**		
0.0	0.5	-	0.0	0.5	4.4%	0.0	-	-	6.2	64.4%	Armenia
0.3	3.3	-	0.0	3.5	7.6%	0.0	0.0	-	55.2	83.7%	Azerbaijan
0.1	7.2	2.5	0.1	9.9	1.1%	0.1	-	-	83.0	75.2%	Belarus
0.1	0.6	-	0.0	0.7	12.2%	0.0	-	0.0	16.9	89.1%	Estonia
0.1	1.5	0.6	0.0	2.3	6.5%	0.0	-	-	12.1	47.9%	Georgia
0.5	9.3	-	0.2	10.0	5.1%	0.1	-	-	168.1	86.6%	Kazakhstan
0.0	3.1	-	0.0	3.2	0.9%	0.0	-	-	11.3	43.8%	Kyrgyzstan
0.1	1.1	-	0.0	1.2	7.4%	0.2	-	-	11.4	68.8%	Latvia
0.1	2.2	-	0.0	2.3	5.8%	0.2	-	-	19.0	68.4%	Lithuania
0.0	1.5	-	0.0	1.5	2.5%	0.0	-	-	11.1	68.9%	Republic of Moldova
4.4	42.9	3.0	2.8	53.1	8.3%	13.9	26.1	8.4	2 151.9	88.7%	Russia
0.0	1.9	-	0.0	1.9	0.5%	0.0	0.1	-	9.4	48.3%	Tajikistan
0.0	3.0	0.5	0.0	3.6	1.0%	0.0	-	-	62.0	88.8%	Turkmenistan
0.9	19.5	8.8	0.3	29.6	3.2%	0.1	0.1	-	410.5	84.3%	Ukraine
0.2	12.1	0.0	0.0	12.4	1.6%	0.2	-	-	180.3	84.7%	Uzbekistan
7.0	**109.8**	**15.4**	**3.6**	**135.8**	**5.2%**	**14.8**	**26.4**	**8.4**	**3 208.6**	**86.6%**	**Former USSR**
0.3	73.3	0.1	1.4	75.2	0.4%	0.3	0.1	0.2	308.0	47.6%	Argentina
0.0	11.1	-	16.0	27.2	0.2%	-	-	0.0	263.5	3.4%	Bolivia
2.6	215.1	7.5	64.3	289.5	0.9%	2.8	3.1	1.0	1 773.9	18.3%	Brazil
0.4	9.8	0.7	0.1	11.0	3.4%	-	-	0.0	87.5	64.3%	Chile
0.4	18.6	0.2	4.9	24.0	1.6%	-	-	0.1	213.7	33.6%	Colombia
0.0	2.8	0.1	0.0	2.9	1.2%	0.0	-	0.0	10.9	42.3%	Costa Rica
0.2	7.5	0.6	0.1	8.5	2.6%	0.0	-	0.0	45.2	57.0%	Cuba
0.1	3.3	-	0.0	3.4	2.8%	-	-	0.0	28.4	62.5%	Dominican Republic
0.1	8.0	-	0.1	8.2	1.3%	0.0	-	0.0	42.8	52.0%	Ecuador
0.1	2.0	-	0.0	2.1	5.1%	0.0	-	0.0	11.7	49.1%	El Salvador
0.2	4.8	-	2.1	7.1	2.8%	0.2	-	0.0	53.7	18.7%	Guatemala
0.1	4.1	-	0.0	4.1	1.4%	-	-	0.0	9.9	17.2%	Haiti
0.1	3.2	-	0.0	3.3	2.5%	-	-	0.0	13.3	36.0%	Honduras
0.0	1.0	-	0.0	1.1	4.0%	0.0	-	0.0	12.5	78.8%	Jamaica
0.0	0.0	-	0.0	0.0	67.5%	-	-	0.0	3.4	96.8%	Netherlands Antilles
0.1	2.7	-	0.0	2.8	3.0%	-	-	0.0	13.2	29.6%	Nicaragua
0.1	1.9	-	0.0	2.0	2.7%	-	-	0.0	10.0	48.8%	Panama
0.1	9.6	-	2.2	11.9	0.8%	-	-	0.0	58.5	6.2%	Paraguay
0.2	14.1	0.0	1.8	16.1	1.5%	0.1	-	0.0	88.8	31.9%	Peru
0.0	0.3	-	0.0	0.3	5.3%	-	-	0.0	26.8	94.3%	Trinidad and Tobago
0.0	16.0	-	0.0	16.1	0.3%	0.0	-	0.0	37.5	14.5%	Uruguay
0.2	19.0	0.0	5.6	24.8	0.9%	1.5	0.3	0.2	296.1	53.9%	Venezuela
0.3	4.4	-	1.2	5.9	4.7%	0.0	0.1	0.0	46.8	32.7%	Other Latin America
5.8	**432.5**	**9.4**	**99.9**	**547.5**	**1.1%**	**5.0**	**3.6**	**1.5**	**3 456.2**	**27.8%**	**Latin America**
1.9	30.6	-	1.0	33.5	5.6%	-	-	0.0	184.1	20.5%	Bangladesh
0.0	0.0	-	0.3	0.4	3.7%	0.1	-	0.0	12.3	57.0%	Brunei Darussalam
0.2	2.5	-	0.8	3.5	4.4%	-			27.3	12.3%	Cambodia
1.0	0.0	0.0	0.0	1.0	96.7%	-	2.1	2.6	236.2	92.6%	Chinese Taipei
15.8	259.3	1.4	2.3	278.7	5.7%	2.3	1.9	4.8	2 173.8	50.6%	India
4.4	50.6	0.2	13.9	69.1	6.4%	-	0.2	0.7	789.2	45.5%	Indonesia
0.6	13.3	-	0.0	13.9	4.2%	1.8	-	0.9	100.6	72.1%	DPR of Korea
1.2	5.8	0.5	1.8	9.3	12.9%	-	0.0	0.5	191.1	70.3%	Malaysia
0.0	16.8	-	0.1	16.9	0.2%	-			35.2	25.5%	Mongolia
0.7	13.5	-	7.9	22.1	3.0%	-	-	0.0	195.8	6.7%	Myanmar
0.7	5.8	-	0.0	6.5	10.8%	-	-	0.0	52.1	14.4%	Nepal
2.0	70.9	0.7	0.0	73.6	2.7%	-	-	0.6	298.6	38.6%	Pakistan
1.0	15.9	0.0	0.0	16.9	6.0%	-	-	0.3	144.4	50.9%	Philippines
0.3	0.1	5.6	0.0	5.9	4.3%	0.8	0.5	0.5	47.7	81.2%	Singapore
0.3	2.5	-	0.0	2.8	10.2%	-	-	0.0	26.7	46.4%	Sri Lanka
0.7	22.7	0.2	2.5	26.0	2.8%	-	-	0.9	310.0	54.1%	Thailand
1.2	25.3	-	0.6	27.1	4.3%	-	-	0.0	168.4	35.1%	Vietnam
0.6	14.5	-	3.8	18.9	3.1%	0.0	-	0.0	113.1	13.1%	Other Asia
32.4	**550.1**	**8.5**	**35.2**	**626.2**	**5.2%**	**5.1**	**4.7**	**12.1**	**5 106.7**	**47.9%**	**Asia**
23.4	517.4	15.1	0.7	556.6	4.2%	62.7	12.1	8.4	5 160.7	65.9%	People's Rep. of China
0.2	0.0	-	0.0	0.2	94.2%	-	-	0.3	42.0	96.3%	Hong Kong, China
23.6	**517.4**	**15.1**	**0.7**	**556.8**	**4.2%**	**62.7**	**12.1**	**8.8**	**5 202.7**	**66.2%**	**China**

2005 Greenhouse gas emissions

Emissions de gaz à effet de serre pour 2005

millions de tonnes d'équivalent CO$_2$ selon le PRC-100

	CO$_2$						CH$_4$					
	Fuel comb.	Fugitive	Industrial processes	Other	Total	Share of energy	Energy	Agricult.	Waste	Other	Total	Share of energy
Monde *	**27 146.3**	**173.4**	**1 342.3**	**3 309.9**	**31 971.9**	**85.4%**	**2 316.1**	**2 968.0**	**1 231.7**	**268.1**	**6 783.9**	**34.1%**
Parties de l'Annexe I	14 179.6	42.9	336.7	52.4	14 611.6	97.3%	1 155.0	518.9	450.4	40.2	2 164.5	53.4%
Parties de l'Annexe II	11 345.1	18.6	244.5	38.3	11 646.6	97.6%	627.1	413.8	343.6	24.9	1 409.4	44.5%
Amérique du Nord	6 340.8	9.9	73.0	20.4	6 444.1	98.5%	505.1	171.9	225.1	12.0	914.1	55.3%
Europe	3 353.2	8.1	124.4	12.5	3 498.2	96.1%	74.4	140.2	79.5	3.4	297.5	25.0%
Pacifique	1 651.1	0.6	47.2	5.4	1 704.3	96.9%	47.6	101.7	39.1	9.4	197.8	24.1%
Annexe I EET	2 618.1	24.3	68.3	13.9	2 724.7	97.0%	524.3	91.3	101.2	15.2	732.0	71.6%
Parties non Annexe I	12 026.2	130.4	1 005.6	3 257.6	16 419.8	74.0%	1 161.1	2 449.1	781.3	227.9	4 619.4	25.1%
Parties Kyoto (Annexe I)	8 117.8	36.7	246.5	32.6	8 433.6	96.7%	687.5	349.7	244.5	32.7	1 314.5	52.3%
Soutes internat.	**940.4**	-	-	-	**940.4**	**100%**	-	-	-	-	-	-
Total Non-OCDE	**13 264.1**	**146.7**	**1 010.7**	**3 206.2**	**17 627.8**	**76.1%**	**1 595.3**	**2 466.5**	**809.8**	**237.0**	**5 108.6**	**31.2%**
Total OCDE	**12 941.7**	**26.6**	**331.5**	**103.8**	**13 403.6**	**96.8%**	**720.8**	**501.5**	**421.9**	**31.1**	**1 675.3**	**43.0%**
Canada	556.3	3.7	8.8	1.0	569.8	98.3%	48.3	23.0	27.8	4.7	103.8	46.6%
Mexique	402.2	8.0	22.1	63.3	495.6	82.8%	26.7	47.5	41.3	4.6	120.1	22.2%
Etats-Unis	5 784.5	6.2	64.2	19.4	5 874.3	98.6%	456.8	148.9	197.2	7.3	810.3	56.4%
OCDE Amérique du N.	**6 743.0**	**17.9**	**95.1**	**83.8**	**6 939.8**	**97.4%**	**531.8**	**219.5**	**266.3**	**16.6**	**1 034.2**	**51.4%**
Australie	387.2	-	5.6	2.8	395.6	97.9%	28.7	71.9	9.5	6.7	116.8	24.6%
Japon	1 227.7	-	41.1	2.2	1 271.0	96.6%	16.0	7.2	27.6	2.7	53.5	30.0%
Corée	468.9	-	26.0	0.9	495.8	94.6%	5.8	9.7	14.9	0.9	31.3	18.5%
Nouvelle-Zélande	36.3	0.6	0.6	0.3	37.7	97.7%	2.9	22.6	2.0	0.0	27.5	10.4%
OCDE Pacifique	**2 120.0**	**0.6**	**73.2**	**6.3**	**2200.1**	**96.4%**	**53.4**	**111.4**	**54.0**	**10.3**	**229.1**	**23.3%**
Autriche	75.0	-	3.8	0.5	79.3	94.6%	1.0	3.6	2.4	0.1	7.2	14.5%
Belgique	120.4	-	5.2	0.2	125.8	95.7%	1.3	4.5	1.5	0.3	7.6	16.9%
République tchèque	119.9	-	2.9	0.1	122.9	97.6%	8.8	2.6	3.4	0.2	14.9	58.7%
Danemark	47.4	0.2	1.2	0.4	49.2	96.8%	0.8	3.3	0.8	-	4.9	16.3%
Finlande	55.1	-	1.0	1.0	57.1	96.5%	0.6	1.7	3.2	0.1	5.5	10.2%
France	386.6	0.3	13.1	3.7	403.7	95.9%	4.7	30.9	7.4	0.5	43.5	10.7%
Allemagne	811.3	1.1	20.2	1.8	834.4	97.4%	26.6	22.8	7.8	0.9	58.1	45.7%
Grèce	95.0	0.0	7.9	0.3	103.2	92.1%	0.7	2.9	3.8	0.0	7.4	9.8%
Hongrie	56.9	-	2.1	0.3	59.3	95.9%	5.8	2.0	3.2	0.1	11.1	52.5%
Islande	2.2	0.0	0.0	0.0	2.3	97.9%	0.0	0.2	0.1	-	0.3	1.7%
Irlande	43.4	-	2.1	-	45.4	95.5%	0.9	1.2	1.6	0.0	3.7	24.4%
Italie	453.8	-	26.4	0.9	481.1	94.3%	7.0	13.8	15.3	0.5	36.7	19.1%
Luxembourg	11.2	-	0.4	0.0	11.6	96.7%	0.1	0.0	0.1	0.0	0.2	40.3%
Pays-Bas	182.6	0.1	1.2	0.4	184.4	99.1%	3.6	7.5	4.0	0.2	15.2	23.7%
Norvège	36.7	0.8	0.8	0.2	38.5	97.4%	7.5	1.7	2.9	0.0	12.1	61.8%
Pologne	294.2	-	7.7	0.6	302.6	97.2%	40.2	11.0	8.6	0.2	60.1	67.0%
Portugal	62.7	0.0	4.6	0.1	67.5	93.0%	0.6	3.8	2.7	0.1	7.1	8.0%
République slovaque	38.1	0.0	2.4	0.0	40.5	94.1%	2.9	1.0	1.3	0.1	5.3	54.2%
Espagne	339.5	0.2	26.1	0.7	366.5	92.7%	4.3	16.8	16.7	0.3	38.0	11.3%
Suède	50.4	0.0	1.8	1.0	53.3	94.6%	0.4	2.7	3.3	0.1	6.5	6.6%
Suisse	44.4	0.0	1.3	0.6	46.4	95.8%	0.4	2.8	1.0	0.0	4.2	8.8%
Turquie	216.4	- 0.0	23.8	0.1	240.3	90.0%	3.5	13.8	5.6	0.2	23.1	15.2%
Royaume-Uni	535.4	5.1	7.2	0.8	548.5	98.6%	14.1	20.0	5.0	0.4	39.4	35.7%
OCDE Europe	**4 078.7**	**8.1**	**163.3**	**13.7**	**4 263.8**	**95.8%**	**135.6**	**170.6**	**101.6**	**4.2**	**411.9**	**32.9%**
Union européenne - 27	3 978.7	7.2	147.2	16.7	4 149.8	96.1%	141.8	164.6	100.3	4.2	410.9	34.5%

* Total Monde inclue le total Non-OCDE, le total OCDE ainsi que les soutes internationales.

Sources: AIE, méthode sectorielle pour les émissions de CO$_2$ dues à la combustion d'énergie. Base de données EDGAR 4 et estimations pour les autres émissions. En général, pour les émissions autres que celles de CO$_2$ dues à la combustion d'énergie, les estimations sont sujettes à une incertitude significativement plus grande.

2005 Greenhouse gas emissions
Emissions de gaz à effet de serre pour 2005

million tonnes of CO$_2$ equivalent using GWP-100

		N$_2$O				HFCs	PFCs	SF$_6$	Total		
Energy	Agriculture	Industrial processes	Other	Total	Share of energy	Industrial processes			Total	Share of energy	
162.0	3 263.7	195.7	321.6	3 943.0	4.1%	559.4	93.0	124.7	43 475.9	68.5%	**World ***
69.8	962.8	133.8	95.8	1 262.2	5.5%	428.2	65.5	91.9	18 624.0	82.9%	*Annex I Parties*
60.8	814.1	97.3	90.7	1 062.9	5.7%	387.2	30.5	82.6	14 619.2	82.4%	*Annex II Parties*
36.6	385.5	27.2	58.2	507.6	7.2%	257.6	7.7	39.0	8 170.1	84.4%	*North America*
15.3	280.5	66.6	26.9	389.3	3.9%	76.3	8.1	19.3	4 288.6	80.5%	*Europe*
9.0	148.0	3.5	5.6	166.0	5.4%	53.4	14.7	24.3	2 160.5	79.1%	*Pacific*
8.1	106.5	32.2	4.6	151.3	5.4%	37.8	34.4	8.5	3 688.6	86.1%	*Annex I EIT*
92.2	2 300.9	61.9	225.8	2 680.8	3.4%	131.2	27.5	32.7	23 911.4	56.1%	*Non-Annex I Parties*
34.9	572.8	101.2	38.7	747.6	4.7%	179.9	60.5	56.7	10 792.8	82.2%	*Annex I Kyoto Parties*
-	-	-	-	-	-	-	-	-	940.4	100.0%	**Internat. bunkers**
95.7	2 299.3	71.0	224.5	2 690.4	3.6%	157.0	58.2	38.0	25 680.0	58.8%	**Non-OECD Total**
66.4	964.4	124.6	97.2	1 252.6	5.3%	402.5	34.8	86.7	16 855.4	81.6%	**OECD Total**
2.7	44.6	2.3	1.8	51.4	5.2%	12.9	3.3	4.6	745.8	81.9%	Canada
1.5	68.0	0.9	5.0	75.5	2.0%	4.2	0.2	0.3	696.0	63.0%	Mexico
33.9	341.0	24.9	56.4	456.2	7.4%	244.7	4.4	34.4	7 424.3	84.6%	United States
38.1	**453.6**	**28.2**	**63.2**	**583.1**	**6.5%**	**261.8**	**7.9**	**39.3**	**8 866.1**	**82.7%**	**OECD N. America**
2.9	108.6	1.5	1.5	114.5	2.5%	5.7	0.8	0.7	634.1	66.0%	Australia
5.9	11.6	2.0	4.1	23.6	25.1%	46.8	13.6	23.5	1 432.0	87.3%	Japan
1.6	8.0	12.5	0.0	22.0	7.2%	3.0	2.8	2.8	557.8	85.4%	Korea
0.1	27.8	0.0	0.0	28.0	0.4%	0.8	0.2	0.1	94.3	42.3%	New Zealand
10.5	**156.0**	**15.9**	**5.6**	**188.1**	**5.6%**	**56.4**	**17.5**	**27.1**	**2 718.3**	**80.4%**	**OECD Pacific**
0.2	3.9	0.4	0.1	4.6	4.1%	1.9	0.2	0.2	93.4	81.6%	Austria
0.5	6.3	1.2	1.7	9.7	5.1%	2.1	0.0	0.2	145.4	84.1%	Belgium
0.4	4.9	1.1	0.2	6.6	6.2%	1.2	0.0	0.0	145.6	88.7%	Czech Republic
0.2	5.8	0.6	0.8	7.4	3.0%	1.4	0.0	0.1	63.0	77.2%	Denmark
0.4	3.2	1.4	0.4	5.3	6.7%	0.8	0.0	0.2	68.8	81.3%	Finland
2.1	60.3	9.4	6.2	78.1	2.7%	13.6	1.4	2.9	543.2	72.5%	France
3.5	51.5	9.2	5.3	69.5	5.0%	16.9	2.6	9.3	990.8	85.0%	Germany
0.5	12.0	0.4	0.2	13.1	4.2%	1.7	0.1	0.1	125.5	76.8%	Greece
0.1	6.7	1.8	0.2	8.8	1.5%	1.3	0.2	0.0	80.7	77.9%	Hungary
0.0	0.4	0.2	0.0	0.7	1.5%	0.0	0.0	0.0	3.3	67.2%	Iceland
0.2	11.4	0.0	0.7	12.3	1.6%	1.0	0.5	0.1	62.9	70.7%	Ireland
1.7	26.2	8.8	0.5	37.2	4.5%	13.5	0.3	1.6	570.4	81.1%	Italy
0.0	-	0.0	0.0	0.1	61.0%	0.1	0.0	0.0	12.0	94.7%	Luxembourg
0.6	8.7	5.7	1.9	16.8	3.3%	3.5	0.0	0.3	220.1	84.9%	Netherlands
0.2	2.5	1.8	0.3	4.7	3.5%	0.3	0.5	1.0	57.0	79.2%	Norway
1.0	18.9	5.8	0.4	26.1	3.8%	1.9	0.4	0.0	391.1	85.8%	Poland
0.3	5.7	0.7	0.4	7.0	3.9%	0.7	0.0	0.1	82.5	77.1%	Portugal
0.1	1.6	0.9	0.2	2.8	2.1%	0.4	0.1	0.0	48.9	83.8%	Slovak Republic
1.5	41.6	1.7	3.7	48.5	3.1%	5.6	0.5	0.5	459.7	75.2%	Spain
0.5	4.7	0.5	0.4	6.1	8.0%	1.2	0.5	0.5	68.1	75.5%	Sweden
0.3	2.2	0.2	0.1	2.8	11.9%	1.7	0.1	0.4	55.6	81.3%	Switzerland
0.9	42.2	4.3	0.6	48.0	1.8%	3.2	0.6	0.9	316.1	69.8%	Turkey
2.6	34.2	24.3	4.4	65.5	4.0%	10.2	1.5	1.8	666.9	83.5%	United Kingdom
17.7	**354.8**	**80.6**	**28.3**	**481.4**	**3.7%**	**84.2**	**9.4**	**20.3**	**5 271.0**	**80.4%**	**OECD Europe**
17.6	325.5	78.8	27.8	449.6	3.9%	82.1	10.5	18.1	5 121.0	80.9%	*European Union - 27*

* Total World includes Non-OECD total, OECD total as well as international bunkers.

Sources: IEA, Sectoral Approach for CO$_2$ emissions from fuel combustion. EDGAR 4 database plus estimates for other emissions. In general, estimates for emissions other than CO$_2$ from fuel combustion are subject to significantly larger uncertainties.

2005 Greenhouse gas emissions

Emissions de gaz à effet de serre pour 2005

millions de tonnes d'équivalent CO_2 selon le PRC-100

	CO_2						CH_4					
	Fuel comb.	Fugitive	Industrial processes	Other	Total	Share of energy	Energy	Agricult.	Waste	Other	Total	Share of energy
Total Non-OCDE	**13 264.1**	**146.7**	**1 010.7**	**3 206.2**	**17 627.8**	**76.1%**	**1 595.3**	**2 466.5**	**809.8**	**237.0**	**5 108.6**	**31.2%**
Algérie	83.8	6.7	4.5	2.0	97.0	93.3%	16.1	3.7	4.4	0.1	24.3	66.3%
Angola	7.8	1.4	0.4	227.1	236.7	3.9%	4.3	14.5	1.4	16.8	37.0	11.7%
Bénin	2.5	-	0.1	18.7	21.4	11.8%	0.4	2.3	0.8	1.4	4.8	8.8%
Botswana	4.3	-	-	-	4.3	100.0%	0.8	3.2	0.3	0.2	4.5	17.8%
Cameroun	2.9	3.1	0.5	26.4	32.9	18.3%	2.7	8.5	2.1	1.8	15.1	17.9%
Congo	1.0	-	0.0	23.8	24.8	4.0%	2.9	0.7	0.5	1.7	5.7	49.7%
Rép. dém. du Congo	2.3	0.5	0.2	370.7	373.7	0.7%	3.9	13.3	6.0	27.2	50.3	7.7%
Côte d'Ivoire	6.3	-	0.3	115.4	122.0	5.1%	1.7	3.2	2.0	8.5	15.3	11.2%
Egypte	149.3	1.5	14.9	5.0	170.7	88.3%	10.3	14.6	8.1	0.1	33.0	31.2%
Erythrée	0.6	-	0.0	0.3	0.9	67.4%	0.2	1.9	0.4	-	2.4	7.5%
Ethiopie	4.8	-	0.8	7.4	13.0	37.2%	4.8	36.9	6.1	-	47.7	10.0%
Gabon	2.1	3.3	0.1	1.9	7.5	72.4%	1.6	0.1	0.2	0.1	2.0	80.2%
Ghana	6.7	-	0.9	14.3	22.0	30.7%	0.9	4.3	2.5	1.0	8.6	10.7%
Kenya	9.9	-	1.0	5.6	16.5	60.0%	3.7	13.2	3.4	-	20.3	18.0%
Libye	42.5	1.6	2.0	0.3	46.4	95.1%	6.6	0.8	1.2	0.0	8.5	77.7%
Maroc	39.3	-	5.4	0.4	45.2	87.0%	0.3	5.5	4.0	3.4	13.2	2.6%
Mozambique	1.5	-	0.2	23.6	25.4	6.0%	2.0	7.5	2.2	-	11.7	16.9%
Namibie	2.9	-	0.0	0.3	3.2	90.8%	0.2	3.8	0.2	0.0	4.3	4.7%
Nigéria	55.6	35.6	1.2	46.8	139.2	65.5%	35.7	26.4	15.1	1.2	78.3	45.5%
Sénégal	4.6	-	0.8	0.7	6.1	75.5%	0.3	4.8	1.2	-	6.3	4.8%
Afrique du Sud	330.4	-	7.5	5.2	343.0	96.3%	32.1	14.1	9.7	3.3	59.2	54.3%
Soudan	10.3	-	0.2	21.7	32.2	31.9%	14.5	49.3	3.5	-	67.3	21.5%
Rép. unie de Tanzanie	4.5	-	0.7	52.0	57.2	7.9%	8.0	25.1	3.6	2.8	39.5	20.3%
Togo	1.0	-	0.4	7.3	8.7	11.3%	0.4	1.4	0.5	0.5	2.8	14.7%
Tunisie	19.3	0.7	3.5	0.7	24.3	82.4%	1.4	1.5	1.5	0.0	4.4	32.1%
Zambie	2.1	-	0.3	43.8	46.2	4.6%	1.0	11.5	1.2	3.1	16.8	5.7%
Zimbabwe	10.4	-	0.2	1.9	12.4	83.4%	2.6	6.3	1.5	0.0	10.4	24.8%
Autres pays d'Afrique	23.1	2.5	1.2	161.5	188.3	13.6%	14.1	98.2	16.1	9.3	137.8	10.3%
Afrique	**831.8**	**57.0**	**47.5**	**1 184.7**	**2 121.0**	**41.9%**	**173.5**	**376.3**	**99.6**	**82.4**	**731.7**	**23.7%**
Bahrein	18.3	-	0.1	0.0	18.4	99.4%	1.8	0.0	0.1	-	2.0	92.6%
Rép. islamique d'Iran	396.7	13.9	18.0	2.6	431.2	95.2%	61.5	20.7	12.8	0.0	95.1	64.7%
Irak	82.1	1.2	1.5	1.0	85.9	97.0%	5.3	1.6	4.0	0.0	11.0	48.7%
Israël	61.5	-	2.4	0.0	64.0	96.2%	0.1	0.4	0.6	0.0	1.2	9.3%
Jordanie	17.9	-	2.0	0.2	20.1	89.0%	0.2	0.4	1.0	-	1.6	12.8%
Koweit	74.3	2.0	1.4	-	77.7	98.2%	10.5	0.2	0.5	-	11.2	93.9%
Liban	15.8	-	1.6	0.2	17.6	89.8%	0.1	0.2	0.7	0.0	1.0	12.1%
Oman	26.9	3.2	1.3	0.1	31.4	95.7%	3.2	0.6	0.5	-	4.3	76.1%
Qatar	35.2	0.5	0.7	0.0	36.4	98.1%	4.9	0.1	0.2	0.0	5.2	94.7%
Arabie saoudite	321.9	0.2	13.1	0.3	335.6	96.0%	58.3	1.2	4.0	-	63.5	91.8%
Syrie	50.1	0.8	2.0	0.6	53.4	95.1%	2.7	2.8	2.5	0.0	8.0	33.8%
Emirats arabes unis	107.3	0.9	4.0	0.2	112.4	96.3%	33.2	0.6	0.5	-	34.2	96.9%
Yémen	19.2	-	0.8	0.6	20.6	93.4%	4.0	2.5	2.5	-	9.0	44.5%
Moyen-Orient	**1 227.2**	**22.7**	**48.9**	**5.8**	**1 304.6**	**95.8%**	**186.0**	**31.2**	**30.0**	**0.1**	**247.2**	**75.2%**
Albanie	4.6	-	0.3	0.2	5.1	90.2%	0.2	1.5	0.4	0.0	2.2	11.3%
Bosnie-Herzégovine	15.7	-	0.5	0.0	16.2	96.7%	1.5	0.9	0.4	0.0	2.9	52.0%
Bulgarie	46.0	-	2.9	0.6	49.6	92.8%	2.0	2.0	2.1	0.1	6.1	31.9%
Croatie	20.7	-	1.9	0.4	23.0	89.7%	1.6	1.1	0.9	0.0	3.7	44.3%
Chypre	7.0	-	0.9	0.0	7.9	88.5%	0.0	0.2	0.1	-	0.3	4.1%
Gibraltar	0.4	-	-	-	0.4	100.0%	0.0	-	0.0	-	0.0	13.4%
ex-RY de Macédoine	8.3	-	0.4	0.3	8.9	92.4%	0.2	0.0	0.3	0.0	0.6	36.8%
Malte	2.6	-	0.0	0.0	2.6	99.8%	0.0	0.0	0.1	-	0.1	2.5%
Roumanie	91.7	-	3.5	1.1	96.3	95.2%	12.2	7.0	4.0	0.1	23.3	52.4%
Serbie	50.2	-	1.4	0.0	51.6	97.3%	1.1	4.0	1.5	0.1	6.7	16.4%
Slovénie	15.3	-	1.7	0.2	17.3	88.9%	0.3	0.8	0.5	-	1.6	21.2%
Europe Non-OCDE	**262.4**	**-**	**13.5**	**2.9**	**278.9**	**94.1%**	**19.2**	**17.6**	**10.3**	**0.4**	**47.5**	**40.4%**

2005 Greenhouse gas emissions

Emissions de gaz à effet de serre pour 2005

million tonnes of CO$_2$ equivalent using GWP-100

N$_2$O						HFCs	PFCs	SF$_6$	Total		
Energy	Agriculture	Industrial processes	Other	Total	Share of energy	Industrial processes			Total	Share of energy	
95.7	2 299.3	71.0	224.5	2 690.4	3.6%	157.0	58.2	38.0	25 680.0	58.8%	**Non-OECD Total**
0.4	9.2	0.7	0.0	10.3	3.7%	0.2	-	0.1	131.9	81.1%	Algeria
0.3	10.2	-	17.9	28.4	0.9%	0.0	-	0.0	302.1	4.6%	Angola
0.0	3.2	-	1.4	4.7	1.1%	-	-	0.0	30.9	9.7%	Benin
0.1	2.4	-	0.0	2.5	2.0%	-	-	0.0	11.3	45.9%	Botswana
0.2	12.4	-	2.0	14.5	1.6%	-	0.9	0.0	63.5	14.1%	Cameroon
0.0	0.4	-	1.9	2.3	1.7%	0.0	-	0.0	32.8	11.9%	Congo
0.6	9.0	-	29.0	38.7	1.7%	-	-	-	462.6	1.6%	Dem. Rep. of Congo
0.2	3.1	-	9.0	12.4	1.9%	-	-	0.0	149.7	5.5%	Côte d'Ivoire
0.8	23.8	3.2	0.0	27.8	2.9%	0.4	0.7	0.9	233.4	69.3%	Egypt
0.0	2.3	-	0.0	2.3	0.9%	-	-	0.0	5.7	14.4%	Eritrea
0.9	62.2	-	0.0	63.1	1.4%	0.0	-	0.0	123.8	8.5%	Ethiopia
0.1	0.2	-	0.1	0.4	12.1%	0.0	-	0.0	10.0	71.4%	Gabon
0.2	9.3	-	1.0	10.5	1.7%	0.0	0.2	0.0	41.3	19.0%	Ghana
0.7	18.4	-	0.0	19.1	3.6%	-	-	0.0	55.9	25.5%	Kenya
0.2	1.9	-	0.0	2.0	8.3%	-	-	0.3	57.2	88.9%	Libya
0.3	11.7	-	3.6	15.5	1.8%	-	-	0.0	73.9	54.0%	Morocco
0.0	9.9	-	0.0	9.9	0.4%	0.1	-	0.0	47.0	7.5%	Mozambique
0.0	4.6	-	0.0	4.6	0.9%	-	-	0.0	12.0	25.8%	Namibia
3.8	34.0	-	1.3	39.0	9.7%	0.4	-	0.1	257.0	50.8%	Nigeria
0.1	10.1	-	0.0	10.3	1.0%	-	-	0.0	22.7	22.2%	Senegal
1.9	24.2	2.1	1.0	29.3	6.5%	0.6	0.5	1.0	433.5	84.1%	South Africa
2.2	57.5	-	0.0	59.8	3.8%	-	-	0.0	159.2	17.0%	Sudan
2.0	26.7	-	3.0	31.7	6.3%	-	-	0.0	128.4	11.3%	United Rep. of Tanzania
0.1	4.9	-	0.5	5.5	1.4%	-	-	0.0	17.0	8.6%	Togo
0.1	6.8	0.3	0.0	7.2	1.6%	-	-	0.0	35.9	60.0%	Tunisia
0.2	7.4	0.4	3.4	11.4	1.7%	0.0	-	0.0	74.4	4.4%	Zambia
0.3	9.9	-	0.0	10.2	2.9%	-	-	0.0	33.0	40.1%	Zimbabwe
2.4	112.3	-	9.4	124.1	1.9%	0.1	-	0.0	450.3	9.4%	Other Africa
18.2	**487.8**	**6.8**	**84.6**	**597.4**	**3.0%**	**1.7**	**2.3**	**2.4**	**3 456.5**	**31.3%**	**Africa**
0.0	0.0	-	0.0	0.1	55.9%	-	0.2	0.0	20.7	97.7%	Bahrain
0.9	64.6	0.6	0.0	66.1	1.4%	-	0.2	1.4	593.9	79.6%	Islamic Rep. of Iran
0.3	3.7	-	0.0	4.0	7.0%	-	-	0.5	101.3	87.8%	Iraq
0.3	1.5	-	0.0	1.8	16.7%	1.5	0.2	0.7	69.3	89.4%	Israel
0.1	1.2	-	0.0	1.2	6.1%	0.1	-	0.0	23.1	78.8%	Jordan
0.1	0.4	-	0.0	0.5	19.0%	0.6	-	0.4	90.5	96.2%	Kuwait
0.1	1.0	-	0.0	1.0	6.2%	-	-	0.0	19.6	81.6%	Lebanon
0.0	1.1	-	0.0	1.1	3.2%	0.2	-	0.0	37.0	90.1%	Oman
0.0	0.2	-	0.0	0.3	13.4%	-	-	0.0	41.9	97.1%	Qatar
0.6	7.1	-	0.0	7.7	7.8%	0.2	-	1.5	408.5	93.3%	Saudi Arabia
0.2	9.0	0.3	0.0	9.4	2.3%	-	-	0.0	70.8	75.9%	Syria
0.3	2.5	-	0.0	2.7	9.7%	-	0.2	0.3	149.9	94.5%	United Arab Emirates
0.1	7.0	-	0.0	7.1	1.2%	-	-	0.0	36.7	63.5%	Yemen
3.0	**99.3**	**0.9**	**0.0**	**103.2**	**2.9%**	**2.6**	**0.7**	**4.8**	**1 663.1**	**86.5%**	**Middle East**
0.0	1.3	-	0.0	1.4	3.1%	0.1	-	0.0	8.7	55.8%	Albania
0.2	0.8	-	0.0	1.0	17.6%	0.5	0.8	0.0	21.4	81.0%	Bosnia-Herzegovina
0.3	3.8	1.8	0.1	5.9	4.7%	0.4	-	0.0	62.0	77.8%	Bulgaria
0.5	2.3	0.8	0.0	3.6	13.0%	0.1	0.1	0.0	30.5	74.6%	Croatia
0.0	0.6	-	0.0	0.6	5.0%	0.2	-	0.0	9.1	77.5%	Cyprus
0.0	-	-	-	0.0	100.0%	-	-	-	0.4	98.8%	Gibraltar
0.1	0.7	-	0.0	0.8	8.1%	0.1	-	0.0	10.4	81.9%	FYR of Macedonia
0.0	0.0	-	0.0	0.0	16.5%	-	-	0.0	2.7	94.8%	Malta
0.3	8.2	3.1	0.2	11.8	2.7%	0.5	2.1	0.0	134.0	77.8%	Romania
0.3	3.8	0.5	0.0	4.7	6.6%	5.1	0.5	0.0	68.6	75.3%	Serbia
0.1	1.0	-	0.0	1.1	9.7%	0.4	0.1	0.0	20.5	76.9%	Slovenia
1.8	**22.6**	**6.1**	**0.4**	**30.9**	**5.9%**	**7.3**	**3.7**	**0.0**	**368.3**	**77.0%**	**Non-OECD Europe**

2005 Greenhouse gas emissions

Emissions de gaz à effet de serre pour 2005

millions de tonnes d'équivalent CO$_2$ selon le PRC-100

	CO$_2$						CH$_4$					
	Fuel comb.	Fugitive	Industrial processes	Other	Total	Share of energy	Energy	Agricult.	Waste	Other	Total	Share of energy
Arménie	4.1	-	0.3	0.1	4.5	91.2%	0.6	1.2	0.5	0.0	2.3	25.4%
Azerbaïdjan	31.1	12.6	0.8	0.2	44.6	97.9%	5.2	5.2	1.1	0.0	11.5	45.2%
Bélarus	61.0	-	2.1	0.2	63.3	96.3%	7.1	6.5	3.0	0.0	16.6	43.0%
Estonie	15.9	-	0.3	0.2	16.5	96.6%	0.5	0.4	0.3	0.0	1.2	42.6%
Géorgie	3.9	-	0.2	1.2	5.4	72.7%	1.3	2.2	0.8	0.0	4.3	29.7%
Kazakhstan	168.2	1.1	2.5	0.1	171.9	98.5%	13.9	10.7	3.0	0.6	28.3	49.1%
Kirghizistan	5.4	-	0.5	0.1	6.0	90.7%	0.4	2.5	0.6	0.0	3.5	10.4%
Lettonie	7.6	-	0.2	0.7	8.4	90.0%	0.9	0.7	0.7	0.0	2.3	40.3%
Lituanie	13.6	-	0.5	1.0	15.1	90.4%	1.6	1.4	0.6	0.0	3.6	44.1%
République de Moldavie	7.9	-	0.2	0.2	8.3	94.1%	1.1	0.8	0.6	0.0	2.6	43.7%
Russie	1 531.2	24.3	30.2	7.2	1 593.0	97.6%	387.4	39.7	61.0	13.2	501.4	77.3%
Tadjikistan	5.6	-	0.1	0.0	5.7	97.3%	0.3	2.2	0.7	0.0	3.3	10.2%
Turkménistan	41.4	-	0.2	0.0	41.6	99.4%	18.9	3.5	0.7	0.0	23.1	81.8%
Ukraine	306.0	-	10.2	1.3	317.5	96.4%	52.1	11.9	10.6	1.1	75.6	68.9%
Ouzbékistan	109.8	-	2.7	0.5	112.9	97.2%	36.1	12.0	3.4	0.0	51.5	70.1%
Ex-URSS	**2 312.7**	**38.0**	**51.1**	**13.1**	**2 414.9**	**97.3%**	**527.5**	**101.0**	**87.7**	**15.0**	**731.2**	**72.1%**
Argentine	139.1	1.6	5.6	2.9	149.2	94.3%	12.2	60.3	14.7	7.2	94.3	13.0%
Bolivie	11.9	0.4	0.7	200.9	213.8	5.7%	0.8	9.4	2.1	14.9	27.1	2.8%
Brésil	327.1	4.3	23.3	770.6	1 125.2	29.4%	12.7	283.1	67.2	58.8	421.8	3.0%
Chili	58.8	0.2	2.3	1.9	63.2	93.3%	2.4	5.9	10.9	0.5	19.6	12.1%
Colombie	59.7	0.7	5.9	63.3	129.7	46.6%	9.7	34.0	13.4	4.6	61.7	15.7%
Costa Rica	5.4	-	1.0	0.1	6.5	83.2%	0.0	1.4	1.0	-	2.5	1.5%
Cuba	24.4	0.2	0.7	1.3	26.5	92.5%	0.6	5.9	3.0	-	9.5	6.5%
République dominicaine	17.5	-	1.3	0.4	19.2	91.0%	0.2	3.7	2.0	-	6.0	4.0%
Equateur	23.5	1.8	1.5	1.1	28.0	90.6%	2.1	7.4	3.4	0.0	12.9	16.3%
El Salvador	5.9	-	0.7	0.8	7.4	79.5%	0.4	1.5	1.3	-	3.2	12.6%
Guatemala	10.9	-	1.2	27.8	39.9	27.3%	1.0	3.8	2.2	2.0	9.0	11.3%
Haïti	1.7	-	0.3	0.5	2.4	69.4%	0.2	2.3	1.2	-	3.7	6.4%
Honduras	6.4	-	1.0	0.6	8.0	80.1%	0.3	3.9	1.2	-	5.4	5.7%
Jamaïque	9.8	-	0.6	0.1	10.5	93.1%	0.0	0.5	0.6	-	1.2	3.1%
Antilles néerlandaises	3.8	-	-	0.0	3.8	99.4%	0.0	0.0	0.1	-	0.1	32.4%
Nicaragua	4.1	-	0.3	0.6	5.1	80.6%	0.3	5.1	1.0	-	6.4	4.8%
Panama	5.7	-	0.4	0.3	6.3	89.2%	0.1	2.2	0.7	-	3.0	4.2%
Paraguay	3.4	-	0.4	25.2	29.0	11.9%	0.3	12.6	1.4	3.5	17.7	1.7%
Pérou	28.5	0.4	2.3	23.5	54.7	52.8%	1.4	10.3	8.1	1.7	21.5	6.4%
Trinité-et-Tobago	23.3	-	0.4	0.0	23.7	98.2%	3.0	0.0	0.8	-	3.8	77.9%
Uruguay	5.2	-	0.5	0.2	6.0	88.0%	0.1	16.0	1.5	0.1	17.7	0.6%
Vénézuela	139.1	3.2	5.2	70.2	217.7	65.3%	27.6	22.1	10.8	5.2	65.7	42.0%
Autres Amérique Latine	16.8	-	1.1	17.7	35.7	47.1%	0.7	3.4	2.4	1.2	7.7	8.5%
Amérique latine	**931.9**	**12.8**	**56.9**	**1 210.2**	**2 211.7**	**42.7%**	**76.3**	**494.8**	**150.7**	**99.7**	**821.5**	**9.3%**
Bangladesh	36.3	-	2.5	31.7	70.5	51.5%	10.7	64.0	16.9	1.0	92.5	11.6%
Brunei Darussalam	5.1	0.7	0.1	4.3	10.2	56.6%	1.7	0.0	0.1	0.3	2.1	80.6%
Cambodge	3.7	-	-	8.1	11.8	31.7%	0.8	10.6	1.6	1.9	14.9	5.4%
Taipei chinois	262.1	-	10.2	1.9	274.2	95.6%	2.7	0.0	1.5	0.3	4.4	60.3%
Inde	1 160.7	1.8	72.3	136.2	1 371.1	84.8%	104.7	461.7	143.0	2.9	712.3	14.7%
Indonésie	331.0	6.5	18.5	208.3	564.2	59.8%	81.2	92.4	37.6	13.1	224.3	36.2%
Rép. pop. dém. de Corée	74.3	-	2.8	2.6	79.6	93.2%	3.1	3.9	3.6	0.1	10.6	29.0%
Malaisie	145.8	6.0	8.8	31.6	192.2	78.9%	14.6	5.7	3.5	1.7	25.5	57.2%
Mongolie	9.6	-	0.1	0.3	10.0	96.5%	0.1	4.1	0.4	0.2	4.8	3.0%
Myanmar	10.1	0.4	0.3	106.0	116.7	9.0%	4.1	42.6	6.7	7.4	60.8	6.8%
Népal	3.0	-	0.2	6.4	9.5	31.8%	3.7	29.0	3.3	0.0	36.0	10.4%
Pakistan	118.3	-	8.9	16.9	144.1	82.1%	15.6	73.2	21.5	0.1	110.3	14.1%
Philippines	72.4	0.3	6.4	7.7	86.9	83.7%	3.6	29.9	11.3	0.0	44.9	8.0%
Singapour	43.1	-	0.1	-	43.2	99.8%	0.3	0.1	0.9	-	1.3	27.0%
Sri Lanka	12.3	-	0.6	2.3	15.2	81.0%	1.3	6.4	2.7	-	10.3	12.2%
Thailande	214.1	-	19.1	33.5	266.8	80.3%	7.4	60.0	9.2	2.3	78.8	9.4%
Viêt-Nam	80.4	0.5	15.6	17.9	114.4	70.7%	13.4	50.1	11.0	0.6	75.1	17.8%
Autres pays d'Asie	15.3	-	0.3	57.1	72.7	21.1%	2.8	14.2	4.2	2.5	23.7	12.0%
Asie	**2 597.7**	**16.3**	**166.8**	**672.6**	**3 453.4**	**75.7%**	**271.8**	**947.8**	**278.8**	**34.4**	**1 532.8**	**17.7%**
Rép. populaire de Chine	5 059.8	-	625.4	116.9	5 802.1	87.2%	340.6	497.9	152.1	5.2	995.8	34.2%
Hong Kong, Chine	40.7	-	0.5	0.0	41.2	98.7%	0.4	0.0	0.6	-	1.1	40.6%
Chine	**5 100.5**	**-**	**625.9**	**116.9**	**5 843.4**	**87.3%**	**341.1**	**497.9**	**152.7**	**5.2**	**996.8**	**34.2%**

2005 Greenhouse gas emissions

Emissions de gaz à effet de serre pour 2005

million tonnes of CO$_2$ equivalent using GWP-100

Energy	Agriculture	Industrial processes	Other	Total	Share of energy	HFCs	PFCs	SF$_6$	Total	Share of energy	
				N$_2$O		Industrial processes			Total		
0.0	0.4	-	0.0	0.4	4.9%	0.4	-	-	7.6	62.0%	Armenia
0.3	3.8	-	0.0	4.0	6.4%	0.1	0.0	-	60.3	81.5%	Azerbaijan
0.1	6.8	3.3	0.1	10.4	0.9%	0.5	-	-	90.8	75.1%	Belarus
0.1	0.5	-	0.0	0.6	15.0%	0.0	-	0.0	18.4	90.0%	Estonia
1.1	1.7	0.6	0.0	3.4	33.1%	0.0	-	-	13.1	48.2%	Georgia
0.4	5.0	-	0.2	5.5	6.5%	0.4	-	-	206.1	89.0%	Kazakhstan
0.0	3.2	-	0.0	3.3	1.0%	0.0	-	-	12.8	45.5%	Kyrgyzstan
0.1	1.2	-	0.0	1.4	10.7%	1.0	-	-	13.1	66.1%	Latvia
0.2	2.6	-	0.0	2.9	8.7%	0.7	-	-	22.3	69.4%	Lithuania
0.0	0.9	-	0.0	1.0	3.8%	0.0	-	-	11.9	75.8%	Republic of Moldova
3.9	32.5	3.4	2.8	42.6	9.2%	24.6	30.7	8.4	2 200.7	88.5%	Russia
0.0	1.6	-	0.0	1.6	0.2%	0.0	0.1	-	10.7	55.2%	Tajikistan
0.0	2.5	0.6	0.0	3.2	0.8%	0.1	-	-	67.9	88.7%	Turkmenistan
0.7	12.6	9.7	0.3	23.3	2.9%	0.3	0.3	-	417.0	86.1%	Ukraine
0.2	14.4	0.0	0.0	14.7	1.3%	0.7	-	-	179.7	81.3%	Uzbekistan
7.2	**89.7**	**17.7**	**3.6**	**118.2**	**6.1%**	**28.7**	**31.1**	**8.4**	**3 332.4**	**86.6%**	**Former USSR**
0.3	81.5	0.2	1.4	83.4	0.4%	0.3	0.1	0.2	327.6	46.8%	Argentina
0.0	12.2	-	16.0	28.3	0.1%	-	-	0.0	269.3	4.8%	Bolivia
3.0	223.4	9.6	64.3	300.3	1.0%	5.1	3.1	1.0	1 856.5	18.7%	Brazil
0.5	11.2	0.9	0.1	12.6	3.6%	-	-	0.0	95.3	64.8%	Chile
0.3	19.1	0.2	4.9	24.5	1.3%	-	-	0.1	216.0	32.6%	Colombia
0.0	2.8	0.0	0.0	2.9	1.2%	0.1	-	0.0	11.9	46.2%	Costa Rica
0.3	7.3	0.7	0.1	8.3	3.0%	0.1	-	0.0	44.5	57.1%	Cuba
0.1	2.7	-	0.0	2.9	3.9%	-	-	0.0	28.0	63.6%	Dominican Republic
0.1	8.3	-	0.1	8.5	1.2%	0.1	-	0.0	49.4	55.7%	Ecuador
0.1	2.1	-	0.0	2.3	5.0%	0.1	-	0.0	13.0	49.6%	El Salvador
0.2	5.6	-	2.1	8.0	3.1%	0.5	-	0.0	57.4	21.2%	Guatemala
0.1	4.2	-	0.0	4.3	1.6%	-	-	0.0	10.4	19.0%	Haiti
0.1	3.8	-	0.0	3.9	2.0%	-	-	0.0	17.3	39.5%	Honduras
0.0	1.0	-	0.0	1.0	4.1%	0.1	-	0.0	12.8	77.4%	Jamaica
0.0	0.0	-	0.0	0.1	70.7%	-	-	0.0	3.9	97.1%	Netherlands Antilles
0.1	3.1	-	0.0	3.2	3.2%	-	-	0.0	14.7	30.8%	Nicaragua
0.1	2.0	-	0.0	2.1	2.8%	-	-	0.0	11.5	51.1%	Panama
0.1	10.5	-	2.2	12.9	0.8%	-	-	0.0	59.6	6.4%	Paraguay
0.2	16.7	-	1.8	18.7	1.3%	0.4	-	0.0	95.3	32.0%	Peru
0.0	0.3	-	0.0	0.4	6.0%	-	-	0.0	27.9	94.2%	Trinidad and Tobago
0.0	15.6	-	0.0	15.6	0.2%	0.1	-	0.0	39.4	13.7%	Uruguay
0.3	20.6	0.0	5.6	26.5	1.0%	2.0	0.3	0.2	312.4	54.5%	Venezuela
0.3	4.5	-	1.2	6.1	4.8%	0.0	0.1	0.0	49.6	35.9%	Other Latin America
6.3	**458.7**	**11.6**	**99.9**	**576.5**	**1.1%**	**8.8**	**3.6**	**1.5**	**3 623.6**	**28.3%**	**Latin America**
2.0	34.1	-	1.0	37.1	5.3%	-	-	0.0	200.2	24.5%	Bangladesh
0.0	0.0	-	0.3	0.4	3.8%	0.3	-	0.0	12.9	57.7%	Brunei Darussalam
0.2	2.8	-	0.8	3.8	4.3%	-	-		30.5	15.4%	Cambodia
1.3	0.0	0.1	0.0	1.4	92.0%	-	2.1	2.6	284.8	93.4%	Chinese Taipei
17.4	279.5	1.5	2.3	300.7	5.8%	2.8	1.9	4.8	2 393.6	53.7%	India
5.0	50.8	0.2	13.9	69.9	7.1%	-	0.2	0.7	859.4	49.3%	Indonesia
0.6	22.6	-	0.0	23.2	2.4%	2.9	-	0.9	117.2	66.5%	DPR of Korea
1.3	6.4	0.4	1.8	9.9	13.3%	-	0.0	0.5	228.2	73.5%	Malaysia
0.0	22.8	-	0.1	22.8	0.1%	-	-		37.6	26.0%	Mongolia
0.7	17.3	-	7.9	25.9	2.7%	-	-	0.0	203.5	7.5%	Myanmar
0.8	6.3	-	0.0	7.1	11.5%	-	-	0.0	52.7	14.4%	Nepal
2.2	77.1	0.7	0.0	80.0	2.8%	-	-	0.6	335.1	40.6%	Pakistan
0.8	18.1	0.0	0.0	18.9	4.2%	-	-	0.3	151.0	51.1%	Philippines
0.3	0.1	7.6	0.0	8.0	3.5%	1.6	0.5	0.5	55.1	79.4%	Singapore
0.3	2.8	-	0.0	3.1	10.8%	-	-	0.0	28.6	48.6%	Sri Lanka
0.7	24.6	0.2	2.5	28.0	2.6%	-	-	0.9	374.5	59.4%	Thailand
1.3	35.6	-	0.6	37.5	3.5%	-	-	0.0	226.9	42.1%	Vietnam
0.6	15.1	-	3.8	19.5	3.2%	0.1	-	0.0	116.0	16.2%	Other Asia
35.5	**615.9**	**10.7**	**35.2**	**697.3**	**5.1%**	**7.6**	**4.7**	**12.1**	**5 707.9**	**51.2%**	**Asia**
23.4	525.3	17.2	0.7	566.7	4.1%	100.2	12.1	8.4	7 485.3	72.5%	People's Rep. of China
0.2	0.0	-	0.0	0.2	94.1%	-	-	0.3	42.9	96.5%	Hong Kong, China
23.6	**525.3**	**17.2**	**0.7**	**566.9**	**4.2%**	**100.2**	**12.1**	**8.8**	**7 528.2**	**72.6%**	**China**

MULTILINGUAL GLOSSARIES

français

Deutsch

Indicateurs principaux

Hauptkennzahlen

français	Deutsch
CO$_2$ Méthode sectorielle (Mt de CO$_2$)	CO$_2$ Sektorspezifischer Ansatz (MT CO$_2$)
CO$_2$ Méthode de référence (Mt de CO$_2$)	CO$_2$ Referenzansatz (MT CO$_2$)
ATEP (PJ)	PEV (PJ)
ATEP (Mtep)	PEV (Mtoe)
PIB (milliards de \$EU 2000 utilisant les taux de change)	BIP (Mrd. 2000 US\$ auf Wechselkursbasis)
PIB (milliards de \$EU 2000 utilisant les PPA)	BIP (Mrd. 2000 US\$ auf Kaufkraftparitätenbasis)
Population (millions)	Bevölkerung (Mio.)
CO$_2$ / ATEP (t CO$_2$ par TJ)	CO$_2$ / PEV (t CO$_2$ pro TJ)
CO$_2$ / PIB (kg CO$_2$ par \$EU 2000)	CO$_2$ / PIB (kg CO$_2$ pro 2000 US\$)
CO$_2$ / PIB (kg CO$_2$ par \$EU 2000 PPA)	CO$_2$ / PIB (kg CO$_2$ pro 2000 US\$ Kaufkraftparität)
CO$_2$ / Population (t CO$_2$ par habitant)	t CO$_2$ pro Kopf

Les rapports sont fondés sur la méthode sectorielle.

Verhältniszahlen basieren auf dem Sektorspezifischer Ansatz.

Emissions de CO$_2$ par secteur en 2006

CO$_2$-Emissionen nach Sektoren (2006)

millions de tonnes de CO$_2$	*Mio. Tonnen CO$_2$*
Méthode sectorielle	**Sektorspezifischer Ansatz**
Production d'électricité et de chaleur (activité principale)	Öffentliche Elektrizitäts- und Wärmeerzeugung
Autoproducteurs non spécifiés	Nicht zugeordnete Eigenerzeuger
Autres industries de l'énergie	Andere Energieindustrien
Industries manufacturières et de construction	Verarbeitende Industrie und Baugewerbe
Transport	Verkehr
dont: transport routier	*davon: Straßenverkehr*
Autres secteurs	Andere Sektoren
dont: résidentiel	*davon: Haushalte*
Méthode de référence	**Referenzansatz**
Ecarts dus aux pertes et/ou aux transformations	Differenzen infolge von Verlusten und/oder Umwandlung
Ecarts statistiques	Stat. Differenzen
Pour mémoire : soutes maritimes internationales	*Anmerkung: Bunkerung von Brennstoffen durch seegehende Schiffe*
Pour mémoire : l'aviation internationale	*Anmerkung: Bunkerung von Brennstoffen im luftverkehr*

La catégorie Autres inclut les déchets industriels et les déchets urbains non renouvelables.

Andern inklusive Industrieabfälle und nichterneuerbane städtische Abfälle.

italiano

Japanese

Principali indicatori

主 要 指 標

italiano	Japanese
CO$_2$ Metodo settoriale (Mt di CO$_2$)	CO$_2$ 排出量 セクター別　アプローチ（二酸化炭素 百万 ト$_ン$）
CO$_2$ Metodo di base (Mt di CO$_2$)	CO$_2$ 排出量 レファレンス・アプローチ（二酸化炭素 百万 ト$_ン$）
ATEP (PJ)	一次エネルギー供 給　（PJ）
ATEP (Mtep)	一次エネルギー供 給　（石油換算 百万 ト$_ン$）
PIL (miliardi di US$ 2000 utilizzando il tasso di cambio)	GDP（10億 米ドル 、2000年 価格）
PIL (miliardi di US$ 2000 utilizzando la PPA)	GDP（10億 米ドル、 2000年 価格、 購買力平価）
Popolazione (milioni)	人口（百万）
CO$_2$ / ATEP (t di CO$_2$ per TJ)	CO$_2$ 排出量 / 一次エネルギー 供 給（CO$_2$ ト$_ン$ / PJ）
CO$_2$ / PIL (kg di CO$_2$ per US$ 2000)	CO$_2$ 排出量 / GDP（CO$_2$ キ$_ロ$ グ$_ラ_ム$ / 米ドル、2000年 価格）
CO$_2$ / PIL (kg di CO$_2$ per US$ 2000)	CO$_2$ 排出量 / GDP（CO$_2$ キ$_ロ$ グ$_ラ_ム$ / 米ドル、2000年 価格、購買力平価）
CO$_2$ / Popolazione (t di CO$_2$ per abitante)	一人当たり CO$_2$ 排出量（二酸化炭素 ト$_ン$ / 人）
I rapporti sono basati sul metodo settoriale.	レートはセクター別アプローチを基に算出

Emissioni di CO$_2$ per settore in 2006

2006年 の 部 門 別 二 酸 化 炭 素 排 出 量

italiano	Japanese
milioni di tonnellate di CO$_2$	CO$_2$ 百 万 ト$_ン$
Metodo settoriale	セクター別　アプローチ
Produzione di elettricità e di calore (attività principale)	電気 ・ 熱供給事業者
Auto-produttori non specificati	自家発
Altri settori energetici	その他のエネルギー産業
Industrie manifatturiere e della costruzione	製造業・建設業
Settore dei trasporti	運輸業
di cui: trasporti stradali	国内道路運送業
Altri settori	その他
di cui: settore domestico	国内民生・家庭用
Metodo di base	レファレンス ・ アプローチ
Differenza dovuta alle perdite e/o alle trasformaz.	転換ロス等に起因する誤差
Differenza statistica	統計誤差
Memo: bunkeraggi marittimi internazionali	メモ：国際海運バンカー
Memo: bunkeraggi aerei internazionali	メモ：国際航空バンカー
La categoria Altri comprende rifiuti industriali e rifiuti urbani non rinnovabili.	「その他」は「産業廃棄物」及び「再利用不可の都市廃棄物」を含む

español	русский
# español	# русский

Indicadores Básicos

Основные показатели

CO$_2$ Metodo Sectorial (Mt de CO$_2$)	CO2 секторный подход (млнт CO2)
CO$_2$ Metodo Base (Mt de CO$_2$)	CO2 системный подход (млнт CO2)
TPES[1] (PJ)	ОППТЭ$_1$ (PJ)
TPES[1] (Mtep)[2]	ОППТЭ$_1$ (млн тнэ2)
PIB (billón de 2000 USA\$ utilizando tipos de cambio)	ВВП (миллиардов долларов США 2000 г. по валютному курсу)
PIB (billón de 2000 USA\$ utilizando PPP[3])	ВВП (миллиардов долларов США 2000 г. по ППС3)
Población (millones)	Население (миллионов человек)
CO$_2$ / TPES (t CO$_2$ por TJ)	CO2/ОППТЭ (т CO2 на тнэ)
CO$_2$ / PIB (kg CO$_2$ por 2000 USA\$)	CO2/ВВП (кг CO2 на доллар США 2000 г.)
CO$_2$ / PIB (kg CO$_2$ por 2000 USA\$ PPP)	CO2/ВВП (кг CO2 на доллар США 2000 г. по ППС)
CO$_2$ / Población (t CO$_2$ per capita)	CO2/Численность населения (тнэ на человека)

Los ratios estan calculados a partir del metodo sectorial. | коэффициенты основаны на секторном подходе.

Emisiones por Sector en 2006

Выбросы CO2 в 2006 г. по отраслям

millón de toneladas de CO$_2$	*миллионов тон CO2*
Metodo Sectorial	секторный подход
Producción de electricidad y calor (actividad principal)	Электростанции и теплоцентрали общего пользования
Autoproductores no especificados	Электростанции и теплоцентрали предприятий
Otras Industrias de Energía	Прочие топливно-энергетические отрасли
Industrias Manufactureras y Construcción	Обрабатывающие отрасли промышленности и строителство
Transporte	Транспорт (включая международную морскую бункеровку)
del cual: Carretera	*в том числе : Автомобильный*
Otros sectores	Прочие отрасли
del cual: Residencial	*в том числе : Жилищно-коммунальное хозяйство*
Metodo Base	системный подход
Diferencias por Pérdidas y/o Transformación	Расхождение от потерь и/или переработки
Diferencias estadísticas	Статистическое расхождение
Memo: Bunkers de Navegación Internacional	*К сведению : Международная морская бункеровка*
Memo: Bunkers de Aviación Internacional	*К сведению : Международная воздушная бункеровка*

Otros incluye residuos industriales y residuos municipales no renovables.

Категория Другие включает промышленные отходы и ком.-быт. твердые отходы.

Energy Data Manager / Statistician

Possible Staff Vacancies

International Energy Agency, Paris, France

The IEA

The International Energy Agency, based in Paris, acts as energy policy advisor to 27 member countries in their effort to ensure reliable, affordable and clean energy for their citizens. Founded during the oil crisis of 1973-74, the IEA's initial role was to co-ordinate measures in times of oil supply emergencies. As energy markets have changed, so has the IEA. Its mandate has broadened to incorporate the "Three E's" of balanced energy policy making: energy security, economic development and environmental protection. Current work focuses on climate change policies, market reform, energy technology collaboration and outreach to the rest of the world, especially major consumers and producers of energy like China, India, Russia and the OPEC countries.

The Energy Statistics Division, with a staff of around 30 people, provides a dynamic environment for young people just finishing their studies or with one to two years of work experience.

Job description

The data managers/statisticians compile, verify and disseminate information on all aspects of energy including production, transformation and consumption of all fuels, renewables, the emergency reporting system, energy efficiency indicators, CO_2 emissions, and energy prices and taxes. The data managers are responsible for receiving, reviewing and inputting data submissions from Member countries and other sources into large computerised databases. They check for completeness, correct calculations, internal consistency, accuracy and consistency with definitions. Often this entails proactively investigating and helping to resolve anomalies in collaboration with national administrations of Member and Non-Member countries. The data managers/statisticians also play a key role in helping to design and implement computer macros used in the preparation of their energy statistics publication(s).

Principal Qualifications

- University degree in a topic relevant to energy, computer programming or statistics. We currently have staff with degrees in Mathematics, Statistics, Information Technology, Economics, Engineering, Physics, Chemistry, Environmental Studies, Hydrology, Public Administration and Business.

- Experience in the basic use of databases and computer software. Good computer programming skills in Visual Basic.

- Ability to work accurately, pay attention to detail and work to deadlines. Ability to deal simultaneously with a wide variety of tasks and to organise work efficiently.

- Good communication skills; ability to work well in a team and in a multicultural environment, particularly in liaising with contacts in national administrations and industry.

- Very good knowledge of one of the two official languages of the Organisation (English or French). Knowledge of other languages would be an advantage.

- Some knowledge of energy industry operations and terminology would also be an advantage, but is not required.

Nationals of any OECD Member country are eligible for appointment. Basic salaries range from 2 900 to 3 800 Euros per month, depending on qualifications. The possibilities for advancement are good for candidates with appropriate qualifications and experience. Tentative enquiries about future vacancies are welcomed from men and women with relevant qualifications and experience. Applications in French or English, accompanied by a curriculum vitae, should be sent to:

Personnel and Finance Division
International Energy Agency
9 rue de la Fédération
75739 Paris Cedex 15, France

Email: recruitment@iea.org

Gestionnaire de données sur l'énergie / Statisticien

Vacances d'emploi éventuelles

Agence internationale de l'énergie, Paris, France

L'AIE

l'Agence internationale de l'énergie, établie à Paris, dispense des conseils de politique énergétique à ses 27 pays membres qui s'emploient à assurer pour leurs citoyens des approvisionnements en énergie fiables, propres et à des prix abordables. Créée pendant la crise pétrolière de 1973-74, l'AIE avait pour mission dans un premier temps de coordonner les mesures à prendre en temps de crise des approvisionnements pétroliers. Au fur et à mesure que les marchés de l'énergie évoluaient, l'AIE a elle aussi changé. Son mandat s'est élargi pour prendre en considération les « trois E » qui sont à la base d'une élaboration équilibrée des politiques énergétiques : la sécurité énergétique, le développement économique et la protection de l'environnement. Les travaux actuels de l'Agence sont axés sur les politiques climatiques, la réforme des marchés, la coopération en matière de technologie de l'énergie et les relations avec le reste du monde, notamment avec de grands producteurs et consommateurs d'énergie tels la Chine, l'Inde, la Russie et les pays de l'OPEP.

La Division des statistiques de l'énergie, qui compte quelque 30 personnes, offre un environnement dynamique pour de jeunes diplômés de fraîche date ou possédant une ou deux années d'expérience professionnelle.

Description de poste

Les gestionnaires de données/statisticiens compilent, vérifient et diffusent des informations sur tous les aspects de l'énergie, notamment la production, la transformation et la consommation de tous les combustibles, les énergies renouvelables, le système de notification des situations d'urgence, les indicateurs d'efficacité énergétique, les émissions de CO_2, ainsi que les prix et la fiscalité de l'énergie. Les gestionnaires de données sont chargés de recevoir, contrôler et introduire dans des bases de données informatisées de taille importante les données communiquées par les pays membres et d'autres sources. Ils en vérifient l'exhaustivité, corrigent les calculs, et s'assurent de la cohérence interne, de l'exactitude et de l'homogénéité de ces données par rapport aux définitions. A cet effet, ils sont souvent amenés à entreprendre activement des recherches, et à aider à résoudre les anomalies en concertation avec les administrations nationales des pays membres et non membres. Les gestionnaires de données/statisticiens jouent également un rôle essentiel en contribuant à la conception et à l'exécution des macros utilisées pour préparer leur(s) publication(s) de statistiques énergétiques.

Principales qualifications

- Diplôme universitaire dans un domaine se rapportant à l'énergie, aux langages de programmation ou à la statistique. Nous comptons actuellement dans nos effectifs des diplômés en mathématiques, statistiques, technologies de l'information, économie, sciences de l'ingénieur, physique, chimie, sciences de l'environnement, hydrologie, administration publique et études commerciales.

- Notions pratiques de l'utilisation de bases de données et de logiciels. Bonnes compétences en programmation en langage Visual Basic.

- Aptitude à travailler avec précision et sens de la minutie, ainsi qu'à respecter les délais. Aptitude à traiter simultanément des tâches variées et à s'organiser avec efficacité.

- Bonne capacité de communication ; esprit d'équipe avéré et aptitude à travailler dans un environnement pluriculturel, notamment en assurant la liaison avec les contacts dans les administrations nationales et dans l'industrie.

- Très bonne connaissance de l'une des deux langues officielles de l'Organisation (anglais ou français). La connaissance d'autres langues constituerait un avantage.

- Une certaine connaissance des activités de l'industrie de l'énergie et de la terminologie correspondante serait également un atout, mais n'est pas indispensable.

Ces postes sont ouverts aux ressortissants des pays membres de l'OCDE. Les traitements de base sont compris entre 2 900 et 3 800 euros par mois, suivant les qualifications. Les candidats possédant les qualifications et l'expérience appropriées se verront offrir des perspectives de promotion. Les demandes de renseignements sur les postes susceptibles de se libérer qui émanent de personnes dotées des qualifications et de l'expérience voulues seront les bienvenues. Les candidatures, rédigées en français ou en anglais et accompagnées d'un curriculum vitae, doivent être envoyées à l'adresse suivante :

Division du personnel et des finances
Agence internationale de l'énergie
9 rue de la Fédération
75739 Paris Cedex 15, France

Email: recruitment@iea.org

On-Line Data Services

Users can instantly access not only all the data published in this book, but also all the time series used for preparing this publication and all the other statistics publications of the IEA. The data are available on-line, either through annual subscription or pay-per-view access. More information on this service can be found on our website: http://data.iea.org

Ten Annual Publications

■ Energy Statistics of OECD Countries, 2008 Edition

No other publication offers such in-depth statistical coverage. It is intended for anyone involved in analytical or policy work related to energy issues. It contains data on energy supply and consumption in original units for coal, oil, natural gas, combustible renewables/wastes and products derived from these primary fuels, as well as for electricity and heat. Complete data are available for 2005 and 2006 and for the first time in this edition, supply estimates are available for the previous year (*i.e.* 2007). Historical tables summarise data on production, trade and final consumption. Each issue includes definitions of products and flows and explanatory notes on the individual country data.

Published July 2008 - Price € 110

■ Energy Balances of OECD Countries, 2008 Edition

A companion volume to *Energy Statistics of OECD Countries*, this publication presents standardised energy balances expressed in million tonnes of oil equivalent. Energy supply and consumption data are divided by main fuel: coal, oil, gas, nuclear, hydro, geothermal/solar, combustible renewables/ wastes, electricity and heat. This allows for easy comparison of the contributions each fuel makes to the economy and their interrelationships through the conversion of one fuel to another. All of this is essential for estimating total energy supply, forecasting, energy conservation, and analysing the potential for interfuel substitution. Complete data are available for 2005 and 2006 and for the first time in this edition, supply estimates are available for the previous year (*i.e.* 2007). Historical tables summarise key energy and economic indicators as well as data on production, trade and final consumption. Each issue includes definitions of products and flows and explanatory notes on the individual country data as well as conversion factors from original units to tonnes of oil equivalent.

Published July 2008 - Price € 110

■ Energy Statistics of Non-OECD Countries, 2008 Edition

This publication offers the same in-depth statistical coverage as the homonymous publication covering OECD countries. It includes data in original units for more than 100 individual countries and nine main regions. The consistency of OECD and non-OECD countries' detailed statistics provides an accurate picture of the global energy situation for 2005 and 2006. For a description of the content, please see *Energy Statistics of OECD Countries* above.

Published August 2008 - Price € 110

■ Energy Balances of Non-OECD Countries, 2008 Edition

A companion volume to the publication *Energy Statistics of Non-OECD Countries*, this publication presents energy balances in million tonnes of oil equivalent and key economic and energy indicators for more than 100 individual countries and nine main regions. It offers the same statistical coverage as the homonymous publication covering OECD countries, and thus provides an accurate picture of the global energy situation for 2005 and 2006. For a description of the content, please see *Energy Balances of OECD Countries* above.

Published August 2008 - Price €110

■ Electricity Information 2008

This reference document provides essential statistics on electricity and heat for each OECD member country by bringing together information on production, installed capacity, input energy mix to electricity and heat production, input fuel prices, consumption, end-user electricity prices and electricity trades. The document also presents selected non-OECD country statistics on the main electricity and heat flows. It is an essential document for electricity and heat market and policy analysts.

Published August 2008 - Price €130

■ Coal Information 2008

This well-established publication provides detailed information on past and current evolution of the world coal market. It presents country specific statistics for OECD member countries and selected non-OECD countries on coal production, demand, trade and prices. This publication represents a key reference tool for all those involved in the coal supply or consumption stream, as well as institutions and governments involved in market and policy analysis of the world coal market.

Published August 2008 - Price €150

■ Natural Gas Information 2008

A detailed reference work on gas supply and demand, covering not only the OECD countries but also the rest of the world. Contains essential information on LNG and pipeline trade, gas reserves, storage capacity and prices. The main part of the book, however, concentrates on OECD countries, showing a detailed gas supply and demand balance for each individual country and for the three OECD regions: North America, Europe and Asia-Pacific, as well as a breakdown of gas consumption by end-user. Import and export data are reported by source and destination.

Published August 2008 - Price €150

■ Oil Information 2008

A comprehensive reference book on current developments in oil supply and demand. The first part of this publication contains key data on world production, trade, prices and consumption of major oil product groups, with time series back to the early 1970s. The second part gives a more detailed and comprehensive picture of oil supply, demand, trade, production and consumption by end-user for each OECD country individually and for the OECD regions. Trade data are reported extensively by origin and destination.

Published August 2008 - Price €150

■ Renewables Information 2008

This reference document brings together in one volume essential statistics on renewables and waste energy sources. It presents a detailed and comprehensive picture of developments for renewable and waste energy sources for each of the OECD member countries, encompassing energy indicators, generating capacity, electricity and heat production from renewable and waste sources, as well as production and consumption of renewable and waste products. It also includes a selection of indicators for non-OECD countries. This report provides a strong foundation for renewables energy policy and market analysis to assess progress towards domestic and international objectives.

Published August 2008 - Price €80

■ CO$_2$ Emissions from Fuel Combustion, 2008 Edition

In order for nations to tackle the problem of climate change, they need accurate greenhouse gas emissions data. This publication provides a basis for comparative analysis of CO$_2$ emissions from fossil fuel combustion, a major source of anthropogenic emissions. The data in this book are designed to assist in understanding the evolution of the emissions of CO$_2$ from 1971 to 2006 for more than 140 countries and regions by sector and by fuel. Emissions were calculated using IEA energy databases and the default methods and emissions factors from the *Revised 1996 IPCC Guidelines for National Greenhouse Gas Inventories.*

Published November 2008 - Price €150

Two Quarterlies

■ Oil, Gas, Coal and Electricity, Quarterly Statistics

This publication provides up-to-date, detailed quarterly statistics on oil, coal, natural gas and electricity for the OECD countries. Oil statistics cover production, trade, refinery intake and output, stock changes and consumption for crude oil, NGL and nine selected oil product groups. Statistics for electricity, natural gas and coal show supply and trade. Import and export data are reported by origin and destination. Moreover, oil as well as hard coal and brown coal production are reported on a worldwide basis.

Published Quarterly - Price €110, annual subscription €350

■ Energy Prices and Taxes

This publication responds to the needs of the energy industry and OECD governments for up-to-date information on prices and taxes in national and international energy markets. It contains prices at all market levels for OECD countries and certain non-OECD countries: import prices, industry prices and consumer prices. The statistics cover the main petroleum products, gas, coal and electricity, giving for imported products an average price both for importing country and country of origin. Every issue includes full notes on sources and methods and a description of price mechanisms in each country.

Published Quarterly - Price €110, annual subscription €350

Electronic Editions

■ CD-ROMs and Online Data Services

To complement its publications, the Energy Statistics Division produces CD-ROMs containing the complete databases which are used for preparing the statistics publications. State-of-the-art software allows you to access and manipulate all these data in a very user-friendly manner and includes graphic facilities. These databases are also available on the internet from our online data service.

Annual CD-ROMS / Online Databases

- Energy Statistics of OECD Countries, 1960-2007   Price: €500 (single user)
- Energy Balances of OECD Countries, 1960-2007   Price: €500 (single user)
- Energy Statistics of Non-OECD Countries, 1971-2006   Price: €500 (single user)
- Energy Balances of Non-OECD Countries, 1971-2006   Price: €500 (single user)
- *Combined subscription of the above four series*   *Price: € 1 200 (single user)*

- Electricity Information 2008   Price: €500 (single user)
- Coal Information 2008   Price: €500 (single user)
- Natural Gas Information 2008   Price: €500 (single user)
- Oil Information 2008   Price: €500 (single user)
- Renewables Information 2008   Price: €300 (single user)
- CO_2 Emissions from Fuel Combustion, 1971-2006   Price: €500 (single user)

Quarterly CD-ROMs / Online Databases

- Energy Prices and Taxes   Price: (four quarters) €800 (single user)

A description of these services are available on our website: **http://data.iea.org**

Other Online Services

■ The Monthly Oil Data Service

The IEA Monthly Oil Data Service provides the detailed databases of historical and projected information which is used in preparing the IEA's monthly *Oil Market Report* (OMR). The IEA Monthly Oil Data Service comprises three packages available separately or combined as a subscriber service on the Internet. The data are available at the same time as the official release of the Oil Market Report.

The packages include:
- Supply, Demand, Balances and Stocks   Price: €5 500 (single user)
- Trade   Price: €1 650 (single user)
- Field-by-Field Supply   Price: €2 750 (single user)
- *Complete Service*   *Price: €8 250 (single user)*

A description of this service is available on our website: **http://modsinfo.iea.org**

■ The Monthly Gas Data Service

The Monthly Gas Data Service provides for OECD countries historical and current data on natural gas supply and demand, as well as detailed information on trade origins and destinations.

The packages include:

- Natural Gas Balances & Trade
  Historical plus 12 monthly updates   Price: €440 (single user)
- Natural Gas Balances & Trade
  Historical   Price: €330 (single user)

A description of this service is available on our website: **http://data.iea.org**

Moreover, the IEA statistics website contains key energy indicators by country, graphs on the world and OECD's energy situation evolution from 1971 to the most recent year available, as well as selected databases for demonstration.

The IEA statistics website can be accessed at: http://www.iea.org/statistics/

The Online Bookshop

International Energy Agency

IEA BOOKS

Tel: +33 (0)1 40 57 66 90
Fax: +33 (0)1 40 57 67 75
E-mail: books@iea.org

www.iea.org/books

International Energy Agency
9, rue de la Fédération
75739 Paris Cedex 15, France

IEA Publications, 9, rue de la Fédération, 75739 Paris Cedex 15
Printed in France by Maulde & Renou Sambre SAS
(61 2008 12 3 P1) ISBN 978-92-64-04238-4